34th EUROPEAN SYMPOSIUM ON COMPUTER AIDED PROCESS ENGINEERING / 15th INTERNATIONAL SYMPOSIUM ON PROCESS SYSTEMS ENGINEERING

VOLUME 2

COMPUTER-AIDED CHEMICAL ENGINEERING, 53

34th EUROPEAN SYMPOSIUM ON COMPUTER AIDED PROCESS ENGINEERING / 15th INTERNATIONAL SYMPOSIUM ON PROCESS SYSTEMS ENGINEERING

VOLUME 2

Edited by

Flavio Manenti
"Giulio Natta" Department of Chemistry, Materials and Chemical Engineering, Polytechnic University of Milan, Milan, Italy

Gintaras V. Reklaitis
Davidson School of Chemical Engineering, Purdue University, West Lafayette, Indiana, United States

Amsterdam – Boston – Heidelberg – London – New York – Oxford
Paris – San Diego – San Francisco – Singapore – Sydney – Tokyo

Elsevier
Radarweg 29, PO Box 211, 1000 AE Amsterdam, Netherlands
The Boulevard, Langford Lane, Kidlington, Oxford OX5 1GB, UK
50 Hampshire Street, 5th Floor, Cambridge, MA 02139, USA

British Library Cataloguing in Publication Data
A catalogue record for this book is available from the British Library

Library of Congress Cataloging-in-Publication Data
A catalog record for this book is available from the Library of Congress

ISBN (Volume 2): 978-0-443-33898-4
ISBN (Set) : 978-0-443-28824-1
ISSN: 1570-7946

For information on all Elsevier publications visit our website at https://www.elsevier.com/

Publisher: Candice Janco
Acquisition Editor: Anita Koch
Editorial Project Manager: Lena Sparks
Production Project Manager: Paul Prasad Chandramohan
Designer: Mark Rogers

Typeset by STRAIVE

Contents

Flavio Manenti, Gintaras V. Reklaitis (Eds.), Proceedings of the 34th European Symposium on Computer Aided Process Engineering / 15th International Symposium on Process Systems Engineering (ESCAPE34/PSE24), June 2-6, 2024, Florence, Italy
 http://dx.doi.org/10.1016/B978-0-443-28824-1.50151-4

Stepwise Parameter Fitting to Combine Industrial and Pilot Plant Datasets

Per Julian Becker[a], Benoit Celse[a]

[a]*IFP Energies nouvelles, Rond-point de l'échangeur de Solaize, BP 3, 69360 Solaize, France*
per.becker@ifpen.fr

Abstract

In kinetic model development for hydrotreatment processes industrial data are generally not used because deactivation must be taken into account, which is very difficult due to the high complexity of chemical phenomena. This is unfortunate because industrial data contains far larger feedstocks variation compared to pilot plant tests. The aim of this work is to propose an innovative method to include industrial data in kinetic model fitting. A stepwise parameter fitting method is proposed to use both pilot plant and industrial data. Pilot plant experiments provide robust data but with small feed variations, on the contrary industrial plant data provide huge feed variation. To obtain more robust models, a combined modeling framework for the kinetic reactor and deactivation models, solved simultaneously, is proposed for the HDN reaction in a hydrotreatment reactor. The kinetic parameters (reaction orders, activation energy) are calibrated on pilot plant points, while the empirical feedstock parameters as well as the deactivation model is calibrated on industrial points. This methodology leverages the strengths of each of the two datasets which results in more robust predictive models.

Keywords: Modeling, Catalyst Deactivation, Hydrotreatment, Industrial Data

1. Motivations & Objectives

Large datasets with thousands of points can be obtained from operating data of industrial units such as hydrotreatment units in fossil- and bio-refineries. This contrasts to the limited number of expensive and time-consuming pilot plant tests. Using industrial data for model fitting is highly desirable but remains challenging because (i) operating conditions generally remain close to the design conditions of a given unit and (ii) catalyst deactivation is very difficult to model due to the high complexity of the chemical phenomena. This leads to issues with the identifiability of kinetic parameters. Pilot plant data is, on the other hand, very well suited for calibration of kinetic models (operating condition variation) with carefully constructed designs of experiment covering a wide range of operating conditions and the absence of deactivation. However, feedstock variability is generally limited which leads to overfitting and consequently less robust models. The aim of this work is to propose an innovative method to include industrial data in kinetic model fitting. The idea is to combine the two datasets (pilot and industrial) in order to leverage their respective strengths. This work presents a methodology for combining industrial and pilot plant datasets.

The model presented in this work was implemented in Fortran and compiled to a shared library (dll) to be used with a high-level scripting language. Data pre-processing and parameter identification was done with R and post-processing was done with Python.

2. Process Description

Hydrotreatment and hydrocracking (HCK) is a very flexible process, which is extensively used in petroleum refining to convert the heavy Vacuum Gas Oil (VGO) fractions of crude oil into high-quality products (Becker 2016). Recently, there has been an increasing interest in this technology for upgrading and conversion of bio-sourced or recycled plastic feeds. A typical HCK unit consists of two fixed-bed reactors in series, under high hydrogen pressure (up to 160 bar), and operating at temperatures between 360 and 430°C. The catalyst of the first reactor is designed for removal of organic impurities via hydro-denitrogenation (HDN), hydro-desulfurization (HDS), or hydro-deoxygenation (HDO) reactions. The second reactor contains a zeolite catalyst, which performs the actual hydrocracking, i.e., breaking up of long-chained hydrocarbons, isomerization, and hydrogenation of aromatic rings. The reactors are followed by a distillation column.

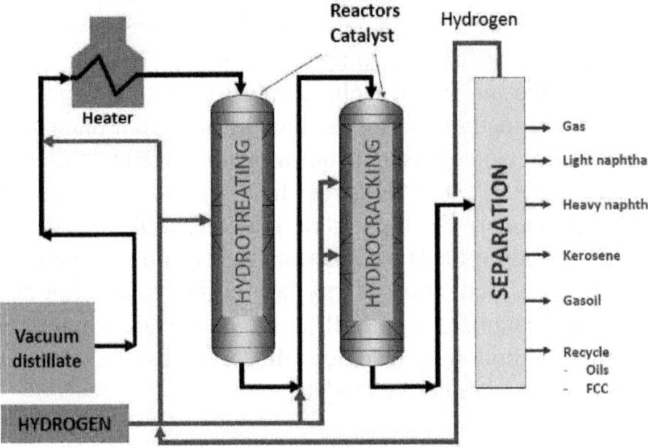

Figure 1 Schematic representation of the Hydrocracking process

The focus of this work is the HDN reaction in the hydrotreatment reactor. Removal of organic nitrogen impurities is important because they act as inhibitors on the zeolite catalysts in the second reactor. The design and operation of the hydrotreatment reactor is based on the required concentration of organic nitrogen (nitrogen slip) at reactor outlet, typically around 10 – 50 ppm. The reactor temperature is used as control variable during operation. A predictive model for the HDN reaction is required at the design phase and to be able to simulate the impact of eventual changes during operation of the unit.

3. Catalyst Deactivation

Hydrotreatment and hydrocracking catalysts deactivate over time (Forzatti 1999), principally due to coke formation, but occasionally also due to presence of heavy metals in the feed. The loss in activity is compensated by increasing reactor temperature. Once reactor temperature reaches the design limitation of the unit (typically < 430°C) the units must be shut down and the catalyst changed. Typical cycle duration is between 2 and 4 years, depending on feedstock characteristics and operating conditions. Shutdowns in large integrated refineries are very costly and need to be planned well in advance. A predictive deactivation model is necessary to correctly predict the required increase of temperature over time and subsequently the cycle lengths. This deactivation model must be combined with a kinetic model to de-correlate instantaneous changes.

4. Model Development

4.1. Kinetic Model for HDN Reaction

The principal difficulty of hydrotreatment reactor modeling is the immense complexity of the system, with typical VGO feeds composed of hundreds of thousands of individual hydrocarbon species (Becker 2016, Chehadeh 2023). Detailed characterization of the chemical composition of feeds and effluents is not feasible with current analytical methods. While some purely data-driven approaches have recently been proposed (Pang 2024) for simulation of hydrocracking units, such methods are generally only applicable for a single refinery. These methods are therefore useful for process control but have poor predictive capabilities. The kinetic model proposed here considers organic nitrogen as a single chemical species and combines well-known reaction kinetics with an empirical term taking macroscopic, easily measured, feed characteristics into account (see Table 1). The kinetic model for the HDN reaction (1) is composed of the kinetic equation for an irreversible reaction with kinetic parameters $\beta_{kin} = [k_0, E_a, n, m]$ combined with an empirical term, g_{corr}, which is used to model the impact of feedstock descriptors (X_{feed}) on reactivity. In this work an explicit form of g_{corr} is used (2), however, it is possible to replace this term with a more complex data-driven model.

$$\frac{dN}{dt} = -k_0 \exp\left(-\frac{E_a}{R_g}\left(\frac{1}{T} - \frac{1}{T_{ref}}\right)\right) N^m \left(\frac{ppH_2}{ppH_2^{ref}}\right)^n * g_{corr}(X_{feed}, \beta_{feed}) \quad (1)$$

$$g_{corr} = \left((1 + A_0 Res)\left(\frac{TMP}{TMP_{ref}}\right)^v \left(\frac{d_{154}}{d_{154}^{ref}}\right)^d \left(\frac{K_{Watson}}{K_{Watson}^{ref}}\right)^k\right)^{-1} \quad (2)$$

Table 1 Definition of descriptors and parameters used in the kinetic model.

N	Nitrogen concentration [ppm]	
T	Temperature (WABT) [K]	ref = 648.15 K (375°C)
t	Time dimension, contact time [s]	
ppH_2	Hydrogen partial pressure [bar]	ref = 128.21 bar
X_{feed}	Feedstock descriptors	
Res	Feed resins [%]	
TMP	Weighted mean boiling point of feed [°C] = (DS5 + 2*DS50 + 4*DS90)/7	ref = 479.2°C
g_{corr}	Correction term for feed descriptors	
d_{154}	Feed density [g/cm^3]	ref = 0.9175 g/cm^3
K_{Watson}	aka K_{UOP} [-]	ref = 11.687
A_0, v, d, k	Feed Parameters: β_{feed}	
k_0, E_a, n, m	Kinetic Parameters: β_{kin}	

4.2. Deactivation Model

Catalyst deactivation is principally due to the formation of coke which accumulates on the catalyst particles and blocks the active sites, thus reducing activity over time (Rodriguez 2018). It is well known that coke formation increases with temperature and tends to be slowed down by increasing hydrogen partial pressure and/or hydrogen-to-hydrocarbon flow ratio (Rodriguez 2018). Feed asphaltene and carbon conradson content of the feedstock are good indicators for the tendency of increased coke formation. A detailed kinetic model for coke formation could not be developed because of the absence of relevant measurements. An semi-empirical deactivation model (3) and (4) was therefore developed, based on the considerations outlined above. Table 2 details the descriptors and models parameters.

$$\frac{dT}{dt} = a_{corr} a_0 e^{bT} \tag{3}$$

$$a_{corr} = \frac{\left(1 + \alpha_{CC}(\max(0, CC - CC_{lim}))^{\beta_{CC}}\right)\left(1 + \alpha_{AS}\left(\frac{\max(0, AS - AS_{lim})}{1000}\right)^{\beta_{AS}}\right)}{\left(\frac{ppH_2}{ppH_{2,std}}\right)^{\beta_{ppH2}}\left(\frac{H2HC}{H2HC_{std}}\right)^{\beta_{H2HC}}} \tag{4}$$

Table 2 Definition of descriptors and parameters used in the deactivation model.

T	Temperature WABT* [°C]	
t	Time on Stream [days]	
CC	Feed Carbon Conradson [%]	lower limit = 0.8 %
AS	Feed Asphaltenes [ppm]	lower limit = 10 ppm
$ppH2$	Hydrogen partial pressure [bar]	std. value = $f(K_{Watson}, TMP)$
$H2HC$	H2 gas to hydrocarbon ratio [L/L]	std. value = $5 * ppH2_{std} + 100$
$a, b, \alpha_{CC}, \beta_{CC}, \alpha_{AS}, \beta_{AS}, a_0, \beta_{ppH2}, \beta_{H2HC}$	Deactivation parameters: β_{deac}	

*WABT = weight averaged bed temperature

5. Datasets

Industrial data was obtained from a total 28 cycles from 19 hydrotreatment units, in addition to 117 pilot plant points performed at IFPEN. The principal differences, with respect to the development of a combined kinetic and deactivation model are summarized in Table 3.

Table 3 Comparison of industrial and pilot plant datasets

	data points	*Feed variability*	*Operating Conditions*	β_{kin} *identifiability*	β_{feed} *identifiability*	*Catalyst De-activation*
Industrial	Large 10,343	High, daily variations	Fixed set-point per cycle	Poor	Good	Yes
Pilot Plant	Small 117	Low, discrete feeds	Varied according to DOE	Good	Poor	No

Pilot plant tests are done on relatively short runs of up to 1.5 months, deactivation is therefore negligible compared to long industrial cycles, the deactivation model cannot be calibrated on this data. Due to careful experimental designs these points are, however, well suited for identification of the kinetic parameters. Data from industrial cycles, on the other hand, allow for the deactivation effect to be observed, but identification of the kinetic parameters is problematic. This is mainly because the nitrogen content in the effluents vary generally very little from the set-point of a particular unit, while temperature is adjusted to correct for loss in catalyst activity, this makes it very difficult to identify the correct reaction order and activation energy. Pilot plant test runs are performed with a limited number of available feedstocks, resulting in a small number (20) of discrete points, which often leads to over-fitting of the β_{feed} parameters in the empirical term of the kinetic model. The feedstock characteristics of the industrial dataset varies at an almost daily rate. This is shown by comparing TMP and d154 in Figure 2. The pilot plant feeds generally fall within the range covered by the industrial data, except for heavier HCGO (feeds 1 and 16), higher boiling point DAO (feeds 13 and 17), and the light feed 15. The feed of plant R cycle 2 is atypical due to higher boiling point than for the other industrial cycles.

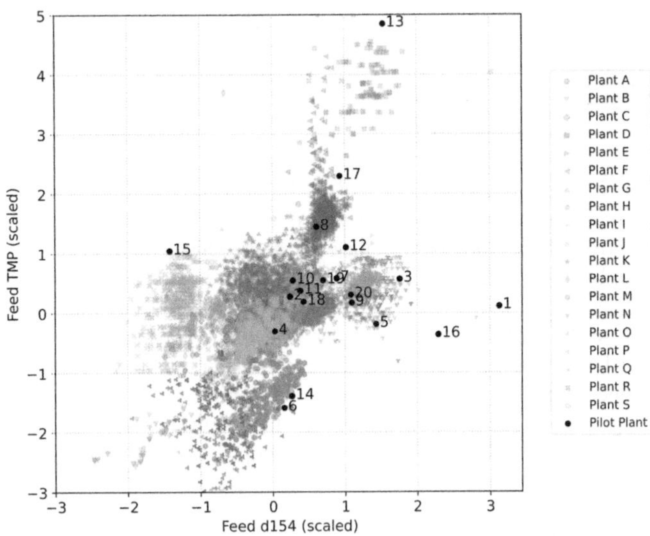

Figure 2 Comparison of feed density and TMP for pilot plant and industrial datasets.

6. Parameter Fitting Algorithm

The combined parameter fitting algorithm consists of two steps: 1) Fit β_{feed} and β_{kin} on the pilot plant dataset, and 2) fit β_{feed} and β_{deac} on the industrial dataset keeping at β_{kin} the value from 1). In the first step the full kinetic model is calibrated only on pilot plant data, this ensures good estimation of the kinetic parameters β_{kin}, while β_{feed} might be poorly estimated or over-fitted. In the second step the empirical feed parameters β_{feed} and the deactivation model β_{deac} are calibrated on the industrial dataset. This step improves the robustness of the empirical term in the kinetic model without compromising the good estimation of β_{kin} from step 1). The "optim" function of R with the "Nelder-Mead" algorithm was used for parameter fitting.

7. Results & Discussion

Results for the combined kinetic/deactivation model with the stepwise parameter fitting procedure (case 2) are shown in Figure 3 with results obtained by either fitting the kinetic model exclusively on pilot plant (case 1) or industrial data (case 3). The target value is an RMSE of ±5°C. Atypical pilot plant feeds are marked in red. The aim here is not to compare the datasets but to show that using both industrial and pilot plant data leads to a more robust model with respect to feed variation thanks to the industrial data, and more robust with respect to operating condition (T, P, LHSV), thanks to the pilot plant data.

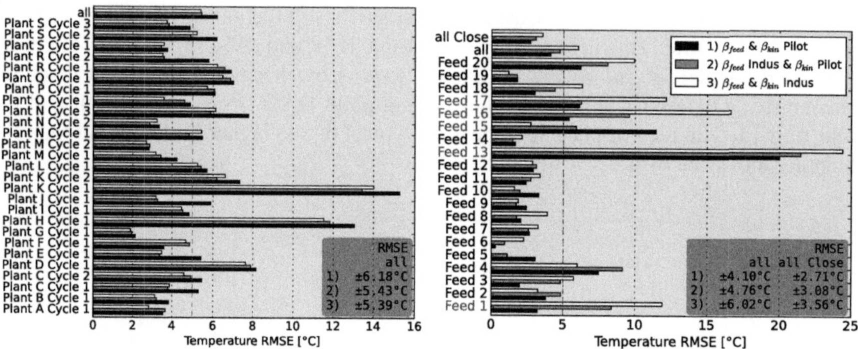

Figure 3 Errors for industrial (left) by cycle and pilot plant (right) by feed.

For the industrial dataset the model error improves by 0.75°C between case 1) and case 2), while the error of the pilot plant dataset is degraded by 0.66°C (0.36°C excluding atypical feeds). No further improvement can be observed when also fitting all parameters of the kinetic model on industrial data (case 3), while the pilot plant error is further degraded by 1.26°C (0.49°C excluding atypical feeds). This suggests that fitting β_{kin} on industrial data leads to over-fitting and these parameters should be identified on pilot plant data. Concerning β_{feed}, the degradation of the pilot plant error is well within the acceptable range, except for the atypical feeds, while significantly improving the error of the industrial data. This method presents a good compromise, for combining the strengths of the two datasets.

8. Conclusions & Perspectives

The proposed parameter fitting algorithm allows both pilot plant and industrial data to be used to fit the parameters of a combined kinetic and deactivation model. Using both datasets for parameter fitting was found to improve model performance compared to the case where only one of the two datasets is used. This is an effective method for combining two very different datasets with different strengths and weaknesses in terms of parameter identifiability. An explicit term was used for the empirical term in the kinetic model, future work includes the implement different data-driven Machine Learning (ML) models for this term. The parameter fitting procedure presented here allows such a hybrid model to leverage the larger industrial dataset for the ML term which generally requires larger volumes of data.

References:

P. Forzatti, L. Lietti, 1999, *Catalyst deactivation*, Catalysis Today. 52, 165-181.

D. Chehadeh, X. Ma, H. Al Bazzaz, 2023, *Recent progress in hydrotreating kinetics and modeling of heavy oil and residue: A review,* Fuel. 334, 126404

E. Rodriguez, et al., 2018, *Modeling of hydrotreating catalyst deactivation for heavy oil hydrocarbons*, Fuel. 225, 118-133

P.J. Becker, B. Celse, D. Guillaume, V. Costa, L. Bertier, E. Guillon, and G. Pirngruber, 2016, *A continuous lumping model for hydrocracking on a zeolite catalysts: model development and parameter identification*, Fuel, pages 73–82.

P.J. Becker, N. Serrand, B. Celse, D. Guillaume, H. Dulot, 2016, *Comparing hydrocracking models: Continuous lumping vs. single events*, Fuel 165, 306-315.

Z. Pang, et al., 2024, *Data-driven prediction of product yields and control framework of hydrocracking unit.* Chemical Engineering Science, 1193386

Flavio Manenti, Gintaras V. Reklaitis (Eds.), Proceedings of the 34th European Symposium on Computer Aided Process Engineering / 15th International Symposium on Process Systems Engineering (ESCAPE34/PSE24), June 2-6, 2024, Florence, Italy
 http://dx.doi.org/10.1016/B978-0-443-28824-1.50152-6

A Bilevel Framework for Environmental and Economic Optimisation of Hydrogen Supply Chains

Vincent Jacquot,[a] Catherine Azzaro-Pantel,[a] Sylvain Bourjade,[b] Catherine Müller[b]

[a]*Laboratoire de Génie Chimique, Université de Toulouse, CNRS, INPT, UPS, Toulouse, France*
[b]*TBS Business School, Toulouse, France*
vincent.jacquot@toulouse-inp.fr

Abstract

Hydrogen is an energy carrier with the potential to decarbonise a portion of the transportation sector. To achieve this, there is a need to deploy a whole supply chain to produce, transport, store, and distribute this low-carbon fuel. Although hydrogen can be low-carbon if produced via the electrolysis of renewable electricity, most of its current production relies on fossil resources such as natural gas. It is thus crucial to develop a hydrogen supply chain that combines the reduction of greenhouse gas emissions to decarbonise mobility with the optimization of economic objectives. Most of the frameworks that model the hydrogen supply chain (HSC) with associated greenhouse emissions use a multi-objective approach to account for it. The whole supply chain is considered as a single actor with the goal of minimising both the total cost and the greenhouse gas (GHG) emissions of the HSC. This paper proposes a new approach involving two stakeholders with competing objectives. The problem is modelled as mixed-integer bilevel programming problem (MIBLPP) including a decision-maker with the aim to minimise GHG emissions as the upper level (UL) and the minimisation of the total cost of the HSC at the lower level (LL). The UL can choose technologies to subsidise in order to support the greenest solutions, while the LL will design the most cost-effective HSC to fulfil the demand based on the availability of technologies and energy sources.

Keywords: Hydrogen Supply Chain, Optimisation, Bilevel, MILP, Evolutionary Algorithm.

1. Introduction

The Paris Agreement sets the goal of maintaining "the increase in the global average temperature to well below 2°C above pre-industrial levels" and further aims "to limit the temperature increase to 1.5°C above pre-industrial levels". To achieve this, participating countries have to cut down their greenhouse gas emissions. According to the French High Council on Climate (HCC), the transport sector was the main source of GHG emissions, accounting for 31% of France's total emissions in 2021 (HCC, 2021). To decarbonise this sector mainly driven by fossil fuels, various technical solutions are being explored, including batteries, biofuels or green hydrogen. The latter refers to hydrogen produced from renewable energy sources, in contrast to grey hydrogen which is fossil-based. Hydrogen is mainly used to produce electricity with fuel cells, powering electric engines

However, for hydrogen to serve as a solution for decarbonising mobility, a whole supply chain is required. This hydrogen supply chain is composed of production plants, hydrogen transport facilities, storage units and distribution stations. The literature review highlights that the predominant engineering model of such energy systems involves a mixed-integer linear programming (MILP) approach (e.g., Almansoori and Shah, 2009 and De-León Almaraz et al., 2014). This modelling approach determines the optimal HSC to satisfy an objective function such as cost minimisation or GHG emissions reduction through cooperation among stakeholders. However, real-world HSC design and management often encompass multiple actors across the different levels, ranging from production to distribution. These challenges involve a hierarchical relationship between two decision levels and are generally formulated as mixed-integer bilevel programs (Bard 1998).

This paper addresses this issue by taking into account the constraint of renewable energy availability in the territory to be considered for hydrogen production and the investment choices for new facilities. To tackle this problem, we propose a bilevel framework using an evolutionary algorithm at the upper level (leader) to select the most consistent subsidies for minimising the total GHG emissions. The lower level (follower) involves a mixed-integer programming formulation to minimise the cost of hydrogen production, transport, storage and distribution based on the model developed by De-León Almaraz (2014). We then apply our methodology to model and optimise an HSC in a sub-area of the Occitanie region in France. The proposed framework has the potential to aid in determining regulations and economic instruments for deploying low-carbon based hydrogen supply chains. Additionally, it allows for the consideration of the impact of policymakers' decisions on the optimal configuration of the HSC.

2. Definition of the MIBLPP model

2.1. Structure of the algorithm

The algorithm designed to model the HSC deployment was implemented using the Python programming language and involves a mixed-integer bilevel programming approach. The

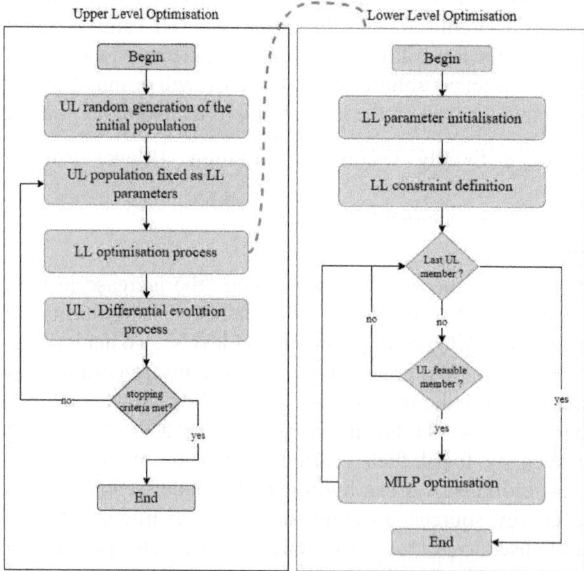

Figure 1: Structure of the MIBLPP algorithm

LL (follower) replicates the approach defined by De León Almaraz et al. (2014) to model the technical aspects of the HSC which is formulated as a mixed-integer linear programming (MILP) problem. It minimises the total cost of the HSC based on the hydrogen demand and techno-economic parameters. The LL also calculates the GHG emissions of the entire supply chain (expressed in $kgCO_2eq$). To transfer the previously designed GAMS (General Algebraic Modelling Language) model to Python, the algebraic modelling language Pyomo (Python based) was used. The UL and the structure of the MIBLPP algorithm are based on the work by Flores-Perez et al. (2020) and Avraamidou and Pitsikopoulos (2019). Figure 1 describes the framework designed to model this MIBLPP. The UL fixes the UL variables (i.e., binaries for the choice of technology or energy sources to subsidise) of each population member and sends them to the LL as parameters. The LL is solved with Gurobi solver and the results are used to calculate the UL objective function. A differential evolution is then performed to generate new population members for the next iteration. For more details on the Python MIBLPP framework, see Jacquot et al. (2023).

2.2. Formulation of the mathematical equations

Eqs. (1-3) describe the UL that minimises the total CO_2 emissions (Eq. 1). The model can choose to subsidise renewable energies or electrolysers procurement (Eq. 2). Eqs. (4-10) are the main equations used by the LL. The objective is to minimise the total operating and investment cost (Eq. 4). Eq. (5) ensures that the level of production or storage respects the maximum and minimum capacities of facilities. The quantity distributed in each portion of the territory (or grid) (Eq. 7) must satisfy the demand (Eq. 8). The subsidies granted by the UL are applied to the units' production costs (Eq. 8) and the plants' capital costs (Eq. 9). Eq. (10) calculates the total CO_2 emissions for the production, storage and transportation of hydrogen (see Table 1). For more details on the equations used by the LL, see De León Almaraz (2014).

Table 1: Sets, parameters and variables

Sets and index	
F, f	Set of facilities (production, storage)
G, g	Set of grids
E, e	Set of primary energy sources
Parameters	
Capmin, Capmax	Minimum and maximum capacities of facilities (kg/day)
Demand	Daily hydrogen demand in each grid (kg/day)
sub	Rate of subsidy
UPC	Hydrogen production cost ($/kg)
USC	Hydrogen storage cost ($/kg/day)
PCC	Investment cost of a production plant ($)
SCC	Investment cost a storage unit ($)
A0	Available primary energy in each grid (GJ/day)
Variables	
x	Binary of choice for subsidising energy purchase
y	Binary of choice for subsidising electrolysers purchase
FOC	Facility operating cost ($)
TOC	Transport operating cost ($)
CEC	CO_2 emissions cost (due to carbon tax) ($)
FCC	Facility capital cost ($)
TCC	Transportation capital cost ($)
Q	Quantity of hydrogen distributed, produced, imported, exported (kg/day)
GWP	Global warming potential of HSC ($kgCO_2eq.$)

$$min_{x,y} GWPtot \quad (1)$$

$$st.\ x + y \leq 1 \quad (2)$$

$$x, y \in \{0, 1\} \quad (3)$$

$$min_{LL\ variables}\ FOC + TOC + CEC + FCC + TCC \quad (4)$$

$$st.\ Capmin_f \leq Level_f \leq Capmax_f \quad (5)$$

$$Qdist_g \geq Demand_g \quad (6)$$

$$Qdist_g = Qprod_g + Qimp_g - Qexp_g \quad (7)$$

$$FOC = \sum_e (UPC_e * (1 - x) * sub_{e,operation} + USC) \quad (8)$$

$$FCC = \sum_e (PCC_e * (1 - y) * sub_{e,investment} + SCC) \quad (9)$$

$$GWPtot = GWPprod + GWPstock + GWPtrans \quad (10)$$

3. Case study

To illustrate this model, we propose a case study on the deployment of the HSC in a sub-area of the Occitanie region in France. Three geographical zone is discretized with an independent demand in each grid: the three grids considered correspond to the departments. The production technologies involved are steam methane reforming (SMR) and electrolysis from wind, photovoltaic, hydraulic, and national grid electricity. Hydrogen is stored and transported in its liquid form. Most of the data used come from the work of De-León Almaraz (2014) and Mashi et al. (2023). Table 2 summarises some of the parameters considered for the case study. SMR is identified as the cheapest technology albeit with the highest CO_2 emissions, and carbon capture technology is not included in this study. In this scenario, investment costs for electrolysers and SMR plants are assumed to be similar (Hecht and Pratt, 2017). Electrolysers can only operate with the primary energy available in their grid, whereas SMR units rely on imported natural gas. A single period of twenty years is considered, with a constant daily demand (see Table 2). A discount rate of 5% is applied to discount costs over time.

Three scenarios for producing low-carbon hydrogen (i.e., hydrogen with a carbon intensity lower than 3 $kgCO_2eq./kgH_2$) are compared: subsidies only, carbon tax only and a hybrid approach combining subsidies, and carbon tax.

Table 2: Parameters of the case study

		PV	Wind	Hydraulic	Electrical grid	SMR
UPC ($/kg)	Small	7.25	6.89	8.67	5.28	2.21
	Medium	7.04	6.68	8.44	5.13	1.82
PCC (M$)	Small	29	29	29	29	29
	Medium	224	224	224	224	224
GWPprod ($kgCO_2eq./kgH_2$)	Small / Medium	3.08	0.984	1.68	2.15	10.3
A0 (GJ/day)	g=1	1,196	533	106	43,835	0
	g=2	1,440	1,751	20	43,835	0
	g=3	1,335	1,114	228	43,835	0
Demand (tH_2/day)	g=1	6.12				
	g=2	15.4				
	g=3	10.9				

4. Results

This section presents the results found for the three scenarios of the case study. The scenarios incorporating subsidies rely on the MIBLPP algorithm previously described, while the scenario only involving a carbon tax is modelled using a conventional single level MILP approach. Table 3 shows the main key performance indicators (KPI) for each scenario compared to a reference scenario without GHG minimisation.

The MIBLPP opted to subsidise the procurement of renewable electricity instead of electrolysers, primarily due to its significantly higher total cost. Even if electrolysers were provided at no cost (unrealistic solution), SMR remains lower, because of the huge difference in primary energy costs. The subsidy needed for the transition away from fossil energies accounts for 95% of the electricity price. This substantial amount is attributed, in part, to the necessity of deploying two electrolysers (medium size, one per grid) as the available wind electricity in a single grid cannot satisfy the whole demand. With unlimited available electricity, a rate of 73% would be sufficient. While this scenario allows to decrease GHG emissions by 88%, it is noteworthy that the decision-maker bears more than half of the total cost.

The carbon tax scenario involves an electrolyser powered by the electrical grid because it enables the production of low-carbon hydrogen at a lower cost than with wind power. This scenario decreases GHG emissions by 77%, but with an 88% increase in the Levelized Cost of Hydrogen (LCOH). The decision-maker earns about 10% of the LCOH through carbon tax revenue.

The hybrid scenario results in the same production configuration as the first scenario with a reduction of 88% of GHG emissions. However, the carbon tax makes the SMR less profitable, leading to a 42% increase in the LCOH. The decision-maker will pay almost 40% of the total cost. To be more realistic, future work should encompass a broader geographical area, involving multiple grids, possibly an entire region. Additionally, this study should explore several different shorter periods and consider alternative technologies, such as SMR with carbon capture, as well as compressed hydrogen transportation and storage.

Table 3: KPIs of the case study

Optimal values of the UL (in brackets)	Subsidies (95% of renewable electricity cost)	Carbon tax (420 $\$/tCO_2$)	Subsidies (67% of renewable electricity cost) + tax (200 $\$/tCO_2$)	Reference (no tax nor subsidy)
LCOH ($\$/kgH_2$)	3.05	5.72	4.35	3.06
GWP ($kgCO_2/kgH_2$)	1.21	2.37	1.21	10.5
Tax ($\$/kgH_2$)	0	0.6	0.1	0
Subsidy ($\$/kgH_2$)	3.9	0	2.8	0
Production plants installed				
g=1	-	-	-	-
g=2	1 medium wind electrolyser	1 medium grid electrolyser	1 medium wind electrolyser	1 medium SMR
g=3	1 medium wind electrolyser	-	1 medium wind electrolyser	-

5. Conclusions

This paper proposes an MIBLPP model for the HSC to help policymakers in making the optimal choices to minimise the GHG emissions of the HSC. The methodological framework includes an evolutionary algorithm to optimise the decision-maker's choices and a MILP approach to optimise a multigrid HSC with investment choices. This approach allows for modelling the vertical relationship between two stakeholders of the HSC. Further work will focus on expanding the model to accommodate a more complex multiperiod HSC with new technologies and additional variables at the UL. To address horizontal competitive relationships and demand elasticity, a combined engineering-economic approach will be explored.

6. Acknowledgments

This work is part of the project GrHyFONDDOR financed by the National Research Agency of France (Agence Nationale de la Recherche).

References

A. Almansoori, N. Shah, 2009, Design and operation of a future hydrogen supply chain: Multi-period model, International Journal of Hydrogen Energy 34 (19), 7883–7897.

S. Avraamidou, E. N. Pistikopoulos, 2019, B-POP Bi-level parametric optimization toolbox, Computers and Chemical Engineering 122, 193–202.

J. F. Bard, 1998, Practical Bilevel Optimization, Vol. 30.

S. De-Leon Almaraz, 2014, Multi-objective optimisation of a hydrogen supply chain, INPT, Toulouse, France

S. De-Leon Almaraz, C. Azzaro-Pantel, L. Montastruc, S. Domenech, 2014. Hydrogen supply chain optimization for deployment scenarios in the Midi-Pyrénées region, France. International Journal of Hydrogen Energy 39 (23), 11831–11845.

J. M. Flores-Perez, C. Azzaro-Pantel, A. Ponsich, A. A. Aguilar Lasserre, 2020, A hybrid strategy for mixed integer bi-level optimization applied to hydrogen energy supply chain management, Modelling and Simulation 2020 – The European Simulation and Modelling Conference, ESM 2020, 277–281.

HCC, 2021, Rapport annuel du haut conseil pour le climat 2021 - Renforcer l'attenuation, engager l'adaptation.

E. S. Hecht, J. Pratt, 2017, Comparison of conventional vs. modular hydrogen refueling stations, and on-site production vs. delivery, Sandia National Laboratories, Albuquerque, New Mexico 87185 and Livermore, California 94550, U.S.A..

V. Jacquot, J. M. Flores-Perez, C. Azzaro-Pantel, S. Bourjade, C. Muller, 2023, Methods and tools for optimising supply chains modelled as mixed-integer bilevel programming problems, Modelling and Simulation 2023 – The European Simulation and Modelling Conference, ESM 2023, 375–382.

R. Mashi, Y. Vincotte, S. De-Leon Almaraz, C. Azzaro-Pantel, 2023, Optimization of Hydrogen Systems for Prospective Life Cycle Assessment: Well-to-Tank Approach, Computer Aided Chemical Engineering – 33 European Symposium on Computer Aided Process Engineering, Vol. 52, 3211–3217.

Flavio Manenti, Gintaras V. Reklaitis (Eds.), Proceedings of the 34th European Symposium on Computer Aided Process Engineering / 15th International Symposium on Process Systems Engineering (ESCAPE34/PSE24), June 2-6, 2024, Florence, Italy
 http://dx.doi.org/10.1016/B978-0-443-28824-1.50153-8

Economic and Environmental Optimization in Sustainable Jet Fuel Production from Butanol

Angel Eduardo García-Hernández,[a] Juan Gabriel Segovia-Hernández,[a] Eduardo Sánchez-Ramírez,[a] José Quiroz-Ramírez[b]

[a]*Department of Chemical Engineering University of Guanajuato, Noria Alta S/N, Noria Alta,36000, Guanajuato, Gto., Mexico.*

[b]*CONACyT-CIATEC A.C Center of Applied Innovation in Competitive Technologies, Omega 201, Industrial Delta, 37545 León, Gto., Mexico.*

ae.garciahernandez@ugto.mx

Abstract

Within the critical context of dwindling oil reserves, the imperative to discover renewable energy alternatives to fossil fuels becomes increasingly acute. Biofuels, derived from organic substrates, emerge as a significant contender. Second-generation biofuels, utilizing non-food biomass, offer an environmentally responsible and cost-effective substitute, alleviating environmental concerns of fossil fuels without jeopardizing food resources.

A pivotal area of development is Sustainable Aviation Fuel (SAF), a biofuel variant. The conventional routes from biomass to SAF are marked by high costs and substantial energy consumption, necessitating innovative approaches that employ stochastic optimization and process intensification. The critical biomass-to-butanol segment encompasses both reaction and separation zones; the former integrates an intensified reactor for simultaneous saccharification and fermentation, guided by kinetic models within MATLAB. The separation zone employs advanced liquid-liquid extraction and distillation techniques, including an intensified column structure. Subsequently, the butanol-to-jet conversion adheres to a standardized protocol involving dehydration, oligomerization, separation, and hydrogenation, with process simulation conducted via Aspen Plus software. The application of the Differential Evolution with Tabu List (DETL) method has been instrumental in refining design and operational parameters, with the strategic aim of reducing the Total Annual Cost (TAC) and lessening the Eco-indicator 99 (EI99) environmental impact. The culmination of this research is the revelation of an optimized SAF production framework, achieving the minimal TAC and EI99, thereby marking a step forward in the quest for sustainable biofuel processes.

Keywords: butanol, SAF, lignocellulosic biomass, stochastic optimization, process intensification.

1. Introduction

Presently, as the scarcity of oil persists, there is a necessity to explore substitutes for fossil fuels, and this is where biofuels derived from biomass come into play as a potential solution. Biofuels are categorized into first-generation, second-generation, and third generation. First-generation biofuels, sourced from food, face limitations due to the potential threat to food supplies. Second-generation biofuels, primarily derived from biomass, offer an affordable, sustainable, and environmentally friendly fuel source.

Third-generation biofuels, extracted from microalgae, are seen as a promising alternative, although their economic viability remains a significant challenge. Within the aviation sector, aviation biofuel has been developed, providing the advantage of reducing reliance on fossil fuels and decreasing CO_2 emissions by 80% throughout its lifecycle, owing to the carbon neutrality of biomass compared to conventional aviation fuel. The physical and chemical properties of aviation biofuel closely resemble those of conventional aviation fuel, enabling it to be easily blended with fossil fuel (aviation fuel) in various proportions without requiring modifications to aircraft and engines.

The manufacturing of second-generation biofuels via biochemical procedures involves four primary phases: pretreatment, enzymatic hydrolysis, fermentation, and separation. The separation stage typically accounts for the highest percentage of the process cost because the mixture subjected to separation is highly diluted, in addition to containing azeotropes. The "alcohol to jet" (ATJ) concept refers to the procedures involved in converting alcohols into aviation fuel. Typically, ethanol and butanol serve as feedstocks for ATJ processes. Both alcohols can be generated from lignocellulosic waste through fermentation, although butanol production technology is still in the research and development stage [1]. Regardless of the feedstock used, the ATJ process follows a uniform set of fundamental steps. It involves four main stages: dehydration, oligomerization, separation, and hydrogenation [1].

In the realm of chemical processing, myriad opportunities emerge, particularly in the domain of process intensification and optimization, pivotal for the integration of Sustainable Aviation Fuel (SAF). Process intensification involves implementing practices aimed at forging technologies that are more efficient, compact, cleaner, and energy-savvy. This encompasses strategies such as unit reduction by amalgamating multiple processes into one, enhancing mass and heat transfer through avant-garde mixing technologies and minimized diffusion pathways, innovating separation methods, and honing control strategies. Optimization, conversely, endeavors to calibrate and augment the overarching efficiency of chemical processes, guaranteeing resource utilization in the most efficacious manner, a cornerstone for the production and implementation of SAF in the aviation industry.

2. Case study

In this instance, we will examine the manufacturing process of biojet fuel derived from lignocellulosic biomass, with butanol serving as an intermediate product. The process will be divided into two segments: biomass-to-butanol and butanol-to-biojet. For the biomass-to-butanol phase, intensification techniques will be applied in both the reaction zone and the purification zone. Conversely, a conventional approach will be employed in the butanol-to-biojet process. The anticipation is that employing optimization methods alongside intensification strategies will lead to a reduction in both the total annual cost and environmental impact.

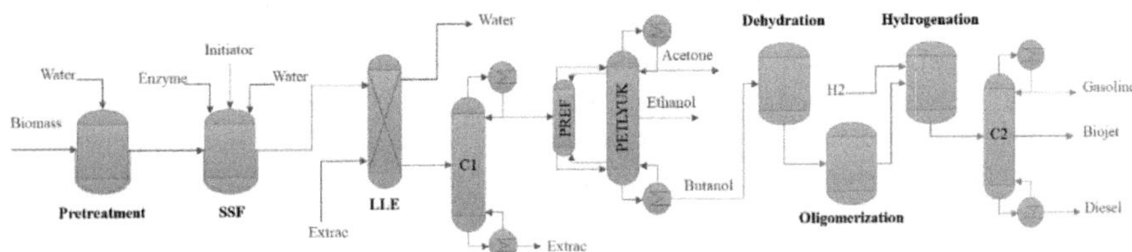

Figure 1. Biomass-biojet process.

3. Process modelling

In the year 2018, the predominant biomass sources in Mexico included sugarcane bagasse and corn straw [2]. Utilizing data from the Agricultural and Fisheries Information Service and SAGARPA (2015), sugarcane bagasse was selected as the primary raw material due to its abundant availability in Mexico during 2018. The process was formulated to extract the necessary sugars from this biomass to facilitate butanol production. The criteria for choosing the pretreatment method included achieving high glucan conversion, alcohol production, and production ratio through intensified systems such as simultaneous saccharification and fermentation (SSF). Among various pretreatment options, liquid hot water (LHW) pretreatment emerged as an effective and economically viable alternative for the chosen raw material.

3.1 Biomass-butanol process

In the reaction phase, an examination can be conducted on the integration of a simultaneous saccharification and fermentation (SSF) reactor. This study aims to decrease the energy and economic requirements of the individual operations. Moving on to the purification phase of the biomass-to-butanol process, the exploration of an intensified distillation system, such as thermally coupled systems, will be undertaken to achieve significant economic and energy efficiencies. Moreover, for the disruption of the azeotropes present, a liquid-liquid extraction system utilizing hexyl acetate as the extraction agent will be implemented.

The development of the intensified simultaneous saccharification and fermentation reactor commences with the concept of merging the two kinetic models (as described earlier) to create a unified model simulating both processes within a single unit. The novel kinetic model for simultaneous saccharification and fermentation (SSF) will be implemented in MATLAB, employing the fourth order Runge-Kutta method for its solution. The kinetic models for hydrolysis and fermentation used as a foundation were those proposed by Kadam and Shinto [3, 4].

The design of the fully thermally coupled column (Petlyuk scheme) is derived from the conventional system design. In both setups, the feed consists of the acetone-butanol-ethanol (ABE) mixture. Both systems undergo design processes using the Aspen Plus simulator. Initial designs are obtained through shortcut methods (DSTWU module), followed by more rigorous methods (RADFRAC module). The selection of the NRTL thermodynamic model is attributed to the presence of azeotropes. It is essential to incorporate a liquid-liquid extraction (LLE) column, employing hexyl acetate as the extraction agent, to disrupt the azeotrope. Furthermore, a distillation column is needed to recover the extracting agent.

3.2 Butanol-biojet process

The conventional simulation of the alcohol-to-jet (ATJ) process, utilizing butanol as the raw material, was carried out using the Aspen Plus software and the NRTL thermodynamic model. The reactors corresponding to the dehydration, oligomerization, and hydrogenation operations were simulated as yield reactors, while the distillation column with a byproduct was designed following the methodology used in the biomass-butanol process.

4. Process optimization

The conversion of lignocellulosic biomass to biojet fuel requires a nuanced multi-objective optimization to discern suitable technologies and optimize design and operational metrics, targeting economic and environmental benefits. Employing the Differential Evolution with Tabu List (DETL) method enables pinpointing of the global optimum with computational efficiency. This approach was pivotal in refining parameters and feedstock scheduling, integrating MS Excel and Aspen Plus via dynamic data exchange for decision variable analysis.

4.1 Total annual cost

In assessing the economic viability of a process under development, the Total Annual Cost (TAC) emerges as a crucial indicator. It reflects not just the final product but is intrinsically linked to the process's characteristics, offering a basis for informative comparison. TAC encompasses both operational expenses, including heating, cooling, and electricity, and capital investment in equipment. The comprehensive formula for TAC is specified in Equation 1.

$$TAC\ (\$USD/kg) = \frac{\frac{Capital\ cost}{Recovery\ time} + Operation\ cost}{F_k} \quad (1)$$

Where F_k represents the product flow.

4.2 Ecoindicator-99

The Eco-indicator 99, a life cycle analysis tool, quantitatively gauges environmental impact across a product's lifespan, from raw material to decomposition. It utilizes ecological indicators to numerically represent this impact, where higher values indicate greater detriment. This method stratifies impact into human health, ecosystem quality, and resource use, with the computational specifics presented in Equation 2.

$$EI99(ecopts/kg) = \frac{\sum_b \sum_d \sum_{k \epsilon K} \delta_d \omega_d \beta_b \alpha_{b,k}}{F_k} \quad (2)$$

Where β_b is the total amount of chemical *b* released per unit of reference flow due to direct emissions, $\alpha_{b,k}$ is the damage caused in category *k* per unit of chemical *b* released to the environment, ω_d is a weighting factor for damage in categories *d*, and δ_d is the normalization factor for damage of category *d*.

4.3 Objective functions

The objective functions used to evaluate the sustainability of the process, considering both environmental and economic aspects, include the Eco-indicator-99 (EI99) and the total annual cost (TAC). The goal is to minimize both energy requirements and operational costs (TAC) while concurrently decreasing the environmental impact of the processes (EI99). These objective functions are represented by the equation:

$$F_{obj}(\vec{X}) = \{\min(TAC, EI99)$$

5. Results

As a result of the optimization, an optimal value for the TAC of 12,614.08 USD/kg of SAF and a value for EI99 of 1.3291E+08 were found. These TAC and EI99 values correspond to a production of 45,833.48 kg/h of biojet or, in its annual equivalent, 389,584.6 tons/year, considering a working year of 8500 hours. Figure 2 shows the Pareto front obtained by plotting both objective functions, highlighting the optimal point found (A1).

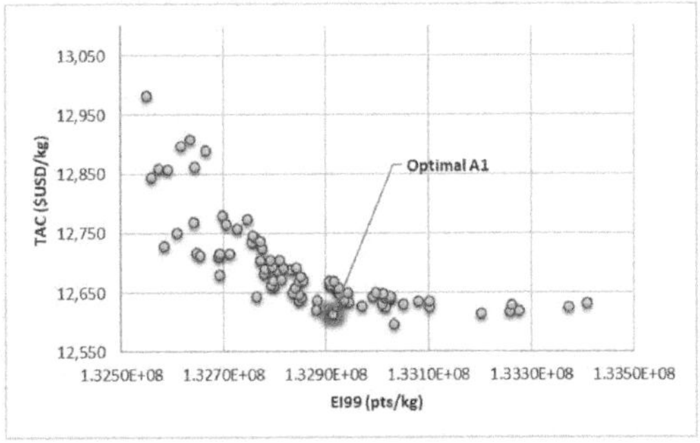

Figure 2. Pareto front for biomass-SAF process.

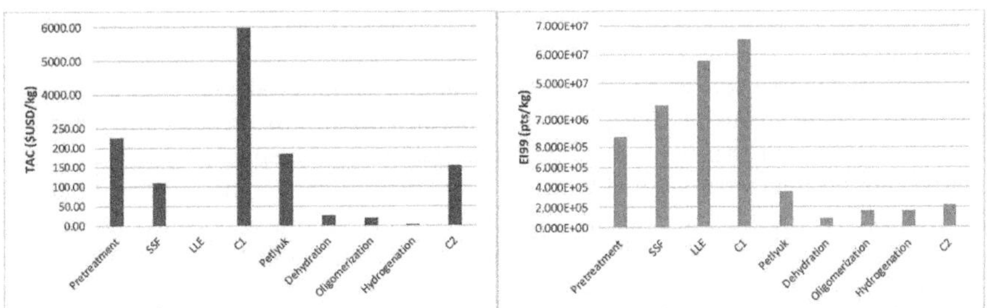

Figure 3. Contribution to the TAC per equipment.

Figure 4. Contribution to the EI99 per equipment.

Figures 3 and 4 depict the team-wise contribution to the objective functions, TAC, and EI99. It is evident that the biomass-butanol process contributes significantly more to both objective functions. Regarding TAC, column (C1), which recovers the extractant agent, has a considerable impact on the total cost. This is due to the high amount of hexyl acetate required to break the azeotrope. On the other hand, in EI99, the biomass-butanol process contributes significantly due to the use of solvent, the flows handled in the process, and consequently, the size of the equipment.

In the following table, the design parameters of the separation stage of the biomass-butanol process, LLE, C1, prefractionator, Petlyuk, are shown, as well as the parameters corresponding to column C2 for the separation stage of the ATJ process. With these separation schemes, the biomass-butanol process was able to produce 40,040.53 kg/h of acetone, 91,358 kg/h of butanol, and 13,590.84 kg/h of ethanol. All three products have a purity of 99.5% wt or higher. On the other hand, in the ATJ process, 20,820.65 kg/h of gasoline, 45,833.48 kg/h of SAF, and 25,430.98 kg/h of diesel were produced.

Table 1. Design parameters of the separation equipment

	LLE	C1	Prefractionator	Petlyuk	C2
Stages	8	41	12	61	17
Feed input stage		28	5		15
Reflux Ratio		0.9098		5.5618	195.32
Input stage of LIF				44	
Input stage of VIF				15	
Output stage of LIF				15	
Output stage of VIF				47	
Output stage of SP				29	8
LIF (kg/h)				23,802.8	
VIF (kg/h)				50,449.3	
SPF (kg/h)				13,787.8	45,615.1
Distillate rate (kg/h)		145,487.9		40,169.8	20,721.4

6. Conclusions

In the biomass-butanol conversion, two process intensification strategies were effectively employed: a simultaneous saccharification and fermentation (SSF) reactor and a Petlyuk column for enhanced thermal coupling. These adaptations facilitated the high-purity production of acetone, ethanol, and butanol. Subsequently, the biomass-derived butanol was efficiently processed via an alcohol-to-jet (ATJ) pathway, yielding 5 kg/h of Sustainable Aviation Fuel (SAF). Post-optimization analysis indicates that the most cost-effective design was achieved, minimizing both Total Annual Cost (TAC) and Eco-Indicator 99 (EI99) impacts. Nonetheless, the metrics remain suboptimal, underscoring the need for alternative intensification and separation techniques to improve sustainability.

References

[1] Kaltschmitt, M., & Neuling, U. (2017). Biokerosene: Status and Prospects. Springer.

[2] SAGARPA, (2015). https://www.gob.mx/. [Online] Available at: https://www.gob.mx/cms/uploads/attachment/file/346978/Manejo_de_residuos_Detallado.pdf

[3] Kadam, L., Rydholm, C., McMillan, D. (2004). Development and Validation of a Kinetic Model for Enzymatic Saccharification of Lignocellulosic Biomass. Biotchnol, 20, pp.698-705.

[4] Shinto, H., Tashiro, Y., Kobayashi, G., Sekiguchi, T., Hanai, T., Kuriya, Y., Okamoto, M., Sonomoto, K. (2008). Kinetic study of substrate dependency for higher butanol production in acetone–butanol–ethanol fermentation. Process Biochemestry, 43, pp.1452-1461.

Flavio Manenti, Gintaras V. Reklaitis (Eds.), Proceedings of the 34th European Symposium on Computer Aided Process Engineering / 15th International Symposium on Process Systems Engineering (ESCAPE34/PSE24), June 2-6, 2024, Florence, Italy
 http://dx.doi.org/10.1016/B978-0-443-28824-1.50154-X

Latent State Space Extension for interpretable hybrid mechanistic models

Judit Aizpuru,[a*] Maxim Borisyak,[a] Peter Neubauer,[a] Mariano Nicolas Cruz-Bournazou[a,b]

[a]*Technische Universität Berlin, Straße 17 des Juni 135, Berlin 10623, Germany*
[b]*DataHow AG, Hagenholzstraße 111, Zurich 8050, Switzerland*
j.aizpuru@campus.tu-berlin.de

Abstract

Mechanistic growth models play a major role in bioprocess engineering, design, and control. Their reasonable predictive power and their high level of interpretability make them an essential tool for computer aided engineering methods. Additionally, since they contain knowledge about cell physiology, the parameter estimates provide meaningful insights into the metabolism of the microorganism under study. However, the assumption of time invariance of the model parameters is often violated in real experiments, limiting their capacity to fully explain the observed dynamics. In this work, we propose a framework for identifying such violations and producing insights into misspecified mechanisms. The framework achieves this by allowing kinetic and process parameters to vary in time. We demonstrate the framework's capabilities by fitting a hybrid model based on a simple mechanistic growth model for E. *coli* with data generated in-silico by a much more complex one, and identifying missing kinetics.

Keywords: mechanistic model, hybrid model, model discovery, bioprocess control, parameter dynamics.

1. Introduction

Mechanistic models are widely applied in bioprocess development, from offline design of experiments to controlling and re-designing experiments in an online manner (Kim et al. 2021). They are typically composed of differential equations describing the kinetics of the uptake and production of different metabolites and biomass, and mass transport and conservation laws. They are typically derived under assumptions of time-invariant parameters and contain the dynamics of just some of the macroscopic species. This makes them simpler and easier to fit with a limited number of experimental measurements, but ignores the very complex metabolic adaptation mechanisms cells are provided with to cope with the cultivation environment, and the possible effects of unmodelled dynamics. This simplification evidently limits their predictive performance since these assumptions are violated in most cultivating conditions, making long term predictions challenging.

In the literature, the problem has been addressed by using hybrid models. These types of models try to use the knowledge that is embedded in the mechanistic models complementing them with data-driven parts. In the literature one can encounter hybrid models where a data-driven component is coupled to the right-hand side of the mechanistic model, for example, by addition of a neural differential equation network to capture missing dynamics (Quaghebeur et al. 2022), or by multiplication of a network to the kinetic reaction rates (Oliveira 2004).

In this work, we propose a framework for hybrid modelling inspired by (Rangapuram et al. 2018), where the authors propose an explainable model based on a linear differential equation system where the parameters can vary in time being the outputs of a recurrent neural network. Our framework in contrast, introduces a linear latent state space model that drives the mechanistic part. Making the mechanistic model parameters linear combinations of these latent states allows them to vary in time, keeping the original interpretation of the model while being flexible enough to express arbitrary adaptation behaviours. We utilise this flexibility to gain important insights into the metabolic activity and the response of the cells to environmental changes. This allows us to detect any deviations from the assumptions and identify possible misspecified mechanisms in the mechanistic model. We demonstrate the framework's capabilities by fitting a hybrid model based on a simple mechanistic growth model for E. *coli* with data generated in-silico by a much more complex one, and detecting the missing kinetics from the base model.

2. Hybrid Model

Consider a mechanistic model f, to which we refer as *the base model* everywhere below:

$$\frac{dx}{dt} = f(x, \theta) \tag{2.1}$$

where x is a vector of states, θ denotes the vector of kinetic and process parameters of the model. As an example, we use E. coli growth model by (Anane et al. 2017) without the acetate dynamics, thus, composed of three states: biomass (X), glucose (S), and dissolved oxygen (DOT). The uptake of substrate will be given by a Monod term, and oxygen is modelled as the difference of oxygen transfer and uptake rate, the latter obtained by mass balancing with glucose.

The proposed hybrid model extends the state space of the base model with latent variables z, whose dynamics are linear with respect to the mechanistic states x and themselves. Linear combinations of these states describe the time evolution of the kinetic and process parameters θ of the base model as:

$$\frac{dz}{dt} = Az + Bx \quad ; \quad \theta(z) = Wz + \theta_0 \tag{2.2}$$

Where $x \in R^n$ and $z \in R^m$ are the base model's state space and states of the model's extension. $\theta_0 \in R^p$ are the values for the base model's parameters when no latent dynamics are present. Finally, A, B and W are parameters of the latent extension, represented as matrices with dimensions $m \times m$, $m \times n$, and $p \times m$ respectively.

The proposed hybrid model allows varying parameters of the base model in time, and in addition, it reduces to the base model when the latent states are constant in time. It is worth noting that the latent extension is a universal approximator i.e., it is capable of expressing arbitrary smooth functions (given that the latent dimensionality is large enough). The main idea behind the proposed method is to detect deviations between the process and the base model by the presence of parameter dynamics.

3. Method

In order to prevent the hybrid model from producing unnecessary parameter dynamics (for example, due to overfitting to measurement noise), and ensure that non-constant dynamics are present only to compensate for the bias in the base model, we introduce a regularisation term to the loss function:

$$loss = -\sum_{i=1}^{n}\sum_{j=1}^{N_i}\frac{\left(x_j^i - y_j^i\right)^2}{\sigma_i^2} + \lambda\left(\sum_{i=1}^{n}\sum_{j=1}^{n} a_{i,j}^2 + \sum_{i=1}^{m}\sum_{j=1}^{n} b_{i,j}^2 + \sum_{i=1}^{p}\sum_{j=1}^{m} w_{i,j}^2\right) \tag{3.1}$$

Where λ controls the strength of the regularisation. Additionally, we restrict the norm of the initial latent state.

It is worth noting three important properties of the model. On the one hand, the proposed model is a strict extension of the base model, i.e., it is able to produce the same dynamics as those to the base model when setting matrices A, B and W to null ones. On the other hand, absolute values of matrix elements are bounded from above by $\sqrt{\frac{L_0}{\lambda}}$, where L_0 is the loss of the base model, and therefore, the matrix norms are bounded as well. Since x(t) is bounded by the loss function, and latent dynamics are bounded by the norm of matrices and the norm of the initial latent state, the parameter dynamics are restricted and dependent on L_0.

Most importantly, any non-negligible parameter dynamics would imply mismatch between the base model and the data. As the regularization term promotes minimal change in the hybrid model's parameters, the dynamics are likely to be related to misspecified kinetics of the base model, thus, offering a valuable insight into these missing mechanisms.

To select an appropriate value for the regularization strength and prevent overfitting, we suggest selecting λ experimentally by fitting the hybrid model to data generated from the base model, with noise, and gradually increasing λ until estimated parameter dynamics become negligible.

4. In-silico experiments

In order to demonstrate the capabilities of the proposed modeling framework, we fit the base and extended model to data generated from a more complex one. This allows us to clearly demonstrate the proposed framework as the differences between the models are known analytically. We select a test scenario that has the usual characteristics of a real experiment. As ground-truth model, we used a slightly modified version of the E. *coli* growth model by (Anane et al. 2017). The model state contains biomass, glucose, acetate (measured at-line), and dissolved oxygen (measured online). 10 different datasets were generated using different sets of parameters and initial conditions. After the batch phase, bolus feeding is applied with constant feed volumes every 12 minutes. Finally, normally distributed noise is added to the observations, using realistic magnitudes. Both models, the base and the hybrid ones, were fitted to each dataset, using a 4-dimensional latent space for the hybrid model.

For simulation, a fixed step Euler integrator was used. With a little modification in the model so that the stiffness is relaxed, this integrator allows fast simulation without much difference in the solution to a more complex multi-step method.

For the optimization, the proposed loss function in Eq. 3.1. has been minimized using an Adam optimizer. To avoid bounded optimization, all parameters of the base model and the corresponding time-varying parameters of the hybrid model are transformed with inverse error function (scaled and shifted by the corresponding ranges) rendering them unbounded. Additionally, to avoid local minima, we use a multi-start procedure with 50 random initial guesses.

5. Results

5.1. Interpolation and extrapolation error

For evaluating the performance of the hybrid model in comparison to the base model, we consider two metrics: interpolation and extrapolation errors. For the calculation of the former, 100 points from the ground truth simulation were sampled randomly. The sum of squared standard errors (SSE) was calculated for each of the models for each dataset. For the calculation of the extrapolation error, 50 observations equally spaced in time within the future 2h were sampled from the simulation. For fitting the hybrid model, we used λ=0.01. Figure 1 shows the distributions and quartiles of these errors, and an overall better performance of the hybrid model for both interpolation and extrapolation tasks. This clearly shows that the hybrid model is expressive enough to approximate the effects of the missing kinetics. Comparing losses to the level expected due to noise, we confirm that: the base model is indeed biased, hybrid model is not overfitted, and, thus, lambda is selected appropriately.

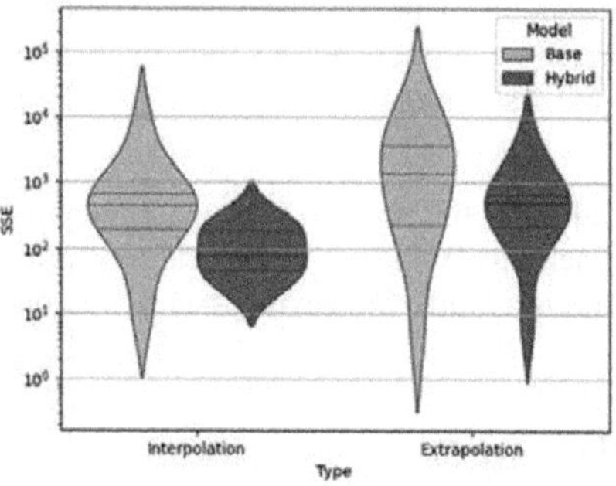

Figure 1: Violin plots showing the distributions of the validation errors for each of the datasets and each of the models. The quartiles of the distributions are highlighted with dashed lines.

5.2. Comparison of two solutions with different levels of acetate accumulation

The base model misses the mechanisms associated with acetate production and consumption. Therefore, in the absence of this metabolite, one should expect both models' predictions to match and the base model to yield a good fit. On the contrary, as soon as a noticeable concentration of this substance is present in the cultivation, one would expect to it to fail, as the kinetic rate for glucose consumption and growth rate are affected by it. We have chosen two scenarios where this effect takes place.

In Figure 2, the low-acetate scenario (the top graph), it can be seen how both models achieve a good fit. At the same time, we observe that parameter dynamics of the hybrid model remain nearly constant (Figure 3, the top graph). The mismatch between the values

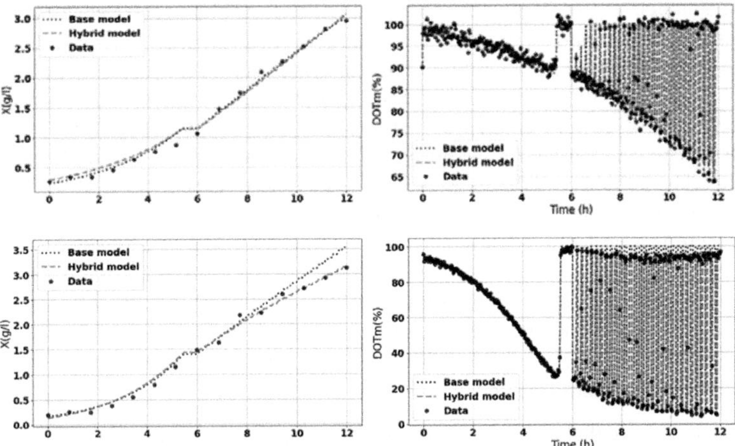

Figure 2: Time-series of the solutions for two optimization scenarios, low acetate (above) and high (below), for the base and the hybrid model, together with the in-silico experimental data.

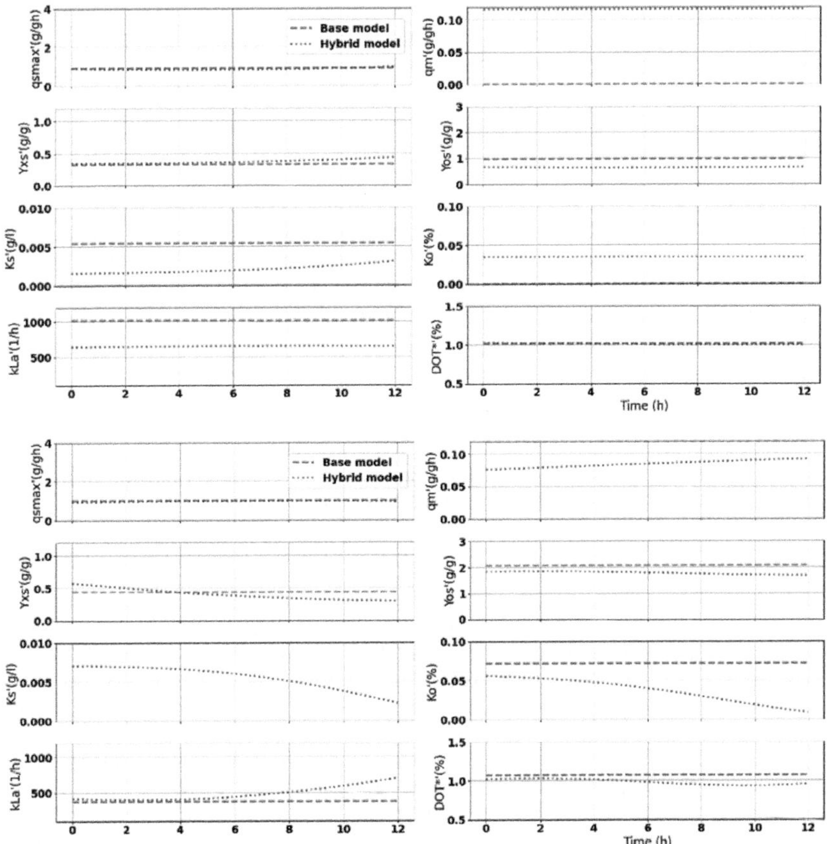

Figure 3: Parameter dynamics predicted by the hybrid model comparing to the static estimates from base model. For the low acetate scenario (above) and high (below).

of the two models are due to the usual identifiability issues, however, as can be seen from the graph, predictions are equivalent. The second case corresponds to an accumulation of around 0.4g/l (Figure 2, the bottom graph). It is noticeable how in the second scenario the base model fails to properly fit the biomass dynamics at the end of the process, and the upper level of oxygen is not well captured during the fed-batch either. The hybrid model is able to compensate for the missing dynamics and improve the fit of both of these quantities. The parameter dynamics (Figure 3, the bottom graph) show how affinity and yield on glucose (K_S and Y_{XS}) decrease, while the maintenance uptake grows (q_m), suggesting there is a larger substrate uptake coinciding with decreased growth of biomass, which happens when acetate is present in the culture. At the same time, the parameters related to oxygen suggest that the saturation of oxygen does not reach the physical maximum (DOT^*), effect encountered when the acetate has not been re-cycled. In addition, the increased volumetric oxygen transfer rate ($k_L a$), might be related to the extra oxygen cells use for metabolizing acetate.

Overall, we observe that parameters that demonstrate significant dynamics are all related to the missing kinetics, namely the inhibition of substrate uptake due to acetate and additional oxygen consumption due to incomplete acetate recycling during the feed pulses.

It is important to note that the parameter dynamics do not necessarily approximate the actual behaviour of the missing mechanisms, however, they still point to the misspecified parts of the base model.

6. Conclusions

In this work, an explainable and novel hybrid model has been presented as a framework for identifying and analyzing misspecifications of macro-kinetic models. The model demonstrates high predictive capacity as shown by our experiments. The proposed fitting procedure allows detecting any deviations from the observed process, as the hybrid model diverges from the base model only when the latter is not sufficient for a proper fit. It serves as a tool for verifying the applicability of existing models, and potentially developing new ones.

Acknowledgments

We gratefully acknowledge the financial support of the German Federal Ministry of Education and Research (01DD20002A – KIWI biolab).

References

Kim, J.W., Krausch, N., Aizpuru, J., Barz, T., Lucia, S., Martínez, E.C., Neubauer, P. and Bournazou, M.N.C., 2022. Model predictive control guided with optimal experimental design for pulse-based parallel cultivation. IFAC-PapersOnLine, 55(7), pp.934-939.

W. Quaghebeur, E. Torfs, B. De Baets, I. Nopens, 2022, Hybrid differential equations: integrating mechanistic and data-driven techniques for modelling of water systems. Water Research, 213, 118-166.

Oliveira, R., 2004. Combining first principles modelling and artificial neural networks: a general framework. Computers & Chemical Engineering, 28(5), pp.755-766.

Rangapuram, S.S., Seeger, M.W., Gasthaus, J., Stella, L., Wang, Y. and Januschowski, T., 2018. Deep state space models for time series forecasting. Advances in neural information processing systems, 31.

Anane, E., Neubauer, P. and Bournazou, M.N.C., 2017. Modelling overflow metabolism in Escherichia coli by acetate cycling. Biochemical engineering journal, 125, pp.23-30.

Flavio Manenti, Gintaras V. Reklaitis (Eds.), Proceedings of the 34th European Symposium on Computer Aided Process Engineering / 15th International Symposium on Process Systems Engineering (ESCAPE34/PSE24), June 2-6, 2024, Florence, Italy
 http://dx.doi.org/10.1016/B978-0-443-28824-1.50155-1

Optimizing deep neural networks through hierarchical multiscale parameter tuning

Bogdan Dorneanu[a], Sushen Zhang[b], Vassilios S. Vassiliadis[b], Harvey Arellano-Garcia[a]

[a]*LS Prozess- und Anlagentechnik, Brandenburgische Technische Universität Cottbus-Senftenberg, Cottbus, 03044, Germany*

Department of Chemical Engineering and Biotechnology, University of Cambridge, Cambridge, CB3 0AS, United Kingdom

arellano@b-tu.de

Abstract

Deep neural networks (DNNs) are frequently employed for information extraction in big data applications across various domains; however, their application in real-time industrial systems is hindered by constraints such as limited computational, storage capacity, energy availability, and time constraints. This contribution introduces the development of a novel hierarchical multiscale framework for the training of DNNs that incorporates neural sensitivity analysis for the automatic and selective training of neurons evaluated to be the most effective. This alternative training methodology generates local minima that closely match or surpass those achieved by traditional approaches, such as the backpropagation method, utilizing identical starting points for comparative purposes.

Keywords: Deep neural networks, Hierarchical multiscale search, Sensitivity analysis.

1. Introduction

Deep neural networks (DNNs) are widely employed across various domains, including manufacturing, waste valorization, or Internet of Things (Samek et al., 2021) owing to their distinctive ability to extract information from large datasets. State-of-the-art frameworks for their training have remained stable, involving neuron optimization through backpropagation, often combined with well-known algorithms such as gradient descent (Shrestha & Mahmood, 2019). However, their deployment in real-time applications faces challenges due to limited computational resources. Solutions involve hardware optimization for data flow and memory, as well as software methods like pruning (Choudhary et al., 2020). A powerful technique for reducing the requirements of DNNs, pruning removes redundant parameters and connections while preserving essential features of the system. Optimizing the network partially during each iteration raises the question of determining the optimal layer for the initial step. A suitable criterion for this is neural sensitivity analysis, widely used in understanding and demystifying the black-box nature of DNNs (Zhang et al., 2021).

Initially focused on how an output or objective changes with input perturbations, neural sensitivity analysis has evolved to consider the relative values of weights or inputs as sensitivity measures (Montaño & Palmer, 2003).

This work introduces a novel hierarchical multiscale framework for training of DNNs integrating neural sensitivity analysis to selectively train neurons identified as most effective. Key contributions include the employment of automatic differentiation and the

inclusion of first- and second-order information for sensitivity evaluation. Furthermore, a new definition of sensitivity measures is introduced, utilizing a scaling factor.
The paper is structured in the following way: Section 2 introduces the neural sensitivity analysis procedure based on scaling factors, while Section 3 describes the proposed hierarchical multiscale parameter tuning. Results from the application of the procedure on a case study are presented and discussed in Section 4, while Section 5 summarizes the conclusions of this work.

2. Scaling factors-based neural sensitivity analysis

The concept of utilizing a scaling factor in the training of a DNN is derived from Conejeros & Vassiliadis (2000) and enables efficient sensitivity ranking of each process step, simplifying the selection and quickly determining a minimal number of critical stages.
For the purpose of the analysis, a neural network is defined as the following process:

$$z_{l,i,k} = f(y_{l,i,k}) \tag{1}$$

Where z = output from a neuron, y = input to the neuron, $l = 1, \dots, NL$ is the layer index, while $i = 1, \dots, NN_l$ is the neuron index within the layer, and $k = 1, \dots, NK$ is the data point index.

In the proposed framework, the scaling factor plays a crucial role in the identification of the most sensitive pathways for optimizing the overall performance of the DNN. In the formulation of the network, this factor pre-multiplies the output value of a neuron as follows:

$$z_{l,i,k} = \theta_{l,i} \cdot f(y_{l,i,k}) \tag{2}$$

Where $\theta_{l,i} \in [0,1]$ are the scaling factors.

The sensitivity analysis procedure implies the solution of an optimization problem involving the set of parameters θ:

$$\begin{aligned} \phi &= \min_{x \in X} f(x;\, \theta) \\ s.t. \quad & h(x;\, \theta) = 0 \end{aligned} \tag{3}$$

Where the function h defines the neuron fitting constraints adopting the scaling factor as:

$$h_{l,i,k} = z_{l,i,k} - \theta_{l,i} \cdot f(y_{l,i,k}) \tag{4}$$

For the solution of the optimization problem defined in Eq. (3), the Lagrangian function is considered as:

$$\mathcal{L}(x, \lambda;\, \theta) = f(x;\, \theta) + \lambda^T h(x;\, \theta) \tag{5}$$

Where x = the set of tuning parameters of the optimization problem, λ = the set of Lagrange multipliers associated with the constraints h.

Finally, the total gradient of the objective function with respect to θ at the optimal point, (x^*, λ^*) is calculated as follows:

$$\frac{Df}{D\theta}\bigg|_{[x^*(\theta),\,\lambda^*(\theta),\theta]} = \left[\frac{\partial f}{\partial x}\frac{\partial x}{\partial \theta}\right]\bigg|_{[x^*(\theta),\,\lambda^*(\theta),\theta]} \quad (6)$$

Other equations that are considered define the influence of the node (l, i) at data point (k):

$$y_{l,i,k} = \sum_{j=1}^{NN_{l-1}} z_{l,j,k} \cdot W_{l,j,i} \quad (7)$$

With W = the bias term.

Based on the discussion above, the sensitivity of the neuron layer is computed by evaluating the partial derivatives of the objective function with respect to the scaling factor. The mean square of errors (MSE) is utilized as an objective function for the purpose of this analysis. The sensitivity value is determined through automatic differentiation.

3. Hierarchical multiscale parameter tuning of DNNs

The concept of the proposed hierarchical multiscale analysis approach (Fig. 1) involves the analysis at the highest level of abstraction, i.e., the entire network structured visualised as an Input/Output (I/O) system. Employing a set bisection strategy, the procedure is moving downward through an expanding binary search tree (Fig. 2), iteratively refining the level of detail considered for optimization, until user-defined criteria are satisfied or the final level of detail is reached. To illustrate the procedure, a DNN with one Input, one Output and seven Hidden layers is considered in Fig. 2.

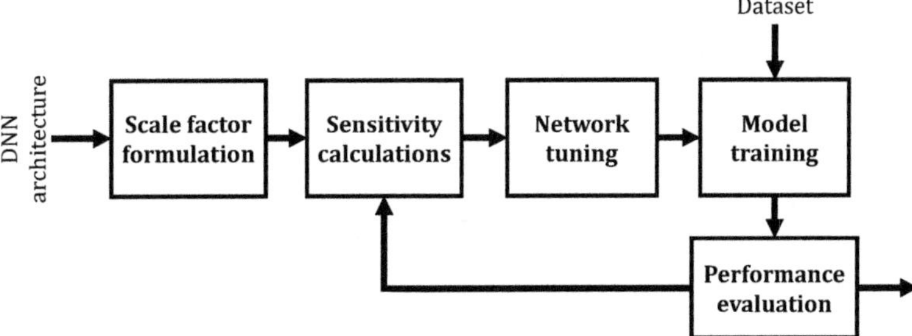

Figure 1: Hierarchical multiscale training of DNNs

At the first level of division, the network is split into two parts, and the focus is on the part of the tree with the highest sensitivity. This leads to subsequent divisions until the most sensitive layer is found. At each iteration, optimization is carried out for a single layer using the backpropagation method, and the process is reiterated through additional binary tree searches, until the convergence criterion is met.

To address the issue of layers being consistently trapped in a loop during selection, a randomized algorithm is introduced based on a probabilistic random factor. This approach introduces a trade-off between exploration and exploitation, allowing the neurons with lower sensitivity the opportunity for optimization.

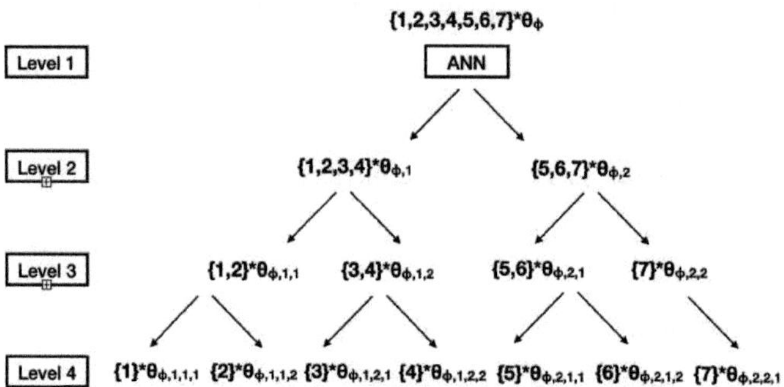

Figure 2: Binary tree partitioning of a DNN with θ sensitivity parameters

4. Results and discussion

The proposed hierarchical multiscale search algorithm for the tuning of the DNNs is implemented to a network with 20 and 50 hidden layers of 5 neurons each, respectively. The hyperparameters used for the performance comparison between the different training methods are summarised in Table 1.

Table 1: Hyperparameters used for the training of the DNN

Hyperparameter	Value
Trust region bound, ϵ	0.001
Learning rate	0.0001
Number of epochs in each iteration	1,000
Upper limit on number of iterations	200
Tolerance	0.001
Number of data points	10,000

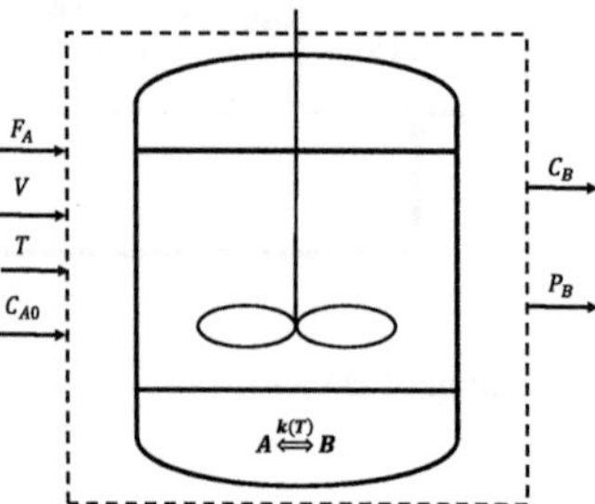

Figure 3: Chemical process with 4 inputs and 2 outputs

The dataset utilised for the training comes from a highly nonlinear chemical process (Fig. 3) that includes a first order chemical reaction, with the reaction rate given by an Arrhenius-type equation. In the figure, F represents flowrate, V the reactor volume, T the reactor temperature, C the concentration of A and B, while P is the productivity.

The algorithm is implemented in Python and run on a macOS Big Sur version 11.0.1 (20B29) with a 2.3GHz Quad-Core Intel Core i5 processor and a memory of 8GB 2133 MHz LPDDR3.

Table 2: Comparison results for a network with 20 hidden layers

Order	Backpropagation	First	Second
Training set MSE	0.93835	0.94697	0.94631
Testing set MSE	0.86888	0.97121	0.93880
Average epochs	200.00	397.26	397.26
Total iterations	97	50	50
Total CPU Time (s)	912.7	1,022.4	1,153.5
Average CPU time (s)	9.376	18.681	18.402

Table 3: Comparison results for a network with 50 hidden layers

Order	Backpropagation	First	Second
Training set MSE	1.00001	1.00000	1.00000
Testing set MSE	1.04468	1.00000	1.00000
Average epochs	200.00	208.83	416.67
Total iterations	100	100	50
Total CPU Time (s)	2,529.4	3,271.9	3,746.6
Average CPU time (s)	25.206	24.519	48.912

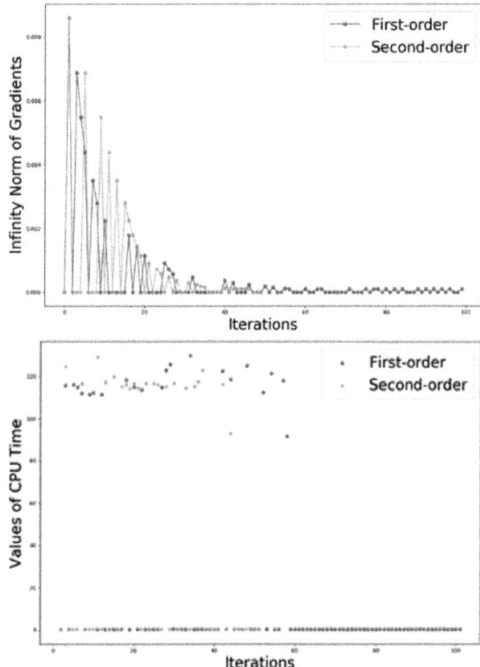

Figure 4: Convergence rate of optimization using first- and second-order information for the 50-layer network: Infinity norm of gradients (top); CPU time across iterations (bottom)

Tables 2 and 3 present the results obtained utilizing the end-to-end backpropagation, as well as the hierarchical approach based on first- and second-order information, for the 20 and 50-layer DNNs, respectively. The average values are obtained for each iteration, while the total values referring to all iterations.

From these results it can be observed that in the case of the 20-layer network, the classical approach is the fastest in terms of total CPU time and CPU time per iteration. Moreover, the approach considering second-order information is slightly faster than the first for the proposed multiscale search method. The number of iterations is the same for the two hierarchical approaches, and significantly lower compared to backpropagation. When looking at the results for the 50-layer network, the first-order approach is the fastest in terms of average CPU time, followed by the classical backpropagation method, demonstrating the advantage of the proposed search algorithm for large scale networks. Nonetheless, the second-order method requires a lower number of iterations. Furthermore, the approach utilizing the second-order information seems to converge slower initially compared to the first-order case, and reaching similar speeds of convergence after several iterations. As the convergence speed is different from the 20-layer case, it can be concluded that there is no fixed dominance of the first- over the second-order information approaches.

Finally, from the results in Fig. 4 it can be concluded that there is a polarization in terms of data points, indicating either very slow or immediate convergence of a particular network layer. These findings suggest that the sluggish convergence may be attributed to layers that exert a substantial influence on the overall performance of the model, implying uneven importance among the different layers within the network.

5. Conclusions

The novel hierarchical multiscale search algorithm for DNN tuning employs a levelled approach where the network undergoes successive divisions, evaluating layer sensitivity using automatic differentiation. The algorithm selects and optimizes one side of a binary tree at each level until a single layer remains. This process repeats iteratively until a convergence criterion is met, offering efficient optimization with $O(\log NL)$ complexity for large DNNs. The innovation lies in selective tuning, enabling rapid convergence and equilibration of sensitivity values, particularly for large-scale networks. Moreover, the algorithm incorporates randomization through a binary selector, enhancing performance by reducing repetition during the optimization. Case studies demonstrate the efficiency of the proposed method, producing solutions comparable to or better than conventional end-to-end backpropagation. Future research will explore leveraging the method for the structure evolution of the DNNs based on sensitivity values.

References

T. Choudhary et al., 2020, A comprehensive survey on model compression and acceleration, Artificial Intelligence Review, vol. 53, pp. 5133-5155

R. Conejeros & V.S. Vassiliadis, 2000, Dynamic biochemical reaction processs analysis and pathway modificaiton predictions, Biotechnol Bioeng, vol. 68, pp. 285-297

J. Montaño & A. Palmer, 2003, Numeric sensitivity analysis applied to feedforward neural networks, Neural Comput Appl, vol. 12, pp. 119-125

W. Samek et al., 2021, Explaining deep neural networks and beyond: A review of methods and applications, Proceedings of the IEEE, vol. 109, no. 3, pp. 247-278

A. Shrestha & A. Mahmood, 2019, Review of deep learning algorithms and architectures, IEEE Access, vol. 7, pp. 53040-53065

T. Zhang et al., 2021, A survey on neural network interpretability, IEEE Trans Emerg Topics Comput Intell, vol. 5, pp. 726-741

Flavio Manenti, Gintaras V. Reklaitis (Eds.), Proceedings of the 34th European Symposium on Computer Aided Process Engineering / 15th International Symposium on Process Systems Engineering (ESCAPE34/PSE24), June 2-6, 2024, Florence, Italy
 http://dx.doi.org/10.1016/B978-0-443-28824-1.50156-3

Simulation of Hydrogen-Methane Separation with Pressure Swing Adsorption

Viktor Kalman [a]*, Aleksander Makaruk [b], Ezgi Engin [c], Anton Balla [c], Michael Harasek [a]

[a]*Technische Universität Wien, Institute of Chemical, Environmental and Bioscience Engineering, Getreidemarkt 9/166-2, Vienna 1060, Austria*
[b]*Axiom angewandte Prozesstechnik GmbH, Wienerstraße 114, Ebreichsdorf 2483, Austria*
[c]*Verbund Green Hydrogen GmbH, Am Hof 6a, Vienna 1010, Austria*
**viktor.kalman@tuwien.ac.at*

Abstract

The global energy landscape is transforming as it shifts towards sustainability, with a growing emphasis on harnessing renewable energy sources and advancing energy storage technologies. Hydrogen plays a pivotal role in this transition as a versatile and potentially clean energy carrier. To address the seasonal variability of renewable energy generation, surplus renewable energy is converted to hydrogen during the summer, which is subsequently stored in depleted natural gas reservoirs for winter recovery, enabling electricity generation or direct use. A high-pressure, 4-bed Pressure Swing Adsorption (PSA) system was designed to separate hydrogen from the cushion gas containing varying amounts of methane. The main challenge lies in the fluctuating feed conditions encountered during winter recovery, where hydrogen concentration in the stream varies from 70% to 98% at pressures ranging from 25 to 60 bar, as direct feed pressurization is eliminated in favour of energy efficiency. A lab-scale PSA system has been constructed, and its experimental results for hydrogen-methane separation are employed to validate a simulation model and support the scale-up. The simulator, developed as open-source software in MATLAB, accurately captures the dynamic behaviour of the high-pressure PSA system, providing insights into breakthrough curves and system performance under realistic conditions. This research contributes to developing efficient and reliable hydrogen storage solutions that align with the current trends in the evolving energy economy, where hydrogen emerges as a key player in achieving a sustainable and resilient energy future.

Keywords: adsorption, hydrogen purification, modelling

1. Introduction

The need for efficient and scalable energy storage solutions is growing as global efforts intensify to transition towards renewable energy sources. The seasonal intermittency of renewable resources, such as solar and wind, necessitates the development of storage technologies capable of accommodating large quantities of energy over extended periods. Hydrogen has the potential to serve as a clean and versatile energy carrier and offers a promising solution for long-term storage. Subsurface geological formations such as salt caverns, aquifers, or depleted oil and gas reservoirs are being investigated globally for this purpose. Porous rock formations, like depleted oil and gas fields and aquifers, are widely available, so several projects, such as HyUnder and HyStories, have been undertaken in Europe to assess the potential sites for hydrogen storage. (Cihlar et al.,

2021) found 80 suitable depleted gas fields around Europe with a total working capacity of 792 TWh. Pure hydrogen or a hydrogen-methane mix can be injected into the porous rock so that the hydrogen content may vary from a few per cent to 100 per cent (Londe, 2021). Ongoing pilot and demonstration projects were collected by (Sambo et al., 2020). Recent projects in Austria and Argentina showed that injection and storage with up to 20 % hydrogen can be safely done. Meanwhile, the storage of pure hydrogen is currently being investigated in Austria in the Underground Sun Storage 2030 project. (Zamehrian and Sedaee, 2022) investigated the effect of cushion gas on underground hydrogen storage in a partially depleted gas reservoir and concluded that the highest purity can be achieved if nitrogen is used as a cushion gas. (Lyssy et al., 2021) showed that different levels of hydrogen injection have different challenges. Pure hydrogen injection resulted in low recovery because most hydrogen remained underground as cushion gas. Recovery can only be increased at the expense of purity, but the impurity levels in the withdrawn gas vary during cyclic operation. (Juez-Larré et al., 2023) used numerical modelling to conduct a feasibility study to quantify the efficiency of different operating strategies at three potential sites for underground hydrogen storage.

Most depleted gas reservoirs are not empty and contain significant amounts of natural gas as cushion gas because the porous structure relies – to some extent – on the gas pressure to prevent the strata from crumbling. The injected hydrogen (pure or mixed form) will blend with the existing cushion gas, especially when stored for an extended period. The hydrogen-natural gas mixture can be withdrawn and injected into the network if local regulations allow it. Alternatively, hydrogen can be separated at the wellhead, for example, using pressure swing adsorption (PSA) technology, to be used directly in mobility applications, transported separately, or transformed into electricity.

PSA is a cyclic separation process with one or more fixed beds going through several pressure-varying and constant pressure steps (Ruthven et al., 1993). The beds are filled with porous material such as activated carbon, molecular sieve, or metal-organic frameworks (MOFs) on which some species are preferentially adsorbed from the gas mixture at high pressure, allowing the light component to be collected as the product. Before the breakthrough of the impurities, the feed is stopped, and the pressure is decreased to regenerate the bed. The number of beds can go up to 12 in Polybed systems, while the number of steps in a single cycle usually ranges from 4 to 12, depending on the complexity and number of pressure equalization steps. Polybed systems are complex, large-scale units that can produce ultrapure H_2 with more than 90 % recovery (Luberti and Ahn, 2022). Hydrogen purification is a common use of PSA but is also used for air separation, biogas upgrading, and spacesuit life support systems (Papale et al., 2006).

In this work, experimental results from (Kalman et al. 2022) are used to validate a simulation model of a 4-bed pressure swing adsorption process to address the challenges from varying hydrogen fractions in the withdrawn gas during cyclic operation, contributing to the development of efficient and reliable hydrogen storage solutions.

2. Models and Methods

The simulations are performed in MATLAB® with the Totally Open Pressure Swing Adsorption Intensification Laboratory (toPSAil) simulation code from (Kim and Scott, 2023) at the Georgia Institute of Technology. toPSAil is an open-source simulation framework for dynamic modeling and simulation of pressure swing adsorption (PSA) processes. The simulator is based on a CSTRs-in-series (CIS) model that describes the adsorbers as a series of continuously stirred tank reactors (CSTRs) in 1-dimensional form. It has a variety of adsorption isotherm models implemented and uses Linear Driving Force approximation for mass transfer description. The resulting system of differential-algebraic equations is solved by built-in solvers from MATLAB®. The complete modelling and simulation framework and its implementation are found in the original publication (Kim and Scott, 2023).

2.1. Lab-Scale Rig

The breakthrough experiments and PSA cycles were carried out in a self-assembled rig. The flow rates and the mixture ratio of feed gases were controlled by mass flow rate controllers. The high pressure in the bed was maintained by a manual back pressure regulator, and the adsorption columns were custom-manufactured and certified to up to 100 bar. The columns were filled with cylindrical activated carbon from Donau Carbon. The adsorbent and the packed bed properties are listed in Table 1.

Table 1: Packed bed properties

Packed bed height [mm]	1800
Column internal diameter [mm]	25
Bed porosity [-]	0.315
Adsorbent mass [g]	480
Bulk density [kg/m3]	795
Particle diameter [mm]	3
Particle porosity [-]	0.83

2.1.1. Adsorption Isotherm

Desorex C33 (from Donau Carbon) was used to fill the bed. The adsorption isotherms were measured in different pressure ranges at 20 °C with the Dynamic Column Breakthrough method as described by (Malek and Farooq, 1996). The results were fitted with the Extended Langmuir Model as in Eq. 1, where n_i is the adsorbed quantity, q_i^* and b_i are isotherm parameters, N is the number of adsorbing species, P is total pressure and y is the mol fraction in the gas phase. The resulting parameters are listed in Table 2.

$$n_i = q_i^* \cdot \frac{b_i P y_i}{1 + \sum_j^N b_j P y_j} \tag{1}$$

Table 2: Adsorption isotherm parameters

Langmuir parameters	**CH_4**	**H_2**
q^* [mol/g]	8.9452	1.0982
b [1/bar]	0.00375	0.073962

2.2. Cycle Design

The proposed PSA cycle in this study has 12 steps, including two pressure equalization steps to improve efficiency. The step sequence for all beds is shown in Figure 1.

2.3. Simulation Conditions

Hydrogen content and overall gas pressure were assumed to decrease through a withdrawal period, and four scenarios in accordance with the four stages from the previously published experimental results were selected (Kalman et al., 2022). The lab-scale columns were assumed to be isothermal, and the mass transfer rate was constant.

The breakthrough curves were evaluated for breakthrough times and compared to experimental results. Breakthrough was defined as the time from feed gas injection to where methane concentration in the product reached 0.1 %. The cyclic simulations were evaluated for hydrogen purity and recovery and compared to experimental results, where applicable. All simulations were conducted on a *Lenovo ThinkCentre M75q Gen 2* desktop computer in MATLAB® 2023a.

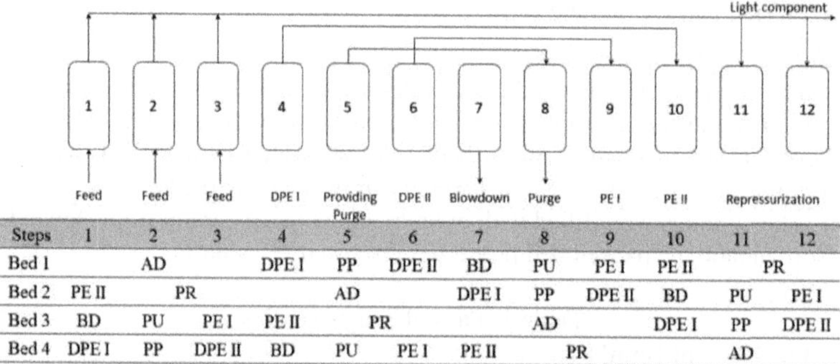

Steps	1	2	3	4	5	6	7	8	9	10	11	12
Bed 1	AD			DPE I	PP	DPE II	BD	PU	PE I	PE II	PR	
Bed 2	PE II	PR		AD			DPE I	PP	DPE II	BD	PU	PE I
Bed 3	BD	PU	PE I	PE II	PR		AD			DPE I	PP	DPE II
Bed 4	DPE I	PP	DPE II	BD	PU	PE I	PE II	PR		AD		

Figure 1: Cyclic configuration of PSA process for hydrogen purification.

3. Results

3.1. Breakthrough Results

Results of breakthrough experiments from (Kalman et al., 2022) were used to validate the kinetic and equilibria model of the simulation. In Fig. 2. the experimental breakthrough curves are compared to isothermal simulations. The low mass transfer resistance, indicated by the sharp initial rise (front), is captured accurately in all four scenarios. The isothermal assumption for the lab-scale columns is acceptable, although the experimental values flatten and show slowing kinetics near equilibrium. This could be due to the increased temperature, which favors desorption in the dynamic equilibrium. However, at this scale, the isothermal assumption is valid as it only introduces a small error in the equilibration time but has no effect on the breakthrough times, the focus of this investigation.

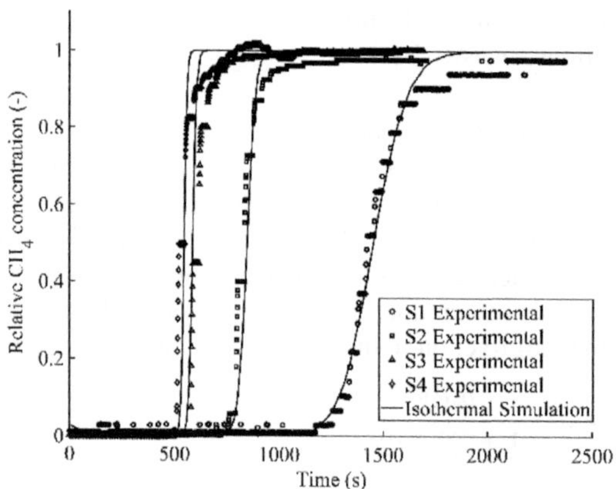

Figure 2: Breakthrough curves for all stages; methane concentration at the end of bed.

Table 3: Breakthrough results

	Breakthrough time [s]	
	Experiment	Simulation
Stage 1	1175	1106
Stage 2	723	733
Stage 3	521	510
Stage 4	495	489

3.2. Results of Cyclic Simulations

After the model validation with breakthrough curves, the cyclic tests from (Kalman et al., 2023) were modelled and correlated well with experimental results. Due to the isothermal solution, a cyclic steady state was reached in tens of cycles. The pressure profile of one column in a full cycle in cyclic steady state (CSS) is shown in Fig. 3a. The rate of pressure decrease in the equalization steps is higher than the theoretical rate. This occurrence could be mitigated by adjusting the valve coefficients. However, this behavior is consistent with the experimental setup where solenoid valves were installed, and precise flow control was unavailable.

Fig. 3b. shows the adsorbed amount of methane along the bed at the end of the adsorption, pressure equalization (PE), and purging steps. Full solid loading and equilibrium are not reached in CSS. At the end of the bed, only 1/6th of the full methane capacity is adsorbed. This allows methane to re-adsorb during the subsequent pressure equalization (PE) steps despite the lowered maximum capacity. It ensures that the connected bed is not contaminated before its adsorption cycle, and by the end of the purging step, no methane is adsorbed, and the clean bed is ready for the next adsorption cycle.

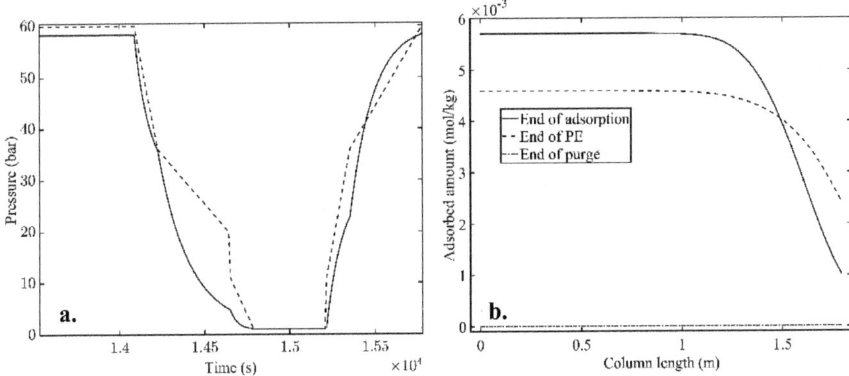

Figure 3: Example results from cyclic simulation. **a.** Pressure profile of a single column in cyclic steady state. **b.** Adsorbed amount of methane along the bed.

3.3. Optimization

For all stages, the step times were adjusted from the experimental baseline to find the Pareto front for each stage where purity is the highest possible while maintaining at least 80 % hydrogen recovery. Results are collected in Table 4. and the Pareto front is shown in Fig. 4. The trade-off between purity and recovery is more challenging in scenarios where the feed concentration of the contaminant is high. However, the results show that the performance can be optimized with careful selection of step times, and the target values can still be achieved. Unfortunately, stage 4 results (where feed methane concentration is highest) were not recoverable due to technical issues during the simulation.

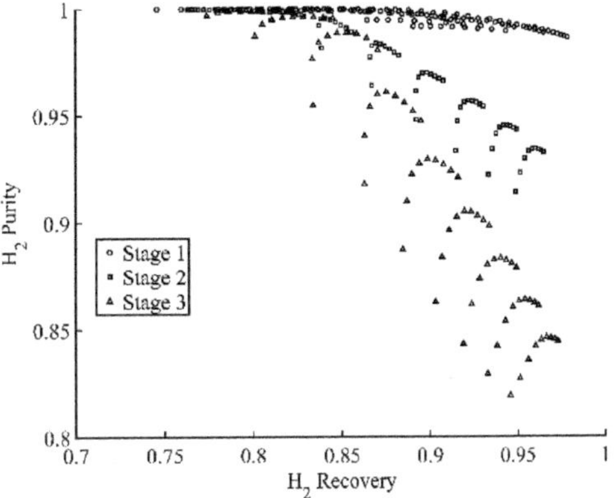

Figure 4: Optimization results of the 12-step PSA process for Stages 1/2/3.

Table 4: PSA process optimization results

	Experimental				Optimization			
	Cycle Time	P/F	Purity	Recovery	Cycle Time	P/F	Purity	Recovery
Stage 1	2320	0.12	99.5 +	80.9	2254	0.15	99.99	80.37
Stage 2	1496	0.38	99.5 +	73.3	1777	0.32	99.91	81.13
Stage 3	1152	0.30	99.5 +	73.1	1644	0.36	99.88	80.51
Stage 4	688	0.30	99.5 +	76	N/A	N/A	N/A	N/A

4. Conclusion

This study used the open-source toPSAil software package to simulate hydrogen-methane separation at four pressures (25, 35, 50, 60 bar) with varying methane concentrations (2 – 30 %) in a 4-bed PSA process. Previous experimental results were used to validate the model with breakthrough and cyclic simulations, both of which showed good correlation. The proposed 12-step PSA process was successfully optimized in three out of the four scenarios. This work demonstrates the capabilities of toPSAil, an open-source process simulation package, and contributes to developing efficient and modular separation systems for hydrogen purification.

References

J. Cihlar, D. Mavins, K. van der Leun, 2021, Picturing the Value of Underground Gas Storage to the European Hydrogen System, The Netherlands, Gas Infrastructure Europe

J. Juez-Larré, C.G. Machado, H. Yousefi, T.-K. Wang, R. Groenenberg, S. Van Gessel, 2023, (Pre)feasibility Study of Underground Hydrogen Storage Potential in Depleted Gas Fields and Salt Caverns in the Netherlands, EGU General Assembly 2023, DOI: 10.5194/egusphere-egu23-10005

V. Kalman, J. Voigt, C. Jordan, M. Harasek, 2022, Hydrogen Purification by Pressure Swing Adsorption: High-Pressure PSA Performance in Recovery from Seasonal Storage, Sustainability, 14, 14037, DOI: 10.3390/su142114037

T. Kim, J.K. Scott, 2023, Dynamic Modeling and Simulation of Pressure Swing Adsorption Processes Using toPSAil, Computers and Chemical Engineering, 176, 108309, DOI: 10.1016/j.compchemeng.2023.108309

L. Londe, 2021, Four Ways to Store Large Quantities of Hydrogen, Paper presented at the Abu Dhabi International Petroleum Exhibition and Conference, Abu Dhabi, UAE, DOI: 10/2118/208178-MS

M. Lysyy, M. Fernø, G. Ersland, 2021, Seasonal Hydrogen Storage in a Depleted Oil and Gas Field, Int. J. Hydr. Energy, 46, 25160-25174, DOI: 10.1016/j.ijhydene.2021.05.030

A. Malek, S. Farooq, 1996, Determination of Equilibrium Isotherms Using Dynamic Column Breakthrough and Constant Flow Equilibrium Desorption, J. Chem. Eng. Data, 41, 25-32, DOI: 10.1021/je950178e

W. Papale, H. Paul, G. Thomas, 2006, Development of Pressure Swing Adsorption Technology for Spacesuit Carbon Dioxide and Humidity Removal, SAE Technical Paper 2006-01-2203, DOI: 10.4271/2006-01-2203

D.M. Ruthven, S. Farooq, K.S. Knaebel, 1993, Pressure Swing Adsorption, VCH Publisher Inc., USA

C. Sambo, A. Dudun, S.A. Samuel, P. Esenenjor, N.S. Muhammed, B. Haq, 2022, A Review on Worldwide underground hydrogen Storage Operating and Potential Fields, Int. J. Hydr. Energy, 47, 22840-22880, DOI: 10.1016/j.ijhydene.2022.05.126

M. Zamehrian, B. Sedaee, 2022, Underground Hydrogen Storage in a Partially Depleted Gas Condensate Reservoir: Influence of Cushion Gas, Journal of Petroleum Science and Engineering, 212, 110304, DOI: 10.1016/j.petrol.2022.110304

M. Zijp, S. Nelskamp, H. Doornenbal, 2017, European Unconventional Oil and Gas Assessment (EUOGA): Resource Estimation of Shale Gas and Shale Oil in Europe, Technical Report

Flavio Manenti, Gintaras V. Reklaitis (Eds.), Proceedings of the 34th European Symposium on Computer Aided Process Engineering / 15th International Symposium on Process Systems Engineering (ESCAPE34/PSE24), June 2-6, 2024, Florence, Italy
 http://dx.doi.org/10.1016/B978-0-443-28824-1.50157-5

Reverse Supply Chain Network Design of a Polyurethane Waste Upcycling System

Dalga Merve Özkan,[a] Sergio Lucia,[a] Sebastian Engell[a*]

[a]*Technische Universität Dortmund, Emil-Figge-Str. 70, 44227 Dortmund, Germany*
sebastian.engell@tu-dortmund.de

Abstract

This paper presents a general mathematical programming framework for the design and optimization of supply chain infrastructures for the upcycling of plastic waste. For this purpose, a multi-product, multi-echelon, multi-period mixed-integer linear programming (MILP) model has been formulated. The objective is to minimize the cost of the entire circular supply chain starting from the collection of post-consumer plastic waste to the production of virgin-equivalent high value polymers, satisfying a large number of constraints from collection quota to the quality of the feedstock. The framework aims to support the strategic planning of future circular supply chains by determining the optimal number, locations and sizes of various types of facilities as well as the amounts of materials to be transported between the nodes of the supply chain network over a specified period. The functionality of the framework has been tested with a case study for the upcycling of rigid polyurethane foam waste coming from construction sites in Germany. The economic potential and infrastructure requirements are evaluated, and it has been found that from a solely economic perspective, the current status of the value chain is not competitive with fossil-based feedstock or incineration. However, with the right economic incentives, there is a considerable potential to establish such value chains, once the upcycling technology is ready and the economic framework conditions have stabilized.

Keywords: plastic waste, optimization, supply chain network design, circular economy

1. Introduction

In response to the urgent need for carbon-neutral economies and a more sustainable future, plastic waste upcycling has gained significant interest. Compared to mechanical recycling, this approach aims to extract valuable molecules from end-of-life or production waste via chemical processing, enabling their reintegration into the production of high-value polymers, and thereby fostering circular value chains. These value chains, with their potential to displace or diminish fossil-based raw material usage in polymer production, hold great promise for a sustainable future. However, design and implementation of such value chains is a demanding and complex task. For example, chemical upcycling often requires a specific type of waste feedstock, which must be carefully separated from other materials. Achieving these standards in waste separation can be logistically challenging and may necessitate substantial modifications to existing collection, sorting and dismantling processes. Secondly, the resource-intensive and complex nature of chemical upcycling technologies pose financial and operational hurdles, such as significant investments in technology and workforce training. Therefore, the successful integration of chemical upcycling technologies with waste management infrastructures and waste separation technologies requires the solution of a complex multi-faceted design problem to achieve regulatory compliance, and economic feasibility.

In this study, we present an adaptable framework that is designed to model, simulate, analyze, and optimize circular supply chains. We formulate the problem as a deterministic mixed-integer linear program (MILP), which computes strategic-level decisions on: (i) the optimal number, locations and sizes of the processing facilities, (ii) the optimal material flows between the nodes of the network under an economic objective. The multi-period deterministic model provides valuable insights into the layout of the system and the interactions among its components. It will be extended to a stochastic model to handle uncertainties in the future. Our framework can be applied to any region or supply chain of interest. We illustrate the proposed approach with the case study of a value chain for the upcycling of rigid polyurethane (PUR) foam waste in Germany as a representative of high-value plastic waste.

2. Model formulation

2.1. Sets

In the formulation, a node represents a geographical location in the studied region. We consider each node as a source of the targeted post-consumer waste material to be collected and as a possible location for installing facilities. The upcycling infrastructure model comprises six echelons: sources, collection facilities, recovery and treatment facilities, chemical processing facilities, downstream processing facilities, and consumers. We denote the set of sources by S^o. The set of materials, including intermediate and final products in the supply chain, is denoted by P. The sets of collection facilities, recovery and treatment facilities, chemical processing facilities and downstream processing facilities are denoted by CF, RTF, CPF and DPF. The set of sinks (i.e. consumers of end products or chemical production facilities) of the upgrading system is denoted by S^i. For each type facility there is a set of discrete size options denoted by C^{CF}, C^{RTF}, C^{CPF} and C^{DPF}. The set of time periods is denoted by T.

2.2. Parameters

Each source $i \in S^o$ has a known waste supply $\sigma_{tpi} \in \mathbb{R}^+$ for a certain material type $p \in P$ in time period $t \in T$. Similarly, each consumer $n \in S^i$ has a demand $\delta_{tpn} \in \mathbb{R}^+$ for a certain product type $p \in P$ in time period $t \in T$. The minimum total processing quota (an environmental policy parameter) for a certain material type $p \in P$ that has to be collected from the sources in time period $t \in T$ is η_{tp}. The transportation cost associated with carrying one ton of material $p \in P$ per unit distance between the nodes is t_p. The transportation distances between the network nodes $i \in S^o$, $j \in CF$, $k \in RTF$, $l \in CPF$, $m \in DPF$ and $n \in S^i$ are represented by D_{ij}, D_{jk}, D_{kl}, D_{lm} and D_{mn}, respectively. All transportation is assumed to be carried out via roads, and the transportation distances are estimated according to the *Haversine distance* formula. Each type of facility has a maximum capacity θ^c_{CF}, θ^c_{RTF}, θ^c_{CPF}, $\theta^c_{DPF} \in \mathbb{R}^+$ for handling all materials $p \in P$ according to the choice of the size and an annualized installation cost $\alpha^I_{CF,c}$, $\alpha^I_{RTF,c}$, $\alpha^I_{CPF,c}$, $\alpha^I_{DPF,c} \in \mathbb{R}^+$ for each size option, an operating cost per ton of processed material α^O_{CF}, α^O_{RTF}, α^O_{CPF}, $\alpha^O_{DPF} \in \mathbb{R}^+$ and a yield factor $\gamma_{p,CF}$, $\gamma_{p,RTF}$, $\gamma_{p,CPF}$, $\gamma_{p,DPF} \in \mathbb{R}$ for certain product $p \in P^{out}_{CF} \subset P, p \in P^{out}_{RTF} \subset P, p \in P^{out}_{CPF} \subset P, p \in P^{out}_{DPF} \subset P$ to be produced from a subset of materials $p \in P^{in}_{CF} \subset P, p \in P^{in}_{RTF} \subset P, p \in P^{in}_{CPF} \subset P, p \in P^{in}_{DPF} \subset P$.

2.3. Decision variables

In the presented model, there are two types of decision variables. The flows of a certain material type $p \in P$ between the nodes of the network are represented by a continuous variable $x \in \mathbb{R}^+$: The flow of material transported from source $i \in S^o$ to sink $j \in CF$ of capacity $c \in C^{CF}$ in time period $t \in T$ is x_{tpijc}, similarly from $j \in CF$ to $k \in RTF$ it is x_{tpjkc}, from $k \in RTF$ to $l \in CPF$ it is x_{tpklc}, from $l \in CPF$ to $m \in DPF$ it is x_{tplmc}, from $m \in DPF$ to $n \in S^i$ it is x_{tpmn}. The installation decisions of facilities are represented by binary variables $b \in \{0,1\}$ and can be stated as follows: The installation decision of $j \in CF$ of capacity $c \in C^{CF}$ is b_{jc}, similarly for $k \in RTF$ of capacity $c \in C^{RTF}$ it is b_{kc}, for $l \in CPF$ of capacity $c \in C^{CPF}$ it is b_{lc}, for $m \in DPF$ of capacity $c \in C^{DPF}$ it is b_{mc}.

2.4. Objective function

The objective is to minimize the total cost of the upcycling infrastructure. The first and second terms in Eq. (1) account for the installation and operating costs of facilities, and the last term accounts for the transportation costs of round trips.

$$
\begin{aligned}
min \Bigg\{ \Bigg(& \sum_{c \in C^{CF}} \sum_{j \in CF} \alpha^I_{CF,c}\, b_{jc} + \sum_{c \in C^{RTF}} \sum_{k \in RTF} \alpha^I_{RTF,c}\, b_{kc} + \sum_{c \in C^{CPF}} \sum_{l \in CPF} \alpha^I_{CPF,c}\, b_{lc} \\
&+ \sum_{c \in C^{DPF}} \sum_{m \in DPF} \alpha^I_{DPF,c}\, b_{mc} \Bigg) + \sum_{t \in T} \Delta T_t \Bigg(\sum_{j \in CF} \alpha^O_{CF} \sum_{c \in C^{CF}} \sum_{p \in P} \sum_{i \in S^o} x_{tpijc} \\
&+ \sum_{k \in RTF} \alpha^O_{RTF} \sum_{c \in C^{RTF}} \sum_{p \in P} \sum_{j \in CF} x_{tpjkc} + \sum_{l \in CPF} \alpha^O_{CPF} \sum_{c \in C^{CPF}} \sum_{p \in P} \sum_{k \in RTF} x_{tpklc} \\
&+ \sum_{m \in DPF} \alpha^O_{DPF} \sum_{c \in C^{DPF}} \sum_{p \in P} \sum_{l \in CPF} x_{tplmc} \Bigg) + 2 \times \sum_{t \in T} \Delta T_t \Bigg(\sum_{c \in C^{CF}} \sum_{p \in P} \sum_{i \in S^o} \sum_{j \in CF} D_{ij}\, t_p\, x_{tpijc} \\
&+ \sum_{c \in C^{RTF}} \sum_{p \in P} \sum_{j \in CF} \sum_{k \in RTF} D_{jk}\, t_p\, x_{tpjkc} + \sum_{c \in C^{CPF}} \sum_{p \in P} \sum_{k \in RTF} \sum_{l \in CPF} D_{kl}\, t_p\, x_{tpklc} \\
&+ \sum_{c \in C^{DPF}} \sum_{p \in P} \sum_{l \in CPF} \sum_{m \in DPF} D_{lm}\, t_p\, x_{tplmc} + \sum_{p \in P} \sum_{m \in DPF} \sum_{n \in S^i} D_{mn}\, t_p\, x_{tpmn} \Bigg) \Bigg\}
\end{aligned}
\tag{1}
$$

2.5. Constraints

The following constraints are added to the problem. Demand satisfaction:

$$
\sum_{m \in DPF} x_{tpmn} \leq \delta_{tpn} \quad \forall\, t \in T, p \in P, n \in S^i \tag{2}
$$

The minimum collection quota is described as:

$$
\sum_{c \in C^{CF}} \sum_{i \in S^o} \sum_{j \in CF} x_{tpijc} \geq \eta_{tp} \sum_{i \in S^o} \sigma_{tpi} \quad \forall\, t \in T,\ p \in P \tag{3}
$$

The flow conservation at the sources can be defined as:

$$
\sum_{c \in C^{CF}} \sum_{j \in CF} x_{tpijc} \leq \sigma_{tpi} \quad \forall\, t \in T, p \in P,\ i \in S^o \tag{4}
$$

The flow conservation at the facilities (written for all other facilities similarly) is:

$$\gamma_{p,CF} \sum_{c \in C^{CF}} \sum_{p \in P_{CF}^{in}} \sum_{i \in S^o} x_{tpijc} = \sum_{c \in C^{RTF}} \sum_{k \in RTF} x_{tpjkc} \quad \forall t \in T, p \in P_{CF}^{out}, j \in CF \tag{5}$$

The maximum treatment capacity at the facilities (written for all other facilities similarly):

$$\sum_{p \in P} \sum_{i \in S^o} x_{tpijc} \leq \theta_{CF}^{c}\, b_{jc} \quad \forall t \in T, j \in CF, c \in C^{CF} \tag{6}$$

The selection of a single facility of same type (written for all other facilities similarly):

$$\sum_{c \in C^{CF}} b_{jc} \leq 1 \quad \forall j \in CF \tag{7}$$

The demand satisfaction constraint in Eq. (2) imposes the compliance with the capacities of the consumers. The constraints given in Eq. (3) and (4) ensure that the waste material is collected from the sources and shipped to collection facilities by respecting both the available waste material amount at the sources and the minimum collection quota. Eq. (5) enforces flow conservation at the facilities so that all the material entering a facility is processed and shipped to the next stage in the supply chain according to the yield factors associated with each technology and material. The maximum treatment capacities at the facilities given in Eq. (6) limit the total amount of material that can be delivered to a facility of chosen size. Eq. (7) makes sure that only one facility is chosen from multiple size (maximum capacity) options.

3. Case study description and assumptions

The proposed model is tested with a real case study for the upcycling of rigid polyurethane foam waste coming from construction sites in Germany. For more details about the estimation of annual PUR waste generation from construction materials and the selection of the nodes of the supply chain network, the reader can refer to Özkan et al. (2023). The potential locations for opening up facilities along with the relative amount of waste generated at the source nodes are shown in Figure 1a.

The supply chain operations are as follows: The PUR containing waste is collected separately in big bags on the construction sites, and not mixed with other construction waste. Then, all of the construction waste and the big bags are taken to CFs via skip trucks. The PUR waste is consolidated at CFs, and it is transported by trucks to RTFs for mechanical separation and compression into briquettes. After this stage, the briquettes are sent to CPFs where they are pre-conditioned and converted into pyrolysis oil via a catalytic pyrolysis process. Then the pyrolysis oil is further purified at DPFs to the desired final products. It is also possible to include the selection among technologies (or processing route) with the presented framework. However, the data on the PUR waste compositions as well as the details about the range of operations inside the facilities and their yields are not yet known precisely and still under research, therefore values that reflect the present state of knowledge are assumed and the selection of the processing routes selection is not considered in the current study.

In this study, for the CFs there are 8, for the RTFs, CPFs and DPFs there are 5 different processing capacity options each. The planning horizon includes three 4-month time periods, because the level of construction and demolishing or renovation activities in a region may vary. In this study, a variation in the volumes of the supplies by 10 to 30% is considered.

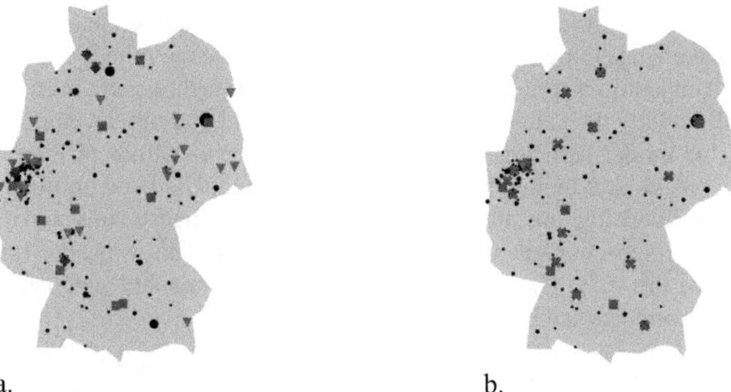

Figure 1. a. The potential locations for opening up CFs (black circles), RTFs (magenta squares), CPFs and DPFs (red triangles) and the existing phosgenation plants to which the output of the chemical recycling can be fed (blue diamonds). The relative amount of waste material generated at the sources is indicated by the sizes of the circles. b. The optimal infrastructure layout with CFs (green crosses), RTFs (magenta squares), CPF and DPF (red triangle).

4. Results and discussion

The number of binary and continuous variables in the presented case study are 1284 and 2,789,388, respectively. The model is implemented using Python programming language and solved with Gurobi 10.0.3 to 3.5% optimality gap within 2.2 h on a computer with 13th Gen Intel® Core™ i9-13900K CPU @ 3.00 GHz and 128 GB RAM.

In the optimal layout, there are 15 CFs, 7 RTFs, one CPF and one DPF. The network has a decentralized structure at the collection stage; but becomes increasingly centralized over the following stages, culminating in a single, integrated chemical and downstream processing facility. The decentralized configuration of CFs and RTFs is primarily driven by the pressure to minimize the transportation costs associated with carrying the lightweight PUR material alongside other high-density construction waste (Each trip contains a very low wt. % of PUR waste). As the processing progresses along the value chain, the material undergoes transformations into denser forms – initially into briquettes and subsequently into pyrolysis oil. This densification significantly increases the transportation efficiency. Also, along the chain, the predominant cost factor shifts to the investment required for establishing technologically advanced chemical upcycling and downstream processing facilities. These facilities are capital-intensive, reaping the benefits of economies of scale. Consequently, establishing a single large-scale facility proves to be more economically viable than maintaining a decentralized structure. Supporting this conclusion, Ma et al. (2023) and Crîstiu et al. (2024) reported similar findings in their recent studies, which explored the reverse supply chain design for post-consumer plastic waste in the United States and Italy. The resulting optimal infrastructure design is shown in Figure 1b. The cost structures are shown in Figure 2 and it can be seen that the total cost is dominated by the investment and operating costs. In Figure 3, the material flows are visualized for a section of the supply chain with the help of Sankey diagrams.

5. Conclusions

This work introduces a general modelling framework that provides a basis for designing and understanding plastics upcycling value chains. The presented multi-period model enables the assessment of the system robustness in the presence of uncertain parameters, considering not only the changes in waste quantities but also changes in other parameter values, such as waste compositions, prices and regulatory constraints that may occur over time. Future work will include the extension to a stochastic model and the development of an independent actor model to better represent the multi-player nature of circular supply chains. Within this kind of model, money flows are also modelled and optimized, providing a basis for influencing the market by tuning the revenue streams and for developing market activating actions at the player-specific levels. This way, the right incentives that will drive the value chain towards a financially sustainable state can be determined and effective policies can be formulated.

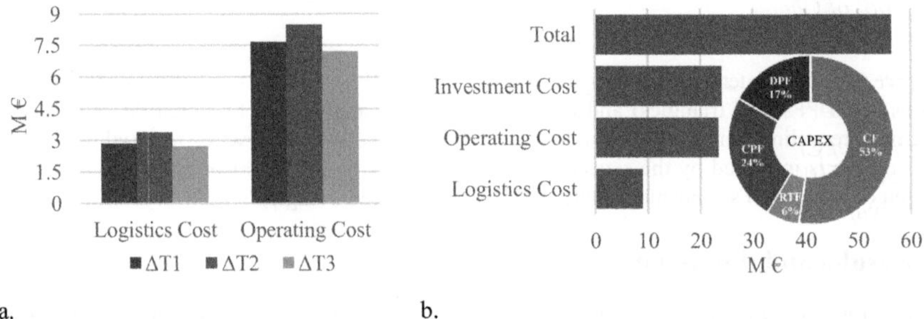

a. b.

Figure 2. a. Logistics and operating costs in each time period, b. Total cost breakdown of the optimal solution.

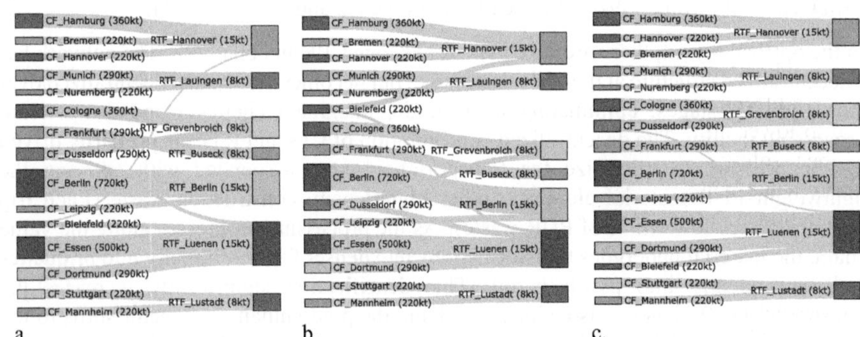

Figure 3. Sankey diagrams showing material flows from CFs to RTFs in a. ΔT_1, b. in ΔT_2, c. in ΔT_3 (Annual maximum processing capacities of the facilities are shown in parentheses).

Acknowledgments

This study has funded by the European Union's Horizon 2020 research and innovation programme as part of the project "Circular Foam" under grant agreement No 101036854.

References

Özkan, D. M., Lucia, S., Engell, S. (2023). Optimal Facility Location and Sizing for Waste Upcycling Systems. Chemical Engineering Transactions (In press)

Ma, J., Tominac, P. A., Aguirre-Villegas, H. A., Olafasakin, O. O., Wright, M. M., Benson, C. H., Huber, G. W., Zavala, V. M. (2023). Economic evaluation of infrastructures for thermochemical upcycling of post-consumer plastic waste. Green Chemistry, 25(3), 1032-1044

Crîstiu, D., d'Amore, F., Bezzo, F. (2024). Economic and environmental optimisation of mixed plastic waste supply chains in Northern Italy comparing incineration and pyrolysis technologies. Computers & Chemical Engineering, 102(17), 7860-7870

Flavio Manenti, Gintaras V. Reklaitis (Eds.), Proceedings of the 34th European Symposium on Computer Aided Process Engineering / 15th International Symposium on Process Systems Engineering (ESCAPE34/PSE24), June 2-6, 2024, Florence, Italy
 http://dx.doi.org/10.1016/B978-0-443-28824-1.50158-7

Design and Optimization of Green Hydrogen Production System with Wind-Solar Coupled Natural Gas Power Generation Considering Carbon Emission: The Case of China

Tingting Zhao,[a] Yan Wu,[a,b] Yufei Wang,[a,*] Xiao Feng[c]

[a]*School of Chemical Engineering and Environment, China University of Petroleum (Beijing), 18 Fuxue Road, Changping, Beijing, 102249, China*

[b]*China Huanqiu Contracting & Engineering CO., LTD, No.1 Chuangda 2nd Road, Laiguangying Hi-tech Industrial Park, Chaoyang District, Beijing, 100012, China*

[c]*School of Chemical Engineering and Technology, Xi'an Jiaotong University, Xi'an, Shaanxi 710049, China*

wangyufei@cup.edu.cn

Abstract

With industrial development and population growth, worldwide energy consumption has increased dramatically, it has become a common consensus to vigorously develop renewable energy. As an efficient storage medium, hydrogen is an important way to store excess energy from wind-solar systems. However, changes in climatic conditions lead to large fluctuations in the output power of renewable energy such as wind and solar, which in turn leads to large fluctuations in hydrogen production from wind and solar. Currently, restrictions on the integration of renewable energy into the grid have led to lower grid security for new projects. Adding natural gas (NG) power stations is one solution. Therefore, a methodology for the integration of hydrogen production from wind, solar, NG, and hydrogen storage is constructed, including solar power generation unit, wind power generation unit, NG power generation unit, electrolyzer unit, hydrogen storage unit, and energy storage unit. Under the premise of fully considering the carbon emission and engineering practical factors, the model optimizes the capacity of each unit of the system under different conditions through a real case study to obtain the most economical scale configuration. Results show that the NG power generation unit can help the system to implement the dispatching scheme and can smooth the fluctuation of wind-solar to hydrogen production, which also keeps hydrogen carbon emissions below the upper limit. The model achieves the deep coupling of wind-solar energy and NG power generation, improves the flexibility of the system, and provides useful assistance for the green and low-carbon transition of energy.

Keywords: Green hydrogen, Natural gas power, Carbon emission, Capacity optimization

1. Introduction

In recent years, the energy crisis and greenhouse effect have become increasingly prominent and have become an urgent challenge for the world (Walmsley et al 2023). Green and low carbon is the main direction of future energy development. In this direction, renewable energy and hydrogen energy play a key role. According to IEA forecasts, the total global renewable energy power generation will reach as high as 4,500 GW in 2024. Hydrogen energy is an ideal zero-carbon energy source. It can not only consume renewable energy but also be used as raw material to produce green products. However, due to the intermittency and fluctuation of wind and solar power generation, the hydrogen produced by wind and solar power fluctuates. Coupling NG with wind-solar hydrogen production can solve this problem well.

As traditional fossil energy, NG has the characteristics of cleanness and low carbon compared with petroleum and coal (Jia et al 2023). Many researchers have focused on integrating renewable energy and NG in microgrids, combined cooling, heating, and power (CCHP) systems, integrated energy systems (IESs), and integrated electricity and NG systems. Ju et al (2016) constructed a CCHP and renewable energy-based hybrid energy system driven by distributed energy resources (DERs CCHP). The system includes three subsystems: the electricity subsystem, the CCHP subsystem, and the auxiliary heating subsystem. The electricity subsystem is powered by wind, solar, and NG. Mei et al (2021) proposed a distributed IES stochastic operation optimization model including renewable energy and NG. It promoted the consumption of renewable energy. Sun et al (2020) developed a shared platform framework that includes NG networks, distributed renewable energy generation systems, and energy storage. The framework focuses on promoting energy sharing throughout the system and increasing system flexibility.

The above researches have achieved the integration of renewable energy and NG, but they did not consider carbon emissions in these models. Therefore, this paper constructs an integrated model of wind-solar coupled NG power generation, hydrogen production, and storage. The model considers many practical engineering factors, such as the efficiency of wind and solar power generation, the carbon emissions of NG and grid power, battery charge and discharge losses. The system capacity is designed and optimized, with a focus on analyzing the impact of NG on system economics.

2. Problem statement

The framework of hydrogen production system from wind-solar coupled NG is shown in Figure 1. The system consists of wind and photovoltaic power generation units, NG power generation unit, grid unit, electricity storage unit, water electrolysis hydrogen production unit, and hydrogen storage unit.

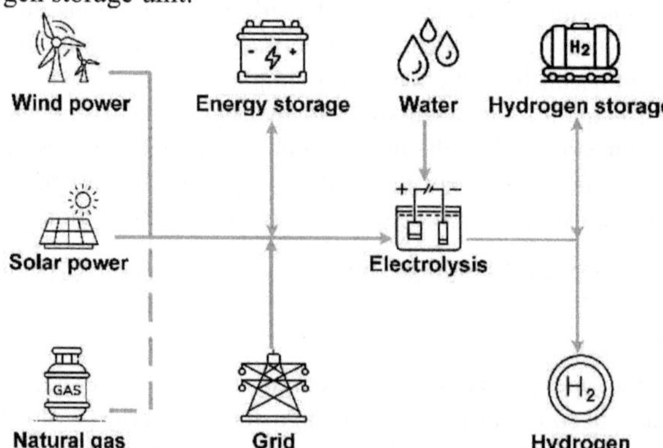

Figure 1. The framework of hydrogen production system from wind-solar coupled NG

Since wind and solar power generation has random fluctuations in seasonal, monthly, and hourly, in order to smooth the volatility of wind and solar power, NG was added to the system to explore changes in the reliability and economy of the NG coupled wind and solar power system. Therefore, this paper constructs two mathematical programming models, one is used to describe the characteristics of the system without NG and solve for the optimization variables, and the other is used to describe the characteristics of the system with NG and solve for the optimization variables.

The models consider the fluctuation of wind, solar, and the grid price. Taking the maximum annual income of the project as the objective function, the impact of NG power on the system is analyzed.

3. Mathematical Model

3.1. Objective function

The objective function is to maximize the annual income (AR), as shown in Eq. (1):

$$\max AR = C^{WS} + C^{B} + C^{E} + C^{S,H_2} + C^{T} + C^{P} + c^{Grid} + c^{NG} - c^{Sale,H_2} \tag{1}$$

Where C^{WS} , C^{B} , C^{E} , C^{S,H_2} are the wind power and photovoltaic investment costs, energy storage investment costs, electrolyzers investment costs, and hydrogen storage tanks investment costs, respectively. C^{T} is the costs of maintenance, repair, management, insurance, etc. C^{P} is the costs of total employee compensation. c^{Grid} is the cost of grid electricity. c^{NG} is the total cost of NG, c^{Sale,H_2} is the income of selling hydrogen.

3.2. Power balance constraints

The amount of electricity in the system follows the principle of energy conservation, that is, the amount of electricity supplied is equal to the amount of electricity consumed, as shown in Eq. (2):

$$\begin{aligned} &P_t^{WT} + P_t^{PV} + p_t^{Eout}\eta^{Eout} + p_t^{G,Off} + p_t^{Gas} \\ &= p_t^{H_2} + p_t^{Ein}/\eta^{Ein} + p_t^{Aba} + p_t^{H_2Com,InS} + p_t^{H_2Com,OutS} \quad (t \in 1,2,3...N^T) \end{aligned} \tag{2}$$

Where P_t^{WT} is the power generated by the WT at t-th hour, P_t^{PV} is the power generated by the photovoltaic at t-th hour, p_t^{Eout} is the discharging power of energy storage at t-th hour, η^{Eout} is the discharge efficiency of energy storage, $p_t^{G,Off}$ is the off-grid electricity at t-th hour. p_t^{Gas} is the power generated by the NG at t-th hour, $p_t^{H_2}$ is the input power of the alkaline electrolyzer at t-th hour, p_t^{Ein} is the charging power of energy storage at t-th hour, η^{Ein} is the charge efficiency of energy storage, p_t^{Aba} is the power curtailment at t-th hour, $p_t^{H_2Com,InS}$ and $p_t^{H_2Com,OutS}$ are the compressor power consumption required for hydrogen to enter and exit the hydrogen storage tank at t-th hour.

3.3. Carbon emissions constraints

According to *Standard and evaluation of low-carbon hydrogen, clean hydrogen and renewable hydrogen* (T/CAB 0078-2020), the system imposes carbon emission constraints on grid power and NG power, as shown in Eq. (3):

$$(EF^{Off}\sum_{t=1}^{N^T} p_t^{Off} + EF^{Gas}\sum_{t=1}^{N^T} p_t^{Gas}) \Big/ \sum_{t=1}^{N^T} v^{PH_2} \le E^{CO_2} \tag{3}$$

Where EF^{Off} is the carbon emission factors of grid electricity, EF^{Gas} is the carbon emission factors of NG, v^{PH_2} is the amount of hydrogen consumed to produce liquid hydrogen at t-th hour, E^{CO_2} is the carbon emissions of the clean hydrogen standard.

4. Case study

To show the effectiveness and feasibility of the proposed method, this section applies the established model to a real case. The wind and solar resource data in this case are taken from Xinjiang Uygur Autonomous Region, China. The installed capacities of photovoltaic and wind power are 635 MW and 150 MW, respectively, and the NG scale is an optimization variable. The system is allowed to buy electricity, but not allowed to sell electricity. Two cases will be analyzed and studied. Case 1 is the system without NG, and Case 2 is the system with NG, the optimization results are shown in Table 1.

The results show that with the same carbon emissions, the annual income and hydrogen production of Case 2 are higher than those of Case 1, which shows that adding NG to the system reduces carbon emissions. The scale of hydrogen storage in Case 1 is much higher than that in Case 2. This is caused by the fluctuations in wind and solar power and grid electricity prices. So, more hydrogen needs to be stored to smooth out the fluctuations of the system and keep the system stable. The fluctuations of wind and solar also lead to the increase of the curtailment rate in Case 1. At the same time, the system with NG promotes the consumption of renewable energy and improves the stability of the system.

Table 1. Comparison of optimization results

Variables	Case 1	Case 2
Consumption of electricity generated by NG (10^8 kWh·y^{-1})	0	0.51
Grid electricity (10^8 kWh·y^{-1})	0.13	0
Proportion of electricity generated by NG to total electricity consumption (%)	0	4.09
Proportion of grid electricity to total electricity consumption (%)	1.10	0
Total electricity consumption (10^8 kWh·y^{-1})	12.10	12.55
Cost of NG (10^8 CNY·y^{-1})	0	0.47
Cost of grid electricity (10^8 CNY·y^{-1})	0.041	0
Total investment cost (10^8 CNY·y^{-1})	55.88	56.20
Annual income (10^8 CNY·y^{-1})	1.18	1.37
Carbon emissions (kgCO_2/kg H_2)	0.49	0.49
Curtailment rate (%)	5.58	5.02
Total hydrogen production (10^8 Nm^3·y^{-1})	2.28	2.37
NG scale (MW)	0	17.99
Energy storage scale (MW)	0	0
Hydrogen storage scale (10^4 Nm^3·h^{-1})	73.79	1.57
Number of electrolyzers	86	88

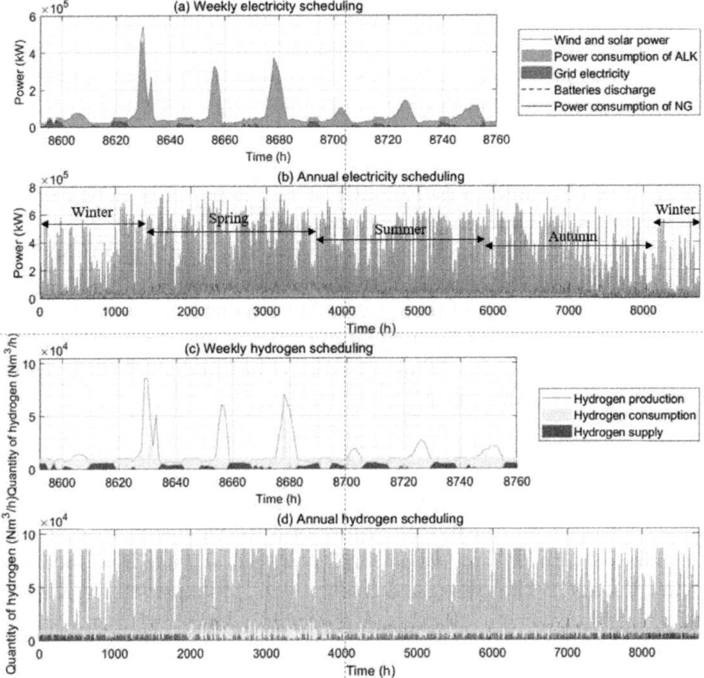

Figure 2. Annual and weekly power/hydrogen scheduling of case 1

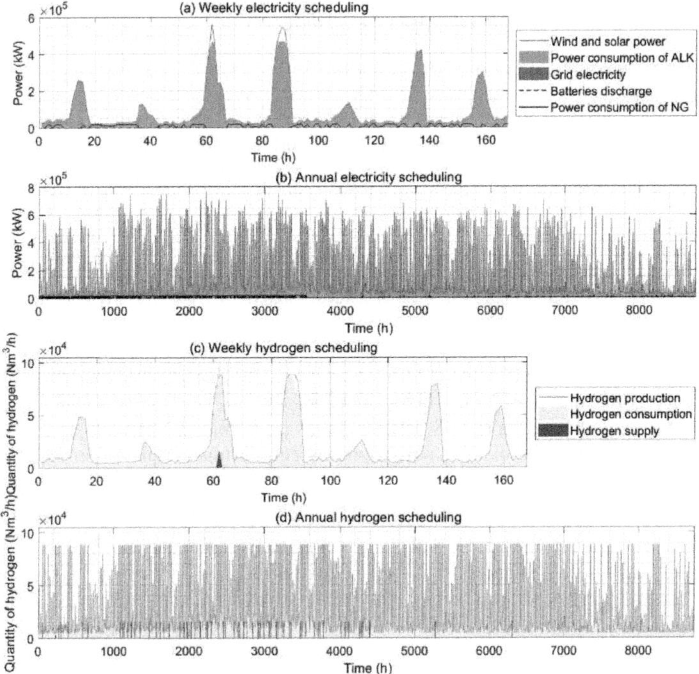

Figure 3. Annual and weekly power/hydrogen scheduling of case 2

Figure 2 shows the annual and weekly power/hydrogen scheduling of Case 1. (a) and (b) show that when wind and solar power generation is insufficient, the system will purchase electricity to reduce the fluctuation of wind and solar power, and more electricity is purchased in autumn and winter, less electricity is purchased in spring and summer. (a) and (c) show that the more wind power is generated, the more hydrogen is produced. when wind and solar power generation is insufficient, the amount of hydrogen supply increases to maintain the relative stability of the hydrogen production load. The scale of energy storage is 0, which indicates that purchasing grid power is more economical than allocating energy storage under the current price system.

Figure 3 shows the annual and weekly power/hydrogen scheduling of Case 2. (a) and (b) show that when wind and solar power generation is insufficient, NG power generation is used to stabilize the fluctuation of the system. At the same time, it can be seen from (c) (d) of Figure 2 and Figure 3 that the amount of hydrogen supplied in Case 2 is less than that in Case 1. This is because by adding NG, the system produces hydrogen more stable, and therefore stores less hydrogen.

5. Conclusion

By taking the maximum annual income as the objective function, this research innovatively establishes an integrated optimization model for wind-solar coupled NG power generation, hydrogen production, and hydrogen storage. The model draws the following conclusions by comparing and analyzing the system with and without NG:

1. The economy of the system with NG is better than that of the system without NG.
2. Wind-solar coupled NG smoothes the fluctuation of wind and solar and improves the flexibility of the system.
3. The system with NG reduces carbon emissions.
4. The system with NG promotes the consumption of renewable energy and reduces the curtailment rate.

Future work will take uncertainties such as wind and solar into account in the model, and consider expanding the downstream products of hydrogen.

References

T. G. Walmsley, M. Philipp, M. Picón-Núñez, H. Meschede, M. T. Taylor, F. Schlosser 2023, Hybrid renewable energy utility systems for industrial sites: A review, Renewable and Sustainable Energy Reviews, 188:113802

L. Ju, Z. Tan, H. Li, Q. Tan, X. Yu and X. Song 2016, Multi-objective operation optimization and evaluation model for CCHP and renewable energy based hybrid energy system driven by distributed energy resources in China, Energy, 111:322-40.

W. Jia, C. Gong, K. Pan and S. Yu 2023, Potential changes of regional natural gas market in China amidst liberalization: A mixed complementarity equilibrium simulation in 2030, Energy, 284:129254.

F. Mei, J. Zhang, J. Lu, J. Lu, Y. Jiang, J. Gu 2021, Stochastic optimal operation model for a distributed integrated energy system based on multiple-scenario simulations, Energy, 219:119629

L. Sun, J. Qiu, X. Han, X. Yin and Z. Y. Dong 2020, Capacity and energy sharing platform with hybrid energy storage system: An example of hospitality industry, Applied Energy, 280:115897

Flavio Manenti, Gintaras V. Reklaitis (Eds.), Proceedings of the 34th European Symposium on Computer Aided Process Engineering / 15th International Symposium on Process Systems Engineering (ESCAPE34/PSE24), June 2-6, 2024, Florence, Italy
 http://dx.doi.org/10.1016/B978-0-443-28824-1.50159-9

A comprehensive gray-box framework for high-fidelity process simulation calibration

Jaime David Ponce-Rocha[a*] , David Camilo Corrales[b]

[a]*Dirección de Ingeniería y Construcción de Plantas, CIATEQ A.C. Centro de Tecnología Avanzada, Av. del Retablo 150, Constituyentes Fovissste, Queretaro, Querétaro, 76150, México.*

[b]*Toulouse White Biotechnology (TWB), INRAE, UMS (1337), 135 Avenue de Rangueil, Toulouse, 31077, France.*

jaime.ponce@ciateq.mx

Abstract

The hybrid models (gray-box models) architecture allows for obtaining a simple and robust tool for chemical process description, where a process simulator represents the white-box model, and an artificial neural network (ANN) involves the black-box model. This study incorporates a case study of calibrating a simulation model based on conventional distillation using a hybrid model that associates operational data from a chemical plant with the results of a process simulator, and six operative scenarios were evaluated for the framework validation. The arrangement of the gray-box model involves a white-box with a black-box model parallel sequence, and later, the results validation was performed in the white-box model. The results showed that a hybrid model allowed obtaining a simulation with a better approximation to the behaviours of the system compared to conventional thermodynamic models, as well as identifying the optimal range of feed flow (425,994.98-475,938.10 kg/h) and the approximated optimal flow design (469,738.80 kg/h).

Keywords: Hybrid models, data-driven models, distillation column, artificial neural networks.

1. Introduction

A chemical process description can be achieved through three ways: a) First-Principia models (White-box models), b) Data-driven models (Black-box models), and c) Hybrid approach model (Gray-box models), which combine the advantages of the a) and b) models into a joint architecture, obtaining a simple and robust model capable of harnessing the advantages of both models (Kurz et al., 2022).

Process simulators as computer-aided tools allow the conceptualization, evaluation, and optimization of any chemical process through a priori knowledge (First-Principia models: Material/Energy balances, thermodynamics, transport laws, kinetic laws, etcetera). Nevertheless, the integration of operational data with a process simulator represents added value for any company because it enables continuous improvement of the simulation model, process understanding, identification of relevant factors, relationships between operational variables, and ensuring an economically competitive operation (Asprion et al., 2019; Foo & Elyas, 2023).

On the other hand, the use of machine learning has become a powerful tool with applications in industrial scenarios, where the data-driven models based on technologies such as artificial neural networks (ANN) have been consolidated as appropriate tools, thus allowing for carry out the calibration and optimization of process systems mentioned above, handling the nonlinearity of process with multivariable inputs and outputs, and often having better results than more sophisticated statistical techniques (Su et al., 1992).

A grey-box model can be represented by different configurations between the black-box and white-box models (serial or parallel arrangements). However, when input and output operational data and the simulation model are available, an integrated model based on a semi-serial arrangement (illustrated in section 3) represents a suitable integrated model, where a first preprocessing of the data inputs is done in a white-box and black box parallel sequence, and later the outputs are taken like a new fed in the white box model for the final validation (Zapf & Wallek, 2021). These model arrangements offer advantages associated with lower computational expenses because they can substitute unknown components of a pure white-box model like finding non-available parameters, fitting numerical deviations of models, or finding a fast model for process optimization. Thus, this work aims to develop a comprehensive framework for gray-box models with high-fidelity results, using computer-aided tools like a process simulator, and data-driven models, as well as to identify the best operational point based on the relevant variables of the process.

2. Case study

This work involves a case study of calibrating a simulation model based on conventional distillation using a grey-box model that incorporates operational data from a chemical plant and the results of a process simulator. The study evaluates six different operating conditions for framework validation. The calibration framework focuses on improving the prediction of liquid-vapor equilibrium using the Soave Redlich Kwong (SRK) equation of state. Figure 1 shows the distillation column diagram, where the separation and purification of methanol in a quaternary mixture is carried out (methanol-MeOH, water-H_2O, dimethyl ether-DME, and ethanol-EtOH) (Adams II et al., 2018).

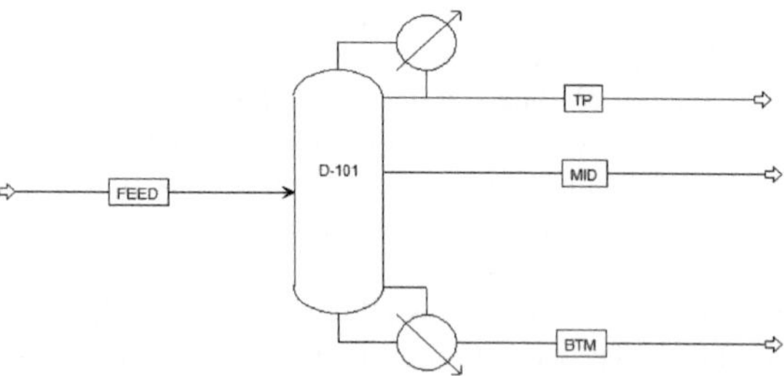

Figure 1. Case study: distillation column with fifty number of stages.

A set of one hundred twenty-two operational data was obtained, where the main variables with upper and lower bounds were: inlet mass flow (313,850.00, 658,095.00 kg/h), top mass flow (267,526.65, 607,342.00 kg/h), top mass composition (0.90, 0.99), condenser duty (-439.96, -180.54 MW), and reboiler duty (178.97, 435.87 MW). Figure 2 shows the operational behavior and correlation of all variables mentioned above. The reflux ratio

(RR=1.00), top pressure (1.36 bar), top temperature (117.00 °C), and input mass fractions (MeOH-0.8312, H_2O-0.1661, DME-0.0019, EtOH-0.0007) were held constant without variations.

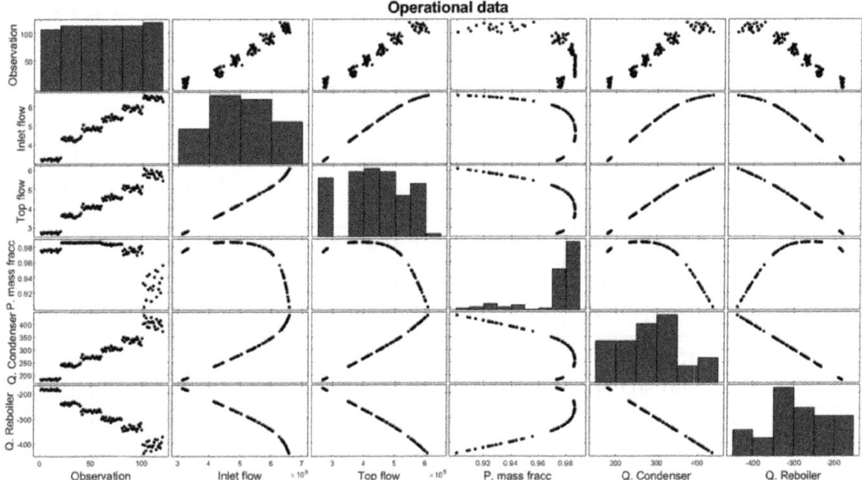

Figure 2. Operational data: observation, inlet mass flow (kg/h), top mass flow (kg/h), product mass fraction, condenser duty (MW), reboiler duty (MW).

3. Methodology

3.1. A comprehensive gray-box framework for high-fidelity process simulation calibration

The framework involves the integration of four systematic steps, where a process simulation and operational data are available: 1) Selection of scenarios, 2) Calibration and validation model in black-box model, 3) Validation of results, and 4) Identification of optimal operative zone. The white-box model was represented through a model simulation developed in Aspen Plus, while the black-box model and the framework were implemented in Python.

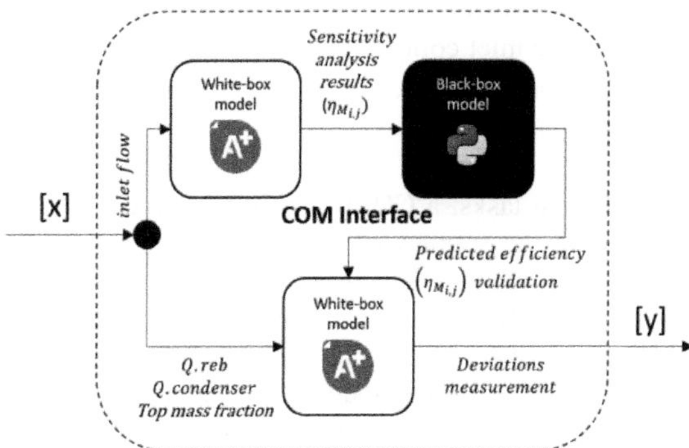

Figure 3. Gray-box model arrangement.

3.2. Selection of scenarios

Based on the graphical results shown in Figure 2, it is possible to observe six representative operating zones considering the inlet mass flows. Therefore, Table 1 shows the selected operational points used as input data for the gray-box model.

Table 1. Operational scenarios.

Scenario	Inlet flow (kg/h)	Top flow (kg/h)	Product mass frac	Condenser duty (MW)	Reboiler duty (MW)
I	328,292.00	278,757.00	0.9771	185.80	-187.40
II	425,995.00	358,720.00	0.9859	237.20	-238.90
III	475,938.00	400,769.00	0.9862	265.00	-266.90
IV	558,616.00	472,852.00	0.9816	314.20	-316.40
V	590,502.00	503,250.00	0.9751	336.60	-339.00
VI	649,336.00	584,499.00	0.9236	410.80	-414.40

3.3. Calibration and validation model

Although rigorous models based on non-equilibrium (mass transfer) for process simulation may be available or developed, these represent a significant computational and mathematical expense mainly, when these are components of a plant simulation or when an optimization task is required. An alternative to detailed mass transfer models involves the use of thermodynamic models based on phase equilibrium calculations, as well as the implementation of correction factors based on theoretical fundaments. For distillation columns, the Murphree efficiencies (Equation 1) is the most widely used equation:

$$\eta_{M_{i,j}} = \frac{y_{i,j} - y_{i,j+1}}{y^{*}_{i,j} - y_{i,j+1}} \tag{1}$$

Where $\eta_{M_{i,j}}$ is the Murphree vapor efficiency for component (*i*) on stage (*j*), and can be seen as a simplified mass transfer parameter that describes, how much the vapor composition changes from the inlet composition ($y_{i,j}$) to the outlet composition ($y_{i,j+1}$) while approaching the equilibrium composition ($y^{*}_{i,j}$) for each column stage (Brunazzi et al., 2018).

For calibration and validation tasks, a COM interface between Python and Aspen Plus was developed to automate the framework steps. Initially, a sensitivity analysis was performed on the process simulator, generating a dataset with different values of the Murphree efficiency (0.10-0.99). This dataset was used in order to train the Artificial Neural Network (ANN) (test size: 30 %) and the obtention of the estimated efficiency value. Subsequently, this estimated value underwent validation in the process simulation, and the Root Mean Square Error (RMSE) was used as a performance metric to measure the differences between predicted and real values.

The neural networks employed were multi-layer perceptron (3) using a rectified linear unit activation function (ReLU) with a sequential model and 750 epochs for each evaluated scenario.

3.4. Identification of optimal operative zones

For the identification of optimal operative zones, the reboiler duty, condenser duty, and product mass fraction were considered relevant variables. Therefore, the use of the utopia-tracking approach was implemented to identify the condition with minimum reboiler and condenser duty and a maximum purity of the product.

4. Results

Table 2 shows a comparative summary between the operative data, results of the hybrid model (calibrated), and the First-Principia model (process simulator results), the six scenarios report the value of the Murphree efficiencies, reboiler duty, condenser duty, top mass fraction, and the RMSE.

Table 2. Summary of the main results.

Scenario	Murphree efficiency (ηM) (%)	Reboiler duty (MW)	Condenser duty (MW)	Top mass fraction	RMSE	
I	-	185.80	-187.40	0.9771	-	OD
	0.67	184.58	-186.03	0.9702	1.06	C
	1.00	181.79	-182.97	0.9841	3.45	NC
II	-	237.20	-238.90	0.9859	-	OD
	0.79	237.58	-239.24	0.9778	0.29	C
	1.00	235.69	-237.31	0.9846	1.27	NC
III	-	265.00	-266.90	0.9862	-	OD
	0.79	265.44	-267.22	0.9780	0.31	C
	1.00	263.35	-265.08	0.9847	1.42	NC
IV	-	314.20	-316.40	0.9816	-	OD
	0.71	313.11	-315.15	0.9740	0.63	C
	1.00	309.13	-311.07	0.9845	4.25	NC
V	-	336.60	-339.00	0.9751	-	OD
	0.66	332.31	-334.46	0.9706	3.61	C
	1.00	326.78	-328.80	0.9850	8.17	NC
VI	-	410.80	-414.40	0.9236	-	OD
	0.60	367.85	-370.20	0.9651	35.58	C
	1.00	359.36	-361.53	0.9851	42.59	NC
OD-Operative data, C-Calibrated simulation, NC-Non-calibrated simulation						

The RMSE implementation allowed quantifying the deviation between operational data and the hybrid model or process simulation results. The predictions for scenarios I to IV exhibit the lowest deviation values, accompanied by the highest product mass fraction. For inlet mass flows greater than 590,502.00 kg/h, the RMSE values for the gray-box model and process simulation show a significant increase. These increases are associated with an overflow in the distillation column; consequently, the prediction of the liquid-vapor equilibrium begins to be affected even with the gray-box model implementation.

The implementation of the utopia-tracking approach enables the identification of the best operative point, characterized by a product mass purity of 0.9863, reboiler duty of 261.46 MW, condenser duty of -263.35 MW, and an inlet mass flow of 469,739.0 kg/h. These conditions correspond to an optimal operative zone between scenario II and III values.

5. Conclusions

The results showed that a hybrid model allowed obtaining a simulation with a better approximation to the system behavior concerning conventional thermodynamic models (SRK), as well as estimating Murphree efficiencies values quickly, accurately, and continuously for the model, reducing the future instrumentation investment and experimental determination of unknown parameters.

On the other hand, it is possible to infer that the increase in the feed flow within the column presents a direct relationship with higher operating costs; however, there is a point at which the purity and, therefore, the efficiency of the stages reaches a maximum, which is associated with an operation close to the column design flow (approximately 469,739.00 kg/h). Finally, the proposed tools and methodology allow obtaining an area of opportunity for the generation of more complex analyses extrapolated towards the dynamic operation of the system and integration of more variables to generate greater robustness in the predictions of the hybrid model.

Acknowledgments

Jaime David Ponce-Rocha acknowledges the financial support from CIATEQ-Advanced Technology Center for the development of this project.

References

T. A. Adams II, T. Thatho, M. C. Le Feuvre, & C. L. E. Swartz, 2018, The Optimal Design of a Distillation System for the Flexible Polygeneration of Dimethyl Ether and Methanol Under Uncertainty, Frontiers in Energy Research, 6(Jun), 41.

N. Asprion, R. Böttcher, R. Pack, M. E. Stavrou, J. Höller, J. Schwientek, & M. Bortz, 2019, Gray-Box Modeling for the Optimization of Chemical Processes, Chemie Ingenieur Technik, 91(3), 305–313.

E. Brunazzi, E. Sorensen, J. Bausa, & J. Steimel, 2018, Extending Murphree Tray Efficiency from Mass to Heat Transfer in Distillation, Chemical engineering transactions, 69.

D. C. Y. Foo, & R. Elyas, 2023, Introduction to process simulation, Chemical Engineering Process Simulation, 3–28.

S. Kurz, H. De Gersem, A. Galetzka, A. Klaedtke, M. Liebsch, D. Loukrezis, S. Russenschuck, & M. Schmidt, 2022, Hybrid modeling: towards the next level of scientific computing in engineering, Journal of Mathematics in Industry, 12(1), 1–12.

H.-T. Su, N. Bhat, P.A. Minderman & T. J. McAvoy, 1992, Integrating Neural Networks with First Principles Models for Dynamic Modeling, IFAC Proceedings Volumes, 25(5), 327–332.

F. Zapf & T. Wallek, 2021, Gray-box surrogate models for flash, distillation and compression units of chemical processes, Computers & Chemical Engineering, 155, 107510.

Flavio Manenti, Gintaras V. Reklaitis (Eds.), Proceedings of the 34th European Symposium on Computer Aided Process Engineering / 15th International Symposium on Process Systems Engineering (ESCAPE34/PSE24), June 2-6, 2024, Florence, Italy
 http://dx.doi.org/10.1016/B978-0-443-28824-1.50160-5

Analysis of Calcium Citrate Salts as Raw Material for Tributyl Citrate Bio-Plasticizer Production: Kinetic Modeling, Process Simulation, and Optimization

Andres F. Cabeza[a,b], Alvaro Orjuela[a*], David E. Bernal Neira[b,c,d]

a Universidad Nacional de Colombia, Department of Chemical and Environmental Engineering, Bogotá, Colombia

b Purdue University, Davidson School of Chemical Engineering, West Lafayette, IN, USA

c Universities Space Research Association, Research Institute of Advanced Computer Science, Mountain View, CA, USA

d Quantum Artificial Intelligence Lab., NASA Ames Research Center, Moffett Field, CA, USA

aorjuelal@unal.edu.co

Abstract

This work studied an alternative intensification approach for the downstream recovery of citric acid (CA) and its further transformation into tributyl citrate (TBC) bio-plasticizer. Avoiding several purification steps required to obtain citric acid, solid calcium citrate (CaCiH) was directly used in the production of the citrates. A set of experiments was conducted and proper kinetic modeling was derived for further process simulation. Three scenarios were evaluated in which the conventional TBC production process was compared to a novel simultaneous acidification-esterification process (SAE process). Based on the process simulation, the SAE process was optimized with respect to gross profits with FOQUS software, selecting the best conditions regarding temperature and Butanol (BuOH):CaCiH molar ratio in the SAE reaction stage. Also, a life cycle assessment (LCA) using OpenLCA was conducted to compare the optimal novel process and the current industrial approach for TBC production. Promising results were obtained since a ~ 25% increase in gross profit compared to the conventional process was achieved alongside a decrease of up to 31% in some environmental impact indicators.

Keywords: Esterification, solid-liquid reaction, Tributyl citrate, FOQUS, process intensification, process optimization

1. Introduction

The global plasticizer market keeps growing, driven by the increased use of plastic materials, mainly PVC. Phthalates, petroleum-derived phthalic acid esters, are the most common plasticizers (Godwin, 2017). However, due to their toxic nature and environmental persistence (Wang & Qian, 2021), they have been banned in various applications leading to the search for eco-friendly alternatives. Among such alternatives, citric acid esters, especially tributyl citrate (TBC), are considered viable substitutes for phthalates. However, TBC production is hindered by high costs due to energy-intensive processes and the need for highly purified raw materials. Citric acid (CA) is produced through aerobic fermentation of sugars and it is precipitated from the fermentation broth as calcium acid citrate (CaCiH) by neutralization with lime. This organic salt is filtrated, resuspended in clear water, and acidified with H_2SO_4 to release CA in a clean medium, with calcium sulfate as a by-product. The remaining CA is fed to highly energy-intensive refining stages (e.g., evaporation, crystallization) (Kristiansen et al., 1998). To avoid all these purification stages, an alternative process (SAE) is proposed in which insoluble CaCiH is used as raw material for direct TBC production. By resuspending it in butanol media instead of water, and with the addition of H_2SO_4, a solid-liquid reaction involving the acidification of the citrate salts enables the release of CA and its simultaneous multi-step esterification, yielding TBC and the intermediates, mono and dibutyl citrates (MBC, DBC respectively). As calcium sulfate forms, it precipitates from the reactive medium, simultaneously removing produced water by capturing it in the hydrated form (Figure 1). In order to assess the proposed process, experiments were conducted to determine the behavior of the reactive system and to obtain a kinetic model. This was used to simulate and optimize the proposed process alongside the industrial process used for TBC production (Osorio-Pascuas et al., 2015); (Fonseca et al., 2020). The optimization of the SAE process was achieved via FOQUS software (Papadopoulos & Seferlis, 2017), where a straightforward link between Python, Aspen Plus, and Excel files was performed.

2. Kinetic Modeling

The reactions were studied in two stages to decouple the mechanisms involved in the solid-liquid acidification-esterification in the production of butyl citrates. Initially, the kinetics of esterification between CA and BuOH using H_2SO_4 as a catalyst was evaluated. The effects of temperature, initial molar ratio, and catalyst loading were considered. Then, solid-liquid reaction experiments using CaCiH as raw material were accomplished. Based on the experimental observations, a combined kinetic model for the solid-solid-liquid media was proposed, and the kinetic parameters were regressed. Details of experiments and the proposed kinetic model were previously reported by the authors (Cabeza, 2023).

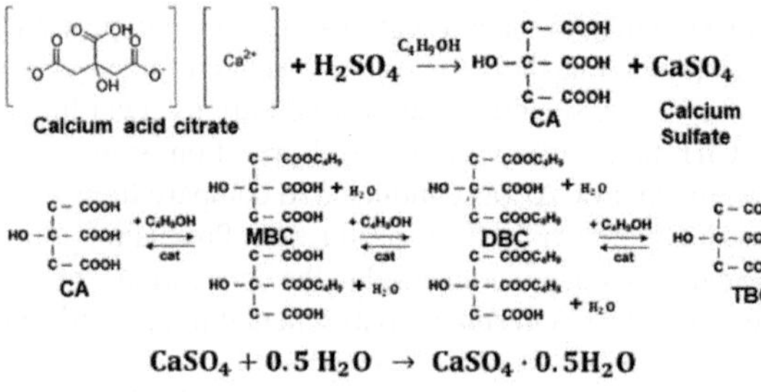

Figure 1: Reaction scheme during Simultaneous Acidification-Esterification

The concentration of involved species was represented in molality (mol compound *i* per kg of liquid). This representation avoids the uncertainties derived by the change in volume or temperature in the reactive medium along the simultaneous acidification-esterification, under batch operation. Then, change in molality can be described as follows:

$$\frac{dC_i}{dt} = \sum_{j=1}^{k} \theta_{i,j} r_{m,j} + \sum_{l=1}^{p} \theta_{i,p} r_{S,p} \quad j = \{1..3\}, l = \{1,2\} \tag{1}$$

Here, index $j = \{1,2,3\}$ corresponds to each of the esterification reaction steps. $l = \{1,2\}$ corresponds to acidification and the calcium sulfate ($CaSO_4$) hydration reaction, respectively. This last reaction is only dependent on the presence of water. For the remaining rate expressions, in which an Arrhenius-type dependence with temperature is assumed ($k_{cat,j} = C_{cat}k_{0cat,j}\exp(Ea_{cat_j}/RT)$), can be expressed as follows:

$$r_{m,1} = k_{cat,1}\left(C_{AC}C_{BuOH} - \frac{C_{MBC}\,C_{H_2O}}{K_{EQ,1}}\right) \quad (2) \qquad r_{m,2} = k_{cat,2}\left(C_{MBC}C_{BuOH} - \frac{C_{DBC}\,C_{H_2O}}{K_{EQ,2}}\right) \quad (3)$$

$$r_{m,3} = k_{cat,3}\left(C_{DBC}C_{BuOH} - \frac{C_{TBC}\,C_{H_2O}}{K_{EQ,3}}\right) \quad (4) \qquad r_S = k_{0s,1}\exp\left(-\frac{Ea_S}{RT}\right)C_{CiCaH}\,C_{H_2SO_4} \quad (5)$$

$$r_{S,2} = k_{S,2}C_{ACaSO_4}C_{H_2O} \quad (6)$$

The corresponding experimentally obtained kinetic parameters are listed in Table 1. For the esterification of citric species in the presence of methanesulfonic acid (MSA), the kinetic model and its parameters are taken from literature (Osorio-Pascuas et al., 2015).

Table 1: Kinetic parameter for the simultaneous acidification-esterification reaction (C.I.: Coinfidencence Interval)

Parameter	Units	Value	C.I	Parameter	Units	Value	C.I.
$k_{0cat,1}$	$kg^2/(mol\cdot mol_{cat}\cdot s)$	723800	±29852	$Ea_{cat,1}$	J/mol	59459	±516
$k_{0cat,2}$		518700	±33541	$Ea_{cat,2}$		60358	±1298
$k_{0cat,3}$		431020	±53585	$Ea_{cat,3}$		62506	±1098
$k_{0s,1}$	$kg/(mol\cdot s)$	4907	±352	Ea_S		32173	±4520
$k_{S,2}$		0.5605	±0.0974	$K_{EQ,2}$	-	3.56	-
$K_{EQ,1}$	-	8.68	-	$K_{EQ,3}$	-	1.4	-

Note. Equilibrium constants were obtained from the literature (Osorio-Pascuas et al., 2015).

3. Methodology

3.1. Process Simulation Considerations

The process to produce CA esters was modeled considering the stages involved in the typical industrial process (Kristiansen et al., 1998). After fermentation and precipitation of the citrate salt, CA is produced by acidification of CiCaH in aquesous solution and fed to purification stages (e.g., evaporation, crystallization, and drying). Part of the produced CA is then dissolved in BuOH for TBC production using MSA as catalyst (Osorio-Pascuas et al., 2015). In the case of the SAE process, it starts by splitting CaCiH into two streams. One part is transformed in CA and the rest is used in the direct acidification-esterification in alcoholic medium with H_2SO_4. Then, to ensure complete conversion to TBC, a further esterification step using MSA as a catalyst was conducted (Figure 2).

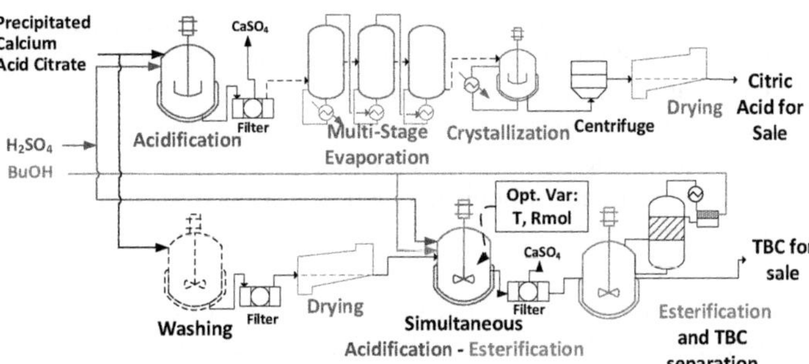

Figure 2: SAE process for the production of citric acid (CA) and TBC

Regarding the phase equilibria of the reactive mixture, these were described using the UNIQUAC equation with previously regressed and validated binary interaction parameters (Santaella et al., 2018, 2022). All process simulations were conducted in Aspen Plus® V12.1 using the corresponding RBatch and BatchSep modules for accurate modeling of batch and semi-batch units involved in the conventional and SAE processes.

3.2. Process Optimization

For process optimization, three scenarios were considered. Each scenario considers the simultaneous production of CA and TBC using fermentative-derivated CaCiH as raw material.

Scenario 1: A non-optimized conventional process for synthesizing tributyl citrate (TBC) is modeled based on industry data (Osorio-Pascuas, 2019)(Finseca et al, 2020). The model assumes a production capacity of 30,000 tons/year of anhydrous CA. About 95% of this CA is sold directly, while the rest is taken to an esterification reaction. Since each batch can process 8000 kg of CA, 180 batches/year can be performed.

Scenario 2: The novel SAE process is implemented in this scenario, considering that 5% of the total citric production plant goes to esterification in calcium citrate. Fixing BuOH loading, the calcium citrate amounts were varied between 8 and 16 BuOH: CaCiH. In this scenario, 180 batches/year are assumed.

Scenario 3: Similar to the second scenario, the SAE process performed the TBC production. As it will be related further in the document, up to 10 hours of savings in batch processing can be achieved in this scenario compared to Scenario 2. In this case, it was possible to perform 230 batches/year.

The optimization of the proposed scenarios was carried out by calculating the gross earnings profits (GEP) (Seider et al., 2017). The acidification-esterification reaction temperature in Kelvin (T) and BuOH:C aCiH initial molar relation ($Rmol$) were selected as decision variables for the optimization. The optimization problem was:

$$\begin{gathered}\min_{T,Rmol} -GEP \\ s.t.\ 313 \leq T \leq 353 \\ 8 \leq Rmol \leq 16\end{gathered} \tag{7}$$

The optimization boundaries were chosen regarding the reaction conditions in which the acidification-esterification kinetic parameters were obtained (Cabeza, 2023). The SAE process scenario optimization was performed via the FOQUS (Framework for Optimization and Quantification of Uncertainty and Sensitivity) tool (Papadopoulos & Seferlis, 2017), allowing the link of different types of simulation and data analysis software. In this study, a link among Python (input pre-processing), Aspen Plus (Process simulation) and Excel (condensed production and capital costs) was used.

Scenarios 2 and 3 were optimized using the solver NLopt and its implementation of the Constrained Optimization via Linea Approximation (COBYLA) algorithm through the FOQUS software. A tolerance difference of the objective function between iterations of 1e-9 was used as the stop criteria. Also, the feasible region was screened using randomly generated data in the Uncertainty Module in FOQUS. This analysis helped to propose the initial point for the optimization.

3.2.1. LCA Analysis

For the comparative LCA analysis, OpenLCA software was used to establish the performance of the novel SAE processes with respect to the conventional process. Thus, a cradle-to-gate analysis was performed. Agribalyse_v301 was used for inventory, and the ReCiPe 2016 Midpoint (H) method was used for environmental assessment.

4. Results and discussion

4.1 Process Optimization

Optimization results are summarized in Table 2, and the optimization contour and pathway are shown in Figure 3. Although the contour plots are similar, small changes are visible. Yet, both scenarios implementing the SAE process improve GEP compared to the conventional process for TBC production (8.803 $MUSD/year). This can be attributed mainly to the reduction of up to 60% in heating energy cost demand per kg of produced TBC using the SAE process.

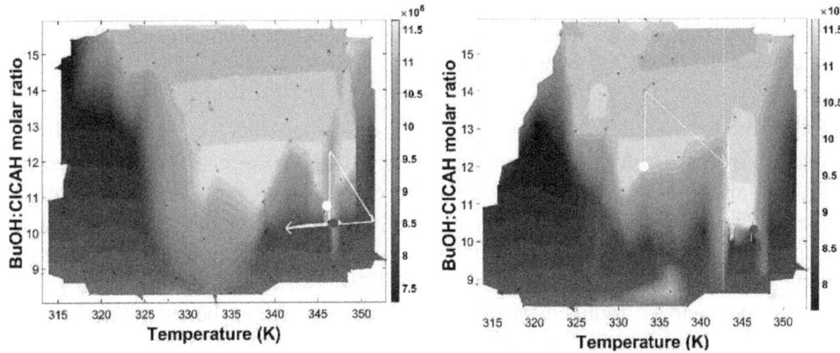

Figure 3: Contour plot and optimization path for the SAE process. Left: Scenario 2, right: Scenario 3. Levels are expressed in $USD/year

Table 2: Results of the optimization of SAE processes

Variable	Scenario 2	Scenario 3
No. Batch/year	180	230
No. Iterations	20	71
Temperature [K]	346.32	346.35
BuOH:CaCiH molar ratio	10.29	10.29
GEP [$MUSD/year]	11.150	11.775

4.2 LCA analysis

A comparative LCA analysis between the three scenarios was performed using OpenLCA. Both SAE processes show a reduction in the environmental impact indicators. The five most affected environmental parameters (figure 3) were reduced up to 10% and 30% with respect to the conventional TBC production process. It was also observed a reduction of up to 60% in steam consumption in the SAE processes in comparison with the traditional processes. This resulted in a reduction in 20% in the global warming impacts and and a 31% decrease in fossil resources usage.

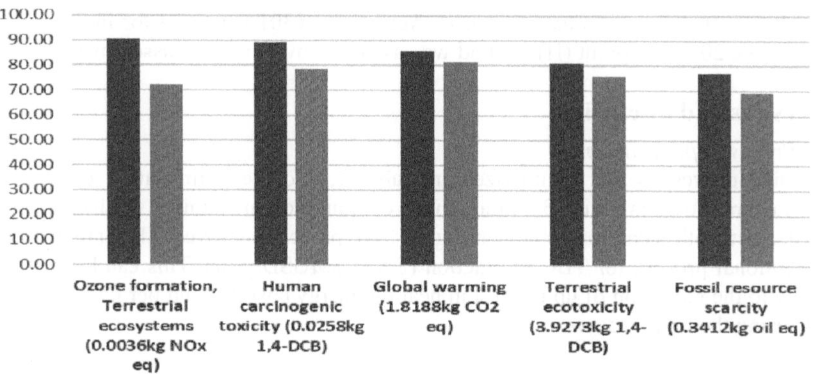

Figure 2: Percentage ratio of environmental impacts with respect to the conventional TBC production process. ■ Scheme 2, ■ Scheme 3

5. Conclusion

The production of TBC from calcium citrate via the novel SAE process was found to be technically feasible and more sustainbale than the conventional process. The optimized SAE process demonstrated significant potential to produce TBC more efficiently with an increase up to 25% in gross earning profits. Also, a relative mitigation in environmental impact indicators (10% to 31%) was achieved. Global warming indicators and Fossil resource scarcity could be reduced by 20% and 31%, which can be associated with a decrease in steam consumption (Up to 60% concerning conventional processes).

References

Cabeza, A. F. 2023. Synthesis of Bio-Plasticizers Derived from Citric Acid from Calcium Citrate (in Spanish). Master's Dissertation. National University of Colombia.

Godwin, A. D. 2017. Plasticizers. Applied plastics engineering handbook. Elsevier.

Kristiansen, B., Linden, J., & Mattey, M. 1998. Citric acid biotechnology. CRC press.

Osorio-Pascuas, O. M. 2019. Production Of Triethyl Citrate And Tributyl Citrate From The Acid Esterification Of Citric Acid With Ethanol And 1-Butanol (in Spanish). Master's Dissertation. National University of Colombia.

Fonseca, J. D., Latifi, A. M., Orjuela, A., Rodríguez, G., Gil, I. D. 2020. Modeling, analysis and multi-objective optimization of an industrial batch process for the production of tributyl citrate. Computers & Chemical Engineering 132, 106603

Osorio-Pascuas, O. M., Santaella, M. A., Rodriguez, G., & Orjuela, A. 2015. Esterification kinetics of tributyl citrate production using homogeneous and heterogeneous catalysts. Industrial & Engineering Chemistry Research, 54 (50), 12534–12542.

Papadopoulos, A. I., & Seferlis, P. 2017. Process systems and materials for CO2 capture: modeling, design, control and Integration. John Wiley & Sons.

Santaella, M. A., Suaza, A., Berdugo, C. E., Rivera, J. L., Orjuela, A. 2018. Phase Equilibrium Behavior in Mixtures Containing Tributyl Citrate, Citric Acid, Butan-1-ol, and Water. Journal of Chemical & Engineering Data 63 (9), 3252-3262

Santaella, M. A., Gutiérrez, M. F., & Orjuela, A. 2022. Tributyl citrate production via reactive distillation: Model reconciliation, optimization, scale up and sustainability indicators. Chemical Engineering Journal, 433, 133199.

Seider, W. D., Lewin, D. R., Seader, J. D., Widagdo, S., Gani, R.,Ng, K. M. 2017. Product and process design principles: synthesis, analysis, and evaluation. John Wiley & Sons.

Wang, Y., & Qian, H. 2021. Phthalates and their impacts on human health. Healthcare, 9 (5), 603

Flavio Manenti, Gintaras V. Reklaitis (Eds.), Proceedings of the 34th European Symposium on Computer Aided Process Engineering / 15th International Symposium on Process Systems Engineering (ESCAPE34/PSE24), June 2-6, 2024, Florence, Italy
 http://dx.doi.org/10.1016/B978-0-443-28824-1.50161-7

Modeling Hydrothermal Gasification of Digestate Sludge: Reaction Kinetic from Molecular Simulations

Do Tuong Ha[a], Khanh-Quang Tran[b*], Thuat T. Trinh[c*]

[a]*Faculty of Applied Sciences, Ton Duc Thang University, Ho Chi Minh city, Vietnam*
[b]*Department of Energy and Process Engineering, Norwegian University of Science and Technology - NTNU, Norway*
[c]*Porelab, Department of Chemistry, Norwegian University of Science and Technology - NTNU, Norway*
* *khanh-quang.tran@ntnu.no; thuat.trinh@ntnu.no*

Abstract

Hydrothermal gasification (HTG) has emerged as a promising technology for converting wet digestate residue from anaerobic digestion processes to valuable fuel gases including hydrogen and methane. To design and optimize HTG reactors for such digestate feedstock, accurate kinetic parameters are essential. Such kinetic parameters can be gained via reactive molecular dynamics simulations, which are the objective of the work presented in this paper. For this purpose, the method of reactive force field (ReaxFF) was employed. Influences of process parameters including temperature, pressure, reactant compositions on the process of digestate HTG were investigated. The obtained activation energy of 141 kJ/mol and product distribution shed light on the mechanistic aspects of the gasification process. The ability to predict reaction kinetics for complex HTG reactions from this work opens new possibilities for optimizing process and advancing sustainable waste-to energy technologies.

Keywords: Molecular simulation, ReaxFF, hydrothermal gasification, digestate sludge, reaction kinetics.

1. Introduction

It is important to optimize the thermal and chemical conversion of biomass (Tran et al., 2020; Mahmoodinia et al., 2017), such as digestate sludge, for sustainable waste-to-energy technologies. Anaerobic digestion (AD) is a common technology for energy recovery form wet and low-cost biomass resources such as sewage sludge from wastewater treatment plants. AD process involves the breakdown of biodegradable organic materials by microorganisms in the absence of oxygen, leading to generation of combustible gas mixtures containing chiefly methane and carbon dioxide (Li et al., 2011). Digestate is a byproduct or residue of AD processes, containing non-digestible organic matter and valuable nutrients such as nitrogen and phosphorus. Digestate sludge can be utilized as fertilizer in agriculture (Mata-Alvarez et al., 2014). However, challenges associated with the application of digestate sludge include variability in composition due to factors such as feedstock type and pretreatment methods used during anaerobic digestion (Nkoa, 2013) and potential risks related to contaminants like heavy metals and pathogens (Verstraete and Vlaeminck, 2011). Because of these challenges, researchers continue to explore new opportunities for utilizing digestate sludge effectively, one of which is hydrothermal gasification.

Hydrothermal gasification (HTG) is a gasification process in supercritical water typically at temperatures within 500-700°C (without catalyst) and their corresponding pressures (Promdej and Matsumura, 2011). The use of water as the reaction environment makes HTG very suitable for valorization of wet feedstock like digestate. This process has garnered increasing attention also due to its potential for producing hydrogen-rich syngas with reduced environmental impact compared to conventional gasification techniques. The product gas from HTG can be combusted directly for heat and power generation. It can also be fed back to the AD reactor in an AD-HTG integrated system to improve the carbon conversion and bio-methane production.

To design and optimize HTG reactors for digestate feedstock, accurate kinetic parameters are essential. Reaction conditions, such as temperature and pressure, also significantly impact the kinetics of hydrothermal gasification reactions. Increasing both temperature and pressure generally leads to an acceleration in reaction rates due to the increased solubility of gases in water under these conditions (Kruse, 2008). However, high-temperature and high-pressure environments can also lead to unwanted side reactions, such as char and coke formation, which may cause fouling or reduce the efficiency of gasification processes (Karayildirim et al., 2008). Therefore, careful optimization of reaction conditions is essential for achieving optimal hydrothermal gasification performance.

The primary objective of this research is to explore the effects of various process parameters such as temperature, and reactant compositions on the HTG of digestate sludges. Employing reactive force field method, our goal is not only to gain insight into the underlying mechanisms but also to predict reaction kinetics for complex HTG reactions. This approach will contribute towards optimizing processes and further advancing sustainable waste-to-energy conversion technologies.

2. Models and Methods

It is a common practice to select specific model compounds to study the kinetic behavior of HTG processes via molecular dynamic (MD) modelling and simulation. In this case, three simple model compounds were chosen for investigation: aspirin (acetylsalicylic acid), xylylenediamine, and sacrylamide (as shown in Figure 1). These representative model compounds were selected as they are presented in digestate sludge solutions (He et al., 2022). By investigating the reactivity, synergy, and kinetics of these three model compounds under HTG conditions, researchers can gain valuable insights into the behavior of more complex feedstocks such as agricultural crops, wood wastes, food processing residues during HTG.

The method of ReaxFF molecular dynamics simulation was employed for this present study due to its ability to accurately describe molecular interactions and chemical reactions. Unlike the method of non-reactive force field, ReaxFF considers dynamic bond length and angle changes in response to alterations in the chemical environment. For a more detailed description of the ReaxFF force field and its underlying methodology, interested readers should be referred to the original paper introducing ReaxFF (van Duin et al., 2001).

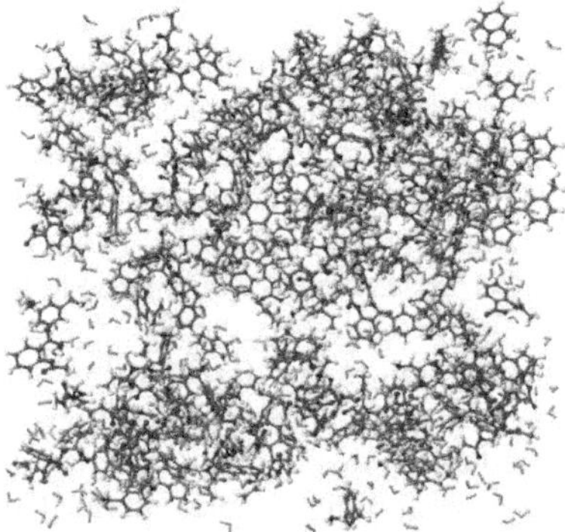

Figure 1: A model digestate sludge used in ReaxFF MD simulation of HTG process.

In this study, we utilized the potential function parameters proposed by (Vashisth et al., 2018). In order to accelerate the reaction kinetics and to overcome the time and length scale limitations, a commonly employed technique in MD is to simulate the system at temperatures higher than that reported in the literature of experimental conditions (Saha and Schatz, 2012; Jiang et al., 2009; Kowalik et al., 2019). The temperature range employed for the HTG simulations of this present work is from 3000 K to 4000 K. A similar temperature range was previously applied in HTG simulation (Liu et al, 2020). The total simulation time was 250 ps with a time step of 0.25 fs. In order to calculate the activation energy values in this study, we utilized the Arrhenius equation.

3. Results and Discussions

3.1. Yield of gaseous products

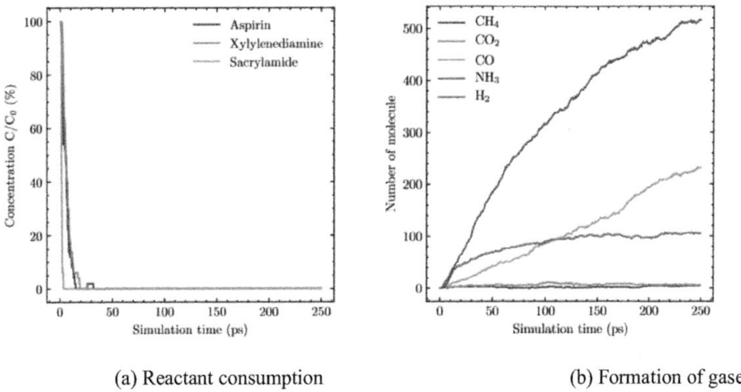

(a) Reactant consumption (b) Formation of gases

Figure 2: Evolution of reactants concentration (a) and formation of gases (b) during HTG simulation. C_0 = initial concentration, C = concentration at simulation time.

The evolution of reactants and gaseous products and intermediates during the HTG simulation, as depicted in Figure 2, provides some insights into the reaction kinetics and product distribution under supercritical water conditions. It is evident that the concentration of all three reactants of the model compounds decreases over time as they are decomposed and converted to intermediates or products. The formation of hydrogen gas is observed to be the most significant among the various gases produced during the HTG process, which aligns with previous research findings (Promdej and Matsumura, 2011) highlighting the potential for hydrothermal gasification to generate high-quality hydrogen-rich syngas from diverse feedstocks. However, it should be noted that the formation of CH_4 and CO_2 gases is minor compared to hydrogen production.

Another important observation is the formation of ammonia gas during the HTG process. This result is consistent with experimental observations and supports previous studies (Kruse, 2008) indicating that nitrogen-containing compounds can play a crucial role in HTG processes by forming stable intermediates or participating in redox reactions.

3.2. Effect of temperature

Figure 3 shows the evolution of intermediates and products in different phases - gas, liquid, and solid - during HTG simulations conducted at two different temperatures 3000K and 3600K. Initially, all reactants are present in their liquid state. As the HTG progresses, the liquid fraction gradually decreases as it is converted into gaseous products through decomposition and partial oxidation reactions.

According to Figure 3.a, the mass fraction of gas during the simulation at 3000 K reaches roughly 66% after 250 ps of simulation time. This indicates that the process is representative of a typical HTG process in which gasification takes place in supercritical water conditions. As the temperature increases to 3600 K (Figure 3.b), the gas fraction further increases to around 78%. This pattern indicates that increasing the temperature minimizes undesirable side reactions like char formation while increasing the efficiency of converting organic resources into syngas.

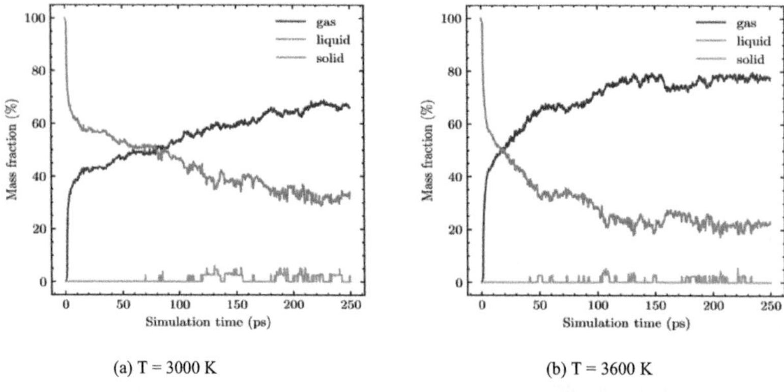

(a) T = 3000 K (b) T = 3600 K

Figure 3: Evolution of different phases during HTG simulation

We observed that the formation of solid or the solid residue during the HTG process is negligible. The trends observed for the revolution of the products in three phases - gas, liquid, and solid during HTG simulations, as depicted in Figure 3, agree with the experimental data obtained from similar studies involving various feedstocks under supercritical water conditions (Promdej and Matsumura, 2011). This consistent behavior across different systems provides convincing evidence that the model compounds chosen for investigation can effectively represent more complex organic materials found in biomass or coal-derived residues.

3.3. Activation barrier of HTG process

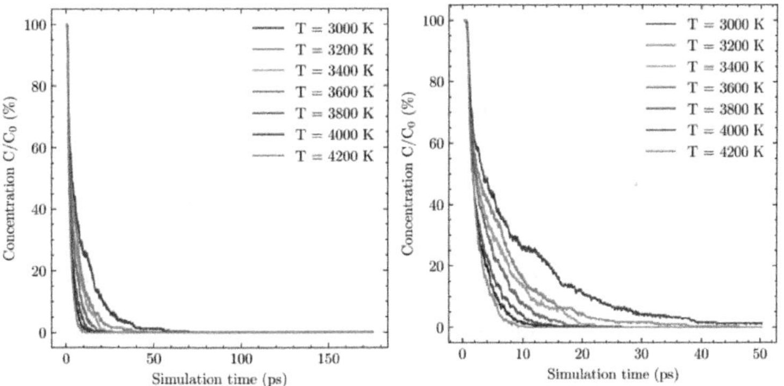

Figure 4: Evolution of reaction concentration at different temperature

To investigate the reaction kinetics, the concentration of reactants over time under varying temperature conditions was monitored (as shown in Figure 4). By assuming a pseudo first-order kinetic model for these reactions, it is possible to calculate the rate constants associated with each of individual steps (such as hydrolysis, dehydration, decarboxylation, and oxidation) in the HTG pathway. The rate constant values obtained at different temperatures can then be used to determine the activation energy barrier. The obtained results show that the activation energy is around 141 kJ/mol, which agrees with experimental findings reported in previous study (Wei et al, 2021).

4. Conclusions

This study has demonstrated the capacity of ReaxFF in investigating HTG of complex organic compounds such as digestate sludge. By employing computational modeling techniques, we can gain valuable insights into the reaction mechanism, kinetics, activation energies, and product yields associated with HTG processes. This can provide essential inputs for more advanced micro-kinetics models employed in chemical engineering applications.

Acknowledgements

The research leading to these results has been co-funded by the Norway Grants 2014-2021 via the National Center for Research and Development, within the frame of the project: "Negative CO2 emission gas power plant" - NOR/POLNORCCS/NEGATIVE -CO2-PP/0009/2019-00 which is co-financed by program "Applied research" under the Norwegian Financial Mechanisms 2014-2021 POLNOR CCS 2019 - Development of CO2 capture solutions integrated in power and industry processes. TTT acknowledge funding from the Research Council of Norway (RCN), the Center of Excellence Funding Scheme, Project No. 262644, PoreLab. Co-financing and support from Ton Duc Thang University and Norwegian University of Science and Technology are gratefully acknowledged.

References

van Duin et al., 2001, ReaxFF: A Reactive Force Field for Hydrocarbons, J. Phys. Chem. A, 105(20), 4663-4672.

He et al., 2022, Molecular diversity of liquid digestate from anaerobic digestion plants for biogenic waste. Bioresource Technology, 347, 126373.

Huelsman and Savage, 2012, Intermediates and kinetics for phenol gasification in supercritical water, Phys. Chem. Chem. Phys., 14(3), 1587-1594.

Jiang et al., 2009, Simulating the Initial Stage of Phenolic Resin Carbonization via the ReaxFF Reactive Force Field, J. Phys. Chem. A, 113(25), 6891-6894.

Karayıldırım et al., 2008, Char and Coke Formation as Unwanted Side Reaction of the Hydrothermal Biomass Gasification. Chemical Engineering & Technology, 31(11), 1561–1568.

Kruse, 2008, Supercritical water gasification. Biofuels, Bioproducts and Biorefining, 2(5), 415–437.

Kowalik et al., 2019, Atomistic Scale Analysis of the Carbonization Process for C/H/O/N-Based Polymers with the ReaxFF Reactive Force Field, J. Phys. Chem. B, 123(25), 5357-5367.

Li et al., 2011, Solid-state anaerobic digestion for methane production from organic waste, Renewable Sustainable Energy Rev., 15(1), 821-826.

Liu et al., 2020, Understanding lignin gasification in supercritical water using reactive molecular dynamics simulations, Renewable Energy, 161(12), 858-866.

Mahmoodinia et al., 2017, Geometrical flexibility of platinum nanoclusters: Impacts on catalytic decomposition of ethylene glycol, Phys. Chem. Chem. Phys., 19(42), 28596-28603.

Mata-Alvarez et al., 2014, A critical review on anaerobic co-digestion achievements between 2010 and 2013, Renewable Sustainable Energy Rev., 36(None), 412-427.

Nanda et al., 2017, An assessment of pinecone gasification in subcritical, near-critical and supercritical water, Fuel Process. Technol., 168(), 84-96.

Nkoa, 2013, Agricultural benefits and environmental risks of soil fertilization with anaerobic digestates: A review, Agron. Sustain. Dev., 34(2), 473-492.

Promdej and Matsumura, 2011, Temperature Effect on Hydrothermal Decomposition of Glucose in Sub- And Supercritical Water, Ind. Eng. Chem. Res., 50(14), 8492-8497.

Saha and Schatz, 2012, Carbonization in Polyacrylonitrile (PAN) Based Carbon Fibers Studied by ReaxFF Molecular Dynamics Simulations, J. Phys. Chem. B, 116(15), 4684-4692.

Tran et al., 2020, Fuel characterization and thermal degradation kinetics of biomass from phytoremediation plants, Biomass Bioenergy, 134, 105469

Wei et al. 2021, Effect of hydrothermal carbonization temperature on reactivity and synergy of co-gasification of biomass hydrochar and coal. Applied Thermal Engineering, 183, 116232.

Vashisth et al., 2018, Accelerated ReaxFF Simulations for Describing the Reactive Cross-Linking of Polymers, J. Phys. Chem. A, 122(32), 6633-6642.

Verstraete and Vlaeminck, 2011, ZeroWasteWater: Short-cycling of wastewater resources for sustainable cities of the future, International Journal of Sustainable Development & World Ecology, 18(3), 253-264.

Flavio Manenti, Gintaras V. Reklaitis (Eds.), Proceedings of the 34th European Symposium on Computer Aided Process Engineering / 15th International Symposium on Process Systems Engineering (ESCAPE34/PSE24), June 2-6, 2024, Florence, Italy
 http://dx.doi.org/10.1016/B978-0-443-28824-1.50162-9

Assessment of the sustainability of intensified CO_2 capture schemes

Melanie Coronel-Muñoz[a], Ana Gabriela Romero-García[a], Brenda Huerta-Rosas[a], Eduardo Sánchez-Ramírez[a*], Juan Gabriel Segovia-Hernández[a]
[a]*Department of Chemical Engineering, Universidad de Guanajuato, Campus Guanajuato, Guanajuato, 36050, Mexico*
eduardo.sanchez@ugto.mx

Abstract

The CO_2 capture process is related to Sustainable Development Goals (SDGs) 7, 9, 12 and 13 of the 2030 Agenda. CO_2 capture involves the use of solvents such as Mono ethanolamine (MEA). Currently there are theoretically more sustainable alternatives such as deep eutectic solvents (DES). In this work two schemes for the CO_2 capture process are evaluated, the first scheme considers Mono-ethanolamine (MEA) and the second scheme considers a DES (ChCl/ urea (1:2)) as green solvent, considering in both schemes the use of natural gas, biogas and coal as fuels that originate the CO_2 flux. The dynamics of the process play an important role when is evaluating the implementation of the new alternatives. Likewise, the evaluation of both alternatives should be considered within a sustainability framework that guarantees the generation of process schemes that comply with the aspects indicated in the United Nations (UN) 2030 Agenda. The results indicate that for both solvents, the alternative that considers coal as fuel in the combustion stage showed the best sustainability indicators evaluated. Also, in a direct comparison between both solvents, it was concluded that DES capture is the best in cost and environmental terms.

Keywords: CO_2 capture, carbon capture, MEA, Deep eutectic solvents, dynamic properties.

1. Introduction

One of the most pressing problems in the world today is climate change, due to various anthropogenic activities that contribute significantly to the release of greenhouse gases (GHG) into the atmosphere, especially CO_2. The Sustainable Development Goals (SDGs) established by the 2030 Agenda have as their main objective to redirect economic, political, and social activities with an approach that prioritizes environmental sustainability. Due to the urgent need to mitigate climate change, various alternatives have been studied to diminish CO_2 emissions, with CO_2 capture being the main option in the industrial sector. Capture technologies in industrial smokestacks are classified into post-combustion, pre-combustion, and oxy-fuel combustion. Post-combustion capture (PCC) technology is more technologically mature and has shown relatively good results in CO_2 capture processes, the classic chemical absorbent for CO_2 separation applications is aqueous Mono-ethanolamine (MEA), due to its great CO_2 capture capacity, commercial availability, relatively low cost, fast absorption rate and extensive research in industrial applications. Despite its high efficiency, MEA is considered highly toxic, so its implementation entails a high environmental impact. Given these drawbacks, there is an opportunity to study new solvents that may be able to replace MEA in the CO_2 capture process. A novel alternative is the implementation of green solvents called deep eutectic solvents (DES) with selective absorption capacity towards CO_2. Previously, several studies have been conducted on the applicability of both solvents for CO_2 capture from combustion processes. For example, Romero-García et al. (2022) evaluated the performance of MEA in a multi-objective optimization framework with several performance indicators. Although promising results were obtained, several indicators that could broaden the perspective of the process in terms of process sustainability were left out. Using a green solvent, Martinez-Lomovskoi et al. (2023) optimized a power generation plant obtaining a minimum of 95 % CO_2 recovery. To evaluate the performance of the capture plant, they used environmental and economic indicators. As a result, the process using coal in the combustion section presented a value of EI99 lower by 56.1 % and 72.8 % with respect to natural gas and biogas. However, the lack of an analysis of the dynamics of the process or a safety evaluation, leaves the results obtained by Martínez-Lomovskoi et al. (2023) relatively incomplete under the light of more performance indexes, since although we could have a plant with a high sustainability index, but highly risky, that is why to achieve a comparative analysis of the use of the DES versus the MEA it is necessary to broaden the approach to other indicators.

Although the use of both solvents was promising due to the capture capacity that was observed, during the exploration of both alternatives, sustainability indicators that allow comparing both alternatives were not jointly evaluated. According to what is proposed by the sustainable development goals of the UN 2030 Agenda, there are several indicators that can provide information regarding their sustainability. For example, the dynamic properties of the process, the inherent safety, as well as the economic and environmental impact. In order to determine the criteria for the implementation of a CO_2 capture process, a comparative analysis was carried out in this article within the framework of sustainability, which is generated by evaluating controllability, economic, environmental, and safety indicators for each of the cases evaluated in the articles by Romero-García (2022) and Martinez-Lomovskoi (2023), taking sample points at different conditions, to compare the feasibility of using DES versus MEA.

2. Case Study

The post-combustion capture process (PCC) consists of removing CO_2 from the flue gas after flaring has been performed. Romero-García et al. (2022) performed a multi-objective optimization project of a power plant coupled to a PCC CO_2 capture process, considering coal, natural gas, associated gas and biogas for electricity production. The CO_2 capture plant used an aqueous solution of Mono-ethanolamine (MEA) at 30 % by weight as solvent. The process consists of an absorption column and a desorption column at the end of the process.

To implement environmentally responsible CO_2 solvents, the use of deep eutectic solvents (DEPs) was proposed, which have advantages over amines, particularly due to the non-toxic and non-corrosive nature of many of them and their high thermal and oxidative stability. Martínez-Lomovskoi et al. (2023), carried out the design and optimization of a carbon capture plant taking up the case study of Romero García et. al. (2022) but now using novel green DES aqueous ChCl/ urea (1:2), under a sustainability scheme, as a first in the reported literature. The process is composed of an absorber and desorber as the traditional process but with the implementation of two flash tanks to treat the DES prior to desorption. Both cases reported their results in a Pareto front as shown in Figure 1. In the traditional process (Figure 1-b), the use of coal stands out as the most viable alternative with respect to environmental and controllability conditions, but with a low return on investment (ROI). While in the implementation of the green solvent (Figure 1-a), Martinez-Lomovskoi highlights the use of coal (C) as the most optimal design obtained, since in terms of environmental impact it presents values 21.9 %, 56.1 % and 72.8 % lower than associated gas (AG), natural gas (NG) and biogas (BG) respectively and also exhibits a higher ROI as well as the best overall performance considering all environmental and economic parameters simultaneously.

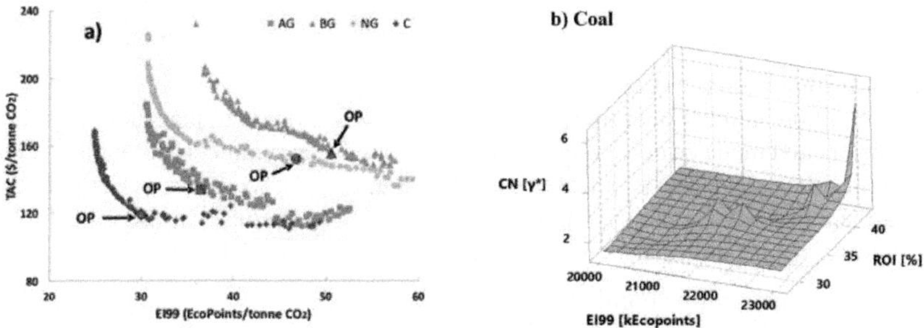

Figure 1. Excerpts from the Pareto fronts reported by Romero-García et al. (2022) and Martínez-Lomovskoi et al. (2023). Being coal (C), associated gas (AG), natural gas (NG) and biogas (BG).

Taking both cases as a precedent, in this article a comparative analysis model was established supported by the evaluation of control and safety indicators, necessary indicators to achieve the integrated evaluation of the designs in a sustainability framework, the evaluation was performed in three crucial points specific to the Pareto fronts, in reference to the cost, that is, a point in the highest, central and cheapest cost for biogas, coal, and natural gas fuels, from the results obtained by Romero-Garcia et al. (2022) and Martinez-Lomovskoi et al. (2023).

3. Performance Indexes and Methodology

Creating or modifying processes towards sustainability requires assessing the feasibility of proposed innovations based on economic, energy, environmental, and control indicators to provide a sustainable manufacturing process and achieve material efficiency. In this article, a set of metrics was selected for the evaluation of environmental impact (Eco-indicator 99, EI99), economic feasibility (Total annual cost, TAC), dynamic process behavior (Condition number), and safety (Risk index, IR).

3.1 Eco-indicator 99 (EI99)

Eco-indicator 99 (EI99) is one of the most widely used environmental impact estimation methods and consists of a quantitative analysis of the life cycle evaluated from beginning to end. The calculation is performed using Eq. (1). Where ω represents the damage weight factor (Pts/kg), Ci represents the impact value for each of the categories i, and α is the value of subcategory j (kg/year).

$$EI99 = \sum_i \sum_j \omega \cdot C_i \cdot \alpha_j \quad (1)$$

3.2 Total annual cost (TAC)

The TAC assumes the annualization of the investment cost of the main process equipment over a 10-year amortization period. To calculate it, Eq. (2) is used. Where $C_{TM,i}$ is the capital cost of the equipment in dollars ($), r represents the payback period in years, and $C_{ut,j}$ is the cost of cooling and heating services, in dollars per year ($/year).

$$TAC = \frac{\sum_{i=1}^{n} C_{TM,i}}{r} + \sum_{j=1}^{n} C_{ut,j} \quad (2)$$

3.3 Condition number (CN)

The Condition Number quantifies the sensitivity of the system to inaccuracies in process parameters and mode errors. Systems with small condition numbers present better control properties. Its calculation is performed as shown in Eq. (3), where (σ_*) is associated with the direction in which the system has more difficulty moving. On the other hand, the magnitude of (σ^*) indicates the easiest direction the system will move to.

$$\gamma^* = \frac{\sigma^*}{\sigma_*} = \frac{\text{maximum singular value}}{\text{minimum singular value}} \quad (3)$$

3.4 Individual risk (IR)

The IR identifies the risk that a person faces based on his position, including the likelihood of an accident resulting in death or serious injury. The IR is defined as shown in Eq. (4). Where, f_i represents the recurrence that one accident will occur, and $P_{x,y}$ is the likelihood that the accident will occur in a particular location.

$$IR = \sum f_i P_{x,y} \quad (4)$$

In the methodology of this project, the instantaneous and continuous risk analysis was performed for each of the equipment involved in the CO_2 capture process that is in contact with the solvent of interest. Catastrophic events such as Boiling Liquid Expanding Vapor Explosion (BLEVE), Unconfined Vapor Cloud Explosion (UVCE), Jet Fire, Flash fire, and toxic explosion were evaluated using specific mathematical models for each case reported in the literature.

4. Results

In this section we present the results of the evaluation of the parameters mentioned in the case study and described in the methodology. In Figure 2-a, the behavior between TAC, EI99, and CN, has a similar trend, so a more sustainable process implies a lower cost and better controllability. At the selected point on the front of Pareto with the highest TAC value for the use of coal as fuel, the total annual cost is lower by 135.34 % and 218.18 % compared to the use of natural gas (NG) and biogas (BG) respectively. At the midpoint of the Pareto front with a central TAC, for coal as fuel, is the lowest CN with 133.0002, while the maximum CN is 6537.4 at the top of the Pareto front with the highest TAC value in the use of NG as fuel. In terms of safety, coal presents the best conditions due to several factors, including lower reboiler heat duty. In Figure 2-b, the relationship EI99 and CN, shows that a more sustainable process is the one with the best controllability. The use of coal with the highest TAC value has the lowest results of CN and EI99 results about the use of natural gas (NG) and biogas (BG) respectively. From the evolution of the sustainability indicators in both schemes, the best designs were obtained for those using coal as fuel in the combustion stage, since it generates a greater flow of CO_2, and greater ease of capture was observed in the face of these CO_2 concentrations.

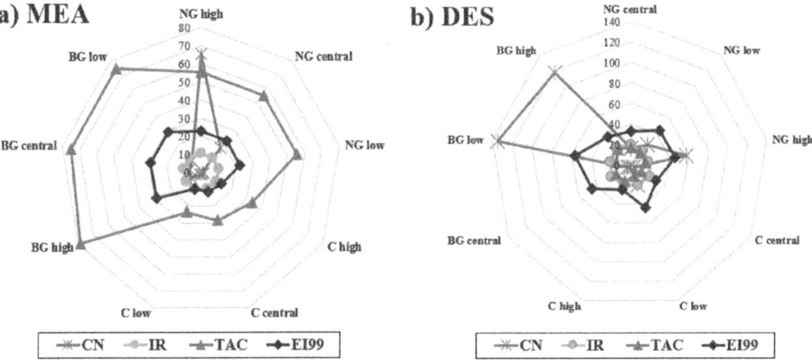

Figure 2. Radial graphs for CO_2 capture with a) MEA and b) DES as solvents. Using natural gas (NG), coal (C) and biogas (BG). Evaluating the indicators of condition number (CN), individual risk (IR), total annual cost (TAC) and eco-indicator 99 (EI99).

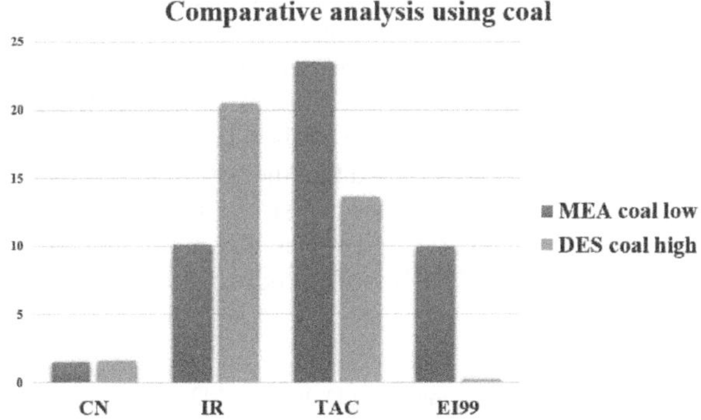

Figure 3. Comparison of the best designs of both schemes using coal (C) as fuel.

In Figure 3.for the same process of post-combustion capture (PCC) with coal, a lower TAC and EI99 were obtained in the use of DES compared to MEA, due to lower equipment costs, operation and lower energy consumption. While DES is more expensive than MEA, the cost of operation is reduced due to the energy used. A higher IR in the case of DES use is due to the implementation of two flash tanks and although the desorption column in the DES PCC process is smaller than the MEA process, reducing the number of stages by about 50 % so, in the flash tanks and in the desorption column occur the pressure drops which significantly influences the individual risk. Regarding condition number, the use of MEA is slightly lower since the controllability of CPC using DES was also affected by the use of the two flash tanks. Finally, for the selection of the best process, the results of Figure 3 were taken into consideration. Therefore, the process with the best results of the indicators is high carbon, in a CPC with the use of DES as a solvent. The process conditions are shown in Figure 4.

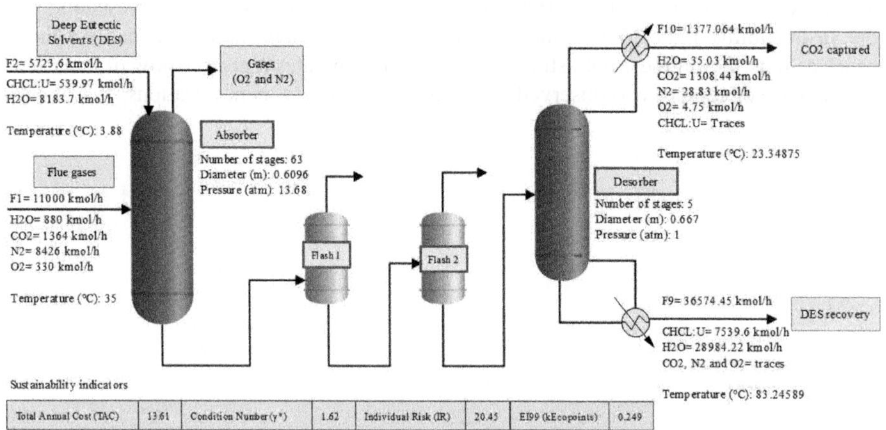

Figure 4. Best proposed scheme of post-combustion CO_2 capture process using high carbon as fuel in a DES scheme as solvent without consider the combustion stage.

5. Conclusions

Regarding the comparative analysis of CO_2 capture using coal as fuel and the conventional solvent MEA as compared to the proposal of a DES solvent, it can be concluded that the model with the best sustainability indexes presents lower costs, good controllability of the process and whose environmental impact is lower compared to the traditional CO_2 capture process. However, in terms of safety, the IR is considerably increased due to pressure drops with the use of flash tanks in the process of treating the DES. After all the analysis it was concluded that the best design is the DES scheme with the use of coal as fuel in your point high the analysis. By implementing this green solvent, it leads to the improvement of existing processes that meet the objectives of the 2030 Agenda, from one of the most used fuels in the production of electricity such as coal.

References

C. Da Silveria Cachola, M. Ciotta, A. Santos and D. Peyerl. 2023. Deploying of the carbon capture technologies for CO2 emission mitigation in the industrial sectors. Carbon Capture Science & Technology, 7, 100102. https://doi.org/10.1016/j.ccst.2023.100102

A. Martinez Lomovskoi, A. G. Romero García, E. Sánchez Ramírez and J.G. Segovia Hernández. 2023. Desing and multi-objective optimization of a CO2 capture plant using deep eutectic solvents. Chemical Engineering Research and Desing, 192, 570-581. https://doi.org/10.1016/j.cherd.2023.03.006.

A. G. Romero García, N. Ramírez Corona, E. Sánchez Ramírez, H. Alcocer García, C. De Blasio and J.G. Segovia Hernández. 2022. Sustentability assessment in the CO2 capture process: multi-objective optimization. Chemical Engineering and Processing-Process Intensification, 182, 109207. https://doi.org/10.1016/j.cep.2022.109207.

G. J. Ruiz Mercado, R.L. Smith and M.A. Gonzalez. 2012. Sustainability Indicators for Chemical Processes: i. Taxonomy. Industrial & Engineering Chemistry Research, 51(5), 2309-2328. https://doi.org/10.1021/ie102116e.

Flavio Manenti, Gintaras V. Reklaitis (Eds.), Proceedings of the 34th European Symposium on Computer Aided Process Engineering / 15th International Symposium on Process Systems Engineering (ESCAPE34/PSE24), June 2-6, 2024, Florence, Italy
 http://dx.doi.org/10.1016/B978-0-443-28824-1.50163-0

Development of Electricity Generation System by Combining Plastic Steam Gasification with Solid Oxide Fuel Cells

Khaled Abouemara, Muhammad Shahbaz, Samir Boulfrad, Gordon McKay, Tareq Al-Ansari*

College of Science and Engineering, Hamad Bin Khalifa University, Qatar Foundation, Doha, Qatar
Email: talansari@hbku.edu.qa

Abstract

This study introduces a novel integration of steam gasification of plastic waste with solid oxide fuel cells (SOFCs) for sustainable electricity generation. Employing Aspen Plus® and Python, the research evaluates SOFC performance under different operational conditions. Key findings reveal that at a gasifier temperature of 1023 K, and with steam and CaO flow rates of 1.00 and 0.50 kmol/hr respectively, the SOFC's power output consistently increases with temperature. The power output rises from 0.639 to 1.157 w by raising the temperature from 1133 to 1293 K, while the output voltage dropping from 0.9141V to 0.793 V in this temperature range. Similarly for the syngas composition for the steam flow rate of 1.5kmol/hr, the power output of system is increased from0.637 to 1.151 W and voltage decreased from 0.910 to 0.788 by raising the SOFC temperature from 1133 to 1293K. Similar profiling is also noticed for the case of CaO flow rate of 0.5 kmol/hr. The study shows the viability of using plastic waste as a renewable energy source, contributing to the global shift towards sustainable energy solutions.

Keywords: SOFC, H_2, Volt. Gasification, Power

1. Introduction

The global surge in electricity demand, driven by digitalization and Industry 4.0, necessitates innovative energy solutions (Karapekmez & Dincer, 2022, Shahbaz et al., 2023). With the projected energy demand set to increase by 40% by 2030, the focus has shifted towards sustainable, environmentally friendly alternatives to traditional fossil fuels, which are currently the primary global energy source (Karapekmez & Dincer, 2022, Ali et al., 2022). The environmental impact of fossil fuel use, particularly the substantial greenhouse gas emissions, highlights the urgency for cleaner, more efficient energy processes (Inayat et al., 2021). The transition towards renewable energy, supported by initiatives like the European Union's "Green Deal," is accelerating (Li et al., 2021). Plastic waste, a prevalent modern material, poses both environmental challenges and opportunities for energy conversion (Chen et al., 2016). The gasification of plastic, transforming it into syngas, stands out for its energy recovery potential. This process, particularly steam gasification, generates a syngas mixture, serving as a promising feedstock for fuel cell technologies (Sharuddin et al., 2016, Asadullah, 2014). Fuel cells, especially SOFCs, are emerging as key players in the renewable energy sector due to their high efficiency and low environmental impact (Kumar & Singh, 2022). The integration of biomass gasification with SOFCs presents a novel approach to electricity generation, combining the advantages of waste management and energy conversion. This study focuses on developing an integrated model using Aspen Plus® and Python to simulate the gasification process and SOFC performance, respectively. The model encompasses a detailed analysis of the gasification parameters (temperature, steam flow low rate and CaO flow rate on syngas and the dynamic behavior of SOFCs in terms of power output. The objective of the study is to investigate the impact of temperature on power and voltage of SOFC based on the H_2 flow rate obtained from gasification system for each optimum parameter.

2. Methodology

The primary aim is to design a carbon-neutral power generation system by integrating a plastic gasification system with a SOFC. This involves using H_2 from steam gasification as fuel for the SOFC, with the overall system consisting of two integrated units developed using Aspen Plus® and Python. Figure 1 shows the combined fuel system.

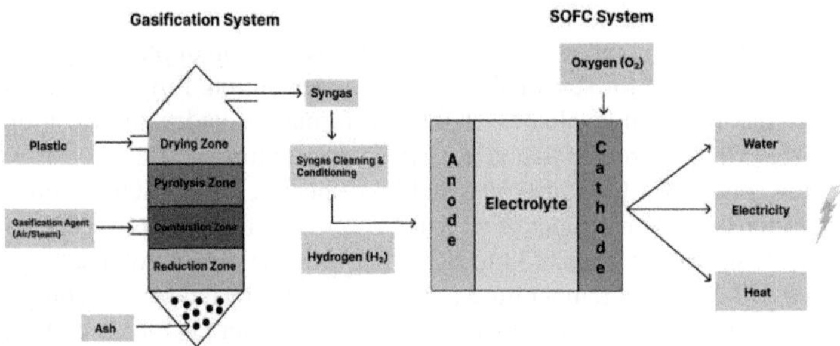

Figure 1: Process scheme for gasification and SOFC fuel system.

The steam gasification process focuses on maximizing hydrogen production, using CaO as a sorbent for CO_2 capture. Key assumptions for the process include uniform temperature and pressure, ideal gas behaviour, and the exclusion of tar and ammonia formation. The system operates under atmospheric pressure, with plastic feedstock and ash considered non-conventional. Utilizing Aspen Plus®, various physical properties packages, like Peng Robinson and Peng Robinson with Boston Modification (PG-RM), are employed to simulate the process. The simulation includes the transformation of plastic into syngas. The process begins with a feed material stream and involves several units like a yield reactor, equilibrium reactors, and separation units to produce clean H_2. The proximate and ultimate analyses of the plastic are shown in Table 1 (Ali et al., 2023). The SOFC utilizes H_2 as fuel, with O_2 sourced separately. Operating on principles of electrochemical conversion, the SOFC model incorporates equations for Nernst voltage and various losses (activation, ohmic, concentration) to determine the cell's voltage and power output are listed in Table 2.

Table 1: Composition of plastic waste (Ali et al., 2023).

Proximate analysis		**Ultimate analysis**	
Element	Value	Element	Value
MC	0.2	Ash	0.1
FC	4.44	Carbon	66.89
VM	95.36	Hydrogen	6.06
Ash	0.1	Nitrogen	0.08
		Sulfur	0.2
		Oxygen*	26.67

Table 1: Correlations for voltage, power output, and partial pressure calculations (Doherty et al., 2010, Gebregergis et al., 2008, Lukas et al., 2001, Qi et al., 2005, Sedghisigarchi & Feliachi, 2004, Ni & Zhao, 2013, Komatsu et al., 2013).

Parameter	***Expression***
Fuel Cell Voltage	$V_{out} = E_{Nernst} - (V_{act} + V_{conc} + V_{ohmic})$
Nernst Voltage	$E_{Nernst} = E_o + \frac{RT}{nF} \frac{P_{H_2} P_{O_2}^{0.5}}{P_{H_2O}}$ Where $E_o = \frac{\Delta gf}{nF}$
Ohmic Losses	$V_{ohmic} = (\gamma \times \exp(\beta(\frac{1}{T_0} - \frac{1}{T})) \times I_{fc}$
Activation Losses	$V_{act} = \frac{RT}{nF}(z + \sqrt{1 + z^2})$ Where $z = \frac{I_{fc}}{2I_0}$
Concentration Losses	$V_{conc} = \frac{RT}{nF}\ln(1 - \frac{I_{fc}}{I_L})$ Where $I_L = K \cdot C\infty$ *and* $I_{fc} = K \cdot (C\infty - Cb)$
Partial Pressure	$P_{H_2} = \frac{\frac{1}{K_{H_2}}}{1+\tau_{H_2}} \times (q_{H_2} - 2K_r I_{fc})$ $P_{O_2} = \frac{\frac{1}{K_{O_2}}}{1+\tau_{O_2}} \times (q_{O_2} - 2K_r I_{fc})$ $P_{H_2O} = \frac{\frac{1}{K_{H_2O}}}{1+\tau_{H_2O}} \times (2K_r I_{fc})$ $q_{H_2} = \frac{2K_r}{U_{opt}} \times (\frac{1}{1+\tau_{fs}})$ $q_{O_2} = \frac{q_{H_2}}{r_{OH}}$
Power output	$Pout = I_{fc} \times V_{out}$

The integration methodology feeds the outputs of the gasification into the SOFC, focusing on the syngas composition and flow rates from the gasifier as inputs for the SOFC. *(i)* Gasification Model Outputs: The model generates syngas components (H_2, CO, CO_2, CH_4) from plastic waste gasification at 1023 K measured in kmol/hr. *(ii)*Unit Conversion: For integration with the SOFC model and real-time applications, the gas component rates are converted from kmol/hr to mol/min using the formula: Rate in mol/sec = Rate in kmol/hr × 0.277 × 60. *(iii)* Calculation of H_2 and O_2: Total H_2 (qh2) is calculated by adding H_2 from gasification and four times the H_2 from CH_4 (as each CH_4 molecule has four H_2 atoms) and total O_2 (qo2) is calculated from CO and CO_2 rates, considering each CO_2 molecule contributes two oxygen atoms. (iv) The calculated H_2 (qh2) and O_2 (qo2) rates are used in the SOFC. H_2 primarily contributes to electricity, water, and heat generation at the SOFC's anode side, while O_2 content aids in maintaining the electrochemical balance. Moreover, sensitivity analysis shows the effects of temperature, steam and CaO flowrate on the system's performance like power and voltage.

3. Results and discussion

As the study investigates the influence of gasification temperature, Steam/feed ratio, and CaO/feed ratio on the SOFC's performance in terms of power, current, and voltage, three data sets were considered for evaluation and discussion: Gasifier temperature at 1023 K, this specific temperature is selected as it represents an optimum operating condition for gasifiers, which shows a higher H_2 flow rate , steam flow rate of 1.00 kmol/h, and CaO flow rate of 0.50 kmol/hr. As shown below in table 3, the syngas composition, obtained from Aspen Plus® for each data set was outlined. The cell performance is measured in terms of output voltage, power with respect to change in temperature.

Table 2: Gasification output at optimum process parameters

Parameters	*H_2 (kmol/hr)*	*CO (kmol/hr)*	*CO_2 (kmol/hr)*	*CH_4 (kmol/hr)*	*Syngas (kmol/hr)*
Temperature (1023 K)	0.0633	0.0092	0.0086	0.00006	0.08126
Steam Flow Rate (1 Kmol/hr)	0.05888	0.01068	0.00639	0.000815	0.07677
CaO Flow Rate (0.5 Kmol/hr)	0.06045	0.0114	0.01469	0.00023	0.08682

In SOFCs, current density represents the electric current per unit area within the cell. This parameter significantly influences the fuel cell's power output, being closely tied to electrochemical processes at the electrodes. As current density increases, FC performance improves up to a certain threshold, known as the limiting current density. Figure 2 below illustrates prevailing Ifc values at various temperatures, along with their corresponding current density (A/cm^2) values.

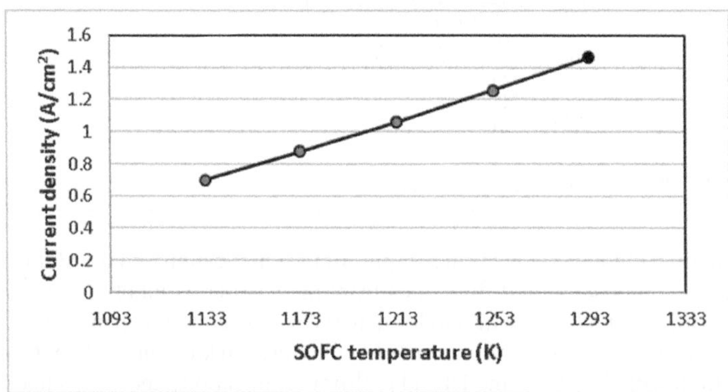

Figure 2: Typical corresponding current density (A/cm^2) at temperatures in (K) (Gebregergis et al., 2008, Udomsilp et al., 2020, Khan et al., 2020).

The SOFC performance, with the gasifier operating at 1023 K, demonstrates a clear relationship between the SOFC temperature, current density, output voltage, and power output. As the SOFC temperature increases from 1133 K to 1293 K, there is a noticeable rise in current density, indicating enhanced electrochemical activity. However, this increase in temperature and current density coincides with a decrease in output voltage, which drops from 0.914 V to 0.793 V. Despite the reduction in voltage, the power output shows a positive trend, increasing from 0.639 W to 1.157 W. This suggests that the SOFC system, becomes more efficient in power generation as the temperature rises, likely due to improved ion conductivity and reaction kinetics at higher temperatures. The SOFC performance under a steady steam flow rate of 1 Kmol/hr follows a similar pattern. As the SOFC temperature increases from 1133 to 1293 K, the output voltage decreases with increasing temperature, moving from 0.910 V to 0.788 V. This inverse relationship between temperature and voltage might be attributed to increased thermal activity impacting the electrochemical potential within the cell. Despite the reduction in voltage, the power output shows an increase, from 0.637 W to 1.151 W. This trend suggests that the SOFC system's efficiency in converting chemical energy to electrical energy improves with temperature, even under a constant steam flow rate. The results indicate that the steam flow rate maintains a conducive environment for the SOFC operation, allowing for effective energy conversion under varying thermal conditions. The SOFC's performance, when operated with a CaO flow rate of 0.50 kmol/hr, displays a notable correlation between the SOFC temperature, output voltage and power output. Interestingly, the output voltage shows a gradual decrease over this temperature range, starting at 0.923 V to 0.803 V. This decrease in voltage could be due to increased ohmic, activation, and concentration losses within the SOFC as temperature rises, which is typical in high-temperature fuel cell operations. The power output grows from 0.646 W to 1.173 W. These results imply that the CaO flow rate effectively maintains syngas quality for efficient SOFC operation, thereby enhancing overall energy conversion efficiency under varying thermal conditions. Results are shown table 4 below.

Table 3: SOFC performance based on a gasifier temperature of 1073 , steam flow rate of 1.00 kmol/hr, and CaO flow rate of 0.50 kmol/hr.

Parameter	***Gasification Temperature at 1023 K***		***Gasification Steam Flow Rate 1.00 kmol/hr***		***Gasification CaO Flow Rate of 0.50 kmol/hr***	
SOFC Temp in K	*Voltage in V*	*Power in W*	*Voltage in V*	*Power in W*	*Voltage in V*	*Power in W*
1133	0.914	0.639	0.910	0.637	0.923	0.646
1173	0.885	0.779	0.881	0.775	0.894	0.787
1213	0.856	0.907	0.852	0.903	0.865	0.917
1253	0.825	1.039	0.820	1.033	0.834	1.051
1293	0.793	1.157	0.788	1.150	0.803	1.172

4. Conclusions

This study successfully demonstrated an innovative approach to sustainable electricity generation by integrating a plastic gasification system with a SOFC. The research focused on evaluating the SOFC's performance under various operational conditions, including different gasifier temperatures, steam flow rates, and CaO flow rates. Key findings from the operational conditions examined revealed that at a gasifier temperature of 1023 K, the SOFC's power output improved significantly with rising temperature. Specifically, power output increased from 0.639 W at 1133 K to 1.157 W at 1293 K, despite a decrease in output voltage from 0.914 V to 0.793 V over this temperature range. Under a steady steam flow rate of 1.00 kmol/hr, a similar pattern was observed, with power output growing from 0.637 W at 1133 K to 1.150 W at 1293 K. Additionally, with a CaO flow rate of 0.50 kmol/hr, the SOFC's power output continued this upward trend, increasing from 0.646 W at 1133K to 1.172 W at 1293K. Future research could expand on this study by exploring the scalability of the integrated system, its economic viability, and the potential for real-world application.

Acknowledgment: The author thanks the GSRA Grant No. GSRA9-L-2-0524-22035 from the Qatar National Research Fund (a member of Qatar Foundation) for financial support. The authors would also like to acknowledge Hamad Bin Khalifa University for the support. Open Access funding provided by the Qatar National Library, Qatar.

References

A. Karapekmez, I. Dincer. Development of a new solar, gasification and fuel cell based integrated plant. International Journal of Hydrogen Energy. 47 (2022) 4196-210.

M. Shahbaz, N. Rashid, J. Saleem, H. Mackey, G. McKay, T. Al-Ansari. A review of waste management approaches to maximise sustainable value of waste from the oil and gas industry and potential for the State of Qatar. Fuel. 332 (2023) 126220.

A.M. Ali, M. Inayat, A.A. Zahrani, K. Shahzad, M. Shahbaz, S.A. Sulaiman, et al. Process optimization and economic evaluation of air gasification of Saudi Arabian date palm fronds for H2-rich syngas using response surface methodology. Fuel. 316 (2022) 123359.

A. Inayat, M. Shahbaz, Z. Khan, M. Inayat, M. Mofijur, S.F. Ahmed, et al. Heat integration modeling of hydrogen production from date seeds via steam gasification. International Journal of Hydrogen Energy. (2021).

Y. Li, Y. Pang, H. Tu, F. Torrigino, S.M.A. Biollaz, Z. Li, et al. Impact of syngas from biomass gasification on solid oxide fuel cells: A review study for the energy transition. Energy Conversion and Management. 250 (2021) 114894.

Y. Chen, Z. Cui, X. Cui, W. Liu, X. Wang, et al. Life cycle assessment of end-of-life treatments of waste plastics in China. Resources, Conservation and Recycling. 146 (2019) 348-57.

S.D. Anuar Sharuddin, F. Abnisa, W.M.A. Wan Daud, M.K. Aroua. A review on pyrolysis of plastic wastes. Energy Conversion and Management. 115 (2016) 308-26.

M. Asadullah. Barriers of commercial power generation using biomass gasification gas: A review. Renewable and Sustainable Energy Reviews. 29 (2014) 201-15.

P. Kumar, O. Singh. A review of solid oxide fuel cell based hybrid cycles. International Journal of Energy Research. 46 (2022) 8560-89.

A.M. Ali, M. Shahbaz, M. Inayat, K. Shahzad, A.A. Al-Zahrani, A.B. Mahpudz. Conversion of municipals waste into syngas and methanol via steam gasification using CaO as sorbent: An Aspen Plus modelling. Fuel. 349 (2023) 128640.

W. Doherty, A. Reynolds, D. Kennedy. Computer simulation of a biomass gasification-solid oxide fuel cell power system using Aspen Plus. Energy. 35 (2010) 4545-55.

A. Gebregergis, P. Pillay, D. Bhattacharyya, R. Rengaswemy. Solid oxide fuel cell modeling. IEEE Transactions on Industrial Electronics. 56 (2008) 139-48.

M.D. Lukas, K.Y. Lee, H. Ghezel-Ayagh. An explicit dynamic model for direct reforming carbonate fuel cell stack. IEEE Transactions on Energy Conversion. 16 (2001) 289-95.

Y. Qi, B. Huang, K.T. Chuang. Dynamic modeling of solid oxide fuel cell: The effect of diffusion and inherent impedance. Journal of Power Sources. 150 (2005) 32-47.

K. Sedghisigarchi, A. Feliachi. Dynamic and transient analysis of power distribution systems with fuel Cells-part I: fuel-cell dynamic model. IEEE Transactions on Energy Conversion. 19 (2004) 423-8.

M. Ni, T.S. Zhao. Solid oxide fuel cells: from materials to system modeling. Royal society of chemistry2013.

Y. Komatsu, S. Kimijima, J.S. Szmyd. Numerical analysis on dynamic behavior of solid oxide fuel cell with power output control scheme. Journal of power sources. 223 (2013) 232-45.

D. Udomsilp, J. Rechberger, R. Neubauer, C. Bischof, F. Thaler, W. Schafbauer, et al. Metal-Supported Solid Oxide Fuel Cells with Exceptionally High Power Density for Range Extender Systems. Cell Reports Physical Science. 1 (2020) 100072.

M.Z. Khan, R.-H. Song, A. Hussain, S.-B. Lee, T.-H. Lim, J.-E. Hong. Effect of applied current density on the degradation behavior of anode-supported flat-tubular solid oxide fuel cells. Journal of the European Ceramic Society. 40 (2020) 1407-17.

Flavio Manenti, Gintaras V. Reklaitis (Eds.), Proceedings of the 34th European Symposium on Computer Aided Process Engineering / 15th International Symposium on Process Systems Engineering (ESCAPE34/PSE24), June 2-6, 2024, Florence, Italy
 http://dx.doi.org/10.1016/B978-0-443-28824-1.50164-2

Integrated Solid Oxide Systems: Advancing Efficiency in Power Generation through Fuel Cell-Electrolyzer Coupling with Diverse Fuels

Xinyi Wei[a,b], Shivom Sharma[a], Arthur Waeber[a], Jan Van Herle[b], François Maréchal[a]
[a]IPESE, EPFL Valais Wallis, 1950 Sion, Switzerland
[b]GEM, EPFL Valais Wallis, 1950 Sion, Switzerland
xinyi.wei@epfl.ch

Abstract

The significant increase in CO_2 concentrations in the atmosphere, which is primarily caused by the combustion of fossil fuels for electricity production. Situated as an auspicious candidate in the realm of environmentally friendly energy and heat generation, the solid oxide fuel cell (SOFC) assumes a pivotal role in confronting this pressing challenge. Usually, owing to the fact that SOFC does not achieve a 100% fuel conversion rate, unconverted fuel is combusted into a burner, and resulting gases are released into the environment. Air is commonly employed in this combustion process. However, the challenge arises when using carbon-based fuels, as the presence of nitrogen makes it challenging to capture CO_2 at downstream of the burner. In this study, an innovative system has been introduced. Solid oxide electrolyzer cells (SOEC) is coupled with SOFC. The novel SOFC-EC configuration achieves a remarkable 100% CO_2 capture rate and purity when utilizing natural gas. Additionally, hydrogen as an alternative SOFC fuel has been considered. A comprehensive performance analysis has been conducted with these two distinct fuels. The evaluation incorporates multi-objective optimization, encompassing various design parameters to provide a comprehensive understanding of the system's capabilities. The active area demand for SOEC is exceptionally low, comprising a mere 4.3% of the active area required for SOFC, all the while attaining a system efficiency close to 60% and adhering to all industrial constraints. With its long-term viability, this innovative SOFC-EC system arises as a promising, compact and cost-effective solution. Significant potential exists for it to influence the course of power generation towards greater sustainability and cleanliness.

Keywords: Solid Oxide Fuel Cell, Solid Oxide Electrolyzer, Carbon Capture, Oxy-combustion, Anode Off-gas Recirculation.

1. Introduction

Solid oxide fuel cells (SOFC) have emerged as a focal point of scientific attention, showcasing promising potential as a power generation technology that could reduce dependence on traditional electricity grids. Their compact design with external fuel storage and its fuel inputs flexibility enhances their adaptability for application in diverse industrial power plants (Sharma et al., 2018). Notably, SOFC operate at elevated temperatures, reaching up to 800°C, enabling the co-generation of high-quality heat or steam that can be efficiently integrated into the system as a valuable heat source (Sharma et al., 2019). Despite their advantages, SOFC face a challenge with a maximum fuel utilization rate of approximately 85%. To address this, a burner is employed to combust any unconverted fuels. While serving the dual purpose of supplying supplementary heat to the SOFC system, the burner introduces an additional aspect by generating additional CO_2. A potential solution involves the direct injection of pure oxygen into the burner. However, this approach brings its own set of challenges, particularly the need for specialized O_2 tanks or production units, such as membrane separation systems, which can be both energy-intensive and costly to implement. Moreover, the production and supply chain of oxygen would require meticulous organization, especially if it is produced at a centralized facility. Solid oxide electrolyzer cell (SOEC), is able to produce O_2 as a byproduct, which can be efficiently utilized in a catalytic burner for the complete combustion of fuel. The flexibility to adjust the quantities of CO_2 and water allows for precise control over the amount of O_2 produced by the electrolyzer. This level of control facilitates a meticulous regulation of the combustion process, leading to the generation of only CO_2 and water, and water can easily be condensed.

In this study, a novel process integration has been thoroughly examined by coupling of SOFC and SOEC. Two distinct types of fuels have been chosen for investigation: natural gas and H_2. The selection of natural gas is driven by the system's ability to easily capture CO_2, presenting an advantageous solution. On the other hand, the inclusion of hydrogen as a fuel allows for a comprehensive understanding of the system's compatibility with different energy carriers. The outcomes of this analysis not only shed light on the suitability of the proposed system for diverse fuel types.

2. Methodology

2.1. SOFC – SOEC system description

This integrated SOFC-EC system is shown in Figure 1, where the incoming fuel - whether natural gas or H_2 - is preheated in H1. To prevent carbon deposition, especially in the case of natural gas, a specific steam-to-carbon ratio must be maintained, therefore, external water is heated in heater H2. Subsequently, the mixture of fuel and steam undergoes further heating in H3 before being introduced into an external reformer. Within the reformer, steam methane reforming occurs, converting a portion of CH_4 into CO and H_2. This step is crucial as it avoids carbon deposition in the fuel cell, particularly when relying solely on internal reforming. It is important to note that when the fuel is H_2, the need for external water or reformer is eliminated. The syngas or H_2 is heated to the necessary SOFC inlet temperature in H5. In SOFC, the chemical energy is converted into electricity.

The anode off-gas (AOG), from the anodic downstream side of SOFC, has three potential routes. Firstly, the AOG can be recirculated back to the inlet of the external reformer after water condensation *via* C2 and C3. This option requires a low-temperature AOG compressor to overcome the pressure drops of the reformer, heat exchangers and stack. Secondly, a potential approach involves partial use of AOG as the inlet to the SOEC, where (co-) electrolysis reactions occur, converting CO_2 and/or steam into CO and/or H_2. Given the similar operating temperatures of the SOFC and SOEC, the advantage lies in the elimination of an additional heat exchanger. The syngas/H_2 produced by SOEC is injected back into the external reformer. Thirdly, the remaining AOG flow is directed to the burner to undergo oxy-combustion, utilizing the oxygen produced from the anodic side of the SOEC. The flue gases at downstream of the burner undergo cooling in C4 and C5 before entering into a water separator/condenser. Notably, when natural gas is used as the fuel and pure O_2 is employed, the process facilitates straightforward carbon capture.

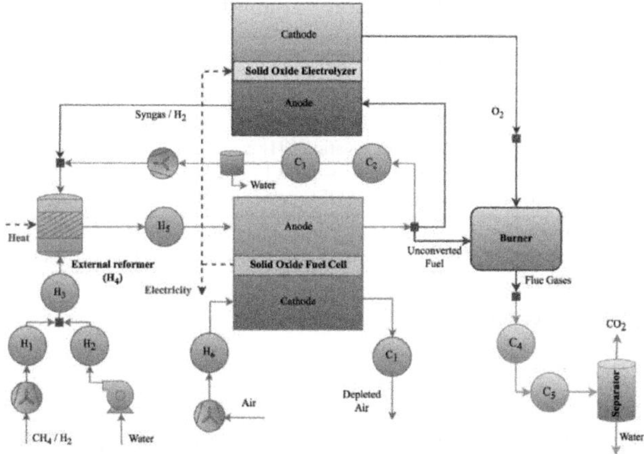

Figure 1. Novel SOFC-SOEC system with oxy-combustion and water separator

The process flowsheet has been simulated in Aspen Plus V12.0, and the key simulation parameters are presented in Table 1. The SOFC system presented has a capacity of 10 kW. The efficiencies of the AOG blower or air blower are derived from the commercial products. Although SOEC is chosen to operate at endothermic or thermally neutral mode based on previous studies.

Table 1. Specifications of SOFC and SOEC systems (T - temperature, P - pressure)

SOFC System: Stack area ~ 3 m^2, Stack P drop = 0.08 bar, Maximum stack ΔT = 100 °C, Stack outlet T = 750 °C, Current density = 4000 A/cm^2, Air blower suction P, P increase, efficiency = 1 bar, 0.3 bar, 0.8
SOEC System: Stack inlet T = 800 °C, Conversion efficiency = 0.9, Operating mode = Thermal neutral, Stack outlet T = 800 °C, Single pass fuel utilization = 0.9, Electricity to H_2 efficiency = 0.95

2.2. Multi-objective Optimization Problem

The multi-objective optimization (MOO) problems formulated were solved using OSMOSE, a decision-making tool developed within our research group. Figure 2 illustrates the basic flowchart depicting the working principle of OSMOSE. Dakota has been used as an external MOO tool to solve the complex optimization problems. OSMOSE is linked with process flowsheet in Aspen Plus to transfer decision variable values and retrieve essential data from the process model. A mixed-integer linear programming (MILP) problem is formulated, utilizing process and utility models to optimize interconnections, mass flows, and heat flows. The MILP problem is then solved using the AMPL/CPLEX solver. Table 2 provides a list of objective functions, decision variables along with their specified ranges, and constraints with set limits. The selection of decision variable ranges and constraint limits is based on the existing literature.

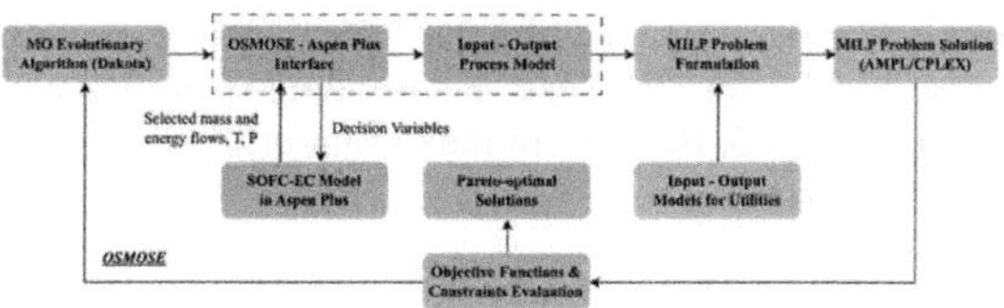

Figure 2. Mechanism of OSMOSE: A Tool for Process Integration and Optimization

Table 2. Objective Functions, Decision Variables and Constraints Information

Objective Functions: F1 - Max Electrical efficiency (%), F2 - Max Global Fuel Utilization (FU), F3 - Min Single Pass FU, F4 - Max the ratio of Global FU/Single FU, F5 – Max Heat Available at 600 °C
Decision Variables with Lower and Upper Limits (CH_4 / H_2 case): External Reforming Temperature (CH_4 case) = 510-550 °C, External Reforming Ratio (CH_4 case) = 0.1 – 0.5, Fuel Input (CH_4 case) = 0.0155 – 0.02 mol/s, External Water Flow (CH_4 case) = 0.1 – 0.09 mol/s, Fuel Input (H_2 case) = 0.0595 – 0.1 mol/s, AOG Recirculation Ratio = 0 – 0.9, SOEC power input = 0.1 – 4 kW
Constraints with Limits: S/C (CH_4 case) > 1.5, Burner Downstream O_2 mole fraction < 0.02, Burner Downstream O_2 mole fraction > 0.00001, ΔT across stack < 100 °C, 0.9 > Single Pass FU > 0.2

3. Results and Discussions

3.1. System performance analysis

3.1.1. CH_4 as SOFC fuel input

The performance of the proposed system has been examined using CH_4 fuel. Figure 3(a) illustrates the outcomes of MOO, considering system electrical efficiency, the ratio between global FU and single pass FU, and the available heat at 600 °C as three objectives. The results reveal a notable trend: as the system electrical efficiency increases, the difference between global FU and single FU becomes smaller. This indicates that a lower AOG recirculation rate is required, a sensible outcome considering the power consumption by the AOG blower. Similarly, for high AOG recirculation, cooling and water removal increase to reduce the AOG blow power consumption. However, this cooling process leads to inefficient use of system heat, resulting in a higher ratio between global and single FU and a smaller amount of high-temperature available heat. In summary, when considering these three objectives, the analysis suggests that the maximum system electrical efficiency achievable is approximately 54%. Transitioning to Figure 3(b), the distinction in this scenario lies in the exclusion of available heat from MOO problem. Beyond the observed conclusions, it is intriguing to note that the achievable system electrical efficiency is approximately 56%, surpassing the efficiency obtained in the previous case.

3.1.2. H_2 as SOFC fuel input

As depicted in
Figure 4 (a), similar conclusions can be drawn when considering H_2 fuel. The maximum achievable system electrical efficiency is approximately 52%. This efficiency is slightly lower compared to CH_4 case. The difference arises from the internal reforming that occurs for CH_4. This internal reforming requires heat, which aids in reducing the air flow rate as it is employed to control the maximum stack outlet temperature. In case of H_2, the reaction is strongly exothermic, resulting in a higher power requirement by the air blower, leading to reduced overall electrical efficiency. When using H_2 fuel, AOG only contains H_2 and steam. This means that after AOG condensation, the flow predominantly consists of H_2 with a small portion of water. If high recirculation is applied, it can lead to a situation where the system has a very low single pass FU, while the global FU remains high. This characteristic is highlighted by the range of these two FUs ratio, with the maximum ratio reaching 2 for H_2 case and 1.3 for CH_4 case. This finding is further supported by
Figure 4 (b). After removing F5, the system maximum efficiency can reach nearly 58%, whereas single FU is less than 0.3.

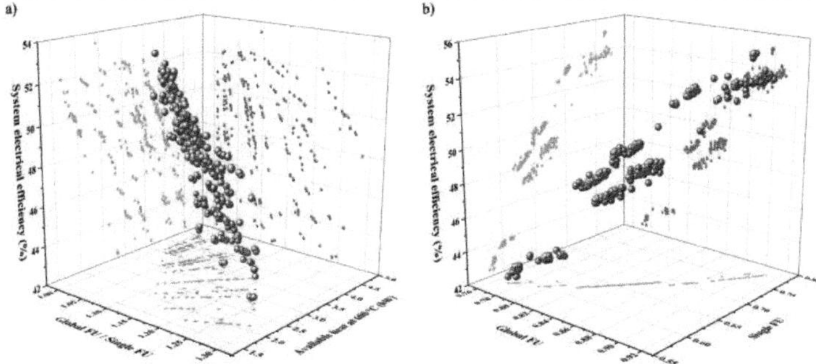

Figure 3. MOO performance analysis by using (a) F1, F4 and F5, (b) F1, F2 and F3.

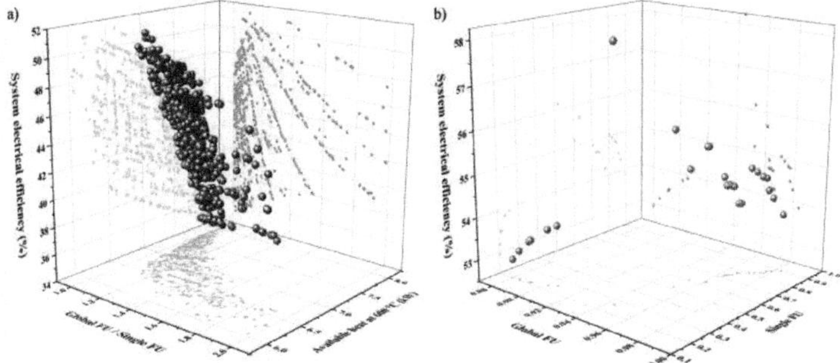

Figure 4. MOO performance analysis by using (a) F1, F4 and F5, (b) F1, F2 and F3.

3.2. Process design parameters analysis

3.2.1. CH_4 as SOFC fuel input

Figure 5 illustrates various relationships between different decision variables and F1 and F5. As anticipated, a lower AOG recirculation rate corresponds to a higher available high-temperature heat. When the efficiency exceeds 52%, the AOG ratio predominantly remains above 0.4. Interestingly, the system can achieve the same efficiency, with different set of parameter values. Additionally, lower external water usage is associated with less heat consumed to convert water into steam. Higher external water usage, indicating a relatively low AOG, tends to result in a slightly lower efficiency. The trend for SOEC power input is clear - higher SOEC input power is linked to lower efficiency. The external reforming temperature, reforming ratio and fuel input flow rate do not have any clear trends. Different combinations of these design parameters can yield similar objectives. However, the system does exhibit a preference for lower external reforming temperature (510 °C), a ratio of 0.2, and a fuel input flow rate less than 0.0165 mol/s.

3.2.2. H_2 as SOFC fuel input

As illustrated in Figure 6, H_2 fuel case has similar conclusions. In CH_4 case, AOG contains LHV compositions (CO and even CO_2); in H_2 fuel case, higher AOG recirculation can indeed bring benefits in efficiency, especially when exceeding 0.56. Regarding fuel input, no clear trend can be observed, consistent with previous observations. However, the system does demonstrate a preference for lower fuel input. Conversely, for SOEC, a lower power input is associated with higher efficiency but poorer performance in terms of high-temperature available heat.

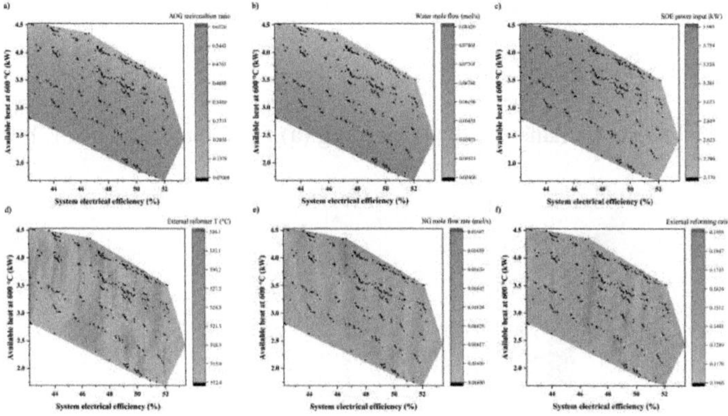

Figure 5. Variation in design parameters with objective functions F1 and F5.

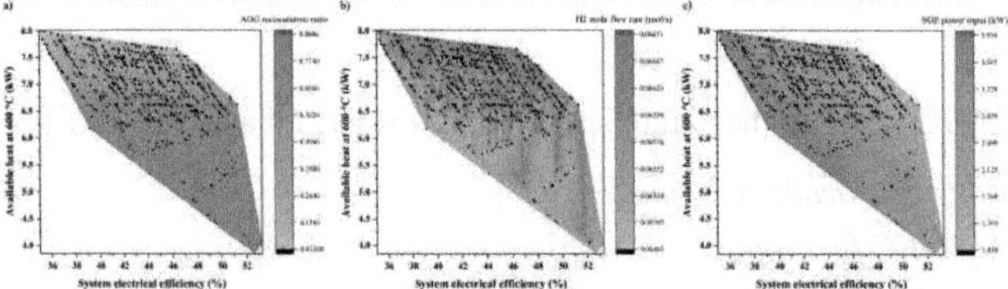

Figure 6. Variations in design parameters with objective functions F1 and F5.

4. Conclusions

In this study, an innovative approach was undertaken to couple SOFC and SOEC, examining two distinct fuel inputs, CH_4 and H_2. The outcomes unveiled subtle patterns in system performance, where factors such as AOG recirculation, external water usage and input power played pivotal roles in shaping efficiency and high-temperature available heat. Particularly noteworthy was the H_2 fuel case, showcasing that elevated AOG recirculation could elevate efficiency to levels surpassing 58%, excluding waste heat valorization. In the CH_4 fuel case, the system achieved a maximum efficiency of around 56%, featuring automatic CO_2 capture. These results underscore the promising prospects of the modular SOFC-EC system.

References

S. Sharma and F. Maréchal, "Robust Multi-Objective Optimization of Solid Oxide Fuel Cell–Gas Turbine Hybrid Cycle and Uncertainty Analysis," J. Electrochem. Energy Convers. Storage, vol. 15, no. 4, p. 041007.

Flavio Manenti, Gintaras V. Reklaitis (Eds.), Proceedings of the 34th European Symposium on Computer Aided Process Engineering / 15th International Symposium on Process Systems Engineering (ESCAPE34/PSE24), June 2-6, 2024, Florence, Italy
 http://dx.doi.org/10.1016/B978-0-443-28824-1.50165-4

Refining SOFC Performance: Parameter Estimation and Model Validation for Dynamic Energy System Optimization

Arthur Waeber[a], Xinyi Wei[a,b], Shivom Sharma[a], Jan Van Herle[b], François Maréchal[a]
[a]IPESE, EPFL Valais Wallis, 1950 Sion, Switzerland
[b]GEM, EPFL Valais Wallis, 1950 Sion, Switzerland
arthur.waeber@epfl.ch

Abstract

As environmental concerns intensify and energy demand rises, the global quest for sustainable energy sources becomes crucial. Given the intermittent nature of renewable electricity, the quest for transient solutions becomes imperative to ensure energy security. Solid oxide fuel cell (SOFC) stands out as a promising technology, characterized by its high electrical efficiency, fuel flexibility, and the capability for co-producing heat. Integrating SOFC into an energy system necessitates a dynamic model capable of handling fluctuations in electricity demand profiles. This underscores the significance of a reliable and reusable SOFC dynamic model. The present study focuses on constructing a detailed electrochemical SOFC stack model using gPROMS. Laboratory data is employed to perform model validation after mathematical pre-treatment. Furthermore, a sensitivity analysis was employed to select the most crucial parameters. Subsequently, parameter estimation was executed by minimizing the likelihood function. To assess the proximity between model predictions and experimental data and to evaluate the potential reuse of the model based on estimated parameter values, statistical analysis incorporated goodness of fit and t-test measures was performed.

Keywords: Solid Oxide Fuel Cell, Model Validation, Parameter Estimation.

1. Introduction

Escalating energy problems have led to a greater emphasis on the study of alternative energy sources. However, the viability of these renewable energy sources is heavily influenced by geographical location, and their intermittency poses limitations, particularly in areas requiring constant energy availability, such as hospitals. While green hydrogen offers promising alternatives to fossil fuels, a full switch to renewables requires modifications to existing pipelines, indicating a gradual process (Sharma et al., 2018). It is therefore necessary to identify interim solutions to provide stable electricity.

Solid oxide fuel cells (SOFCs) can convert chemical energy into electricity. Recent attention has focused on the remarkable efficiency of these systems, which exceeds 60%, and their high operating temperature of 800°C. This high temperature facilitates the production of heat as a valuable co-product (Xu et al., 2022). This high temperature facilitates the production of heat as a valuable co-product (Xu et al., 2022). This high temperature facilitates the production of heat as a valuable co-product (Xu et al., 2022). In addition, SOFC is flexible in the use of various fuel sources, including hydrocarbons, syngas, hydrogen and biofuels. The incorporation of biofuels indicates that it is possible to consider this electricity generation technology as carbon neutral. If combined with downstream carbon capture, it can even be considered carbon negative. When using a SOFC system to generate electricity, it is essential to take account of dynamic responses, particularly in residential areas. This behavior can be effectively managed with SOFC by simply adjusting the fuel input. However, it is essential to understand the performance of the system and refine the process conditions, which highlights the need for a validated dynamic model for the SOFC system. Previous validations of SOFC models can be found in the literature, but they are mainly based on steady-state performance or simplified mathematical models that significantly reduce the set of parameters. In this research, an elaborate electrochemical SOFC model was developed in the gPROMS library. The experimental data was provided by the Energy Materials Group (GEM) laboratory at EPFL, which is renowned for its expertise in the field of fuel cells. The subsequent critical step involved the validation of the model using the acquired experimental data, correctly accounting for the propagated error due to the intrinsic uncertainty of the measuring instruments.

This SOFC stack model encompasses more than 70 parameters. These parameters include pivotal factors such as exchange current density, stack area, and electrical conductivity, directly impacting the SOFC stack's performance. Additionally, parameters defining the microscopic structure of the electrodes (porosity, tortuosity or even equivalent pore radius) may exert a significant influence on the activation overpotentials or on the gas diffusion. Consequently, there arises a necessary task of discerning which sets of parameters are indispensable for estimation, particularly when confronted with a limited number of experiments to avoid overfitting. While parameter estimation is acknowledged as the initial step of a wider dynamical study, it is a fundamental and pivotal process. This paper introduces and executes the processing and pretreatment of experimental data, and its error propagation, alongside detailed parameter estimation. The results of this study highlight the robust and dependable nature of the SOFC stack model, rendering it well-suited for application in later stages of dynamic energy system development.

2. Methodology

2.1. SOFC stack model description

gPROMS Process Academic Research is among the most advanced modelling software available today. It features Global System analysis, together with design of experiments and model validation tools that can be carried out on highly sophisticated models. In this section, the electrochemical model of an SOFC is briefly described to enable a good overview of its structure.

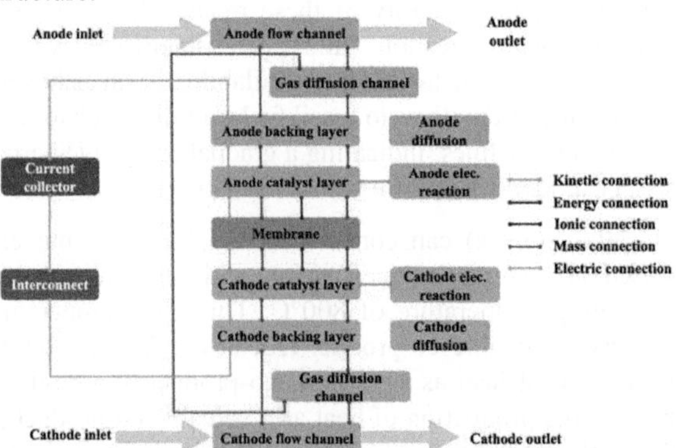

Figure 1. gPROMS SOFC model - modelling structure

In Figure 1 a process flow diagram illustrates the different layers for a precise SOFC modelling. The gases with a defined composition, temperature and pressure are injected through the flow channel in co-flow configuration. There, the molecules will diffuse through the backing layers (i.e. substrate layers) to reach the catalyst layer where the effective electrochemical reactions will take place. Each of these layers can be precisely characterized in terms of thickness, diffusion properties, thermal conductivity or even chemical reactivity. Between the 2 electrodes, the membrane should enable the propagation of O^{2-}ions, while limiting its electric conductivity to avoid any significant losses in the cell voltage. The electrons are then transferred to the current collector through interconnect, where, between others, the contact resistance and electrical conductivity can again be specified. This complex modelling enables very precise calculations even along the flow direction, requiring obviously a large set of parameters.

2.2. Methodology for the Model Validation mechanism

The model validation process is part of a more general scientific approach. As shown in Figure 2, it includes primarily the laboratory work like carrying out the experimental tests, processing the data and the extracting the interesting experiments. Secondly, the error propagation and sensitivity analysis for selecting the crucial parameters have to be performed. Once these first steps are accepted, one can finally turn to the model validation followed by a statistical analysis to assess the results. This procedure can then be repeated several times in order to gain accuracy on the final validated model. Indeed, after a first trial, one might want to diversify the experiments, or seek for new parameters to be estimated. Each of these steps is detailed in the results to stress out their importance and enable a clear overview of the procedure.

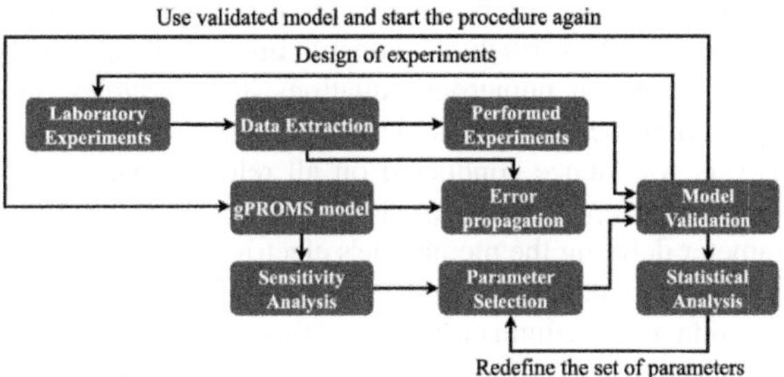

Figure 2. Working mechanism of model validation

3. Results and Discussions

3.1. Lab data analysis

The experimental data, sourced from GEM lab, is intended for the analysis of a SolydEra short stack performance. This stack comprises 6 cells in series, each possessing an active surface area of 80 cm^2. Over a duration of 6 months, measurements were conducted at the anode/cathode inlet and outlet, and on individual cell performance. The extensive set of measurements underwent processing, and 4 current ramps were isolated. Notably, the "dry ramps," involving a H_2/N_2 mixture at the anode inlet, are distinguished from "wet ramps," where steam, CO_2, and methane are additionally injected at the fuel electrode.

3.1.1. Error propagation

Given the complexity of the gPROMS model, a non-mathematical approach has been favored, opting for error calculation through the Sobol sampling method. Assuming normally distributed errors, the gPROMS model underwent 1000 calculations, selecting input conditions quasi-randomly based on their mean and standard deviation.

Figure 3 shows the j-V curve with the 95%-interval for the dry and the wet experiments. It clearly emphasizes that the error on the voltage increases with increasing current densities and underscores that wet experiments are more susceptible to significant deviations from the actual value. It is important to clarify that a literature-based gPROMS model was employed at this stage, potentially introducing some relaxation in the computed errors. Additionally, for wet experiments, the system transitions to the concentration-limited regime at relatively low current density, resulting in a wider error range. This finding serves as a guideline for further experiment design.

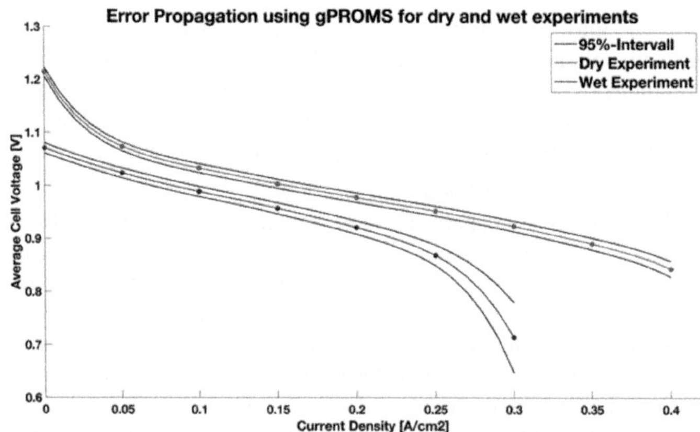

Figure 3. Error propagation of dry and wet experiments

3.2. Sensitivity Analysis for Parameter Selection

Employing a 2D-SOFC model offers advantages in comprehending the bidirectional behaviors of the stack. Nevertheless, constructing such a highly sophisticated mathematical model relies on numerous equations and variables. Given the limited quantity of data, discerning sensitive variables is crucial for enabling efficient validation. A sensitivity analysis was hence conducted on all relevant parameters across various current densities. Figure 4 depicts the methodology for four typical parameters. It appears that only the parameter defining the membrane's electrical conductivity has a discernible impact on the open circuit voltage. While the mass specific area of the anode catalyst has a major impact on voltage at medium current densities, the parameter describing the mass transfer at the anode has a considerable influence close to the limiting current density. On the contrary, a variation in the density of the anode backing layer produces a flat voltage response which indicates that the density is not crucial for this analysis. Employing this strategy allowed the reduction of parameters relevant for model validation from 70 to 8, which are detailed in Table 1.

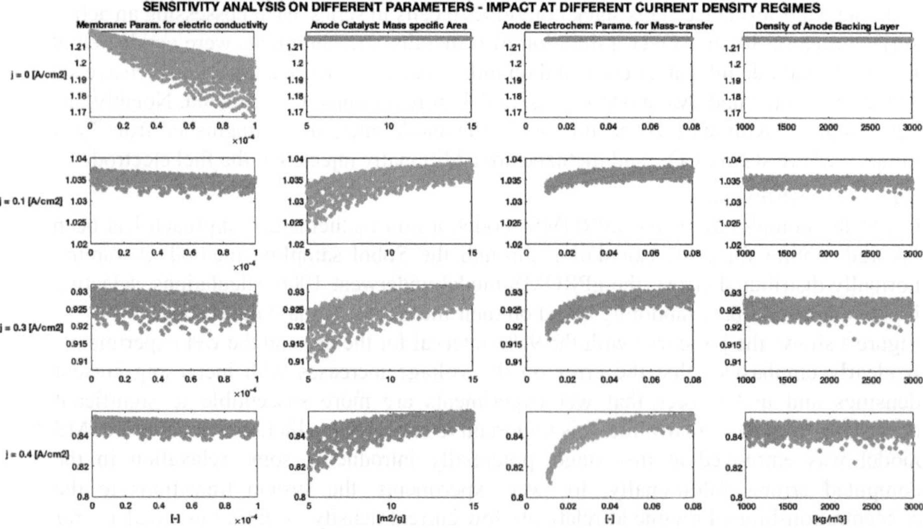

Figure 4. Sensitivity analysis on stack parameters

Table 1. List of potential variables for parameter estimation

Location	Variables	Default Value	Range	Unit
Anode Backing Layer	Tortuosity	2	[1 – 9]	-
Anode Catalyst Layer	Catalyst loading	0.005	[0.001 – 0.1]	kg/m^2
Anode Catalyst Layer	Mass specific area of catalyst	10	[2 – 20]	m^2/g
Anode Electrochemistry	Parameter for mass transfer	0.05	[0.005 – 0.1]	-
Anode Electrochemistry	Reference exchange current density	18	[10 – 1000]	A/m^2
Membrane	Ionic conductivity	5	[1 – 50]	-
Membrane	Parameter for electrical conductivity	1E-5	[1E-6 – 1E-4]	-
Membrane	Thickness	5	[2 – 20]	μm

3.3. Parameter estimation

With limited experimental data, the selection of parameters becomes a critical aspect. Attempting to estimate too many parameters simultaneously would inevitably result in overfitting. Therefore, to prevent this, three parameters have been selected, as pre-analysis indicates that these parameters induce a strong impact on the stack average voltage. In this section, the outcomes of the parameter estimation are presented and discussed in statistical terms to thoroughly evaluate the fitting performance.

3.3.1. Overall system performance

In this section, a visual interpretation of the model validation performance is given and fitting performance are briefly discussed. From Figure 5, one can directly see that the validated model provides a better fit of the experimental data compared to the original non-validated model. The fitting performance appears to be slightly better for the first experiment, probably due to the higher number of points. For the same reason, the wet experiment is slightly disregarded, and the fitting performance is lower. This fact is also explained by the larger error in the wet experiment, due to the presence of water. Finally, the overall performance seems to be satisfying at least from a visual interpretation. Further investigations on the statistical analysis will decide and evaluate more deeply the validity of this fit.

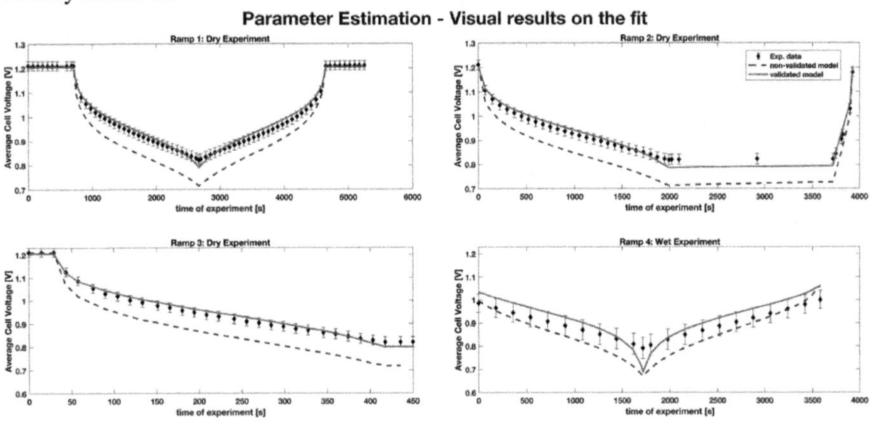

Figure 5. Visual interpretation - Original vs. validated model

3.3.2. Goodness of fit

The primary goal in parameter estimation is to minimize the likelihood function, which serves as a measure of the agreement between experimental and model data. Nevertheless, depending solely on the likelihood function for assessment poses difficulties in gauging the model's ability to faithfully depict reality. Goodness of fit encompasses a broader perspective by evaluating how well the model aligns with the observed data across various dimensions. A chi-squared test has been conducted, to compare the weighted residuals with the expected weighted residuals derived from the dataset. A chi-squared value below the critical threshold indicates that the experiment is suitably fitted by the model. Table 2 indicates that all experiments have successfully passed, affirming the model's capability to accurately represent the experimental data.

Table 2: Goodness of fit - χ^2 results for Exp 1, Exp 2, Exp 3: Dry ramps, Exp 4: Wet ramp

Exp 1		**Exp 2**		**Exp 3**		**Exp 4**		**Overall results**	
χ^2	$\chi^2_{critical}$	χ^2	$\chi^2_{critical}$	χ^2	$\chi^2_{critical}$	χ^2	$\chi^2_{critical}$	χ^2	$\chi^2_{critical}$
31.29	89.39	30.59	48.60	12.51	41.34	16.04	30.14	90.43	189.42

3.3.3. T-test

An additional consideration pertains to the reusability of the model, signifying the importance of ascertaining the confidence in the estimated parameters. To assess the confidence in estimated parameters, a pertinent statistical tool is the t-test. The application of the t-test enables a formal evaluation of the reliability of parameter estimates.

Table 3. t-value for the estimated parameters

Model Parameters	**Initial Value**	**Final Value**	**CI 95%**	**95% t-value**
Exchange current density	18	142.63	24.05	5.93
Param. for mass transfer	0.05	0.0083	0.0021	3.91
Param. for elec. conductivity	1E-5	5.4E-5	2.7E-5	1.99

Firstly, a ref. t-value is calculated for the set of experiments that was provided. In this study, it amounts to 1.654. Each parameter is then individually analyzed with a given final value and a 95% t-value. For the available data to be sufficient to estimate the set of parameters, the t-value of each parameter should be greater than the reference one. In Table 3, it is noteworthy that all parameters have successfully passed the t-test, signifying a high confidence in the estimated parameters and the potential reuse of this model.

4. Conclusions

In this study, the use of experimental data, sensitivity analysis and parameter estimation have been conducted and could provide a validated SOFC model. This work emphasizes further the need for other testing conditions, in presence of steam, thus allowing more parameters to be estimated and yielding more precise fitting results. The outlet temperatures and pressures could also be included. Moreover, linking this model with other programming languages could be an interesting dimension for further study in this field. Finally, this validated model should be tested in real case application, where the dynamics is crucial for system efficiency calculation or even meeting electricity demand profiles. It is hence to be integrated in dynamic energy system for further applications.

References

H. Alhumade, A. Fathy, A. Al-Zahrani, M.J Rawa, H. Rezk, 2021, Optimal Parameter Estimation Methodology of Solid Oxide Fuel Cell Using Modern Optimization. *Mathematics*, no. *9*, p. 1066

A. Rahayu, Purhadi, Sutikno, DD. Prastyo, 2020, Multivariate Gamma Regression: Parameter Estimation, Hypothesis Testing, and Its Application. *Symmetry, no.* 12(5), p.813

S. Sharma, F. Maréchal, 2018, Robust Multi-Objective Optimization of Solid Oxide Fuel Cell–Gas Turbine Hybrid Cycle and Uncertainty Analysis, Electrochem. Energy Convers. Storage, vol. 15, no. 4, p. 041007

Q. Xu, Z. Guo, L. Xia, Q. He, Z. Li, I.T. Bello, M. Ni, 2022, A comprehensive review of solid oxide fuel cells operating on various promising alternative fuels, Energy Conversion and Management, no. 253, p. 115175.

Flavio Manenti, Gintaras V. Reklaitis (Eds.), Proceedings of the 34th European Symposium on Computer Aided Process Engineering / 15th International Symposium on Process Systems Engineering (ESCAPE34/PSE24), June 2-6, 2024, Florence, Italy
 http://dx.doi.org/10.1016/B978-0-443-28824-1.50166-6

Modeling of the coupling of dissolution and crystallization in the digestion tank of a wet phosphoric acid manufacturing process

Sanae Elmisaoui[a,b,c], Abderrazak M. Latifi[a,b], Fadoua Farghi[a] , Safae Elmisaoui[a] Lhachmi Khamar[a]

[a]*Mohammed VI Polytechnic University, 43150 Benguerir, Morocco*
[b]*Université de Lorraine, CNRS, LRGP, F-54000, Nancy, France*
[c]*Mohammed V University, Rabat, Morocco*
abderrazak.latifi@univ-lorraine.fr

Abstract

This work deals with the development of a first-principles model describing the digestion tank of a wet phosphoric acid manufacturing process. Phosphate dissolution and gypsum crystallization, which both occur simultaneously in the tank, are taken into account. The dissolution model is based on the mass balance equations of the reactants and products in the liquid bulk, in the liquid film surrounding the ore particles, and in the particles (Elmisaoui et al., 2024). The gypsum crystallization model is based on a population balance equation involving both crystal growth and nucleation. By means of a global estimability analysis approach, the values of the unknown parameters of the model are determined from experimental measurements. The predictions of the identified model exhibit a good agreement with the experimental data.

Keywords: Dissolution, Crystallization, Phosphoric acid, Modelling and simulation, Global estimability analysis, Parameter identification.

1. Introduction

Optimal design and operation of the digestion tank is of utmost importance to improve the performance of industrial phosphoric acid manufacturing processes. Hence, the understanding of the complex phenomena involved in the digestion tank is therefore necessary to develop fine and accurate models in close and permanent interactions with the experiments. The dissolution of the phosphate ore and the crystallization of gypsum are the two main complex phenomena taking place simultaneously within the digestion tank, and obviously their progress influences the process performances. Indeed, the first one leads to the extraction of P_2O_5 from the phosphate ore particles, while the second one has an impact on the filterability and washing characteristics of the gypsum. Hence, a model combining the two phenomena is therefore required to correctly predict the process performance. It is the objective of the present paper which aims to develop a first-principles model describing the dissolution of ore particles and the crystallization of gypsum formed in the digestion tank.

2. Model formulation

To describe the mechanisms of dissolution and crystallization involved in the digestion tank, four phases are considered: the liquid film, the liquid bulk, a first solid phase constituted by the phosphate particles, and a second solid phase represented by the formed gypsum crystals. Two main reactions occur simultaneously:

- The phosphate dissolution reaction (Van der Sluis et al., 1987):

$$Ca_3(PO_4)_2 + 4\,H_3PO_4 \rightarrow 3\,Ca(H_2PO_4)_2 \tag{1}$$

- The gypsum crystallization reaction (Abu-Eishah et Abu-Jabal, 2001):

$$Ca(H_2PO_4)_2 + H_2SO_4 + 2\,H_2O \rightarrow 2\,H_3PO_4 + CaSO_4.2H_2O \tag{2}$$

2.1. Mechanism description

The shrinking core model is adopted to represent the evolution of the particle radius during its dissolution in the digestion tank. The mechanism considered assumes that phosphoric acid H_3PO_4 (ACP), sulfuric acid H_2SO_4 (ACS), and water H_2O (W) diffuse through the film toward the solid, and only ACP adsorbs on the particles of phosphate ore and eventually reacts with the Tri-Calcium Phosphate $Ca_3(PO_4)_2$(TCP). The Mono-Calcium Phosphate $Ca(H_2PO_4)_2$ (MCP) product takes the opposite path where it desorbs first from the solid surface, then diffuses through the liquid film and transfers to the liquid bulk. It is important to point out that MCP reacts with the sulfuric acid in the liquid film and in the liquid bulk to produce phosphoric acid and dissolved gypsum $CaSO_4.2H_2O$ (G). When the liquid bulk is saturated with gypsum, crystals begin to form. They are characterized by a shape and a size distribution.
The model of the tank is based on the following assumptions : (i) the particles are spherical and well dispersed in the liquid bulk, (ii) the digestion tank is perfectly mixed, (iii) the adsorption/desorption and mass transfer steps are non-limiting, (iv) the dissolution reaction (Eq.1) is irreversible, (v) the crystallization reaction (Eq.2) occurs simultaneously in the film and in the liquid bulk, (vi) the transfer of MCP to the liquid bulk is considered to be the limiting step of the dissolution mechanism, (vii) the crystallization reaction rate is proportional to the amount of gypsum produced, (viii) the digestion tank is isothermal. The model is thus provided by the system of mass balance equations below.

2.2. Liquid film

Fick's second law is used to describe the diffusion of substances in the liquid film with the associated initial and boundary conditions, as:

$$\frac{\partial C_i}{\partial t} = D_i\left(\frac{\partial^2 C_i}{\partial r^2} + \frac{2}{r}\frac{\partial C_i}{\partial r}\right) + \nu_i \frac{dC_G^D}{dt} \qquad i = ACP, ACS, MCP, W, G \tag{4}$$

$$r = R \quad \left| \begin{array}{ll} -D_i \dfrac{dC_i}{dr} = \nu_i k_r C_{ACP}^b & i = ACP, MCP \\ -D_j \dfrac{dC_j}{dr} = 0 & j = ACS, W, G \end{array} \right. \tag{5}$$

$$r = R + \delta \qquad C_i = C_i^b \qquad i = ACP, ACS, MCP, W, G \tag{6}$$

where C_i(mol. m^{-3}) and D_i(m$^2 \cdot$ s^{-1}) are the molar concentration in the liquid film and the diffusion coefficient of substance (i), respectively. C_i^b(mol $\cdot$ m^{-3}) is the molar concentration in the liquid bulk, $k_r(m.s^{-1})$ the reaction rate constant, and $\delta(m)$ is the thickness of the liquid film.

2.3. First solid phase

The equation describing the temporal profile of the dissolution rate (X) of ore particles (first solid phase) in a solution of phosphoric and sulfuric acids, in the presence of a non-uniform particle size distribution, represented by the Gate-Gaudin-Schuhmann distribution, is written as (Elmisaoui, 2023):

$$\frac{dX}{dt} = \frac{3M_{TCP}D_{MCP}}{x_{TCP}\rho_S}\int_{R_{\min}}^{R_{\max}} \frac{[C_{MCP|r=R}(R_0) - C^b_{MCP}(R_0)][1 - X(R_0)]^{\frac{2}{3}}f(R_0)}{R_0\delta(R_0)}dR_0 \tag{7}$$

where M_{TCP} is the molar weight of TCP, x_{TCP} is the mass fraction of TCP in the solid, ρ_s is the density of the solid, and $f(R_0)\mathrm{d}R_0$ is the mass fraction of particles whose size is between R_0 and $R_0 + dR_0$. The size distribution is characterized by a coefficient of variation (CV) which is a model parameter.
The thickness of the liquid film is expressed by (Elmisaoui, 2023):

$$\delta = \int_{R_{\min}}^{R_{\max}} R_0[1 - X(R_0)]^{\frac{1}{3}}\left[1 + \alpha\left(1 - X(R_0)\right)^{\frac{8}{27}}D_{MCP}^{-\frac{1}{3}}\right]^{-1} \tag{8}$$

where α is a parameter of the hydrodynamic conditions in the stirred digestion tank.

2.4. Liquid bulk

Taking into account the stoichiometry of the substances in the reactions Eqs. (1) and (2), the concentrations in the liquid bulk are expressed as:

$$\begin{aligned} C^b_{ACP} &= C^b_{0ACP} - 4\frac{n^0_{TCP}}{V_L}X + 2C^b_G \\ C^b_{MCP} &= 3\frac{n^0_{TCP}}{V_L}X - C^b_G \\ C^b_{ACS} &= C^b_{0ACS} - C^b_G \\ C^b_W &= C^b_{0W} - 2C^b_G \end{aligned} \tag{9}$$

where $C^b_{0i}(\mathrm{mol.m^{-3}})$ is the initial molar concentration of substance (i) in the liquid, and $V_L(m^3)$ is the volume of liquid in the digestion tank.

2.5. Second solid phase

The production of gypsum crystals (second solid phase) in the liquid bulk can be described by means of the following equation (Bakir, 2006):

$$\frac{d(V_L C^b_G)}{dt} + \frac{d(V_T C^S_G)}{dt} = 0\,, with\ V_L = V_T\left(1 - \frac{M_G}{\rho_G}C^S_G\right) \tag{10}$$

where $V_T(\mathrm{m^3})$ is the volume of the suspension, $M_G(\mathrm{kg.mol^{-1}})$ is the molecular weight of gypsum, $\rho_G(\mathrm{kg.m^{-3}})$ is the density of gypsum, and $C^S_G(\mathrm{mol.m^{-3}})$ is the concentration of solid gypsum formed calculated from the crystal size distribution using the following relationship :

$C_G^S = \frac{K_v \rho_G}{M_G}\left[\int_0^\infty L^3 N dL\right]$, K_v is a form factor (for spherical particles $K_v = \frac{\pi}{6}$). (11)

Calculation of C_G^S requires determination of the crystal size distribution using the population balance equation. In this work, discontinuous crystallisation without seeding is considered. We also assume that crystal growth does not depend on crystal size (L). The mono-dimensional population balance is then expressed as (Barbier et al., 2009):

$$\frac{\partial N(L,t)}{\partial t} + G\frac{\partial N(L,t)}{\partial L} = 0, \quad N(0,t) = \frac{R_{N_1} + R_{N_2}}{G} \tag{12}$$

$$R_{N_1} = A_1 \times \exp\left(\frac{-B_1}{\sigma^2}\right) \tag{13}$$

$$R_{N_2} = A_2 \times (C_G^b - C_G^{sat})^{B_2} \times C_G^S \tag{14}$$

$$G = K_c \frac{M_G}{2\rho_G}\eta(C_G^b - C_G^{sat})^g \tag{15}$$

$$\left[\frac{K_c}{K_d}(C_G^b - C_G^{sat})^{g-1}\right]\eta + \eta^{1/g} + 1 = 0 \tag{16}$$

$$S = \frac{a_{SO_4^{2-}} a_{Ca^{2+}} a_w^2}{K_s}, \qquad \sigma = \ln(S) \tag{17}$$

where $N(L,t)$ (number. $m^{-3} \cdot m^{-1}$) is the crystal size distribution, R_{N_1} is the primary nucleation rate, R_{N_2} is the secondary nucleation rate, G is the crystal growth rate, S is the supersaturation ratio which depends on the activities of the sulphate ions $a_{SO_4^{2-}}$, of the calcium $a_{Ca^{2+}}$ and of the water a_w, as well as of the equilibrium constant K_s. σ is the relative supersaturation, C_G^{sat} is the solubility, the term $C_G^b - C_G^{sat}$ represents the crystallization driving force, and η is the efficiency factor given by the solution of the equation (16). k_r, α, D_{MCP}, CV, $A_1, B_1, A_2, B_2, K_c, K_d$ and g are unknown parameters to be determined from experimental measurements.

3. Results and discussions

The estimability of the unknown parameters involved in the model is first carried out, then the most estimable parameters are identified from existing experimental data, i.e., temporal profiles of crystal size distribution and ACP concentration in the liquid bulk. Matlab environment is used to implement and solve the model equations.

3.1. Estimability analysis results

The unknown parameters are ranked in decreasing order of estimability as follows:
$g > K_d > K_c > A_1 > CV > k_r > B_1 > \alpha > D_{MCP} > A_2 > B_2$. This ranking shows the importance of the growth phenomenon in the gypsum crystallization mechanism, and that the parameter g, is the most estimable. This is obvious, since it represents the power of the crystallization driving force. This ranking analysis also shows that the coefficient of variation, CV, is more estimable than the kinetic constant, k_r, the MCP diffusion coefficient, D_{MCP}, and the hydrodynamic parameter, α. To determine the number of estimable parameters, it is necessary to set a value for the estimability threshold. This estimability cut-off allows to distinguish between estimable parameters and non-estimable ones. Using the algorithm of Wu et al. (2011), the optimal value of the

estimability threshold allowing the CV parameter to be estimable is 0.016 (Elmisaoui, 2023) . The set of estimable parameters is therefore constituted by: g, K_d, K_c, A_1 and CV.

3.2. Parameter estimation

We considered a batch reactor of volume V= 1L, initially containing a mass of 100g of raw phosphate of size between 250 and 500 μm. The ACP and ACS solutions introduced in the digestion tank are characterized by 18% of P_2O_5 and an excess of free sulphates of 2%, respectively. The temperature of the reaction medium was maintained at 70°C, with a corresponding stirring speed of 200 rpm. Crystal size L was assumed to be in the range of 0-100 μm. Table 1 shows the identified values of the estimated parameters of the model with their corresponding 95% confidence intervals (CIs).

CIs show that the optimal values of the global model parameters were determined with good accuracy. These findings were confirmed by the good agreement between the model predictions and the experimental data, as shown in Figure 1. It can be seen that the concentration of ACP in the solution increases over time (Fig. 1.C). This increase is attributed to the production of phosphoric acid as crystallization proceeds, leading to the appearance of gypsum crystals formed simultaneously.

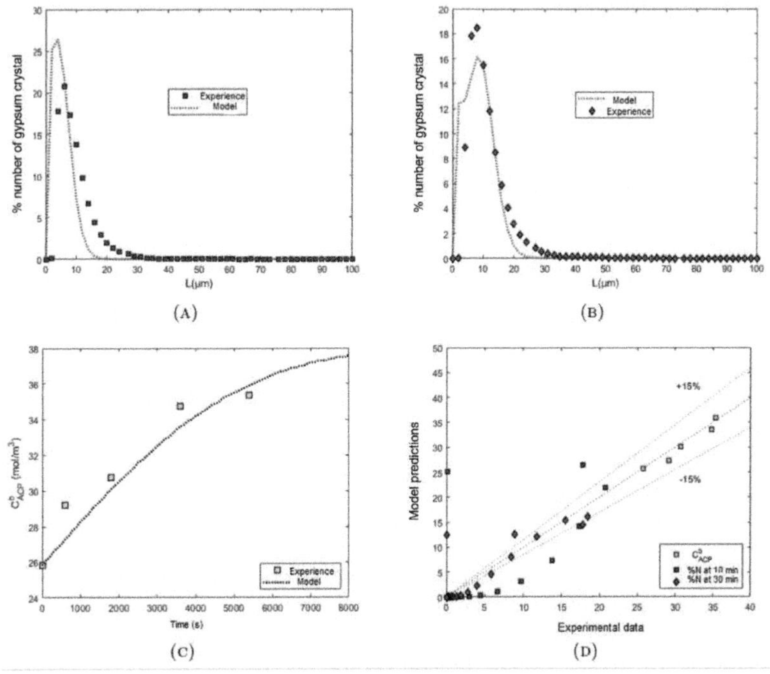

Figure 1: Comparison between experimental measurements and predictions of the number distribution of crystals as a function of their size after (A) 10 min, (B) 30 min, (C) molar concentration of ACP, (D) parity diagram

In addition, the size of the crystals increases from [0-16 μm] after 10 minutes (Fig. 1.A) to [0-25 μm] after 30 minutes (Fig. 1.B) in the digestion tank. The parity diagram in Figure 1.D shows the comparison between the experimental measurements and the global model predictions. It is clear that the majority of the predictions obtained for phosphoric acid concentration and crystal number after 30 min of digestion are within the range of 15 % of uncertainty, thus showing the good quality of the developed model.

Table 1: Optimal values identified for estimable parameters.

Parameter	Optimal value	95% CI	Unit
g	1.96	0.05	-
K_d	1.14×10^{-3}	0.05×10^{-3}	$m.s^{-1}$
K_c	9.59×10^{-4}	0.75×10^{-4}	$mol^{-1} \cdot m^4 \cdot s^{-1}$
A_1	2.224×10^8	0.63×10^8	$nb.m^{-3}.s^{-1}$
CV	1.69×10^{-1}	0.11×10^{-1}	-

4. Conclusions

A first-principles model for the digestion tank of a phosphoric acid manufacturing process is developed and identified from available experimental data. It combines two sub-models : a model for the dissolution of phosphate ore in a phosphoric acid solution, and a model based on population balance for gypsum crystallization. The estimability of the unknown parameters involved in the resulting global model was analysed by means of a global estimability analysis, and the most estimable ones are identified from the available experimental data. The results obtained showed that the model predictions are in good agreement with the experimental data. However, further research still needs to be carried out to improve the accuracy of the model.

References

Abu-Eishah, S. I., & Abu-Jabal, N. M. (2001). Parametric study on the production of phosphoric acid by the dihydrate process. Chemical Engineering Journal, 81(1-3), 231-250.

Elmisaoui, S. (2023). Modélisation, simulation et expérimentation du réacteur de production d'acide phosphorique à partir du minerai de phosphate, PhD thesis, Université de Lorraine, Nancy, France.

Elmisaoui, S., Latifi, A. M., & Khamar, L. (2024). Analysis of the dissolution of phosphate ore particles in phosphoric acid: Influence of particle size distribution. Hydrometallurgy, Vol. 223, pp.106197.

Van der Sluis, S., Meszaros, Y., Marchee, W. G., Wesselingh, H. A., & Van Rosmalen, G. M. (1987). The digestion of phosphate ore in phosphoric acid. Industrial & engineering chemistry research, 26(12), 2501-2505.

Bakir, T. (2006). Estimation d'un procédé de cristallisation en batch (Doctoral dissertation, Université Claude Bernard-Lyon I).

Barbier, E., Coste, M., Genin, A., Jung, D., Lemoine, C., Logette, S., & Muhr, H. (2009). Simultaneous determination of nucleation and crystal growth kinetics of gypsum. Chemical Engineering Science, 64(2), 363-369.

Wu, S., McLean, K. A., Harris, T. J., & McAuley, K. B. (2011). Selection of optimal parameter set using estimability analysis and MSE-based model-selection criterion. International Journal of Advanced Mechatronic Systems, 3(3), 188-197.

Flavio Manenti, Gintaras V. Reklaitis (Eds.), Proceedings of the 34th European Symposium on Computer Aided Process Engineering / 15th International Symposium on Process Systems Engineering (ESCAPE34/PSE24), June 2-6, 2024, Florence, Italy
 http://dx.doi.org/10.1016/B978-0-443-28824-1.50167-8

Optimization of High-Performance Membrane Processes for Post-Combustion Carbon Capture

Marina Micari*, Kumar Varoon Agrawal

Laboratory of Advanced Separations, EPFL, Rue de l'Industrie 17, Sion, Switzerland
marina.micari@epfl.ch

Abstract

Membrane processes are emerging as an attractive alternative to absorption for carbon capture, thanks to the high energy efficiency and modularity. To assess the real potential of membrane technology at a large scale, operating conditions need to be optimized in combination with the selected material. In this work, for the first time, we report the results of the techno-economic optimization of a double-stage membrane process for post-combustion carbon capture in the presence of a wide range of membranes, corresponding to several combinations of CO_2 permeance and CO_2/N_2 selectivity.
The optimization maps identify impact of various performance parameters on the cost. Also, the optimization results are used to chart out targets for permeance and selectivity, beyond which a further improvement does not result in cost reduction.
Overall, this work gives important insights into the impact of membrane performances on the techno-economic feasibility of the optimized capture process and into the performance targets to make the technology more competitive.

Keywords: membrane process, post-combustion carbon capture, cost minimization, techno-economic analysis, process design

1. Introduction

Membrane technology has shown to be highly promising for post-combustion carbon capture, since it can reduce energy consumption with respect to state-of-art absorption from 3-4 MJ/kg to below 1 MJ/kg. This allows an important cost reduction for capture from coal power plant flue gas from 50 $/t to 20-30 $/t (Merkel et al., 2010).

Literature has reported several techno-economic studies on capture processes based on different membranes. (Merkel et al., 2010) showed the attractiveness of membrane processes by designing a double-stage process based on polymeric membranes by MTR Polaris™. Recent studies focused also on composite membranes (Xu et al., 2019), facilitated transport membranes (Han & Ho, 2020), graphene membranes (Micari et al., 2021) and mixed matrix membranes (Fujita et al., 2022).
Depending on the membrane performance, several operating conditions and process configurations should be considered to optimize process performances. In this context, various contributions concerned the optimization of multi-stage processes and the minimization of total capture cost (Zamarripa et al., 2018). These include different approaches, from superstructure-based (Arias et al., 2016) to surrogate-based optimization (Graciano et al., 2018).
Generally, the optimized process configurations are reported for a selected membrane with a given performance. Therefore, it becomes challenging to compare membranes with varying performances (combination of CO_2 permeance and CO_2/N_2 selectivity) because of the different techno-economic assumptions used in the literature.

In this work, for the first time, we report and compare the minimized capture costs and the relevant energy and membrane area requirements for a wide range of membrane performances. These results will allow to assess the impact of the membrane parameters on the optimal operating conditions and on the techno-economic feasibility of the optimized process. Finally, the findings will serve as guidelines for membrane developers and manufacturers to identify improvement targets for membrane performance parameters.

2. Mathematical model

We developed a techno-economic model to simulate and design multi-stage membrane processes for gas separation and to assess their economic feasibility.

2.1. Technical model

First, we built a modular technical model where multi-stage processes are represented as combinations of single membrane stages (Micari et al., 2021). Each single stage has a cross-flow arrangement (Figure 1, left) and is modelled under the following assumptions: (i) fixed temperature, (ii) permeance independent of concentration, (iii) negligible pressure drops and concentration polarization, (iv) no mixing in the permeate channel.
To model the single stage, we estimate the transmembrane flux of each component (*i*) along the z axis by applying the solution diffusion model, as in Eq. (1). The flux J is proportional to the partial pressure difference between feed and permeate channel, where the partial pressure is given by the product of the total pressure in the channel (P) and the molar fraction (X_i). The calculated fluxes are then used in mass balances, to assess the variation of flow rates and concentrations of each component along the length of the stage. More details on the model are reported in our previous work (Micari et al., 2021).

$$J_i(z) = \boldsymbol{Permeance}_i \left(P_{feed} X_{i,feed}(z) - P_{perm} X'_{i,perm}(z) \right) \quad (1)$$

The process performances are defined in terms of purity and recovery. The purity corresponds to the concentration of the main component (CO_2) in the outlet permeate stream. The recovery is given by the ratio between the flow rate of the main component in the permeate and that in the feed. To achieve high recovery and purity, a single stage process is often not enough and multi-stage processes need to be designed. This work presents the results for a double-stage process where the permeate produced by the first stage is fed to the second stage and the retentate produced by the second stage is recycled and mixed with the feed of the first stage, to increase driving force (Figure 1, right).

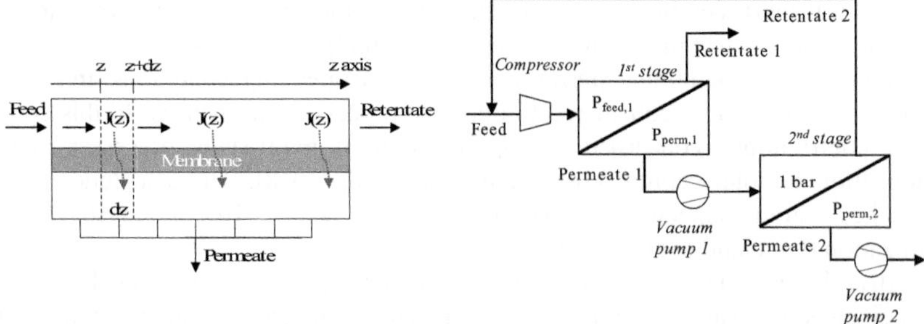

Figure 1. Schematic representation of the single-stage process (left) and of the double-stage process with recycle of the retentate from the second stage (right).

We design double-stage processes with given sets of pressures in the feed and permeate channel by identifying the membrane areas in the two stages that minimize the difference between calculated and target values of recovery and purity (design objective function).

2.2. Economic model

The economic model calculates the capital and operating costs of the membrane process based on the outputs of the technical model, i.e., membrane area and energy consumption. The model is reported in detail in (Micari et al., 2023). The capital costs are given by the direct costs for purchase and installation of all pieces of equipment (membrane modules with specific membrane cost of 100 $\$/m^2$, compressors, vacuum pumps, and blowers), the indirect costs (14% of the direct costs) and the contingency and fee costs (35% of the sum of direct and indirect costs). These costs are then annualized by assuming a capital charge factor (equal to 0.125) to obtain the CAPEX [$/y].

The operating costs include the cost for energy, for maintenance and labor, and for membrane replacement. The specific cost of energy is taken equal to 0.05 $/kWh and the membranes are replaced every 5 years. The total operating cost is defined as OPEX [$/y]. The capture penalty is given by the sum of CAPEX and OPEX divided by the total amount of CO_2 produced per year [t/y].

2.3. Process optimization

For each set of CO_2 permeance and CO_2/N_2 selectivity, we found the set of operating pressures ($P_{feed,1}$, $P_{perm,1}$ and $P_{perm,2}$ as in Figure 1 (right), while $P_{feed,2}$ is equal to 1 bar) that minimizes the capture penalty (techno-economic objective function).

For the optimization, we used the shooting method, where a coarse grid search is followed by optimization via Sequential Least Square Programming (SLSQP from *scipy* library in Python). Figure 2 shows an example for the case of permeance of 500 GPU and selectivity of 20, where the grid search allowed to identify narrow ranges of the optimization variables within which we performed local optimization (minimum value of 72 $/t, represented with a circular marker in the map of Figure 2).

3. Description of the system and the operating conditions

The membrane process presents two stages as in the scheme of Figure 1 (right), where the membrane areas are designed to achieve the targets of 90% CO_2 recovery and 95% CO_2 purity. The flue gas fed to the membrane process is produced by a coal power plant, the flow rate is 4385 mol/s (corresponding to 0.6 million ton_{CO2}/y captured) and the composition is: 13.5% CO_2, 15% H_2O, 3% O_2 and 68.5% N_2 (Micari et al., 2021). The simulations take into account the multicomponent feed and assume a fixed CO_2/H_2O and CO_2/O_2 selectivity of 1 and 12.6, respectively (Micari et al., 2021). We vary CO_2 permeance and CO_2/N_2 selectivity from 500 to 10000 GPU (Gas Permeation Unit, 1 GPU = 3.35×10^{-10} mol/ (m^2 s Pa)) and from 20 to 100, respectively.

4. Results and discussion

The optimization maps of membrane area, energy consumption, and capture penalty are reported in Figure 3. From the map of membrane area (Figure 3A), we observe that in general membrane area is controlled by permeance. This is particularly evident when the permeance is low (< 1000 GPU) or when the permeance is high (> 7000 GPU). In the intermediate region, the selectivity plays a role, and an increase of selectivity causes an increase in membrane area. This can be explained by considering that: (i) at higher selectivity, the optimal feed pressure is lower and the optimal permeate pressure is higher, since lower driving force is preferred to reduce energy; (ii) for a given CO_2 permeance, when CO_2/N_2 selectivity increases, the N_2 permeance decreases; (iii) the higher CO_2 concentration in the permeate given by the higher selectivity reduces driving force along the length of the stage.

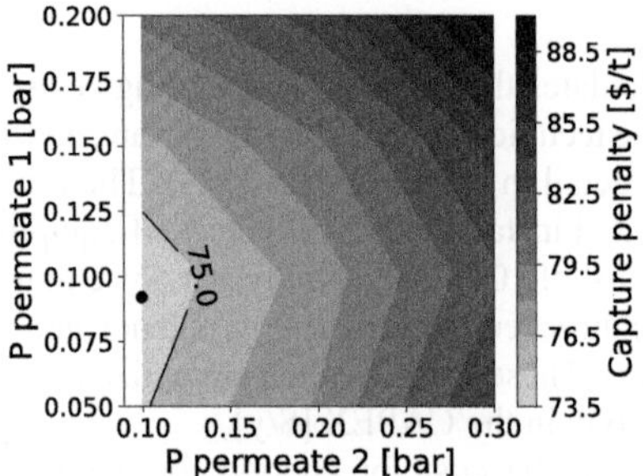

Figure 2. Example of optimization process for permeance of 500 GPU and selectivity of 20.

In the map of specific energy (Figure 3B) we can identify a region (selectivity < 40) where the energy is almost only controlled by the selectivity. Conversely, at higher selectivity values, the permeance starts to play a role and, in particular, the energy increases when permeance decreases below 3000 GPU. As evident from the curve at 1.0 MJ/kg, the selectivity needs to increase when permeance reduces to keep the same value of specific energy, because of the higher feed compression requirement at lower permeance.

The overall effect of membrane permeance and selectivity is shown in the map of capture penalty (Figure 3C). Here, we can isolate three regions: (i) selectivity < 40; (ii) selectivity > 40 and permeance < 3000 GPU; (iii) selectivity > 40 and permeance > 3000 GPU.

In the first region, as shown in the curves at 40 and 50 $/t, the capture penalty is controlled by selectivity as it is driven by the operating cost (specific energy, Figure 3B). In the second region, as shown by the same curves in the range of higher selectivity values, the capture penalty is controlled by the permeance because of the larger investment cost for membrane area which changes sharply with permeance (Figure 3A). Finally, in the last region, as shown in the curve at 30 $/t, both membrane parameters play a role in determining the capture penalty and, within this range, the higher the parameters, the lower the minimized capture penalty.

It is also important to mention that minimized capture penalties below 40 $/t are found for a wide range of membrane parameters. We can define a feasibility space of parameters with permeance > 2000 GPU and selectivity > 40, where membranes are highly competitive with absorption process.

Figure 4 shows the Pareto curves in the specific energy vs. specific area charts for given couples of permeance and selectivity. The Pareto curves are obtained from all the points representing double-stage processes with variable pressures in the first and second stage, that fulfill the recovery and purity targets. When permeance is varied from 500 to 10000 GPU, the membrane area also varies by one order of magnitude. The specific area in the Pareto curves ranges from 10 to 50 × 10^3 $m^2/(kg/s)$ for permeance of 500 GPU and from around 1 to 2.5 × 10^3 $m^2/(kg/s)$ with 10000 GPU. Importantly, for a fixed permeance, the Pareto curves at variable selectivity shift vertically along the specific energy axis and show a much bigger drop when selectivity increases from 20 to 40 than when it increases from 40 to 100. This is due to the fact that the system performance is controlled by selectivity when this is below 40, as observed also in the maps of Figure 3. Thus, a further increase in selectivity has a lower impact on the overall capture cost.

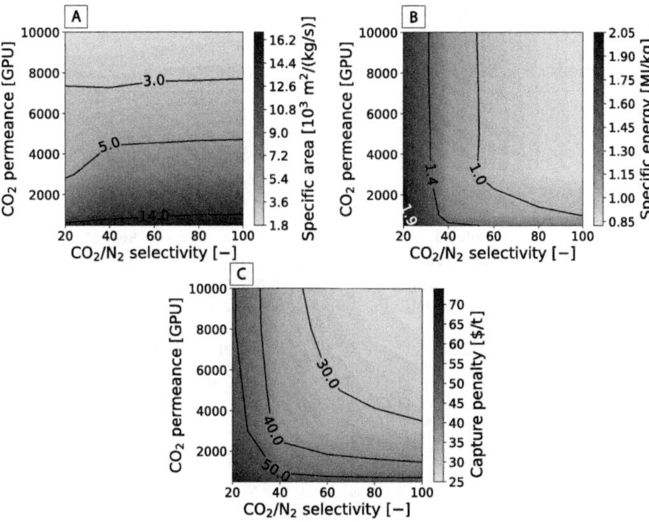

Figure 3. Maps of specific area (A) and energy (B) corresponding to the minimum capture penalty (C) at variable permeance and selectivity. Targets: 90% CO_2 recovery and 95% CO_2 purity.

On the other hand, in the lower charts, the Pareto curves at different permeances are located in the region of 2 MJ/kg of specific energy when selectivity is 20 and of 1 MJ/kg when selectivity is 100.

Notably, when permeance increases, the curves shift to left along the specific area axis, showing how permeance mostly impacts membrane area rather than energy consumption. The gap between the curves at 500 and 3000 GPU is larger than that between the curves at higher permeances. Analogously to selectivity, this comparison shows that the effect of permeance variations is stronger when permeance is lower than 3000 GPU and a further increase has limited impact on global system performances.

5. Conclusions

This work presents a comprehensive assessment of the impact of membrane performance parameters, namely CO_2 permeance and CO_2/N_2 selectivity, on the techno-economic figures of the optimized double-stage membrane processes for post-combustion capture from coal power plants flue gas. The maps of minimized capture penalty and of the corresponding specific membrane area and energy consumption are powerful tools to identify regions with different roles of the two parameters. In particular, we can identify three regions: (i) selectivity-controlled, when selectivity is below 40 at any permeance, (ii) permeance-controlled, when permeance is below 3000 GPU and selectivity is above 40, (iii) both permeance- and selectivity-controlled, when permeance is higher than 3000 GPU and selectivity higher than 40. Also, the Pareto curves reported at variable selectivity or permeance values are important to understand to what extent the parameters impact the technical and economic figures and when their further increase starts to have a negligible role in terms of cost reduction. These results are very important as they provide useful guidelines to the membranes manufacturers concerning the parameters to improve and the impact of parameters variations depending on the region to which the specific membranes belong. Finally, a wide feasibility space of parameters reports optimized capture penalties below 40 \$/t, thus showing the high competitiveness of membrane technology for post-combustion capture from the coal-fired power plants.

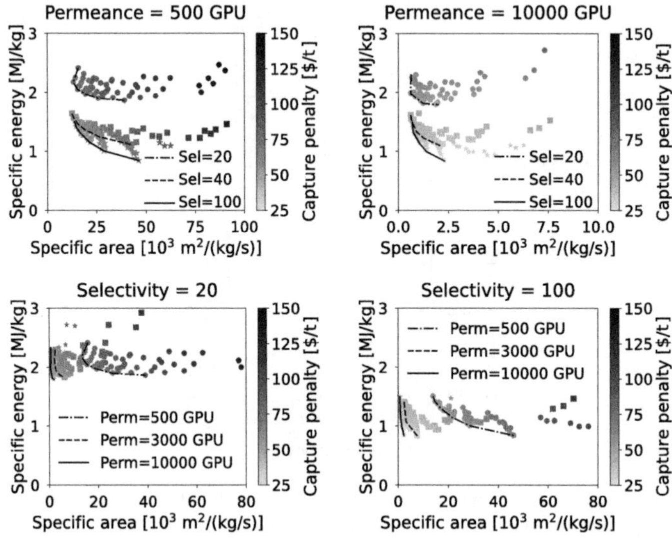

Figure 4. Pareto curves of specific energy vs. specific area at fixed CO_2 permeance and variable CO_2/N_2 selectivity (upper charts) and at fixed selectivity and variable permeance (lower charts). The points represent the systems at 90% recovery and 95% purity with variable pressures.

References

Arias, A. M., Mussati, M. C., Mores, P. L., Scenna, N. J., Caballero, J. A., & Mussati, S. F., 2016, Optimization of multi-stage membrane systems for CO2 capture from flue gas, International Journal of Greenhouse Gas Control, 53, 371–390

Fujita, K., Akimoto, R., Suzuki, Y., Ogasawara, Y., Nakaiwa, M., & Matsuda, K., 2022, Evaluation of Economic Performance of Co2 Separation Process Using Mixed Matrix Membrane, 14th International Symposium on Process Systems Engineering, 49, 265–270

Graciano, J. E. A., Alves, R. M. B., & Chachuat, B., 2018, Surrogate-based Optimization Approach to Membrane Network Synthesis in Gas Separation, 28th European Symposium on Computer Aided Process Engineering, 43, 597–602

Han, Y., & Ho, W. S. W., 2020, Design of Amine-Containing CO2-Selective Membrane Process for Carbon Capture from Flue Gas, Industrial and Engineering Chemistry Research, 59, 12, 5340–5350.

Merkel, T. C., Lin, H., Wei, X., & Baker, R., 2010, Power plant post-combustion carbon dioxide capture: An opportunity for membranes, Journal of Membrane Science, 359, 1–2, 126-139.

Micari, M., Dakhchoune, M., & Agrawal, K. V., 2021, Techno-economic assessment of postcombustion carbon capture using high-performance nanoporous single-layer graphene membranes, Journal of Membrane Science, 624, 119103.

Micari, M., Duan, X., & Agrawal, K. V., 2023, Atmospheric water harvesting in semi-arid regions by membranes: A techno-economic assessment, Journal of Membrane Science, 672, 121437.

Xu, J., Wang, Z., Qiao, Z., Wu, H., Dong, S., Zhao, S., & Wang, J., 2019, Post-combustion CO2 capture with membrane process: Practical membrane performance and appropriate pressure, Journal of Membrane Science, 581, 195–213.

Zamarripa, M. A., Eslick, J. C., Matuszewski, M. S., & Miller, D. C., 2018, Multi-objective Optimization of Membrane-based CO2 Capture, 13th International Symposium on Process Systems Engineering, 44, 1117–1122.

Flavio Manenti, Gintaras V. Reklaitis (Eds.), Proceedings of the 34th European Symposium on Computer Aided Process Engineering / 15th International Symposium on Process Systems Engineering (ESCAPE34/PSE24), June 2-6, 2024, Florence, Italy
 http://dx.doi.org/10.1016/B978-0-443-28824-1.50168-X

Modeling of the dynamic behaviour of Fischer-Tropsch fixed-bed reactors: a pseudohomogeneous approach

Egydio Terziotti Neto,[a] Rita M. B. Alves,[a] Reinaldo Giudici[a]*

[a]*Universidade de São Paulo, Escola Politécnica, Department of Chemical Engineering, São Paulo, São Paulo, Brazil*

**rgiudici@usp.br*

Abstract

This work aims to model and evaluate the dynamic behaviour of a conceptual reactor for Fischer-Tropsch synthesis based on a first principle model using classical mass and energy conservation equations. The system was designed to produce hydrocarbons within the commercial fuel ranges such as gasoline and aviation diesel. The model was coded in Aspen Custom Modeler® v12 and component properties as well as the Soave-Redlich-Kwong equation of state were embedded in the model through the connection with Aspen Properties® v12 software or by direct implementation of literature correlations. Upon achieving a stable numerical solution for different operating conditions, a sensitivity analysis was conducted by varying the flow rate, temperature, and composition at the system's inlet in order to evaluate the impact of these variables on the dynamic behaviour of the reactor and the yield of hydrocarbons in the desired range. It was observed that the system reaches steady state within short times, of approximately one minute for most tested cases. Furthermore, it was noted that, among all evaluated scenarios, a slight increase in the system temperature would allow for a CO conversion of 84.22% (higher than the 72.87% in the base case) with 48.25% selectivity for hydrocarbons in the C2-C7 range and 24.27% in the C8-C16 range, which could then be blended in order to produce commercial fuels.

Keywords: Fischer-Tropsch, Fixed-bed, Mathematical Modeling, Biofuels, Dynamic Model

1. Introduction

Despite extensive efforts to diminish greenhouse gases emissions, global demand for petroleum continues to rise. For instance, in 2017, daily production exceeded 90 million barrels, from which 85% were used to manufacture different fuels types accountable for emitting not only carbon dioxide, but also sulfur based and oxygenated organic compounds (Mahmoudi et al., 2017). Within this scenario, the Fischer-Tropsch (FT) process emerges as a technology not only proven to efficiently convert greenhouse gases (CO_2 or CO) into usable fuels, but it is already implemented in industrial scale. Such technology makes it is possible to synthesize a wide range of hydrocarbons suitable for blending into gasoline and/or sustainable aviation fuels (SAFs) (Méndez et al., 2017). However, it is worth noting that, in spite of the great benefits FT reaction is able to provide, it also faces several obstacles, such as unknown kinetic mechanisms, unpredictable nature of product distribution and the high reaction exothermicity, which can lead to the formation of hot-stops in the reaction system.

As a result of the above-mentioned drawbacks, it is thus imperative that the process available technologies are refined, in an effort to facilitate its implementation on a larger scale and to avoid operational problems. Mathematical models are a useful tool due to its capacity of describing, through constitutive equations, the characteristic phenomena occurring in a given system, allowing a deep understanding of its performance and also makes room for optimization studies. Nevertheless, few studies have been published regarding the dynamics of a FT reactor (Sauerhöfer-Rodrigo et al., 2023). To fill this gap, the present study focuses on modeling the dynamic behavior of a fixed-bed FT reactor by means of a one-dimensional pseudohomogeneous approach in different operating conditions. Additionally, the proposed model incorporates several enhancements. The proposed model incorporates enhancements, such as: 1. Using the Soave-Redlich-Kwong Equation of State to represent the system non-idealities; 2. The model encompasses 42 different substances, with their properties directly computed from Aspen Properties® interface. This modeling strategy not only enhances the realism of the reactor's behavior but also facilitates the computation of the properties involved. The sensitivity analysis was conducted to evaluate the effects of inlet composition, temperature and molar flow-rate according to available literature data, which reflects the industrial operating conditions of such reactors (Espinoza et al., 1999; Lee & Chung, 2012; Jess & Kern, 2009). The results underscored the significant influence of these operating variables in the stabilization of a stationary regime and yield of higher chain hydrocarbons.

2. Methods and Modeling

The conceptual model proposed in this study encompasses a tubular arrangement, measuring 12 meters in length and 4.6 centimeters in inner diameter, within a multitubular fixed-bed reactor designed for Fischer-Tropsch synthesis. It utilizes spherical particles of $Co\text{-}Al_2O_3$ catalyst with 3 mm diameter. The reactor has an outer cooling mechanism, consisting of boiling water at a temperature 5 to 10 °C lower in respect to that of the incoming syngas in order to avoid thermal runaways. Moreover, due to the intrinsic complexity of such process, the following considerations were made: 1. Dynamic operation; 2. One-dimensional pseudohomogeneous model; 3. Solid-gas model (as it was observed that over 99% of the system exists in vapor phase); 4. No resistance to thermal convection at the external tube wall; 5. Formation of alcohols or aromatics was not considered; 6. Reaction enthalpy and bed porosity remain constant alongside the reactor length; 7. Paraffins and olefins formation is considered up to a chain length of 20 carbons. As a result, the constitutive equations describing this model are represented in Eqs. (1) to (3) with initial and boundary conditions included in Table 1.

$$\varepsilon \frac{\partial C_i}{\partial t} = -u_s \frac{\partial C_i}{\partial z} + \rho_b \sum_{n} r_i \tag{1}$$

$$\left(\varepsilon \rho_f c_{p_f} + (1-\varepsilon)\rho_s c_{p_s}\right)\frac{\partial T}{\partial t} = -u_s \rho_f c_{p_f} \frac{\partial T}{\partial z} + \frac{4}{d_i} U_{wall}\left(T - T_{wall}\right) + \rho_b \underset{n}{} (-\Delta H_{rxn}) r_{i,n} \tag{2}$$

$$\frac{dP}{dz} = -\frac{u_s}{d_p}\frac{(1-\varepsilon)}{\varepsilon^3}\left(150\frac{(1-\varepsilon)*\mu_m}{d_p} + 1.75\rho_f u_s\right) \tag{3}$$

Where ε is the bed porosity (Benyahia and O'Neill, 2005), C_i is the component concentration (mol/m^3), u_s is the fluid superficial velocity (m/s), ρ_b is the bulk density (kg/m^3), r_i is the component reaction rate (mol/kg.s), ρ_f is the fluid density ($kmol/m^3$), ρ_p is the catalyst density (kg/m^3) (Wang et al., 2016), cp_f is the fluid heat capacity (kJ/kmol.K), cp_s is the solid heat capacity (kJ/kg.K) (Wang et al., 2016), T is the temperature (K), U_{wall} is the global heat transfer coefficient evaluated at the wall (kJ/m².K) and its calculation procedure has been reported in extensive detail by Rafiq et al (2011), T_{wall} is the temperature at the tube wall, ΔH_{rxn} is the reaction enthalpy (kJ/mol) (Méndez et al., 2017), P is the pressure (Pa), d_p is the catalyst particle diameter and μ_m is the fluid viscosity (Pa.s).

Table 1. Initial and boundary conditions for the set of differential equations.

Condition	Variables		
$t = 0, 0 < z \leq L$	$C_i = 0$	$T = 25\ °C$	$P = P_{in}$
$t > 0, z = 0$	$C_i = C_{i,in}$	$T = T_{in}$	$P = P_{in}$

The reaction rate expression is obtained according to Eq. (4).

$$r_i = \nu_i S_i \varphi_i r_{FT} \quad (4)$$

Where ν_i is the component's stoichiometric coefficient, S_i is the component's selectivity following the Anderson-Shulz-Flory distribution (Förtsch et al., 2015) by means of a variable chain growth probability factor (Vervloet et al., 2012), φ_i is the distribution factor for the Olefin/Paraffin ratio (Pandey et al., 2020) and r_{FT}, denoting the reaction kinetics, is related to the commercial Co-Al_2O_3 catalyst and have been obtained from Kaiser et al. (2014) comprehensive study.

In addition, the remaining properties concerning the system's components were computed using the databases within the Aspen Properties® v12 software, employing the Soave-Redlich-Kwong equation of state (Karimi et al., 2012). The resulting system of differential equations was subsequently implemented as a model in Aspen Custom Modeler® v12 software. The solution was obtained by employing the lines method, using backward finite differentiation for discretizing the axial domain in 50 slices of 0.24 m each and Implicit Euler as the integration method for the time derivatives up to t = 300 s and variable step size.

In order to test the developed model, a sensitivity analysis varying syngas inlet molar flow-rate, temperature and syngas composition was conducted in order to evaluate how long the system would take to achieve steady-state, CO conversion and selectivity towards different chain length hydrocarbons. Table 2 presents an overview of both the base case and the varied conditions examined, which further allowed to analyze alterations and deviations from the base case scenario clarifying how the operational variables impact the system behavior.

3. Results and discussion

Modeling a dynamic system that represents the Fischer-Tropsch process has proven to be a complex task, despite the usage of simplifying assumptions. The numerical initialization is highly sensitive to initial conditions, given the nonlinearities inherent not only in the overall constitutive equations of the model but also in the calculations of the system's parameters and properties.

Table 2. Conditions tested in the sensitivity analysis.

Case	Inlet Temperature (°C)	Syngas inlet flow-rate (mol/s)	Inlet H_2/CO Ratio
Base	210	0.5	2:1
1	205	0.5	2:1
2	215	0.5	2:1
3	210	0.25	2:1
4	210	1	2:1
5	210	0.5	1:1
6	210	0.5	3:1

Furhermore, due to the high exothermicity of the reaction, operating at wall temperatures lower than those of the syngas is imperative to prevent thermal runaways, which excessively raise the fluid temperature and cause numerical instabilities in the final solution of the model. Figure 1 shows the variations in the profiles of the base case for the CO flow-rate, C5+ hydrocarbons flow-rate and temperature in respect with the reactor length considering four different times. Specifically for this case, steady-state operation was achieved at 44 s.

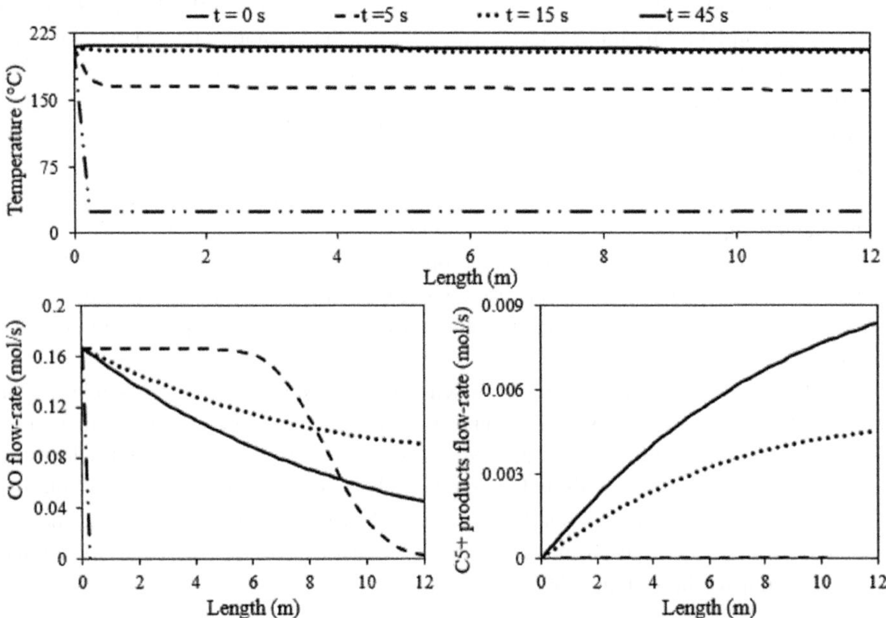

Figure 1. Simulated profiles for the base scenario considering four different times.

It can be noted that the system behaves as it would be expected. In the initial seconds, while the temperature is low and still stabilizing, no reaction is observed in the system, only the passage of CO through the tube. The first product fractions alongside the axial length are observed after the bed reaches approximately 180 °C. The reactor then continues to heat, not only due to the energy transfer between the wall and the bed but also because of the heat released by the reaction, until it is thermally stable. Eventually, with the interior temperature stabilized, the system evolves for a few more seconds until it reaches steady-state, with the flow rates of reactants and products stabilizing along the reactor. Table 3 summarizes the final results obtained during the sensitivity analysis. The 'SS', 'X_{CO}' and 'S' abbreviatures address the time required for the system to reach the steady-state operation, CO conversion and product selectivity for the specified hydrocarbon chain length, respectively.

Table 3. Overall results obtained in the sensitivity analysis.

Case	SS (s)	X_{CO} (%)	S-C1 (%)	S-C2-C7 (%)	S-C8-C16 (%)	S-C17+ (%)
Base	44	72.87%	8.26%	35.91%	26.87%	28.96%
1	45	57.45%	5.20%	24.97%	23.10%	46.73%
2	94	84.22%	13.56%	48.25%	24.27%	13.91%
3	120	86.19%	6.27%	28.60%	23.95%	41.18%
4	35	42.76%	7.83%	34.72%	26.95%	30.50%
5	43	26.09%	0.71%	3.97%	5.09%	90.23%
6	137	99.73%	45.67%	49.06%	5.01%	0.25%

The system takes an average of 74 seconds to reach steady-state operation, with 35 seconds as the minimum time and 137 seconds as the maximum. The obtained results align with what would be theoretically expected from the system, as in case 4, for instance, a great impact was assessed from a flow rate twice as high compared to the base case. The increased fluid spatial velocity caused it to traverse the reactor length more rapidly, resulting in a direct negative impact on CO conversion. For the 6th case, a notable observation is the extended duration required to attain the steady-state condition. This prolonged period correlates with a heightened CO conversion, consequently amplifying the thermal effects within the system due to the escalated heat release from the reaction, thereby prolonging temperature stabilization.

Other evaluated cases also align with theoretical expectations. The temperature increase demonstrated the capability to rise CO conversion. However, at the same time, it reduced the selectivity towards larger hydrocarbon chains, showcasing a disadvantage to processes aiming, for example, to produce aviation kerosene (which encompasses hydrocarbons with chains with more than 8 carbons in it). The syngas ratio also yielded significant impacts, especially towards products selectivities. A higher ratio of H_2/CO has been showed to be capable of achieving higher selectivities solely for lighter hydrocarbons, jeopardizing the production of higher chain compounds. Finally, the scenario 2 was considered to be the best, regardless of the higher required time to reach its equilibrium or the slightly lower selectivities towards higher chain hydrocarbons, the operation condition was able to convert the most out of CO and had the highest overall yield of hydrocarbons that could be blended together into fuels.

4. Conclusions

A dynamic model of a fixed-bed reactor for Fischer-Tropsch synthesis was developed and its behavior studied. Employing mass and energy balances and utilizing the Ergun Equation to assess pressure drop in the bed, not only conversions and selectivities were unveiled but also the theoretical time for the system to reach steady-state was evaluated. In general terms, the system exhibited short times to achieve equilibrium, with an average value close to one minute. Furthermore, it was observed that reductions in inlet flow rates and the increment in inlet temperature or H_2/CO ratio led to longer times required for the system's stabilization. Among the evaluated conditions, the temperature increase tested in case 2 yielded the most favorable results for hydrocarbon yields with chain lengths suitable for blending into commercial fuels.

5. Acknowledgements

The authors gratefully acknowledge the support of the São Paulo Research Foundation (FAPESP) (2022/04751-0; 2023/08268-4), the National Council for Scientific and Technological Development (CNPq) (310125/2021-9; 314598/2021-9), and the Coordination for the Improvement of Higher Education Personnel (CAPES) (Finance Code 001).

References

A. Jess, C. Kern, 2009, Modeling of Multi-Tubular Reactors for Fischer-Tropsch Synthesis, Chemical Engineering & Technology: Industrial Chemistry-Plant Equipment-Process Engineering-Biotechnology, 32, 8, 1164-1175.

C. I. Méndez, J. Ancheyta, F. Trejo, 2017, Modeling of catalytic fixed-bed reactors for fuels production by Fischer–Tropsch synthesis, Energy & fuels, 31, 12, 13011-13042.

D. Förtsch, K. Pabst, E. Groß-Hardt, 2015, The product distribution in Fischer–Tropsch synthesis: An extension of the ASF model to describe common deviations, Chemical Engineering Science, 138, 333-346.

D. Vervloet, F. Kapteijn, J. Nijenhuis, J.R. Van Ommen, 2012, Fischer–Tropsch reaction–diffusion in a cobalt catalyst particle: aspects of activity and selectivity for a variable chain growth probability, Catalysis Science & Technology, 2, 6, 1221-1233.

D. Wang, C. Chen, J. Wang, L. Jia, B. Hou, D. Li, 2016, High thermal conductive core-shell structured Al_2O_3@ Al composite supported cobalt catalyst for Fischer-Tropsch synthesis, Applied catalysis a: General, 527, 60-71.

F. Benyahia, K. E. O'Neill, 2005, Enhanced Voidage Correlations for Packed Beds of Various Particle Shapes and Sizes, Particulate Science and Technology, 23, 2, 169-177.

F. Sauerhöfer-Rodrigo, I. Díaz, M. Rodríguez, P. Pérez, 2023, Modelling of fixed bed and slurry bubble column reactors for Fischer–Tropsch synthesis. Reviews in Chemical Engineering.

H. Mahmoudi, M. Mahmoudi, O. Doustdar, H. Jahangiri, A. Tsolakis, S. Gu, M. LechWyszynski, 2017, A review of Fischer Tropsch synthesis process, mechanism, surface chemistry and catalyst formulation, Biofuels Engineering, 2, 1, 11-31.

M. H. Rafiq, H. A. Jakobsen, R. Schmid, J.E. Hustad, 2011, Experimental studies and modeling of a fixed bed reactor for Fischer–Tropsch synthesis using biosyngas, Fuel processing technology, 92, 5, 893-907.

P. Kaiser, F. Pöhlmann, A. Jess, 2014, Intrinsic and Effective Kinetics of Cobalt-Catalyzed Fischer-Tropsch Synthesis in View of a Power-to-Liquid Process Based on Renewable Energy, Chemical Engineering & Technology, 37, 6, 964-972.

R. L. Espinoza, A. P. Steynberg, B. Jager, A. C. Vosloo, 1999, Low temperature Fischer–Tropsch synthesis from a Sasol perspective, Applied Catalysis A: General, 186, 1-2, 13-26.

T. S. Lee, J. N. Chung, 2012, Mathematical modeling and numerical simulation of a Fischer–Tropsch packed bed reactor and its thermal management for liquid hydrocarbon fuel production using biomass syngas, Energy & Fuels, 26, 2, 1363-1379.

U. Pandey, A. Runningen, L. Gavrilović, E.A. Jørgensen, K.R. Putta, K.R. Rout, E. Rytter, E.A. Blekkan, M. Hillestad, 2021, Modeling Fischer–Tropsch kinetics and product distribution over a cobalt catalyst, AIChE Journal, 67, 7, e17234.

Z. Karimi, M. Rahmani, M. Moqadam, 2012, A study on vapour-liquid equilibria in Fischer-Tropsch synthesis, Procedia Engineering, 42, 25-33.

Flavio Manenti, Gintaras V. Reklaitis (Eds.), Proceedings of the 34th European Symposium on Computer Aided Process Engineering / 15th International Symposium on Process Systems Engineering (ESCAPE34/PSE24), June 2-6, 2024, Florence, Italy
 http://dx.doi.org/10.1016/B978-0-443-28824-1.50169-1

Variable structure simulation and optimization of start-up of batch distillation columns

Nikhil Sharma,[a*] Kannan M. Moudgalya,[a] Sunil Shah,[b]

[a] *Dept. of Chemical Engg, Indian Institute of Technology Bombay, Powai 400076, India*
[b]*Modelicon Infotech LLP, Bengaluru, 560066, India*
nikhilsharma1207@gmail.com

Abstract

A versatile hybrid simulator, capable of including only the active units, useful especially for start-up and shut-down simulations, has been developed using the scheduler developed by Paknikar et al. (2022). This simulator has been used to study the start-up operations of a methanol-water batch distillation column. The results of these simulations are validated with that of Elgue et al. (2004). After rigorously simulating the start-up, the reflux rate profile is optimized to achieve 99 % product purity in the shortest time. This exercise is repeated for the approximate modeling in which liquid in every tray is taken to be at feed composition, with vapor-liquid equilibrium established. Optimization with accurate initial conditions leads to 75 % reduction in batch time. This simulator is capable of start-up and shut-down also of continuous distillation columns, and extendable to that of entire flowsheets.

Keywords: Variable-structure modeling, start-up of batch distillation, optimal start-up

1. Introduction

Understanding of distillation column operation especially during start-up is an important step to enable "1st time right" policies for establishing optimal time and energy policies. Modeling of dynamic operations of start-up and shut-down operations is beneficial in the design, control, and operability of distillation columns. Fieg et al. (1993) tried to answer when and how proper valve switching should be done to achieve desired purity safely and in a short time. Scenna et al. (1998) demonstrated for reactive distillation systems how a given start-up policy may be better or worse. Modeling start-up operations is also of interest for optimizing a distillation system. Wang et al. (2003) suggested a trial and error method to obtain the pseudo-warm state for initializing optimization. Gonzalez-Velasco et al. (1987) suggested the improvement in batch distillation start-up without considering changes in the phases. Ruiz et al. (1988) developed a dynamic model for batch distillation start-up. Flender et al. (1998) also developed a start-up model for distillation but did not consider the transition from the empty column.

Modeling of start-up processes is an inherently difficult problem due to sequential on-streaming of unit operations and components. For example, cold start-up of distillation columns, will gradually bring on-stream trays till the whole column is filled, and vapor-liquid traffic is established. This requires a structurally changing set of equations that need to be modeled and solved.

Wang et al. (2003) simulated rigorously the start-up of a distillation column from a cold state using gPROMS Barton et al. (1994), handling the structurally changing set of equations indirectly: they solved one set of equations, with inactive units being modeled by trivial equations. They also validated their prediction with experimental results. Their model was improved by Elgue et al. (2004), who carried out a similar study. Hoffmann et al. (2020) suggested a pressure-driven dynamic model for the start-up of distillation columns through smooth reformulations of min/max operators and step functions.

In this work, the approach of Wang et al. (2003) and Elgue et al. (2004) is used without resorting to the use of trivial equations: a part of the column is simulated only if there is any liquid or vapor traffic in it. Feed is charged into the reboiler and heated. Tray models are used as and when the vapor reaches them, condenses, and VLE is established. Accordingly, the number of equations in the model keeps increasing, as and when a tray is brought into focus, using the scheduling engine developed by Paknikar et al. (2022). The results of this simulation are compared with a study in which all trays participate from the beginning, with the composition in every tray being equal to that of feed. Optimization studies confirm the benefits of using correct initial conditions.

2. Simulator for variable structure modeling and simulation

A scheduling engine developed by Paknikar et al. (2022) in OpenModelica has been leveraged to execute sequential operations during a distillation column start-up. This simulator facilitates the inclusion of only active units, which can be considered as *just-in-time* modeling. Inactive units are not included, and hence their model equations are excluded from the simulation. Consequently, there is no need to provide trivial equations or guesses for inactive units. The scheduling engine of Paknikar et al. (2022) enables event monitoring for variable structure modeling and simulation.

The start-up procedure may vary based on the column geometries and modes of operation. For validation purposes, an experimental Oldershaw-type Methanol-Water column used by Elgue et al. (2004) is selected for modeling. A methanol-water feed with 18% methanol is charged to the reboiler in a 20-stage column operating at atmospheric pressure. The resulting temperature profiles of select trays during the start-up, as calculated by our simulator, are compared with that of Elgue et al. (2004) in Figure (1).

There are slight differences between the two profiles, which can be attributed to the differences in hold-up values and in the modeling of the reboiler. As the current simulator solves a unit only when it is active, temperature profiles it predicts do not start from time

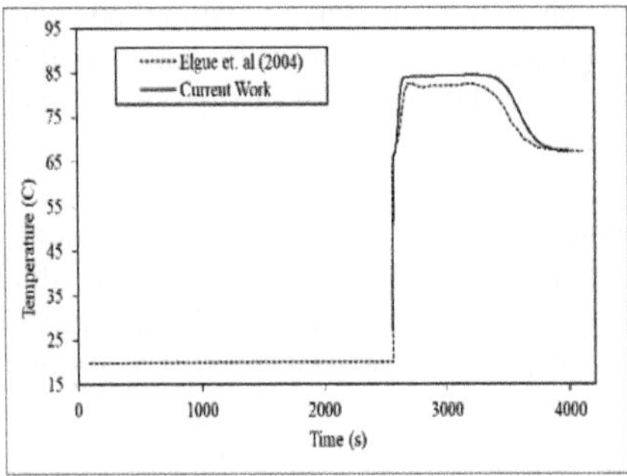

(a) Bottom tray

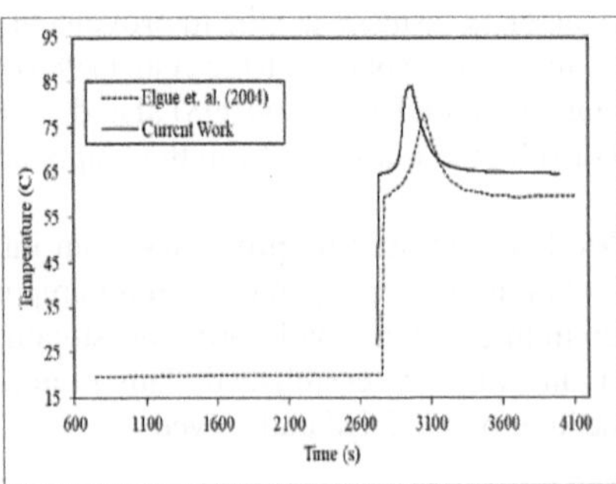

(b) Intermediate tray

zero: a tray becomes active only when vapor reaches the wall of the tray.

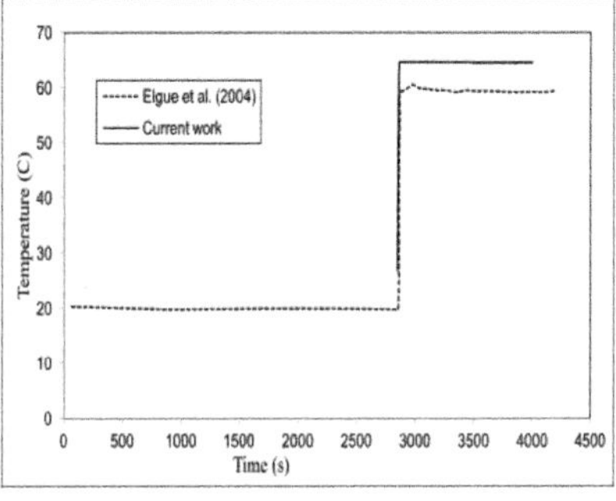

(c) Top tray

Figure 1: Comparison of temperature profiles of the current work with that of Elgue et al. (2004) (a) Bottom tray (b) Intermediate tray (c) Top tray

3. Start-up and optimization

The importance of using correct initial conditions is brought out in this section. Just-in-time modeling, explained above, is used to carry out the start-up in an equimolar Methanol-Water system (see Table 1), using the realistic model equations of Elgue et al. (2004).

Table 1: Column Specification for the Methanol-Water system

Column Specifications	
Components	Methanol- Water (Equimolar)
Initial charge	800 Moles
Number of Trays	20 (each with 10 Moles Hold-up)
Reflux Drum Hold-up	200 Moles
Pressure	101325 Pa
Heat Duty	3 kW
K Values	NRTL

Start-up is said to be complete when the vapor-liquid traffic is established and in equilibrium in the entire column. In this example, the start-up is considered complete when the bottom tray is completely filled with the incoming liquid from the tray just above it. Figures 2(a) and 2(b), respectively, show the temperature and composition profiles for a few select trays during the startup. As mentioned earlier, profiles of different trays begin at different times, depending on when they become active and hence get included in the simulation.

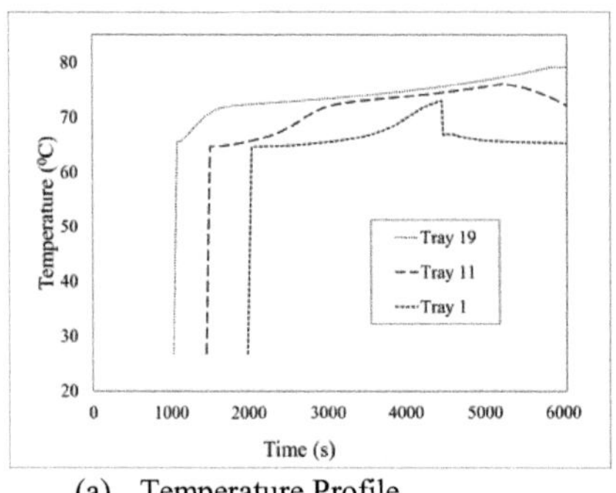

(a) Temperature Profile

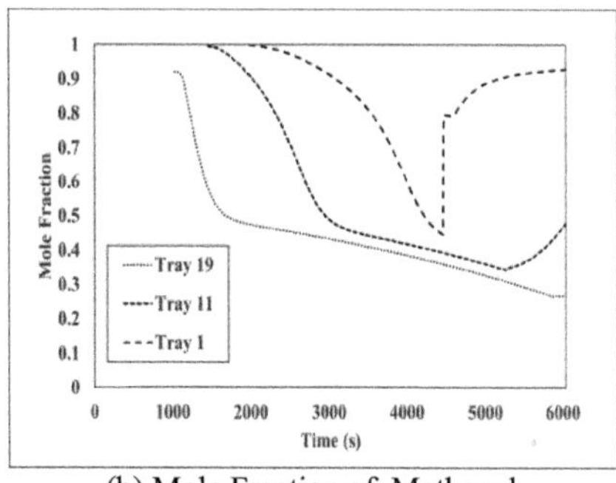

(b) Mole Fraction of Methanol

Figure 2: Temperature and composition profiles of select trays, numbered from top to bottom during start-up

After the start-up, the reflux ratios are optimized so as to complete the separation in minimum time, with the constraint that 99% pure methanol is obtained at the top of the distillation column. As it is a batch operation, the product is taken to be the sum of the liquid collected at the reflux drum, and what is already withdrawn in the accumulator. The optimization problem is stated in Eq. (1).

$$\min_{rr} \frac{T_{Batch}}{H_a} \quad \text{Sub. to} \quad X_{p,1} \geq 0.99 \tag{1}$$

Where, rr is reflux ratio and is defined as an internal reflux i.e., the ratio of liquid returning to vapor flow rate and varies from 0 to 1. T_{Batch} is the batch time, H_a is the accumulator hold-up, and $X_{p,1}$ is the combined mole fraction of methanol in the accumulator and the reflux drum. The batch time is divided into five equal intervals with a constant reflux ratio in each. The approach of constrained optimization by linear approximations (Powell, 1994) is used. In this particular implementation, scipy.optimize.COBYLA is used in OpenModelica.

In the traditional method of start-up, however, it is assumed that every tray, the reboiler, and the reflux drum are filled with the liquid at feed conditions: equimolar composition at the bubble point, in this case. This assumption is at best approximate as vapor-liquid equilibrium is not possible even if every tray is charged with liquid at the feed composition with vapor-liquid traffic established. The reflux ratio for this initial condition is subsequently optimized to obtain 99% purity of methanol at the top.

Results of the traditional approach (left) and the just-in-time modeling approach (right) are now reported in Table 2. The optimal reflux ratio profiles for the two cases are compared in Figure 3. To handle different batch times, the model equations are integrated to unit time instant and multiplied by the actual batch time. Figure 4 compares the composition profiles in the reflux drum and the accumulator.

It is evident from Table 2 that initial conditions have a critical role in optimization. It takes less than 75 % time in separating components in the just-in-time modeling, as compared to the traditional method. Although the just-in-time modeling approach slightly overestimates startup as can be seen in Figure 1, it helps arrive at better optimal values (the improvement observed is around 75 %). Since 200 moles of holdup are present in the reflux drum, which is also 99% pure, implies that 370 moles out of 400 moles are obtained with 99% purity. Figure 3 and 4 shows for traditional approach column needs to be operated at total reflux for considerable amount of time to achieve the desired purity.

Table 2: Comparison of optimization results

Optimized Variable	**Results for different initial conditions**	
	Accurate (proposed in this work)	**Traditional (feed composition in every tray)**
Batch Time	11002 sec	48713 sec
Accumulator Hold-up	170 moles	173 moles
Total top product	370 moles	373 moles
Accumulator purity	98.8 % Methanol (moles)	99.7 % Methanol (moles)
Reflux drum purity	99.1 % Methanol (moles)	97.7 % Methanol (moles)
Total Purity	98.9 % Methanol (moles)	98.6 % Methanol (moles)

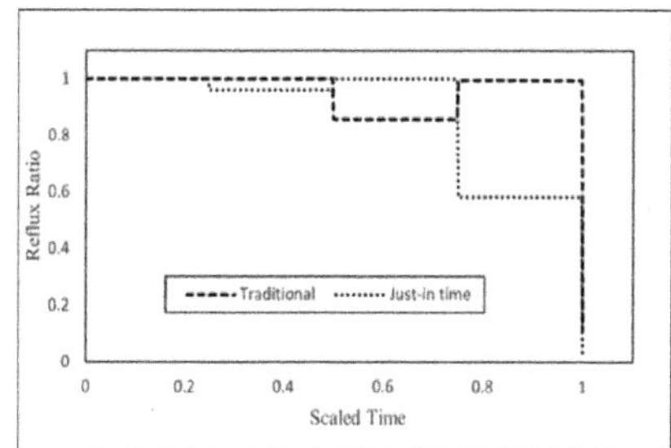

Figure 3: Comparison of Optimum reflux ratio profiles

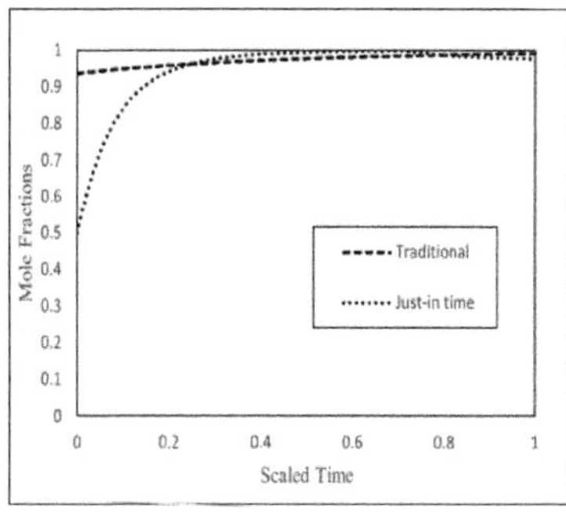

(a)

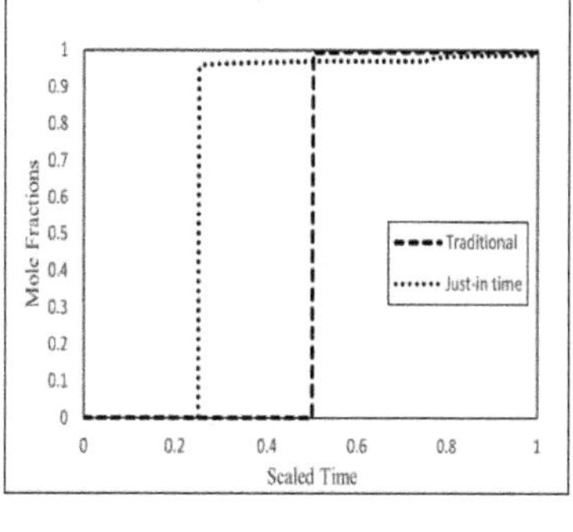

(b)

Figure 4: (a) reflux drum profiles and (b) accumulator profiles

Conclusions

A versatile hybrid simulator capable of doing just-in-time simulations, incorporating only the active units, has been developed in OpenModelica. Simulating only the active units obviates the need to come up with trivial models, to develop which, considerable effort may be required (Paknikar et al. (2022)). The simulator's utility has been demonstrated through the start-up simulation of a batch distillation column. This simulator can be easily extended to the start-up and shut-down of continuous distillation columns and to the start-up and shut-down of entire flowsheet. Start-up and shut-down operations can be considered as batch processes.

The traditional method of taking the liquid composition in every tray to be equal to that of feed could be much less optimal than the rigorous start-up using just-in-time modeling. More importantly, this traditional method could give simulation results that are quite different from the actual situation, portrayed more correctly by the rigorous just-in-time simulation.

Future work includes optimizing these operations using variable structure optimization, implementing control strategies, and extending the scheduling framework for the startup and shutdown of process plants.

References

J. R. Gonzalez-Velasco, M. A. Gutierrez-Ortiz, J. M. Castresana-Pelayo, and J. A. Gonzalez-Marcos, "Improvements in batch distillation startup," Industrial & engineering chemistry research, vol. 26, no. 4, pp. 745–750, 1987.

C. A. Ruiz, I. Cameron, and R Gani, "A generalized dynamic model for distillation columns—iii. study of startup operations," Computers & chemical engineering, vol. 12, no. 1, pp. 1–14, 1988.

G Fieg, G Wozny, and C. Kruse, "Experimental and theoretical studies of the dynamics of startup and product switchover operations of distillation columns," Chemical Engineering and Processing: Process Intensification, vol. 32, no. 5, pp. 283–290, 1993.

M Flender, G Wozny, and G Fieg, "Time-optimal startup of a packed distillation column," IFAC Proceedings Volumes, vol. 31, no. 11, pp. 111–116, 1998.

N. Scenna, C. Ruiz, and S. Benz, "Dynamic simulation of start-up procedures of reactive distillation columns," Computers & chemical engineering, vol. 22, S719–S722, 1998.

L. Wang, P. Li, G. Wozny, and S. Wang, "A startup model for simulation of batch distillation starting from a cold state," Computers & Chemical Engineering, vol. 27, no. 10, pp. 1485–1497, 2003.

Barton, Paul I., and Constantinos C. Pantelides. "Modeling of combined discrete/continuous processes." AIChE journal 40.6 (1994): 966-979.

S. Elgue, L. Prat, M. Cabassud, J.-M. Le Lann, and J. Cezerac, "Dynamic models for start-up operations of batch distillation columns with experimental validation," Computers & chemical engineering, vol. 28, no. 12, pp. 2735–2747, 2004.

N. Russell, W. M. Van Der Aalst, and A. H. Ter Hofstede, Workflow Patterns: The Definitive Guide. MIT Press, Feb. 2016, isbn: 9780262029827.

C. Hoffmann, J. Weigert, E. Esche, and J.-U. Repke, "A pressure-driven, dynamic model for distillation columns with smooth reformulations for flexible operation," Computers & chemical Engineering, vol. 142, p. 107 062, 2020.

R. Paknikar, N. Sharma, P. Nayak, K. Moudgalya, and B. Raman, "Simulation scheduling of variable-structure systems in OpenModelica," in Modelica Conferences, 2022, pp. 147–155.

Powell, Michael JD. A direct search optimization method that models the objective and constraint functions by linear interpolation. Springer Netherlands, 1994.

Flavio Manenti, Gintaras V. Reklaitis (Eds.), Proceedings of the 34th European Symposium on Computer Aided Process Engineering / 15th International Symposium on Process Systems Engineering (ESCAPE34/PSE24), June 2-6, 2024, Florence, Italy
 http://dx.doi.org/10.1016/B978-0-443-28824-1.50170-8

Dynamic Modeling and Validation of an Industrial Vacuum Thermodeasphalting Column for the Regeneration of Used Oil

Francesco Negri[a,b], Kristiano Prifti[b], Simone Caspani[b], Francesco Gallo[a], Flavio Manenti[b,*]

[a]*Itelyum Regeneration S.p.A., Via Tavernelle 19, Pieve Fissiraga 26854, Lodi, Italy*
[b]*Politecnico di Milano, CMIC Dept. "Giulio Natta", Piazza Leonardo da Vinci 32, Milan 20133, Italy*
**flavio.manenti@polimi.it*

Abstract

Dynamic process simulation is a valuable strategy to enhance the reliability of transient operations in chemical plants. Deviations from normal operating conditions may be necessary to perform corrective actions against any external disturbance that may alter the performance of some process units. Moreover, some standard plant operations are intrinsically transient in nature, such as start-up and shut-down procedures. Used oil waste re-refining industry is beginning to explore this strategy, which could lead to successful outcomes, similarly to what has been observed in the crude oil refining industry. This work proposes a modeling approach for the dynamic simulation of a thermodeasphalting column for the regeneration of used oil, currently operative in the Itelyum Regeneration re-refining facility in Pieve Fissiraga. The modeling strategy introduces a discretization of the column sections, a reasoned choice of appropriate thermodynamic methods, and the calculation of the main equilibrium and transport parameters necessary to solve mass, energy, and momentum balances on the column sections. The model is validated with experimental data, showing good agreement regarding both manipulated and controlled variables, thus becoming a valuable tool for the aprioristic evaluation of critical transient operations such as start-up, shut-down, and accidents simulation.

Keywords: AVEVA Dynamic Simulation, Dynamic modelling, Revivoil, Thermodeasphalting, Used oil.

1. Introduction

Historically, the complexity of operations in chemical plants was governed by relying on steady-state simulation tools, which are representative of normal operations. However, transient operations are also critical for the correct conduction of a chemical plant, they occur in extremely delicate timeframes during which the change from a stable, steady-state condition to a new one may lead to problematic events. Management of these transient timeframes that may occur during normal operations is a research topic that identifies dynamic process simulation suites as the main tool to assist plant personnel (Srinivasan et al., 2005). The domain of crude oil refining has shown significant advancements in dynamic simulation, including case studies regarding typical unit operations such as crude oil atmospheric distillation (Sotelo et al., 2019), and hydrogen purification through PSA systems (Agarwal et al., 2009), but also alternative applications such as fouling monitoring (Díaz-Bejarano et al., 2015) and personnel training (Vasconcelos et al., 2005). The domain of used oil waste re-refining, which has a large number of technologies already available and operating on the market (Kupareva et al., 2013), is much less developed in this sense, showing only preliminary approaches centered around the dynamic validation of controllers response (Haura et al., 2017). This paper introduces a new, important step in the domain of dynamic modeling within the used oil re-refining industry, by developing a methodology for the modeling and validation of a thermodeasphalting column, key process component of the Revivoil® process that is currently run in the Itelyum Regeneration re-refining facility (Gallo, 2016).

2. Materials and Methods

The thermodeasphalting (TDA) section of the Revivoil® process is a crucial step for the proper regeneration of used oil. The TDA section performs the separation of dehydrated used oil into semi-finished base lube oil cuts, those being spindle, light, and heavy lubricant fractions (SLF, LLF, HLF, respectively). Vacuum gasoil (VGO) and bitumen (VISCOFLEX) are also produced as byproducts (Gallo, 2016). The T-401 vacuum column of the section is a packed column that is internally divided into sectors, each one dedicated to the separation of adjacent cuts. It is possible to identify five different sections, each one having a liquid collection device at the bottom. Each section has one or multiple beds composed of several types of structured packing, being of different type and height. The authors of this work propose a modeling approach for the dynamic simulation of the T-401 column that describes it as a discrete ensemble of five distinct sections, each one interconnected with the two adjacent ones and representing the real sections into which the column is divided. The software chosen for the dynamic modeling is AVEVA Dynamic Simulation (AVEVA, 2023). The modeling strategy can be implemented in the software by building each section as a discrete entity having three components: a sump to represent the liquid collection system, pack equilibrium stages to model structured packing, and vertical tubes to represent the empty space above each section in which vapor and liquid flow towards adjacent sections. The conceptual representation of this modeling approach is shown in Figure 1 with simplified diagrams.

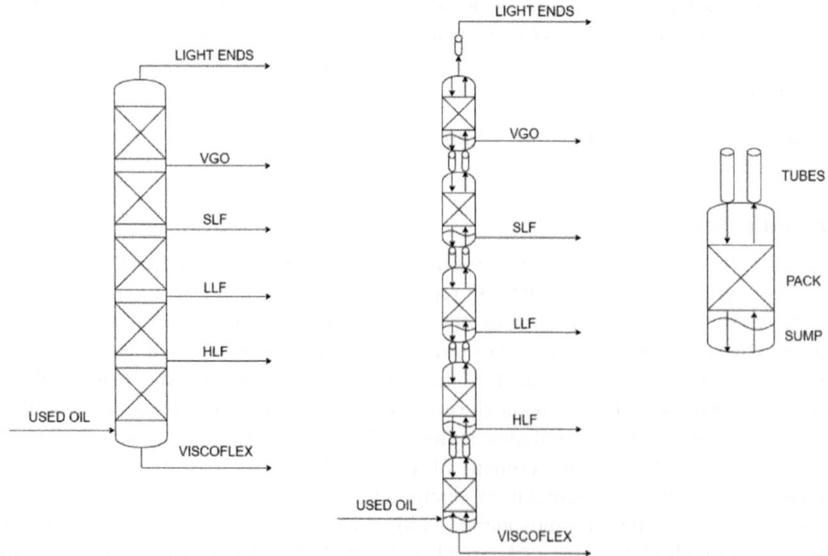

Figure 1. Simplified schemes for T-401 column (left), discrete modeling approach (middle), and detail of the fundamental simulation block (right)

Input data required for the dynamic simulation of T-401 include two different types, the first being thermodynamic data and the second one being design and operative data of the equipment to be simulated. Some data require preliminary information about the column to be available, such as temperature and pressure profiles. While some of these data can be retrieved directly from field instrumentation, this is not true for all the required entries. To overcome this limitation, the authors have considered an already functioning steady-state simulation developed in Aspen HYSYS® software (AspenTech, 2023) as the source of the missing data, since this simulation is currently used in the plant with good agreement with experimental data. Thermodynamic data include ASTM D1160 curves considered at the atmospheric equivalent temperature (AET), available as sets of experimental laboratory data, which are converted by the simulation software into 31 pseudo-components to simulate correctly the real mixtures. The Peng-Robinson cubic equation of state is used to describe almost all of the properties of the mixtures (Peng and Robinson, 1976). Some exception with their alternative methods are liquid density, calculated using Rackett method, molecular weight, critical pressure, critical temperature, and acentric factor, all calculated using both the standard and the extended Twu method, and liquid viscosity, calculated using the Bergmann-Sutton method. AVEVA Dynamic Simulation also requires data to solve mass, energy, and momentum balances for each discrete section in which the column is divided. Mass balances can be solved by assigning a certain number of ideal equilibrium stages to each packed section, also referred to as Equivalent Theoretical Plates (ETP), values that can be obtained from the Aspen HYSYS® simulation. Energy balances can be solved by calculating both the external (h_e) and the internal (h_i) liminal heat transfer coefficients. The h_e parameter is calculated by considering natural convection from the metal surface to the environment according to Eq. (1), where k_{air} is the thermal conductivity of air, H is the height of the packed section, Ra is the Rayleigh number (Bird et al., 2007).

$$h_e = 0.13 \cdot \frac{k_{air}}{H} \cdot Ra^{\frac{1}{3}} \tag{1}$$

The h_i parameter is calculated using Carpenter-Colburn's expression, which describes a forced vapor flowrate in counter current with a descending liquid film, according to Eq. (2), where all the parameters are referred to the vapor, G is the mass velocity, f is the friction coefficient, C_p is the specific heat, k is the thermal conductivity, μ is the dynamic viscosity, and v is the superficial velocity (Green and Southard, 2019).

$$h_i = 0.065 \cdot G \cdot \sqrt{f \cdot \frac{C_p \cdot k}{2 \cdot \mu \cdot v}} \tag{2}$$

Momentum balances can be solved by calculating pack flow rate conductance (K), which describes how easily the vapor can flow through a certain packed section, according to Eq. (3), where all the physical parameters refer to the vapor and the geometrical ones refer to the packed sections, v is the superficial velocity, f is the friction coefficient, ε is the void fraction, ρ is the density, H is the height, ΔP is the pressure drop, and D_{eq} is the characteristic dimension.

$$K = v \cdot \sqrt{\frac{3}{4} \cdot \frac{f \cdot \frac{1-\varepsilon}{\varepsilon^{4.65}} \cdot \rho \cdot H}{1000 \cdot \Delta P \cdot D_{eq}}} \tag{3}$$

The parameters introduced previously allow to solve the balances on the column, thus solving the main body of the T-401. Ancillary units such as pumps, heat exchangers, pipes, and valves are modeled by selecting the appropriate type among the list available in the simulation software, and introducing design and operations data from P&IDs. Controller parameters are directly taken from the control room DCS. Numerical values calculated for the main parameters of the T-401 column balances are reported in Table 1, where each section is named after the product exiting from the corresponding bottom sump.

Table 1. Main parameters for mass, energy, and momentum balances for T-401

Packed section	ETP [n.]	h_e [W/m^2/K]	h_i [W/m^2/K]	K [-]
VISCOFLEX	3.00	9.2	19.9	0.2632
HLF	1.00	9.1	24.1	0.8532
LLF	3.78	8.7	28.7	1.8844
SLF	6.12	7.4	23.9	2.3815
VGO	4.00	4.6	14.8	3.1358

3. Results and Discussion

The detailed view of the LLF section is shown in Figure 2 as a case study. It is possible to notice the discrete modeling approach as introduced previously, with the combination of sump, packed section, and tubes. The LLF pack includes controllers, recirculation pump, and a split between the LLF product sent to storage and the LLF reflux that is used in the adjacent HLF section below. It is also possible to notice the SLF flowrates exiting from the corresponding section above, which is similarly divided into product to be stored, and a reflux to be fed to the LLF section. This kind of topology is common among vacuum-based, used oil re-refining technologies (Kupareva et al., 2013).

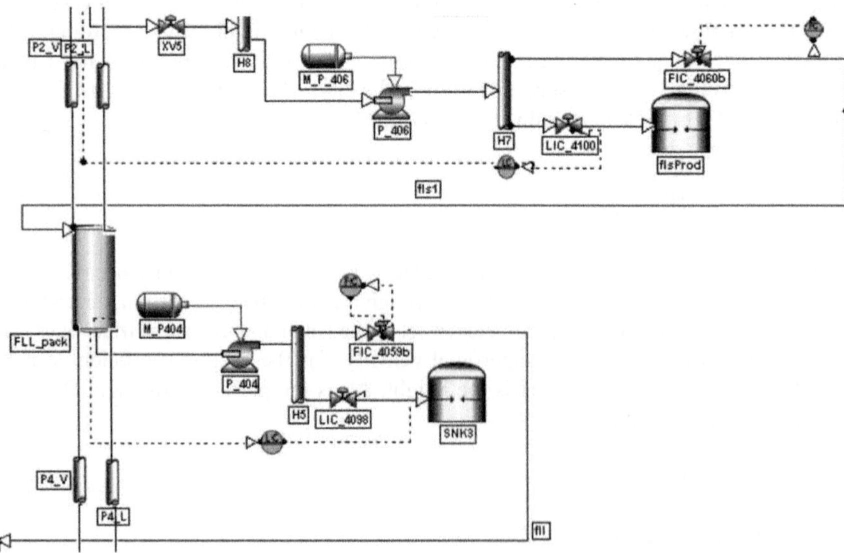

Figure 2. Detail of the LLF section including SLF reflux from the adjacent top section

It is possible to analyze the performance of simulated sections by considering a transient operation that was executed by plant operators, in which the feedstock to the TDA column was increased by 20%. The chosen indicator will be the normalized deviation of appropriate variables from their initial value (δ), defined as in Eq. (4), where x(t) and x^0 are the variables as a function of time and the corresponding initial value, respectively.

$$\delta(t) = \frac{x(t)-x^0}{x^0} \quad (4)$$

The first parameter to be analyzed is the responsiveness of the simulated control loops, which refers to manipulated variables that are determined by the user in the simulation. The SLF reflux to the LLF pack is shown in Figure 3 for this purpose. There is good agreement between simulation and experimental values.

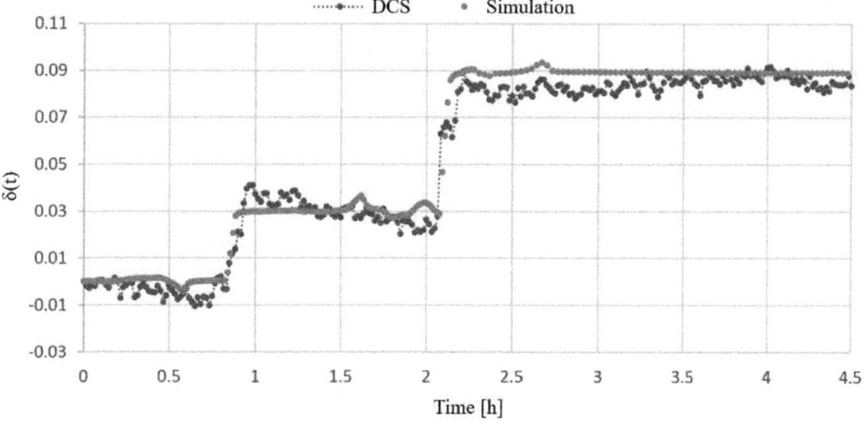

Figure 3. Comparison between DCS and simulation for SLF flowrate, manipulated variable

The second parameter to be analyzed is the dynamic evolution in time of the controlled variables, that are not determined by the user and that are automatically calculated by the software. The LLF liquid sump temperature is shown in Figure 4 for this purpose. There is good agreement between simulation and experimental values. Results similar to what is shown in Figures 3 and 4 are obtained for all the simulated column sections.

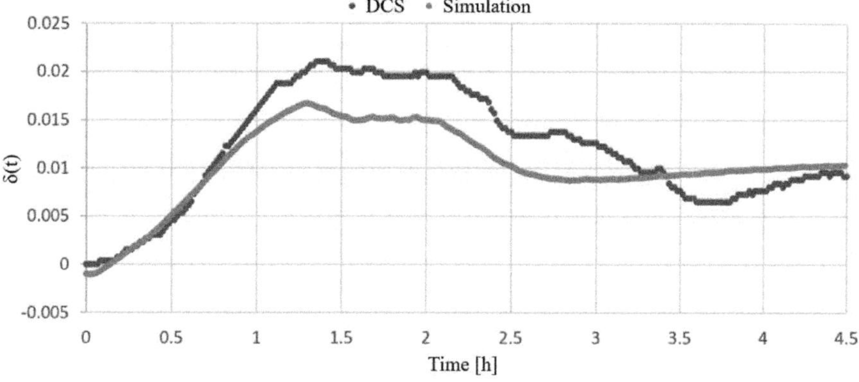

Figure 4. Comparison between DCS and simulation for LLF sump temperature, controlled variable

4. Conclusions

This work introduced a methodology to build a dynamic process simulation for the thermodeasphalting T-401 column currently operating in the Itelyum Regeneration re-refining facility located in Pieve Fissiraga, Lodi, Italy. A discrete, equation-based modelling approach was followed, introducing appropriate thermodynamic methods and showing the main results for equilibrium and transport parameters. Validation of the model has been carried out by comparing the output from the simulation with real plant data from the DCS. Good agreement between simulated time-dependent profiles and real DCS data is shown both for manipulated and controlled variables. The case of the LLF pack is shown here as a meaningful example, in which the evolution in time of the SLF reflux and the LLF sump temperature are shown. The dynamic simulation is a reliable tool that can be used for the aprioristic study and evaluation of transient operations such as start-up, shut-down, or even the simulation of accidents caused by equipment failure.

References

A. Agarwal, L.T. Biegler, S.E. Zitney, 2009. Simulation and optimization of pressure swing adsorption systems using reduced-order modeling. Industrial and Engineering Chemistry Research 48, 2327–2343.

AspenTech, 2023. Aspen HYSYS | Process Simulation Software | AspenTech. https://www.aspentech.com/en/products/engineering/aspen-hysys.

AVEVA, 2023. DYNSIM Dynamic Simulation - Setting New Standards for Rigor, Robustness, and Ease of Use. https://www.aveva.com/en/products/dynamic-simulation/

R.B. Bird, W.E. Stewart, E.N. Lightfoot, 2007. Transport Phenomena, 2nd ed. Wiley, New York.

E. Díaz-Bejarano, F. Coletti, S. Macchietto, 2015. Detection of changes in fouling behavior by simultaneous monitoring of thermal and hydraulic performance of refinery heat exchangers. Computer Aided Chemical Engineering 37, 1649–1654.

F. Gallo, 2016. Procedimento di rigenerazione di olii usati. ITUB20151298A1.

D.W. Green, M.Z. Southard (Eds.), 2019. Perry's Chemical Engineers' Handbook, 9th Edition. ed. McGraw-Hill Education, New York.

A.L. Haura, K.Q. Ma'mun, J.P. Sutikno, R. Handogo, 2017. Re-refinery used oil vacuum distillation column control by using internal model control. Chemical Engineering Transactions 56, 1471–1476.

A. Kupareva, P. Mäki-Arvela, D.Y. Murzin, 2013. Technology for rerefining used lube oils applied in Europe: A review. Journal of Chemical Technology and Biotechnology 88, 1780–1793.

D.-Y. Peng, D.B. Robinson, 1976. A New Two-Constant Equation of State. Industrial and Engineering Chemistry Fundamentals 15, 59–64.

D. Sotelo, A. Favela-Contreras, C. Lozoya, F. Beltran-Carbajal, G. Dieck-Assad, C. Sotelo, 2019. Dynamic simulation of a crude oil distillation plant using Aspen-Hysys®. International Journal of Simulation Modelling 18, 229–241.

R. Srinivasan, P. Viswanathan, H. Vedam, A. Nochur, 2005. A framework for managing transitions in chemical plants. Computers and Chemical Engineering 29, 305–322.

C.J.G. Vasconcelos, R.M. Filho, R. Spandri, M.R. Wolf-Maciel, 2005. Dynamic models towards operator and engineer training: Virtual environment. Computer Aided Chemical Engineering 20, 565–570.

Flavio Manenti, Gintaras V. Reklaitis (Eds.), Proceedings of the 34th European Symposium on Computer Aided Process Engineering / 15th International Symposium on Process Systems Engineering (ESCAPE34/PSE24), June 2-6, 2024, Florence, Italy
 http://dx.doi.org/10.1016/B978-0-443-28824-1.50171-X

Integrated Recycling of End-of-Life Tires through Pyrolysis for Fuels Production with Hydrogen Recovery

Simone Caspani [a], Anna Nova [a], Francesco Negri [a, b], Flavio Manenti [a, *]

[a]*Politecnico di Milano, Dipartimento CMIC "Giulio Natta", Piazza Leonardo da Vinci, 32, Milano 20133, Italia*

[b]*Itelyum Regeneration S.p.A., Via Tavernelle 19, Pieve Fissiraga 26854, Lodi, Italia*

flavio.manenti@polimi.it

Abstract

Waste tire management is a crucial and actual problem. Exploiting new technologies for their treatment is a key point in an optical of circularity. The objective of this preliminary project is to design and simulate a novel approach for recycling of end-of-life tires. This involves implementing tire pyrolysis, followed by well-known processes to enhance the quality of the resulting gaseous and liquid outputs. Enhancing treatment methods are crucial, given the substantial sulfur content in the feedstock (approximately 2 w.t.%). Indeed, this sulfur can lead to the generation of numerous impurities during pyrolysis.

This contribution is proposing a conceptual process design utilizing Aspen Plus V11 coupled with MATLAB for specific unconventional units. The process is divided into three main blocks: pyrolysis; oil upgrading via hydrotreating; hydrogen recovery system. This allowed to assess the performance of each plant section and make preliminary evaluations regarding hydrogen consumption.

Keywords: Process Simulation, Waste Tire, Chemical Recycling, Pyrolysis, H_2S

1. Introduction

In the context of contemporary production, the management of waste tires has emerged as a significant concern.

Mechanical recycling technologies have attained a high level of industrial readiness, particularly within the construction sector and in the reutilization of tires (retreading). Especially, a substantial volume of end-of-life (EoL) tires is typically consigned to landfill (Valentini and Pegoretti, 2022). To advance towards a comprehensive circular approach, numerous treatment methods are presently under investigation. Of particular interest are the potential thermal processes such as: gasification, pyrolysis and liquefaction, aimed at converting EoL tires into chemicals (Nkosi et al., 2021).

Pyrolysis stands out as the most commonly employed and extensively developed chemical treatment among various options. Waste tires undergo an intense thermal treatment (T > 400 °C) under atmospheric pressure to generate a gaseous and liquid stream (scrap tire pyrolytic oil, STPO) as desired products, together with a solid residue. Because the feedstock contains a relatively high sulfur fraction (approximately 2 w.t.%), several impurities, such as H_2S and benzothiazole, are detectable in the gas and liquid output. Hence upgrading treatments as sulfur removal and oil cracking are necessary.

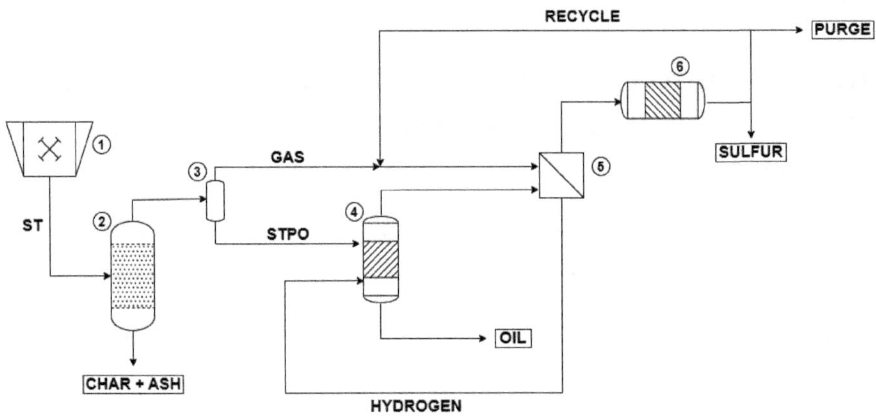

Figure 1: Process flow diagram of the conceptual process for EoL tires recycling.

2. Materials and Methods

The key concept behind this study is to explore the possibility of a fully self-sustainable process for waste tire recycling and following upgrading of the products in terms of hydrogen consumption. A schematic representation of the plant scheme is reported in Figure 1. A stream of 100 kg/h of waste tires, previously treated to remove metals and fibers, is firstly crushed in a miller (Unit 1), to obtain homogenous solid particles distribution (i.e., 0.006 – 0.015 m). The feed stream is a non-conventional solid. Properties and composition are estimated starting from Ultimate, Proximate analysis, as reported in Table 1, in accordance with literature (Ismail et al., 2017). The waste stream is firstly processed in a pyrolysis reactor (Unit 2), operating at 500 °C and atmospheric pressure. Pyrolysis is a complex thermo-chemical process. Its behavior depends on many factors such as temperature, pressure, and the characteristic dimension of the feed, among others. The conducted simulation of this step is a simplification. Indeed, by breaking down the non-conventional solid into its elemental components, it becomes possible to integrate fictitious lumped reactions among these elements according to the conventional product distribution obtained during pyrolysis, without taking into account the effects of other parameters. The unit modelled in Aspen Plus V11. is the combination of a yield reactor and a plug flow reactor (PFR) (Ismail et al., 2017). In the first reactor the non-conventional solid feed is decomposed in a pseudo component, in the form $C_aH_bO_cN_dS_e$ + ASH, that takes into account only of the atom composition. The fictitious component obtained is then processed in the PFR.

Table 1: Feedstock's Ultimate Analysis[a] and Proximate Analysis[b].

UA[a] [w.t.%]		PA[b] [w.t.%]	
ASH	13.5	Moisture	1.5
C	75.0	Fixed Carbon	30.0
H	7.0	Volatile Matter	55.0
N	0.3	ASH	13.5
S	1.5		
O	2.7		

Lumped kinetic reactions among the elements occur in the unit, following the kinetic scheme described by Olazar et al. (2008). Kinetics are based on a conventional power law, with Arrhenius' kinetic parameters estimated in accordance with typical products distribution down pyrolysis for gaseous and liquid output. According to the kinetic scheme adopted the limiting reactant is hydrogen. The characteristic dimension and residence time of the unit have been selected according to a sensitivity analysis in order to obtain a hydrogen concentration in the gaseous stream similar to literature (Kyari et al., 2005). To avoid the presence of unreacted oxygen in the gaseous stream, the kinetic adopted has been slightly adjusted. Indeed, to favor oxygen conversion, water synthesis reaction has been introduced and also CO_x synthesis has been favored adopting equilibrium reactions. The solid output obtained, mainly composed by unreacted carbon and ASH, is stored. The liquid and gaseous output is then splitted in an ideal flash (Unit 3) operating at 35 °C.

The liquid output, scrap tire pyrolysis oil (STPO), is an oil composed of C_5 up to C_{20} molecules. The oil is characterized in cuts, according to carbon atoms number and normal boiling point (N.B.P.), and functional groups. The oil is, then, grouped in Gasoil, Diesel, Naphtha fractions for the cuts and Aromatics, Naphthene and Paraffines according to the different functional groups. Oil upgrading treatments are typically required, due to the significant amount of Aromatics and Gasoil together with the relevant content of sulfur in the oil. Indeed, the liquid stream is processed into a catalytic hydrotreating reactor (Unit 4), operating at 65 bars, 375 °C and an H_2/STPO ratio equal to 1000 Nm^3/m^3. The reaction occurs in presence of Ni/Mo catalyst over Al_2O_3 support. The time of stream is set equal to 8 h and the space time equal to 0.5 $g_{cat}\,h/g_{feed}$. Reaction conditions have been selected in accordance with literature to keep hydrogen content inside the liquid constant in the unit, and to favor the conversion of STPO. Inside the unit three main reactions occurs: Hydrocracking (HC), Hydrodearomatization (HDA) and Hydrodesulfurization (HDS) (Hita et al., 2015). The hydrotreating unit is modelled in MATLAB following the lumped kinetics scheme for HC and HDA. The HDS reaction has not been simulated due to lack in kinetics. Although according to literature benzothiazole, selected as representative sulfur contaminant in the liquid product, is easily converted due to the low amount of carbon atoms. Sulfur conversion has been set equal to 80 w.t.% of the total amount fed. H_2S production has been estimated according to the elemental stoichiometric reaction among hydrogen and sulfur.

Globally an upgraded oil is obtained, by lowering the Aromatic and Gasoil content and increasing the Paraffine and Diesel fraction of the fuel.

The hydrogen consumption in the hydrotreating unit is estimated adopting semi-empirical strategies (Castañeda et al., 2011). Hydrogen consumption is simply a function of the abatement efficiency of the unit. In this first approach, it is based on the amount of sulfur and Aromatics converted.

The gaseous stream obtained down the pyrolysis is mainly composed by H_2, CO_x, light hydrocarbons (i.e., C_1-C_4) and H_2S as contaminant. The stream is mixed with a recycle rich in hydrogen, exiting from the hydrogen recovery unit (Unit 6). The mixture is compressed and cooled at 35 °C and 8 bar and sent to a membrane (Unit 5) for the separation of hydrogen. Separation occurs thanks to high selective membrane (i.e., Matrimid 5218), that can perform a complete removal of hydrogen (Scholes et al., 2011). Only CO_2 as contaminant is detected in the filtered stream. In this first analysis no effect of H_2S have been considered. The filtered stream obtained, rich in hydrogen, is then compressed and sent to the Hydrotreating unit (Unit 4). The residual stream, instead, is processed to a hydrogen recovery reactor for H_2S conversion (Unit 6). Hydrogen recovery

occurs in a thermal unit operating at high temperature (i.e., around 800 °C) and ambient pressure conditions in which the reaction of dissociation of H_2S into hydrogen and elemental sulfur takes place (Nova et al., 2023). Full conversion of H_2S into element has been considered in this unit.
The solid sulfur residual is then stored, while the gaseous output, rich in H_2 is split: part is recycled back to the membrane separation section (Unit 5) previously described, the remaining part is purged, to avoid the buildup in the cycle loop.

3. Results and Discussion

The simulation carried out a preliminary investigation on the integration of EoL tires pyrolysis with upgrading treatments. In this first study the in-depth simulation have been carried out only for pyrolysis and hydrodesulfurization process. However interesting prime approach results have been obtained.

3.1 Pyrolysis

Down pyrolysis EoL tires feed is decomposed in solid, liquid and gas. As expected, the liquid product represents the majority of the output (i.e., 62.27 w.t.%), the gaseous stream, instead, is the less favored product (i.e., 3.01 w.t.%). The remaining part is the solid residue (i.e., 34.73 w.t.%). The phase products distribution relies with literature results (Kyari et al., 2005). The solid residual obtained is composed by the whole ASH fed, inert in the reactor, the unreacted carbon and sulfur. In accordance with typical results almost the 50 w.t.% of the sulfur present in the feed is trapped in the solid residual. However, no hydrogen content has been detected in the solid. This unusual result can be explained on the base of the simulation model adopted. Indeed, the elemental hydrogen reacting in the pseudo component is a pure gas.
The gas stream is a mixture of light hydrocarbons (i.e., $C_1 - C_4$), CO_x, H_2 and H_2S, as reported in Table 2. Oxygen content in the gaseous output is negligible, as expected. The significant amount of CO_x can be justified by the variation adopted in the kinetic model that maximizes their production. Hydrogen content has been established in accordance to literature results. The significant amount of light hydrocarbons is justified by the presence of cracking reactions that occurs at this conditions. To maximize the amount of gas a slow pyrolysis set-up and longer residence time should be adopted. The relevant amount of H_2S can be explained thanks to the adoption of an equilibrium reaction. The liquid output, as mentioned above, is the main product of pyrolysis. By assuming a perfect separation stage after pyrolysis, water is completely condensed in the liquid stream. The relevant amount of water detected is due to the insertion of water synthesis reaction in the kinetics, extremely favored at these conditions.

Table 2: Pyrolysis products distribution, Gas[a] molar fractions, STPO[b] mass fractions.

Gas[a] [mol.%]	
H_2	22.4
CO_x	22.3
C_1	24.9
C_2	14.1
C_{3+}	6.1
H_2S	7.8
Others	2.4

STPO[b]			
Oil Cut [w.t.%]		Functional Group [w.t.%]	
Gasoil	19.4	Aromatic 2-ring	26.5
Diesel	43.6	Aromatic 1-ring	16.3
Naphtha	31.1	Naphthenes	32.2
Water	5.9	Paraffines	19.1

Benzothiazole is selected as representative compound of sulfur species in the oil, its content even though is low is non negligible (i.e., 0.43 w.t.%). STPO has a global H/C ratio equal to 1.45. The results obtained assuming the subdivision based on N.B.P. temperatures and functional groups are reported in Table 2.As can be observed STPO is a light oil that has a wide range of boiling points and a large number of aromatics, as expected for an unrefined oil. The significant amount of aromatics can be justified by the nature of the feedstock, a mixture of natural rubber and synthetic rubber.

3.2 Hydrotreating

Under the above-mentioned operative conditions, the hydrotreating stage provide a sensible improvement in oil composition. Figure 2 and Figure 3 illustrates the variations in mass fractions for both the oil cut and functional groups, by varying the space time velocity. As can be observed after the hydrotreating the content of heavy compounds is drastically diminished. Indeed, the upgraded oil is a mixture of lighter hydrocarbons with Diesel as main cut. The asymptotic conditions are achieved for higher space velocity, due to the higher amount of catalyst used. As can be observed in the plots reported below the two rings' Aromatics content is drastically decreased. The global number of Aromatic compounds drop of 4.6 w.t.%. Sulfur content is decreased according to the imposed conversion leading to the formation of H_2S. The resulting liquid stream is then a lighter oil with less Aromatics and sulfur components and a higher content of Paraffines.
The amount of hydrogen consumed in the hydrotreating stage is equal to 0.14 kg/h, corresponding to a specific consumption ratio H_2/STPO equal to 22.2 Nm^3/m^3.

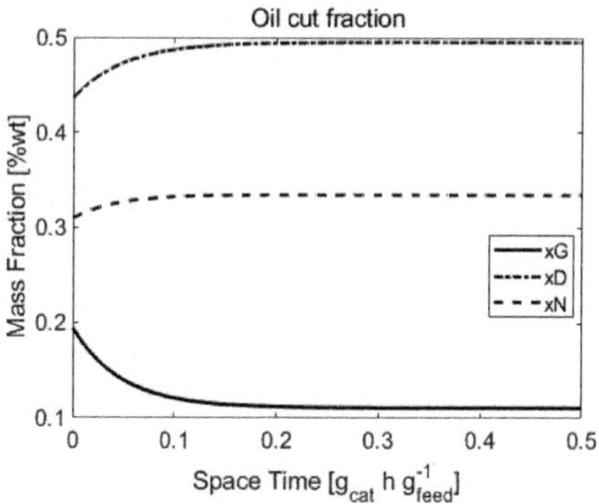

Figure 2: Hydrotreating effects on oil's cut cut mass fractions of Gasoil (xG) Diesel (xD) and Naphhta (xN).

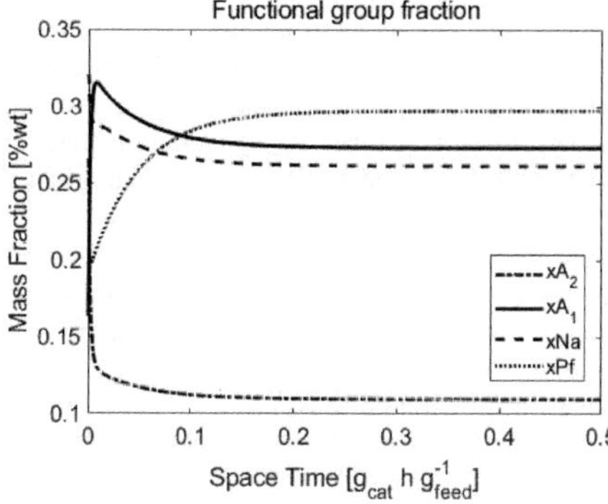

Figure 3: Hydrotreating effects on functional groups fractions of Aromatics 2 and 1 ring (xA_2 ; xA_1), Naphthene (xNa), Paraffine (xPf).

4. Conclusions and Future Developments

The research activity provides a first Aspen Plus V11-MATLAB process simulation filling the literature gap. Promising preliminary results indicate a significant improvement in oil quality down hydrotreating, particularly in reducing heavy and Aromatic fractions, at a hydrogen consumption ratio H_2/STPO equal to 22.2 Nm^3/m^3. Future developments dealing with an accurate estimation of hydrogen consumption are required.

For a more robust and comprehensive simulation of the process, it is necessary to integrate the presented work with other relevant research. Simulation and accurate estimation of hydrogen, recovered from the thermal unit adopting detailed simulation with more accurate kinetics, should be adopted. Detailed simulation of the distillation and separation units for the refining of the upgrade oil must be integrated. Once obtained a more comprehensive simulation, an energy analysis should be carried out. Further improvements that have to be investigated are a sensitivity analysis on pyrolysis conditions, to get a fully hydrogen self-sustainable system.

The interest in this work is high, indeed the choice of waste tire as feed is in line with the current problematics of waste recycling. The choice of maximizing liquid production is interesting, indeed the production of fuels and base chemicals, avoiding the use of virgin oil, is fundamental.

References

L.C. Castañeda, J.A.D. Muñoz, J. Ancheyta, 2011. Comparison of approaches to determine hydrogen consumption during catalytic hydrotreating of oil fractions. Fuel, Environmental Modeling of Catalytic Reactions in the Oil Refining Industry 90, 3593–3601.

I. Hita, A.T. Aguayo, M. Olazar, M.J. Azkoiti, J. Bilbao, J.M. Arandes, P. Castaño, 2015. Kinetic Modeling of the Hydrotreating and Hydrocracking Stages for Upgrading Scrap Tires Pyrolysis Oil (STPO) toward High-Quality Fuels. Energy Fuels 29, 7542–7553.

H.Y. Ismail, A. Abbas, F. Azizi, J. Zeaiter, 2017. Pyrolysis of waste tires: A modeling and parameter estimation study using Aspen Plus®. Waste Management, Special Thematic Issue: Urban Mining and Circular Economy 60, 482–493.

M. Kyari, A. Cunliffe, P.T. Williams, 2005. Characterization of Oils, Gases, and Char in Relation to the Pyrolysis of Different Brands of Scrap Automotive Tires. Energy Fuels 19, 1165–1173.

N. Nkosi, E. Muzenda, J. Gorimbo, M. Belaid, 2021. Developments in waste tyre thermochemical conversion processes: gasification, pyrolysis and liquefaction. RSC Advances 11, 11844–11871.

A. Nova, F. Negri, F. Manenti, 2023. Multi-scale Modelling and Experimental Investigation of Hydrogen Sulphide Thermal Decomposition, in: Kokossis, A.C., Georgiadis, M.C., Pistikopoulos, E. (Eds.), Computer Aided Chemical Engineering, 33 European Symposium on Computer Aided Process Engineering. Elsevier, pp. 2411–2416.

M. Olazar, G. Lopez, M. Arabiourrutia, G. Elordi, R. Aguado, J. Bilbao, 2008. Kinetic modelling of tyre pyrolysis in a conical spouted bed reactor. Journal of Analytical and Applied Pyrolysis 81, 127–132.

C.A. Scholes, G.Q. Chen, W.X. Tao, J. Bacus, C. Anderson, G.W. Stevens, S.E. Kentish, 2011. The effects of minor components on the gas separation performance of membranes for carbon capture. Energy Procedia, 10th International Conference on Greenhouse Gas Control Technologies 4, 681–687.

F. Valentini, A. Pegoretti, 2022. End-of-life options of tyres. A review. Advanced Industrial and Engineering Polymer Research, Recycling of Rubbers 5, 203–213.

Flavio Manenti, Gintaras V. Reklaitis (Eds.), Proceedings of the 34th European Symposium on Computer Aided Process Engineering / 15th International Symposium on Process Systems Engineering (ESCAPE34/PSE24), June 2-6, 2024, Florence, Italy
 http://dx.doi.org/10.1016/B978-0-443-28824-1.50172-1

Dynamic Modelling and Surrogate-based Optimization of Auto-thermal Reforming for Enhanced Hydrogen Production

Hao Chen,[a*] Konstantinos Kyprianidis[a]

[a]*School of Business, Society and Engineering, Mälardalen University, SE 72123 Västerås, Sweden*
Hao.Chen@mdu.se

Abstract

Hydrogen energy has been considered as one of the solutions to achieve the net-zero emission scenario by 2050. Steam methane reforming is a widely used industrial process for producing hydrogen from natural gas or methane nowadays. Considering that methane could be utilized as a suitable carrier for hydrogen energy, it is anticipated that steam methane reforming will still play an important role in the future energy sector when it comes to hydrogen production, storage, and transportation. In this work, a one-dimensional dynamic model is established to simulate the performance of an auto-thermal reforming reactor, which allows for capturing the localized phenomena inside the reactor over time. A set of input parameters is selected based on the Latin Hypercube Sampling method to generate the training data for the surrogate model development. Singular value decomposition and Gaussian Process regression are then implemented on the training data to construct a surrogate model of the reformer. This surrogate model is subsequently utilized in the optimization process to enhance hydrogen production and lower the maximum catalyst temperature within the reactor. The results show that the surrogate model, developed by using singular value decomposition and Gaussian Process, exhibits a high level of accuracy when compared to the physics-based reformer model. Furthermore, the optimization framework built upon surrogate modelling offers the potential to substantially reduce the computational expenses associated with the optimization process, while preserving the precision of the optimization results. This method could efficiently serve as a tool for parameters optimization of such reactors and could be used to guide the operation of these systems toward improved performance.

Keywords: auto-thermal reforming, dynamic modelling, multi-objective optimization, surrogate modelling.

1. Introduction

Hydrogen finds extensive utilization in many critical industrial processes, including but not limited to petroleum refining, the production of methanol, and the synthesis of ammonia (Kojima and Tahara, 2001). Hydrogen is also a clean energy carrier and has great potential to help decarbonize a range of hard-to-abate sectors, including long-haul transport, chemicals, and iron and steel (Noussan et al., 2020). Today, hydrogen production is still dominated by natural gas reforming (Younas et al, 2022). Given the increasing attention on the Power-to-Methane concept (Blanco et al, 2018), it is envisaged that methane reforming will persist in maintaining an important role in the processes of hydrogen production and utilization.

Autothermal reforming (ATR) combines the steam reforming reaction and partial oxidation reaction into a single unit (Lamb et al, 2020). In this process, the exothermic partial oxidation of methane generates the necessary heat to support the endothermic methane reforming reactions (Brett et al, 2012). Optimization and simulation are widely adopted approaches to obtain insights into the complicated heat and mass transfer process coupled with chemical reactions inside the reactor (Wang et al., 2021). Simulation conducted within at least a one-dimensional (1D) domain is imperative for capturing localized phenomena within the reactor. This necessity, particularly when integrated with optimization algorithms demanding iterative processes, increases the computational cost and makes it unfavorable for implementation.

In this work, a dynamic 1D model of an auto-thermal reforming reactor is established by solving the governing heat and mass transfer equations, coupled with chemical reactions within the ATR process. A surrogate model built on singular value decomposition (SVD) and Gaussian Process (GP), by using the training data obtained from different operating parameters, is developed to reduce the computational cost of simulation with the capability to capture the localized phenomena inside the reactor. Subsequently, a multi-objective Genetic Algorithm is applied to the surrogate model for the purpose of optimizing the autothermal reforming process. The proposed approach holds promise for efficient and effective exploration of optimal operating parameters of the ATR process with enhanced computational efficiency.

2. Dynamic modelling of ATR reactor

A one-dimensional dynamic ATR reactor model accounting for mass transfer in solid and gas phases, and heat transfer across the entire reactor is constructed. Only those dominating reactions in the overall ATR process are considered in this work. The main chemical reactions used in the simulation are shown below:

$$R1: CH_4 + 2O_2 \leftrightarrow CO_2 + 2H_2O,\ \Delta H_{298K} = -802.7\ \mathrm{kJ/mol} \tag{1}$$

$$R2: CO + H_2O \leftrightarrow CO_2 + H_2,\ \Delta H_{298K} = -41.1\ \mathrm{kJ/mol} \tag{2}$$

$$R3: CH_4 + H_2O \leftrightarrow CO + 3H_2,\ \Delta H_{298K} = +206.2\ \mathrm{kJ/mol} \tag{3}$$

$$R4: CH_4 + 2H_2O \leftrightarrow CO_2 + 4H_2,\ \Delta H_{298K} = +164.9\ \mathrm{kJ/mol} \tag{4}$$

The rate equations for total oxidation reaction (R1), water-gas shift reaction (R2), and steam methane reforming reactions (R3, R4) based on Langmuire Hinshelwood methodology are given below, according to Xu and Froment (1989).

$$R_1 = \frac{k_{1a} p_{CH_4} p_{O_2}}{\left(1 + K_{CH_4}^C p_{CH_4} + K_{O_2}^C p_{O_2}\right)^2} + \frac{k_{1b} p_{CH_4} p_{O_2}^{0.5}}{1 + K_{CH_4}^C p_{CH_4} + K_{O_2}^C p_{O_2}} \tag{5}$$

$$R_2 = \frac{k_2}{p_{H_2}} \left(p_{CO} p_{H_2O} - \frac{p_{H_2} p_{CO_2}}{K_I}\right) \times \frac{1}{\Omega^2} \tag{6}$$

$$R_3 = \frac{k_3}{p_{H_2}^{2.5}} \left(p_{CH_4} p_{H_2O} - \frac{p_{H_2}^3 p_{CO}}{K_{II}}\right) \times \frac{1}{\Omega^2} \tag{7}$$

$$R_4 = \frac{k_4}{p_{H_2}^{3.5}} \left(p_{CH_4} p_{H_2O}^2 - \frac{p_{H_2}^4 p_{CO_2}}{K_{III}}\right) \times \frac{1}{\Omega^2} \tag{8}$$

$$\Omega = 1 + K_{\mathrm{CO}}p_{\mathrm{CO}} + K_{H_2}p_{H_2} + K_{\mathrm{CH_4}}p_{\mathrm{CH_4}} + K_{H_2O}\frac{p_{H_2O}}{p_{H_2}} \tag{9}$$

Where R is the reaction rate; P is the partial pressure of gas specie; k denotes the Arrhenius kinetic parameters; K_I, K_{II}, K_{III} are the reaction equilibrium constants; K_{CO}, K_{H_2}, $K_{\mathrm{CH_4}}$, K_{H_2O}, $K_{O_2}^{C}$, $K_{CH_4}^{C}$are the Van't Hoff parameters for species adsorption. More details about these parameters are available in Halabi et al. (2008). According to energy and mass balance, the governing equations in the ATR reactor can be summarized as follows:

In the gas phase:

$$\varepsilon_b\frac{\partial C_i}{\partial t} + \frac{\partial(uC_i)}{\partial X} + k_{g,i}a_v\left(C_i - C_{i,s}\right) = \varepsilon_b D_X\frac{\partial^2 C_i}{\partial X^2} \tag{10}$$

$$\varepsilon_b\rho_g C_{p,g}\frac{\partial T}{\partial t} + u\rho_g C_{p,g}\frac{\partial T}{\partial X} = h_f a_v(T_s - T) + \lambda_X^f\frac{\partial^2 T}{\partial X^2} \tag{11}$$

In the solid phase:

$$k_{g,i}a_v\left(C_i - C_{i,s}\right) + \frac{\partial C_{i,s}}{\partial t} = (1-\varepsilon_b)\rho_{cat}r_i \tag{12}$$

$$\rho_{cat}C_{p,cat}\frac{\partial T_s}{\partial t} + h_f a_v(T_s - T) = (1-\varepsilon_b)\rho_{cat}\sum\left(\Delta H_{rxn,j}n_j R_j\right) \tag{13}$$

Where u is the average gas viscosity; C_i denotes the concentration of gas species in the mainstream; $C_{i,s}$ is the concentration of gas component i in the catalyst; ε_b is the bed porosity; ρ_{cat} and ρ_g are the density of catalyst and gas mixture respectively; $C_{p,g}$ and $C_{p,cat}$ are the heat capacity of gas mixture and catalyst; a_v is the external surface area per unit volume of catalyst bed; $k_{g,i}$ is the gas to solid mass transfer coefficient of component i; D_X is the axial dispersion coefficient; λ_X^f is the effective thermal conductivity; r_i is the rate of formation or consumption of species i; h_f is the gas to solid heat transfer coefficient; the $\Delta H_{rxn,j}$ is the reaction heat of reaction *j*; n_j denotes the effectiveness factor of reaction *j*; R_j denotes the rate of reaction *j*. More details about the parameters used in the governing equations, and the geometric parameter of the ATR reactor can be found in De Smet et al. (2001).

Based on the governing equations established above, finite volume method is employed to discretize these partial differential equations and solve them in Matlab/Simulink environment. The entire domain along the reactor length is divided into 200 intervals to obtain the independent results of discretization.

3. Surrogate-based modelling and optimization

In this work, the training data matrix, *M*, for surrogate model development is obtained from the results (catalyst temperature distribution and H_2 composition distribution) of the physics-based ATR model under a range of inlet parameters. The inlet parameters investigated in this study are shown in table 1.

Table 1 selected inlet parameters for the ATR model

Inlet parameters	Range (which are also the boundary constraints for optimization)
Steam to carbon ratio	2.0 - 6.0
Oxygen to carbon ratio	0.1 - 1.0
Inlet gas temperature	673 - 973 K
Inlet gas mass flowrate	0.1 - 0.55 kg/(m^{2}s)

To effectively explore the parameter space, Latin hypercube sampling is employed to obtain training data from a range of inlet parameters (Chen et al., 2017). After obtaining the data from the physics-based ATR model, the training data matrix is decomposed to find the principal components (PCs) by using singular value decomposition (SVD), which is illustrated by equation (14).

$$M = U\Sigma V^T \tag{14}$$

Here, U and V are left- and right-singular vectors of matrix M, and $\Sigma = \text{diag}\,(s_1, s_2, \ldots, s_n)$ indicates singular values of the data matrix. Then, the ith row of V^T could be considered as the ith principal components of the training data matrix with a principal score as s_i. The training data can be represented as the linear combination of all the principal components.

After identifying the PCs, Gaussian Process (GP) prediction, also known as Kriging prediction, is used to predict the PC scores based on different inlet parameters. More details about the Gaussian Process prediction can be found in our previous work (Chen et al., 2022). The surrogate ATR reactor model is then constructed by using SVD to identify the PCs and by using GP prediction to predict the PC scores.

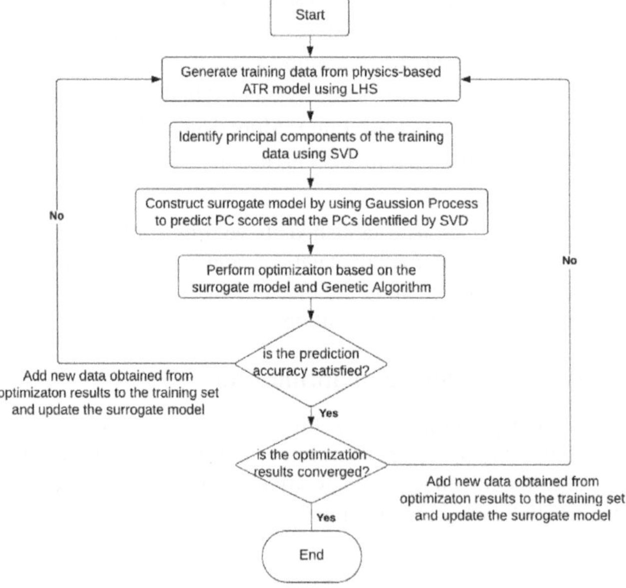

Figure 1 Process diagram of the surrogate-based optimization

Once the surrogate model is established, Multi-objective Genetic Algorithms will be applied to optimize the performance of the ATR reactor. In this work, maximum catalyst temperature and outlet H_2 composition are considered as the two objective functions for the optimization (Maximize H_2 composition, minimize catalyst temperature). It is worth noting that after each optimization, the obtained optimal results will be compared with the results from the physics-based model. The new data generated from the physics-based model will be added to the training data to update the surrogate model until results converge. The entire process diagram of the surrogate-based optimization is illustrated in Figure 1.

4. Results and discussion

The initial training data size was set at 320 in this work. LHS was then performed on the parameter space to select inlet parameters for the physics-based ATR model to obtain training data. By using SVD to decompose the training data matrix, the principal components of the catalyst temperature distribution profile and H_2 composition distribution profile are identified. Figure 2 shows the 2 most important PCs of the catalyst temperature distribution profile, which captures 98% of the variation in the training data.

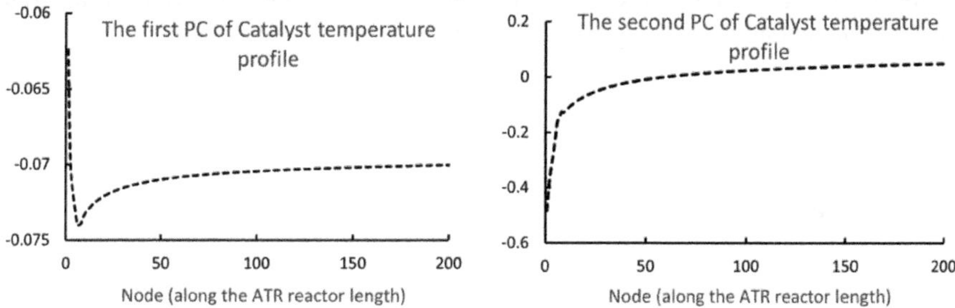

Figure 2 The first 2 principal components of the catalyst temperature profile

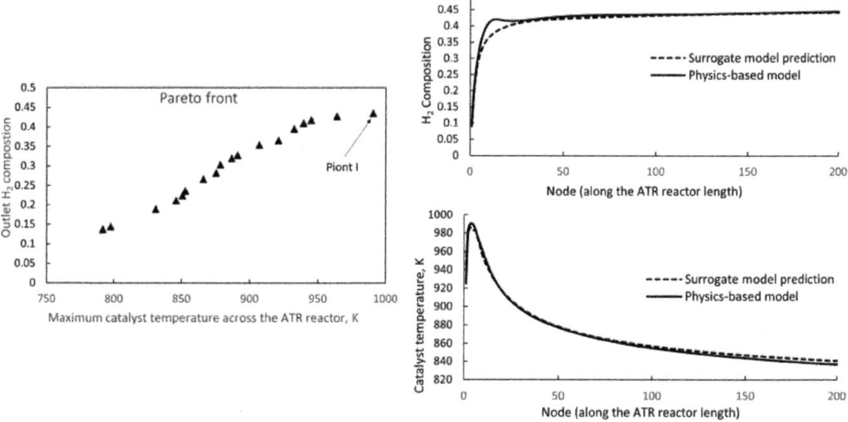

Figure 3 Pareto front obtained from surrogate-based optimization and the comparison of results predicted by the surrogate model and the physics-based model for Point I in the Pareto front.

Figure 3 shows the Pareto front obtained from the surrogate-based optimization. It is noted from the Pareto front that, to increase the H_2 composition at the reactor outlet, the cost would be the increase of the catalyst temperature, which might lead to higher degradation of the catalyst. As shown in the right of Figure 3, the surrogate model shows good accuracy in predicting the H_2 composition distribution profile and catalyst temperature distribution profile across the ATR reactor.

5. Conclusions

A surrogate-based modelling and optimization framework is proposed in this work to improve the performance of an ATR reactor. The surrogate model built on SVD and GP could considerably reduce the computation cost of optimization without losing the capability to capture the localized phenomena across the reactor. Combined with the Multi-objective Genetic Algorithm, this approach could serve as a tool for parameters optimization of such reactors and could be used to guide the operation of these systems toward improved performance.

Acknowledgment

This work was carried out in the IFAISTOS project (Intelligent electroFuel production for An Integrated STOrage System), which is funded under the framework of the joint programming initiative ERA-Net Smart Energy Systems.

References

T. Kojima, K. Tahara, 2001. Refinement and transportation of petroleum with hydrogen from renewable energy. Energy conversion and management, 42(15-17), pp.1839-1851.

M. Noussan, P.P. Raimondi, R. Scita, and M. Hafner, 2020. The role of green and blue hydrogen in the energy transition—A technological and geopolitical perspective. Sustainability, 13(1), p.298.

M. Younas, S. Shafique, A. Hafeez, F. Javed, and F. Rehman, 2022. An overview of hydrogen production: current status, potential, and challenges. Fuel, 316, p.123317.

H. Blanco, W. Nijs, J. Ruf, and A. Faaij, 2018. Potential of Power-to-Methane in the EU energy transition to a low carbon system using cost optimization. Applied energy, 232, pp.323-340.

J.J. Lamb, M. Hillestad, E. Rytter, R. Bock, A.S. Nordgård, K.M. Lien, O.S. Burheim, and B.G. Pollet, 2020. Traditional routes for hydrogen production and carbon conversion. In Hydrogen, biomass and bioenergy (pp. 21-53). Academic Press.

D.J.L. Brett, E. Agante, N.P. Brandon, E. Brightman, R.J.C. Brown, M. Manage, and I. Staffell, 2012. The role of the fuel in the operation, performance, and degradation of fuel cells. In Functional materials for sustainable energy applications (pp. 249-278). Woodhead Publishing.

J. Wang, S. Wei, Q. Wang, and B. Sundén, 2021. Transient numerical modeling and model predictive control of an industrial-scale steam methane reforming reactor. international journal of hydrogen energy, 46(29), pp.15241-15256.

J. Xu, and G.F. Froment, 1989. Methane steam reforming, methanation, and water-gas shift: I. Intrinsic kinetics. AIChE journal, 35(1), pp.88-96.

M.H. Halabi, M.H.J.M. De Croon, J. Van der Schaaf, P.D Cobden, and J.C. Schouten, 2008. Modeling and analysis of autothermal reforming of methane to hydrogen in a fixed bed reformer. Chemical Engineering Journal, 137(3), pp.568-578.

C. R. H. De Smet, M. H. J. M. De Croon, R. J. Berger, G. B. Marin, and J. C. Schouten. "Design of adiabatic fixed-bed reactors for the partial oxidation of methane to synthesis gas. Application to production of methanol and hydrogen-for-fuel-cells." Chemical Engineering Science 56, no. 16 (2001): 4849-4861.

H. Chen, C.Yang, K. Deng, N. Zhou, and H. Wu, 2017. Multi-objective optimization of the hybrid wind/solar/fuel cell distributed generation system using Hammersley Sequence Sampling. International Journal of Hydrogen Energy, 42(12), pp.7836-7846.

H. Chen, Y. Zhou, Q. Li, Z. Liu, F. Qi, C. Ma, B. Zhao, and Y. Huang, 2022. Multi-objective optimization design of U3Si2–FeCrAl accident tolerant fuel elements based on Gaussian process and genetic algorithm. International Journal of Energy Research, 46(9), pp.12108-12121.

Flavio Manenti, Gintaras V. Reklaitis (Eds.), Proceedings of the 34th European Symposium on Computer Aided Process Engineering / 15th International Symposium on Process Systems Engineering (ESCAPE34/PSE24), June 2-6, 2024, Florence, Italy
 http://dx.doi.org/10.1016/B978-0-443-28824-1.50173-3

Using Mathematical Optimization for the Transition to Sustainable and Circular Agriculture

Jan Drofenik[a], Bojan Pahor[b,a], Zdravko Kravanja[a], Zorka Novak Pintarič[a]*

[a]*University of Maribor, Faculty of Chemistry and Chemical Engineering, Smetanova 17, 2000 Maribor, Slovenia*
[b]*Saubermacher Slovenija d.o.o., Sp. Porčič 4a, 2230 Lenart, Slovenia*
**zorka.novak@um.si*

Abstract

This paper introduces a novel index, the Agricultural Circularity and Sustainability (ACS) index, for evaluating the circularity and sustainability of agriculture. Implemented as a multi-criteria objective function within a MILP model of the food supply chain, the ACS index optimizes various measures for transition of agriculture to circular and sustainable performance. Inspired by the circularity index developed by Baratsas et al. (2022) for companies, the ACS index is tailored for agricultural applications. It assesses measures such as reducing artificial fertilizer use, food waste generation, and a change of dietary habits, while promoting organic farming, enhancing food production efficiency, and balancing the import and export of animal-origin food products. A case study for Slovenia demonstrates that implementing these measures would more than double the overall ACS index. The optimization model, equipped with the new ACS index, serves as a unique tool for systematically planning and implementing long-term measures to transform national agriculture towards a sustainable and circular economy.

Keywords: circular, sustainable, agriculture, food supply chain, MILP optimization

1. Introduction

Food production and the agricultural sector are of paramount strategic importance for every country and the world as a whole, especially in light of a growing population and the increasing rate of climate change. The current state of agriculture, however, raises significant environmental and social concerns. Agriculture is a major contributor to climate change, accounting for approximately 10.3% of the EU's greenhouse gas (GHG) emissions (European Commission, 2020). Overuse of fertilizers and pesticides pollutes soils, watercourses, and groundwater. Excessive soil cultivation leads to erosion and fertility loss. Another issue in the food sector is the excessive consumption of animal protein, resulting in vast areas of arable land being used for animal feed, and substantial food loss and waste (Circle Economy, 2020). Agriculture remains predominantly linear, necessitating a shift towards circularity to mitigate its environmental impact. A unified metric for quantitatively assessing agricultural circularity is yet to be adopted. Despite the absence of a standardized metric, the theoretical principles and some indicators for measuring agricultural circularity are established (Velasco-Muñoz et al., 2021). Circular agriculture adheres to the principle of maximizing resource efficiency, utilizing both raw materials and waste effectively (Circle Economy, 2020). This can be achieved through various measures, such as localizing livestock, feed and food production, minimizing edible food waste and GHG emissions, optimizing bio-waste utilization within the chain (e.g., for animal feed) or bio-based products and fuels production (Circle Economy, 2020). Agricultural practices must incorporate the principles of regeneration, recycling, and minimization (Dagevos et al., 2021), such as composting and anaerobic systems that reduce waste generation. Advanced production techniques also play an important role, including conservation agriculture, precision agriculture utilizing drones and sensors, digitalization, and geographically adapted food production to address the ongoing negative impacts of global warming (Ali Chandio, 2023). The intricate nature of the food supply chain necessitates a systemic approach to developing effective measures that promote circular and sustainable agriculture. In our previous work, a mixed-integer linear programming (MILP) model for optimizing arable land allocation to major food and feed crops was developed (Drofenik et al., 2023). This model helped identify key conflicts and synergies within the food supply chain. The aim of this study is to extend previous work by: a) developing a novel multi-criteria metric to maximize circularity and sustainability of agriculture and b) assessing the impact of different measures on the transition of agriculture to a circular economy.

2. Methodology

2.1. Basic mathematical model

The basis of the present study is the MILP model by Drofenik et al. (2023), encompassing primary food production, processing, distribution, consumption, and waste management. This model optimizes distribution of crop cultivation areas, crop yields, agricultural production types, livestock numbers, and various indicators such as GHG emissions, fertilizer consumption, self-sufficiency rates, economic potential etc. The model's implementation was validated using a case study on the optimization of the entire food chain in Slovenia. This work identified the crucial trade-offs and clearly demonstrated that food production decisions must prioritize food security and environmental protection beyond mere economic considerations.

2.2. Agriculture circularity and sustainability (ACS) index

To drive circular and sustainable solutions within the food supply chain, a novel Agricultural Circularity and Sustainability (ACS) index is developed and integrated into the mathematical model as a multi-objective function. Inspired by the MICRON system (Baratsas et al., 2022) initially designed for the industrial sector, the ACS index incorporates the three pillars of sustainable development (economy, society, and environment) as primary categories. Additionally, food losses and waste (FLW) were included as a separate category due to its significance in achieving the United Nations' (2015) goals and its detrimental impact on all sustainability aspects.

Table 1 shows the indicators of the principal categories Economy, Society, Environment and FLW. Economy indicators (econ) are defined on the production side as annual production costs and revenues per capita. Indicators for the Society category (soc) are defined as modified self-sufficiency rates for Slovenia's seven most consumed food groups. The self-sufficiency rate for each food group (SS_i) is reduced by the export-to-consumption ratio (Eq. 1), thus reflecting the proportion of domestically produced food that is available for local consumption. This modified indicator promotes local food production and thus corresponds to the objectives of this main category.

$$soc_i = \frac{production_i - FLW_{\text{production},i} - export_i}{consumption_i} = SS_i - \frac{export_i}{consumption_i} \qquad i=1,...,7 \qquad (1)$$

The first three indicators of Environment principal category (env), focusing on GHG emissions, mineral fertilizers, and organic farming, align with the objectives of the Farm to Fork Strategy (European Commission, 2020). Our previous research (Drofenik et al., 2023) revealed that minimizing agriculture's environmental impact could lead to increased food imports, potentially causing carbon leakage. Therefore, indicators for annual food and feed imports (env4) and exports (env5) were incorporated to mitigate cross-border environmental impact transfers. The indicators of the category Food loss and waste (FLW) are the amount of total and edible food waste. Edible food waste is given a special indicator as it can be directly influenced by encouraging residents to handle food more responsibly, while the amount of inedible food waste is very difficult to reduce.

Table 1: Indicators of principal categories

Metric	Indicator	Unit	Formula used
econ1	Production costs per capita	EUR/y	100·(1-norm[econ1])
econ2	Production revenue per capita	EUR/y	100·norm[econ2])
soc1	Social indicator – cereals	-	100·soc1
soc2	Social indicator – potatoes	-	100·soc2
soc3	Social indicator – vegetables	-	100·soc3
soc4	Social indicator – fruit	-	100·soc4
soc5	Social indicator – meat	-	100·soc5
soc6	Social indicator – milk and dairy products	-	100·soc6
soc7	Social indicator - eggs	-	100·soc7
env1	GHG emissions per capita	kg/y	100·(1-norm[env1])
env2	Mineral fertilizers use per hectare of land	t /(ha·y)	100·(1-norm[env 2])
env3	Share of land for organic farming	-	100·env3
env4	Food and feed imported per capita	t/y	100·(1-norm[env4])
env5	Food and feed exported per capita	t/y	100·(1-norm[env5])
flw1	FLW per capita	kg/y	100·(1-norm[flw1])
flw2	Edible FLW per capita	kg/y	100·(1-norm[flw1])

Indicators are normalized using the method of Baratsas et al. (2022), ranging from 0 point (complete linearity) to 100 points (complete circularity). Category sub-indices are calculated as the average of category indicators, and the overall ACS index is obtained by combining category sub-indices.

2.3. Measures for circular agriculture and sustainable food production

2.3.1. Narrow use of fertilizers and pesticides

The Farm to Fork strategy calls for a minimum 20% reduction in fertilizer and pesticide use. Decreasing mineral fertilizer consumption can mitigate water pollution, nitrogen oxide emissions, and contribute to climate protection (European Commission, 2020). This measure also enhances agricultural circularity by enabling the utilization of waste products like compost, manure, and litter as organic fertilizer alternatives to mineral fertilizers.

2.3.2. *Use regeneration strategies*

The Farm to Fork strategy seeks to expand the share of land dedicated to organic food production to at least 25%. Organic farming plays a significant role in enhancing agricultural circularity by employing various measures to minimize waste and optimize resource utilization. It produces sustainable crops without resorting to artificial chemicals. Organic farms have well-established practices for recycling and composting waste, along with the utilization of organic fertilizers. Organic farmers typically raise fewer animals compared to their conventional counterparts, contributing to soil fertility preservation and pollution reduction.

2.3.3. Narrow food consumption

According to the CGR report for the Netherlands, the ratio of animal to plant protein in the human diet used to be around 40/60, while in Western countries it is now around 60/40 (Circle Economy, 2020). In Slovenia, this ratio is even higher at 68.6/31.4, leading to excessive consumption of resources for animal feed and health problems due to obesity and environmental pollution. Balancing the dietary habits with more plant-based foods and less meat consumption is an important measure for circular agriculture. For example, halving red meat consumption (RMC) would reduce total daily protein intake from 100 g per capita to 86 g and the ratio of animal to plant protein to 63.4/36.6, still providing more than enough protein for the average person, according to health recommendations.

2.3.4. Reduce waste

Minimizing food loss and waste is crucial for the circular economy, because producing food that is ultimately not eaten consumes large amounts of resources. United Nations Sustainable Development Goal 12.3 targets a 50% reduction in food loss and waste (United Nations, 2015). Edible food waste (eFLW) should be addressed through dietary changes, humanitarian initiatives, and education. Unavoidable food loss and waste should be transformed into bio-based products and bioenergy through cascading utilization.

2.3.5. Produce local

Local feed and meat production is crucial for a circular economy, according to the CGR report for the Netherlands (Circle Economy, 2020). Eliminating animal product and feed imports and exports could boost the Netherlands' circularity metric by 1.5% and reduce its material footprint by 5.4%. Prioritizing local production would lessen cross-border transportation emissions. The EU's principle of free movement of goods and services may hinder agricultural circularity and sustainability. Importing cheap food from abroad while exporting the same type of domestically produced food leads to unnecessary transportation emissions. Home-grown animals can consume local agricultural and food waste, reducing reliance on external sources. This shift would require political and financial incentives to discourage animal product imports and exports while supporting local producers through subsidies.

2.3.6. Minimize inputs, maximize outputs

Circular food production necessitates maximizing output with minimal resource utilization. According to the European Commission (2016), crop yields have increased steadily, with cereal yields rising from an average of 5 t/ha to 6.2 t/ha between 1993 and 2015, representing a 24% increase. Yield improvements are expected to continue due to technological advancements, new crop varieties, enhanced management practices, and improved organization. Considering the uncertainty surrounding these forecasts, a conservative assumption was made for the next measure: a 10% increase in yield per hectare and a 10% reduction in mineral fertilizer use over the coming decades.

3. Results

The estimated value of the ACS index for the current situation of Slovenian agriculture is 32.1 points (left rectangle in Figure 1), with the highest value for the Economy sub-index (45 points, grey column) following by the Environment (39, green) and Society (36, blue), while the lowest value is for the FLW sub-index (8, brown).

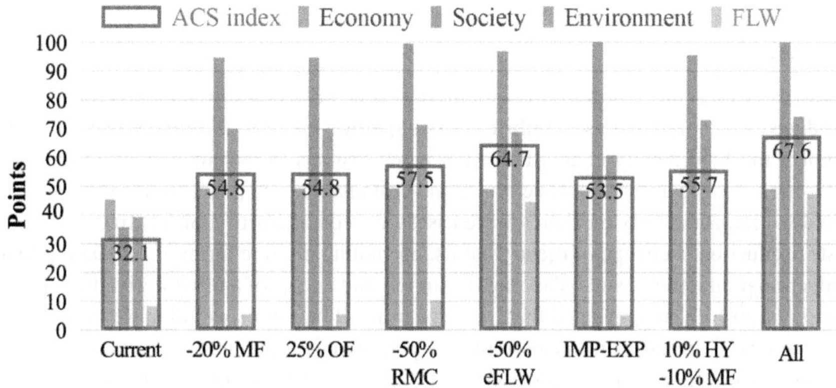

Figure 1: ACS index and principal category sub-indexes

Limiting mineral fertilizer use to a maximum of 80% of current levels (-20% MF in Figure 1) raises the ACS index to 54.8 points. This significant uplift stems from a substantial surge in the Society sub-index (from 36 to 95 points), primarily attributed to the enhanced local food production which is the result of the optimized distribution of agricultural land. The Environmental sub-index also experiences a substantial boost, reaching 70 points. This advancement is driven by a 66% reduction in mineral fertilizer consumption compared to the current level, coupled with an increase in the share of organic agriculture from 7.7% to 43.5%. This achievement aligns with the Farm to Fork strategy's mandate of at least 25% organic agriculture, explaining that the same optimal solution was attained also by implementing the second measure (25% OF in Figure 1).

Reducing red meat consumption by half (-50% RMC) increases the ACS index to 57.5 points. The Society sub-index value nears its maximum (99.5), indicating an abundant supply of local food. The Environment sub-index also reaches a high value of 71 points, as emissions, particularly from animal husbandry, would fall. Eliminating half of the edible FLW (-50% eFLW) would double the ACS index, surpassing the impact of all other measures. Abolishing animal product imports and exports (IMP-EXP), as proposed in the Netherlands' CGR report, would raise the ACS index. However, if meat consumption remains unchanged, this measure leads to an increase in GHG emissions and fertilizer use compared to previous measures as all animal-based foods are produced domestically. A 10% increase in agricultural productivity (10% HY, -10% MF) would additionally improve the ACS index compared to implementing the measures of Farm to Fork strategy (-20% MF and 25% OF). This improvement is primarily due to the higher Environment sub-index, as the higher productivity enables an increase in the share of organic production to 50%, which substantially reduces the use of mineral fertilizers.

Implementing all proposed measures would boost the ACS index from the current 32.1 to 67.6 points. This scenario would maximize the Society sub-index to 100 points, indicating local availability of essential food groups. This would significantly mitigate environmental impact, reduce food waste, and maintain economic performance. It is noteworthy that the ACS index of the solution obtained by maximizing the production of food and feed in our previous work (Drofenik et al., 2023) was a mere 39 points. This highlights the central role of optimization with an appropriately tailored multi-objective function. This approach can lead to solutions that not only achieve a high level of food security, but are also environmentally and economically sound.

4. Conclusions

A novel metric, the 'Agriculture Circularity and Sustainability index' (ACS), was introduced and integrated as a multi-criteria objective function into the MILP model to optimize the food supply chain. The ACS index enables the evaluation of agricultural sector performance and promotes circular and sustainable food production solutions. The individual impacts of six measures were assessed: reducing artificial fertilizer use, food waste production, a change of dietary habits, promoting organic farming, enhancing food production productivity, and balancing the import and export of animal-derived food. The case study for Slovenia revealed that implementing all measures would more than double the overall ACS index, from the current 32.1 points to 67.6 points. Food waste reduction and red meat consumption reduction have the most significant contributions to this improvement. Additionally, investing in increased agricultural productivity is crucial due to projected population growth and climate change.

Acknowledgement

The authors thank the Ministry of the Environment, Climate and Energy and Slovenian Research and Innovation Agency (Project V2-2279 and Program P2-0414) for support.

References

A. Ali Chandio, D. Ozdemir, Y. Jiang, 2023, Modelling the impact of climate change and advanced agricultural technologies on grain output: Recent evidence from China, Ecological Modelling, 485, 110501.

S. G. Baratsas, E. N. Pistikopoulos, S. Avraamidou, 2022, A quantitative and holistic circular economy assessment framework at the micro level, Computers & Chemical Engineering, 160, 107697.

Circle Economy, 2020, The Circularity Gap Report: the Netherlands, https://www.circularity-gap.world/netherlands, accessed on September 27, 2023.

H. Dagevos, C. de Lauwere, 2021, Circular Business Models and Circular Agriculture: Perceptions and Practices of Dutch Farmers, Sustainability, 13, 1282.

J. Drofenik, B. Pahor, Z. Kravanja, Z. Novak Pintarič, 2023, Multi-objective scenario optimization of the food supply chain – Slovenian case study, Computer and Chemical Engineering, 172, 108197.

European Commission, 2016, Productivity in EU agriculture – slowly but steadily growing, https://agriculture.ec.europa.eu/system/files/2019-10/agri-market-brief-10_en_0.pdf, accessed November 26, 2023

European Commission, 2020, Farm to Fork Strategy, ec.europa.eu/food/system/files/2020-05/f2f_action-plan_2020_strategy-info_en.pdf, accessed October 18, 2021.

United Nations, 2015, Sustainable Development Goals, Target 12.3, https://sdgs.un.org/goals/goal12#targets_and_indicators, accessed November 26, 2023.

J. F. Velasco-Muñoz, J. M. F. Menoza, J. A. Aznar-Sánchez, A. Gallego-Schmid, 2021, Circular economy implementation in the agricultural sector: Definition, strategies and indicators, Resources, Conservation and Recycling, 170, 105618.

Flavio Manenti, Gintaras V. Reklaitis (Eds.), Proceedings of the 34th European Symposium on Computer Aided Process Engineering / 15th International Symposium on Process Systems Engineering (ESCAPE34/PSE24), June 2-6, 2024, Florence, Italy
 http://dx.doi.org/10.1016/B978-0-443-28824-1.50174-5

An industrial case study of dynamic adsorption simulation for Volatile Organic Compound (VOC) pharmaceutical emission abatement

Vasiliki E. Tzanakopoulou,[a] Michael Pollitt,[b] Daniel Castro-Rodriguez,[c] Dimitrios I. Gerogiorgis[a,*]

[a] *Institute for Materials & Processes (IMP), School of Engineering, University of Edinburgh, EH9 3FB, UK*
[b] *GlaxoSmithKline (GSK), Montrose, Angus, Scotland, DD10 8EA, UK*
[c] *Haleon, No. 5 The Heights, Brooklands Business Park, KT13 0NY, Weybridge, UK*
D.Gerogiorgis@ed.ac.uk

Abstract

Volatile Organic Compound (VOC) emissions have a toxic impact on both environment and human health, so many pharma processes comprise adsorption beds for VOC capture. Optimal management of activated carbon use therein is a key operational and cost issue. This paper presents the application of a validated, non-isothermal adsorption model for an industrially relevant binary (hexane-toluene) mixture under dynamic inlet conditions. Specifically, two VOC inlet concentration patterns are examined in the 100-250 ppm range, emulating industrial VOC generation, revealing preferential adsorption of toluene. Breakthrough times and transitional period durations are also computed and discussed. Longer operation times may be needed for more dilute mixtures, as our results portray. Dynamic models paired with industrial data can deepen our operational insight, enabling extensive technoeconomic VOC mitigation system optimisation towards efficiency maximisation and environmental impact and cost minimisation, towards Industry 4.0.

Keywords: Volatile Organic Compound (VOC), dynamic simulation, adsorption.

1. Introduction

Global demand for life-saving medicine will steadily increase over the next decades. Primary pharmaceutical manufacturing relies heavily on Volatile Organic Compounds (VOCs) as solvents, but their potential emissions endanger human health and ecosystems alike (DEFRA, 2023). End-of-pipeline methods, such as adsorption (Das et al., 2004) are ideal and widely applied for industrial emissions abatement. However, as gas waste streams from multiple processes are fed to the same unit, frequent and costly adsorbent regeneration is inevitable, as irregular bed saturation hampers process efficiency greatly.

We present here the application of a validated dynamic, nonisothermal adsorption model (Tzanakopoulou et al., 2023) to study a binary mixture (hexane-toluene) under industrial conditions. Adsorption is a profound field of study (Tefera et al., 2014; Knox et al., 2016), but the literature on pharma-relevant VOCs under industrial conditions is rather limited. This study therefore considers two dynamic VOC feed concentration patterns, in order to examine relevant breakthrough trends in an Activated Carbon (AC) adsorption column. The VOC concentration range (100-250 ppm) emulates realistic industrial (multi-unit) feed conditions for both cases, aiming to probe the effect of component/concentration sequencing on bed breakthrough time, cost implications and wider environmental impact.

2. Multicomponent, nonisothermal adsorption model development

The validated model we use (Tzanakopoulou et al., 2023) employs the next assumptions:
1. The temperature difference between particles and the gas phase as well as carrier gas adsorption are considered negligible, while the ideal gas law applies (Ruthven, 1984).
2. Equilibrium obeys the Extended Langmuir model for binary mixtures (Ruthven, 1984).
3. Solid phase mass transport is approximated by the LDF model which is characterized as "simple, analytical and physically consistent" (Sircar, 2000).
The equations are derived from these sources, with Eqs. (17-21) from Knox et al. (2016). The Bosanquet formula, Eq. (12) thus Eq. (5), is verified (Krishna & van Baten, 2012).

$\frac{\partial C_i}{\partial t} = D_{z,i}\frac{\partial^2 C_i}{\partial z^2} - \frac{\partial (uC_i)}{\partial z} - \frac{(1-\varepsilon_b)}{\varepsilon_b}\rho_p\frac{\partial q_i}{\partial t}$	(1)	$k_{eff} = k_g(\frac{k_p}{k_g})^n$	(17)
$D_{z,i} = \left(\alpha_0 + \frac{Sc_i Re_p}{2}\right)\frac{D_{AB,i}}{\varepsilon_b}$	(2)	$n = 0.28 - 0.757\log_{10}\varepsilon_b - 0.057\log_{10}\left(\frac{k_p}{k_g}\right)$	(18)
$D_{AB,i} = 10^{-3}T^{1.75}\frac{\sqrt{\left(\frac{M_A+M_B}{M_A M_B}\right)}}{P((\sum v)_A^{0.33} + (\sum v)_B^{0.33})^2}$	(3)	$k_{ez} = k_g(\frac{k_{eff}}{k_g} + 0.75PrRe)$	(19)
$\frac{\partial q_i}{\partial t} = k_{LDF}(q_{e,i} - q_i)$	(4)	$\frac{1}{h_o d} = \frac{1}{dh_{int}} + \frac{x}{k_w d_{lm}}$	(20)
$k_{LDF} = \frac{60\varepsilon_p C_{0,i} D_{eff,i}}{\tau_p C_{s0,i} d_p^2}$	(5)	$h_{int} = \frac{k_g}{2R}[2.03Re^{0.8}\exp\left(-6\frac{R_p}{R}\right)]$	(21)
$\rho_p = \frac{\rho_b}{1-\varepsilon_b}$	(6)	$-\frac{\partial P}{\partial z} = 150u\mu\frac{(1-\varepsilon_b)^2}{\varepsilon_b^2 d_p^2} + 1.75\rho_g u^2\frac{(1-\varepsilon_b)}{\varepsilon_b d_p}$	(22)
$\varepsilon_b = 0.379 + \frac{0.078}{\left(\frac{D}{d_p}\right) - 1.8}$	(7)	$D_{z,i}\frac{\partial C_i(z=0,t)}{\partial z} = -u(C_{o,i} - C_i)$	(23)
$\varepsilon_p = V_{pore}\rho_p$	(8)	$k_{z,i}\frac{\partial T(z=0,t)}{\partial z} = -uC_{pg}\rho_g(T_{in} - T)$	(24)
$\tau_p = \frac{1}{\varepsilon_p^2}$	(9)	$u(0) = \frac{V_s}{\varepsilon_b}$	(25)
$C_{s0,i} = \rho_b q_{e,i}$	(10)	$\frac{\partial C_i(z=L,t)}{\partial z} = 0$	(26)
$D_{k,i} = 97r_p\sqrt{\frac{T}{M_{rA}}}$	(11)	$\frac{\partial T(z=L,t)}{\partial z} = 0$	(27)
$\frac{1}{D_{eff,i}} = \frac{1}{D_{AB,i}} + \frac{1}{D_{k,i}}$	(12)	$\frac{\partial u(L)}{\partial z} = 0$	(28)
$\frac{\partial C_t}{\partial t} = -\frac{\partial (uC_t)}{\partial z} - \frac{(1-\varepsilon_b)}{\varepsilon_b}\rho_p\sum\frac{\partial q_i}{\partial t}$	(13)	$C_i(z,t=0) = 0$	(29)
$q_{e,i} = \frac{q_{m,i} b_i C_i}{1 + \sum b_i C_i}$	(14)	$q_i(z,t=0) = 0$	(30)
$b_i = b_{o,i}exp\left(\frac{-\Delta H_{ad,i}}{RT}\right)$	(15)	$T = (z,t=0) = T_{in}$	(31)
$\left(\rho_g C_{pg} + \frac{(1-\varepsilon_b)}{\varepsilon_b}\rho_p C_{pp}\right)\frac{\partial T}{\partial t} = k_{ez}\frac{\partial^2 T}{\partial z^2} - \rho_g C_{pg}\frac{\partial (uT)}{\partial z} + \frac{(1-\varepsilon_b)}{\varepsilon_b}\sum_{i=1}^{n}\Delta H_{ad,i}\frac{\partial q_i}{\partial t} - \frac{2h_o}{\varepsilon_b R_p}(T - T_w)$	(16)	$Q = V_s A$	(32)

3. Dynamic Model Parameters for Adsorption Systems

The developed model is used to simulate multicomponent VOC adsorption under dynamic inlet concentration. The set of PDEs is solved using RADAU solver and orthogonal collocation on finite elements for space discretization in gPROMS Process 2.0.0. The adsorption of binary hexane – toluene mixture, with air as the carrier, has been examined on beaded activated carbon (Tefera et al., 2014) and a wall temperature of 295 K. The system viscosities are computed from Wilke's equation for binary mixtures, while Langmuir isotherm parameters are taken from Delage et al., (2000) and Shim et al., (2003) for toluene and hexane respectively. Air is assumed as a binary mixture (N_2:O_2 = 79:21 % v/v). Table 1 presents the values for the main simulation parameters.

Table 1. Main model parameter values.

	V_s (m s^{-1})	L (m)	R (m)	ε_b	x (m)	ρ_b (kg m^{-3})	T_{in} (K)	T_w (K)
HEX / TOL	0.914	0.065	0.0076	0.38	0.001	606	300	295

	C_{pp} (J kg^{-1} K^{-1})	k_w (W m^{-1} K^{-1})	k_p (W m^{-1} K^{-1})	ε_p	b_0 (m^3 mol^{-1})	ΔHad (J mol^{-1})	q_m (mol kg^{-1})
HEX	706.7	14.2	0.17	0.56	$2.35 \cdot 10^{-8}$	50,000	3.801
TOL					$4.06 \cdot 10^{-7}$	45,500	4.610

Table 2 presents the main dynamic inlet parameter values employed for both patterns.

Table 2. Pattern 1 and 2 parameter values.

Pattern 1	$C_{0,i}$ (ppm$_v$)	k_{LDF} (s^{-1})	$D_{z,i}$ (m^2 s^{-1})	C_{pg} (J kg^{-1} K^{-1})	h_o (W m^{-2} K^{-1})	k_{ez} (W m^{-1} K^{-1})
HEX	200	$1.88 \cdot 10^{-4}$	$1.32 \cdot 10^{-3}$	1,014	37.17	0.67
TOL	250	$5.43 \cdot 10^{-5}$	$1.34 \cdot 10^{-3}$			
HEX	230	$1.94 \cdot 10^{-4}$	$1.32 \cdot 10^{-3}$	1,014	37.17	0.67
TOL	250	$5.50 \cdot 10^{-5}$	$1.34 \cdot 10^{-3}$			
HEX	250	$1.95 \cdot 10^{-4}$	$1.32 \cdot 10^{-3}$	1,014	37.17	0.67
TOL	250	$5.53 \cdot 10^{-5}$	$1.34 \cdot 10^{-3}$			
HEX	165	$1.82 \cdot 10^{-4}$	$1.32 \cdot 10^{-3}$	1,014	37.17	0.67
TOL	250	$5.38 \cdot 10^{-5}$	$1.34 \cdot 10^{-3}$			
HEX	150	$1.85 \cdot 10^{-4}$	$1.32 \cdot 10^{-3}$	1,014	37.16	0.67
TOL	250	$5.33 \cdot 10^{-5}$	$1.34 \cdot 10^{-3}$			
HEX	130	$1.83 \cdot 10^{-4}$	$1.32 \cdot 10^{-3}$	1,014	37.16	0.67
TOL	250	$5.32 \cdot 10^{-5}$	$1.34 \cdot 10^{-3}$			
Pattern 2	$C_{0,i}$ (ppm$_v$)	k_{LDF} (s^{-1})	$D_{z,i}$ (m^2 s^{-1})	C_{pg} (J kg^{-1} K^{-1})	h_o (W m^{-2} K^{-1})	k_{ez} (W m^{-1} K^{-1})
HEX	200	$1.59 \cdot 10^{-4}$	$1.32 \cdot 10^{-3}$	1,014	37.19	0.67
TOL	100	$4.63 \cdot 10^{-5}$	$1.34 \cdot 10^{-3}$			
HEX	230	$1.62 \cdot 10^{-4}$	$1.32 \cdot 10^{-3}$	1,014	37.19	0.67
TOL	100	$4.69 \cdot 10^{-5}$	$1.34 \cdot 10^{-3}$			
HEX	250	$1.65 \cdot 10^{-4}$	$1.32 \cdot 10^{-3}$	1,014	37.19	0.67
TOL	100	$4.73 \cdot 10^{-5}$	$1.34 \cdot 10^{-3}$			
HEX	165	$1.57 \cdot 10^{-4}$	$1.32 \cdot 10^{-3}$	1,014	37.19	0.67
TOL	100	$4.58 \cdot 10^{-5}$	$1.34 \cdot 10^{-3}$			
HEX	150	$1.58 \cdot 10^{-4}$	$1.32 \cdot 10^{-3}$	1,014	37.19	0.67
TOL	100	$4.54 \cdot 10^{-5}$	$1.34 \cdot 10^{-3}$			
HEX	130	$1.52 \cdot 10^{-4}$	$1.32 \cdot 10^{-3}$	1,014	37.19	0.67
TOL	100	$4.50 \cdot 10^{-5}$	$1.34 \cdot 10^{-3}$			

4. Results and Discussion

Figure 1 presents the breakthrough curves (outlet concentration vs time) and temperature and pressure variations of the examined binary system (hexane-toluene). In this work the adsorption behaviour of the binary mixture hexane-toluene (with air as the carrier gas) has been examined, for an activated carbon column, under two different dynamic inlet concentration cases (Patterns 1, 2) of industrial relevance. For both scenaria considered, hexane undergoes a series of inlet concentration step changes (as occurring from upstream batch production steps), accompanied by a toluene stream of steady inlet concentration. The latter is fixed at a high (250 ppm) or low (100 ppm) level, for the said Patterns 1-2.

The breakthrough onset time ($t_{5\%}$) is calculated as the time that the component's outlet concentration reaches 5% of its equilibrium outlet concentration (after all transitions). Breakthrough completion for toluene ($t_{95\%}$) is considered to occur at the time that the outlet concentration of the VOC reaches a 95% fraction of the equilibrium (final) value. For hexane (the weakly adsorbing component), the $t_{105\%}$ value is taken to be the breakthrough completion time (as it is approached from higher values after an overshoot). The breakthrough intervals are thus defined as 5-95% for toluene, and 5-105% for hexane.

Fig. 1 (a-b) present the inlet and outlet concentrations for the Pattern 1 case, respectively. Hexane breaks through the column outlet first at t = 1037 s, while toluene breaks through the column second at t = 3190 s. Breakthrough completion comes after the indicative points of $t_{95\%}$ = 6769 s for toluene, and $t_{105\%}$ = 5200 s for hexane (due to a clear overshoot).

Fig. 1 (c-d) present the inlet and outlet concentrations of pattern two. As observed in pattern one, hexane breakthrough onset precedes toluene's, at $t_{5\%}$ = 1021 s followed by toluene at $t_{5\%}$ = 3368 s. Breakthrough completion for toluene is at $t_{95\%}$ = 8220 s, which makes it's duration in pattern 2, 18 % longer than in pattern 1, due to the lower concentration of toluene in the mixture. For hexane, breakthrough completion is $t_{105\%}$ = 5038 s, 3 % shorter than in pattern 1. Interestingly, in pattern 2 the breakthrough onset time for hexane is 2 % quicker than in pattern one, despite the lower toluene concentration, while toluene's breakthrough onset is 5 % larger compared to pattern one, as expected due to the decrease in inlet concentration between the two scenarios.

Fig. 1 (e-f) show temperature and pressure variations for both said Patterns investigated. Continuous dark lines denote Pattern 1, while dashed light lines correspond to Pattern 2. As can be seen in plot (e), adsorption causes a temperature rise when taking place due to its exothermicity. Interestingly, the temperature rise of Pattern 1 leads to a marginally higher temperature rise (T_{max} = 299.37 K) compared to Pattern 2 (T_{max} = 299.17 K), in which toluene concentration is lower, before stabilising once the mass transfer zone has moved to later parts of the bed. The pressure drop, depicted in panel 1(f), is nearly the same for the two patterns, as expected due to flow conditions and feed concentrations.

Fig. 1 (g-h) present the key metrics of breakthrough, quantifying the transition intervals. All breakthrough time metrics for both cases are summarised in Fig. 1 (g-h) histograms. Breakthrough durations therein are denoted by respective Δt symbols and lighter shading. For Pattern 2, where we have considered toluene at a 60% lower inlet concentration vs. Pattern 1, the breakthrough duration is 74% shorter; for hexane, it is only 4% shorter.

A remarkable observation emerges: though Pattern 1 has a clearly heavier VOC load vs. Pattern 2 (due only to the higher toluene level, as the hexane transient is kept invariant), the adsorption breakthrough duration is shorter for Pattern 1 vs. Pattern 2, for which it is longer. The strongly adsorbing component (toluene) affects the time to reach steady state.

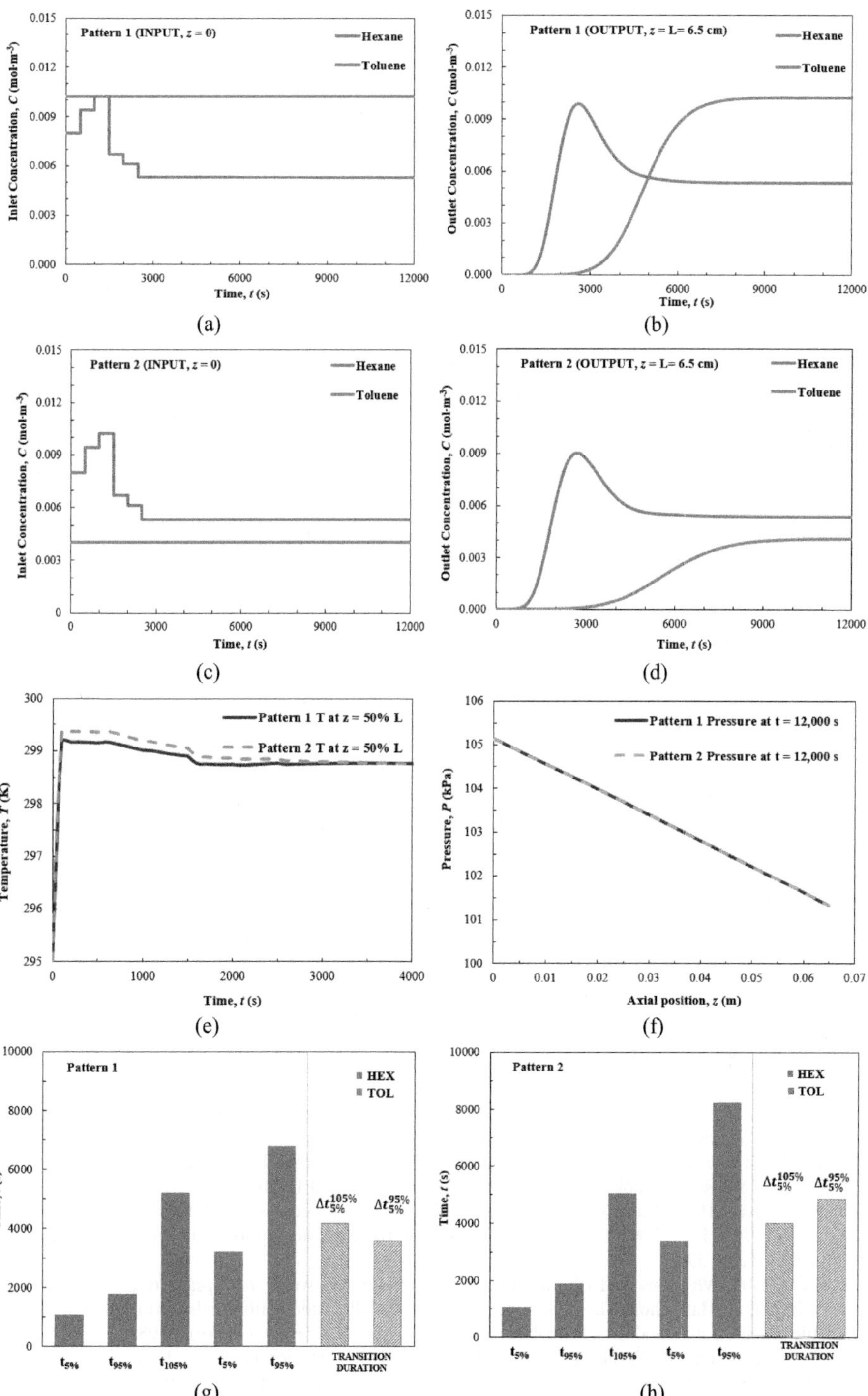

Figure 1. Simulation results for dynamic inlet patterns 1 and 2 of the hexane-toluene mixture.

5. Conclusions

In an era of global efforts towards sustainable manufacturing, limiting Volatile Organic Compound (VOC) emissions emerges as a priority for the pharma industry, where solvent substitution is not always an option due to the stringent regulatory approval constraints. In tandem to unit operation-specific counter-emission measures, the existence of end-of-pipe adsorption columns safeguards compliance with all environmental protection laws. Nevertheless, feeding adsorption beds with a multitude of VOC-laden gas streams from many process unit vents in batch operation induces irregular activated carbon saturation. Frequent and expensive adsorbent regeneration and changeover thus become inevitable. Despite a vast literature body, industrial VOC adsorption under transient feeds is elusive.

This work presents the application of a validated (Tzanakopoulou et al., 2023), multicomponent, nonisothermal adsorption model to investigate dynamic feed concentration volatile organic compound adsorption. To this end, the mixture of hexane-toluene with air as the carrier gas is studied under inlet conditions informed by industrial data. Two VOC inlet patterns are studied where ehxane undergoes a series of inlet concentration changes and toluene reamins at a constant high (250 ppm) inlet concentration in one scenario and toluene remains at a constant low (100 ppm) inlet concentration in the second scenario. Results reveal a later breakthrough onset time for hexane when in a mixture with a high (250 ppm) toluene inlet concentration, while the opposite happens for toluene. The transient duration is longer for the lower VOC load. Temperature rises in the bed as well as pressure drop increase with increased VOC solvent stream load. This work paves the way for waste stream sequencing efforts, not only under batch, but also future continuous pharmaceutical manufacturing optimisation efforts.

Acknowledgements

The authors gratefully acknowledge the SRPe-NMIS IDP PhD Scholarship awarded to V.T., as well as the financial support of UKRI and the Engineering & Physical Sciences Research Council (EPSRC), under the auspices of an ongoing grant (*RAPID: ReAltime Process ModellIng & Diagnostics – Powering Digital Factories*, EP/V028618/1).

References

D. Das, V. Gaur, N. Verma, 2004, Removal of VOC by ACF, *Carbon,* 42(14), 2949.

F. Delage, P. Pre, P. Le Cloirec, 2000, Mass transfer and warming during adsorption of high concentrations of VOCs on AC. *Environ. Sci. Technol.*, 34, 4816.

Department for Environment, Food and Rural Affairs, 2023, Emissions of air pollutants in the UK https://www.gov.uk/government/statistics/emissions-of-air-pollutants/ (Accessed 11/09/2023)

J.C. Knox, A.D. Ebner, M.D. LeVan et al, 2016, Limitations of breakthrough curve analysis in fixed-bed adsorption, *Ind. Eng. Chem. Res.,* 55(16), 4734.

R. Krishna, J.M. Van Baten, 2012, Investigating the validity of the Bosanquet formula for estimation of diffusivities in mesopores, *Chem. Eng. Sci.*, 69(1), 684–688.

National Institute of Standards and Technology (NIST), 2023, NIST Chemical WebBook, SRD69. Available at: https://webbook.nist.gov/chemistry/fluid/. (Accessed 10/10/2023)

D. M. Ruthven, 1984, Principles of adsorption and adsorption processes, D. M. Ruthven, Wiley.

W.G. Shim, J.W. Lee, H. Moon, 2003, Equilibrium and fixed bed adsorption of n-hexane on AC, *Separ. Sci. Technol.*, 38, 3905.

S. Sircar, 2000, Why does the LDF model for adsorption kinetics work, *Adsorption,* 6, 2, 137.

D.T. Tefera, Z. Hashisho, J.H. Philips, et al. 2014, Modeling competitive adsorption of mixtures of volatile organic compounds in a fixed-bed of BAC, *Environ. Sci. Technol.,* 48(9), 5108.

V. Tzanakopoulou, M. Pollitt, D. Castro-Rodriguez, D.I. Gerogiorgis, 2023, Dynamic modelling, simulation and theoretical performance analysis of VOC abatement systems in pharma, *Comput. Chem. Eng.,* 174, 108248.

Flavio Manenti, Gintaras V. Reklaitis (Eds.), Proceedings of the 34th European Symposium on Computer Aided Process Engineering / 15th International Symposium on Process Systems Engineering (ESCAPE34/PSE24), June 2-6, 2024, Florence, Italy
 http://dx.doi.org/10.1016/B978-0-443-28824-1.50175-7

Techno-Economic Analysis for Biogas Reforming using PSWA: Case Study on Methanol Synthesis

Loretta Salano[a], Marcello M. Bozzini[a], Flavio Manenti[a]

Politecnico di Milano, Dipartimento di Chimica, Materiali ed Ingegneria Chimica "G.Natta", Piazza Leonardo da Vinci 32,, 20133, Milano, Italy

flavio.manenti@polimi.it

Abstract

The production of biogas, a mixture of methane and carbon dioxide, from anaerobic digestion from different biowaste sources has been interesting for its application in chemical processes. Currently, it is invested in the production of thermal and electrical energy, but it has also been investigated for the production of syngas, which is usually derived from fossil fuels. A fundamental step for this application is the conditioning of biogas to produce valuable syngas, this can be achieved through a water absorption column among other technologies. This study aimed at the optimal configuration of a pressure swing water absorption (PSWA) tower for the optimal operation of a biogas reforming process. Results show how the placement of the water column has an impact on capital and operating costs, and how the level of conditioning can be useful for chemical synthesis.

1. Introduction

The demand for lower harmful emissions and a lower impact from the process industry on the total number of greenhouse gases (GHG) emissions has pushed the chemical sector towards innovative processes. The main molecule to mitigate is the CO_2, this molecule can be mitigated by substituting thermal with electrical energy sources, with its capture and storage (CCS) and its capture and utilization (CCU) technologies. Biogas is a mixture of gases produced by anaerobic digestion of either agricultural, animal or municipal waste. This stream is usually composed of 55-60 % of methane and 38-40 % of CO_2, with different amounts of impurities, depending on the feedstock. Biogas is considered a carbon-neutral renewable energy source, its capture of CH_4 contributes to avoiding further emissions of GHG (Chen et al., 2015). In recent years some studies have emerged with the concept of Biogas-to-Fuel and its use as a direct substitute for natural gas for chemical processes (Bozzano et al., 2017). The typical route is to upgrade the biogas to biomethane and then undergo the well-known process of methanol production (Sheets & Shah, 2018). This approach requires the system to clean the biogas and then adjust the content of CO_2 in the syngas to the desired quality. It has also been suggested by previous authors a partial upgrading (Previtali et al., 2018; Santos et al., 2023, Rinaldi et al., 2023) before sending it to the reformer. This study investigates an optimal layout for the biogas to syngas route with the partial upgrading of biogas through a water absorption column unit for quality syngas production for methanol synthesis.

2. Methodology

The process under study is built by two main blocks: the conditioning of the biogas and the reforming unit for the production of valuable syngas. The so-called conditioning of biogas is acted by the absorption of CO_2 in a water scrubbing unit, in which the biogas passes through water inside a packed tower in a counter-current configuration. This method takes advantage of the high-water solubility of CO_2 compared to CH_4 (Yang & Ge, 2016). The amount of carbon dioxide removed strongly depends on the amount of water circulated inside the column. The top of Figure 1 reports such a relationship, the highest flow rate, the lowest CO_2 residual in the biogas. The tenor of carbon dioxide in the biogas translates into a change in demand for fuel from the furnace and in the production of syngas. The top image in Figure 1 shows the impact on the quality of the syngas, this is evaluated from the stoichiometric ratio, Eq. (1). The optimal value for methanol synthesis is around 2.00 to ensure the best condition for the catalytic reactors.

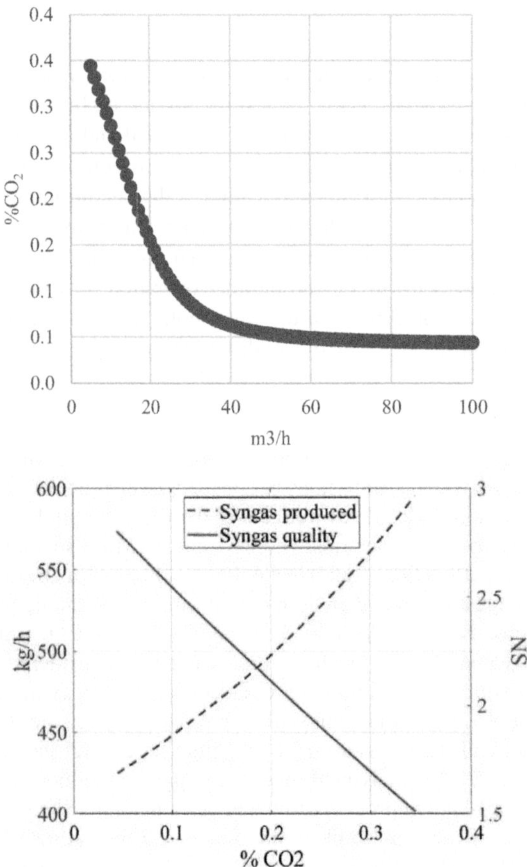

Figure 1 – top: carbon dioxide tenor depending on the water circulated in the column; bottom: syngas production versus quality of the syngas depending on the carbon dioxide tenor in biogas.

The reforming section is composed of a fire-heated furnace and the catalytic tube reactors. Standard reforming technologies takes into consideration natural gas as a feedstock, and steam to ensure the steam methane reforming reaction, reported in Eq. (2). Along with this reaction there is the presence of the water gas shift reaction, Eq. (3). Having a high percentage of CO_2 introduces the so-called bi-reforming: the methane will react in part with the CO_2, Eq. (3), with higher production of the syngas mixture.

Two configurations of the two blocks were taken under study. The difference lies in the placement of the fuel feed. In configuration (a), top, the total amount of biogas is distributed in a reacting feed and a fuel one, which has a very high tenor of inert CO_2 for combustion.

$$SN = \frac{y_{H_2} - y_{CO_2}}{y_{CO_2} + y_{CO}} \quad (1)$$

$$CH_4 + H_2O \rightarrow CO + 3H_2 \quad (2)$$

$$CO + H_2O \rightarrow CO_2 + H_2 \tag{3}$$

$$CH_4 + CO_2 \rightarrow 2CO + 2H_2 \tag{4}$$

In the second layout, Figure 2 bottom, the biogas to be fed furnace-side is retrieved by the PSWA unit. In this way, the tenor of CO_2 in the fuel is mitigated as well.

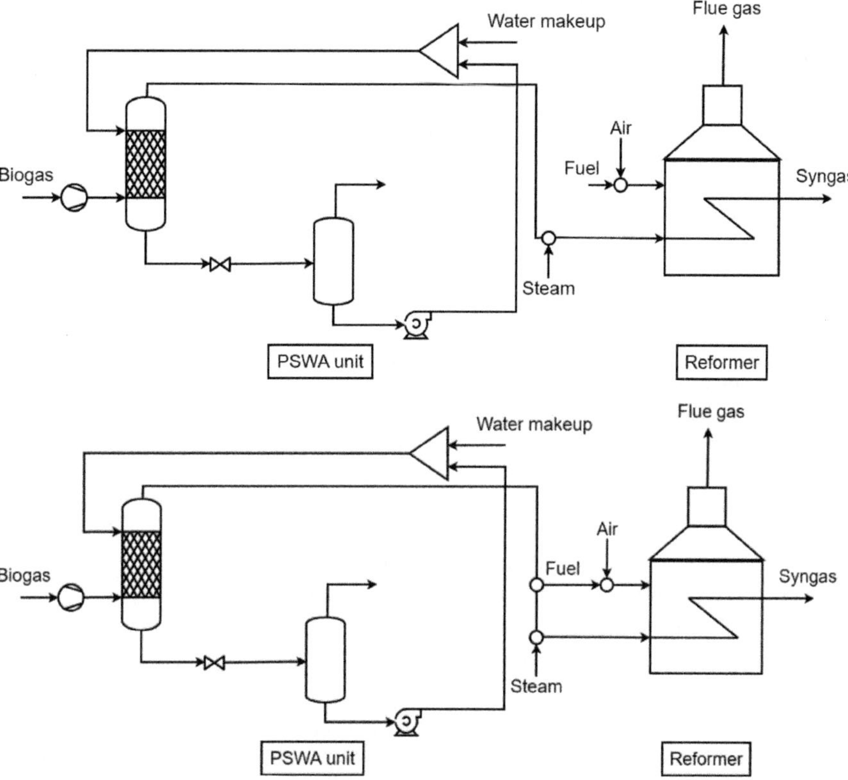

Figure 2 – top: configuration (a); bottom: configuration (b)

The first step taken was to optimize the system to minimize the costs of syngas production, according to the operating conditions, reported in Table 1. The physical constraints of the process refer to the steam-to-carbon ratio (S/C), Eq. (4), at the inlet of the reforming reactor, set equal to 3, the amount of biogas fed to both systems, fixed at 600 Nm3/h, equivalent to 1 MW power plants, and the excess of air to the furnace set to 105 % of the stoichiometric ratio. The S/C is relevant for avoiding coke formation inside the catalytic tubes and for optimal production while the amount of methane to feed is equal to the standard capacity of a biogas CHP plant in Italy (Previtali et al., 2018).

$$S/C = \frac{F_{steam}}{F_{CH_4}} \tag{5}$$

For the evaluation of the economics, the capital costs (CAPEX) were estimated based on the bare module cost of each piece of equipment, according to the method proposed by Turton et al., (2018) and then actualized in recent years through the Chemical Engineering Plant Cost Index (CEPCI). As operational costs were only considered the utility consumptions, the reference prices are reported in Table 2. The total working hours per year considered were 8000, and the plant lifetime for the investment was assumed to be 5 years (Santos et al., 2023). The objective function of the problem is the cost of syngas production, Eq. (7), calculated from the total annual costs (TAC), Eq. (6), and the flow rate of syngas obtained.

$$TAC = \frac{CAPEX}{Plant\ lifetime} + OPEX \tag{6}$$

$$Syngas\ cost = \frac{TAC}{Syngas\ production} \tag{7}$$

Table 1 - Operating conditions of the main process units

	T [K]	P [bar]	Ref.
PSWA	293.15	27	(Santos et al., 2023)
Reformer	1125.15	27	(Hiller et al., 2011)
Furnace	1373.15	1.013	(Hiller et al., 2011)

Table 2 - Utilities costs

	Cost [$/kWh]	Ref.
Electricity	0.1058	(Santos et al., 2023)
Cooling Water	0.001408	(Turton et al., 2018)
Steam	0.01801	(Turton et al., n.d.)

The overall goal of the optimization was to find the correct amount of water to circulate in the PSWA to obtain the minimum amount of energy requested from the system and its equivalent costs to compare the two setups. The simulation of the process was carried out in Aspen HYSY V11, using the Sour Peng-Robinson thermodynamic package.

3. Results and discussion

As already stated, the optimal conditions were found for each configuration, according to the constraints of the system. In the first configuration, as expected, the amount of water needed to remove around 50 % of carbon dioxide is lower than in the second configuration. This result is a direct consequence of the quality of the fuel that is sent to the furnace to sustain the reformer heat demand. Upon these conditions, the economic analysis was carried out. The capital costs differ due to higher demand from the compressor and pump, which in the second configuration face a higher intake in flow rate. The difference in production price is approximately 15 %. This value has a high impact on the overall costs, but considering the higher production of quality syngas, this value should be included in a wider economic study of the comprehensive methanol production chain.

Table 3 - Performance summary for configuration (a) with biogas as fuel and (b) with upgraded biogas as fuel

		(a)	(b)
Water circulating	m3/h	14.89	21.9
Syngas Production	kg/h	505.6	509.1
CAPEX	$	2,439,716.46	2,613,626.69
OPEX	$/y	145,028.88	211,381.69
TAC	$/y	625,463.41	734,183.10
Syngas cost	$/kg	0.1546	0.1803

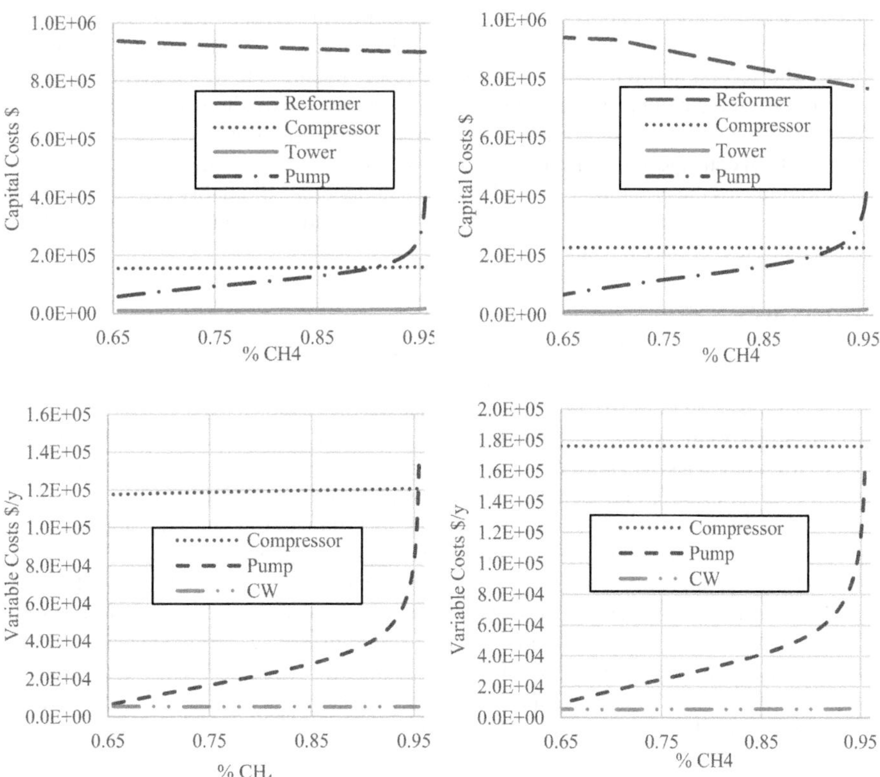

Figure 3 - top: capital costs for configuration (a), left, and (b), right; bottom: operating costs for (a), left, and (b), right

A sensitivity analysis was carried out on the tenor of methane in the biogas. In terms of capital costs, for both scenarios, the reformer takes up to around 75 % of total costs; the compressor and tower don't show any fluctuations, while the pump sees a great increase for a high regime of CO_2 separation. In scenario (b), the capital costs of the reformer have a significant decrease due to the lower tenor of CO_2 on the fuel side. Operating costs are strongly affected by the compressor power, expectably, the more fluid to compress, the higher the demand. The same concept is applicable to explain the pump cost behaviour. The recovery in capital costs and higher syngas production isn't enough to compensate for the very high operational costs of the system.

4. Conclusions

In this work, two process configurations were taken under study to maximise the production of quality syngas for methanol synthesis for the least expense. The goal of the study was to try and propose a new process layout that involves the least amount of biogas possible to be spent as fuel. The size of the plant considered corresponds to 1MW, a common CHP Italian plant size with biogas feed. The biogas available both as reactant and fuel was kept constant for both scenarios. The first one translated into a lower production of syngas, due to the energy to spend in the furnace for the heating of the endothermic reforming reactor, but an overall lower cost of production of only 0.1546 \$/kg. The second configuration has a higher price, mostly due to the higher electricity demand from the compressor and pump, the operational costs show an increase of 45 % compared to the first configuration, while capital costs differ only by 7 %.

The study overall showed no definitive improvement from the alternative layout, the main upbringing was the possibility of producing higher amounts of quality syngas from equal feedstock, this aspect is to be further studied in an economic evaluation of the methanol comprehensive production chain.

References

Bozzano, G., Pirola, C., Italiano, C., Pelosato, R., Vita, A., & Manenti, F. (2017). Biogas: a Possible New Pathway to Methanol? In *Computer Aided Chemical Engineering* (Vol. 40, pp. 523–528). Elsevier B.V.

Chen, X. Y., Vinh-Thang, H., Ramirez, A. A., Rodrigue, D., & Kaliaguine, S. (2015). Membrane gas separation technologies for biogas upgrading. In *RSC Advances* (Vol. 5, Issue 31, pp. 24399–24448). Royal Society of Chemistry.

Hiller, H., Reimert, R., & Stönner, H. (2011). Gas Production, 1. Introduction. In *Ullmann's Encyclopedia of Industrial Chemistry*. Wiley.

Previtali, D., Vita, A., Bassani, A., Italiano, C., Amaral, A. F., Pirola, C., Pino, L., Palella, A., & Manenti, F. (2018). Methanol synthesis: A distributed production concept based on biogas plants. *Chemical Engineering Transactions*, *65*, 409–414

Santos, R., Prifti, K., Prata, D., Secchi, A., & Manenti, F. (2023). Techno-economic Analysis of the Syngas Conditioning from Biogas Using PSA and Pswa: Case Study of Methanol Synthesis. *Chemical Engineering Transactions, 2023*, 673–678.

Sheets, J. P., & Shah, A. (2018). Techno-economic comparison of biogas cleaning for grid injection, compressed natural gas, and biogas-to-methanol conversion technologies. *Biofuels, Bioproducts and Biorefining*, *12*(3), 412–425.

Turton, R., Bailie, R. C., Whiting, W. B., Shaeiwitz, J. A., & Bhattacharyya, D. (n.d.). *Analysis, Synthesis, and Design of Chemical Processes Fourth Edition*.

Yang, L., & Ge, X. (2016). Biogas and Syngas Upgrading. In *Advances in Bioenergy* (Vol. 1, pp. 125–188). Elsevier Inc.

Flavio Manenti, Gintaras V. Reklaitis (Eds.), Proceedings of the 34th European Symposium on Computer Aided Process Engineering / 15th International Symposium on Process Systems Engineering (ESCAPE34/PSE24), June 2-6, 2024, Florence, Italy
 http://dx.doi.org/10.1016/B978-0-443-28824-1.50176-9

A Novel Approach to Scheduling Water Injection for Energy Efficiency in Ghawar Oilfield

Abdullah Alghazal

Process & Control Systems Department, Saudi Aramco, Dhahran 31311, Saudi Arabia abdullah.ghazal@aramco.com

Abstract

Optimizing water injection processes in oil production is crucial for reducing energy consumption and operational costs. This paper considers the problem of optimally operating seawater injection for the Ghawar oilfield, unequivocally the world's largest conventional oilfield. Focusing on a complex water distribution and injection network, which draws millions of barrels daily from the Arabian Gulf, the model utilizes mixed-integer linear programming to minimize operational costs. It prescribes optimal daily injection rates at each flank, efficient pump operational parameters, and supply strategies for swing flanks. The model accommodates user-defined constraints, ensuring month-end compliance targets are met. By introducing penalty terms in the objective function, the model minimizes daily operational variations, producing a practical and operationally acceptable schedule. Employing techniques to enhance computational efficiency, the model reduces CPU times from hours to an average of 340 seconds. Results demonstrate the model's ability to reduce energy consumption for the water injection network by up to a 7%, yielding an implementable schedule with minimal disruptions and accordingly a significant reduction in GHG emissions.

Keywords: seawater, injection, optimization, emissions, energy.

1. Introduction

In the world of oil production, the injection of substantial volumes of seawater into subterranean reservoirs plays a pivotal role in maintaining pressure and enhancing oil recovery. Accordingly, the potential for optimizing this process to reduce energy consumption and operational costs is a compelling challenge. While numerous studies explored various aspects of oilfield optimization, a noticeable gap exists in the literature regarding the comprehensive optimization of water injection networks in giant fields.

Liu et al. (2016) addressed the optimal operation of a network of gas oil separation plants (GOSPs) in the Arabian Gulf Coast Area. Their mixed integer linear programming (MILP) model optimizes crude transfer through swing pipelines, showcasing potential cost savings in operating expenditures. On the other hand, addressing the issue of energy consumption in high water-cut reservoirs, Bai et al. (2021) presented an integrated energy-consumption calculation model. Leveraging a Particle Swarm Optimization algorithm and reservoir numerical simulation, their model showcased notable reductions in energy consumption. Gas lift optimization, a crucial aspect for maximizing crude oil production from well platforms, is highlighted by Sudhanshu and Chaturvedi (2021). Their approach, utilizes regression and linear programming based on field data to allocate compressed gas to wells.

In the domain of strategic/tactical planning of offshore oilfield development, Gupta and Grossmann (2012) presented a multiperiod nonconvex mixed-integer nonlinear programming (MINLP) model. Originally designed for offshore fields, this model offers versatility for optimizing infrastructure and production planning over long-term horizons. In continuation of this work, Awasthi and Grossmann (2019) provided insights into multiperiod optimization models for oilfield production planning. Their models emphasized the significance of multiperiod optimization in oil and gas production planning and introduce a bicriterion optimization model for determining an ideal compromise solution between net present value (NPV) and total oil production.

In the domain of reservoirs waterflooding, Zhou et al. (2019), amongst a few others, developed optimization models for optimal flooding strategy and control of a surface waterflooding pipeline network. However, in their approach, the total profit of waterflooding development was defined as the objective function and they did not consider the potential of minimizing energy consumption of surface equipment.

In this paper, we introduce a pioneering model to optimize the daily scheduling of a water injection network in the Ghawar oilfield. This network comprises a multitude of nodes, where seawater first undergoes a series of preliminary treatments. The treated seawater is then pumped through an extensive network of plants, which either further pressurize the water for transfer to other plants or directly inject it underground through remote wells, which are located along piping flanks. Notably, certain flanks can be supplied by multiple injection plants. Our model offers optimal guidance on daily injection rates for each flank, ensuring the fulfillment of month-end compliance targets. It prescribes the most efficient operational parameters for each pump, should they be selected by the optimizer for use, and outlines the optimal supply strategy for swing flanks. Furthermore, it allows for the incorporation of user-defined constraints, such as specifying the maximum number of days with no injection.

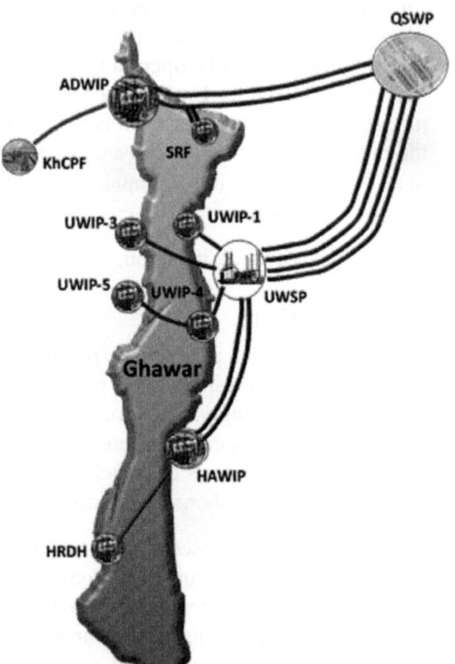

Figure 1 Ghawar Oilfield Water Injection Network

2. Problem Definition

The starting point of the water injection network is the Qurayyah Seawater Plant, located on the Arabian Gulf (Figure 1). The facility is capable of processing some 14 million barrels of seawater daily, more than any other comparable water treatment facility in the world. The treated water leaves Qurayyah south bound to the 'Uthmaniyah Water Supply Plant (UWSP) and north to the Ain Dar Water Injection Plant (ADWIP). From UWSP, water is pumped to a network of water injection plants (WIPs). Each WIP directs water to a number of remote injection wells located along flanks.

Table 1 Equipment at Water Injection Plants

Plant/Equipment	Gas Turbine Pump	Motor Pump	Capacity (Thousand Barrels per Day - MBD)
UWSP	6	-	970 - 1900
UWIP-1	2	-	384 - 450
UWIP-3	3	-	205 - 350
UWIP-4	4	-	205 - 350
UWIP-5	4	-	205 - 350
HAWIP	6	-	240 - 500
HAWIP Shipping	-	3	335 - 665
ADWIP	4	-	420 – 680
ADWIP Shipping	-	3	620 – 1570
SRF	-	4	85 – 150

Four 'Uthmaniyah WIPs sustain pressure in the Ghawar's North section, while the Hawiyah WIP (HAWIP) injects to wells that are connected directly to it and additional ones further south at HRDH. In the North, water is pumped to the Sulfate Removal Facility (SRF) and ADWIP. At ADWIP water is directed to remote injection wells and is also sent to Khurais Central Processing Facility (KhCPF), which is responsible for injecting water at the Khurais field.

Each WIP is equipped with a set of motor or gas turbine driven pumps with varying minimum and maximum capacities (Table 1). Each WIP is connected to a set of flanks. In this work, we do not model wells explicitly and will group their assigned production targets into their respective flanks. Two flanks are shared between UWIP-1 and UWIP-3. One Flank is shared between UWIP-4 and HAWIP and one flank is shared between UWIP-5 and HAWIP. The objective of this work is to build a model which minimizes the overall energy consumption of the network. It shall issue a schedule with minimal disruptions both in the pumping and injection rates. This is crucial for the usability of the models and the applicability of the results as it is not preferred to frequently adjust the injection flowrate for each well or flank. It is also possible to shutdown injection for a given maximum number of days. If not shutdown, the flank must operate between given minimum and maximum rates. It is also mandatory to meet month end total targets within a given compliance limit, which can be separately specified for each flank. For this work, it is assumed that if pumps are used, the model will sustain a fixed base cost, which varies per pump, but is not a function of the flowrate.

3. Mathematical Model

Our mathematical model has a MILP formulation with binary and continuous variables. Its objective is to minimize the cost of operating the network, which is primarily composed of running injection pumps. This is in addition to various terms that aims to make the schedule practical and implementable.

$$\text{Min} \quad \sum_t \sum_p z_{t,p}^{pumps} \times Cost_p^{WIP} - \sum_t \sum_f y_{t,f}^{inject} + \sum_t \sum_f x_{t,f}^{DIR} + \sum_t \sum_p x_{t,p}^{DPR} \tag{1}$$

subject to

$$x_{t,p}^{pump\,rate} \leq z_{t,p}^{pumps} \times MaxRate_p^{WIP} \quad \forall t \in T,\, p \in P \tag{2}$$

$$x_{t,p}^{pump\,rate} \geq z_{t,p}^{pumps} \times MinRate_p^{WIP} \quad \forall t \in T,\, p \in P \tag{3}$$

$$\sum_p x_{p,f,t}^{supply} \geq MinRate_f^{flank} \times y_{t,f}^{inject} \quad \forall t \in T, f \in F \tag{4}$$

$$\sum_p x_{p,f,t}^{supply} \leq MaxRate_f^{flank} \times y_{t,f}^{inject} \quad \forall t \in T, f \in F \tag{5}$$

$$\sum_p x_{p,f,t}^{supply} = 0 \quad \forall t \in T^*, f \in F \tag{6}$$

$$\sum_f x_{p,f,t}^{supply} = x_{t,p}^{pump\,rate} \quad \forall t \in T,\, p \in P \tag{7}$$

$$\sum_t 1 - y_{t,f}^{inject} \leq MaxZeroFlowDays_f \quad \forall f \in F \tag{8}$$

$$\sum_t \sum_p x_{p,f,t}^{supply} \geq (1 - MaxDev_f) \times \sum_t InitialRate_{f,t}^{flank} \quad \forall f \in F, \tag{9}$$

$$\sum_p x_{p,f,t+1}^{supply} - x_{p,f,t}^{supply} \leq x_{t,f}^{DIR} \quad \forall f \in F \tag{10}$$

$$\sum_p x_{p,f,t}^{supply} - x_{p,f,t+1}^{supply} \leq x_{t,f}^{DIR} \quad \forall f \in F \tag{11}$$

$$x_{t+1,p}^{pump\,rate} - x_{t,p}^{pump\,rate} \leq x_{t,p}^{DPR} \tag{12}$$

$$x_{t,p}^{pump\,rate} - x_{t+1,p}^{pump\,rate} \leq x_{t,p}^{DPR} \tag{13}$$

$$x_t^{UWSP} = \sum_p x_{t,p}^{pump\,rate} \quad \forall t \in T \quad p \in [UWIP-1,\, UWIP-3,\, UWIP-4,\, UWIP-5,\, HAWIP,\, HAWIP\ Shipping] \tag{14}$$

Sets T, P and F refer to time periods, WIPs and flanks, respectively. Variables x, y and z refer to continuous, binary and integer variables, respectively.

The first term in Eq. (1) calculates the total cost of used pumps at each WIP, where z^{pumps} is the number of running pumps at the WIP and $Cost^{WIP}$ is the cost of using a pump, which is assumed to be the same for all pumps at the same WIP to reduce the problem size. The second term penalizes the model for setting zero injection rate at a given day to avoid unnecessary shut down of injection, where y^{inject} is a binary variable which is activated when there is zero injection. The third and fourth terms minimize fluctuations in injection and pumping rates, respectively, where x^{DIR} is a variable that equals or exceeds daily variations in injection rates and x^{DPR} is defined to equal or exceed daily variations in pumping rates as will be illustrated in the constraints.

The constraints in Eqs. (2) and (3) ensure that the total supply of each WIP falls between the aggregated minimum and maximum limits of operating pumps, where $x^{pump\,rate}$ is the water rate supplied by a given WIP. $MaxRate^{WIP}$ and $MinRate^{WIP}$ are the maximum and minimum rates of pumps at each WIP, which are assumed to be equal for each pump at each WIP. The constraints in Eqs. (4) and (5) limit the total injection to each flank between the minimum and maximum allowed rates, where $x^{supply}$is the supply from each WIP to each flank. They also control for limiting the number of shutdown days by embedding the term y^{inject}. Eq. (6) ensures that injection to a given flank is zero for user define periods T*. Eq. (7) balances the supply from each WIP with the rate from its pumps. Eq. (8) limits the number of shutdown days to those defined by the user. Eq. (9) ensures the model meets the month end injection target within a user-defined minimum compliance. Eqs. (10) and (11) activate the variable x^{DIR}, which is minimized in the objective function to reduce injection fluctuations. Similarly, Eqs. (12) and (13) minimize fluctuations in pump rates. Finally, Eq. (14) ensures the water rate supplied by plant UWSP is equal the water rate of the connected receiving plants. To reduce solve time, we ensured variables are strictly defined between their feasibility limits. We also, added constraints that ensures no more than 2 rate changes are allowed, which is operationally sensible and computationally advantageous. Also, for symmetry breaking, we assigned a cost for shutting down injection to each flank, which increases along the periods in the schedule. This incentivized the model to place any shutdowns in the beginning of the schedule, therefore reducing solve time significantly.

The MILP problem was formulated in Python v3.7 using the PuLP library and solved using the COIN CLP/CBC LP solver.

4. Results

We conducted multiple experiments to assess the efficacy of the proposed model. Table 2 represent the base schedule. It includes a majority of Ghawar flanks supplied by the model. Injection should be as close as possible to the Base supply.

4.1. Case (1): Minimum 90% Supply of Base, 95% Month End Deviation and Zero Shutdown Days

In this case, the minimum supply to each flank must be 90% of the base supply, each day and the model must meet 95% of the month-end supply without shutting down injection to any flank. In this case, the model solves in 210 seconds. The model reduces injection to UWIP-1 flanks by 90% for half of the month then

Table 2 Flanks Supply Case

Flank	Base Supply (MBD)	Supplier
1N-U	28	UWIP-1
1N-S	102	UWIP-1
1N-S-E-S	99	UWIP-1/3
1S-U	130	UWIP-1
1E-U	41	UWIP-1
3N-S W	59	UWIP-3
3N-S W S	99	UWIP-3/1
3N-U	14	UWIP-3
3S-U	186	UWIP-3
4N	91	UWIP-4
4S	108	UWIP-4
4E	342	UWIP-4
5N	105	UWIP-5
5S	179	UWIP-5
5W	454	UWIP-5
5W - S	46	UWIP-5/ HAWIP
HA-NE	307	HAWIP
HA-NE S	38	UWIP-4/ HAWIP
HA-NE SE	568	HAWIP
HA-HDE-1	409	HAWIP
HA-NW	88	HAWIP
HA-SW	248	HAWIP
HA-HDW-1	270	HAWIP
HA-HD-2E	185	HAWIP
HA-HD-2W	241	HAWIP
HA-HD-3	576	HAWIP
A-EF	239	ADWIP
A-WF	302	ADWIP
SHWIP	280	ADWIP
NAD	258	ADWIP
FZRN	291	SRF
S Injection	1968	ADWIP
LFDL	240	ADWIP

ramps up injection to full capacity for the rest of the month. It supplies flank '3N-S W S' for half of the month from UWIP-1 and the other half from UWIP-3. It reduces injection to flank '3S-U' by 9% for half of the month and by 1% for the other half. The model reduced injection to UWIP-4 flanks by 9% for half of the month, then 1% for the other half. UWIP-5 flanks injection was reduced by 9% for half of the month. Overall, this allowed the model to operate 3 pumps at UWSP for half of the month and 4 pumps for the other half, as opposed to 4 pumps throughout the month. It also allowed operating one pump at UWIP-1 throughout the month as opposed to 2 pumps in the base case. This reduces energy consumption by 4.8% in comparison to the base case where 4 pumps at UWSP are operated.

4.2. Case (2): Minimum 90% Supply of Base, 85% Month End Deviation and one day of allowed shutdown per flank

The major changes in this case include shutting down ADWIP injection for one day then operating at max capacity for the rest of the month. The model also shuts down injection at UWIP-3, 4 and 5 and HAWIP for one day. It then operates at the minimum supply for most of the month. This allows reducing the number of operating pumps at HAWIP to 3 for 2 days and operate 6 for the remainder of the month. It also allows operating 2 pumps at UWSP for 2 days and 3 for the remainder of the month as opposed to 4 in the base case proposed by the user. UWIP-1 behaves similarly as in case (1) but the reduction lasts for the entire month. This allows reducing energy consumption by 8.5%.

5. Conclusions

In this work, we developed a first of a kind MILP model for the optimization of water injection operation at the Ghawar field. The model allows uncovering optimization opportunities that would be very challenging to arrive at manually. This results in reducing energy consumption by an average of 7%. The model provides minimal fluctuations in injection and pumping rates. It can also allow for user-defined constraints, such as specifying the number of maximum shutdown days. The formulation results in a model that generates practical and implementable schedule, which supports its usability.

References

Awasthi, U., Grossmann, I. E. (2019). "Multiperiod Optimization Model for Oilfield Production Planning: Bicriterion Optimization and Two-Stage Stochastic Programming Model." Journal of Optimization Theory and Applications, 20, 1227–1248.

Bai, Y., Hou, J., Liu, Y., Zhao, D., Bing, S., Xiao, W., Zhao, W. (2021). "Energy-Consumption Calculation and Optimization Method of Integrated System of Injection-Reservoir-Production in High Water-Cut Reservoir." Journal of Petroleum Engineering.

Gupta, V., Grossmann, I. E. (2012). "An Efficient Multiperiod MINLP Model for Optimal Planning of Offshore Oil and Gas Field Infrastructure." Industrial & Engineering Chemistry Research, 51(19), 6823–6840.

Liu, S., Alhasan, I., Papageorgiou, L. G. (2016). "A Mixed Integer Linear Programming Model for the Optimal Operation of a Network of Gas Oil Separation Plants." Journal of Chemical Engineering.

Sudhanshu, R., Chaturvedi, N. D. (2021). "Gas Lift Optimization for Optimum Oil Production from a Well Platform." Journal of Chemical and Biochemical Engineering.

Zhou, X., Liang, Y., Xin, S., Di, P., Yan, Y., Zhang, H. (2019). "A MINLP Model for the Optimal Waterflooding Strategy and Operation Control of Surface Waterflooding Pipeline Network Considering Reservoir Characteristics." Journal of Petroleum Science and Engineering.

Flavio Manenti, Gintaras V. Reklaitis (Eds.), Proceedings of the 34th European Symposium on Computer Aided Process Engineering / 15th International Symposium on Process Systems Engineering (ESCAPE34/PSE24), June 2-6, 2024, Florence, Italy
 http://dx.doi.org/10.1016/B978-0-443-28824-1.50177-0

Modeling the Market Fluctuations of Ammonia Price

Andrea Isella, Davide Manca*

PSE-Lab, Process Systems Engineering Laboratory, Dipartimento di Chimica, Materiali e Ingegneria Chimica "Giulio Natta", Politecnico di Milano, Piazza Leonardo da Vinci 32, 20133 Milano, Italy

**davide.manca@polimi.it*

Abstract

The fertilizer industry is one of the most prominent sectors of chemical engineering and manufacturing: by way of example, it generates in the United States of America more than USD 155 billion in economic revenues annually and provides more than 495,000 jobs (The Fertilizer Institute, 2022). Indeed, since half of all food grown worldwide today is made possible through fertilizers, and, as demand continues to increase, their role will only become more important as a key ingredient in feeding a rising global population. Among fertilizers, ammonia is the primary reference compound, as it represents the raw material for the vast majority of their manufacturing and shows the highest production volumes (Isella and Manca, 2022). Based on the previous, pioneering works of Manca (2013, 2015, 2016) on commodity price forecasting, this paper presents a systematic approach to predict the evolution of the ammonia price in the next years for the feasibility-study framework of dynamic conceptual design. Specifically, different autoregressive models are proposed to forecast the distribution of (i) commodity prices that contribute to the definition of the ammonia price and (ii) the ammonia price itself.

Keywords: dynamic conceptual design, econometric modeling, price and cost forecast, short-/long-term predictions, fertilizer industry.

1. Introduction

Feasibility studies for designing, retrofitting, or revamping chemical plants unavoidably require updating capital (CapEx) and operating (OpEx) expenditures. While several tools are longtime established for CapEx estimation (*e.g.*, Guthrie's formulas and cost indexes), very few have been developed for the OpEx. Indeed, raw materials, products, and utility costs/prices are mostly evaluated through a "discounting back approach", *i.e.* they are assumed constant for the whole time horizon embraced by the feasibility study. However, such an assumption often proves to be too simplistic as it does not consider at all the oscillations and fluctuations that can strongly affect market prices. These are the main motivations behind the works of Manca (2013, 2016), which proposed a novel methodology to model the time evolution of commodity prices for feasibility studies and dynamic conceptual design. The present manuscript reflects those considerations in the fertilizer sector and, specifically, in the ammonia industry. Indeed, since ammonia synthesis is the most carbon-intensive process in the chemical industry (Isella and Manca, 2022), many feasibility studies regarding alternative, carbon-mitigating process layouts (to cite only a few: Armijo and Philibert, 2020; Wang *et al.*, 2021; Isella *et al.*, 2023) have been published to push the decarbonization of the fertilizer industry. Therefore, the main goal of this work is to provide a tool for ammonia price forecasting that might lead to much more robust feasibility studies for ammonia (and its derivatives) production.

2. Methodology

As extensively discussed in Manca (2013), the dynamic evolution of commodity prices may be traced back to one or more reference components, which must be chosen according to the market field of interest. By doing so, the economic dynamics of the commodity may be expressed as a function of the time series of the reference components' market quotations. More precisely, Autoregressive Distributed Lag (ADL) models have been identified as the optimal candidates for identifying such functional dependencies.
Concerning the ammonia (NH_3) price, two reference components have been taken into account: crude oil and natural gas. Indeed, being ammonia currently synthesized almost entirely from fossil fuels, its price shows a remarkable correlation with them. Specifically, as far as the Northern American geopolitical scenario is concerned, West Texas Intermediate (WTI) and Henry Hub (HH) are considered for crude oil and natural gas prices, respectively. In this regard, U.S. Energy Information Administration (EIA, 2023) databases allow retrieving both WTI and HH prices, while Illinois production cost reports from the Agricultural Marketing Service of the U.S. Department of Agriculture (USDA AMS, 2023) are considered for the ammonia prices. The monthly price datasets were limited to a time frame spanning from January 2018 to September 2023 (69 months). The next paragraphs focus on each component assessed (the two references, *i.e.* WTI and HH, and the commodity, *i.e.* ammonia), and highlight the ADL models used to describe their economic dynamics.

2.1. WTI price modeling

The ADL model for WTI price forecast grounds on its autocorrelogram (see Fig. 1A). Indeed, the correlation peaks of WTI price as against itself subjected to increasingly long-time shifts occur at 1- and 2-month time lags (0-month time lag is neglected instead since autocorrelograms are by definition equal to 1).

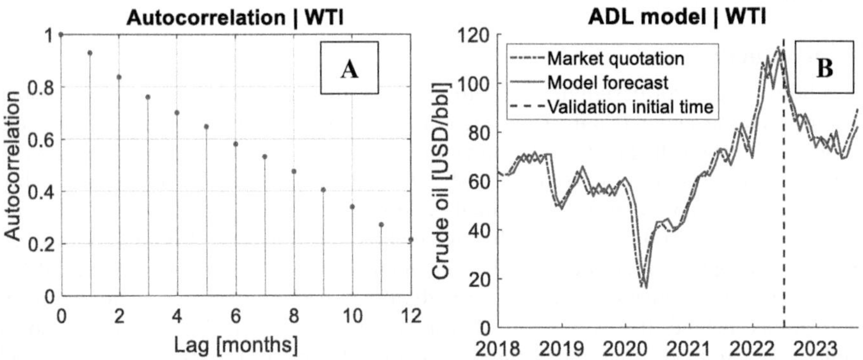

Figure 1: (Panel A) WTI price autocorrelogram; (Panel B) WTI price forecast model.

From this, it follows that a suitable ADL model for WTI price forecast is:

$$P_{WTI}^{(t)} = a_{0,WTI} + a_{1,WTI} \times P_{WTI}^{(t-1)} + a_{2,WTI} \times P_{WTI}^{(t-2)} \quad (1)$$

To perform the regression, the whole dataset was split into two subsets: 80% of data points (*i.e.* from January 2018 to July 2022) were used for the identification procedure, while the remaining 20% was used to run the cross-validation procedure. Fig. 1B shows the model's accuracy, while Table 1 reports the resulting parameters.

Table 1: Parameters of the linear regression for the WTI price.

$a_{0,WTI}$ [USD/bbl]	$a_{1,WTI}$ [-]	$a_{2,WTI}$ [-]	R^2_{adj} [-]
4.4439	1.2386	−0.3028	0.8888

2.2. HH price modeling

The ADL model for HH price forecast builds on its autocorrelogram (see Fig. 2A) and on its correlogram to WTI quotations (see Fig. 2B). Indeed, crude oil is a valid reference component to natural gas, and the correlogram shows that the highest correlation between HH and WTI market quotations occurs when introducing a 2-month time lag. On the other hand, the autocorrelogram shows the best autocorrelation in HH prices at a 1-month time lag.

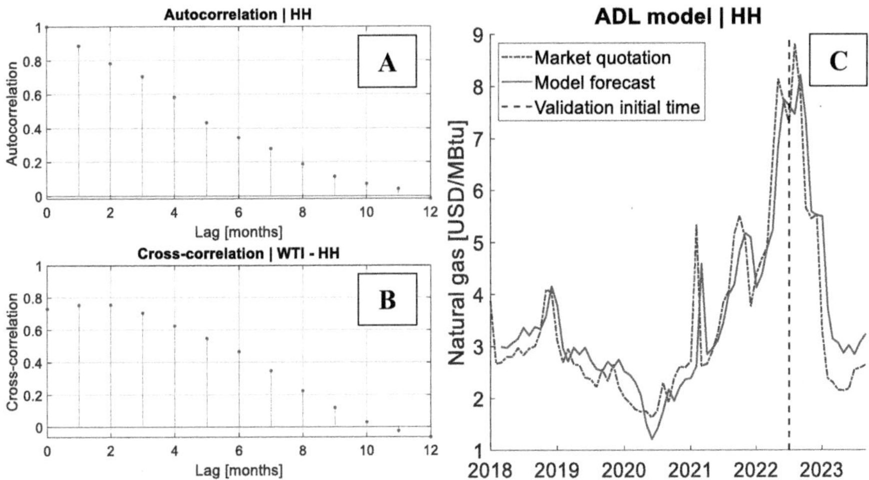

Figure 2: (Panel A) HH price autocorrelogram; (Panel B) WTI-HH price correlogram; (Panel C) HH price forecast model.

It follows that a suitable ADL model for HH price forecast is:

$$P_{HH}^{(t)} = a_{0,HH} + a_{1,HH} \times P_{WTI}^{(t-2)} + b_{1,HH} \times P_{HH}^{(t-1)} \quad (2)$$

Once again, to perform the regression, two subsets were considered: 80% of data points (*i.e.* from January 2018 until July 2022) for identification and 20% for cross-validation. Fig. 2C shows the model's accuracy, while Table 2 reports the resulting parameters.

Table 2: Parameters of the linear regression for the HH price.

$a_{0,HH}$ [USD/MBtu]	$a_{1,HH}$ [bbl/MBtu]	$b_{1,HH}$ [-]	R^2_{adj} [-]
−0.4208	0.0243	0.6999	0.7969

2.3. NH_3 price modeling

The ADL model for NH_3 price forecast is based on its autocorrelogram (see Fig. 3A), on its correlogram as against WTI quotations (see Fig. 3B), and on its correlogram as against HH quotations (see Fig. 3C). Indeed, ammonia price shows a good correlation with WTI and HH prices: on one hand, a 0-month time lag for the WTI-NH_3 correlogram, and, on the other hand, a 2-month time lag for the HH-NH_3 correlogram. The autocorrelogram shows instead that the highest autocorrelation in NH_3 prices happens at a 1-month time lag.

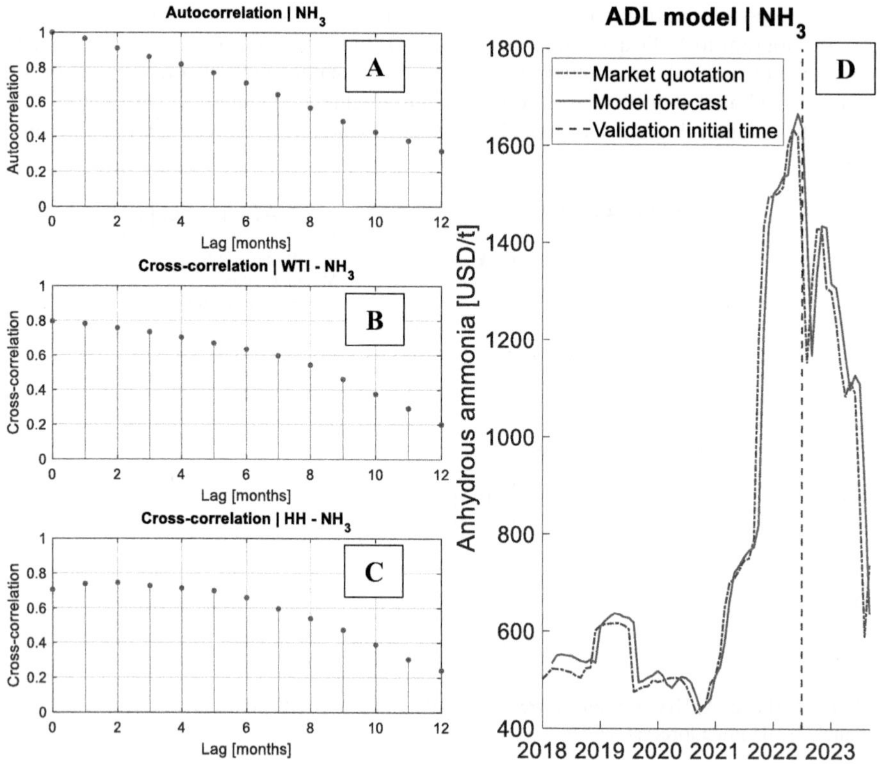

Figure 3: (Panel A) NH_3 price autocorrelogram; (Panel B) WTI-NH_3 price correlogram; (Panel C) HH-NH_3 price correlogram; (Panel D) NH_3 price forecast model.

It follows that a suitable ADL model for NH_3 price forecast is:

$$P_{NH_3}^{(t)} = a_{0,NH_3} + a_{1,NH_3} \times P_{WTI}^{(t)} + a_{2,NH_3} \times P_{HH}^{(t-2)} + b_{1,NH_3} \times P_{NH_3}^{(t-1)} \quad (3)$$

Again, two subsets were considered: 80% of data points (*i.e.* from January 2018 until July 2022) for identification and 20% for cross-validation. Fig. 3D shows the model's accuracy, while Table 3 reports the resulting parameters.

Table 3: Parameters of the linear regression for the NH_3 price.

a_{0,NH_3} [USD/t]	a_{1,NH_3} [bbl/t]	a_{2,NH_3} [MBtu/t]	b_{1,NH_3} [-]	R^2_{adj} [-]
−15.6096	0.9674	−1.7087	0.9676	0.9365

3. Results

After having developed the ADL models for WTI, HH, and NH_3, the ammonia price forecast tool can predict future ammonia price scenarios. For this purpose, an additional source of stochasticity is introduced in Eqs. (1), (2), and (3) by multiplying them by a random contribution term for each specific commodity.

$$P_{WTI}^{(t)}=(a_{0,WTI}+a_{1,WTI}\times P_{WTI}^{(t-1)}+a_{2,WTI}\times P_{WTI}^{(t-2)})\times(1+rand\times\sigma_{WTI}+\chi_{WTI}) \quad (4)$$

$$P_{HH}^{(t)}=(a_{0,HH}+a_{1,HH}\times P_{WTI}^{(t-2)}+b_{1,HH}\times P_{HH}^{(t-1)})\times(1+rand\times\sigma_{HH}+\chi_{HH}) \quad (5)$$

$$P_{NH_3}^{(t)}=(a_{0,NH_3}+a_{1,NH_3}\times P_{WTI}^{(t)}+a_{2,NH_3}\times P_{HH}^{(t-2)}+b_{1,NH_3}\times P_{NH_3}^{(t-1)})\times(1+rand\times\sigma_{NH_3}) \quad (6)$$

Table 4: Additional parameters from the linear regressions performed for WTI, HH, and NH_3.

χ_{WTI} [-]	χ_{HH} [-]	σ_{WTI} [-]	σ_{HH} [-]	σ_{NH_3} [-]
−0.0113	−0.0746	0.1424	0.2201	0.1081

Specifically, σ_i and χ_i (see Table 4) are the ith-component relative error's standard deviation and mean, respectively, from the previous regression procedures. Conversely, $rand$ returns a random scalar drawn from the uniform distribution in the interval $(-1,+1)$.

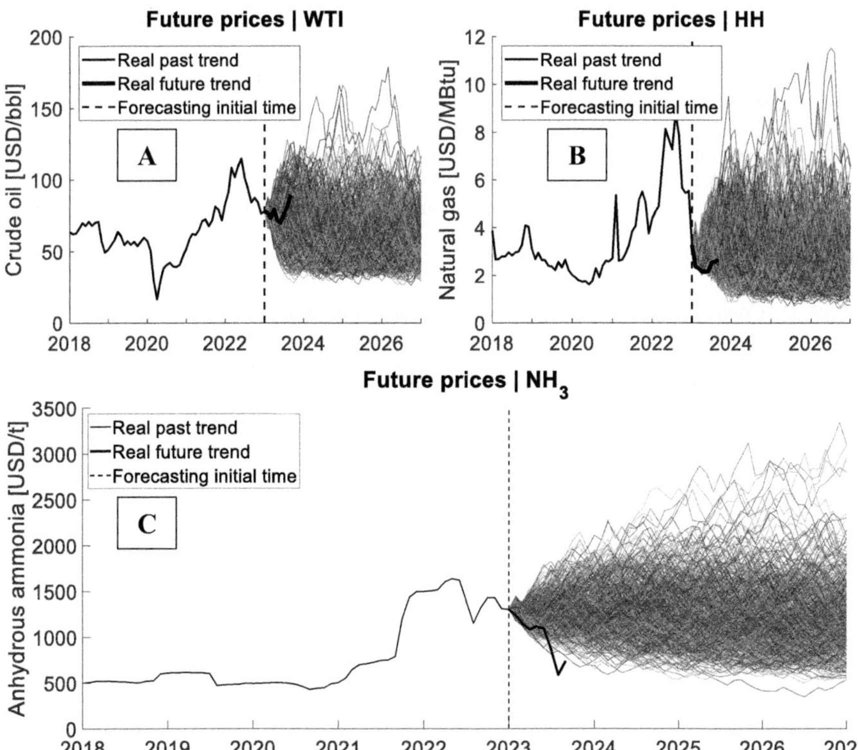

Figure 4: (Panel A) Future WTI price forecasts; (Panel B) Future HH price forecasts; (Panel C) Future NH_3 price forecasts. All forecast periods span from January 2023 to January 2027.

Finally, 500 distinct scenarios were assessed to predict future ammonia prices. The forecast procedure was initialized in January 2023 (to allow the outcomes' partial validation, since the prices up to September 2023 are already known to date) and carried out until January 2027. Figure 4 shows the results for all three components.

4. Discussion and conclusions

This paper showed a methodology aimed at forecasting ammonia price dynamics so that forthcoming feasibility studies of ammonia and fertilizer manufacturing plants may be more accurate and robust than if the conventional "discounting back approach" (*i.e.* all commodity and utilities prices kept constant over the entire timescale assessed) is considered. As it relies just on econometric considerations (*i.e.* it regards the price trends only), this criterion does not take into account economic real variables such as the supply-and-demand law. However, it copes better with medium- and long-term time horizons compared to more rigorous (but short-sighted) economic models.
Moreover, the whole procedure is pretty simple, being essentially based on linear regressions (ADL models are employed) which simply need as input data the historical prices of crude oil, natural gas (*i.e.* the reference components), and, of course, ammonia.

References

Armijo, J., & Philibert, C. (2020). Flexible production of green hydrogen and ammonia from variable solar and wind energy: Case study of Chile and Argentina. Int. J. Hydrog. Energy, 45(3), 1541–1558.

EIA (2023). U.S. Energy Information Administration. Available at: https://www.eia.gov/ (accessed on Oct 12th, 2023).

Isella, A., & Manca, D. (2022). GHG Emissions by (Petro)Chemical Processes and Decarbonization Priorities—A Review. Energies, 15(20), 7560.

Isella, A., Lista, A., Colombo, G., Ostuni, R., & Manca, D. (2023). Gray and hybrid green ammonia price sensitivity to market fluctuations: the Russia-Ukraine war case. Computer Aided Chemical Engineering, 52, 2285–2290.

Manca, D. (2013). Modeling the commodity fluctuations of OPEX terms. Computers and Chemical Engineering, 57, 3–9.

Manca, D., Conte, A., & Barzaghi, R. (2015). How to account for market volatility in the conceptual design of chemical processes. Chemical Engineering Transactions, 43, 1333–1338.

Manca, D. (2016). Price model of electrical energy for PSE applications. Computers and Chemical Engineering, 84, 208-216.

The Fertilizer Institute (2022). About the fertilizer industry. Available at: https://www.tfi.org/our-industry/state-of-industry-archive/2017/about-the-industry (accessed on Sep 15th, 2023).

Wang, S., Fernandes, D., Xu, Q., & Chen, D. (2021). New Conceptual Design of an Integrated Allam-Cycle Power Complex Coupling Air Separation Unit and Ammonia Plant. Industrial & Engineering Chemistry Research, 60(49), 18007–18017.

USDA AMS (2023). Agricultural Marketing Service, U.S. Department of Agriculture. Available at: https://www.ams.usda.gov/ (accessed on Oct 12th, 2023).

Flavio Manenti, Gintaras V. Reklaitis (Eds.), Proceedings of the 34th European Symposium on Computer Aided Process Engineering / 15th International Symposium on Process Systems Engineering (ESCAPE34/PSE24), June 2-6, 2024, Florence, Italy
 http://dx.doi.org/10.1016/B978-0-443-28824-1.50178-2

Economic Optimization of the Synthesis Section of a Small-Scale Biogas-to-Methanol Plant

Marcello M. Bozzini,[a] Loretta Salano,[a] Carlo Pirola,[b] Flavio Manenti[a,*]

[a]CMIC Department "Giulio Natta", Politecnico di Milano, Piazza Leonardo da Vinci 32, Milan 20133, Italy

[b]Dipartimento di Chimica, Università degli Studi di Milano, via Golgi, 19, Milan 20133, Italy

flavio.manenti@polimi.it

Abstract

As global concerns about carbon emissions and the sustainability of energy sources grow, the utilization of biogas has gained significant attention for reducing greenhouse gas emissions and moving away from fossil-based chemicals. Biogas, predominantly composed of methane and carbon dioxide, is generated through the anaerobic digestion of organic materials, such as agricultural residues, municipal waste, and wastewater sludge. To exploit the full potential of biogas and increase its energy density, the conversion of biogas into valuable chemical products seems to be a viable and feasible solution. Specifically, the production of methanol and the development of small-scale biogas-to-methanol plants has received notable recognition. This study focuses on the economic optimization of the synthesis section within such plants. The optimization of this section plays a crucial role in ensuring both the economic viability and the sustainability of the process. The synthesis section is modeled with two reactors arranged in series, where liquefaction of the methanol and water produced takes place after each reactor. To maximize methanol production, unreacted gases are recycled back to the first reactor. This article presents the economic optimization perspective on the reactor's design and operating conditions, finding a compromise between maximizing methanol yield and minimizing reactor costs. This study highlights the potential for biogas-based methanol in the transition between greener energy alternatives. Moreover, it offers a systematic procedure for optimizing the design of the synthesis sections, which is applied to a typical case study. By addressing the complex factors involved in this process, this research actively contributes to the progress of sustainable energy solutions and provides a valuable baseline for future development.

Keywords: Biogas, Methanol, Economics, Optimization, Modeling

1. Introduction

The current trend in the chemical industry and energy sector is entirely directed toward de-fossilization and, consequently, the exploration of renewable resources. Among these, biogas stands out as one of the most promising. Biogas is a mixture composed mainly by methane and carbon dioxide (CO_2) produced through the anaerobic digestion of biomasses. While the current valorization of biogas takes place in Combined Heat and Power (CHP) plants to generate electricity and heat, recent investigations have explored new alternatives, especially the production of methanol (*MeOH*) (Bozzano et al., 2017). *MeOH* is considered a key component in the energy transition process due to its highly energy-intensive synthesis and significant global production. CO_2 hydrogenation appears as a highly promising pathway for carbon utilization, contributing to the de-fossilization of the methanol production industry (Prifti et al., 2023). In these plants, biogas is firstly treated and reformed to produce syngas, a mixture of H_2, carbon monoxide (CO) and CO_2. Subsequently, the syngas is heated up and passes through a catalytic reactor where three reactions take place: the Reverse Water Gas Shift, CO hydrogenation and the CO_2 hydrogenation (Bisotti et al., 2022). Recent studies on biogas-to-methanol plants have been lately conducted focusing mostly on process simulation and layout (Moioli and Schildhauer, 2022). Additionally, various works have extensively analyzed different feedstocks and operating conditions (Santos et al., 2018). It is noteworthy that the techno-economic analysis conducted by Rinaldi et al., (2023) provides a comprehensive assessment of such plants, simulating the overall process with different configurations. However, the scale of the plant analyzed is considerably larger compared to the average biogas plant in Europe (Софія, 2020). This study aims to evaluate the economic feasibility and optimize, from an economic standpoint, the synthesis section of such plants through rigorous modeling of reactors and ancillaries.

2. Methods

The primary object of this paper is to assess the economic feasibility of an optimized synthesis section of a small-scale biogas-to-methanol plant. Rigorous modeling and design have been implemented for each unit for economic optimization of the overall section by varying the volume of the reactors. This study specifically focuses on the economic viability and optimization of the synthesis section in these plants. The economic procedure adopted, and the parameter's database used to estimate the cost of the units, follows the Bare Module Costing technique explained in Turton et al. (2018). The costs have been actualized using the 2023 CEPCI index. The price of *MeOH* is sourced from Methanex's regional contracts to estimate the revenues of the plant. The capital expenditures for both the feed compressor and the recycle compressor have been neglected. Respectively, the first one's cost does not depend on the synthesis section, while the second one's cost depends on fluid power, which does not significantly change since the compression ratio is limited. It is assumed that the electric boiler's electricity consumption is the only operating expenditure in the system.

2.1. Syngas Preparation

Biogas-to-methanol simulated plants typically consist of four main sections: capture of carbon dioxide, reforming of methane, methanol synthesis and purification. This study concentrates on the synthesis section of the plant. The feed stream to the synthesis section has been derived from a rigorous simulation in Aspen HYSYS of such a process. The scale of the process is 1 MW equivalent of biogas on Lower Heating Value basis, which corresponds to the average biogas capacity plant in Italy. Table 1 illustrates the feed stream's parameters, which have been fixed throughout the assessment and optimization procedures.

Table 1. a) Flow and parameters and b) mass fractions of syngas to synthesis section

Operative conditions		Mass Fraction	
Mass Flow	726.3 [kg/h]	ω_{CO}	0.4662
Volumetric Flow	1433 [STD_m^3/h]	ω_{H_2}	0.1131
Temperature	25 [°C]	ω_{CO_2}	0.391
Pressure	61 [bar]	ω_{H_2O}	0.0089
SN	1.85	ω_{CH_4}	0.0208

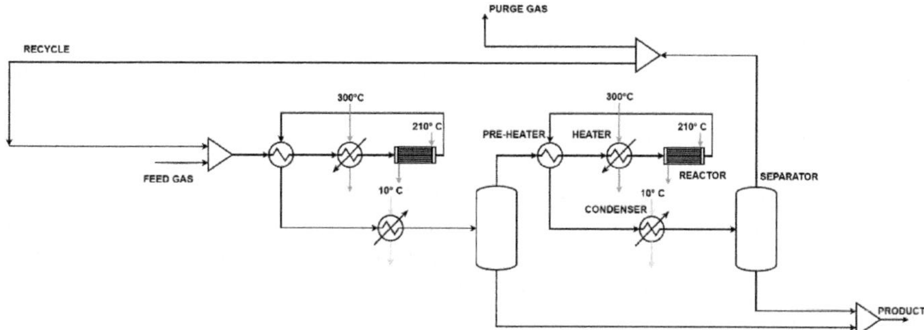

Figure 1. Process Flow Diagram of the synthesis section

2.2. Modeling of the synthesis section

Figure 1 represents the synthesis section as modeled in this study. The feed gas combines with unreacted gas from the last separator and is fed to the synthesis. Subsequently, the reagent mixture, primarily composed of CO, CO_2 and H_2, passes through the pre-heater and the heater to reach the reactor inlet temperature. Then, it enters the reactive unit producing *MeOH*. The resulting mixture is cooled down to extract the main product and the water, while the unreacted gases proceed to the second part of the synthesis, duplicating the first. The products from both reactors are collected for further processing in the purification section, while the unreacted gases are 95 % recycled and 5 % purged. The compressor within the recycle loop has been neglected in this study. Cooling water entering at 10 °C is used to cool down the product stream, while diathermic oil is chosen both to heat up the reagent mixture and to provide refrigeration throughout the reactor length. The pre-heaters and the condensers are modeled as fixed tube heat exchangers solving global energy and mass balances. In contrast, the heaters before the reactors have been designed as double-pipe heat exchangers due to their lower exchange area. The reactors are modeled as oil-cooled multi-tubular reactors, with several assumptions made to replicate the unit over its length. The system of ordinary differential equations for each reactor consists of eight equations with their respective initial conditions. Specifically, five mass balance equations, one for each component, two heat balance equations, one for the shell side and one for the tube side, and the Ergun equations to account for pressure drop along the reactor's length. The separators have been solved using the ϕ/ϕ method, applying the Soave-Redlich-Kwong equation of state. The design of the units follows the procedure explained by Towler and Sinnott (2012).

The operating pressure is set at 61 bar for the first reactor inlet, while the second reactor's pressure is determined by subtracting the pressure drop evaluated with the Ergun equation from the initial pressure. The pre-heater inlet temperature of the reactive mixture is estimated through an energy balance. The minimum temperature approach is constrained to 30 °C. Diathermic oil is employed at 300 °C and 210 °C for heating and cooling, respectively, in the heater and reactor units. The multi-tubular reactor's inlet temperature is fixed at 250 °C, with the constraint that it remains below 300 °C due to catalyst deactivation. The separation of water and *MeOH* is carried out at 45 °C.

2.2.1. Reactor modeling

Synthesis reactors are modeled as multi-tubular heat exchangers with a reactive section within the tube bundle. The pseudo-homogeneous model proposed by Manenti et al. (2011) has been applied to describe the evolution of the reactive mixture along the reactor's length, maintaining the assumptions made by the original authors. In addition, mass transfer limitations have been neglected and the catalyst particle efficiency value has been fixed equal to 1. This simplifying assumption is made with the consideration that the reactions are limited by thermodynamics. Regarding the description of the kinetic region inside the tube bundle, the Vanden Bussche-Froment kinetic model has been applied (Bussche and Froment, 1996). This kinetic model is extensively implemented in both academic and industrial practice. The kinetic model is characterized by its dependence on partial pressures of each component, and the kinetic structure is composed only by the RWGS and the CO_2 hydrogenation reactions. The rate of reaction is influenced by catalyst's density and void fraction. In this work, values corresponding to commercial $CuO/ZnO/Al_2O_3$ catalyst have been picked, specifically 1170 kg/m^3 for the catalyst's density and 0.4 for the void fraction.

3. Results and Discussion

Figure 2 illustrates the relation between the volume of a single reactor and the CO_X conversion through both reactors and the overall synthesis section. The range of the reactor's volume has been limited within the common range applied in the literature to design the unit. As expected, the conversion of the CO_X, and, consequently, methanol production, increases with the volume of the reactors. Both curves reach an asymptotic value due to the thermodynamic limit, corresponding to a production rate of *MeOH* of around 530 kg/h. It must be noted that increasing the volume of the reactors leads to a lower mass flow inside the synthesis loop due to the higher conversion. Both operating and capital expenditures depend more or less significantly with the reactor's volume. Specifically, the former always increases as the independent variable grows. On the contrary, despite the higher volume and cost of the reactor, the capital expenditure decreases, reaching a minimum due to the lower flow circulating. It then increases as the reactor approaches the thermodynamic limit due to the higher reactor dimensions.

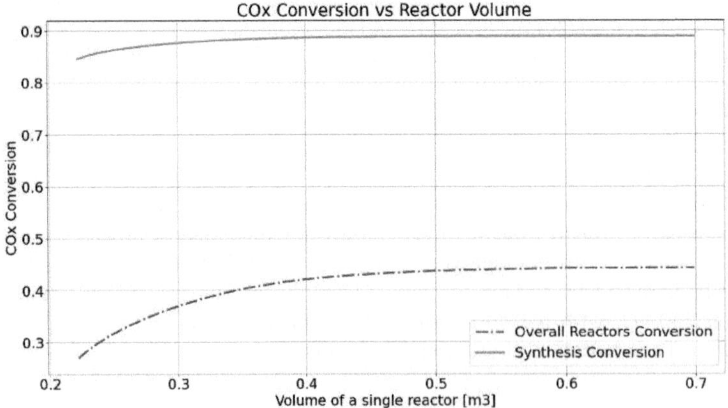

Figure 2. Dependence of CO_X conversion on reactor volume

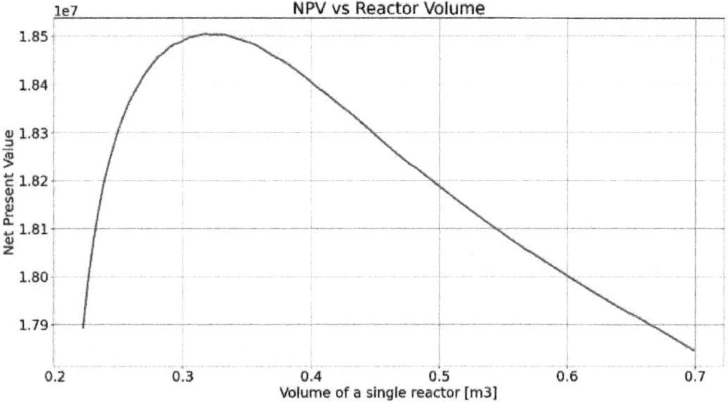

Figure 3. Trends of Net Present Value over reactor volume

The key parameter indicator chosen to assess the synthesis section and determine the optimal volume and its impact on the economics is the non-discounted Net Present Value (NPV). Despite assuming constant costs for both the first section of the plant and the purification section, without specific estimation, NPV has been chosen for its simplicity, assuming a plant lifetime of 10 years. Figure 3. illustrates the NPV with respect to the volume of a single reactor. The trend exhibits a significative peak, corresponding to a volume of each reactor of around 0.3 m^3, which aligns with the volume needed to approximately achieve thermodynamic equilibrium. The corresponding optimal conversions of both reactors and the synthesis section are respectively equal to 41 % and 89 %. Figure 4. represents the Gas Hourly Space Velocity (GHSV) and the Stoichiometric Number (SN) concerning the same independent variable. As commonly known in the literature, the corresponding optimal SN has been found to be 2.0, while the optimal GHSV parameter, commonly used in describing the reactive unit, has been estimated at 17,000 h^{-1}. Simultaneously, these results validate the model outlined in Section 2, opening new routes for more advanced and complex optimizations.

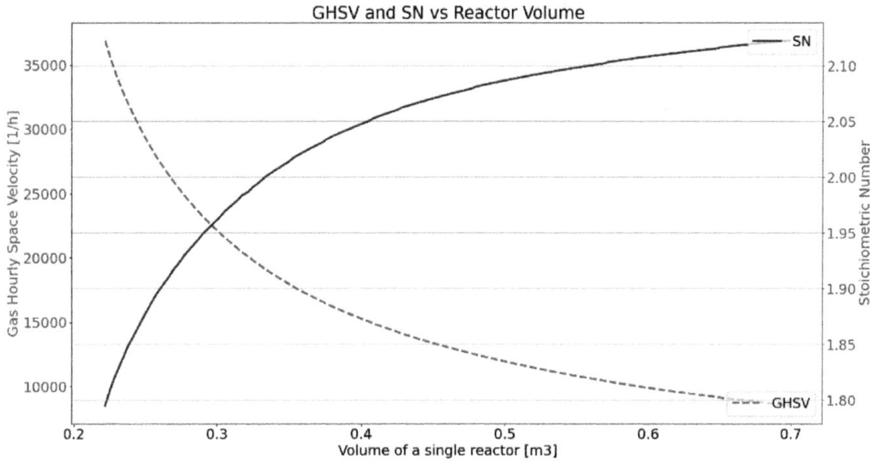

Figure 4. Dependence of GHSV and SN on the volume of each reactor

4. Conclusions and Further Developments

This study focuses on the economic viability and optimization of the synthesis section of a small-scale biogas-to-methanol plant. This section can be divided into two identical parts, each one composed by three heat exchangers for heating and cooling the mixture, a multi-tubular reactor and a separator. The unreacted gases are recycled, with a fraction vented. The plant economics were estimated using a common procedure to assess its feasibility. Subsequently, economic optimization of the NPV by varying the volume of the reactors within its common range of operation was performed to evaluate its impact on the economics of the section. The NPV trend, concerning the volume of each reactor, exhibits a clear peak at around 0.3 m^3. The SN and GHSV values at the optimal point, under fixed operating conditions, are 2.0 and 17,000 h^{-1}, respectively, consistent with literature values. Both operating and capital costs are highly sensitive to the chosen independent variable. The capital costs of the reactors and process-to-process heat exchangers are the most impactful, while the operating expenditure related to the synthesis section is relatively less significant due to the energy-integrated process layout. Although this study neglected costs related to pre- and post-processing, the process appears economically feasible, given the considerable methanol production and potential revenues. This work demonstrates the feasibility of small-scale biogas-to-methanol plant. Furthermore, the optimization of such a process significantly influences its economics, addressing the economic disadvantage compared to traditional, less environmentally friendly solutions. As a result, more advanced and exhaustive optimization of the synthesis section, considering operating conditions, and of the overall process will be carried out. In parallel, optimization procedures based on both economic and environmental criteria will be explored.

References

F. Bisotti, M. Fedeli, K. Prifti, A. Galeazzi, A. Dell'Angelo, F. Manenti, 2022. Impact of Kinetic Models on Methanol Synthesis Reactor Predictions: In Silico Assessment and Comparison with Industrial Data. Ind. Eng. Chem. Res. 61, 2206–2226.

G. Bozzano, C. Pirola, C. Italiano, R. Pelosato, A. Vita, F. Manenti, 2017. Biogas: a Possible New Pathway to Methanol?, in: Espuña, A., Graells, M., Puigjaner, L. (Eds.), Computer Aided Chemical Engineering, 27 European Symposium on Computer Aided Process Engineering. Elsevier, pp. 523–528.

K.M.V. Bussche, G.F. Froment, 1996. A Steady-State Kinetic Model for Methanol Synthesis and the Water Gas Shift Reaction on a Commercial Cu/ZnO/Al2O3Catalyst. Journal of Catalysis 161, 1–10.

F. Manenti, S. Cieri, M. Restelli, 2011. Considerations on the steady-state modeling of methanol synthesis fixed-bed reactor. Chemical Engineering Science 66, 152–162.

E. Moioli, T. Schildhauer, 2022. Eco-Techno-Economic Analysis of Methanol Production from Biogas and Power-to-X. Ind. Eng. Chem. Res. 61, 7335–7348.

K. Prifti, A. Galeazzi, F. Manenti, 2023. Design and Simulation of a Plastic Waste to Methanol Process: Yields and Economics. Ind. Eng. Chem. Res. 62, 5083–5096.

R.O. dos Santos, L. de S. Santos, D.M. Prata, 2018. Simulation and optimization of a methanol synthesis process from different biogas sources. Journal of Cleaner Production 186, 821–830.

G. Towler, R. Sinnott, 2012. Chemical Engineering Design: Principles, Practice and Economics of Plant and Process Design, 2nd edition. ed. Butterworth-Heinemann, Boston, MA.

R. Turton, J. Shaeiwitz, D. Bhattacharyya, W. Whiting, 2018. Analysis, Synthesis, and Design of Chemical Processes, 5th edition. ed. Pearson, Boston.

Софія, 2020. European Biogas Association Statistical Report 2020. UABIO.

Flavio Manenti, Gintaras V. Reklaitis (Eds.), Proceedings of the 34th European Symposium on Computer Aided Process Engineering / 15th International Symposium on Process Systems Engineering (ESCAPE34/PSE24), June 2-6, 2024, Florence, Italy
 http://dx.doi.org/10.1016/B978-0-443-28824-1.50179-4

Present Status of Mixed Plastic Waste Pyrolysis: Plant Simulation through Aspen Hysys

Stefano Redaelli[a], Maurizio Masi[a,*], Davide Alberti[b], Edoardo Vitto[b], and Flavio Manenti[a]

[a]Politecnico di Milano, CMIC department, piazza Leonardo da Vinci 32, Milan 20133, Italy
[b]a2a S. p. A., Corso di Porta Vittoria 4, Milan 20122, Italy
**corresponding author. E-mail: maurizio.masi@polimi.it*

Abstract

The widespread use of plastics results in plastic waste generation. After reuse, recycling is the preferred pathway to reduce the need for virgin feedstock. Concerning mechanical recycling, pyrolysis, consisting of heating the feedstock to promote the thermal degradation of polymers, allows to process Mixed Plastic Wastes (MPW) which cannot be easily sorted. Nowadays, chemical recycling through pyrolysis has reached the demonstration scale, but it is still challenging its further scale-up. In this work, a simulation of a MPW pyrolysis plant coherent with the present technology status is presented. The simulation was performed on Aspen Hysys v11. Unit operations composing the system were chosen according to literature and patent reviews. The process flow diagram of the system is composed of 4 lines in parallel, each one constituted by a reactor, one or more condensation (flash) steps, and a water scrubber (ex-situ dehalogenation) for incondensable gases before their combustion to sustain the reactor energy demand. Each line processes 5000 t/y, representing current scalability limits. The MPW feedstock mass composition assumed is the following: 45 % for both polypropylene (PP) and polyethylene (PE), 8 % for polystyrene (PS), and 1 % each for polymethylmethacrylate (PMMA) and polyvinylchloride (PVC). The reactor has been modeled as a conversion reactor which satisfies the conservation of atoms yielding gaseous, liquid, and solid products of 20, 70, and 10 % of the feedstock mass respectively. After the condensing units, a single distillation column collects the oil produced by each line. The influence of changing the number of condensation (i.e., flash) steps has been investigated. The maximum condensate production was observed for one flash unit. Employing fewer flash units allows to obtain more condensate, paying a slightly larger reboiler duty.

Keywords: chemical recycling, pyrolysis, plastic waste, steady-state simulation

1. Introduction

Current waste treatment solutions are energy recovery, landfilling, and mechanical recycling, end-of-life of 42, 35 and 23 % of plastic wastes respectively. As highlighted in scientific reports commissioned by the European Union (Garcia-Gutierrez et al., 2023), after waste prevention and reuse, material recycling is the preferred path to reduce the environmental impact of plastic wastes. Mechanical recycling, the current strategy for plastic wastes, is a well-established process but it requires single-sorted polymers, and it induces degradation of the polymeric material due to β-scissions following undesired formation of radicals (Schyns & Shaver, 2021). Therefore, to increase the recycling rate in Europe researchers are looking for alternatives. In the literature, several processes are proposed. Among others, chemical recycling processes gained interest. They are all characterized by a common element. Differently from current recycling, polymers degradation is promoted, producing monomers or complex hydrocarbon mixtures. Some processes focus on single polymers. They are depolymerizations (i.e., pyrolysis) and solvolysis of polyethylene terephthalate (PET), where the output is constituted by monomers. Other chemical recycling processes, gasification, and pyrolysis allow to process Mixed Plastic Wastes (MPW). Gasification allows to obtain syngas from MPW. It is a versatile process, since it is possible, for instance, to convert the syngas obtained to base chemicals such as methanol, but it is not expected to be economically viable in the next decades in Europe (Garcia-Gutierrez et al., 2023). Pyrolysis is expected to be the preferred route in the next decades for MPW chemical recycling. It consists in heating the feedstock in an inert environment at temperatures spanning from 400 to 800 °C. In these conditions carbon chains constituting polymeric backbones are broken, owing to complex hydrocarbon mixtures. Some companies achieved a scale of ten thousand t/y (Soni et al., 2021). However, limitations related to poor heat transfer inside the polymeric matrix and high feedstock viscosity hinders its further scale-up. The objective of this work is to simulate present conditions of MPW pyrolysis, trying to represent a realistic MPW pyrolysis plant. Several authors produced relevant works on the simulation of plastic waste pyrolysis. They focused on different feedstocks, mainly plastic wastes constituted by carbon and hydrogen, and different outputs, from heavy oil substitutes (Fivga & Dimitriou, 2018) to hydrocarbon gases (Somoza-Tornos et al., 2020). Here it is proposed, through a simple conversion reactor as first modeling attempt, simulation of a complex MPW feedstock has been addressed. Pyrolysis is expected to play a relevant role in recycling mixed plastics since better alternatives for single polymers already exist.

2. Process description

Pyrolysis consists of heating a carbon-containing feedstock in inert conditions to promote the formation of a hydrocarbon mixture that ranges from gases to char. Focusing on plastic wastes, with respect to other conversion strategies, pyrolysis is of interest for MPW, although they must have a sufficiently high olefinic content, otherwise product distribution would shift towards coke and aromatics. A model MPW mixture has been selected according to this principle and consistent with the composition of wastes obtained after sorting processes. The polymeric composition of the model MPW is the following (expressed in mass fractions): 45 % for both PP and PE, 8 % for PS, and 1 % each for PMMA and PVC. The presence of PVC allows to include the impact of HCl formation on downstream separation units. Simulation is performed on Aspen Hysys v11. To model the plastic feedstock, a hypothetical solid is created. Specific heat was determined averaging the specific heat of each polymer with respect to its mass fraction in the inlet stream. Figure 1 shows a block flow diagram of the modeled process. Concerning simulation boundaries, this work focuses on MPW assumed to be already shredded and ends with the production of three streams of raw pyrolysis oil after distillation. Stream 1, MPW, contains the polymeric mixture with 1 % of moisture. It enters the pyrolysis reactor, working at 450 °C, which is a common operating temperature of most patented processes (Fareid Erik, 2018). Under these conditions, mixed plastics are converted to a hydrocarbon mixture consisting of paraffins, olefins, naphthenes, and aromatics. Due to the high complexity of the reacting system, constituted by a wide variety of reactions involving radicals, proper reactor simulation is not straightforward.

For this reason, it has been chosen, as a first attempt, to employ a simple conversion reactor yielding 20, 70, and 10 % of gaseous, liquid, and solid products.

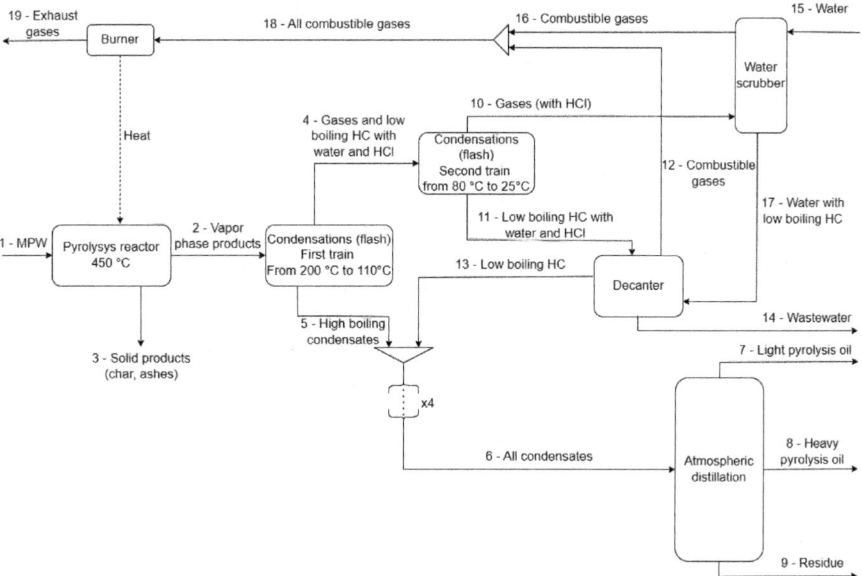

Figure 1: block flow diagram of the MPW pyrolysis process simulated in this study.

Products were selected to fulfil the constraint of the conservation of atoms between reactants and products.

Table 1: composition of stream 2.

Species	**Molar fraction**	**Species**	**Molar fraction**
Water	0.053	Styrene	0.047
HCl	0.015	n-Nonane	0.031
Methane	0.029	n-Decane	0.019
Ethane	0.107	n-C11	0.017
Ethylene	0.114	1-Undecanol	0.001
Propane	0.073	n-C12	0.026
n-Butane	0.148	n-C13	0.044
n-Pentane	0.012	n-C20	0.030
Benzene	0.144	1-Eicosanol	0.015
n-Heptane	0.045	n-C25	0.025
1-Heptanol	0.002	n-C30	0.004

It has been assumed complete conversion of plastics to products. To represent the gaseous and liquid products, 22 species ranging from c1 to c30 are selected. Table 1 shows the composition of stream 2. 1-heptanol, 1-undecanol, and 1-eicosanol are selected to balance oxygen atoms. Solid products are assumed to be constituted by char and ashes, present in equal amounts (yield of 5% each) in the solid products stream. Reaction enthalpy has been evaluated forcing the MPW pseudo-component (polymers are not present in Aspen Hysys) to have a formation enthalpy that satisfies an overall pyrolysis energy demand of 5.4 MJ/kg, 50 % larger than a value found in the literature (3.6 MJ/kg) (Dogu et al., 2021). After the reactor, condensation steps are needed to obtain the liquid hydrocarbon product. The Peng-Robinson-Stryjek-Vera (PRSV) equation of state was selected to model both condensation and downstream decanting and distillation units, due to the co-presence of hydrocarbons and oxygenated compounds. Condensation is a sequence of flash units. The first train of flash units cools down vapors to 110 °C. These liquids do not have significant quantities of hydrogen chloride or water and can be sent to a distillation column. In addition, a stepwise condensation might be necessary to avoid wax deposition. Variations in the number of flash units in the first and the second condensation trains have been explored. Their impact is analyzed in the next paragraph. Vapors from the first flash units are sent to additional condensation steps achieving 25 °C. Stream 11 contains water and most of HCl. Acid water and hydrocarbons are separated by using a decanter. PRSV does not model properly migration of HCl to the water stream. For this reason, two-component splitters are modeled after the decanter to assume the complete migration of HCl to water from both liquid and gaseous hydrocarbon streams. Stream 13, constituted by low-boiling hydrocarbons, is mixed with 5 and sent to the distillation column. Due to the relatively small dimensions of a pyrolysis reactor according to the present technological level, it has been assumed to employ a single column for 4 lines to simulate a 20 kt/y plant. For this reason, streams 5 and 13 have been multiplied by 4 before entering the column. It has been modeled as an atmospheric distillation column. Degrees of freedom were saturated imposing component recoveries on distillate and residue of 0.85 (of n-nonane and n-eicosane) and 3 kmol/h as side draw flow rate. In this way, it is possible to impose a sharp separation between top and bottom streams. Then, the column feed plate, side draw plate, and the number of stages were optimized according to the minimization of the condenser and reboiler power without achieving a temperature larger than 350 °C in the bottom tray (to avoid cracking of hydrocarbons). According to this methodology, a column with 18 trays, and with feed and side draw in the middle tray, has been obtained. The column produces three streams: a heavy hydrocarbon residue (c20>), an intermediate (between c12 and c20), and a light pyrolysis oil (c12<). Gaseous stream 10, containing residual HCl, is sent to a three-stage absorption column with water. Water flow rate have been minimized. Absorber stages were selected to allow obtaining rather low quantities of hydrogen chloride (less than 10^{-19}) in the outlet gas stream. In addition, water promotes the condensation of residual hydrocarbons. For this reason, it is sent to the decanter before wastewater treatment. Electrolyte-NRTL equation of state is selected to model water absorption. After the absorber, gaseous streams are mixed with gases coming from the decanter and sent to a burner, modeled as a Gibbs reactor, providing heat to sustain the pyrolysis reactor. The Peng-Robinson equation was employed in this unit. The flow of air has been selected according to the lowest threshold limit for temperature inside burners (750 °C) presented in the Best Available Techniques (Lecomte et al., 2017).

3. Energetic and material considerations

In this section, the most relevant results related to energy and material balances are presented. However, it must be highlighted that these are preliminary results and proper reactor simulation is needed to obtain a finer estimation of energy and mass flows.
Firstly, reactors are the energetic hotspots of the process. A single MPW pyrolysis reactor needs 822 kW to process 5000 kt/y of plastics, while the column reboiler, processing condensates coming from 4 lines, needs between 305 and 307 kW according to different number of flash units. The choice to simulate different flash configurations is related to the fact that is common practice in patents to consider multiple condensation steps working in series at progressively lower temperatures. Table 1 summarizes the configurations explored. Table 2 shows some relevant parameters associated with different flash configurations.

Table 1: flash configurations explored.

Number of the simulation	Flash configuration	Temperatures first train [°C]	Temperatures second train [°C]
1	2-2	200-110	80-25
2	1-2	110	80-25
3	2-1	200-110	25
4	3-2	200-155-110	80-25
5	2-3	200-110	80-50-25

Table 2: summary of relevant parameters according to different simulations.

Parameter	Simulation 1	Simulation 2	Simulation 3	Simulation 4	Simulation 5
Stream 7 flow rate [kg/h]	584.2	586.6	599.6	583.7	567.6
Stream 9 flow rate [kg/h]	487.4	487.4	487.5	487.4	487.2
Reboiler duty [kW]	305.9	306.1	306.6	305.9	305.3
Air flow rate [kg/h]	6202.8	6174.0	6000.9	6231.7	6433.6
Water flow rate [kg/h]	18.8	18.8	18.3	18.8	18.0
Wastewater flow rate [kg/h]	24.6	24.5	24.3	24.6	23.4

When the number of flash units is reduced, stream 7 mass flow rate progressively increases, with a maximum obtained for simulation 3, being 5.7 % larger than its lowest value, observed in simulation 5. A stream with a larger flow rate is subjected to a lower temperature of the considered condensation train. Conversely, a higher fraction of hydrocarbons remains in the gas phase when multiple condensations are employed. This justifies the behavior of the air flow rate, which is opposite to stream 7, with its minimum value corresponding to simulation 3. Species contributing largely to this phenomenon are hydrocarbons such as n-butane and n-pentane, which, for instance, have, respectively, mass flow rates of 28.7 and 8.52 kg/h in simulation 4, while 29.7 and 8.64 kg/h in simulation 2. The opposite is found for the increasing number of flash units. Accordingly, reboiler power increases for decreasing number of flash units (more low boiling hydrocarbons present in the column feed). In common patents design, the choice of employing multiple flash units in series is probably related to the proper design of condensation units, to avoid the need for a single unit with large dimensions.

4. Conclusions

Plastic waste pyrolysis would play a significant role in processing mixed plastics only, since conventional (i.e., mechanical) recycling or other novel processes allow to process single sorted plastics in a more effective way than pyrolysis. For this reason, when simulating or modeling plastic pyrolysis, it is necessary to focus on mixed polymeric feedstocks. To perform an analysis about energy and material balances in MPW pyrolysis, a steady-state simulation of a MPW pyrolysis plant was done. Particular attention is paid to PVC, which produces hydrogen chloride during the heating step. Although with some simplistic approximations, the simulation performed allowed to estimate the energetic consumption of the units composing the system, highlighting the fact that the reactor is the energetic hot spot. In addition, the impact of multiple flash unit in series, common practice to reduce unit dimensions, have been explored. More flash units result in lower pyrolysis oil production. A further step would be proper modeling of the pyrolysis reactor, needed to allow estimate in a more defined way energy consumptions and process yield, and to explore influence of reactor temperature variations on process performances.

References

Dogu, O., Pelucchi, M., Van de Vijver, R., Van Steenberge, P. H. M., D'hooge, D. R., Cuoci, A., Mehl, M., Frassoldati, A., Faravelli, T., & Van Geem, K. M. (2021). The chemistry of chemical recycling of solid plastic waste via pyrolysis and gasification: State-of-the-art, challenges, and future directions. In *Progress in Energy and Combustion Science* (Vol. 84). Elsevier Ltd. https://doi.org/10.1016/j.pecs.2020.100901

Fareid Erik. (2018). *Production of hydrocarbon fuels from waste plastic* (Patent WO2020008050A1).

Fivga, A., & Dimitriou, I. (2018). Pyrolysis of plastic waste for production of heavy fuel substitute: A techno-economic assessment. *Energy*, *149*, 865–874. https://doi.org/10.1016/j.energy.2018.02.094

Garcia-Gutierrez, P., Amadei, A. M., Klenert, D., Nessi, S., Tonini, D., Tosches, D., Ardente, F., Saveyn, H., & European Commission. Joint Research Centre. (2023). *Environmental and economic assessment of plastic waste recycling : a comparison of mechanical, physical, chemical recycling and energy recovery of plastic waste.*

Lecomte, T., Félix Ferrería de la Fuente, J., Neuwahl, F., Canova, M., Pinasseau, A., Jankov, I., Brinkmann, T., Roudier, S., & Delgado Sancho, L. (2017). *Best Available Techniques (BAT) Reference Document for Large Combustion Plants - Industrial Emissions Directive 2010/75/EU (Integrated Pollution Prevention and Control).*

Schyns, Z. O. G., & Shaver, M. P. (2021). Mechanical Recycling of Packaging Plastics: A Review. In *Macromolecular Rapid Communications* (Vol. 42, Issue 3). Wiley-VCH Verlag. https://doi.org/10.1002/marc.202000415

Somoza-Tornos, A., Gonzalez-Garay, A., Pozo, C., Graells, M., Espuña, A., & Guillén-Gosálbez, G. (2020). Realizing the Potential High Benefits of Circular Economy in the Chemical Industry: Ethylene Monomer Recovery via Polyethylene Pyrolysis. *ACS Sustainable Chemistry and Engineering*, *8*(9), 3561–3572. https://doi.org/10.1021/acssuschemeng.9b04835

Soni, V. K., Singh, G., Vijayan, B. K., Chopra, A., Kapur, G. S., & Ramakumar, S. S. V. (2021). Thermochemical Recycling of Waste Plastics by Pyrolysis: A Review. In *Energy and Fuels* (Vol. 35, Issue 16, pp. 12763–12808). American Chemical Society. https://doi.org/10.1021/acs.energyfuels.1c01292

Flavio Manenti, Gintaras V. Reklaitis (Eds.), Proceedings of the 34th European Symposium on Computer Aided Process Engineering / 15th International Symposium on Process Systems Engineering (ESCAPE34/PSE24), June 2-6, 2024, Florence, Italy
 http://dx.doi.org/10.1016/B978-0-443-28824-1.50180-0

Evaluation on Various Pathways for Converting CO2 into Chemicals

Bor-Yih Yu*

Department of Chemical Engineering, National Taiwan University
Email: boryihyu@ntu.edu.tw

Abstract

To mitigate the damage caused by climate change, significant research efforts have been made in the field of CO_2 utilization. However, the existing data obtained from process analysis has still been inconsistent due to the varying levels of complexity of the models used for analysis and the different groups conducting the analysis. Aiming to accurately compares various CO_2 conversion pathways, our research group is currently establishing a platform based on rigorous process simulation. With this paper, the key findings from our recent studies in the field of CO_2 utilization are summarized and compared.

Keywords: CO_2 utilization, process simulation, techno-economic analysis, decarbonization, rigorous model.

1. Introduction

The concept of CO_2 capture, utilization, and storage (CCUS) has emerged as a highly researched topic in both academia and industry, in order to mitigate excessive CO_2 emissions. Among them, the utilization of CO_2, which aims to convert CO_2 into green and value-added chemicals, plays a key role.

The CO_2 conversion pathways can be categorized as either non-reductive or reductive. The non-reductive pathways do not involve a change in the oxidation states of CO_2 during the reaction. Such a process converts CO_2 directly into alkyl carbonates when combined with alcohols, into aliphatic polycarbonates when combined with diols, into ureas when combined with amines, and into carbamates when combined with both alcohols and amines simultaneously (Tomishige et al., 2020; Tomishige et al., 2019). Despite their atomic efficiency, the main challenge of such processes is the issue of severe chemical equilibrium. This indicates that a suitable catalyst and an intensified reactor system may be necessary to enhance the performance of the reaction.

In contrast, reductive conversion occurs when the oxidation state of the carbon center in CO_2 changes. Such pathways require the addition of a highly active co-reactant to react with CO_2. Some well-known reductive pathways include the direct hydrogenation of CO_2 to form hydrocarbons (e.g. methane, syngas, and liquid fuels), the reaction with epoxide to form carbonates (e.g. ethylene carbonate, by reacting with ethylene oxide), and so on. Overall, the reductive reactions can proceed more easily. However, incorporating an additional co-reactant, especially hydrogen, leads to economic barriers.

There have been several previous studies aimed at evaluating various CO_2 conversion processes, primarily in terms of their economic viability and potential for decarbonization. However, some issues have remained unresolved. First, simplified process models were used for performance evaluation in many previous studies. The alternative process configurations have not been the main focus of study, either. This limits the results obtained from the analysis. Second, different research groups used different process models for analysis. This causes the evaluation results to diverge and lacks a consistent basis. To address this issue, our research group has been developing a rigorous simulation-based framework that presents the most recent discoveries in various CO_2 conversion processes. Within this framework, different CO_2 conversion processes can be compared on a fair basis. In this paper, the important findings from our recent studies are summarized.

2. Rigorous Modeling of CO_2 Utilization Processes

This section highlights the selected processes. To conduct rigorous process simulation, special attention has been paid to the kinetics and thermodynamics, which are the foundation for designing the reaction and separation sections, respectively. Aspen Plus V12 was used for process modeling. The economic feasibility (using the minimum required selling price, or MRSP, in USD/kg) and decarbonization potential (measured by the amount of CO_2 emissions per unit of product formed, or CO_2-e, in kg/kg) of each process can be evaluated and compared together. The specific details of each process can be referred to as indicated.

2.1. Reductive conversion pathways

2.1.1 Synthesis of methane

Methane can be synthesized from direct hydrogenation of CO_2. In a recent paper by Uddin et al. (2022), eight alternative configurations based on fixed-bed reactors were developed and compared. The proposed schemes differ in the number of reactors and the format of heat management (e.g., adiabatic, non-adiabatic with co-current or counter-current exchange). The analysis recommended the use of a two-reactor configuration, with the first stage being a non-adiabatic reactor equipped with internal recycle and counter-current cooling, and the second stage being an adiabatic reactor. A suitable control strategy for this process configuration was also proposed.

2.1.2 Synthesis of methanol

In the context of CO_2 utilization, methanol can be produced by reacting the CO_2 captured from waste gas (such as flue gas) with green hydrogen (generated from the electrolysis of alkaline water). Recently, Chiou et al. (2023) proposed six commercially viable reactor configurations for CO_2-based methanol process and evaluated them in terms of MRSP (in USD/kg) and CO_2-e (in kg/kg). The recommended configuration is to use two reactors. The first stage should be an adiabatic reactor with current-cooling, followed by another adiabatic reactor. A suitable control strategy was also developed for the selected scheme.

2.1.3 Synthesis of dimethyl carbonate

Yu et al. (2018) proposed two processes that convert CO_2 into dimethyl carbonate (DMC). The first process follows an indirect and reductive pathway. It reacts CO_2 with ethylene oxide (EO) to form ethylene carbonate (EC) in the first step, while it further reacts EC with methanol (MeOH) to form DMC and ethylene glycol (EG) in the second step. The second process proposed reacting CO_2 directly with MeOH to form DMC and water, with the addition of butylene oxide (BO) as a chemical dehydrant. As reported in this paper, the first process is superior to the second due to its higher per-pass conversion of CO_2. Although the second process incorporated in situ water removal, the per-pass conversion can only be enhanced to around 10%. This leads to the heavy separation tasks following the reaction section. However, although the first process can be economically viable, it did not show promise in terms of decarbonization (CO_2-e = +0.049), even with the implementation of the extreme heat integration strategy. The main cause is the separation of the azeotrope between MeOH and DMC. As the azeotropic composition leans towards the pure MeOH end, the separation of this azeotrope requires distilling a large amount of lighter species to the distillate, thereby resulting in high energy consumption.

2.1.4 Synthesis of glycerol carbonate

Wu et al.(2024) proposed a novel process for producing glycerol carbonate (GC) through the indirect conversion of CO_2. The process converts CO_2 and propylene oxide (PO) into propylene carbonate (PC) in the first step, while further converting PC with glycerol (GLY) to GC and a co-product, propylene glycol (PG), subsequently. This paper also proposes using GC as a heavy entrainer, enabling the separation of the close-boiling PC and PG through extractive distillation. This method would simultaneously facilitate the purification of PG and the recycling of unreacted PC. Based on the findings, we have concluded that this process shows promise in both economics (MRSP = 0.628 USD/kg) and decarbonization (CO_2-e = -0.238). Considering the appealing properties of GC and its favorable process analysis results, further development of this process is recommended.

2.1.5 Other possibilities

There are still many potential pathways to produce chemicals through the reductive conversion of CO_2. For example, the production of hydrocarbons (either light or heavy) through Fischer-Tropsch synthesis and higher-order alcohols has been investigated both experimentally and computationally. Note that most of the well-known reductive conversion processes of CO_2 produce commodity chemicals. Their features include fewer barriers in production, a large scale of production, and a lower unit price for the products. As the processes incorporate expensive co-reactants, there is a growing trend towards exploring reductive conversion to produce more valuable components.

2.2. Non-reductive pathways

2.2.1 Synthesis of alkyl carbonates

A globally renowned team in the field of non-reductive conversion of CO_2, led by Tomishige et al. at Tohoku University, has proposed over fifty viable pathways for directly converting CO_2 into carbonates, carbamates, or ureas (Tomishige et al., 2020; Tomishige et al., 2019). However, it can be impractical to perform rigorous simulations and comprehensive analyses for all of these processes. To identify processes with potential both in economics and decarbonization, Lee et al. (2021) proposed a screening method based on thermodynamics and process understanding. There are three rules for the screening: (1) No azeotropes or close-boiling behavior should form between the reactants and the products; (2) high selectivity towards the product should be reported from the experiment; (3) the reacting conditions should be industrially relevant. The pathways that meet these three screening rules can be highly productive while emitting a lower amount of indirect CO_2 emissions during the separation of reactor effluents.

Lee et al. (2021) analyzed 15 pathways that convert CO_2 into various carbonates and carbamates using these screening rules. Relevant experiments were conducted using a highly efficient CeO_2 catalyst with the addition of 2-cyanopyridine (2-CP) to facilitate *in situ* water removal (Tomishige et al., 2019). There are four process pathways that pass the screening step, including the production of dimethyl carbonate (DMC), diethyl carbonate (DEC), dipropyl carbonate (DPC), and isopropyl n-phenyl carbamate

(IPPhCM). The process models for these four processes were thereby developed, which subsequently served as the basis for conducting techno-economic and decarbonization analyses. As indicated from this study, the production of DEC can be appealing in both economics (MRSP=2.38 USD/kg) and decarbonization (CO_2-e = -0.154).

The key aspect of whether these processes can be further scaled up lies in the regeneration of 2-CP. As mentioned by Honda et al.(2013), the regeneration of 2-CP proceeded very slowly in a solvent. To investigate this issue, Yu et al. (2020a) obtained the most extreme operating conditions for the regeneration section of the DEC process which resulted in the overall process becoming carbon neutral. In general, the issues surrounding the handling of 2-CP have sparked new discussions on non-reductive conversion pathways. If 2-CP is not regenerated, it could be crucial to find ways to manage the hydration product, 2-picolinamide (2-PA). Besides, it is also necessary to find a reliable source that consistently supplies 2-CP in order to make the process feasible. Otherwise, it is urgently necessary to develop a more suitable reaction system that efficiently regenerates 2-CP. Relevant discussions can also be referred to in a more recent paper by Huang et al. (2023).

2.2.2 Synthesis of isopropyl n-phenyl carbamate (IPPhCM)

The production of IPPhCM was further investigated by Huang et al. (2023), with more rigorous description of the reaction kinetics and reactor configurations. Due to the numerous side reaction occurring the system, the optimal operating conditions were obtained based on different combinations of conversion and yield. With proper strategies for heat integration and thermal coupling, and the addition of ammonia into the reactor to facilitate the regeneration of side products, the process can achieve an exergy efficiency of 71.8% while slightly producing net CO_2 emissions (CO2-e to +0.118 kg/kg).

2.2.3 Synthesis of polycarbonates

Another process that produced poly(butylene carbonate) by reacting CO_2 with 1,4-butanediol was proposed by Yu et al. (2020b), based on the previous experimental findings reported by Tomishige et al. The original experiment involved excessive use of solvents (methanol and tetrahydrofuran) and a scrubbing agent (water), making the separation section of this process highly energy-intensive. To make this process achievable, it is necessary to reduce the amount of solvent used.

2.2.4 Other possibilities

Since the non-reductive conversion processes mentioned above involved the use of a chemical dehydrating agent (i.e. 2-CP), this complicates the separation processes and also leads to undesired side reactions. Exploring alternative pathways or reacting systems that can proceed with fewer chemical equilibrium limitations may still be recommended.

3. Results and comparisons

The evaluation results for all the processes mentioned in Section 2 are summarized **Table 1**. The readers may refer to the indicated papers for more details. The MRSPs (i.e., calculated at a 15% internal rate of return) for producing each chemical are compared with its current market price. The CO_2-e of the designed scenario are compared with the theoretical values, both with and without consideration of the footprint of CO_2 capture. A negative value of CO_2-e indicates that the overall process in is net decarbonization. The theoretical CO_2-e can be calculated directly from the reaction formula, representing the theoretical amount of CO_2 (in kg) required to produce one kg of the product.

Table 1. Comparisons of MRSP and CO_2-e for various CO_2 conversion processes.

	Economics (USD/Ton)		CO_2-e (kg/kg)		
	MRSP	Market	Design (w/o footprint)	Design (w/ footprint)	Theoretical
Reductive					
Methane	32.80[a]	2.03-6.49[a]	-3.338	-2.777	-2.750
MeOH	986	322-434	-1.254	-0.974	-1.375
GC	628	2400	-0.238	-0.162	-0.373
DMC	768	690	0.054	0.154	-0.488
Non-Reductive					
DMC	1500-4960	690	0.049	0.149	-0.488
DPC	2070-4060	3000	0.088	0.149	-0.301
PBC	1580[b]	n.a.	4.340	4.417	-0.379
DEC	1120-2810	1100-1900	-0.237	-0.161	-0.372
IPPhCM	1759	n.a.	0.118	0.168	-0.246

[a]In a unit of USD/MMBTU; [b]The yearly manufacturing cost is listed.

Table 1 shows that products produced through direct hydrogenation (i.e., methane and methanol) have significantly higher MRSP compared to their market prices. The main reason is the inclusion of green hydrogen, which costs 2.4 USD/kg. It is also concluded that such processes can be economically comparable to the existing processes only if green hydrogen is available at a low to moderate cost. In addition, the two indirect processes that produce GC and DMC by reacting epoxides with CO_2 show better economic viability. However, the value of MRSP may change as the costs of the co-reactants and the values of the co-products vary.

There have been few cost data available to compare the MRSPs of the product generated through non-reductive pathways. Within the limited data, the MRSP of DMC was found to be much higher than its market price. The necessary separation of high-boiling species related to 2-CP and its derivative should be the main cause. For the other chemicals, the MRSPs of DEC and DPC generally lie within the range of the corresponding prices. No existing data can be used to compare the MPSPs of IPPhCM and PBC.

In terms of decarbonization, it is generally observed that each process has a higher CO_2-e value than its theoretical value. This is because indirect emissions produced by utility consumption are considered. The methanation process is an exception. In this process, the steam generated through waste recovery is more than sufficient to meet its own requirements. The recovered waste heat can be used in other processes, thereby resulting in further reduction in CO_2 emissions. Note that the theoretical CO_2-e is lower if producing molecules with larger molecular weight. Hence, the overall CO_2-e may become positive if the separation section consumes a significant amount of energy, even if the process uses CO_2 as the starting material.

Considering the carbon footprint associated with CO_2 capture, the results of decarbonization analysis may become less favourable. Here, the calculation incorporated the emission data for the commercially available CO_2 capture process using monoethanolamine (MEA) solution. This includes an average specific energy consumption of 2.8 GJ/Ton-CO_2, and 0.204 kg of indirect CO_2 emissions per kg of CO_2 captured. The inclusion of this term causes the slightly negative CO_2-e of certain processes to become positive.

There are still many factors to consider when providing comprehensive evaluations of CO_2 conversion processes. For example, Chiou et al. (2023) pointed out the trade-off between economics and decarbonization caused by the utilization of various hydrogen sources. Huang et al. investigated the economic uncertainties resulting from the incorporation of 2-CP as a dehydrant in the production of IPPhCM. Yu et al. (2020a) and Lee et al. (2021) conducted a series of sensitivity tests to investigate the impact of varying unit prices on the MRSPs. Although the various items were investigated in different studies, the use of a rigorous model ensures that all the analysis results are comparable.

Note that comparing the MRSP and CO_2-e of the proposed processes provides a unified approach to their evaluation. This also makes the framework flexible for comparing the newly proposed CO_2-based processes to the previous ones.

4. Conclusions

This paper summarizes our recent findings of various CO_2 conversion processes (i.e. th e production of methane, methanol, various carbonates, n-phenyl carbamate, and poly(butylene carbonate). Within this framework, different CO_2-based processes were rigorously developed and were compared on a fair basis. In the foreseeable future, our research team aims to develop an integrated platform that will disclose the latest simulation-based analysis of various CO_2 conversion processes. The rigorous models used for process analysis will be made open to the public to provide a consistent basis.

References

Chiou, H.H., Lee, C.J., Wen, B.S., Lin, J.X., Chen, C.L., Yu, B.Y., 2023. Evaluation of alternative processes of methanol production from CO2: Design, optimization, control, techno-economic, and environmental analysis. Fuel 343.

Honda, M., Tamura, M., Nakagawa, Y., Sonehara, S., Suzuki, K., Fujimoto, K., Tomishige, K., 2013. Ceria-Catalyzed Conversion of Carbon Dioxide into Dimethyl Carbonate with 2-Cyanopyridine. Chemsuschem 6, 1341-1344.

Huang, T.H., Chen, Y.S., Yu, B.Y., 2023. Techno-economic, environmental, and exergetic evaluation of a novel isopropyl n-phenylcarbamate production process through non-reductive conversion of CO2. Process Saf Environ 179, 124-136.

Lee, C.T., Tsai, C.C., Wu, P.J., Yu, B.Y., Lin, S.T., 2021. Screening of CO_2 utilization routes from process simulation: Design, optimization, environmental and techno-economic analysis. J Co2 Util 53.

Tomishige, K., Gu, Y., Nakagawa, Y., Tamura, M., 2020. Reaction of CO2 With Alcohols to Linear-, Cyclic-, and Poly-Carbonates Using CeO2-Based Catalysts. Front Energy Res 8.

Tomishige, K., Tamura, M., Nakagawa, Y., 2019. CO2 Conversion with Alcohols and Amines into Carbonates, Ureas, and Carbamates over CeO2 Catalyst in the Presence and Absence of 2-Cyanopyridine. Chem Rec 19, 1354-1379.

Uddin, Z., Yu, B.Y., Lee, H.Y., 2022. Evaluation of alternative processes of CO2 methanation: Design, optimization, control, techno-economic and environmental analysis. J Co2 Util 60.

Wu, P.J., Hsu, C.C., Yu, B.Y., Lin, S.T., 2024. Rigorous simulation and comprehensive analysis for the novel glycerol carbonate (GC) production process via indirect conversion of CO2. Fuel 357.

Yu, B.Y., Chen, M.K., Chien, I.L., 2018. Assessment on CO2 Utilization through Rigorous Simulation: Converting CO2 to Dimethyl Carbonate. Ind Eng Chem Res 57, 639-652.

Yu, B.Y., Wu, P.J., Tsai, C.C., Lin, S.T., 2020a. Evaluating the direct CO2 to diethyl carbonate (DEC) process: Rigorous simulation, techno-economical and environmental evaluation. J Co2 Util 41.

Yu, Y.C., Wang, T.Y., Chang, L.H., Wu, P.J., Yu, B.Y., Yu, W.Y., 2020b. Conceptual design, environmental, and economic evaluation of direct copolymerization process of carbon dioxide and 1,4-butanediol. J Taiwan Inst Chem E 116, 36-42.

Flavio Manenti, Gintaras V. Reklaitis (Eds.), Proceedings of the 34th European Symposium on Computer Aided Process Engineering / 15th International Symposium on Process Systems Engineering (ESCAPE34/PSE24), June 2-6, 2024, Florence, Italy
 http://dx.doi.org/10.1016/B978-0-443-28824-1.50181-2

Transferable mini-blender performance impact on continuous direct compaction tablets using a modified Kushner-Moore approach.

Hikaru G. Jolliffe[a*], Colette Tierney[a], Ecaterina Bordos[a], Carlota Mendez Torrecillas[a], Martin Prostredny[a], Ebenezer Ojo, Richard Elkes[b], and John Robertson[a].

[a]*CMAC, 99 George Street, Glasgow, G1 1RD, UK.*
[b]*GSK Ware R&D, Harris's Lane, Ware, Hertfordshire, SG12 0GX, UK.*
hikaru.jolliffe@strath.ac.uk

Abstract

Small-scale blenders capable of operating in batch mode are a key tool for many pharmaceutical R&D programs and production processes. In current times there is a strong drive to increase efficiency and reduce waste and development time, and there is high utility in transferable modelling approaches that allow the use of one blender to determine the performance in another. In the present work a modified Kushner-Moore approach is used to model the sensitivity to lubrication for tablets produced by Direct Compaction. A model formulation has been mixed in a Gericke GBM 10 P Mini Blender at intensities inaccessible to most batch blenders, with the blends then used to produce tablets, the properties of which have been analysed. The modified Kushner-Moore approach presented here shows a lubrication sensitivity trend that is also applicable in a Pharmatech bin blender, allowing transferability between mixing regimes that have significantly low intensity (Froude number $Fr < 0.4$) and high intensity ($Fr >> 1$), as well as equipment types.

Keywords: modelling, powder, blending, lubrication, compaction.

1. Introduction

Increasing R&D costs and a drive to improve efficiency and product quality have led to significant research interests in alternative production methods for pharmaceutical products (Cervera-Padrell et al., 2011; Gerogiorgis and Barton, 2009; Lee et al., 2015; Plumb, 2005). In particular, Continuous Direct Compaction (CDC) is attractive as a way to reduce material use and development time during the production of solid dosage forms, from key benefits of a simple manufacturing route and a reduction in scale-up needs (Ierapetritou et al., 2016; Vanarase and Muzzio, 2011). Understanding powder mixing phenomena becomes key, and models that are transferable across mixing durations, intensities and scales have high utility (Gao et al., 2013; Moghtadernejad et al., 2018).

In the literature, various batch blenders have been characterized and their operation in terms of impact on tablet tensile strength at solid fraction of 0.85 ($\sigma_{\mathrm{SF=0.85}}$) can be generalized by the following equation (Kushner and Moore, 2010):

$$\sigma_{\mathrm{SF=0.85}} = \sigma_{\mathrm{SF=0.85,min}} - \left(\sigma_{\mathrm{SF=0.85,max}} - \sigma_{\mathrm{SF=0.85,min}}\right)\mathrm{e}^{-\gamma V^{1/3} FR} \quad (1)$$

Where there are three formulation-dependent fitting parameters ($\sigma_{SF=0.85,min}$, lowest achievable tensile strength; $\sigma_{SF=0.85,max}$, theoretical tensile strength of an unblended mixture; γ, a rate constant) and three process-dependent variables ($V^{1/3}$, cube root of volume and a measure of mixing length scale; F, headspace fraction; R, number of revolutions and the product of blending time and speed *i.e.* rotation rate). Batch blenders to which Eq. (1) applies are restricted to mixing speeds that result in a Froude number Fr value below 0.4 due to centrifugal forces (Brone et al., 1998); Froude number (dimensionless) is the ratio of gravitational forces to inertial forces:

$$Fr = \frac{v^2 r}{g} \tag{2}$$

Where v is rotation rate, r is radius of mixing, and g is the gravitational constant.

In the present work the impact on lubrication extent of mini-blender is evaluated. A mini-blender is a horizontal cylinder with blades about a mixing shaft that can be operated semi-continuously as well as in batch mode. As mixing is imparted by rotating blades and not rotation of the vessel itself, significantly higher Froude numbers (in practice meaning higher mixing speeds) can be used (Jaspers et al., 2023). The present work evaluates how applicable Eq. (1) is to a mini-blender, and if any modifications are required.

2. Materials and Methods

2.1. Materials and equipment

The formulation is based on a literature composition of 2:1 microcrystalline cellulose (Pharmacel® 102, DFE) to lactose monohydrate (SuperTab® 11 SD) adding up to 99 weight % of the blend and 1 weight % magnesium stearate (Ligamed® MF-2-V, Peter Greven). Fixed composition allows exploration of blending effects on lubrication extent. The blenders used are a 10 L horizontal, single-shaft GBM 10 P Mini Blender (Gericke AG Switzerland) and a 5 L bin blender (Pharmatech). A KORSCH XP 1 single-punch tablet press was used for tablet compaction.

Table 1. Mini blender run conditions. a: standard conditions in mini-blender (66 % MCC, 33 % lactose, 1 % MgSt). b: bin blender runs. Bulk density of the formulation was measured at 0.42 g/cm^3, giving headspace fraction values of 0.38 for the mini-blender and 0.29 for the bin-blender.

Run	Blend time (s)	Blend speed (RPM)	Blend mass (kg)	Run	Blend time (s)	Blend speed (RPM)	Blend mass (kg)
01[a]	5	100	3.00	16[a]	112	200	3.00
02[a]	10	100	3.00	17[a]	50	300	3.00
03[a]	30	100	3.00	18[a]	659	50	3.00
04[a]	120	100	3.00	19[a]	1198	50	3.00
05[a]	60	100	3.00	20[a]	1797	50	3.00
06[a]	60	200	3.00	21[a]	2396	50	3.00
07[a]	60	300	3.00	22[a]	2995	50	3.00
08[a]	600	100	3.00	23[a]	187	200	3.00
09[a]	1200	100	3.00	24[a]	83	300	3.00
10[a]	600	300	3.00	25[b]	180	20	1.50
11[a]	600	200	3.00	26[b]	300	20	1.50
12[a]	41	200	3.00	27[b]	1800	20	1.50
13[a]	18	300	3.00	28[b]	3600	20	1.50
14[a]	75	200	3.00	29[b]	8400	20	1.50
15[a]	33	300	3.00	30[b]	26400	20	1.50

2.2. Mini-blender operation

Blending speed and time were varied (Table 1) to explore degrees of mixing covering all potential regimes (Jaspers et al., 2023). For all experiments, a fixed routine of blend material addition and experiment execution is followed: 1) stationary blades and open inlet; 2) add Pharmacel® 102 followed by SuperTab® 11 SD (2:1 ratio, total mass 3.0 kg) set blade speed to 10 RPM for 1 s (complete equipment filling stage with minimal mixing; 4) pre-blend major components at 100 RPM for 60; 5) stationary blades and open inlet; 6) add Ligamed® MF-2-V; 7) set blade speed to 10 RPM for 1 s; 8) blend time and speed according to Table 1; 9) discharge at 10 RPM for 1200 s to allow complete discharge.

2.3. Bin blender operation

Bin blends were prepared with a Pharmatech bin blender (5 L vessel, internal agitator present but not used during experiments). Pharmacel® 102 added first followed by SuperTab® 11SD (2:1 ratio, total mass of 1.5 kg) with pre-blending of 600 s at 20 RPM. For the lubricant addition a fixed speed of 20 RPM was used and blending time was varied as described in Table 1.

2.4. Tablet compaction and analysis

Tableting was performed with a KORSCH XP1 tablet press equipped (9 mm round flat faced punches, 20 strokes per minute). Target tablet mass of 200 mg. Tablets were compressed at 8 upper main compression forces (UMCF) from 1–36 kN. A total of 100 tablets were prepared for each compression point. From these 10 were used for hardness/ tensile strength determination, with thickness measured; remaining ones were retained for further analysis. Tablet weight was measured with a 5DP analytical balance. Tablet thickness and hardness were measured using a calibrated hardness tester (Kraemer Elektronik) with two different load cells: 0–50 N or 50–500 N crushing force according to the expected tablet hardness. Tensile and porosity data have been used to regress Ryshkewitch-Duckworth equation parameters (Duckworth, 1953; Ryshkewitch, 1953):

$$\sigma = \sigma_0 e^{-k_b \varepsilon} \tag{3}$$

Where σ is tensile strength, fitting parameters are tensile strength at zero porosity σ_0 and bonding capacity and k_b, and ε is porosity (1 – solid fraction). Regression has been done in Matlab with error bars included in weighting. For further analysis values of tensile strength at 0.85, 0.80 and 0.75 solid fraction have been used (typical range for tablets of target tensile strength 1.5 – 2.5 MPa, (Nassar et al., 2021).

3. Results and discussion

Interpolating for tensile strength values at 0.85 solid fraction using Eq. (3) and plotting (Figure 3) mini-blender data according to Eq. (1) shows that while there are common maximum ($\sigma_{SF=0.85,max}$) and minimum ($\sigma_{SF=0.85,min}$) tensile strength parameters in across the four Froude number datasets, multiple rate constants γ are required which should not be the case as these should be process-dependent parameters (Kushner and Moore, 2010).

As stated previously, Eq. (1) was developed using batch blenders that are restricted to low Froude numbers due to mixing otherwise being prevented by centrifugal forces (Brone et al., 1998; Kushner and Moore, 2010). Given that Figure 3A shows clear differences in data trends between datapoints with different Froude numbers, modifications to Eq. (1) that incorporate an *Fr* term in some form have been explored.

Table 2. Regressed parameters of Eq. (1), regressed under assumption that datasets share a common maximum and minimum ($\sigma_{SF=0.85,max}$ and $\sigma_{SF=0.85,min}$, respectively).

v (RPM)	Fr (-)	$\sigma_{SF=0.85,max}$ (MPa)	$\sigma_{SF=0.85,min}$ (MPa)	γ (-)
50	0.33	5.299	1.266	0.0023
100	1.33	5.299	1.266	0.0037
200	5.32	5.299	1.266	0.0061
300	11.97	5.299	1.266	0.0132

The approach which showed promise is to include the root of Fr but only for conditions where Fr is above 1 – the hypothesis being that below this value it is number of revolutions R experienced that matters, and that above it is both the number of revolutions experienced and the intensity at which they are experienced (represented by Froude number) which matters. Whilst Fr values below 2.5 are described as one regime of mixing in the literature (Nassar et al., 2021) there is a clear difference in data between Fr values of 0.33 and 1.33 (Figure 3). In summary, the modified equation approach is:

$$\sigma_{SF=0.85} = \sigma_{SF=0.85,max} - \left(\sigma_{SF=0.85,max} - \sigma_{SF=0.85,min}\right)e^{-\gamma V^{1/3} FR (Fr)^n}, \quad n = \begin{cases} 0 & \text{if} \quad Fr < 1 \\ 1/2 & \text{if} \quad Fr > 1 \end{cases} \tag{4}$$

Plotting the data in this manner results in a collapse of all datapoints into one overall trend (Figure 3), with regressed parameters $\sigma_{SF=0.85,max} = 4.761$ MPa, $\sigma_{SF=0.85,min} = 1.369$ MPa, $\gamma = 0.0027$. The approach also holds for other pharmaceutically relevant (Nassar et al., 2021) solid fractions of 0.85, 0.80 and 0.75 (Figure 3).

The overall trend represented by Eq. (4) could, for a given formulation, allow use of experiments conducted at one RPM (*i.e.* Froude number) for predicting performance at any RPM, or alternatively, runs across several RPMs (but few in each specific RPM) to be used to predict said performance. Whilst the present work has been developed on one

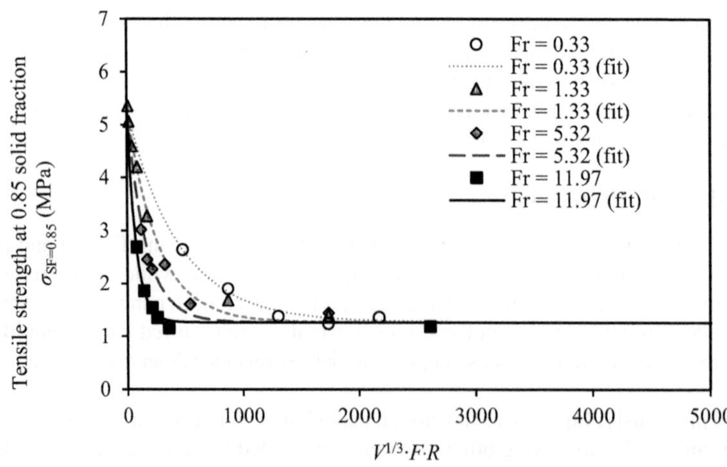

Figure 1. Compaction data for varying with blending speed and time (Table 1). Speeds of 50, 100, 200 and 300 RPM correspond to Froude number Fr values of 0.33, 1.33, 5.32, and 11.97. Mini-blender data (runs 01–24, Table 1) plotted according to Eq. (1); regressed parameters in Table 2.

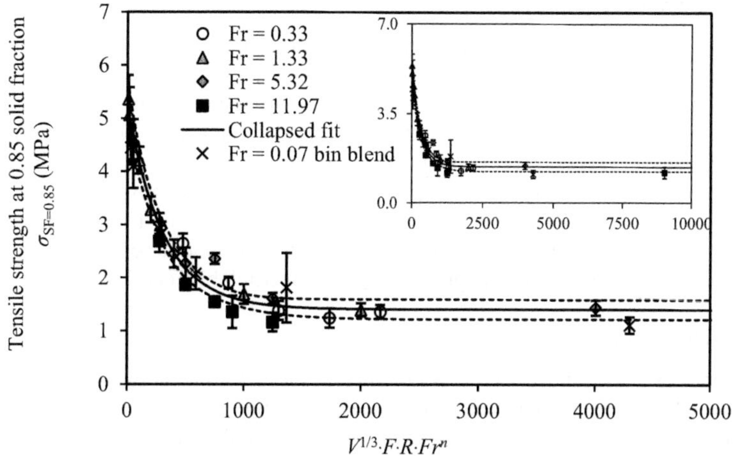

Figure 2. Compaction data for varying with blending speed and time (Table 1). Speeds of 50, 100, 200 and 300 RPM correspond to *Fr* values of 0.33, 1.33, 5.32, and 11.97. Mini-blender data (runs 01–24, Table 1) plotted alongside bin-blender data (runs 24–30, Table 1) according to Eq. (4).

scale of equipment, the fact that bin blender data is overlaid with mini-blender data when Eq. (4) is used suggests that the approach shows promise (Figure 3), especially as the literature shows that there is a commonality of performance across many batch blenders (Kushner, 2012; Kushner and Moore, 2010; Kushner and Schlack, 2014).

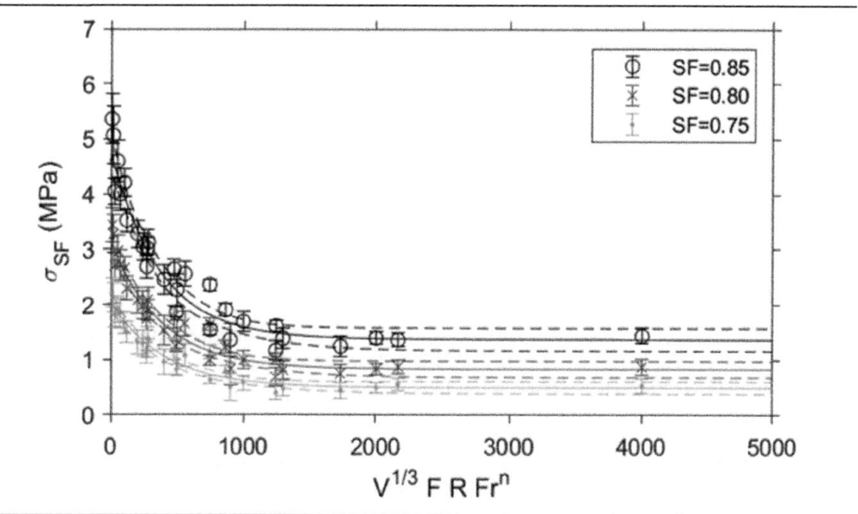

Figure 3. Compaction data for varying with blending speed and time (Table 1). Speeds of 50, 100, 200 and 300 RPM correspond to *Fr* values of 0.33, 1.33, 5.32, and 11.97. Mini-blender data (runs 01–24, Table 1) according to Eq. (4) for solid fraction (SF) of 0.85, 0.80, and 0.75.

4. Conclusions

There is significant research interest in novel pharmaceutical production methods, and this is the case for dry powder blending, relevant for Continuous Direct Compaction. Evaluations of existing approaches in literature for modelling the impact that batch blender operation has on lubrication extent (assessed via tablet tensile strength) suggests that modifications are required to extend the model to devices such as a mini-blender (that can operate at substantially higher blending speeds). Results show that modifying the existing approach to include a new term based on the root of the Froude number shows promise, with this modification resulting in one overall trend across different blending speeds. Moreover, the approach appears to work for batch blender data as well.

Acknowledgements

This work has been funded by the Medicines Manufacturing Innovation Centre project (MMIC), UK (project ownership: Centre for Process Innovation, CPI). Funding has come from Innovate UK and Scottish Enterprise. Founding industry partners with significant financial and technical support are AstraZeneca and GlaxoSmithKline. The University of Strathclyde (via CMAC) is the founding academic partner. Pfizer are project partners and have provided key technical input and data. Project partners DFE Pharma have provided materials and technical input, and project partners Gericke AG have provided technical equipment support and advice. Project partners Siemens and Applied Materials have provided key software and software/IT expertise.

References

Brone, D., Alexander, A., Muzzio, F.J., 1998. AIChE J. 44, 271–278.

Cervera-Padrell, A.E., Gani, R., Kiil, S., Skovby, T., Gernaey, K.V., 2011. In: 21st European Symposium on Computer Aided Process Engineering, Computer-Aided Chemical Engineering. Elsevier, AMSTERDAM, pp. 271–275.

Duckworth, W., 1953. Discussion of Ryshkewitch Paper. J. Am. Ceram. Soc. 36.

Gao, Y., Muzzio, F.J., Ierapetritou, M.G., 2013. Powder Technol. 235, 55–69. https://doi.org/10.1016/j.powtec.2012.09.036

Gerogiorgis, D.I., Barton, P.I., 2009. In: Rita Maria de Brito Alves, C.A.O. do N. and E.C.B. (Ed.), Computer Aided Chemical Engineering, 10th International Symposium on Process Systems Engineering: Part A. Elsevier, pp. 927–932.

Ierapetritou, M., Muzzio, F., Reklaitis, G., 2016. AIChE J. 62, 1846–1862. h

Jaspers, M., Roelofs, T.P., Lohrmann, A., Tegel, F., Maqsood, M.K., Song, Y.L., Meir, B., Elkes, R., Dickhoff, B.H.J., 2023. Powder Technol. 428,

Kushner, J., 2012. Int. J. Pharm. 429, 1–11.0

Kushner, J., Moore, F., 2010. Int. J. Pharm. 399, 19–30.

Kushner, J., Schlack, H., 2014. Int. J. Pharm. 475, 147–155.

Lee, S.L., O'Connor, T.F., Yang, X., Cruz, C.N., Chatterjee, S., Madurawe, R.D., Moore, C.M.V., Yu, L.X., Woodcock, J., 2015. J. Pharm. Innov. 1–9.

Moghtadernejad, S., Escotet-Espinoza, M.S., Oka, S., Singh, R., Liu, Z., Román-Ospino, A.D., Li, T., Razavi, S., Panikar, S., Scicolone, J., Callegari, G., Hausner, D., Muzzio, F., 2018. Pharm. Innov. 13, 155–187.

Nassar, J., Williams, B., Davies, C., Lief, K., Elkes, R., 2021. Int. J. Pharm. 592, 119980.

Plumb, K., 2005. Chem. Eng. Res. Des. 83, 730–738.

Ryshkewitch, E., 1953. J. Am. Ceram. Soc. 36, 65–68.

Vanarase, A.U., Muzzio, F.J., 2011.Powder Technol. 208, 26–36.

Flavio Manenti, Gintaras V. Reklaitis (Eds.), Proceedings of the 34th European Symposium on Computer Aided Process Engineering / 15th International Symposium on Process Systems Engineering (ESCAPE34/PSE24), June 2-6, 2024, Florence, Italy
 http://dx.doi.org/10.1016/B978-0-443-28824-1.50182-4

Design and Planning of Socially Responsible Pharmaceutical Supply Chains Considering Procurement Strategies

Inês Duarte[a*], Bruna Mota[a], Tânia Pinto-Varela[a], Ana Amaro[b], Ana Paula Barbosa-Povoa[a]

[a] *Centre for Management Studies of IST (CEG-IST), University of Lisbon. Av Rovisco Pais, 1, 1049-001 Lisbon, Portugal*

[b] *Coimbra Business School-ISCAC/ IPC, Quinta Agrícola, 3045-601 Coimbra, Portugal*

ines.r.duarte@tecnico.ulisboa.pt

Abstract

Pharmaceutical supply chains operate in a complex global environment, facing challenges such as medicine shortages caused by raw material scarcity and demand fluctuations. In this context, the awareness of creating sustainable supply chains is high, and ensuring both economic viability and social responsibility is essential. This work proposes a decision-support tool based on a multi-objective mixed-integer linear programming model for the design and planning of pharmaceutical supply chains. The proposed tool leverages the Kraljic matrix to categorize raw materials based on their supply risk and profit impact, enabling the identification of efficient procurement strategies. The optimization model aids in making strategic and tactical decisions while fulfilling economic and social objectives. The economic objective intends to maximize the Net Present Value. The social dimension is explored through two different approaches: a) an objective function that prioritizes the location of entities in areas with higher incidence of diseases and b) the concern of affordability of different markets exploring the concept of demand-to-price elasticity. The model is applied to a case-study where several scenarios are analysed showing how strategic and tactical decisions are impacted by variations on both supply and demand sides, and how it impacts the performance of sustainability indicators. Moreover, it provides insights into creating socially responsible pharmaceutical supply chains and strategies to reduce vulnerabilities in raw materials sourcing.

Keywords: Pharmaceutical Supply Chains; Sustainability; Procurement strategies; Accessibility; Optimization.

1. Introduction

In the face of several challenges within globally dispersed supply chain entities that demand close integration in an uncertain environment, supply chains face an increasing awareness on establishing sustainable practices (Barbosa-Póvoa et al., 2018). Pharmaceutical supply chains are no exception, and they are crucial to support the health and quality of life of populations. However, medicines shortages caused by raw material scarcity, quality issues, and demand fluctuations persist, leading to unequal access to these products (FDA, 2019). Hence, promoting global access to medicines is crucial, making it imperative to integrate social concerns in the management of pharmaceutical supply chain objectives (Milanesi et al., 2020). Moreover, suppliers' failures and insufficient raw material availability represent significant risks that can have far-reaching implications as they mark the initial phase of a supply chain, and effects can ripple through the entire supply chain (Jaberidoost et al., 2013). Given this, establishing effective procurement strategies can significantly impact the supply chain performance. Based on the challenges outlined, this work presents the following contributions:

- Proposes a multi-objective model for the design and planning of pharmaceutical supply chains that includes both strategic and tactical decisions;
- Addresses vulnerabilities in the supply of raw materials and identifies effective procurement strategies envisioning the reduction of supply risk and profit impact, according to Kraljic Matrix's classification of raw materials;
- Explores two social approaches focused on improving equitable access to pharmaceutical products;
- Incorporates economic and social considerations as objective functions, allowing the analysis of trade-offs between these two sustainability pillars.

2. Problem Definition and Mathematical Formulation

In this work, the Kraljic matrix is used to classify raw materials regarding their supply risk and profit impact. This classification enables the identification of procurement strategies aimed at reducing supply risk and minimizing profit impact (Kraljic, 1983). This framework allows to categorize materials into strategic items, leverage items, bottleneck items and non-critical items, depending on two main factors: a) supply risk – associated with the availability of suppliers, substitution opportunities, make-or-buy opportunities, and storage risks; b) profit impact – related with the volume of materials purchased, the percentage it represents on the total purchase costs, and the impact that it has on product quality and business growth. When designing and planning pharmaceutical supply chains, it is important to consider appropriate procurement strategies for each raw material, as they play a key role in managing supply risk and optimizing profit impact. The strategic and tactical decisions made during this process significantly influence the overall performance of the supply chain. The mathematical model proposed is based on the model initially introduced by Duarte et al. (2022), which is further developed to integrate decisions on the selection of raw materials' suppliers with diverse attributes such as location, capacities, and fluctuating costs over time. Moreover, planning decisions on the levels of supply of raw materials from each supplier are included, together with production, inventory, and distribution decisions. The objectives being considered intend to contribute to economic and social sustainability improvement of the supply chain and are integrated into the model through two objective functions. Moreover, an additional social approach is integrated to, together with the social objective function, fulfil two strong pillars of equity in access to pharmaceutical products: availability and affordability.

2.1. Economic Sustainability objective

The economic assessment aims to maximize the Net Present Value (NPV) by summing the cash flows of each time-period at an interest rate. These cash flows are achieved through the net earnings (NE_t), which are given by the difference between revenues (amount of products sold (X_{maijt}) at a certain price (ps_{mit})), and the overall costs. As seen in Eq. (1), the supply chain costs considered are raw material costs (first term), production operating costs (second term), storage costs (third term), variable transportation costs (fourth term), hub handling costs (fifth term), contracted costs with airline/freighter (sixth term), inventory costs (seventh term), labour costs at entities (eighth and ninth terms), and finally the labour costs for the use of technologies (tenth term).

$$NE_t = (1-tr)\left[\sum_{\substack{(m,i,j)\in F_{INCFP}\\(a,m,i,j)\in NetP}} ps_{mi}X_{maijt} - \left(\sum_{\substack{(m,i,j)\in F_{OUTSUPRM}\\(a,m,i,j)\in NetP}} rmc_{mi}X_{maijt} + \sum_{\substack{(m,g)\in H_{prod}\\ i\in I_f}} opc_g P_{mgit}\right.\right.$$
$$+ \sum_{\substack{(m,g)\in H_{stor}\\ i\in(I_f\cup I_w)}} opc_g S_{mgit} + \sum_{\substack{(a,m,i,j)\in NetP\\ a\in(A_{plane}\cup A_{boat}\cup A_{trucks})}} tc_a.pw_m.d_{ij}.X_{maijt} + \sum_{\substack{(a,m,i,j)\in NetP\\ (j\in I_{plane/boat}\wedge i\notin I_{plane/boat})}} hhc_j.X_{maijt}$$
$$+ \sum_{i\in(I_{plane}\cup I_{boat})} cfp_i.Y_i + \sum_{\substack{(m,g)\in H_{stor}\\(m,i)\in V}} sc_m S_{mgit} + \sum_{i\in(I_f\cup I_w)} w_i.lc_i.wwh.wpt.Y_i$$
$$\left.\left. + \sum_{i\in(I_f\cup I_w)} wpsq.lc_i.wwh.wpt.YC_i + \sum_{\substack{(m,g)\in H\\ i\in I_f}} w_g.lc_i.wwh.wpt.Z_{gmi}\right) + tr.DP_t\right] \quad (1)$$

2.2. Social Sustainability assessment

The social sustainability assessment is focused on improving equity in access to pharmaceutical products, by improving two strong pillars: Availability and Affordability. The Availability pillar aims to prioritize populations with higher incidence of a disease to which the product being produced and distributed is essential for prevention or treatment. Hence, the objective function defined in Eq. (2) maximizes the location of entities in areas with higher DALY (Disability-Adjusted Life Years) - a metric that reflects the burden of a disease as a rate per 100,000 population. In Eq. (2) the parameter p_i^{DALY} is used together with the binary decision variable, Y_i, to prioritize the location of entity i in geographical areas with higher DALY value. Additionally, a restriction is used to ensure that, when a manufacturing facility is open for production, it produces a percentage of its production to satisfy the local demand, guaranteeing the improvement of accessibility of the population of its geographical area.

$$\max PharmaAccess = \left(\sum_{i\in(I_f\cup I_w)} p_i^{DALY}.\ Y_i\right) \quad (2)$$

The Affordability pillar is explored through demand-to-price elasticity (Duarte et al., 2023). This approach aims to balance the supply and demand sides while considering affordability concerns. The elasticity coefficient, ϵ_{mi}, translates the connection between demand and price and is determined by the absolute value of the logarithmic change in demand concerning price. Demand is categorized as elastic if its relative change is greater than or equal to the corresponding relative price fluctuation ($|\epsilon_{mi}| \geq 1$), and inelastic otherwise ($|\epsilon_{mi}| < 1$). This elasticity coefficient varies with the product (m) and the market (i) since different markets have different affordability levels, affecting their sensitivity to price fluctuations. This approach aims to explore how the demand-to-price elasticity can be related with the quantity and price that a company can set, as well as the population's capacity to afford that price, as defined in Eq. (3). The demand (D_{mit}) is derived from a polynomial relationship with the corresponding price (ps_{mit}), and B_{mit} establishes the minimal demand threshold for the minimum feasible price (Eq. (4)).

$$Dm_{mit} = \beta_{mit}\,(pm_{mit})^{\epsilon_{mi}} \quad \leftrightarrow \quad \ln(Dm_{mit}) = \ln(\beta_{mit}) + \epsilon_{mi}\ln(pm_{mit}) \quad (3)$$

And considering $D_{mit} = \ln(Dm_{mit})$; $B_{mit} = \ln(\beta_{mit})$; $ps_{mit} = \ln(pm_{mit})$ a linear relation is achieved: $D_{mit} = B_{mit} + \epsilon_{mi}\ ps_{mit}$ (4)

3. Case-study

The pharmaceutical company investigated in this study manufactures and distributes a meningitis conjugate vaccine. Low- and middle-income countries do not acquire this vaccine due to its price. Africa and Eastern Mediterranean region countries have expressed the desire to incorporate this vaccine into their standard immunization programmes but have encountered challenges in obtaining these vaccines because of its high price and limited availability (World Health Organization, 2019). The considered global pharmaceutical supply chain is composed of multiple suppliers, two factories (located in France and the U.S.), airports, seaports, and five markets - U.S, Australia, Europe, Africa and Middle East. A possible new factory location in Africa explores the possibility of increasing accessibility for this vaccine in this market. The vaccine under study (final product – Fp) requires four main raw materials for it to be produced: Active Pharmaceutical Ingredients (Rm1), supporting chemical materials (Rm2), vials (Rm3) and card package (Rm4). These raw materials are categorized in terms of supply risk and profit impact in the Kraljic matrix. **Rm1** is a **strategic material** (high percentage of the total purchase costs of the company and high risk of supply with only one supplier available, located in UK). Hence, the most efficient procurement strategy is to focus on long-term contracts with the supplier in order to minimize the supply risk. **Rm2**, a **leverage item**, has a high profit impact but lower supply risk. Exploiting purchasing power and minimizing costs should be considered as procurement strategies for this material. Diversifying suppliers is guaranteed by the possibility of supplying this material from two different suppliers, located in Texas and Lyon. **Rm3** and **Rm4** are **non-critical items**, characterized by a lower percentage of the total purchase costs representing a lower impact on profit, and a lower supply risk. Efficient procurement strategies involve simplification and automation of procurement processes, as well as guaranteeing abundant supply to keep supply risk low. Hence material Rm3 has three suppliers available located in Lyon, Kosamba, and Morganton, and material Rm4 has three suppliers available located in Essen, Mumbai, and Chicago. These suppliers differ between them not only in their location, but also in the price of the material they supply. As mentioned previously, demand is a decision variable and the obtained value is influenced by changes in the price of the product along time and the elasticity coefficient of the corresponding market namely, -4.94, -3.45, -0.69, -0.14, -0.05 for U.S., Australia, Middle East, Europe, and Africa, respectively. These values were calculated using procurement data from WHO's MI4A/VP3 database (Market Information for Access to Vaccines/Vaccine Product, Price, and Procurement) for the year 2022. The first two markets are characterized by an elastic demand to price, while the others are inelastic.

4. Results and Discussion

The results focus on three scenarios (1, 2 and 3) over two cases (A and B).

In the **first scenario (base scenario)** two cases are studied where lexicographic optimization was used: Case A corresponds to the optimum economic performance; Case B corresponds to the optimum social performance of the *Pharma Access* objective. Results for scenario 1 are shown in Table 1. Different supply chain structures are obtained depending on the prioritized sustainability pillar. The social sustainability pillar can be improved from 37.7 (Case A) to its maximum performance of 252.72 (case B). In its optimum performance, corresponding to Case B, all factories produce the vaccine at a production capacity at least equal to the local demand with a profit decrease of 1.3% (nearly 22.5M€). This decrease in profit for Case B is primarily due to higher labor and transportation costs, along with investments in technologies and entities necessary for the installation of the two additional factories, in U.S. and Africa.

Table 1. Supply chain topology and performance indicators' results for scenario 1

Scenario 1		Case A	Case B
	NPV (€)	1.810E+09	1.787E+09
	s- Suppliers and f- Factories	sUK (Rm1), sLyon (Rm2), sLyon (Rm3), sEssen (Rm4); fFrance	sUK (Rm1), sLyon and sTexas (Rm2), sLyon and sMorganton (Rm3), sEssen and sChicago (Rm4); fFrance, fUS, fAfrica
	Transportation network	Predominantly high-capacity trucks; Intercontinental transportation by plane (4 airports) and boat (4 seaports)	Predominantly high-capacity trucks; Intercontinental transportation by plane (3 airports) and boat (4 seaports)

The **second scenario** explores the impact of a rise in the cost of raw materials on the design and planning decisions. Only Case A is analysed. Variations on the cost of a raw material are introduced on the supplier chosen on the base scenario. These variations (increase of 20%, 60%, and 150%) are introduced in the 5th year of a planning period of 10 years and aim to explore disruptive situations that significantly influence supply chain decisions. From the obtained results for scenario 2 (Table 2) it is observed that an increase of Rm1's price by sUK will have implications on the profit reached, while the same supply chain configuration is obtained, since there is no other supplier available. An increase of 60% on the price of Rm2 by sLyon results in a different supply chain structure since a different supplier with a lower price is chosen (sTexas), even so, a global profit decrease of 1.8% is obtained. An increase of 150% leads to the selection of sMumbai to supply Rm4 to the factory fFrance, instead of sEssen initially chosen, and a profit decrease of 4%, corresponding to 72 million euros. It is relevant to point out that for the present case-study, considerable percentual increases on the price of the raw materials are necessary to lead to changes in the suppliers' selection since the factory chosen in scenario 1 – Case A to produce the final product is located in France and the suppliers selected are the–ones located closer to this factory. Hence, the choice of other suppliers is associated with an increase of transportation costs, leading to a decrease of the NPV. In scenario 2, the optimum performance obtained for Pharma Access indicator was 37.7 as in scenario 1- Case A.

Table 2. Supply chain topology and performance indicators' results for scenario 2

Scenario 2		Case A		
	Variations*	**↑20%**	**↑60%**	**↑150%**
	NPV (€)	1.799E+09	1.780E+09	1.737E+09
	s- Suppliers and f- Factories	sUK (Rm1), sLyon (Rm2), sLyon (Rm3), sEssen (Rm4); fFrance	sUK (Rm1), sLyon (Rm2, $t < 5$), sTexas (Rm2, $t \geq 5$), sLyon (Rm3), sEssen (Rm4); fFrance	sUK (Rm1), sLyon (Rm2, $t <$ 5), sTexas (Rm2, $t \geq 5$), sLyon (Rm3), sEssen (Rm4, $t < 5$), sMumbai (Rm4, $t \geq$ 5); fFrance

*Percentual increase on the price of raw materials by suppliers chosen in scenario 1 – Case A, introduced in period 5 of a total planning period of 10 years.

An increase in the cost of purchased raw materials may lead to an increase in the price of the final product as a strategy for the company to recover the profit lost. This study proposes to account not only for the economic performance of a company, but also to consider social concerns related with availability and affordability of pharmaceutical products. In scenario 2, a 60% increase in the raw material cost provided by the initially selected suppliers in the base scenario was introduced. Building upon this, **scenario 3** introduces an additional variation of the price of the final vaccine in each market. These variations include an increase of 2% in the price of the vaccine for high income markets, U.S. and Australia, whereas a decrease of 15% is applied to the remaining markets. These price variations are introduced in the 5th year of a planning period of 10 years.

The same supply chain structure was obtained but with different demand responses, depending on the market and its sensitivity to the introduced price variations. In the markets where a price decrease of 15% was introduced, demand rose by 10.5% in Middle East, 1.96% in Europe and 0.75% in Africa, therefore increasing the affordability of this vaccine to these markets. On the other hand, a demand decrease of 9% in U.S. and 7% in Australia was obtained due to a price increase of 2%. Although the effect of the same variation results in consistent behaviour among markets, the magnitude of these responses is distinct, depending on the demand-price elasticities experienced by each market. The increase in the price of the vaccine being distributed and sold to the high-income markets of the U.S. and Australia leads to a decrease in the demand of these markets which can be explained by the existence of substitute vaccines produced by other companies in these two markets. This means that for the vaccine under consideration, the markets with greater purchasing power and higher affordability levels, are also the markets with higher product availability, leading to a higher sensitivity to price variations (higher elasticity coefficients). Hence, the markets' response to the variations introduced results in a 6% decrease in NPV compared to the base scenario. In conclusion, to offset the profit loss from increased raw material costs, the company should consider more effective strategies other than raising prices in higher purchasing power markets.

5. Conclusions

This work proposes an optimization model for the design and planning of economically and socially sustainable supply chains. Different scenarios are proposed which reveal the importance of having efficient procurement strategies that allow a company to reduce the risk associated with raw materials supply, such as increased costs or disruptive situations. Moreover, this study highlights the importance and impact of considering both economic and social concerns when designing and planning pharmaceutical supply chains.

Acknowledgements: The authors acknowledge the support provided by FCT under the project PTDC/EME-SIS/6019/2020 and UIDB/00097/2020, and PhD Grant 2022.11365.BD.

References

Barbosa-Póvoa, A. P., da Silva, C., & Carvalho, A. (2018). Opportunities and challenges in sustainable supply chain: An operations research perspective. *European Journal of Operational Research*, *268*(2), 399–431. https://doi.org/10.1016/j.ejor.2017.10.036

Duarte, I., Mota, B., Pinto-Varela, T., Amaro, A., & Barbosa-Povoa, A. P. (2023). Modelling availability and affordability concerns in the design and planning of pharmaceutical supply chains. *Computer Aided Chemical Engineering*, *52*, 3369–3374. https://doi.org/10.1016/B978-0-443-15274-0.50537-0

Duarte, I., Mota, B., Pinto-Varela, T., & Barbosa-Póvoa, A. P. (2022). Pharmaceutical industry supply chains: How to sustainably improve access to vaccines? *Chemical Engineering Research and Design*, *182*, 324–341. https://doi.org/10.1016/j.cherd.2022.04.001

FDA. (2019). Drug Shortages: Root Causes and Potential Solutions: A Report by the Drug Shortages Task Force. *U.S. Food and Drug Administration (FDA)*, 1–6.

Jaberidoost, M., Nikfar, S., Abdollahiasl, A., & Dinarvand, R. (2013). Pharmaceutical supply chain risks: A systematic review. *DARU, Journal of Pharmaceutical Sciences*, *21*(1), 1–7. https://doi.org/10.1186/2008-2231-21-69

Milanesi, M., Runfola, A., & Guercini, S. (2020). Pharmaceutical industry riding the wave of sustainability: Review and opportunities for future research. *Journal of Cleaner Production*, *261*, 121204. https://doi.org/10.1016/j.jclepro.2020.121204

World Health Organization (2019). *Global Market Study: Meningococcal Meningitis Vaccines*. https://cdn.who.int/media/docs/default-source/immunization/mi4a/who_meningococcal_vaccines_public_summary.pdf

Flavio Manenti, Gintaras V. Reklaitis (Eds.), Proceedings of the 34th European Symposium on Computer Aided Process Engineering / 15th International Symposium on Process Systems Engineering (ESCAPE34/PSE24), June 2-6, 2024, Florence, Italy
 http://dx.doi.org/10.1016/B978-0-443-28824-1.50183-6

Techno-economic and environmental assessment of plastic waste pyrolysis: From a linear to a circular economy

Christine El Khoury, Laureano Jiménez, Carlos Pozo*

Departament d'Enginyeria Quimica, Universitat Rovira i Virgili, Av. Països Catalans 26, 43007 Tarragona, Spain
corresponding author: carlos.pozo@urv.cat

Abstract

Single use plastics, although beneficial, pose environmental challenges when discarded. Chemical recycling offers a sustainable solution by breaking down plastic waste into monomers, allowing for continuous production of plastic without downgrading its properties. In this contribution, a lab-sized pyrolysis reaction of polypropylene waste was transformed into an industrial process using a simulation-optimization approach with Aspen HYSYS. This baseline simulation, which includes energy integration, was used as a basis to create nine alternative scenarios using different technologies. In addition, a circularity metric was used to assess the degree of material circularity obtained in the pyrolysis process. Heat integration allowed for a 61% reduction in energy costs of the process. In addition, our study proves that product recovery from waste polypropylene pyrolysis could be 94% circular, which can play a significant role in reduction of raw material extraction and carbon emissions. Pyrolysis has the potential of processing a wide range of plastic types, making it a promising technology to combat and add value to plastic waste.

Keywords: Plastic Waste, Pyrolysis, Circular Economy, Process Systems Engineering

1. Introduction

Since the mid-20th century, plastics have been known for significantly impacting our lives. However, they also pose a substantial environmental threat, with over 8300 million tons produced globally, 70% becoming waste, and 84% of that waste finding its way into the environment (Smet et al., 2019). In Europe, approximately 32% of plastic waste is recycled, 43% is incinerated, and the remaining 25% is sent to landfills (Mortensen & Tange, 2021). However, both landfills and incineration pose long-term threats to the environment, with incineration offering a minor detour with energy recovery (Payne et al., 2019). Recycling, mostly done mechanically today, cannot preserve plastic properties, resulting in a product that is no longer suitable for the original application. Hence, it can only reduce partially the accumulation of plastic waste and raw material extraction.

The need to incorporate the circular economy concept into advanced recycling technologies is a key driver for adding value to plastic waste, thereby lessening carbon emissions as well as the reliance on fossil-based feedstock to produce commodity plastics. In this context, chemical recycling emerges as a promising alternative. Chemical recycling, unlike mechanical, enables the return to the monomer, ensuring the production of high-quality plastic further down the value chain. This form of recycling can be considered as a closed-loop process, where the recycled plastics are used completely and entirely to produce again plastics (the same or others) with the original properties. Pyrolysis, a form of chemical recycling, operates at moderate to high temperatures in the absence of oxygen, breaking down the polymer chain into shorter carbon-based chains

(Stallkamp et al., 2023). Prior research has examined the use of pyrolysis oil extracted from polypropylene waste as a promising diesel substitute, finding that it has the potential to contribute significantly to mitigating the increasing challenge of waste disposal (Pacheco-López et al., 2021). Somoza-Tornos et al. (2020) utilized techno-economic and life cycle assessment to compare different end-of-life alternatives for polyethylene waste, concluding that pyrolysis can be both economically and environmentally beneficial. However, these contributions did not assess the degree of circularity that could be achieved through the pyrolysis process.

In this contribution, we study the conversion of plastic waste into value-added chemicals from an economic and an environmental perspective, the latter addressed through a circularity metric. To this end, we created a preliminary design of an industrial process for the chemical recycling of waste polypropylene (PP) and used it as a case study to explore the degree of circularity that can be achieved under different scenarios, and at which cost.

2. Methodology

We departed from lab scale experimental data of a pyrolysis reaction, which we turned into the core of a scaled-up industrial process, that we designed using a simulation-optimization approach with Aspen HYSYS, with Peng-Robinson as fluid package. The real-life model generated potential products and was further optimized. Primarily, the pyrolysis of polypropylene (PP) waste takes place at 700°C, yielding a myriad of products (Honus et al., 2016). Major components were retained, representing 92.9% of the total mass, and we normalized their composition to add to 100%. Hence, the reaction products considered are, on a mass basis: 6.7% methane, 10.4% ethylene, 7.6% ethane, 47.1% propylene and 28.3% 1-butene. Finally, the stoichiometric coefficients for the adjusted pseudo-reaction were obtained considering a molecular weight of 12,000 g/mol for PP, and a composition of 85.6% carbon and 14.4% hydrogen (equation (1)).

$$0.0833\ PP \rightarrow 4.176\ CH_4 + 3.697\ C_2H_4 + 2.514\ C_2H_6 + 11.188\ C_3H_6 + 5.042\ C_4H_8 \quad (1)$$

We assumed that the plant operates 330 days a year and 24 hours a day, with a feed rate of 19,000 kg/h. The pyrolysis furnace modelled as a conversion reactor, uses diesel as a fuel and achieves a 100% conversion, as reported from lab experiments.

After the reactor, a multi-stage compressor was added to minimize the cryogenic operating temperatures in the condensers of the distillation columns downstream. The compressor operating conditions (inner temperatures and stage pressures) were optimized to minimize the annualized cost using Aspen HYSYS optimizer tool. For economical analysis, the following unit costs, retrieved from literature, were considered: plastic waste (175 €/ton), sorting (314.56 €/ton), methane (1.43 €/litre), ethylene (1.12 €/kg), ethane (0.26 €/kg), propylene (0.89 €/kg), 1-butene (1.13 €/kg), natural gas (0.07 €/kWh), gasoline (1.63 €/litre), ethanol (1.93 €/litre), diesel (1.59 €/litre), steam ($2.29 \cdot 10^{-4}$ €/kJ), electricity (0.12 €/kWh), cooling water (1.4 €/kJ).

After the compressor, a separation train, comprising four distillation columns, was incorporated to ensure 98% recovery for the five products. The optimal sequence for this train was obtained based on the minimum vapour flow method (Modi & Westerberg, 1992). In addition, the design of each column was optimized separately to minimize its total annualized cost (Towler & Sinnott, 2008), using the number of stages as the decision variable. With pyrolysis being an energy intensive process, energy integration was implemented to reduce energy consumption. Applying the pinch methodology is essential to optimize the recovery of process heat, enabling the ideal equilibrium between capital (size of the heat exchanger network) and operational expenditure (utility cost).

With the process simulation for the baseline case at hand, nine different scenarios were created by varying different technological decisions. On the one hand, four different fossil-based fuels were employed in the furnace: diesel (baseline), ethanol, gasoline and natural gas. Five additional scenarios were also explored where pyrolysis products were individually reused as fuel in the furnace, instead of sold as a products. No additional fuel was needed to fulfill the furnace requirements in all these cases, which hilighlights the energetic value of pyrolysis gases. In addition, the nine scenarios consider the implementation of carbon capture and sequestration (CCS) in the pyrolysis furnace, with a capture rate of 90% of the CO_2 in the flue gas. The application of CCS aligns with environmental goals of mitigating carbon emissions and contributing to the overall reduction of greenhouse gases, thereby addressing climate change concerns.

Finally, we introduce the concept of the material circularity index (MCI), which serves the purpose of facilitating the assessment of material circularity. This index could help decision-makers to identify processes with a high degree of circularity, emphasizing on the extension of resource lifespan, and reducing the need for raw material extraction. The MCI (equation 3) employs a straightforward scale ranging from 0 to 1, where 0 represents a linear process, and 1 signifies a fully circular one, indicating the potential for both resource and product lifespan extension. In our case, the numerator represents all the products obtained from the pyrolysis, while the denominator denotes the amount of feed (i.e., sorted waste polypropylene) (Circle Economy & Deloitte, 2023). We considered all products recovered since they can be reused as virgin material in other processes, either to produce PP or other products.

$$Material\ Circularity\ Index\ (MCI) = \frac{Product\ mass\ recovered}{Total\ material\ consumption} \quad (3)$$

3. Results and discussion

3.1. Process simulation and economic performance

The optimized process flowsheet is depicted in Figure 1, where we intentionally avoided most of the heat exchanger network to facilitate visualization.

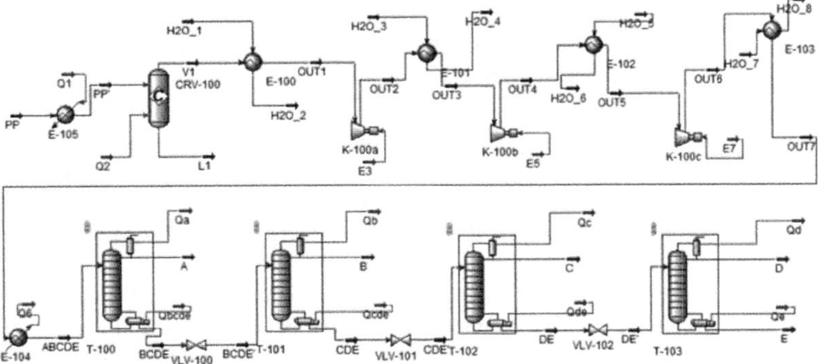

Figure 1: Flowsheet of the polypropylene pyrolysis process

In this case, we found the direct separation sequence to be the optimal, where we first separate methane (stream A), then ethylene (B), then ethane (C) and finally propylene

(D) and 1-butene (E). Purities of the major components in each product stream range 91%-99% on a molar basis. As aforementioned, we next use the results (mass and energy balance) from this baseline simulation to explore the performance of nine alternative scenarios in terms of cost and circularity.

We next turn our attention to a comprehensive economic assessment of the nine scenarios considered (Figure 2). Bars provide the breakdown of process expenditures, with product sales depicted as negative values. The final net cost is given by markers over the bars.

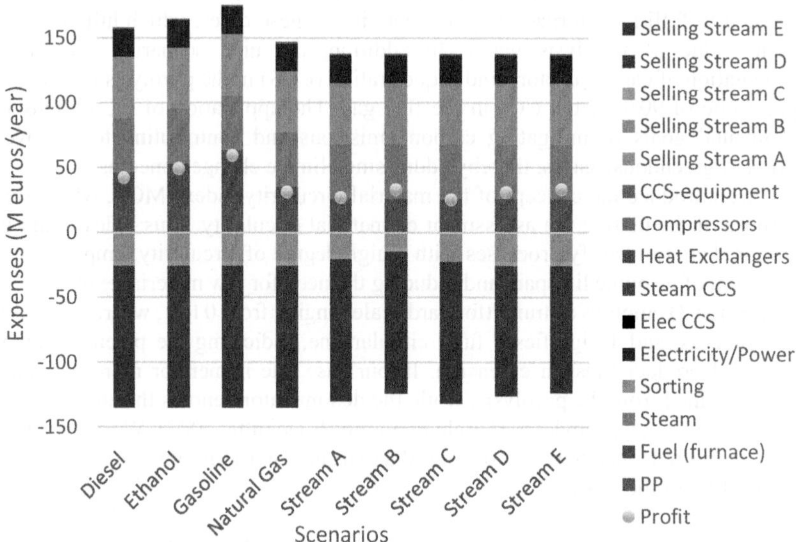

Figure 2: Annual cost breakdown of the optimized pyrolysis process for the nine scenarios studied.

Importantly, we found no scenario with the capacity to become economically appealing, since product sales are always lower than process expenditures. This situation can be explained by the large cost of sorting the plastic waste, which is the most expensive item in the nine scenarios. Sorting costs represent between 25% and 31% of the total expenditure of the process. We note that the sorting process is crucial to separate specific plastic fractions, which sometimes allow for more efficient chemical recycling processes, therefore aligning with the principles of circular economy.

In this case, heat integration resulted in 23 heat exchangers, which allowed us to bring down the annual costs of energy from 188 million euros to 74 million euros (61% reduction). Note that these results include the condensers and the reboilers of the distillation columns. Considering a lifespan of 30 years for the heat exchangers, this one-time purchase accounts for less than 1% of the total energy costs of the process.

In the first four scenarios, where the products obtained are sold to other industries, these contribute with sales worth 135 million euros annually, thus reducing the (gross) process expenditures. Stream D, mostly propylene, adds large benefit to each of these scenarios, covering about 46% of the total sales. Stream E, mainly 1-butene, is responsible for 34% of total sales. This is because both streams are produced in large quantities, in addition to their high value, with a propylene price of 0.89 €/kg and 1-butene of 1.13 €/kg. On the other hand, these scenarios are also characterized by a high process cost, ranging 159-187 million euros annually, since outsourced fuels are used to operate the furnace. In this

regard, gasoline emerges as the costliest option (0.08 €/MJ), while natural gas is the cheapest alternative (0.02 €/MJ).
In the other five scenarios, pyrolysis products are reused as fuel in the furnace, reducing sales as only the unused portion of the streams is marketed. In turn, this leads to significant savings, as there is no requirement for outsourced fuels in the furnace. The magnitude of these savings depends on the reference fuel used in the furnace and on the process stream reused as fuel. According to our estimates, reusing methane (stream A) and ethane (C) are the best options among all the scenarios considered. This is not surprising given that methane and ethane have the largest MJ/€, standing at 101 and 186 MJ/€, respectively.

3.2. Environmental Assessment: material circularity

In the initial four scenarios, where all the product streams are sold to other industrial processes and fossil-fuels are used in the furnace, a 100% MCI for the pyrolysis process is achieved. This value can be deemed as an upper bound on the overall material circularity that could not be achieved in practice, since losses will likely occur in other parts of the supply chain (e.g., transformation of monomers back into polymers).
In the other five scenarios, where some product streams are reused as fuel in the pyrolysis furnace, not all the material is recovered, thus decreasing the MCI to approximately 94%. Recall that these were the scenarios achieving the best economic performance, which shows that a trade-off exists between these two metrics. Hence, to substantiate the decision-making process, we plot these metrics in Figure 3.

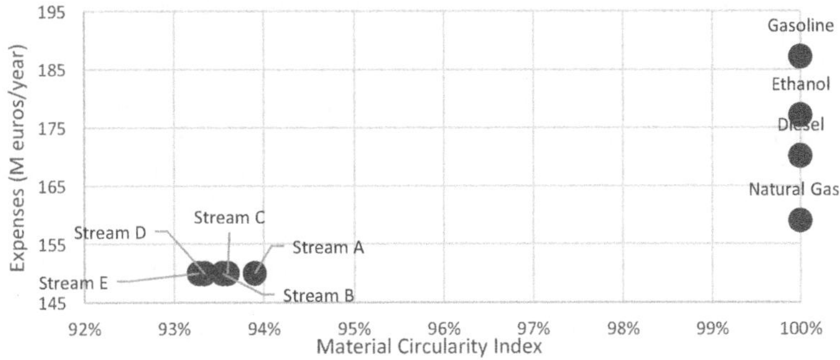

Figure 3: Scatter plot depicting the material circularity vs the process expenses for the nine scenarios studied.

Indeed, we found that using outsourced fuels in the furnace leads to higher circularity, despite not being as cost effective as when product streams replace them. Analysing these results through the lens of multi-objective optimization, only two strong Pareto optimal solutions are found: selling all products and outsourcing natural gas for the furnace (Natural Gas scenario), and reusing methane as fuel in the furnace (Stream A). Hence, methane (the main component of natural gas) at 99% purity, proves to be an excellent substitute for natural gas. It displays 21% lower expenses compared to the other strong Pareto scenario, while maintaining a commendable MCI 94%. The remaining scenarios explored can all be regarded as weak Pareto points (within a certain numerical tolerance), and therefore inferior to the two aforementioned cases.

4. Conclusions

This study capitalized on laboratory-scale data of a pyrolysis reaction of waste PP to design an industrial process for its chemical recycling. To this end, we used a simulation-optimization approach, complemented with a heat-exchanger network that allowed to reduce the process costs by 61%. Results from this baseline simulation were used to examine nine scenarios involving different options for the fuel used in the furnace: four scenarios with different outsourced fuels, and five scenarios utilizing the products streams as fuels. We found scenarios to achieve high values for material circularity in the pyrolysis process, ranging from 93%-100%. These values should be understood as upper bounds on the real material circularity that can be achieved, since material losses are expected to occur in other transformation processes necessary to close the circle. Unfortunately, these promising results are not paired by an equally appealing economic performance, since none of the scenarios managed to achieve a positive profit (net expenses ranging from 159 to 187 million euros annually). This demonstrates the need to devote further research efforts to improve this process. Meanwhile, subsidies could help penetrate chemical recycling in the market, as these processes generate valuable chemicals from plastic waste, while achieving significant degrees of material circularity. Our contribution can aid with generating a solution to the accumulation of plastic waste.

References

A. Pacheco-López, F. Lechtenberg, A. Somoza-Tornos, M. Graells & A. Espuña, 2021, Economic and Environmental Assessment of Plastic Waste Pyrolysis Products and Biofuels as Substitutes for Fossil-Based Fuels, Frontiers in Energy Research, 9.

A.K. Modi, & A.W. Westerberg, 1992, Process Engineering and Design Distillation Column Sequencing Using Marginal Price, In Chem. Res.

C. Stallkamp, M. Hennig, R. Volk, F. Richter, B. Bergfeldt, S. Tavakkol, F. Schultmann, & D. Stapf, 2023, Economic and environmental assessment of automotive plastic waste end-of-life options: Energy recovery versus chemical recycling, Journal of Industrial Ecology.

Circle Economy & Deloitte, 2023, Closing the Circularity Gap in Switzerland-Report.

European Commission, Directorate-General for Research and Innovation, De Smet, M., Linder, M., Koopmans, R. et al., A circular economy for plastics – Insights from research and innovation to inform policy and funding decisions, De Smet, M., Linder, M., Publications Office, 2019.

G. Towler, & R. Sinnott, 2008, Chemical Engineering Design Principles, Practice and Economics of Plant and Process Design.

J. Payne, P. McKeown, & M.D. Jones, 2019, A circular economy approach to plastic waste, In Polymer Degradation and Stability, Vol. 165, pp. 170–181, Elsevier Ltd.

L. F. Mortensen, & I. L. Tange, 2021, Plastics, the circular economy, and Europe's environment-A priority for action.

S. Honus, S. Kumagai, O. Němček, & T. Yoshioka, 2016, Replacing conventional fuels in USA, Europe, and UK with plastic pyrolysis gases – Part I: Experiments and graphical interchangeability methods. Energy Conversion and Management, 126, 1118–1127.

Flavio Manenti, Gintaras V. Reklaitis (Eds.), Proceedings of the 34th European Symposium on Computer Aided Process Engineering / 15th International Symposium on Process Systems Engineering (ESCAPE34/PSE24), June 2-6, 2024, Florence, Italy
 http://dx.doi.org/10.1016/B978-0-443-28824-1.50184-8

Modeling Substrate Degradation in Upflow Anaerobic Sludge Blanket Reactors

Federico Moretta, Luisa Carbone, Giulia Bozzano

Politecnico di Milano, Dipartimento di Chimica, Materiali ed Ingegneria Chimica, p.zza Leonardo da Vinci, 32, 20133, Milano (MI), Italy.
giulia.bozzano@polimi.it

Abstract

Anaerobic digestion concerns the conversion of organic resources into biogas, providing clean energy. The upflow anaerobic sludge blanket (UASB) reactor, known for its efficiency in wastewater treatment, utilizes biomass as granules, enhancing efficiency and reducing costs. However, the understanding around its substrate-biomass reactivity and interaction is limited, leading to complex and scarce modeling for biogas production and morganic matter remotion prediction. This work develops a dynamic model for UASB reactors, using a tanks-in-series model to better treat the hydrodynamic complexity. A lumped kinetic mechanism identifies key components: substrate, active biomass, inactive biomass, and methane. Emphasis is on granule dynamics, considering reaction-diffusion equations. Diffusion through particle boundary layers is analyzed for a realistic substrate concentration profile. Granule kinetics use the Monod equation, solved numerically through python programming language. The model, validated against literature and industrial data, enhances understanding of UASB reactor substrate degradation, aiding in system optimization for wastewater treatment.

Keywords: Anaerobic Digestion, Sludge, Mathematical Modelling, Transport Phenomena.

1. Introduction

Anaerobic digestion (AD) is an established technology in the wastewater treatment field which, through the metabolization of organic matter, can recover energy by producing biogas, a mixture of methane and carbon dioxide.

1.1. The process

The upflow anaerobic sludge blanket (UASB) is an anaerobic digester in which the microorganisms, that perform the digestion, are in granular form. This determines the capability of treating higher organic loading rates (OLR), a higher efficiency, compact volumes, and lower costs. It is comprised of two sections: a cylindrical column and a gas-solid separator. The influent wastewater enters at the bottom and flows upwards. The first section that it passes through is the sludge bed at the bottom of the reactor, which consists of very active biomass in the form of dense granules and heavy and sedimentable flocs. Here is the region in which the digestion proceeds at the highest rate. The next layer is the sludge blanket, where the microorganisms are present in the form of a suspension of lighter flocs. The various reactions keep going, but at a significantly slower pace. Finally, the three-phase separator divides the gas from the effluent wastewater, while most of the biomass is retained in the reactor.

1.2. The problem and purpose of the work

The aim of this work is to develop a generalized dynamic model to describe the behavior of the reactor, both at the particle scale and at the reactor level. The result proposed is highly innovative, as there is an evident lack of research focus on this type of reactor, despite being one of the most used technologies in its field (Mainardis et al., 2020). Furthermore, a focus is reserved for the dynamics of the granules, considering both kinetics and mass transfer, resulting in a model able to estimate their growth during operations using typical computational fluid dynamics techniques. No kinetic constant and transport parameters regression have been made but derived from common mathematical relations. Most models proposed in the literature are extremely complex, resulting in too high computational times and the necessity of complex input data, thus making them unsuitable for industrial purposes (Boiocchi et al., 2022; Michalopoulos et al., 2018).

1.3. Model key points

The problem under study presents complexities from several points of view: the hydrodynamics are non-ideal, with the fluid behavior being in between that of a plug-flow reactor (PFR) and a continuous stirred tank reactor (CSTR); the biochemical reactions are not describable with simple kinetics due to the inability to identify all the species that participate in the reactions. Finally, mass transport phenomena need to be taken into consideration, because of the heterogeneous nature of the system. Many methods can be identified to describe the fluid dynamics of the process, and the one used for this is the *tanks-in-series* models. This is considered as one-parameter model, since the variable that describes the flow is respectively the number of tanks in series (N) used to model the real reactor. This indicates how close the flow is to either a plug flow or a completely mixed regime, as it is linked to the Peclet (Pe) number. The kinetics are usually expressed by the Monod equation, the most used expression to model the growth of microorganisms. For the transport phenomena, some authors propose to neglect the external mass transfer due to the relatively high upflow velocities in the reactor, while others conclude that it may have a relevant impact on the system. Conversely, the internal mass transfer should not be disregarded.

2. Model description

The model here developed has been called GRANULE (generalized diffusion sludge particle model). It takes into consideration the non-ideal hydrodynamics of the reactor using a tanks-in-series (TIS) model. The core of the work can be identified in the reaction-diffusion equation, solved with the Finite Difference Method. Because of the focus on particle dynamics, a better understanding of the internal and external mass transfer phenomena affecting the granules can be achieved. To have comprehensive knowledge of the behavior of the main components present in the reactor environment, a lumped approach for the kinetics is chosen, with mass balance equations for the substrate, the active and inactive biomass, and the methane produced during the reactions. Because of the impossibility of solving analytically this type of problem, the model was implemented in Python and solved with numerical techniques. The model automatically select the amount of TIS needed for the simulation; through an iterative approach, until steady states conditions are reached.

2.1. Transport Phenomena

To model the particle dynamics, a mass balance of the substrate concentration is written, based on the following hypotheses:

- The granules can be assumed to be spherical in shape and uniform in size.

- The problem is spherically symmetric, meaning that considering a spherical polar system with r as the radial coordinate, θ as the polar angular coordinate and φ as the azimuthal angular coordinate, the only gradient is in the radial direction, making the problem one-dimensional.
- The convective term can be neglected, as it is assumed that the transport due to diffusion is much higher with respect to this (Rodríguez-Gómez et al., 2013).
- A quasi-steady state is assumed to simplify the ODE resolution.
- The biomass concentration inside the particle is uniform.
- The reaction term can be described using the Monod equation.
- The diffusion flux is expressed by Fick's law, and to evaluate the diffusion coefficient $\mathcal{D}$ the Wilke-Chang correlation is used, assuming that the physical characteristics of both the substrate and the wastewater can be approximated with the water ones.
- The external mass transfer coefficient is evaluated using the Kolmogorov theory for turbulent flows.

The resulting expression is:

$$\mathcal{D}\frac{1}{r^2}\frac{d}{dr}\left(r^2\frac{dS_P}{dr}\right) - \frac{\mu_{MAX}}{Y}\frac{X}{K_S+S_P}S_P = 0 \tag{1}$$

Where S_P is the substrate concentration inside the particle [kg/m^3], X is the biomass concentration [kg/m^3], μ_{MAX}[d^{-1}] and K_S [kg/m^3]are respectively the maximum growth rate of the microorganisms and the half-saturation constant, and Y is the stoichiometric yield. With the boundary conditions:

$$\left.\frac{dS_P}{dr}\right|_{r=0} = 0 \tag{2}$$

$$\mathcal{D}\left.\frac{dS_P}{dr}\right|_{r=R} = k_m(S - S_P|_{r=R}) \tag{3}$$

Where Equation (2) is the condition of symmetry at the center of the granule, and Equation (3) states that the diffusive flux at the surface of the particle must be equal to the external convective transport, expressed as the product of the external mass transfer coefficient k_m [m/s] and the difference between the bulk concentration S [kg/m^3] and the concentration on the surface of the particle. S_P is the substrate concentration inside the particle, which differs from S because of the resistance to the transport of the substrate given both by the wastewater (external resistance) and by the particles themselves (internal resistance). Because of this difference, it is more accurate to use S_P in the model. Equation (1) does not have an analytical solution; therefore, the Finite Difference Method was utilized to solve it. The first order derivative was discretized using a *first-order forward difference* scheme and the second derivative was discretized with a *second-order central difference* scheme.

2.2. Kinetic system and mass balances

To take into consideration the non-ideal hydrodynamics of the UASB, a tanks-in-series model has been utilized. The reactor is thus divided into a N number of CSTRs, each of equal volume V_j [m^3]

$$V_j = \frac{V}{N} \tag{4}$$

For each j-th reactor it is possible to write:

$$\frac{dS_j}{dt} = \frac{Q}{V_j}(S_{j-1} - S_j) - \eta R_j \tag{5}$$

$$\frac{dX_j}{dt} = \frac{Q}{V_j}(X_{j-1} - X_j) + \eta R_j Y - K_d X_j \tag{7}$$

$$\frac{dE_j}{dt} = \frac{Q}{V_j}(X_{j-1} - X_j) + K_d X_j \tag{8}$$

These are the mass balances respectively for the concentration of substrate S [kg/m^3], the active biomass X [kg/m^3], and the inactive E [kg/m^3]. The latter is an indication of how much biomass dies during operations. The microbial decay is an inevitable phenomenon due to several factors, especially the lack of nutrients. It is assumed that it can be modeled with a first order kinetic expression, depending on the biomass concentration, and described by the decay constant K_d [d^{-1}]. The reaction term R_j at the macro scale is different with respect to the Monod kinetics, because it needs to consider what is occurring to the particles. It is defined as the diffusion flux, multiplied by the surface that it traverses, *i.e.*, the surface of the particle, and by the number of particles present in the reactor (N_p).

$$R_j = -\mathcal{D}\,\nabla S_P \cdot 4\pi R^2 N_p \tag{8}$$

It is assumed that no new granules are formed, hence the microbial growth manifests itself simply as the growth of the already-formed particles. N_p is calculated at the start of the simulation through the formula:

$$N_p = \frac{X_0 + E_0}{\rho_{biomass}} \frac{1}{\frac{4}{3}\pi R_0^3} \tag{9}$$

Where X_0 and E_0 are the entirety of the biomass that enters the first CSTR, $\rho_{biomass}$ is the density of the biomass and R_0 [m] is the initial average radius of the particles. From Equation (9), because of the assumption of constant N_p, it is then possible to calculate the new radius of the particles, after the ODE system is solved. Furthermore, η is the internal mass transfer efficiency, defined as follow:

$$\eta = \frac{\int R dV}{R_{surface} V} = \frac{3\mathcal{D}\frac{dS_P}{dr}\Big|_{r=R_P}}{\frac{\mu_{MAX}}{Y}\frac{X}{K_S + S_P(r=R_P)} S_P(r=R_P)\; R_P} \tag{10}$$

In each reactor the same flowrate Q enters, and it is assumed that the inlet one is equal to the outlet (steady conditions). To describe the concentration of methane calculated, Equation 11 is considered. It is assumed that in each CSTR no methane enters, as it is only formed in the reactor through the reaction, and the methane formed exits each reactor.

$$\frac{dM_j}{dt} = -\frac{Q}{V_j} M_j + \eta R_j \tag{11}$$

Where M is the methane concentration [kg/m^3]. Finally, the number of reactors into which the UASB is divided is chosen by the user.

3. Results and Discussion

To validate the model, it was compared to two other works proposed in the literature: the model presented by Bolle et al. (1986) and by Pontes and Pinto (2006). In both models the UASB is divided into two CSTRs to describe respectively the bed and the blanket, and one PFR to represent the settler, in which it is assumed that no reactions take place. In the bed there is the presence of dead volumes, while two short circuiting flows are defined. Consequently, two different simulations were performed: the first one (Scenario 1, Figure 1a) was done in batch mode, meaning in an ideal situation in which the reactor was assumed to not have input and output flows; while the second simulation (Scenario

2, Figure 1b) the UASB is in continuous mode. The results are represented in Figure 1a-b, with the GRANULE trend described by the continuous line, and the literature models expressed by their main values, reported respectively by the red and blue dots.

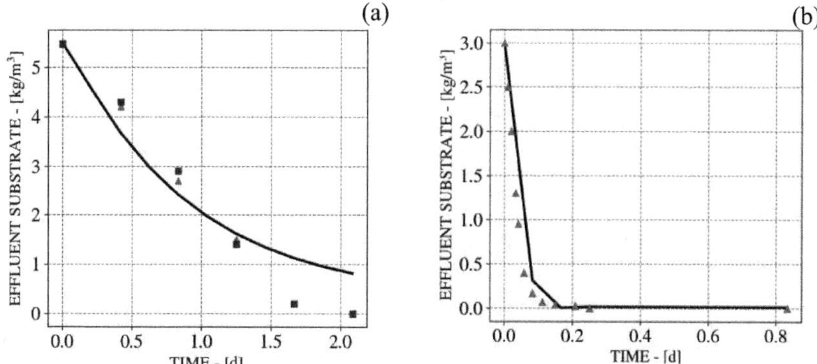

Figure 1. Effluent substrate comparison between model (black line) simulation in (a) Scenario 1, with Bolle et al. (red triangles) and Pinto ed al. (blue squares) data; and (b) Scenario 2 with Pinto et al. data.

As is it possible to see, the model adequately describes the trend of both the literature models, with negligible discrepancy. This may be due to the differences in the kinetics used in the models. Other experimental data set were taken from the work of Leitão et al., (2005), and from Shanmugam and Akunna (2008); which comparison is shown in Figure 2a and 2b respectively.

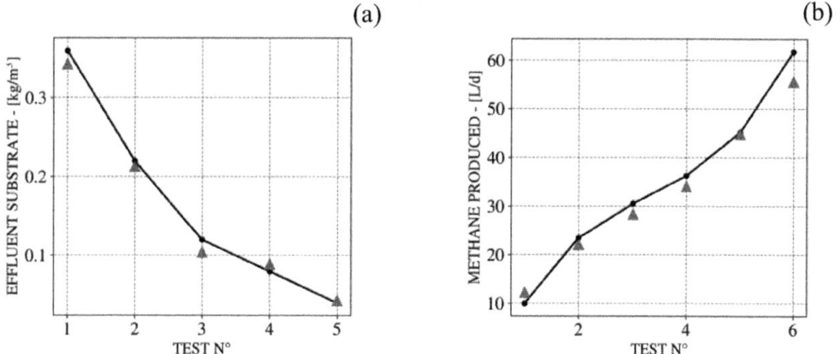

Figure 2. Results of comparison of model (line with mark) with experimental data from (a) Leitao et al. and (b) Shanmugam & Akunna data (red triangles).

As it is possible to see, the model adequately describes methane production too. It is possible to confirm that in all cases, the model can describe properly the trends delineated by the experimental data.

4. Conclusions

This work successfully brings to the development of a dynamic UASB reactor model, which has a significantly low computational time, and correctly describe the dynamics of an extremely complex process, despite its simplicity. As confirmation to this, comparison done with simulation and experimental data from the literature has been made, bringing successful results.

However, improvements are suggested, such as refining lumped kinetics to distinguish substrate types and bacterial species. Specifically, modeling volatile fatty acids and differentiating microbial species (acidogenic, acetogenic, and methanogenic) would enhance its accuracy. For kinetic parameters, calibration using more data and regression analysis is proposed, since here phenomenological approach have been used. Despite these possible enhancements, the presented work marks great progress in modeling UASB reactors, with the potential to become a valuable tool in wastewater treatment.

References

Boiocchi, R., Zhang, Q., Gao, M., Liu, Y., 2022. Modeling and optimization of an upflow anaerobic sludge blanket (UASB) system treating blackwaters. J. Environ. Chem. Eng. 10, 107614. https://doi.org/10.1016/j.jece.2022.107614

Bolle, W.L., van Breugel, J., van Eybergen, G.C., Kossen, N.W., van Gils, W., 1986. An integral dynamic model for the UASB reactor. Biotechnol. Bioeng. 28, 1621–1636. https://doi.org/10.1002/bit.260281106

Leitão, R.C., Silva-Filho, J.A., Sanders, W., van Haandel, A.C., Zeeman, G., Lettinga, G., 2005. The effect of operational conditions on the performance of UASB reactors for domestic wastewater treatment. Water Sci. Technol. J. Int. Assoc. Water Pollut. Res. 52, 299–305.

Mainardis, M., Buttazzoni, M., Goi, D., 2020. Up-Flow Anaerobic Sludge Blanket (UASB) Technology for Energy Recovery: A Review on State-of-the-Art and Recent Technological Advances. Bioengineering 7, 43. https://doi.org/10.3390/bioengineering7020043

Michalopoulos, I., Kamperidis, T., Seintis, G., Pashos, G., Lytras, C., Papadopoulou, K., Boudouvis, A.G., Lyberatos, G., 2018. Experimental and numerical assessment of the hydraulic behavior of a pilot-scale Periodic Anaerobic Baffled Reactor (PABR). Comput. Chem. Eng. 111, 278–287. https://doi.org/10.1016/j.compchemeng.2018.01.014

Pontes, R., Pinto, J., 2006. Analysis of integrated kinetic and flow models for anaerobic digesters. Chem. Eng. J. - CHEM ENG J 122, 65–80. https://doi.org/10.1016/j.cej.2006.02.018

Rodríguez-Gómez, R., Renman, G., Moreno, L., Liu, L., 2013. A model to describe the performance of the UASB reactor. Biodegradation 25. https://doi.org/10.1007/s10532-013-9656-z

Shanmugam, A.S., Akunna, J.C., 2008. Comparing the performance of UASB and GRABBR treating low strength wastewaters. Water Sci. Technol. J. Int. Assoc. Water Pollut. Res. 58, 225–232. https://doi.org/10.2166/wst.2008.338

Flavio Manenti, Gintaras V. Reklaitis (Eds.), Proceedings of the 34th European Symposium on Computer Aided Process Engineering / 15th International Symposium on Process Systems Engineering (ESCAPE34/PSE24), June 2-6, 2024, Florence, Italy
 http://dx.doi.org/10.1016/B978-0-443-28824-1.50185-X

Modeling Framework for Optimization of the Life Cycle Sustainability of Lithium-Ion Batteries by Nickel Manganese Cobalt Recycling Process

Minseong Kim[a], Jeongdong Kim[a], Junghwan Kim[a], Hyungjoon Yoon[a], Pieter Nachtergaele[b], Il Moon[a*]

[a] *Department of Chemical and Biomolecular Engineering, Yonsei University, 50 Yonsei-ro, Seodaemun-gu, Seoul 03722, Republic of Korea*

[b] *Research Group Sustainable Systems Engineering (STEN), Ghent University, Coupure Links 653, 9000 Ghent, Belgium*

email of the corresponding author: *ilmoon@yonsei.ac.kr

Abstract

The increasing utilization of lithium nickel manganese cobalt oxide (NCM) batteries has led to a greater demand for the retrieval of cathode materials to support sustainable battery recycling. This is essential due to the finite availability of metals and the need to reduce the adverse environmental consequences associated with battery disposal. Despite attempts to enhance the sustainability of Lithium-Ion Batteries (LIB) life cycle, few studies have comprehensively addressed both economic and environmental aspects. Several end-of-pipe chemical processes for recycling LIB have been proposed, along with their techno-economic analyses, without considering their environmental sustainability. Thus, this study introduces multi-objective optimization considering economic profit and life cycle environmental performance simultaneously by applying it to optimize the NCM battery recycling process. A hydrometallurgical intensified process model of LIB recycling was developed using a process simulator Aspen Plus, transforming LIB waste into NCM hydroxide. A model of the cradle-to-gate life cycle of LIBs was developed in the LCA software OpenLCA. Following, based on multi-objective Bayesian optimization, the optimal pareto points were identified. The results of this study make decisions on selecting and optimizing battery recycling processes, contributing to achieving both economic viability and sustainability while closing the material loop of LIBs. Also, this is the first study which interconnects Aspen Plus with OpenLCA to perform optimization, thereby contributing to the potential development of automated life cycle assessments.

Keywords: Life Cycle Assessment Automation, Lithium-ion Battery Recycling Process, Circular Economy, Techno-economic Analysis, Bayesian Optimization

1. Introduction

Concerns regarding resource depletion and environmental impacts of battery waste pose a potential obstacle to a sustainable energy transition (Mohr et al., 2020). Thus, recycling waste batteries is crucial to manage the expected stream of discarded batteries and minimize the potential depletion of critical resources such as lithium, manganese, and cobalt. Hydrometallurgical processes stand out as primary LIB recycling technologies. This process involves the use of acids to dissolve the metals of the cathode and recovers the targeted metals by selective precipitation. Despite its high recovery efficiency and no gaseous pollutants through this process, this has some limitations concerning its environmental footprint due to its substantial space requirement and wastewater production.

Efforts to address these limitations have led to the proposal of novel hydrometallurgical processes and subsequent assessment of their environmental impacts using life cycle assessment methodology to identify environmental hotspots (Arshad et al., 2022; Dewulf et al., 2010; Kim et al., 2022; Kim et al., 2023; Quan et al., 2022). The research from Kim et al. (2023) proposed and simulated an innovative LIB recycling process integrated with a hydrogen roasting and carbon dioxide waste gas stream generated from a combustion process for district heating. This novel process achieves 98.10% Li recovery without emissions and demonstrated economic feasibility, surpassing the net present value of the proposed process by 3.08% compared to conventional hydrometallurgy. In addition, Du et al. (2022) present a life cycle assessment of the Chinese hydrometallurgical process using the ReCiPe 2016 methodology. This reveals that the leaching and extraction process and pretreatment process contributed 35.08% and 34.66% to the Global Warming Potential (GWP) of the process.

In this context, this study proposes an intensified hydrometallurgical process, modelled using Aspen Plus, aiming to maximize economic profits of NCM hydroxide (the end-product of this process) and minimize potential environmental impacts of the process simultaneously. While maximizing the product yield is essential with respect to the economic feasibility and profitability of the targeted process, it is crucial to recognize that this may exacerbate the possible environmental impact of the process. The outcomes of this study can be used to serve as valuable insights for making informed decisions regarding selecting and optimizing battery recycling processes (Guillén-Gosálbez et al., 2019; Köck et al., 2023).

2. Method

2.1. Process description

Figure 1 illustrates the schematic diagram detailing both the conventional NCM recycling process and the proposed recycling process (Kim et al., 2023). While the entire process comprises multiple unit processes aimed at recuperating metals from spent LIB cathodes, the proposed process utilizes a single batch process that produces NCM hydroxide. This process uses an optimized sequencing batch reactor cycle comprising three main steps: leaching process, crystallization, and filtration. Initially, the spent batteries are subjected to a leaching process using sulfuric acid and hydrogen peroxide chemicals. Following leaching, the pH of the leachate solution containing Cobalt ions, Nickel ions, and Manganese ions is adjusted to pH 10.6 by adding sodium hydroxide and ammonia. These chemicals facilitate co-precipitation to form NCM hydroxide. The resulting ferrous solid mixture is precipitated as a single clump and then filtered. Any remaining components are considered to be dissolved in wastewater.

(a)

(b)

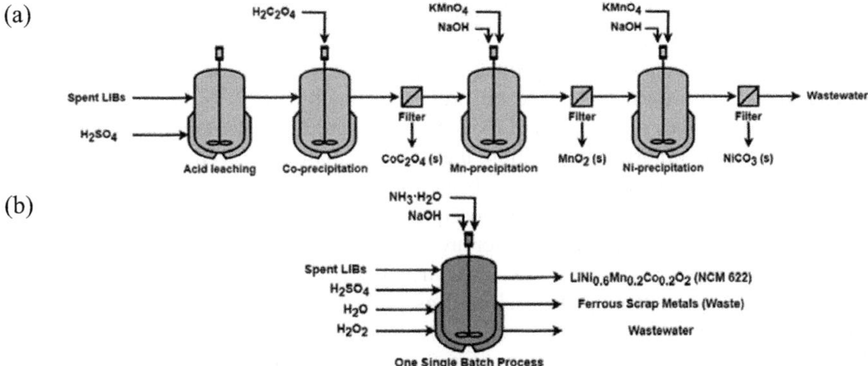

Figure 1 Schematic Diagram of Conventional Hydrometallurgical NCM Recycling Process (a) and Proposed NCM Recycling Process (b)

The crystallization process following leaching was modeled using the population balance equation (Hu et al., 2004). The population balance equation describes the evolution of population density under nucleation and particle growth.

$$\frac{\partial Vf(L,t)}{\partial t} + V\frac{\partial[G(L)f(L,t)]}{\partial L} = VB\delta(L - L_0)$$

where V represents slurry volume, f denotes the population density of crystals, L signifies the particle size, G stands for the crystal growth rate, B is the nucleation rate, and $\delta(L)$ represents the Dirac delta function. This model determines the evolution of crystal size distribution.

The crystal growth rate $G(L)$ is a function of temperature, crystal size, and supersaturation ratio.

$$G(L) = k_0 \, exp\left(-E_g/RT\right)(1 + k_1L)^{k_2}(S - 1)^{\alpha}$$

where k_0, E_g, k_1, k_2, and α are parameters to be estimated by experimental data and S denote the supersaturation ratio.

The methodology employed simulates the crystal size distribution evolution in each time step. Hence, the population density of the precursor is as follows.

$$f\left(L_{j+1,i}\right) \approx \frac{f\left(L_{j,i-1}\right)V_j}{\left(1+\frac{\partial G}{\partial L}\Big|_{L=L_{j,i-1}}\right)V_{j+1}\Delta t}$$

and $L_{i,j}$ and V_j represent particle size points and slurry volume at time interval j.

When calculating the economic profit of this process, only operating expenses were considered, given that this process is based on a single unit batch reactor. The economic profit was determined as the difference between the market price of the NCM products and the total sum of input streams price.

2.2. Life cycle assessment

The environmental assessment was performed according to the ISO 14040/44. The goal of this study is to assess the environmental impact of the proposed hydrometallurgical recycling process. This assessment follows a cradle-to-gate system boundary. The

functional unit is defined as 1 g of NCM hydroxide produced. The life cycle was modelled using OpenLCA software developed by Greendelta, Germany.
The life cycle inventory of the foreground system was retrieved from stream results and operating conditions from the proposed process using pywin32 Python library. This retrieved inventory was processed and loaded onto OpenLCA software via olca-schema and olca-ipc Python libraries. In addition, the LCA database Ecoinvent 3.91 was used to quantify the environmental impacts of the background system. It is assumed that the waste and the wastewater do not undergo the subsequent treatment process. In other words, the waste and the pollutants in the wastewater are considered emissions in this study.
The life cycle impact assessment was done using IPCC 2013 GWP 100a calculation methodology. Global warming was selected as indicator for this study because it is a major public concern. Also, the GWP indicator can be used to help decision-making when selecting one technology over the alternative.

2.3. Mathematical formulation for optimization

The original design problem can be mathematically formulated as follows.

$$\min_{x} \{\psi_1(x), \psi_2(x)\}$$
$$subject\ to : LB \leq x \leq UB,\ \ x \in \mathrm{R}^n$$

where $\psi_1(x)$ and $\psi_2(x)$ refer to the objective functions (i.e., economic profit and environmental indicator (GWP)), x denotes 15 decision variables (5 scenarios and 3 operating conditions), and LB and UB refer to the lower and upper bounds on the continuous variables, respectively.
Here, the multi-objective Bayesian optimization was used to maximize the economic profits and minimize the environmental impacts using botorch Python library. This is a sequential model-based optimization technique used for optimizing expensive-to-evaluate black-box functions. The surrogate model utilized is the gaussian process regression. Also, the acquisition function used is the expected improvement.

3. Results and Discussion

Table 1 and Figure 2 present the outcomes derived from the optimization process, highlighting key findings. Economic profits plateau at 890 US dollars per one batch process operation, while the global warming potential reaches a minimum of 140 kg CO_2 eq. The optimization also reveals a peak recovery efficiency of approximately 80% for nickel, cobalt, and manganese, resulting in a maximum total recovery of 500 g NCM hydroxide per 1kg of spent batteries. Figure 2 emphasizes an inverse relationship between economic profit and global warming potential. Notably, the use of NH_3 in the process significantly impacts global warming due to its energy-intensive production, emitting substantial carbon dioxide. Reducing NH_3 consumption can mitigate these environmental effects.
Conversely, NH_3 functions as a chelating agent facilitating the recovery of nickel, cobalt, and manganese, leading to increased NCM hydroxide production and, subsequently, higher economic profits. Therefore, decision-makers need to balance NH_3 usage for optimal outcomes. Operational time is another crucial factor. Prolonged operational time increases NCM hydroxide crystallization, augmenting its production and economic benefits. However, this also amplifies environmental impacts, notably the consumption of steam produced by burning coal. The longer operational time results in more coal burning, elevating the global warming potential. Thus, decision-makers must consider

both economic and environmental factors when determining operational time, guided by their knowledge and priorities.

Table 1 Process Optimization Result

Optimum	#1	#2	#3	#4	#5	#6	#7	#8	#9
Economic Profit (US $)	846.7	851.6	856.5	857.4	857.6	858.1	875.3	880.1	890.2
GWP (kg CO_2 Eq.)	148.0	169.2	204.6	216.7	218.4	232.6	243.3	253.7	253.7

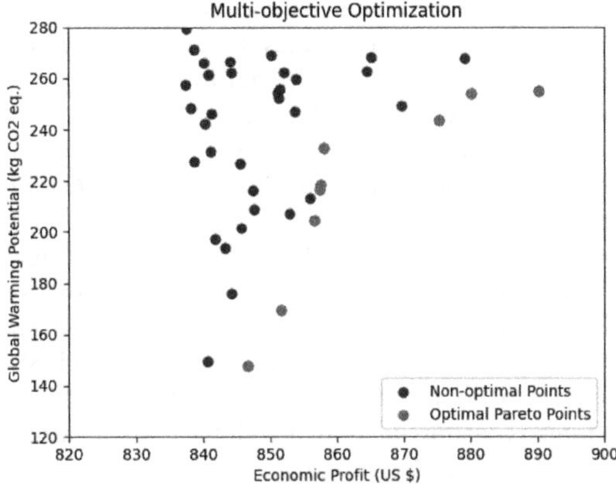

Figure 2: Multi-objective Bayesian Optimization Pareto Points

4. Conclusion

This work introduces an intensified hydrometallurgical LIB recycling process with the primary goal of maximizing the output of NCM hydroxide while simultaneously reducing the potential environmental footprint of the process. The NCM hydroxide output is expected to be used in the LIB manufacturing process, replacing some of the resources from mining.

The optimization of this process yields optimal profits ranging from 840 US dollars to 890 US dollars. However, it is noteworthy that as profits increase, the environmental impact, measured by the Global Warming Potential (GWP), also increases, ranging from 148 kg CO2 eq to 254 kg CO2 eq. It is crucial to recognize that while maximizing profitability is a key goal, it comes with the trade-off of heightened environmental consequences. Therefore, maintaining a balance between economic gains and environmental sustainability is essential for achieving long-term operational viability.

This study provides valuable insights that can guide decision-makers in selecting a battery recycling operational strategy. By considering the interplay between economic outcomes and environmental impacts, stakeholders can make well-informed decisions, contributing to the development of sustainable practices in the field of LIB recycling.

References

Arshad, F., Lin, J., Manurkar, N., Fan, E., Ahmad, A., Tariq, M. un N., Wu, F., Chen, R., & Li, L. (2022). Life Cycle Assessment of Lithium-ion Batteries: A Critical Review. In *Resources, Conservation and Recycling* (Vol. 180). Elsevier B.V. https://doi.org/10.1016/j.resconrec.2022.106164

Dewulf, J., Van der Vorst, G., Denturck, K., Van Langenhove, H., Ghyoot, W., Tytgat, J., & Vandeputte, K. (2010). Recycling rechargeable lithium ion batteries: Critical analysis of natural resource savings. *Resources, Conservation and Recycling*, *54*(4), 229–234. https://doi.org/10.1016/j.resconrec.2009.08.004

Du, S., Gao, F., Nie, Z., Liu, Y., Sun, B., & Gong, X. (2022). Life cycle assessment of recycled NiCoMn ternary cathode materials prepared by hydrometallurgical technology for power batteries in China. *Journal of Cleaner Production*, *340*. https://doi.org/10.1016/j.jclepro.2022.130798

Guillén-Gosálbez, G., You, F., Galán-Martín, Á., Pozo, C., & Grossmann, I. E. (2019). Process systems engineering thinking and tools applied to sustainability problems: current landscape and future opportunities. In *Current Opinion in Chemical Engineering* (Vol. 26, pp. 170–179). Elsevier Ltd. https://doi.org/10.1016/j.coche.2019.11.002

Hu, Q., Rohani, S., Wang, D. X., & Jutan, A. (2004). Nonlinear kinetic parameter estimation for batch cooling seeded crystallization. *AIChE Journal*, *50*(8), 1786–1794. https://doi.org/10.1002/aic.10163

Kim, J., Kim, S., Lim, J., Moon, I., & Kim, J. (2022). Sequential flue gas utilization for sustainable leaching and metal precipitation of spent lithium-ion battery cathode material: Process design and techno-economic analysis. *Journal of Cleaner Production*, *380*. https://doi.org/10.1016/j.jclepro.2022.134988

Kim, J., Kim, Y., Moon, I., Cho, H., & Kim, J. (2023). Process design and economic analysis of hydrogen roasting integrated with CCU for a carbon-free spent LIB recycling process. *Chemical Engineering Journal*, *451*. https://doi.org/10.1016/j.cej.2022.139005

Kim, J., Moon, I., & Kim, J. (2023). Integration of wastewater electro-electrodialysis and CO2 capture for sustainable LIB recycling: Process design and economic analyses. *Journal of Cleaner Production*, *391*. https://doi.org/10.1016/j.jclepro.2023.136241

Köck, B., Friedl, A., Serna Loaiza, S., Wukovits, W., & Mihalyi-Schneider, B. (2023). Automation of Life Cycle Assessment—A Critical Review of Developments in the Field of Life Cycle Inventory Analysis. In *Sustainability (Switzerland)* (Vol. 15, Issue 6). MDPI. https://doi.org/10.3390/su15065531

Mohr, M., Peters, J. F., Baumann, M., & Weil, M. (2020). Toward a cell-chemistry specific life cycle assessment of lithium-ion battery recycling processes. *Journal of Industrial Ecology*, *24*(6), 1310–1322. https://doi.org/10.1111/jiec.13021

Quan, J., Zhao, S., Song, D., Wang, T., He, W., & Li, G. (2022). Comparative life cycle assessment of LFP and NCM batteries including the secondary use and different recycling technologies. *Science of the Total Environment*, *819*. https://doi.org/10.1016/j.scitotenv.2022.153105

Flavio Manenti, Gintaras V. Reklaitis (Eds.), Proceedings of the 34th European Symposium on Computer Aided Process Engineering / 15th International Symposium on Process Systems Engineering (ESCAPE34/PSE24), June 2-6, 2024, Florence, Italy
 http://dx.doi.org/10.1016/B978-0-443-28824-1.50186-1

Efficient Numerical Methods for Dynamic Simulation of Fixed-bed Reactors

Joachim Weel Rosbo[a*], Anker D. Jensen[a], John Bagterp Jørgensen[b], Jakob K. Huusom[a]
[a]*Dept. of Chemical and Biochemical Engineering, Technical University of Denmark,*
[b]*Dept. of Applied Mathematics and Computer Science, Technical University of Denmark,*
**jwro@kt.dtu.dk*

Abstract

The intermittent nature of renewable energies requires Power-to-X (P2X) plants to operate flexibly in contrast to traditional stable operation with fossil feedstocks. This emphasises the need for accurate and efficient dynamic models of P2X plants. In this paper, we study a partial differential algebraic equations (PDAEs) model for a fixed-bed gas phase reactor. The model is discretized in space by the finite volume method (FVM). The dispersion term from back-mixing in the bed is approximated by numerical diffusion by using an appropriate number of discretization cells. Five different numerical implementations of the Euler step are investigated for solving in time: One traditional explicit scheme and four implicit formulations. The performance of the numerical schemes is tested by solving the response of the bed to a step change in the inlet temperature. The most efficient implicit method is an order of magnitude faster than the traditional explicit method, while the slowest implicit method is an order of magnitude slower.

Keywords: Fixed-bed reactors, PDAE, Finite Volume Method, Implicit methods

1. Introduction

Catalytic fixed-bed reactors are the most used reactor type for synthesizing large-scale chemicals such as methanol, ammonia and sulphuric acid. Often literature and textbooks focus on steady-state modelling as chemical plants are traditionally built for stable operation with as few fluctuations in production as possible. But with today's focus on out-phasing fossil-based feedstocks and replacing them with renewable energy, new challenges are arising for the operation of chemical plants. Dynamic and flexible operation of power-to-X (P2X) plants is required to comply with the intermittent nature of renewable energies such as wind and solar power. This emphasizes the importance of dynamic models, which are fundamental for advanced control and critical in ensuring the safe and optimal operation of renewable-powered chemical plants. Steady-state 1D models of industrial fixed-bed reactors for ammonia or methanol production are common in the literature, and have proven an accurate model approach for industrial reactors in several studies (Shamiri & Aliabadi, 2021). Based on 1D PFR models several papers have set up dynamic models for fixed-bed ammonia and methanol reactors. Morud & Skogestad, (1998) transformed the fixed-bed partial differential equations (PDEs) model into an ordinary differential equations (ODEs) system by the finite volume method, while Manenti & Bozzano, (2013) applied a finite difference scheme. The papers use an explicit Euler step for the integration. The models qualitatively match transient behaviors observed for fixed-bed ammonia and methanol reactors, but quantitative accuracy is not discussed. The papers assume constant thermodynamic properties and do not account for deviations from ideal gas in the high-pressure reactors (up to 250 bar). Rosbo et al., (2023) presented a PDEAs model for the ammonia reactor beds, incorporating rigorous thermodynamics for calculating temperature and pressure dependent system properties. The PDEA was transformed into a DAEs problem via the FVM method, and an implicit Euler step was used for the timewise integration. However, the computational speed of the solution method was not assessed. In this paper, we investigate the optimal numerical implementation of the PDAE model presented by Rosbo et al., (2023) in terms of computational cost. Furthermore, we assess the influence of numerical diffusion on the transient solution and propose a strategy for coupling this to the physical dispersion term.

2. Fixed-Bed Model

Fig. 1 displays a schematic illustration of the catalytic fixed-bed. For the packed bed reactor, we define the porosity, $\boldsymbol{\epsilon_B}$, as the void fraction of the reactor volume,

$$\epsilon_B = \frac{V^g}{V_R}, \qquad 1 - \epsilon_B = \frac{V^s}{V_R} \qquad (1)$$

where V^g is the gas volume, V^s is the solid catalyst volume, and V_R is the total reactor bed volume. We model the bed as a 1-dimensional packed bed reactor with the following assumptions:

A1. The reactor beds are adiabatic as the reactor is well insulated.
A2. The reactor is isobaric both in time and space.
A3. The particle and gas phases are isothermal.

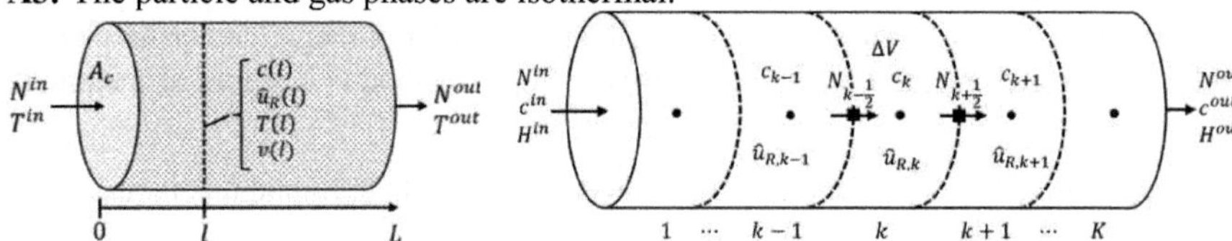

Figure 1: Schematics of the fixed-bed. Figure 2: Finite volume discretization of the fixed-bed.

2.1. Material and energy balances

For the 1-dimensional model with assumptions **A1-A3** the material and energy balances for the fixed-bed are given by the partial differential equations (Rosbo et al., 2023),

$$\partial_t c = -\partial_l N + R \qquad (2)$$

$$\partial_t \hat{u}_R = -\epsilon_B \, \partial_l \overline{H} \qquad (3)$$

where c is the gas phase concentration vector, l is the spatial coordinate, N is the molar flux vector, and R is the production rate vector per gas volume.

The molar flux vector, N, consists of an advection and dispersion term,

$$N = vc - D_L \partial_l c \qquad (5)$$

in which v is the interstitial flow velocity and D_L is the axial dispersion coefficient. In the energy balance, $\overline{H}$ denotes the flux of enthalpy given by,

$$\overline{H} = H(T, P, N) \qquad (6)$$

The thermodynamic function H is calculated via a thermodynamic tool as described in Rosbo et al., (2023). The equation of state (EOS) must be satisfied in the entire domain,

$$V(T, P, c) = 1 \qquad (7)$$

Eq. 2-7 define the bed model as a partial differential algebraic equations system (PDAEs).

2.2. Discretization in space

The fixed-bed PDAEs model (Eq. 2-7) can be solved by discretization of the spatial coordinate. We apply the finite volume method (FVM) where the bed is divided into K cells as illustrated in Figure 2. For the discretized system the mass and energy balances are,

$$\Delta V_k^g \partial_t c_k = A_c^g N_{k-\frac{1}{2}} - A_c^g N_{k+\frac{1}{2}} + \Delta V_k^g R_k \quad 8$$

$$\Delta V_{R,k} \partial_t \hat{u}_{R,k} = A_c^g \bar{H}_{k-\frac{1}{2}} - A_c^g \bar{H}_{k+\frac{1}{2}} \quad 9$$

Where the flux over cell surfaces is given from an upwind scheme,

$$N_{k+\frac{1}{2}} = c_k v_{k+\frac{1}{2}} \quad 10$$

We deliberately choose not to include the dispersion term. The FVM method introduces numerical diffusion, which we use to represent the physical dispersion (see Section 3.2). The EOS is enforced through,

$$V(T_k, P_k, c_k) = 1 \quad 11$$

Eq. 8-11 constitute a DAE system, which is expressed in semi-explicit form by,

$$\dot{\mathbf{x}} = f(\mathbf{x}, \mathbf{y}), \qquad 0 = g(\mathbf{x}, \mathbf{y}) \quad 12$$

where f contains the balance equations and g represents the thermodynamic functions.

2.3. Discretization in time

A first order Euler scheme is applied for the discretization in time of the material and energy balance. We can solve the Euler step either explicitly or implicitly depending on whether the spatial derivatives are approximated at the current or future time step,

Explicit: $$\mathbf{x}^{n+1} = \mathbf{x}^n + f(\mathbf{x}^n, \mathbf{y}^n)\Delta t \quad 13$$

Implicit: $$\mathbf{x}^{n+1} = \mathbf{x}^n + f(\mathbf{x}^{n+1}, \mathbf{y}^{n+1})\Delta t \quad 14$$

where Δt is the size of the Euler step. The studied literature has exclusively utilized explicit methods, which are relatively simple to implement. But the stability of the explicit algorithms is restricted by the Courant number, Co,

$$Co = \frac{v\Delta t}{\Delta L} < 1 \, for \, stability \, of \, explicit \, schemes \quad 15$$

Where ΔL is the length of the discretization cell. This implies, the time step is required to be smaller than the residence time of the cell for stability. The implicit method evaluates f and g at the next time step. This yields a nonlinear equation system, which we solve by Newton's iteration method.

$$\mathbf{z}_{new}^{n+1} = \mathbf{z}_{old}^{n+1} - M(\mathbf{z}_{old}^{n+1})^{-1}\mathbf{R}(\mathbf{z}_{old}^{n+1}) \quad 16$$

Where $\mathbf{z}$ is a concatenation of $\mathbf{x}$ and $\mathbf{y}$, $\mathbf{R}$ combines Eq. 14 and the algebraic equations in a residual function, and M is the iteration matrix equal to the Jacobian of $\mathbf{R}$.

2.4. Numerical formulations

We investigate one explicit (**E1**) and four different implicit (**I1-I4**) implementations of the Euler step as tabulated in Table 1. For the implicit formulations, we can choose to keep the algebraic equations and variables as a part of the equation system or express the algebraic variables explicitly as indicated in Table 1. The variable, x, is the mole fractions which is required for the partial pressures in the reaction rate expression,

$$x = \frac{c}{\sum c} \quad 17$$

In Rosbo et al., (2023), we utilized implicit method **I2.**

Table 1: Labeling of the numerical methods.

Method name	E1	I1	I2	I3	I4
States, x	$c, \hat{u}_R$	$c, \hat{u}_R$	$c, \hat{u}_R$	$c, \hat{u}_R$	$c, \hat{u}_R$
Algebraic variables, y	T	T	T, x	T, v	T, x, v

Figure 3 displays the size and sparsity of the iteration matrices (with $K = 10$ cells) for the implicit formulations. The size of the iteration matrix increases when more algebraic equations and variables are included in the formulation (I4). However, expressing the algebraic variables from the states may lead to a denser structure of the iteration matrix (I1 and I2). Figure reveals, that especially eliminating the velocities, v, from the algebraic variables increases the density of the iteration matrices. When expressing v in terms of the states, a change in the states is influencing the velocities throughout the bed – hence the staircase structure.

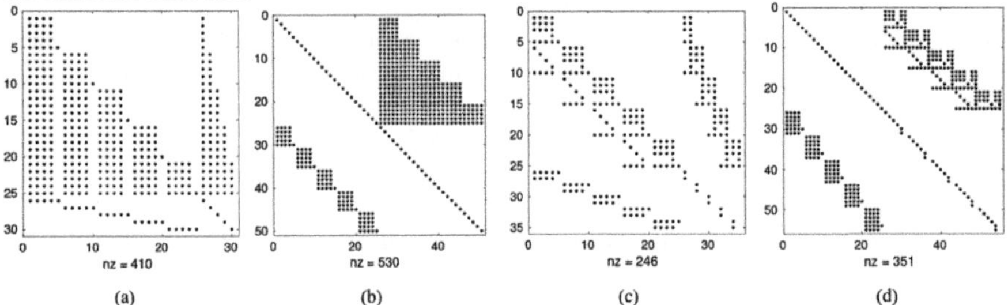

Figure 3:Structure of the iteration matrices for different implementations of the implicit Euler: a) I1, b) I2, c) I3, and d) I4. The matrices are constructed for $K = 10$, and nz = non-zero elements.

3. Simulation efficiency

The simulation case is the first bed in an ammonia reactor system defined in (Rosbo et al., 2023). We investigate the 3 min system response for a step disturbance of 10 K in the bed feed temperature, $\boldsymbol{T^{in}}$. The simulations are performed in Matlab on an Intel(R) Core(TM) i7-6700 3.40GHz CPU.

3.1. Size of the time step

From the stability limit (Eq. 15), we find that using a fixed time step of, $\Delta t = 1/K$, ensures numerical stability for the explicit method. For the implicit methods, larger steps in time are feasible wrt. stability, but at the cost of numerical accuracy. Fig. 4a displays the simulated step response of the bed outlet temperature for an increasing size of the time step (with $K = 80$ cells). The response shows an initial decrease in the bed outlet temperature (inverse response) to the 10 K step increase in the inlet temperature. This is a known phenomenon for exothermic fixed-bed reactors. Fig. 4b shows the maximum numerical error compared to a refined solution. The dotted line depicts a unit slope illustrating the first order global error of the Euler scheme. With a step size of $\Delta t = 20/K$, the maximum error is well below 1 K, smaller than the error we expect from applying the simplifying assumption **(A1-A3)**, and the bed response is almost identical to those for smaller time steps.

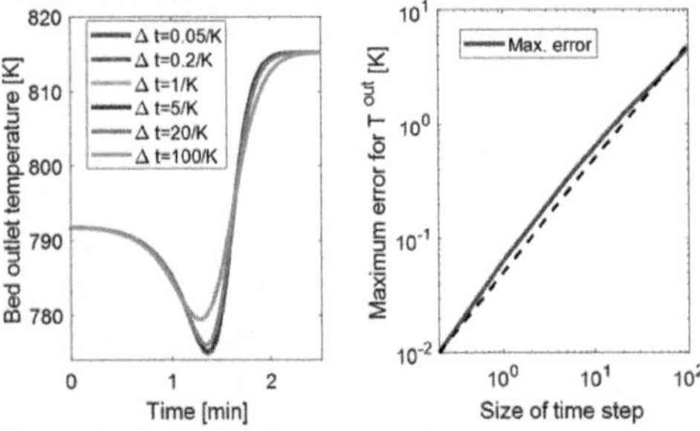

Figure 4: a) Bed outlet temperature response to a 10 K step increase in the inlet temperature simulated with different timewise discretizations. b) Maximum error as a function of the time step size.

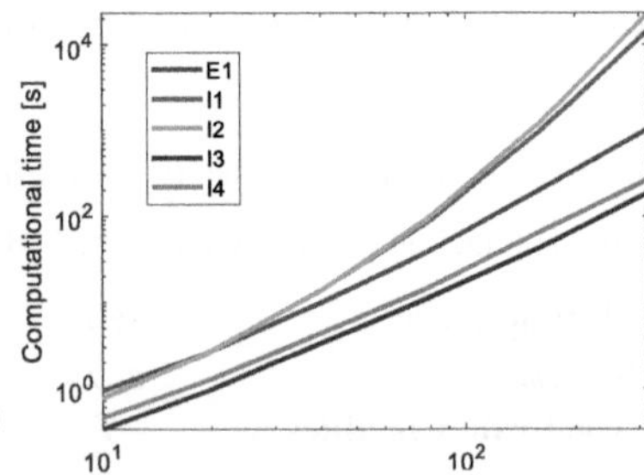

Figure 5: CPU time versus the number of cells for simulating 3 min physical time. The curves represent the five different numerical formulations.

For $\Delta t = \frac{100}{K}$, the bed response begins to deviate significantly from the finer timewise discretization, and the inverse response is not captured properly. Thus, in the following analysis, a time step of $\Delta t = 10/K$ is used for the implicit methods.

3.2. Spatial refinement

Figure 6 displays the bed outlet temperature response for increasing refinement of the spatial discretization. The inverse temperature response is larger and narrower for a higher number of cells. This reflects the effect of numerical diffusion as the truncation error of the FVM method (Froment et al., 2010). The numerical diffusion is not identical to a physical dispersion term, but the properties of the solution are very similar.

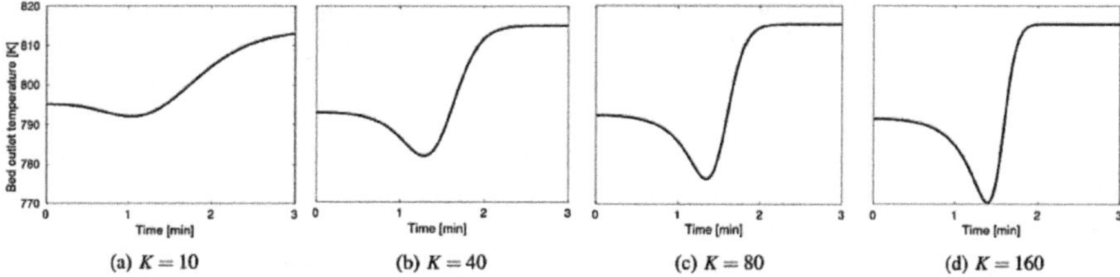

Figure 6: Step response for the bed outlet temperature to a 10 K step change in inlet temperature with FVM of a) 10 cells, b) 40 cells, c) 80 cells, and d) 160 cells.

For simulating physical dispersion with numerical diffusion, Froment et al. suggest using an equal standard deviation of the residence time distribution for a series of CSTRs and the analytical solution to a pure diffusion/advection problem,

$$K \cong \frac{\text{Pe}}{2} + \frac{1}{2}, \quad \text{Re} > 2 \qquad 18$$

where $\text{Pe} = vL/D_L$ is the Peclet number. At high Reynolds numbers ($\text{Re} > 2000$) the axial dispersion from backmixing in packed beds can be approximated

$$D_L = \frac{1}{2} v d_p, \quad \text{Re} > 2000 \qquad 19$$

in which d_p is the diameter of the catalyst particles. For a fixed-bed ammonia reactor, the Reynolds number in the bed is around $\text{Re} = v d_p \rho^g / \mu^g \approx 15{,}000$, where ρ^g is the gas density and μ^g is the gas viscosity. Thus, we are well within the regime where Eq. 18 is applicable. Inserting the definition of Pe and Eq. 19 in Eq. 18,

$$K = \frac{\text{Pe}}{2} + \frac{1}{2} = \frac{vL}{2D_L} + \frac{1}{2} = \frac{L}{d_p} + \frac{1}{2} = \frac{1.2441 \text{ m}}{8.00 \cdot 10^{-3} \text{ m}} + \frac{1}{2} = 156.0 \qquad 20$$

Thus, the physical dispersion can be resembled with numerical diffusion by discretizing the bed into 156 cells. For fixed-bed gas phase reactions L/d_p typically ranges between 100-500. Note, if one wants to simulate the physical dispersion term by including it in the discretization, a significant higher number of cells are required to eliminate the effects from numerical diffusion.

3.3. Computational efficiency

Section 3.2 illustrated that typically 100-500 cells are required to resemble the physical dispersion with numerical diffusion. This is a relatively fine discretization associated with significant computational effort. Figure 5 displays the computational time versus the number of discretization cells for solving 3 min physical time of the step response for the different numerical formulations in Table 1. We see significant differences between the efficiency of the algorithms. The algorithms expressing the flow velocities, v_k, explicitly (I1 and I2) are substantially more computationally expensive as the iteration matrices are not sparse. The number of elements in matrices of Figure 3a and 3b scales quadratically with the number of cells, K^2, which dramatically increases the computational cost for increasing number of cells. The iteration matrices for methods I3 and I4 (Figure 3c and 3d) scale linearly with the number of cells. Thus, the matrices become sparse for more cells, and the algorithms (I3 and I4) require significantly less computational effort as seen in Figure 5. Compared with the traditional explicit method (E1), I3 and I4 solve about a factor of ten times faster. The speed-up matches the ten times larger time step applied for the implicit methods.

3.4. Discussion

Figure 5 shows that with 156 cells the traditional explicit method simulates the 3 min step response with a computational time of around 200 s, while the implicit method I3 requires about 40 s with the applied software. For P2X applications, the aim for dynamic modelling of fixed-bed reactors is ultimately to set up advanced dynamic control. For advanced control, e.g. nonlinear MPC, it is crucial that the simulator simulates faster than physical time. An ammonia plant contains a multi-bed reactor system with up to four beds in addition to several heat-exchangers, compressors, valves and a separator. Thus, the simulation results for one bed in this paper indicate, that computational time might be a concern especially using conventional explicit methods even with high-performance software and hardware. The implicit numerical methods presented in this paper might provide the basis for reducing the computational effort. The implicit Euler schemes can relatively easily be converted to higher-order schemes, which provide significant better numerical accuracy at larger time steps. Thus, higher-order implicit methods may bridge the computational gap for advanced control of fixed-bed reactors.

4. Conclusion

In this paper, we have solved a PDAEs model for a fixed-bed catalytic gas phase reactor by converting the system to a DAEs problem via the finite volume method. The simulations were based on a bed in an ammonia reactor, and the number of discretization cells required to resemble the physical dispersion was determined to 156 cells. We investigated the numerical efficiency of five different numerical implementations of the Euler step: One traditional explicit scheme and four implicit formulations. The efficiency of implicit formulation depended heavily on, which algebraic variables were implemented implicitly. Thus, the least effective implicit algorithm simulated significantly slower than the traditional explicit method, while most efficient implicit scheme was about 5 times faster. This is a promising speed up regarding model based advanced control of P2X plants.

References

Froment, Gilbert F. Bischoff, K. B., & De Wilde, J. (2010). *Chemical Reactor Analysis and Design* (3rd ed.). Wiley.

Manenti, F., & Bozzano, G. (2013). Optimal control of methanol synthesis fixed-bed reactor. *Industrial and Engineering Chemistry Research*, *52*(36), 13079–13091.

Morud, J. C., & Skogestad, S. (1998). Analysis of Instability in an Industrial Ammonia Reactor. *AIChE Journal*, *44*(4), 888–895.

Rosbo, J. W., Ritschel, T. K. S., Hørstholt, S., Huusom, J. K., & Jørgensen, J. B. (2023). Flexible operation, optimisation and stabilising control of a quench cooled ammonia reactor for Power-to-Ammonia. *Computers & Chemical Engineering*, *176*(108316).

Shamiri, A., & Aliabadi, N. (2021). Modeling and Performance Improvement of an Industrial Ammonia Synthesis Reactor. *Chemical Engineering Journal Advances*, *8*, 100177.

Flavio Manenti, Gintaras V. Reklaitis (Eds.), Proceedings of the 34th European Symposium on Computer Aided Process Engineering / 15th International Symposium on Process Systems Engineering (ESCAPE34/PSE24), June 2-6, 2024, Florence, Italy
 http://dx.doi.org/10.1016/B978-0-443-28824-1.50187-3

Modelling and Investigation of Continuous Ideal Flow Crystallizer with Multidimensional Population Balance Equations

László Balogh[a*], Attila Egedy[a], Ágnes Bárkányi[a]

[a] *Department of Process Engineering, Faculty of Engineering, University of Pannonia, Egyetem street 10., Veszprém, Hungary*
* *balogh.laszlo@mk.uni-pannon.hu*

Abstract

The importance of the continuous processes are increasing in the pharmaceutical sector, and the model based design and optimization is a powerful tool for the health safety and of adequate quality fabrication of the crystalline product. The two most important property of the crystal product are the particle characteristic size (for example diameter) and the size distribution. In this work we wish to investigate a continuous industrial size crystallizer on model base. The solution of these extended model is not an easy task because the breakage is a probability variable based phenomenon, so the integration of the population balance equation is not possible. So, we need to search for an adequate method for the solution for example Monte Carlo (MC) simulation.

Keywords: population balance, crystallizer, breakage

1. Introduction

In our research we want to investigate a continuous crystallizer (CMSMPR – Continuous Mixed Suspension Mixed Product Removal), the emerging crystals have two-dimension distributions. During the modelling we solve the model parametrically, so we do not handle a specific material system. Borsos and Lakatos (2012) investigated a continuous crystallizer with breaking events. In their model the crystals break into half, and the solution was made by standard method of moments. In our works we recreate their model and results in addition we compare it with our solution of MC simulation. Borsos and Lakatos (2014) modified their model, thus in this version the breaking of the crystals are happening in random in length. The solution method is a moments method but every integration step they integrate a random function for the breaking. Szilágyi et al. (2015) investigate a high aspects ratio crystals breaking with two-dimensional population balance. They used SMOM (standard method of moments) method and QMOM (quadratic method of moments) for the solution. Peborgh Gooch and Hounslow (1996) was engaged with MC simulation for different complexity population balance equation (PBE). They found the MC simulation gives very accurate results in comparison with analytical solution. Piotrowski and Piotrowski (2004) modelled a CMSMPR crystallizer with monte MC method, with two material systems. Their model does contain a heat balance, they handled the crystallizer as adiabatic. In this work we make a model for a CMSMPR crystallizer with heat balance, and we solve it with two different methods.

2. Mathematical Model for Continuous Crystallizer

During the modelling process we want to formalize a mathematical model of a CMSMPR crystallizer. The crystallizer is supplemented with cooling jacket. In the crystallization we consider three kinetic processes, the growing, the nucleation and the breaking process. The parameters of the model were used from Borsos and Lakatos (2012) and Borsos and Lakatos (2014). The following assumptions was implemented:

- The crystallizer perfectly mixed, the product removal is representative.
- Agglomeration is neglected.
- The crystals break into half, and only in the length of the crystal .
- The level control is ideal, so the volume of the inside is constant (V = constant)
- The growing of the crystals is independent from the crystal sizes.
- Volume of the crystallized solute is the same as its volume in the dissolved state.
- The inlet stream does not contain crystals ($\epsilon_{in} = 0$) or any impurities.

2.1. Crystal Growing

The crystals have two-dimensional distribution; thus, we handled the crystals as square based column. The length of the crystals denotes by z and the diameter denote by r. The growing in dimension r and dimension z can be described with the same expressions (when i = z, r) (Eq. (1)) (Borsos et al., 2012).

$$G_i = k_{g,i} \exp\left(\frac{-E_{g,i}}{RT}\right)\left(\frac{c-c_S}{c_S}\right)^{g_i} \qquad \text{where} \qquad k_{g,i}, g_i, E_{g,i} > 0 \tag{1}$$

In the Eq. (1) the $k_{g,i}$; g_i and $E_{g,i}$ are constants, the c is the actual concentration of solutes material, the c_s is the solubility concentration, the T denotes the temperature of the inside while R is the universal gas constant. This form of the equations takes into account the relative supersaturations. The solubility concentration can be described with the following polynomial equation (Eq. (2)), the temperature is understood in °C and the parameters and comes from Szilágyi et al (2015).

$$c_s(T) = a - bT + cT^2 \tag{2}$$

2.2. Nucleation

In case of nucleation, we count with primer (N_p) and seconder (N_s) nucleation, that's two expressions are the following (Eq. (3) and (4)) (Borsos et al., 2012).

$$N_p = (1-\epsilon)\, k_p \exp\left(\frac{-E_p}{RT}\right) \exp\left(\frac{-k_e}{\ln^2\left(\frac{c}{c_S}\right)}\right) \qquad \text{where} \qquad k_p, E_p, k_e > 0 \tag{3}$$

$$N_s = k_s \exp\left(\frac{-E_S}{RT}\right)\left(\frac{c-c_S}{c_S}\right)^s \mu_{1,2}^b$$

$$\text{where} \qquad k_s, E_s, s, b > 0 \tag{4}$$

$$N_s = k_s \exp\left(\frac{-E_S}{RT}\right)\left(\frac{c-c_S}{c_S}\right)^s V_S^m$$

The ϵ denotes the solid volume fraction and that calculated with the following (Eq. (5)), this interpretation of the solid volume rate comes from Balogh et al. (2023).

$$\epsilon = \frac{V_S}{V_S+V_F} \tag{5}$$

In the Eq. (3) the k_p, E_p, k_e are constants of the primary nucleation, and in the Eq. (4) the k_s, E_s, s, b are the constants of the secondary nucleation. The secondary nucleation is dependent on the volume of the solid fraction, so in case of SMOM the $\mu_{1,2}$ modify the value of secondary nucleation while in case of MC we calculate directly the solid volume (V_S). The full rate of nucleation (N_Σ) is the sum of the primary and secondary nucleation rate.

2.3. Crystal Breaking

The breaking of the crystals is characterized with the selection function ($S(z,r)$) and the breaking function ($b_z(z,\lambda_z)b_r(r,\lambda_r)$). The previous function characterized the probability of the breaking the last determine the size after the breaking event. The selection function has the following form (Eq. (6)) (Borsos et al., 2012).

$$S(z,r) = k_B z^\beta r^\gamma \tag{6}$$

In the Eq. (6) the β and γ are the parameters of the function. The $\gamma = 0$ because the breaking happens only in z coordinates, the β was chosen to 1, because the moments equations give an unclosed system if $\beta > 1$ (Szilágyi et al. (2015)). In case of breaking functions, we assume that the crystals break into half, thus the function has the following form (Eq. (7)) (Borsos et al., 2012).

$$b_z(z,\lambda_z)b_r(r,\lambda_r) = 2\delta\left(z - \frac{\lambda_z}{2}\right)\delta(r - \lambda_r) \tag{7}$$

The δ denotes the Dirac delta function, the λ is the size of the mother crystal. The meaning of the Eq. (7): after the breaking event we get two of equal length crystal with same diameter.

2.4. Population Balance equation

The population balance equation can be formulized with the following multivariable partial integro-differential equation (Eq. (8)). It has a same form with Borsos et al. (2012).

$$\frac{\partial\Psi(z,r,t)}{\partial t} + G_z\frac{\partial\Psi(z,r,t)}{\partial z} + G_r\frac{\partial\Psi(z,r,t)}{\partial r} = -\frac{B\,\Psi(z,r,t)}{V} + N_\Sigma\,\delta(z - z_0, r - r_0)$$
$$-k_B\int_0^z\int_0^r z^\beta\delta\left(\lambda_z - \frac{z}{2}\right)\delta(\lambda_r - r)\Psi(z,r,t)d\lambda_z d\lambda_r \tag{8}$$
$$+k_B\int_z^\infty\int_r^\infty \lambda^\beta\delta\left(z - \frac{\lambda_z}{2}\right)\delta(r - \lambda_r)\Psi(\lambda_z,\lambda_r,t)\,d\lambda_z d\lambda_r$$

In the Eq. (8) the Ψ denotes the crystal size density function, B means the volume flow rate. The initial condition (Eq. (9)).

$$\Psi(z,r,0) = \Psi_0(z,r) \tag{9}$$

The two boundary conditions (Eq. (10)):

$$\lim_{z\to 0; r\to 0}[G_z\Psi(z,r,t) + G_r\Psi(z,r,t)] = 0 \qquad \lim_{z\to\infty; r\to\infty}\Psi(z,r,t) = 0 \tag{10}$$

The macroscopic properties of the crystallizer were calculated with a same mathematical expression as Balogh et al. (2023) and the assumed equipment also a same.

3. Solution of the Model

In the following we would to introduce the two method what we use for the solution. The first is the standard method of the moments, the second is the Monte Carlo simulation.

3.1. Standard Method of Moments

One of the solution methods is the method of moments. At the first step we need to transform the Eq. (8) to moments equations. The definition of the moments is the following (Eq. (11)).

$$\mu_{k,m} = \int_0^\infty\int_0^\infty z^k r^m\,\Psi(z,r,t)dzdr \tag{11}$$

After the moments transformation we get the following general equations (Eq. (12) for the 0,0-th moment and Eq. (13) for the m,k-th moments).

$$\frac{d\,\mu_{0,0}}{dt} = -\frac{B}{V}\,\mu_{0,0} + N_{\Sigma} + k_B\mu_{1,0} \tag{12}$$

$$\frac{d\,\mu_{k,m}}{dt} = -\frac{B}{V}\,\mu_{k,m} + kG_z\mu_{k-1,m} + mG_r\mu_{k,m-1} + k_B\left(\frac{1}{2^{k-1}} - 1\right)\mu_{k+1,m} \tag{13}$$

Thus, we get an ordinary differential equation system. In case of standard method of moments, the source term formulized by the following equation (Eq. (14)).

$$R_{V_S} = k_V V(G_z\mu_{0,2} + 2G_r\mu_{1,1}) \tag{14}$$

3.2. Monte Carlo Simulation

During the MC simulation we need to distinguish continuous processes and discrete events in time. In our case the volume, the concentration, and the temperature were handled by continuous process, only the breaking is the discrete event. The continuous part of the model was solved by Euler method with fixed simulation step ($h = 0.1$ s). The general form of the used formula is the following (Eq. (15)).

$$y_{i+1} = y_i + h\,f(t_i, y_i) \tag{15}$$

In the Eq. (15) the f means the right side of the differential equation. In every simulation step the number of size fractions are expanding, and we collect the number of the crystals in every fraction and the size of the fractions. The source term in case of MC simulation is interpreted by the following figure (Figure 1.).

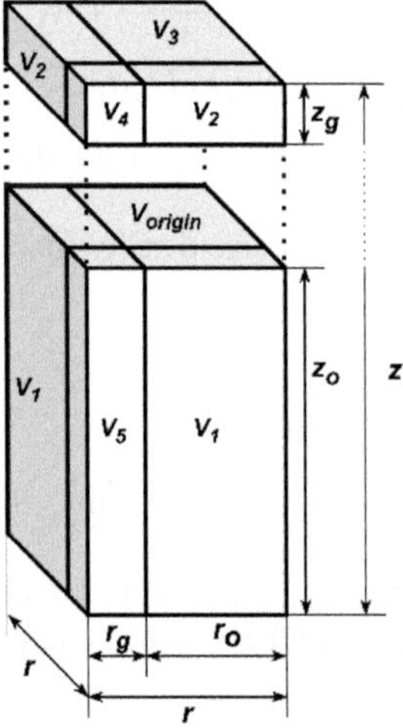

Figure 1.: Interpretation of the connection of the growing and the volume source term during one step (V means the volume, the o and g in the lower index denotes the origin and the gain length)

The growing is gaining the size of the crystal in 3 dimensions; thus, we need to calculate the volume increase. The growing in specific size direction is independent from the size, but not independent from the other size coordinate. In case of MC simulation, the source term of one step formalized by the following (Eq. (16)) based on Figure 1.

$$R_{V_S} = 2V_1 + 2V_2 + V_3 + V_4 + V_5 \tag{16}$$

And because we calculate all crystal size we can determine the volume increase of each crystal, and the sum of that gives the full volume source.

4. Results and Discussion

In the following, we compare the simulation results of the SMOM and the MC simulations. At first, we plotted in common diagram the two method's results with the break free case (Figure 2.)

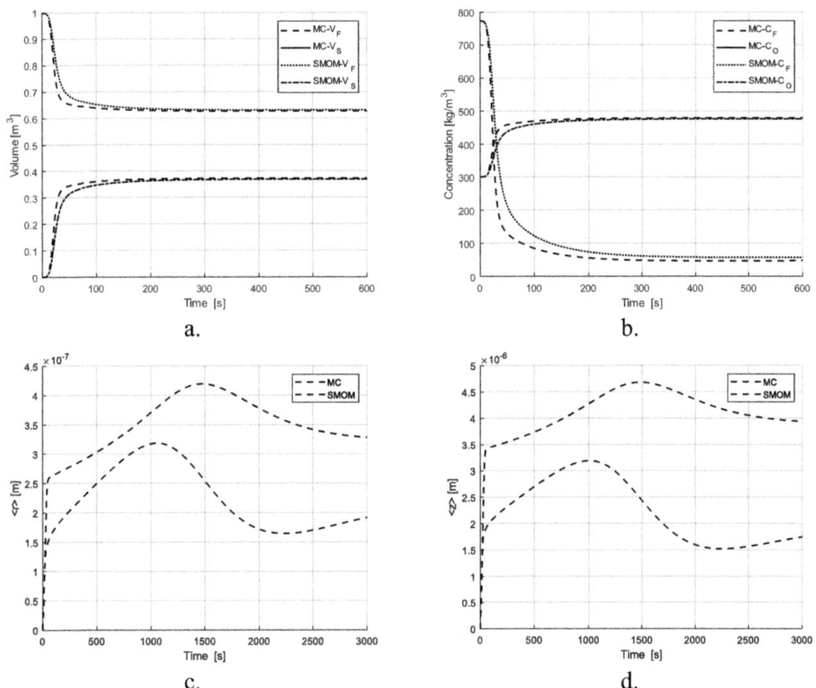

Figure 2.: Comparison of the results of the SMOM and MC simulations in time (a.: volume of the solid and liquid fraction; b.: concentration of the mother liquid, and the solvent; c.: average size of crystal diameter; d.: average size of crystal length)

In the Figure 2. can be seen a difference between the two methods. This can be explained by in one hand the inaccuracy of Euler method, in other hand the two methods from different approaches. At the next we compare the two methods with breaking event. In this work we don't want to give a same result from the two simulations, just want to present the two methods give a same tendency. Matching the two methods is not easy for two reasons. The first is the breaking is dependent on the k_B in case of SMOM and dependent on the breaking number in case of MC simulation, but these two parameter effects on different variable (in SMOM to the moments, in MC directly to the crystal length). The Figure 3. shows the comparison of the results of the two methods with breaking and breaking free case.

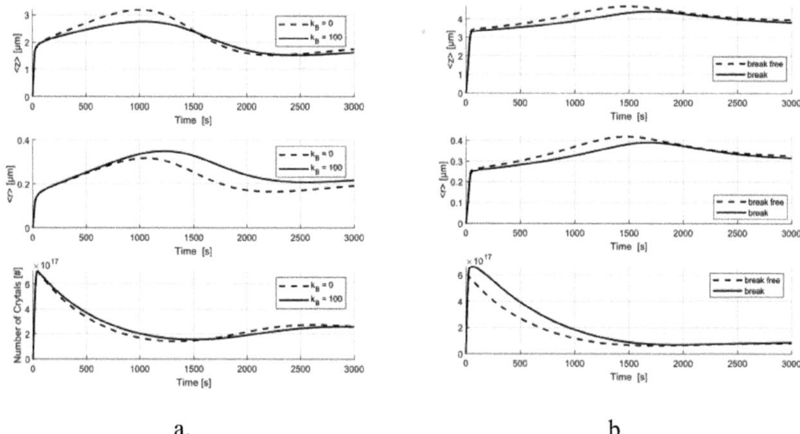

a. b.

Figure 3.: Comparison of the result of breaking and breaking free case (a. SMOM; b. MC)

During the comparison of breaking case, we have chosen for the k_B 0 and 100 value in case of SMOM and in case of MC we drew lots 100 random fraction and we assumed 0.1% of braking in one fraction. In Figure 3. can be seen the two method gives a different result in case of average size of crystals. That discrepancy also comes from the different approach and the random variable. The parametric matching of the two methods to each other is the fact of future research. In terms of simulation time the SMOM can be calculated only a few seconds, the MC simulation took 1000s approximately.

5. Conclusions

In this work we compare two methods for solve the same model and we compare the two results. The advantage of the SMOM is the short solution time, and the easy handling of the ordinary differential system, but disadvantage are the complex mathematical transformation and the losing of the information. The run of the MC simulation is slower but gives more information about the system and this method suitable to non-ideal and more complex system modelling. The matching of the two method is a hard task because the two approach is different. Unfortunately, in the absence of measurement results we do not choose which method is better. In the future work we would to make a parameter set for the identic solution.

Reference

Á. Borsos, B. G. Lakatos, 2012, Influence of breakage on crystal size distribution in a continuous cooling crystallizer, Periodica Polytechnica, Chemical Engineering, 56, 2, 65-69

Á. Borsos, B. G. Lakatos, 2014, Investigation and simulation of crystallization of high aspect ratio crystals with fragmentation, Chemical Engineering Research and Design, 92, 1133–1141

B. Szilágyi, P. S. Agachi, B. G. Lakatos, 2015, Numerical analysis of crystallization of high aspect ratio crystals with breakage, Powder Tecnology, 283, 152-162

L. Balogh, A. Egedy, Zs. Ulbert, Á. Bárkányi, 2023, Comparison of the Dynamic and Thermal Behavior of Different Ideal Flow Crystallizers, ChemEngineering, 7, 2, 2-21

J.R. van Peborgh Gooch, M.J. Hounslow, 1996, Monte Carlo Simulation of Size-Enlargement Mechanisms in Crystallization, Particle Technology and Fluidization, 42, 7,1864-1874

K. Piotrowski, J. Piotrowski, 2005, Monte Carlo modelling of continuous adiabatic MSMPR crystallizer, Chemical Engineering and Processing, 44, 517–529

Flavio Manenti, Gintaras V. Reklaitis (Eds.), Proceedings of the 34th European Symposium on Computer Aided Process Engineering / 15th International Symposium on Process Systems Engineering (ESCAPE34/PSE24), June 2-6, 2024, Florence, Italy
 http://dx.doi.org/10.1016/B978-0-443-28824-1.50188-5

Hydrogen production from biogas with electrified steam methane reforming: system optimization with renewable generation and storages

Andrea Nava,[a*] Davide Remondini,[b] Matteo Lualdi,[b] Stefano Campanari,[a] Matteo C. Romano,[a]

[a]*Politecnico di Milano, Department of Energy, Via Lambruschini 4, Milano 20156, Italy*
[b]*Snam S.p.A., San Donato Milanese, Milano 20097, Italy*
andrea.nava@polimi.it

Abstract

Biogas is a renewable resource produced by anaerobic digestion, that had a significant deployment in Europe in the last 20 years for electricity and heat generation. The biogenic CO_2 emission associated with biogas and biomethane utilization in 2020 was 24 Mton in Europe (EBA, 2022). Therefore, introducing alternative pathways such as the production of decarbonised energy carriers from biogas with CO_2 capture and storage would allow to achieve negative emissions and generate significant carbon credits.

This work analyses a process for biogas conversion into hydrogen with CO_2 separation and liquefaction using the novel electrified steam reforming (eSMR) technology. The chemical plant is simulated with Aspen Plus software and consists of two main sections: syngas generation by means of eSMR and water gas shift (WGS); gas separation section, where CO_2 is separated from syngas with MDEA-based absorption process and pure hydrogen is recovered with a Pressure Swing Adsorption (PSA) unit. The whole system is thermally integrated and the only external energy supply is electricity. System integration with renewable sources, battery energy storage system (BESS), gas storages and connection with power grid is optimized with GAMS, that allows to calculate the optimal renewable energy plant and storage system capacity , as well as the optimal equipment size.

The proposed biogas conversion system consumes 18 kWh/kg_{H2} of electricity (1.1 MW with an input of 390 Nm^3/h of biogas) and 80% of this consumption is absorbed by the electrified reformer. 96% of the chemical energy of biogas is converted to hydrogen while 75% of the carbon is converted to high purity CO_2. The resulting cost of hydrogen depends on the share of renewable energy used, the renewable capacity factor and the size of the plant: in the short term, the cost varies between 6.2 and 7.1 €/kg on a small scale, while in future scenarios with reduced cost of renewable energy, the hydrogen cost would reduce to 4.2 €/kg. With 10 times larger plant, the cost can be further lowered at 2.5 €/kg.

Keywords: biogas, hydrogen, CO_2 separation, electrified steam methane reforming, economic optimization

1. Introduction

Electrified steam methane reforming is a novel technology that allows to reduce CO_2 emissions and provide flexible and compact heat generation (Wismann et al., 2019), enabling process intensification and design of reactors for syngas production suitable for small-scale applications such as biogas plants. In 2021, Europe produced 159 TWh of biogas and 37 TWh of bio-methane, and potential growth is estimated at 1326 TWh in

2040 (IEA, 2020). It is therefore interesting to evaluate the potential of alternative biogas conversion pathways for the production of decarbonized energy carriers with separation and capture of biogenic CO_2, which are able to yield negative emissions. The scope of this work is to evaluate bio-H_2 production from biogas plants such as those located far from the gas grid and unsuitable for conventional bio-methane production.

2. System design

2.1. Chemical Island

The conversion system is presented in Figure 1 and exploits 390 Nm^3/h of biogas, representative of an average biodigester size in the typical agriculture context of north Italy. Biogas properties and main plant assumptions are reported in Table 1.

Table 1 – Biogas properties (left) and summary of main process assumptions (right).

Mass	500	kg/h	Saturator	H_2O/CH_4 molar ratio	3.5	-
LHV	15.4	MJ/kg	eSMR	Temperature out	800	°C
Molar	28.6	kg/kmol	eSMR	Pressure out	7	bar
Thermal	2.14	MW_{LHV}	WGS	Adiabatic, Temperature In	300	°C
			CO2 sep.	Capture efficiency	95	%
Molar fractions			PSA	H2 recovery efficiency	90	%
CH_4	55	%	Compressors	Isentropic efficiency	70	%
CO_2	45	%	Compressors	Mech-electric eff.	92	%

Biogas is compressed to 9 bar and feeds the saturation column, where the amount of circulating hot water is adjusted to reach the desired H_2O/CH_4 ratio. The wet biogas is pre-heated before feeding the eSMR, where syngas is produced at 800 °C and 7 bar. Syngas is cooled to generate saturated steam and is then fed to the adiabatic WGS at 300°C. Shifted syngas is further cooled and heat is exploited for pre-heating reactants and the biodigester water loop. Condensed water from the syngas is recovered and recycled to the saturator, while dry syngas is compressed to 30 bar and CO_2 is separated by means of MDEA-based absorption process. The CO_2 rich stream undergoes a compression and liquefaction process, delivering high-purity CO_2 transportable by truck (15 bar; -31 °C). Hydrogen from clean syngas is purified in a PSA unit. PSA off-gases are burned to generate additional steam. The total amount of steam generated in the plant is used (i) to regenerate the CO_2-enriched solvent in the reboiler of the CO_2 absorption process, (ii) to heat up the water feeding the saturator and the water loop of the bio-digester.

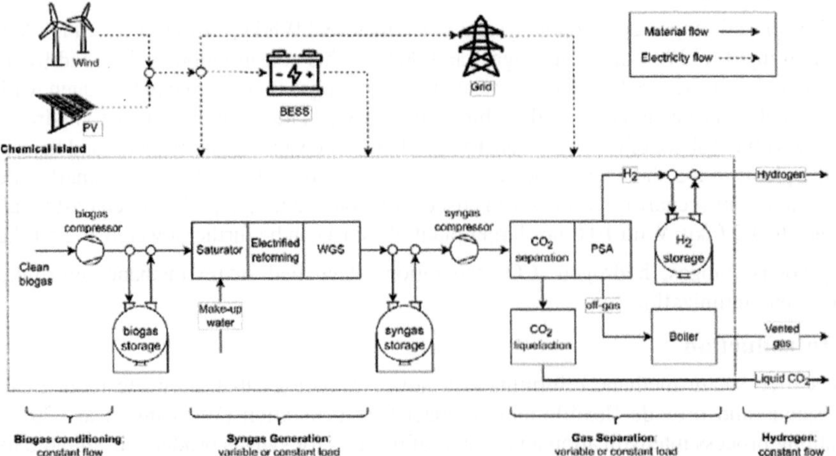

Figure 1 - Schematic of biogas conversion system with power supply and storage units.

2.2. System integration

The only external energy supply of the chemical island is electricity, which can be supplied to the system via renewable sources (e.g. PV panels, wind) or from the electric grid. BESS is charged when the renewable production is greater than the load and discharged at times of low availability. As shown in Figure 1, the plant is equipped with gas storage units, that allow flexible operation of the chemical island. Syngas generation increases by emptying the biogas storage to take advantage of renewable production peaks, while it decreases in periods of reduced renewable availability by filling the biogas tank. The syngas storage allows to decouple the two sections of the chemical island dedicated to reforming and CO_2 separation, while the hydrogen storage allows delivering a constant hydrogen flow at the plant outlet.

3. Methods and key performance indicators

The chemical island was modelled and simulated in Aspen Plus® for both design and part-load conditions, by using the Peng-Robinson equation of state and the Electrolyte-NRTL model for the amine-based absorption process, the saturation column and the water separation vessels. Columns were modelled with a rate-based approach, while eSMR and WGS reactors are calculated at chemical equilibrium. At part load, the electric power for the eSMR is controlled to keep the outlet temperature constant, while the solvent flowrate is adjusted to keep the CO_2 capture efficiency at 95%.

Heat exchangers area is fixed at design conditions, while the heat transfer coefficients are varied depending on the fluids flow rate with an exponential law (exponent n=0.8 for shell and tube and n=0.67 for plate heat exchangers) as in Eq. (1).

$$h_{off} = h_{design}\left(\frac{\dot{m}_{off}}{\dot{m}_{design}}\right)^n;\ U_{off} = \left(\frac{1}{h_{hot,off}}+\frac{1}{h_{cold,off}}\right)^{-1} \quad \left[\frac{W}{m^2K}\right] \tag{1}$$

Integration with renewable sources, grid and storage units is modelled with GAMS optimization software and mixed integer linear programming (MILP) method, using energy and mass balance equations of the chemical plant from Aspen Plus. Mass balances at gas storages boundaries, energy balance for the state of charge of the battery, energy balances between power production, BESS, grid and electricity absorbed by the plant are computed along the year with hourly resolution. The optimization variables are the capacity of renewable plants, BESS and gas storage units. Nonlinear economic equations coupling gas flow rate with plant cost allow the calculation of the optimal size of chemical island equipment and were linearized with the piecewise method. The objective function is the total annual costs, which is minimized using the CPLEX solver. Wind and solar power distribution is taken from Pfenninger et al. (2016) for different locations.

The key performance indicators are the hydrogen production, the carbon capture ratio, specific electric consumption and the Renewable Energy Share, that represents the percentage of renewable energy used by the chemical plant during the year, as defined in Eq. (2).

Renewable Energy Share
$$RENS = \frac{\sum_{t=1}^{8760}(E_{renew,to\ chemical\ island}(t))\cdot\Delta t}{\sum_{t=1}^{8760}(E_{chemical\ island})\cdot\Delta t}\cdot 100\ [\%] \tag{2}$$

The economic analysis was carried out with the methodology of Turton (2012), whose tables were used for estimating the cost of conventional components. The cost of the WGS and PSA units was taken from Rath et al (2010) and thc electrified reformer cost was estimated with an in-house model using the technology developed by Politecnico di Milano (Ambrosetti et al., 2023). The currency is updated to $€^{2019}$ with the CEPCI index. Costs of renewable technologies were taken from IRENA (2022), gas storages from Apt et al. (2008), while future cost forecasts were derived from Ram et al. (2020). The cost of

electricity from the grid was assumed flat and equal to 150 €/MWh in the current scenario and 100 €/MWh in the future scenario. As for CO_2 produced, a credit of 100 €/t and a transport cost of 50 €/t were considered, resulting in a net revenue of 50 €/t.
Emissions from Italian grid, equal to 356 g_{CO2}/kWh (Scarlat et al., 2022) and embedded emission from PV (645 kg_{CO2}/kW_{el} from Müller et al., 2021), wind turbines (500 kg_{CO2}/kW_{el} from Schreiber et al., 2019) and Li-Ion batteries (129 kg_{CO2}/kWh_{el} from Bonalumi & Kolahchian Tabrizi, 2022) are considered for power production.

4. Results

The main results of the chemical island are shown in Table 3, where it can be noted that 96% of the chemical energy of biogas is converted into hydrogen while 75% of the biogenic carbon is available as high purity CO_2. Electric consumption of the chemical island is equal to 17.7 kWh/kg_{H2}, 78% of which goes for the electrified reforming, 13% for biogas and syngas compression and 7% for CO_2 compression (132 kWh/t_{CO2}), while the CO_2 separation thermal duty is equal to 2.15 MJ/kg_{CO2}.
The total CAPEX of the chemical island is 3.5 M€, including 1.4 M€ for CO_2 capture (40 €/t_{CO2}) and 1.4 M€ for syngas generation (0.35 M€ for the eSMR).
Considering a biodigester located in north Italy as a reference, the optimal renewable energy share (RENS) is 27%, as shown in the first column of the optimization results in Table 3, and system emissions are equal to -4.7 kg_{CO2}/kg_{H2}.

Table 2 Main results of the chemical island operating parameters and optimization results.

Chemical island results								
H_2O/CH_4 at reformer inlet					-		3.50	
CH_4 conversion in eSMR					%		95.1%	
CO conversion in WGS					%		73.2%	
Biogas input					kW_{LHV}		2142	
Hydrogen output					kW_{LHV}		2064	
CO_2 specific capture					kg_{CO2}/kg_{H2}		-9.42	
Carbon capture ratio					%		75.9	
H_2 production					MW_{H2}/MW_{BG}		96.3%	
Electricity consumption					kWh_{el}/kg_{H2}		17.7	
Optimization results (flexible system located in north Italy)								
RENS		*27%*	*40%*	*60%*	*80%*	*90%*	*95%*	*100%*
PV capacity	MW	2.01	2.61	2.57	3.29	3.75	4.30	6.23
Wind capacity	MW	-	0.47	2.42	3.99	4.49	4.70	11.49
BESS capacity	MWh	-	-	-	-	3.21	6.35	17.44
BESS equivalent cycles	-	-	-	-	-	202	164	28
Biogas storage size	m^3	-	120	205	1036	1251	1367	973
Biogas storage hours	h	-	2.4	4.1	20.9	25.3	27.6	19.7
Syngas storage size	m^3	-	479	729	1411	2285	3370	2378
Syngas storage hours	h	-	2.4	3.6	7.0	11.3	16.7	11.8
Hydrogen storage size	m^3	-	-	-	270.7	276.5	187.9	102.2
Hydrogen storage hours	h	-	-	-	9.5	9.7	6.6	3.6
Syngas generation size	%	100%	100%	132%	165%	164%	159%	119%
Gas Separation size	%	100%	100%	102%	147%	145%	138%	102%
Captured CO_2	kg_{CO2}/kg_{H2}	-9.42	-9.42	-9.42	-9.42	-9.42	-9.42	-9.42
Net emissions	kg_{CO2}/kg_{H2}	-4.69	-5.44	-6.64	-7.81	-8.36	-8.60	-8.42

By constraining the RENS, the optimal capacity of PV and wind increases, and for RENS greater than 80% a battery has to be installed. The solution with RENS=100% is hardly feasible and leads to slightly higher emissions than the case with RENS=95% due to oversizing of renewable and battery capacity and the curtailment of 60% of electricity.
The hydrogen production cost breakdown is shown in Figure 2, and is equal to 4.7 €/kg in the optimal solution, where the contribution on the hydrogen cost of the chemical island is 0.6 €/kg, PV is 0.3 €/kg and grid electricity accounts for 1.9 €/kg as for biogas.

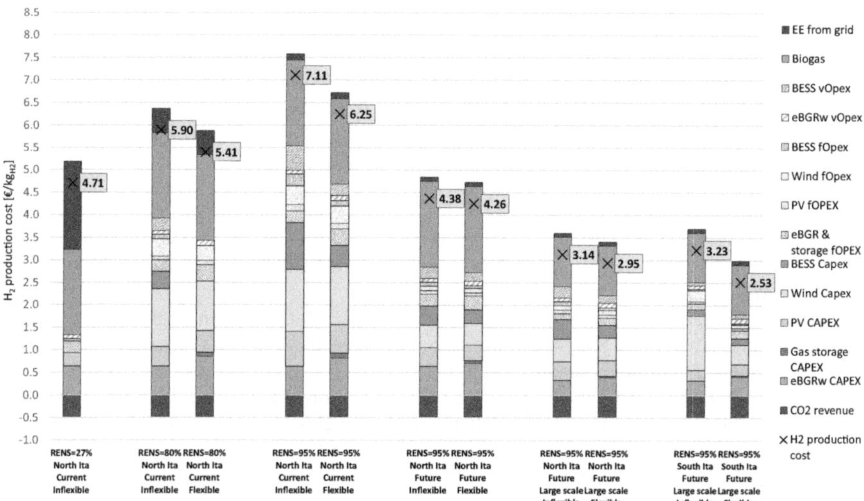

Figure 2 H_2 cost breakdown for different RENS values, plant size and locations

As RENS increases, the lower contribution of grid electricity is not offset by the higher cost of renewables and battery, and consequently the cost of hydrogen production increases to 7.1 €/kg.

In Flexible systems, the CAPEX of the chemical island rises to 0.9 €/kg$_{H2}$, while the contribution of gas storage units is always very low and at most equal to 0.1 €/kg$_{H2}$. Therefore, the option of a flexible operation decreases the hydrogen cost, as the economic burden of an oversized chemical island and of the gas storage units is offset by the smaller renewable plant and battery capacity. For example, with RENS=95% it is possible to reduce the cost of hydrogen from 7.1 to 6.3 €/kg by making the system flexible. The difference between flexible and inflexible plants is reduced in the future scenario, due to the reduced specific cost of renewable energy technologies.

Biogas production cost for the small biodigester is equal to 55 €/MWh and represents the largest share on hydrogen cost (1.9 €/kg). By increasing the size of the biodigester, the cost of biogas can be reduced at 32 €/MWh (IEA, 2020). Considering a system with a biodigester capacity of 3900 Nm^3/h (i.e. 10 times the size of the reference case), the cost of hydrogen would reduce significantly to 2.9-3.1 €/kg, thanks to the economies of scale. The cost difference between a flexible and inflexible system increases on a large scale, and is greater when the availability of renewable energy increases, as can be observed in the case of south Italy, where flexibility can reduce the cost from 3.2 €/kg to 2.5 €/kg.

5. Conclusions

With the electrification of the reformer, it is possible to intensify the syngas generation process even at small-scale and convert almost all of the energy from the biogas into hydrogen, since no gas needs to be burned to sustain the endothermicity of the process and heat is provided by electrical elements. With the separation and capture of CO_2 from the generated syngas, it is possible to achieve a system with negative emissions of up to -8.6 kg$_{CO2}$/kg$_{H2}$ through the use of renewable electricity and gas and electricity storage units. Hydrogen production cost was minimized by using results from Aspen as input to an optimization algorithm developed in GAMS. Hydrogen cost increases with RENS because of the higher renewable and BESS capacity required to meet the plant load, and varies between 4-7 €/kg in the short-term scenario for a small-scale plant located in north

Italy. Locations with higher solar and wind availability (e.g., south Italy) allow to decrease the renewable capacity required for the same amount of energy, and thus reduce the cost of hydrogen production. Moreover, by increasing the size of the system and taking advantage of economies of scale in the chemical island and biodigester, it is possible to further reduce the cost of production, up to 2.5 €/kg in the most favourable case of high availability of PV and wind as typical of south Italy.

References

Ambrosetti, M., Beretta, A., Groppi, G., Romano, M. C., & Tronconi, E. (2023). *Reactor with electrically heated thermo-conductive structure for endothermic catalytic process* (Patent No. WO 2023/062591 A1).

Apt, J., Newcomer, A., Lave, L. B., Douglas, S., & Dunn, L. M. (2008). An Engineering-Economic Analysis of Syngas Storage. *U.S. Department of Energy's National Energy Technology Laboratory, January 2015*, 143.

Bonalumi, D., & Kolahchian Tabrizi, M. (2022). Re-evaluation of the Global Warming Potential for the Production of Lithium-Ion Batteries with Nickel-Manganese-Cobalt Cathode Chemistries in China. *Energy and Fuels*, *36*(22), 13753–13767. https://doi.org/10.1021/ACS.ENERGYFUELS.2C02204/ASSET/IMAGES/MEDIUM/EF2C02204_0013.GIF

EBA. (2022). *Statistical Report 2022 Tracking biogas and biomethane.*

IEA. (2020). *Sustainable supply potential and costs – Outlook for biogas and biomethane: Prospects for organic growth – Analysis - IEA*. https://www.iea.org/reports/outlook-for-biogas-and-biomethane-prospects-for-organic-growth/sustainable-supply-potential-and-costs

IRENA. (2022). IRENA (2022), Renewable Power Generation Costs in 2021, International Renewable Energy Agency, Abu Dhabi. ISBN 978-92-9260-452-3. *International Renewable Energy Agency*, 160. https://www.irena.org/-/media/Files/IRENA/Agency/Publication/2018/Jan/IRENA_2017_Power_Costs_2018.pdf

Müller, A., Friedrich, L., Reichel, C., Herceg, S., Mittag, M., & Neuhaus, D. H. (2021). A comparative life cycle assessment of silicon PV modules: Impact of module design, manufacturing location and inventory. *Solar Energy Materials and Solar Cells*, *230*, 111277. https://doi.org/10.1016/J.SOLMAT.2021.111277

Pfenninger, S., & Staffell, I. (2016). Long-term patterns of European PV output using 30 years of validated hourly reanalysis and satellite data. *Energy*, *114*, 1251–1265. https://doi.org/10.1016/j.energy.2016.08.060

Ram, M., Galimova, T., Bogdanov, D., Fasihi, M., Gulagi, A., Breyer dena, C., Micheli, M., & Crone, K. (2020). *POWERFUELS in a Renewable Energy World.* www.dena.de

Rath, Lawrence K and Chou, Vincent H and Kuehn, N. J. (2010). Assessment of Hydrogen Production with CO2 Capture Volume 1: Baseline State-of- the-Art Plants. In *Doe/Netl-2010/1434* (Vol. 1). www.netl.doe.gov

Scarlat, N., Prussi, M., & Padella, M. (2022). Quantification of the carbon intensity of electricity produced and used in Europe. *Applied Energy*, *305*, 117901. https://doi.org/10.1016/J.APENERGY.2021.117901

Schreiber, A., Marx, J., & Zapp, P. (2019). Comparative life cycle assessment of electricity generation by different wind turbine types. *Journal of Cleaner Production*, *233*, 561–572. https://doi.org/10.1016/J.JCLEPRO.2019.06.058

Turton, Richard and Bailie, Richard C and Whiting, Wallace B and Shaeiwitz, J. A. (2012). *Analysis, synthesis, and design of chemical processes*. Prentice Hall.

Wismann, S. T., Engbæk, J. S., Vendelbo, S. B., Bendixen, F. B., Eriksen, W. L., Aasberg-Petersen, K., Frandsen, C., Chorkendorff, I., & Mortensen, P. M. (2019). Electrified methane reforming: A compact approach to greener industrial hydrogen production. *Science (New York, N.Y.)*, *364*(6442), 756–759. https://doi.org/10.1126/SCIENCE.AAW8775/SUPPL_FILE/AAW8775-WISMANN-SM.PDF

Flavio Manenti, Gintaras V. Reklaitis (Eds.), Proceedings of the 34th European Symposium on Computer Aided Process Engineering / 15th International Symposium on Process Systems Engineering (ESCAPE34/PSE24), June 2-6, 2024, Florence, Italy
 http://dx.doi.org/10.1016/B978-0-443-28824-1.50189-7

Ontology-driven automation of process modelling and simulation

Alberto Rodríguez-Fernández, Vinay Kumar Gautam, Heinz A Preisig*

Department of Chemical Engineering, Norwegian University of Science and Technology, N-7491 Trondheim, Norway

Heinz.Preisig@chemeng.ntnu.no

Abstract

NTNU's **Pro**cess **Mo**delling suite, ProMo, adopts a rigorous ontology-driven modelling paradigm that aligns with the foundational tenets of physical, chemical, and biological systems. This approach serves as the basis for the systematic development of models. Creating a coherent variable/expression list, manifested as a multi-bipartite graph, forms the bedrock for assembling fundamental building blocks. These building blocks, in turn, expedite the construction of complex models, ensuring coherence across the modelling lifecycle. This work showcases our method for preparing model data to be integrated into the code generation process.

Keywords: Ontology, simulation, computational engineering, automatic code generation.

1. Ontology-Driven Simulations

A user-friendly graphical interface augments the user experience when utilising simulation software. Block diagrams are the most common technology for visualisation. They connect activities, often spiced with logical components, implementing a logic-driven control structure. Some application domains, like process control, use them as a preferred tool, and chemical engineering uses flowsheeting as the primary plant design tool. People grab pictorial information much quicker than corresponding textual. It is not a surprise then that these tools were some of the very early developments when computing arrived, and various tools emerged consequently. Monsanto's FLOWTRAN was released in 1966, triggering several projects, such as ASPEN (1981), HYSYS (ASPEN), UniSim (Honeywell). The need for dynamic simulators started SPEEDUP (Imperial College) and later gPROMS (Imperial College, PSE, now Siemens). The last 20 years saw a development towards an ontology-driven model-development environment with ASCENT (Carnegie Mellon), MODEL.A (MIT), MODKIT (RWTH), Modeller (TU/E), and ProMo (NTNU), driven by the objective to produce internally correctly structured models. NTNU's ProMo builds on the concept of fundamental entities, representing the modelled process as a communicating network of these entities. NTNU has been working with a graphical representation for teaching and designing processes, with the graphical language eventually evolving into a standard (Preisig, 2022).

ProMo constructs first an ontology that captures the main structures and items. In the second step, the ontology is used to build a *variable := expression* bipartite graph, which in the third step are the ingredients for defining the behaviour of the entities' specialised varieties by a modelling specialist. The next step is the construction of process models, done by what we now refer to as a translator, a person who learns about the process and maps it into a process model using the expert's fundamental building blocks. The final stage is the generation of target code, which is a parameterised simulation in either a stand-alone task or a script for the target simulation environment. In contrast to most other simulation systems where the equations are spread over different model modules, ProMo implements a **single module** with all the equations.

When users interact with the different modules, they provide information in several ways, such as variables and defining expressions, construction of entity models, visual construction of the process model, and instantiation of variables. The Task Factory module of ProMo uses all this information to generate the target code automatically. A templating engine performs the translation to a specific language as the last step in the code generation. This approach allows for great flexibility, making it possible to switch between different languages, such as C++, Python, or Matlab, by selecting the appropriate template. Modifying the templates so the generated code can be used as a standalone file or as input for another program like an orchestrator is possible. This paper focuses on transforming the user-supplied information into a form that the templating engine can consume. In Section 2, we introduce the structure of the data entered by the user, followed by a description of the input that the templating engine requires. Section 3 details the data processing necessary to fulfil those requirements. Section 4 summarises the procedure and presents other uses it can have in the future.

2. The ProMo Automation Workflow

2.1. *User input data*

2.1.1. *Entity Models*

Entity models represent elementary parts of the modelled system. The CWA (Preisig, 2022) defines a set of elementary entities. Their definition in the context of the modelled process depends on the granularity required to capture the modelled object's behaviour. It is thus application dependent. Each entity model contains a subset of variables and equations from the bipartite graph, forming a coupled equation forest. Mathematically, each entity model is seen as an input/output function, and the equation forest computes variables as a function of other variables. On the function level, the variables are classified as follows:

- *Input* variables originate from other entities and are the external quantities needed to calculate the *output* variables.
- *Output* variables are the result of computing the entity models. They are the inputs to other entity models.
- *Instantiation* variables represent quantities related to the characteristics of the part of the modelled system the entity model describes. Initial conditions and parameters are typical class members, and the user must introduce numerical values later in the modelling process.
- The variable/equation forest links all the variables in an entity by defining equations. Each *output* variable is the root of one tree in the forest. Each node in a tree will contain either a variable or an equation. Variable nodes can have at most one child, its defining equation. Equation nodes can have one child for each variable on the right-hand side of the equation. This structure ensures that going from the leaves of a particular tree to the root yields the sequence of equations necessary to compute the corresponding *output* variable. Finally, variables in each tree are available to all the other trees, ensuring the uniqueness of the nodes in the forest.

In addition, each entity model contains a unique index set name. An entity model is complete when all the variables are *input*, *instantiation* or have a defining equation in the variable/equation forest. This completeness guarantees the feasibility of computing all variables if the entity model has access to the *input* variables and numerical values for all *instantiation* variables. Only complete entity models can be used as blocks to construct the topology of the process model.

2.1.2. *Topology graph*

The Modeller module of ProMo allows a user to map a process into a process model using a graphical tool. This visual representation is automatically converted and stored as a topology graph with nodes that store "tokens" and arcs that control their transfer between nodes (Preisig 2021). The nodes and arcs contain references to the entity models. That is why, while constructing this graph, we simultaneously define the connections between entity models. As a rule, entity models can only receive *input* variables from others directly connected to them.

The topology graph presents a visual and intuitive way of splitting a system into smaller components and their relationships. The entity models help to distinguish between these components and provide the necessary mathematical structure. The graphic nature of this representation also comes in handy to assign numerical values to the *instantiation* variables, allowing the user to orient himself in a commonly complex system.

2.1.3. *Instantiation*

All *instantiation* variables in an entity model require a numerical value. The user provides these values, transforming a general representation of the model into a parameterised instance. ProMo stores this information as a group of equations (assignments) in the form:

$$x := \# \tag{1}$$

where x is an *instantiation* variable, and # is a numerical value.

A more advanced case appears when the user assigns numerical values to variables not classified as *instantiation*. This action triggers a restructuring of the variable/equation forest of one or multiple entity models. It is beyond the scope of this paper to go into the details of the required manipulations, but the resulting entity models behave in the same way as the previously defined ones.

Several checks ensure that no *instantiation* variable remains without a numerical value. Failure to comply with this condition will lead to a mathematical representation of the model that is not solvable.

2.2. *Processed output data*

The final step in the ProMo is the automatic code generation. The task factory module writes all the necessary information into a format defined by the target language. A templating engine takes the essential data and uses language-specific templates to complete this step. The required input data to the templating engine consists of:

1. A list of variables used and values for the ones marked as *instantiation*.
2. A list of equations used and their computing order.
3. Index sets indicate the relation of entity models to elements in the topology.

4. Information about language-specific ways of representing the variables and equations.

Items 1 and 2 require some additional processing of the user input data, which will be detailed in the following section. The data in items 3 and 4 is already available at this stage. The former comes from the topology graph. Each index set name belongs to one of the entity models used, and all nodes and arcs referencing the entity model belong to the set. The latter originates from creating the bipartite graph in the first steps of our modelling journey. The user can supply additional data to document the variables and equations at that step. This data can be marked as language-specific to comply with language rules or guidelines specified by different communities, ensuring the resulting code aligns with the preferences and needs of its end-users.

ProMo generates the code automatically using a templating engine. The general user is advised not to change the automatically generated code manually. Instead, to go back and make necessary changes to previous steps.

3. Equation sequencing

As previously mentioned, our starting point is the topology graph, where each node and arc are linked to an entity model and has a set of already instantiated variables (Figure 1a). We use different incidence matrices to capture the relationship between nodes and arcs under certain constraints (nodes and arcs containing specific tokens, transfer mechanisms, etc.). These matrices are variables in our bipartite graph and will preserve the information of the topology graph once we move on from this representation.

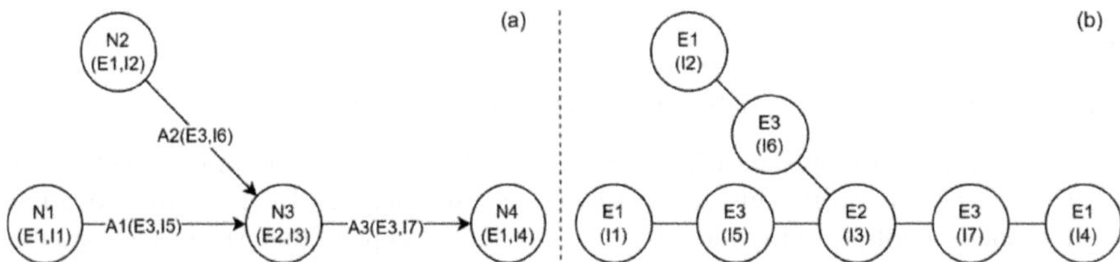

Figure 1. (a) Example topology graph: each node and arc have a link to an entity and a group of instantiated variables. (b) Entity model graph constructed from the topology graph on the left.

Our first step is constructing an undirected graph where each vertex corresponds to an entity model and associating it with the corresponding values of the *instantiation* variables. We add one vertex for each node and arc in the topology graph. At this stage, the entity models are the main focus, and it is irrelevant whether there was a link to one type of element or the other in the previous graph. Edges between the new graph's vertices indicate an arc going in or out from a node in the topology graph. Figure 1b shows the resulting graph obtained from the one shown in Figure 1a. In this new graph, adjacency between two vertices means that the corresponding entities can exchange *input* and *output* variables, as previously mentioned, which simplifies the process of finding the required *input* variables.

At this point, variables and equations are spread over the entity model graph, each vertex containing its own subset. Next, we will create a new directed graph containing only variables and equations. We will use this final form of our data to find the correct computing order for the equations.

As illustrated in Figure 2a, each vertex in the new graph contains a tuple of three elements: a variable, an equation, and a list of index set names corresponding to the entity models where this specific variable/equation combination appears. Arcs between vertices imply that the equation in the tail vertex contains the variable in the head one.

At first, we add variable/equation pairs representing balance or conservation for the state variables. If the same variable/equation combination appears in multiple entity models, we group all the index set names together in one vertex instead of creating a new one each time. This rule is observed in general and implies that each combination appears only once in the graph. Each equation provides a new group of variables that are added to a queue.

From now on, we process the variables in the queue. First, we search to find their defining equations. In the case of *input* variables, this implies a search in the adjacent entity models. For *instantiation* variables, an equation like Eq. (1) is constructed for each instantiated value. Given that all utilised entity models adhere to the completeness condition outlined in Subsection 1.1.1, each of the remaining variables will possess a defining equation within the variable/equation forest. For each new variable/equation pair, a new vertex is created. If the pair exists already in the graph, the index set name is added to the existing vertex. In both cases, we add an arc connecting the vertex containing the parent equation to the vertex with the children variable/equation pair. New variables are added to the queue when a vertex with a new equation is created. This process is repeated until the queue is empty. Figure 2a shows an illustrative example of this type of graph.

At last, we are ready to find the computation order for the equations. We have transformed our data and ended up with what is, at first sight, a dependency resolution or scheduling problem (Beeri et al. 1981). Our solution uses a modified version of the topological sort algorithm (Kahn 1962), tailored to accommodate the following two constraints in our computational model.

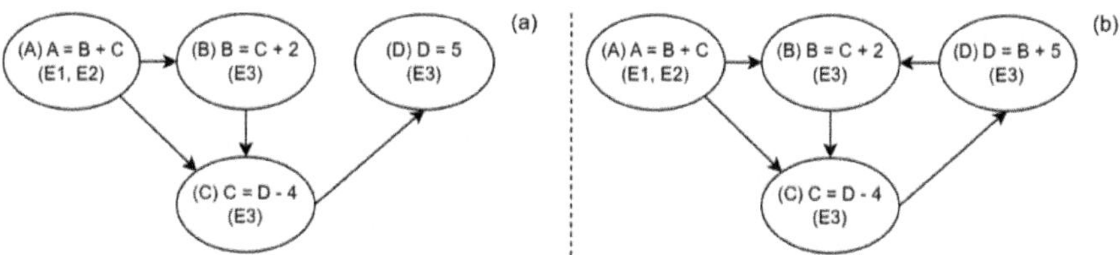

Figure 2. Example variable/equation graph. (a) Simple case. (b) Case with a cycle.

First, equations corresponding to the *instantiation* variables should be collected independently. Usually, this type of equation is evaluated only once at the beginning of the generated code, so it makes sense to separate them. From looking at Eq. (1), it is evident that vertices containing this type are always head vertices. This understanding facilitates their removal from the graph without affecting the ordering of the remaining vertices.

Second, the variable/equation digraph is not restricted to being a Directed Acyclic Graph (DAG) (See Figure 2b), which implies that the topological sorting algorithm will fail if cycles are not handled appropriately. Cycles in this graph indicate the presence of equations that need to be solved simultaneously. They commonly appear as part of strongly connected components (SCCs) (Tarjan 1972). All the equations in vertices belonging to an SCC must be solved at the same time. In our case, we use Tarjan's algorithm (Tarjan 1972) with Nuutila's modifications (Nuutila 1994) to find all SCCs and replace each with a single vertex. Each of these vertices contains all the equations in the corresponding SCC and is labeled accordingly so the templating engine can process them correctly.

The subsequent procedure is straightforward. We execute the topological sorting algorithm and reverse the resulting order to obtain the computation order for the equations. A list of index set names is attached to each equation so the correct values for the variables can be used.

After all these steps, the data is ready to be consumed by the templating engine. The resulting code contains all the necessary equations in one place, disregarding the entity models where they were used. This is only possible because the bipartite variable/equation graph is built as a whole at the beginning of the process and referenced from there on. This approach reduces the number of mistakes derived from defining the same equations in several places. Furthermore, it facilitates the analysis for consistency of the equations used in the model.

4. Conclusions

To automatically generate code using the information provided by users at different levels, ProMo uses a templating engine with templates written for each target language. Several data processing steps are necessary to convert the user's input to the information that feeds the template manager. First, we transform the topology graph into one where the entity models are the main component, which allows for an effective search of equations corresponding to *input* variables in the entity models. Next, we collect all variables and equations into a directed graph, allowing the use of topological sorting to find the computing order for the equations. Equations for instantiation variables and systems of equations are handled specially and labelled accordingly. This procedure has been implemented in the Task Factory module of ProMo, and the current tests have shown great success.

Acknowledgements

VIPCOAT H2020-NMBP-TO-IND-2020, Grant Agreement No. 952903; MEDIATE-net project, DigiPass CSA, HORIZON-CL4-2023-RESILIENCE- 01-39, Grant Agreement No. 101138510, NanoLodge NFR 299363, MEDIATE a European net project; Bio4Fuels (Norwegian Centre for Environment-friendly Energy Research (FME), project 257622).

References

A.B. Kahn, 1962, Topological Sorting of Large Networks, Commun. ACM, 5(11), 558–562.

C. Beeri and M.Y. Vardi, 1981. The implication problem for data dependencies. In: Even, S.,

H.A. Preisig, 2010, Constructing and maintaining proper process models, Comp & Chem Eng, 34(9), 1543-1555.

H.A. Preisig, 2021, Ontology-Based Process Modelling-with Examples of Physical Topologies, Processes, 9.

H.A. Preisig et al., 2022, ModGra - a Graphical representation of physical process models; CWA 1796, CEN-GENELEC Management Centre, Brussels.

E. Nuutila. and E. Soisalon-Soinen, 1994, On finding the strongly connected components in a directed graph, Information Processing Letters, 49(1), 9-14.

O. Kariv, (eds) Automata, Languages and Programming. ICALP 1981. Lecture Notes in Computer Science, vol 115. Springer, Berlin, Heidelberg.

R. Tarjan, 1972, Depth-first search and linear graph algorithms, SIAM Journal of Computing, 1(2):146-160.

Flavio Manenti, Gintaras V. Reklaitis (Eds.), Proceedings of the 34th European Symposium on Computer Aided Process Engineering / 15th International Symposium on Process Systems Engineering (ESCAPE34/PSE24), June 2-6, 2024, Florence, Italy
 http://dx.doi.org/10.1016/B978-0-443-28824-1.50190-3

Towards a Combined, Integrated, and Adaptable Bioethanol and -Ethylene Process Leveraging Flexible Ratios in Hybrid Production

Christoph Huber[a,b], Merlin Alvarado-Morales[a], Gürkan Sin[a]

[a]*Process and Systems Engineering Center (PROSYS), Department of Chemical and Biochemical Engineering, Technical University of Denmark (DTU), 2800 Kgs.Lyngby, Denmark*

[b]*School of Engineering and Design, Chair of Energy Systems Department, Technical University of Münich (TUM), 85747 Garching, Germany*

meal@kt.dtu.dk

Abstract

The production of bioethanol and ethylene offers significant potential as carbon-neutral fuel and raw material *e.g.*, for polyethylene production, respectively. We present a new approach, where we combined a) the bioethanol production process (pretreatment, hydrolysis, fermentation), b) the ethanol purification under the consideration of trace compounds and their removal to reach solvent-grade ethanol, and c) the coupling of the ethylene process to the ethanol process. The simulation results showed the feasibility of a flexible hybrid production process that fulfills the high-purity grades of both products. In addition, there is a high heat integration potential for all product ratios, thereby offering significant potential for adaptation to different market situations.

Keywords: bioethanol and -ethylene, hybrid production, heat integration, simulation

1. Introduction

Bioethanol and ethylene offer the potential for sustainable fuel, and carbon-neutral plastics production, respectively. While bioethanol production, especially first-generation concepts, is already established on larger-scale plants, ethylene is still mostly produced from fossil sources in a highly energy-intensive process. In most cases, these processes are still cheaper than the carbon-neutral alternative of bioethanol dehydration (Bayens *et al.*, 2015). Further, as economic uncertainties increasingly affect the planning of energy-intensive processes, adaptability and flexibility are required for the profitable operation of such processes. As a step towards biobased processes with such desired properties, this work presents an approach that features a hybrid production concept with flexible product ratios that can be adapted in response to price fluctuations of raw materials, products, energy, and heat utility. Further, this approach targets higher-purity products to increase the economic viability as well as to analyze the effects of impurities in raw materials. We present an integrated concept for a standalone plant that fully exploits its heat integration potential. Several aspects of this work have already been analyzed in different works. The effect of trace compounds in the fermentation broth on the bioethanol product was analyzed by Bisgaard *et al.* (2017), focusing on ethanol purification performance. Ethanol (Bayens *et al.*, 2015, Humbird *et al.*, 2011) and ethylene processes (Frosi *et al.*, 2021), (Mohsenzadeh *et al.*, 2017) have been separately analyzed in many studies, thereby focusing on process configurations, equipment design, and heat integration. However, a combination and optimization of both processes with the target of a hybrid production concept have, to the best of the authors' knowledge, not been performed. In the following, section two provides an overview of both bioethanol purification and the ethylene production processes, and the proposed combined process is presented. This is followed by the used models and methods in section three, and finally, section four presents and discusses the simulation results.

2. Process Description

2.1. Background scenario

The background scenario considered in this work is the second-generation bioethanol plant-wide simulation model developed by Prunescu *et al.* (2017) for a large-scale plant. The model includes pretreatment, enzymatic hydrolysis, and co-fermentation sections, respectively. The output of the plant-wide simulation model –the fermentation broth coming out of the co-fermentation section –is used as the input for the bioethanol purification model analyzed in this work.

2.2. Bioethanol Purification

Bioethanol can be produced in fuel-grade purity, which can contain fractions of water, methanol, and other volatiles and higher saturated mono alcohols. Figure 1 illustrates the downstream purification process where the feed is the fermentation broth coming from the second-generation bioethanol plant-wide model. The process configuration is based on Bisgaard *et al.* (2017). In a first step, the beer stripper column separates the solids from the fermentation broth by stripping the product stream with steam.

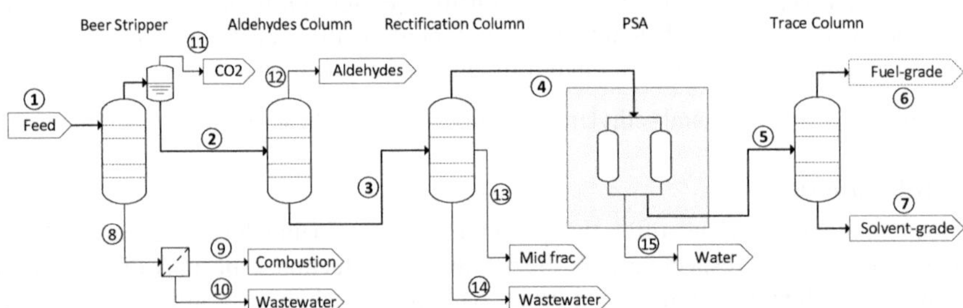

Figure 1: Model flowsheet of the second-generation bioethanol purification process

The aldehydes column removes acetaldehyde, 1-propanal, 1-butanal, crotonaldehyde, and ethyl acetate. The main function of the third column, the rectification column is to further concentrate ethanol up to a distillate with an azeotropic mixture of ethanol and water. The side draw is implemented to remove benzaldehyde, 1-propanol, 1-butanol, 2-butanol (s-butanol), 2-methyl-1-propanol, 2-methyl-1-butanol, and 3-methyl-1-butanol. The top product from the rectification column is sent to a molecular sieve unit to produce anhydrous ethanol. A fourth column, the trace column is required to separate the remaining impurities, which are mainly methanol. Thereby, methanol can be separated with ethanol as the top product. In order to combust the remaining solids, these are separated from the beer column bottoms with a filter press, thereby targeting a low remaining water content. In this work, we target solvent-grade ethanol with a purity of over 99.9 % (*w*/*w*).

2.3. Bioethylene

Ethanol can be dehydrated to ethylene. Using bioethanol as raw material in this process, carbon-neutral bio-based ethylene can be obtained. The basic process layout of the ethylene process is shown in Figure 2.

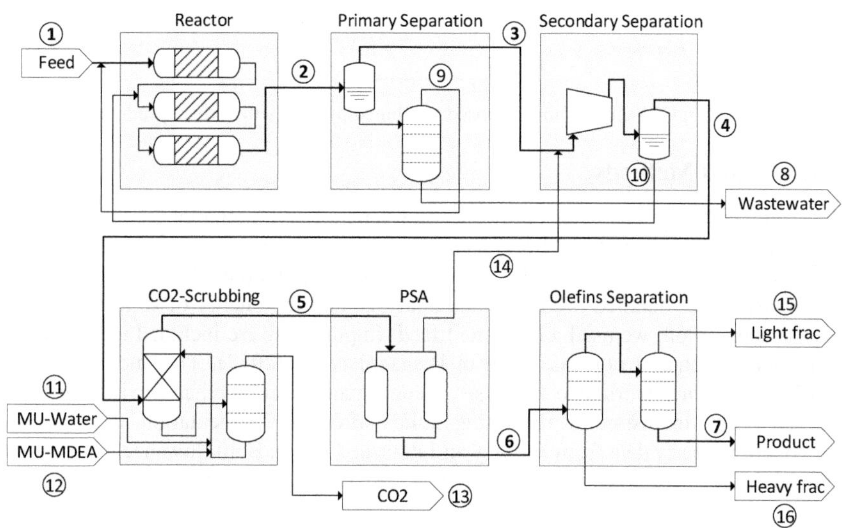

Figure 2: Model flowsheet of the ethylene process

In a first step, ethanol is dehydrated to ethylene in a train of adiabatic fixed-bed reactors. Before being fed to the reactor, the ethanol is heated since the dehydration reaction to ethylene is strongly endothermic. As water is produced during the reaction, this is separated in two steps, namely a primary and secondary separation, where the pressure is increased to around 16 bar to further condense the remaining water. Carbon dioxide, a side product of the dehydration reaction, is separated in an absorber column using methyl diethanolamine (MDEA). After that, the remaining humidity is removed using pressure-swing adsorption (PSA) columns followed by a cryogenic olefin separation that removes methane, hydrogen, acetaldehyde, and other impurities to achieve polymer-grade ethylene (high purity, suitable for polymerization).

2.4. Hybrid process

A flexible, hybrid production of both solvent-grade ethanol and polymer-grade ethylene is considered. Figure 3 shows the configuration of the proposed process: For solvent-grade ethanol production, the previously explained process is used, *i.e.* the rectification column features a side-drain to remove components such as benzaldehyde, 1-propanol, and 1-butanol. The distillate with azeotropic composition is dried in a molecular sieve and goes to the trace column, where primarily the methanol is separated to get solvent-grade ethanol (1). Using this configuration, there remain two unused streams with high ethanol content, which are the column side drain (M) and the top product of the trace column (2). In this scenario, these streams are mixed and used as feed for polymer-grade ethylene production. By varying the ratio between the side-drain and distillate outlet flows of the rectification column, the ratio of the products can be adjusted.

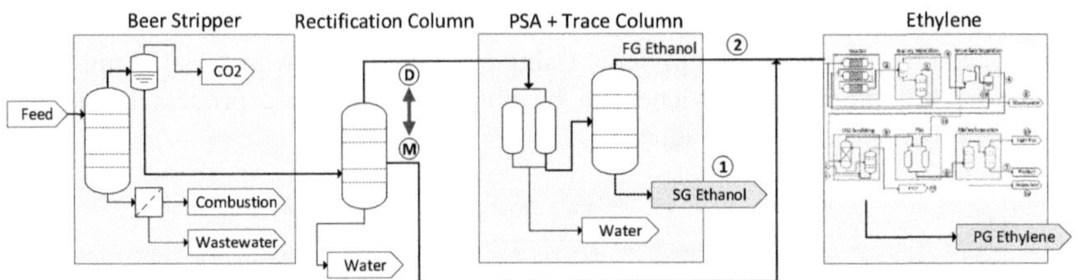

Figure 3: Overview of the proposed combined process with hybrid production

3. Model and Methods

Mass and enthalpy balances of the second-generation bioethanol plant-wide model developed by Prunescu *et al.* (2017) have been derived to investigate the possibilities of comprehensive heat integration. To further include the potential of the optimized model, the impurities for detailed product grade analysis, and the energy of solids combustion for heat integration, we used a combined feed. Impurities were included using the same component-to-ethanol ratio as given in Bisgaard *et al.* (2017). This inclusion can be justified since their work also addresses second-generation bioethanol with similar raw materials. The inclusion of remaining solids after the fermentation was based on component property data from Wooley and Putsche (1996). Both flowsheets are modeled with AVEVA® Process Simulator (AVEVA, 2023). We use a vapor-liquid equilibrium with activity-coefficient-based UNIQUAC method data for component pairs provided by AVEVA®. The gas phase is modeled as an ideal gas, and the solubility of CO_2 is modeled using Henry's law. Comparing thermodynamic methods, it was found that both NRTL and UNIQUAC only lead to small deviations. For validation of the simulation model, the results of Bisgaard *et al.* (2017) could be replicated with only small deviations. In this work, the initial configuration and equipment specifications were iteratively adapted using a Python-based sensitivity analysis tool that offers an interface to AVEVA®. An adiabatic, fixed-bed plug-flow reactor with three sections was selected for ethanol dehydration, which is standard in the industry (Yakolewa et al, 2016). The reactor was modeled as a first principle model and implemented in MATLAB® utilizing kinetic models from Maia *et al.* (2018), and Tripodi *et al.* (2019) of which both had plant/experimental data using a Syndol catalyst. After the reactor parameters were optimized, the model was transferred to AVEVA®. In the CO_2-stripping section, electrolyte NRTL was used to correctly simulate the interactions between the charged species. The vapor-liquid equilibrium is based on an activity-coefficient model. The solubility of the light components CO, CO_2, O_2, N_2, H_2, CH_4, ethane, and propylene is modeled using Henry's law. The reactions taking place in the amine-based CO_2 absorption were implemented on all absorber stages, assuming equilibrium.

4. Results

4.1. Feasibility of the hybrid process

Simulation results showed that a flexible, hybrid production of high-purity chemicals, namely solvent-grade ethanol and polymer-grade ethylene is technically feasible with the given process concept and technologies. Utilizing the remaining solids after fermentation for combustion, the obtained heat can be fully used to cover the heat demands of other units. It was found that the ethylene process is feasible with lower ethanol concentrations as input, while still maintaining a high yield. To exploit this, the rectification column was configured so that the side-drain delivers a stream with a low ethanol concentration of 50-60 mol%, thereby saving energy for further concentration of ethanol. Note that when maximum ethanol production is targeted, there is still a small side-drain flow as well as a significant top product flow in the trace column, which cannot be utilized for solvent-grade ethanol. Therefore, the maximum possible ratio in favor of solvent-grade ethanol is 0.72:0.28 (mole-based). In contrast, when full ethylene production is targeted, the whole ethanol product stream can be used as ethylene process feed by closing the side-drain and reducing the distillate ethanol concentration to 59 mol%, meaning that a 0:1 ratio is possible (results not shown). Expectedly, the obtained rectification column duties reduce significantly with lower required distillate purity.

4.2. Varying the Product Ratio

The results presented in Table 1 show the obtained values of economically important process parameters for different product ratios. Note that the hot and cold utility targets are significantly lower than the heating and cooling demand of a non-integrated process, meaning that there is a high heat integration potential. The results further indicate that there are several opposing trends regarding specific parameters when changing the ratio of the product. Interestingly, the pinch analysis in Figure 4 shows that there is an optimal point regarding heat recovery potential and minimization of hot and cold utility, respectively.

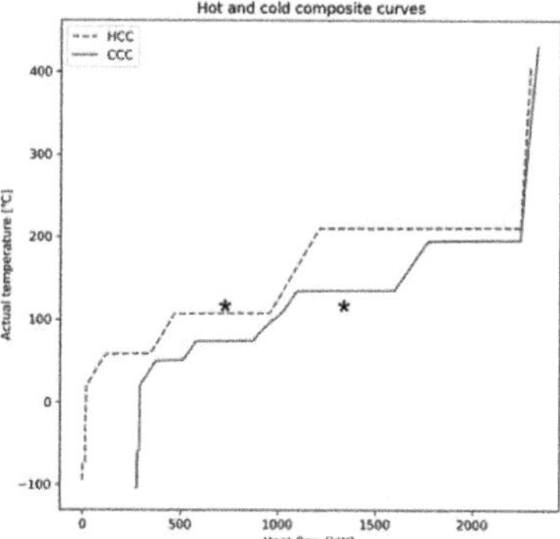

Figure 4: Composite Curves of the hybrid process for 0.5 SG Ethanol:0.5 PG Ethylene

This minimum is located around the 0.5:0.5 ratio of both products. In contrast, the sum of electric duty, mainly determined by the compressors in the ethylene process, increases with a higher ethylene product ratio.

Table 1: Results of important process parameters for different product ratios

Ethanol (SG): Ethylene (PG)	0.72:0.28	0.5:0.5	0.25:0.75	0:1
Ethanol product, kmol/h	3.80	2.65	1.32	-
Ethylene product, kmol/h	1.48	2.65	3.98	5.30
Ethylene reaction yield in %	99.0	99.3	99.3	99.2
Sum of electric duty in kW	7	10	17	23
Heating demand in kW	2201	2055	1971	2024
Cooling demand in kW	2447	2286	2178	2230
Hot utility target in kW	226	39	67	157
Cold utility target in kW	471	269	273	362

Depending on prices for electricity as well as heating and cooling utility, the economically optimal product ratio will differ. A more detailed analysis as well as dynamic behaviour during variation of product ratios will be part of future work.

5. Conclusions

The results showed that a flexible, hybrid production is possible that maintains the high-purity grades of both products at all points. Configuration one (only polymer-grade ethylene) showed a reduction of 31 % in hot and 23 % in cold utilities and an increase of 229 % in electric demand compared to configuration two with a product ratio of 72 % solvent-grade ethanol to 28 % polymer-grade (molar-based). For all configurations and product ratios, there is a high heat integration potential as the obtained heat from the combustion of solids after fermentation can be fully used to cover the heat demands of other units. Overall, the hot and cold utility can be drastically reduced. Further, by varying the product ratio, the sensibility of the heat integration towards the solid fraction and its heating value, respectively, can be reduced, thereby ensuring more robust operation. Further, a minimum for utility was found between these extreme points. Therefore, the presented process offers a versatile concept with potential for adaptation to different market situations.

References

AVEVA Simulation Building Guide, 2023

Baeyens, J., Kang, Q., Appels, L., Dewil, R., Lv, Y., Tan, T., 2015, Challenges and opportunities in improving the production of bio-ethanol, Progress in Energy and Combustion Science, 47:60–88

Bisgaard, T., Mauricio-Iglesias, M., Huusom, J. K., Gernaey, K. V., Dohrup, J., Petersen, M. A., Abildskov, J., 2017, Adding value to bioethanol through a purification process Revamp, Industrial & Engineering Chemistry Research, 56(19):5692–5704

Frosi, M., Tripodi, A., Conte, F., Ramis, G., Mahinpey, N., Rossetti, I., 2021, Ethylene from renewable ethanol: Process optimization and economic feasibility assessment, Journal of Industrial and Engineering Chemistry, 104:272–285

Humbird, D., Davis, R., Tao, L., Kinchin, C., Hsu, D., Aden, A., Schoen, P., Lukas, J., Olthof, B., Worley, M., Sexton, D., Dudgeon, D., 2011, Process design and economics for biochemical conversion of lignocellulosic biomass to ethanol: Dilute-acid pretreatment and enzymatic hydrolysis of corn stover. United States. https://doi.org/10.2172/1013269

Maia, J. G. S. S., Demuner, R. B., Secchi, A. R., Melo, P. A., do Carmo, R. W., Gusmão, G. S., 2018, Process modeling and simulation of an industrial-scale plant for green ethylene production, Ind. Eng. Chem. Res., 57,18, 6401– 6416

Mohsenzadeh, A., Zamani, A., Taherzadeh, M. J., Bioethylene production from ethanol: A review and techno-economical evaluation, 2017, Chem. Bio. Eng. Reviews, 4(2):75–91.

Prunescu, R.M. et al., 2017, Model-based plantwide optimization of large scale lignocellulosic bioethanol plants, Biochemical Engineering Journal,124, 13-25

Tripodi, A., Belotti, M., Rossetti, I., 2019, Bioethylene production: From reaction kinetics to plant design, ACS Sustainable Chemistry & Engineering, 7(15):13333–13350.

Wooley, R J, and Putsche, V., 1996, Development of an ASPEN PLUS physical property database for biofuels components. United States: N. p.. Web. doi:10.2172/257362

Yakovleva, I.S., Banzaraktsaeva, S.P., Ovchinnikova, E.V. et al., 2016, Catalytic dehydration of bioethanol to ethylene. Catal. Ind. 8, 152–167

Flavio Manenti, Gintaras V. Reklaitis (Eds.), Proceedings of the 34th European Symposium on Computer Aided Process Engineering / 15th International Symposium on Process Systems Engineering (ESCAPE34/PSE24), June 2-6, 2024, Florence, Italy
 http://dx.doi.org/10.1016/B978-0-443-28824-1.50191-5

Leveraging Digital Twin Modeling for Anaerobic Digesters using Anaerobic Digestion Model No. 1 (ADM1) and Neural Network within the Pyomo Framework

Mayowa F. Oladele,[a,b] George M. Bollas[a,b]

[a]*University of Connecticut, Department of Chemical and Biomolecular Engineering, Storrs, CT, USA*

[b]*Pratt & Whitney Insitute for Advanced Systems Engineering, Storrs, CT, USA*

george.bollas@uconn.edu

Abstract

Harnessing the power of physics-based modeling and machine learning, this study delves into the development of a digital twin model for anaerobic digesters. The integration leverages the Anaerobic Digestion Model No. 1 (ADM1) in tandem with a Neural Network (NN) algorithm, implemented within Pyomo, an open-source optimization modeling language in Python. Central to this work is a sensitivity analysis conducted on eleven key practical measurements crucial for estimating ADM1 input variables. The results show that measurements such as Particulate Chemical Oxygen Demand (COD_p), Volatile Fatty Acids (VFA), and Total Organic Carbon (TOC) have a significant influence on biogas production. This insight gives a better understanding of anaerobic digester dynamics and strengthens the predictive accuracy and control capabilities of digital twin models, marking a significant stride toward the optimization of waste-to-energy processes.

Keywords: Digital Twin, Anaerobic Digestion, ADM1, Neural Network, Sensitivity Analysis.

1. Introduction

In the pursuit of sustainable waste management and energy generation, anaerobic digestion (AD) has emerged as a promising technology. Its unique ability to merge waste treatment with energy production positions AD as a suitable option for methane capture and renewable energy (Curry and Pillay, 2012). However, the efficacy of the AD process is marred by inherent instabilities under specific operating conditions, that can lead to process failure, impacting biogas production and overall system efficiency. In response to these challenges, the integration of digital twin technology emerges as a transformative solution, providing unparalleled insights into AD system dynamics and a means to mitigate operational uncertainties. By harnessing digital twin capabilities, operators and researchers can gain a comprehensive understanding of the underlying processes, identify potential points of failure, control and predict AD system performance under various operational scenarios (Therrien et al., 2020).

This study presents a nuanced approach to building a digital twin for the AD process, combining the mechanistic insight of Anaerobic Digestion Model No. 1 or ADM1 (a physics-based model) and the adaptability of a Neural Network algorithm (data-driven model) implemented in Pyomo. Integrating the ADM1 into the digital twin however poses two challenges: characterization of the influent variables and calibration of numerous parameters (Fatolahi et al., 2020; Girault et al., 2012). These challenges can lead to inaccurate predictions. To address the first challenge, a sensitivity analysis is conducted on practical measurements used to characterize ADM1 inputs. This analysis identifies key measurements impacting biogas production (output of interest), leading to a more accurate and reliable AD system. Our methodology sheds light on the development of the digital twin, particularly emphasizing the sensitivity analysis conducted on the practical measurements needed for the ADM1 inputs.

2. Digital Twin Integration and Implementation

2.1 Anaerobic Digestion Model No. 1 (ADM1)

The core of our digital twin architecture is the ADM1, a well-established physics-based model developed by the International Water Association (IWA) task group. ADM1 is implemented as a differential algebraic system (DAE), encompassing 28 dynamic state variables and 19 biochemical rate processes (Batstone et al., 2002). This model serves as the foundation for capturing fundamental biochemical reactions and processes within the anaerobic digester, providing a comprehensive framework for understanding system dynamics.

2.2 *Neural Network (NN) Integration*

To complement the strengths of ADM1, a NN is integrated into the digital twin. Trained on historical data from a specific AD system of interest, the NN captures subtle nuances and non-linear relationships that may be challenging for ADM1. The NN introduces adaptability, enabling the digital twin to dynamically adjust to evolving operational conditions and enhance overall predictive accuracy throughout the entire life cycle of the AD system.

2.3 Digital Twin Architecture

The digital twin is constructed by stacking the outputs from both ADM1 and NN into a unified network. We automatically update the weights for each model to ensure accurate representation and responsiveness to changing conditions. The system input (X) and output (Y) collected over a time interval are utilized as a training set (X, Y) to continually train and update the digital twin, adjusting the weights (w_{physi} *and* w_{nn}) for both the physics-based and data-driven components.

The NN employs a multi-layer feed-forward architecture with k hidden layers. The structure incorporates activation functions for non-linearity, with weights (w) and biases (b) initialized at random. The final output (q_{nn}) is calculated by combining outputs from each layer, contributing to the overall prediction. The final output of the digital twin is the sum of the contributions from both ADM1 and NN.

2.4 Pyomo Framework Implementation

The digital twin is implemented within the Pyomo framework, a powerful optimization modeling language capable of handling the intricate constraints associated with AD operation. ADM1 equations are represented using the Pyomo.DAE package, facilitating the modeling of differential equations and applying discretization (finite differences) to convert the equations to algebraic form. The Ipopt solver was used for solving these equations.

The NN component is specifically implemented using the Optimization and Machine Learning Toolkit (OMLT), an open source-software package integrated also with Pyomo.

OMLT enables the transformation of pre-trained machine learning models, including NNs, into the Pyomo algebraic modeling language. The OmltBlock, a Pyomo block, is utilized to create input/output objects and constraints, linking the surrogate model to the broader optimization problem. OMLT supports NNs through interfaces such as ONNX and Keras, providing a seamless integration with Pyomo's optimization approaches.
This integrated digital twin, combining the strengths of ADM1 and NN within the Pyomo framework, offers a powerful tool for understanding, optimizing, and predicting the dynamics of AD processes throughout their life cycle.

3. Characterization of ADM1 Input variables

In characterizing the input variables of the ADM1, practical measurements of the feedstock entering the anaerobic digestion system are crucial for estimating the model input variables. However, not all of these practical measurements are analyzed in wastewater treatment plants and hence, existing literature provides six methods to characterize the ADM1 input variables based on the available measurements (Girault et al., 2012, 2020; Lübken et al., 2015). These methods include physico-chemical analysis (Lübken et al., 2007), elemental analysis (Kleerebezem and Van Loosdrecht, 2006), anaerobic respirometry (Girault et al., 2020), physico-chemical analysis combined with online gas curve calibration procedure (Girault et al., 2020), conversion of other measurement to the ADM1 inputs required (Nopens et al., 2009), and elemental analysis for high solids waste, also known as the transformer model(Zaher et al., 2009). This study focuses on the transformer model, by conducting a sensitivity analysis to understand the model responses to input variations.

3.1 Transformer Model

The transformer model, an upgrade over elemental analysis measurements, was developed based on principles of mass balance of macronutrient elements (carbon, hydrogen, oxygen, and phosphorus [CHNOP]), Chemical Oxygen Demand (COD) and charge intensity. Developed with the specific aim of generating detailed ADM1 inputs, the transformer model considers 11 practical measurements: particulate COD, COD_s – VFA, volatile fatty acid, total organic carbon, organic nitrogen (N_{org}), total ammonia nitrogen, organic phosphorus (TP-orthoP), orthophosphate, total inorganic carbon, total alkalinity, and Fixed Solid (FS). Calculations involve simple differences between existing measurements, as described by Zaher et al. (2009), making the transformer model a practical and well-understood way to generate ADM1 inputs.

4. Sensitivity Analysis

Due to the limited availability of measurements for the ADM1 transformer model inputs, a sensitivity analysis was conducted to evaluate the impact of the 11 key practical measurements on biogas production. Each sensitivity analysis involved varying one input variable while keeping others at baseline values. The results of this analysis are shown in Figures 1 and 2.
Figure 1 shows that biogas production exhibited higher sensitivity to particulate COD, volatile fatty acid, and total organic carbon compared to CODs – VFA. Specifically, Figure 1A shows a decrease in biogas production with an increase in particulate COD. The same trend is observed in Figure 1C where biogas production decreases with an increase in volatile fatty acid, aligning with common understanding of AD systems where

an accumulation of volatile fatty acid leads to a decrease in the pH and biogas production. Figure 1D shows that a decrease in total organic carbon also decreases biogas production. While higher total organic carbon content generally supports increased biogas production due to more organic matter for microbial breakdown and conversion into methane and carbon dioxide, an optimal total organic carbon threshold exists depending on the type of organic matter being digested and exceeding it can result in reduced biogas production. Figure 1B indicates relative insensitivity of biogas production to changes in CODs – VFA.

In Figure 2, organic nitrogen, organic phosphorus, and total ammonia nitrogen are identified to have a relatively significant influence on biogas production. Figures 2A, 2B, and 2C depict increased biogas production with decreasing values of organic nitrogen, organic phosphorus, and total ammonia nitrogen, respectively. Generally, elevated organic nitrogen levels can induce ammonia toxicity, inhibiting methanogen activity, while excessive organic phosphorus can lead to struvite formation, reducing reactor volume and biogas production. Conversely, Figure 2D shows low sensitivity to changes in orthophosphate.

Furthermore, the analysis showed that biogas production exhibited low sensitivity to total inorganic carbon, total alkalinity, and Fixed Solid. Incremental values of total alkalinity, and Fixed Solid, as well as decreasing total inorganic carbon values, showed negligible impact on biogas production. While these observations are pivotal, visual representations of these plots are omitted due to their inconsequential influence on biogas production.

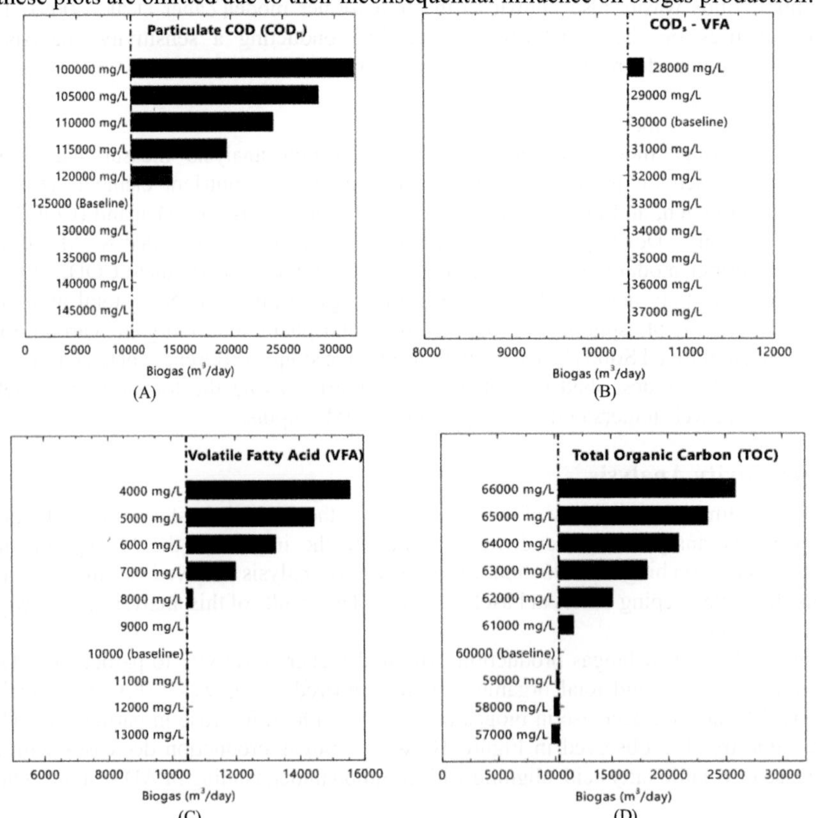

Figure 1: Sensitivity analysis of biogas production with respect to (A) COD_p; (B) COD_s – VFA; (C) VFA; (D) TOC

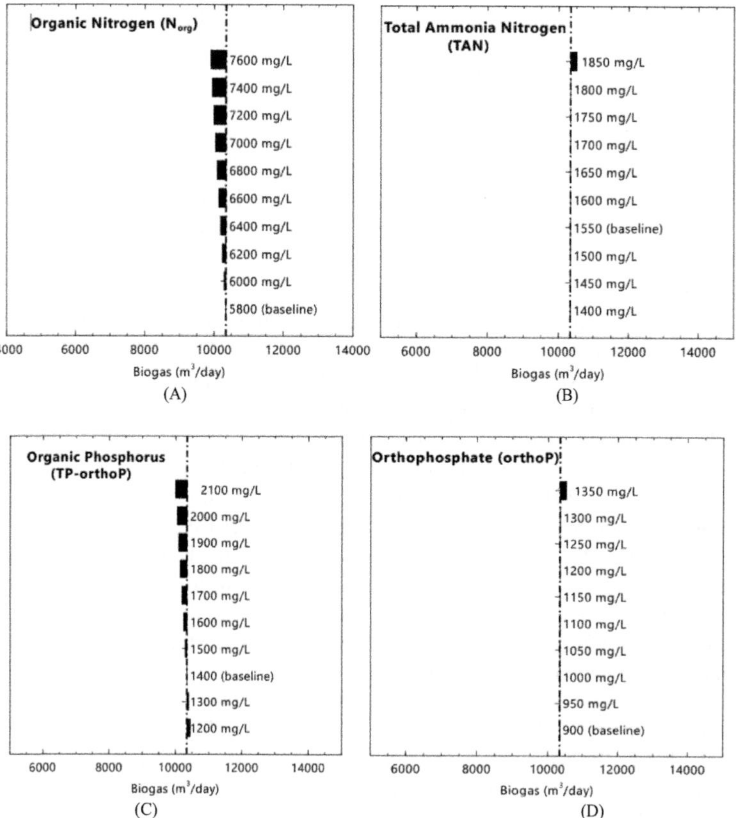

Figure 2: Sensitivity analysis of biogas production with respect to (A) N_{org}; (B) TAN; (C) TP-orthoP; (D) orthoP

These sensitivity analysis results provide valuable insights into the most important practical measurements influencing biogas production within the AD system. Particulate COD, Volatile Fatty Acids, and Total Organic Carbon were observed to have the highest impact on biogas production, emphasizing the necessity for accurate characterization to optimize and predict biogas production effectively.

5. Conclusion

This study underscores the significance of leveraging a digital twin in the context of anaerobic digesters, using the Anaerobic Digestion Model No. 1 (ADM1) within the Pyomo framework. A pivotal aspect of this study is the sensitivity analysis conducted on key practical measurements of the ADM1 transformer model, which is crucial for estimating ADM1 input variables. The result highlights the significant influence of particulate COD, Volatile Fatty Acids, and Total Organic Carbon on biogas production. This insight enriches our understanding of anaerobic digester performance and helps the predictive accuracy and control capabilities of AD digital twin models. Despite the challenges in ADM1 integration, particularly in input characterization, this study addresses these challenges and lays the groundwork for future research endeavors aimed at optimizing these important measurements.

Acknowledgment

This study was supported by the U.S. Department of Energy's Office of Energy Efficiency and Renewable Energy (EERE) under the Advanced Manufacturing Office, Award Number DE-EE0009497.

References

Curry, N., Pillay, P., 2012. Biogas prediction and design of a food waste to energy system for the urban environment. Renew Energy 41, 200–209.

Fatolahi, Z., Arab, G., Razaviarani, V., 2020. Calibration of the Anaerobic Digestion Model No. 1 for anaerobic digestion of organic fraction of municipal solid waste under mesophilic condition. Biomass Bioenergy 139.

Girault, R., Bridoux, G., Nauleau, F., Poullain, C., Buffet, J., Steyer, J.P., Sadowski, A.G., Béline, F., 2012. A waste characterisation procedure for ADM1 implementation based on degradation kinetics. Water Res 46, 4099–4110.

Girault, R., Steyer, J.-P., Zaher, U., Sadowski, A.G., Nopens, I., Béline, F., Zak, A., Kujawski, O., Holm, N.C., Rönner-Holm, S.G.E., n.d. Influent fractionation and parameter calibration for ADM1: Lab-scale and full-scale experiments.

IWA Task Group for Mathematical Modelling of Anaerobic Digestion Processes., 2002. Anaerobic digestion model no. 1 (ADM1). IWA.

Kleerebezem, R., Van Loosdrecht, M.C.M., 2006. Waste characterization for implementation in ADM1. Water Science and Technology 54, 167–174.

Lübken, M., Kosse, P., Koch, K., Gehring, T., Wichern, M., 2015. Influent fractionation for modeling continuous anaerobic digestion processes. Adv Biochem Eng Biotechnol 151, 137–169.

Lübken, M., Wichern, M., Schlattmann, M., Gronauer, A., Horn, H., 2007. Modelling the energy balance of an anaerobic digester fed with cattle manure and renewable energy crops. Water Res 41, 4085–4096.

Nopens, I., Batstone, D.J., Copp, J.B., Jeppsson, U., Volcke, E., Alex, J., Vanrolleghem, P.A., 2009. An ASM/ADM model interface for dynamic plant-wide simulation. Water Res 43, 1913–1923.

Therrien, J.D., Nicolaï, N., Vanrolleghem, P.A., 2020. A critical review of the data pipeline: How wastewater system operation flows from data to intelligence. Water Science and Technology.

Zaher, U., Buffiere, P., Steyer, J. -P., Chen, S., 2009. A Procedure to Estimate Proximate Analysis of Mixed Organic Wastes. Water Environment Research 81, 407–415.

Flavio Manenti, Gintaras V. Reklaitis (Eds.), Proceedings of the 34th European Symposium on Computer Aided Process Engineering / 15th International Symposium on Process Systems Engineering (ESCAPE34/PSE24), June 2-6, 2024, Florence, Italy
 http://dx.doi.org/10.1016/B978-0-443-28824-1.50192-7

Revitalizing Plastic Waste with Pyrolysis: a UniSim Design© Simulation Case study for Renewable Energy Production from Car Fluff

Mariangela Guastaferro, Letizia Marchetti, Marco Vaccari*, Cristiano Nicolella, Leonardo Tognotti

University of Pisa, Department of Civil and Industrial Engineering, Largo Lucio Lazzarino 2, 56126 Pisa (Italy)

*marco.vaccari@unipi.it

Abstract

This study addresses the imperative of substituting fossil fuels with energy from wastes, focusing on car fluff pyrolysis. The environmental viability of fuels produced through this method is assessed, aligning with the European Union's Renewable Energy Directive II (RED II) emissions assessment methodology. Using UniSim Design©, the entire inventory for an industrial-scale process is modeled, examining emissions contributions from each facility. By repurposing automotive waste, waste reduction and renewable energy generation are simultaneously achieved, in line with RED II objectives. UniSim Design© optimizes the heat integration system, minimizing energy wastage and reducing reliance on external sources, thereby lowering associated greenhouse gas emissions. Therefore, this research not only meets sustainability goals and regulatory compliance but also ensures the long-term viability of the plant in a changing regulatory environment.

Keywords: Plastic Pyrolysis, Simulation, Renewable Energy, process system, Renewable Fuel.

1. Introduction

The plastic industry faces challenges due to soaring demand, production growth, and insufficient recycling, necessitating innovative solutions (Qureshi et al., 2020). Recent studies have revealed that only 7% of generated plastic wastes are recycled, about 8% incinerated, and the rest landfilled (Nyika and Dinka, 2022), resulting in greenhouse gas (GHG) emissions, soil and water contamination, and economic loss (Fahim et al., 2021; Maitlo et al., 2022). The most effective solution is recycling, which involves primary, secondary, tertiary, and quaternary processes. Tertiary recycling involves plastic wastes thermal degradation, leading to chains breakage. Pyrolysis, a non-oxidizing thermochemical process, is promising for chemical recycling and power generation. Unlike incineration, it converts materials into versatile gas, solid, or liquid products, crucial for producing power and biofuels, contributing to CO_2 emissions reduction (Honus et al., 2016). However, derived liquid fuels require upgrading for transport use, involving chemical modifications for thermal stability, volatility, and viscosity compliance with current legislation standards (Jahirul et al., 2022; Palos et al., 2021). Post-treatments units significantly impact the economic analysis, with small plant (~15000 million l/year) breakeven potentially taking 25 years (Faisal et al., 2023). Gaseous stream products from pyrolysis of plastic types, i.e. polyethylenes (PEs) and polypropylene (PP), include H_2, CH_4, ethane, ethene, propene, propane, butane and butene; PET pyrolysis emits more CO_2 and CO, while PVC pyrolysis produces mainly hydrochloric acid (HCl) (Williams and Williams, 1999). Gas from PE or PP pyrolysis has high heating value (HHV) of 42 - 50 MJ/kg, making it a potential heat source for industrial pyrolysis plants. Ethene and propene, separated from other components, can also serve as valuable feedstocks chemicals production. Additionally, pyrolytic gas can be used in internal combustion engines (ICEs) for electricity generation and directly employed in boilers without requiring fuel gas treatment (Maqsood et al., 2021). Simultaneously, evaluating the current legislative landscape is essential for producing sustainable fuels. To determine if recycled carbon-based fuels (RCFs) qualify as renewable energy sources, their GHG emissions during production and use must be compared to those of fossil fuels. This assessment is vital for understanding the RCFs potential in reducing environmental pollution. On February 10th 2023, the Recast Renewable Energy Directive empowered the European Commission (EC) to the Directive (EU) 2018/2001 (RED II), aiming to set a minimum threshold for GHG emissions savings from RCFs and establishing an assessment methodology (Annex I of the delegated act). Proposed criteria deem RCFs renewable if their total emissions are reduced by at least 70% compared to those associated with using a fossil fuel, set at a default value of 94 gCO_2eq/MJ (paragraph 19, Annex V, part C, of Directive 2018/2001). In this framework, the objectives of this work are threefold: 1) conduct experimental activities to determine yields for pyrolysis process simulation; 2) develop a rigorous UniSim Design© simulation of the pyrolysis process for enhanced thermal efficiency and avoiding external energy supply; 3) use CO_2 equivalent flow rates from the simulation model for emission calculation in different scenarios, adhering to Annex I guidelines in the delegated act.

2. Materials and Methods

2.1. Process Description

The car fluff material, representing the light fraction of automobile shredder residues, is the plastic material processed in the first part of this study, undergoing pyrolysis in a lab-scale double-stage thermal reactor, including a pyrolysis reactor and a homogeneous cracking reactor. The pyrolysis process occurs in an inert atmosphere, at atmospheric pressure and fixed temperature (500 °C). Thermal cracking of pyrolytic vapors is carried out at 800 °C. After operative temperature is reached, 5 g of car fluff material is fed midway into the pyrolysis unit where the reaction lasts 30 minutes. Liquid and gaseous phases are collected post-separation: condensable vapors separate through cooling, with a liquid CO_2 and ethanol mixture, while the gaseous phase is collected in the 5 L Tedlar Bag and analyzed using a gas chromatograph (Agilent 990) equipment.

2.2. Process Modeling Methodology

Experimental results, specifying gaseous and liquid yields, serve as the basis for modeling simulation, to predict plant performance and enable process optimization for efficient industrial-scale operations. A flowsheet of the car fluff pyrolysis process is built using the simulation software UniSim Design© to evaluate the operative conditions, and estimate material, energy balances and utility requirements. The Peng–Robinson thermodynamic property fluid package is chosen for accurate modeling of hydrocarbon and light gases components in refinery applications (Fivga and Dimitriou, 2018). Through differential scanning calorimetry (DSC) analysis, PP is identified as the primary hydrocarbon in car fluff and modeled using group contribution methods (UNIFAC). All pyrolysis products, including compounds (H_2, CO and CO_2) and the hydrocarbons (CH_4, C_2H_4, C_2H_6, C_3H_6 and C_4H_8) in the gaseous phase, are selected/defined to model the process, providing essential thermodynamic data for energy balances computation. Hydrocarbon compounds, namely octene for the gasoline fraction and octacosane, for the diesel fraction, represent the primary components in the liquid phase. Yield shift reactors (*R1* and *R2* in Figure 1) simulate both pyrolysis units utilizing product yield data from experimental results. These reactors calculate thermal energy requirements for maintaining constant temperatures profiles at 500 and 800 °C in the pyrolysis (*R1*) and homogenous cracking reactor (*R2*), respectively. The heat reaction value (set at 2000 kJ/kg) in the model configuration section of yield shift reactor block, is determined by summing the enthalpy of the PP pyrolysis reaction (541 kJ/kg, Jin et al., 2018), sensible and latent heats to raise the fed material temperature up to 500°C (80 kW). The vapor-liquid stream resulting from pyrolysis and cracking reactions (stream *3*), leave the top of the simple solid separator (*S1*), while char residue (stream *4*) is collected at its bottom. Simulating coke end-of-life uses a conversion reactor (*R-coke*), providing enthalpy and post-incineration CO_2 amount (assumed stoichiometric). Stream *3* is cooled down to 0 °C (in *E-1*) and then separated in *V-1*, allowing near-complete separation of octane and octacosane from the compounds identified by micro-GC in the gaseous stream during the experimental analysis. The internal combustion engine (ICE) is simulated using a combination of unit operations. First, in a conversion reactor (*R-ICE*), complete combustion of pyrolytic gases is achieved by adding air (stream *AIR7*). Subsequently, a first cooling step (*E-ICE*), adjust the outlet gas temperature to reach a thermal power of 562.5 kW (*En-ICE*), representing the energy production phase. The chosen heat power value, when multiplied by the electrical efficiency of the ICE (0.4) and divided by its thermal efficiency (0.45), results in the specified target electrical power of 500 kWe. The next cooling operation (*E-ICErec*) focuses only on thermal power recovery (*En-ICErec*). Process simulation uses a car fluff mass flow rate of 200 kg/hr, obtained iteratively to achieve the target electrical power, at atmospheric pressure. Two scenarios for supplying energy required for the pyrolysis endothermic reactions in *R1* are considered: in the first one (scenario A) fossil fuel (FF) combustion is performed in *R3*, as shown in Figure 1; in the second one (scenario B) thermal integration of process streams is applied. Specifically, half of the pyrolytic oils (stream *13* containing 0.22 wt% of octene and 0.78 wt% of octacosane) from *V-1* (stream *8*) undergo combustion in *R3* and the energy stream (*E-CG*) derived from flue gases cooling is used for heat integration in *R1*. Combustion in both scenarios involves an excess of air equal to 12% with the temperature of air entering *R3* set at 300 °C. Moreover, in scenario B, the thermal duty recovered by the second cooling (*En-ICErec*) of the ICE flue gases is used to pre-heat stream *Air13*. The heat integration does not involve the *R2* section since it is assumed an autothermal behavior of this reactor due to a partial combustion of the pyrolytic vapors (stream *5*).

2.3 Emission Calculation Methodology

The correlation to assess GHG emissions from production and use of RCFs for transport, in Eq. (1), and the correlation to evaluate the GHG emission savings, in Eq. (2) are reported in 1(A) and 2(A) of Annex I of the Delegated Act 20/05/22.

$$E = e_i + e_p + e_{td} + e_u - e_{ccs} \tag{1}$$

$$Savings = (E_f - E)/E \tag{2}$$

The term E_f, representing fossil fuel emissions, is set at 94 gCO_2eq/MJfuel (paragraph 19 of Annex V, part C of Directive (EU) 2018/2001). If emissions savings exceed 70%, the produced gas distributed as electrical power qualifies as renewable. The term e_i accounts for inputs supply emissions, including power use, feedstock transportation to the site, and conventional treatments. Emissions from processing (e_p), encompass pyrolytic oils transport, the CO_2 from solid residue disposal, and gaseous fuel combustion in ICE unit. Emissions from final fuel use (e_u) are assumed zero, considering direct use in the pyrolysis process through the ICE, included in the process boundaries, that allow to exploit thermal and electrical recovery. Transport and distribution (e_{td}) and carbon capture and geological storage savings (e_{ccs}) are set at zero, as the fuel is directly injected into the ICE, and no carbon capture is involved. Contributions of e_i and e_p terms affecting co-products yields undergo to the emission allocation criterion (paragraph 15 of Annex I, part A of Delegated Act 20/05/22) and, according to the Annex I, they should be multiplied for the allocation factor (fA). In this study, fA is evaluated based on physical causality as the ratio of gaseous fuel mass and total co-products mass (i.e., oil and gas).

3. Results and Discussion

The flowsheet resulting from the scenarios described in Section 2.2 and obtained using Unisim Design© is reported in Figure 1.

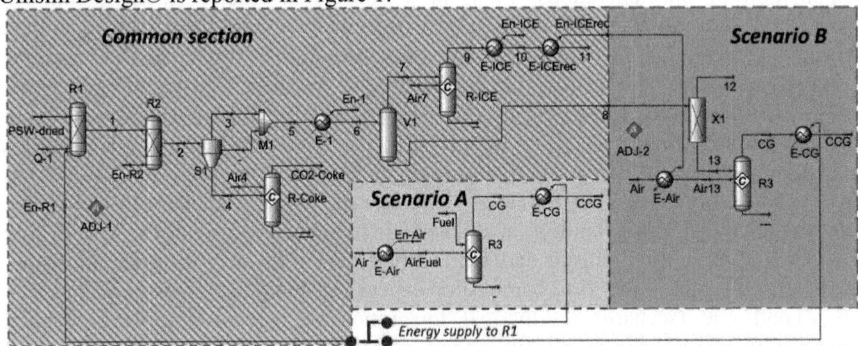

Figure 1 Flowsheet of the two scenarios considered in which the striped fill represents the common section shared by both. The grey fill indicates the boundaries of Scenario A; green fill indicates the boundaries of Scenario B.

Based on the simulation outcomes, the pyrolysis plant produced 126 kg/h of gaseous fuel (stream *7*) having a low heating value equal to 5104 MJ/h. In Scenario A, the resulting mass flows are M_8= 19 kg/h and M_4= 48.39 kg/h for pyrolytic oils and char, respectively, while in Scenario B, M_8= 11.64 kg/h and M_4= 48.39 kg/h. Pyrolysis is an endothermic reaction requiring a constant source of energy and the available thermal energies from burning FF or pyrolytic oils are calculated in the model to be 98.69 kW and 99.44 kW, respectively. As discussed in Section 2.2, the total thermal energy for the pyrolysis reactor (*R1*) is approximately 99 kW; therefore, an additional duty is not required. In Scenario B, thermal power, is recovered from the flue gases produced in the ICE, generating up to 572.8 kWth, that are partially used (i.e., 10 kWth) to pre-heat air stream up to 300 °C. In Scenario A, the same value of thermal power, needed to pre-heat the air to be mixed with FF (*AirFuel*), is ensured by providing heat from an external source. Moreover, mass balances results carried out by the simulation software are used as inventory to assess the GHG emissions according to the guidelines reported in Annex I of the Delegated Act 20/05/22. To evaluate the e_p term, reported in Eq. (1), the mass flows of CO_2 derived from FF/pyrolytic oils combustion (*R3*), coke incineration (*R-coke*) and pyrolytic gases burning in *R-ICE* resulted equal to $M_{CO2,CG}$ =24.3 kg/h, $M_{CO2-Coke}$ =177.3 kg/h and $M_{CO2,9}$ =274.8 kg/h, respectively. On the contrary, the e_i term is calculated using literature data and making some assumptions. To evaluate the $e_{i,elastic}$ term, the emissions intensity of generated grid electricity in Italy are considered. They are set equal to 103 gCO_{2eq}/MJfuel (Table A of Annex I) and multiplied for the electrical process inputs (reactor screwing, 10 kWe, and cooling system, 0.47 kWe). The manufacturing term of $e_{i,rigid}$ is considered zero since the processed material is classified as waste (Table 3 of Annex I). To evaluate the term describing the emissions associated with the plastic transport to the production site, it is assumed that 150 5-LH per year are used to transport 13 tons of waste, covering 100 km, and characterized by an emission factor of 56.60 gCO_{2eq}/t·km (International Council of Clean Transportation (ICCT). Moreover, the $e_{i,rigid}$ also considers the difference in energy between what would be produced by waste-to-energy treatment and what is produced by the simulated pyrolysis plant. The energy amount recovered by waste-to-energy is equal to $5.9 \cdot 10^6$ MJe/y, that is obtained considering that only 66% of the processed material generally undergoes to this treatment and setting the electrical process efficiency equal to 0.21; whereas the pyrolysis plant analyzed in this scenario provides $1.3 \cdot 10^7$ MJ_e/y, that corresponds to the chosen target value. The $e_{i,ex-use}$ value determined is 49.7 gCO_{2eq}/MJ_{fuel}, evaluated considering the amount of GHG emissions that would be produced by conventional treatments and that are avoided by replacing them with pyrolysis. Specifically, the waste-to-energy, incineration, and landfill processes produce emissions equal to 898, 2894, and 60 gCO_2eq/t_{fuel} respectively, that are then multiplied by the corresponding plastic weight percentages subjected to these treatment methods (i.e., 66.5%, 12.6%, and 20.9%, respectively). The values of each term contributing to determine the final value of E in Eq. (1) are reported in Figure 2 and they are evaluated by multiplying them for a period corresponding to full-time 300 working days per year (ft = 300*24 h/y) and dividing each emission value for the gaseous fuel low heating value previously reported (5104 MJ/h).

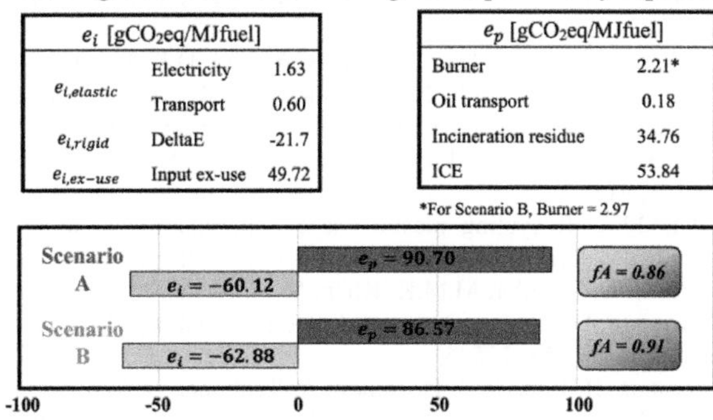

e_i [gCO_2eq/MJfuel]		
$e_{i,elastic}$	Electricity	1.63
	Transport	0.60
$e_{i,rigid}$	DeltaE	-21.7
$e_{i,ex-use}$	Input ex-use	49.72

e_p [gCO_2eq/MJfuel]	
Burner	2.21*
Oil transport	0.18
Incineration residue	34.76
ICE	53.84

*For Scenario B, Burner = 2.97

Figure 2. e_i/e_p and allocation factor (fA) terms calculation for the two scenarios.

Even though, almost each term has the same value for the two considered scenarios, the calculation of the overall GHG emissions provides different results (as reported in Fig. 2). This variation is due to the calculation of fA. Indeed, for Scenario A, fA is evaluated as the ratio between M_7= 126 kg/h (Fig. 1) and the sum of M_7= 126 kg/h and M_8= 19 kg/h (Fig. 1), leading to 0.87 value. Regarding Scenario B, the resulting allocation factor increased with respect to that corresponding to Scenario A (i.e., 0.91) since the burning of bio-oil produced (M_{13}= 6.5 kg/h) lowered the total amount of the obtained co-products. Therefore, the variation of e_i and e_p between the two analyzed scenarios is mainly affected by the different allocation methods. Indeed, the allocation factor is increased and in the second case not only the emissions from the burner are allocated, but also those derived from ICE, since its fumes are also used as source of heat integration. Then, the emission savings are calculated using Eq. (2) and resulted equal to 65% and 73% for Scenario A and B, respectively. According to the threshold value reported in the REDII (i.e., 70%), it is possible to claim that only the gaseous fuel produced considering the second scenario can be considered renewable.

4. Conclusions

The scrap from automobile shredder residues was effectively processed in a pyrolysis plant to yield co-products of higher economic value compared to the original waste. The methodology outlined in Annex I of the Delegated Act 20/05/22 was applied to assess GHG emissions for each analyzed scenario. Each emission factors, as specified in Annex I, were determined based on simulation outcomes, accounting for CO_2 from combustion reactions, energy supply, and heat integration. This analysis revealed that, despite being produced from recycled carbon, fuels may not always qualify as renewable under the overarching directive framework. Engineering choices, such as minimizing energy demand through thermal integration and by-product valorization, strongly influence emission factor values, making simulation models a useful tool to predict such trends. Future perspective, include exploring additional scenarios to enhance gaseous fuel production and corresponding emission savings.

5. References

A. Fivga, I. Dimitriou, 2018, Pyrolysis of plastic waste for production of heavy fuel substitute: A techno-economic assessment, Energy, 149, 1, 865–874.

F. Faisal, M.G. Rasul, A.A. Chowdhury, M.I. Jahirul, M.A. Hazrat, 2023, Performance and emission characteristics of a CI engine with post-treated plastic pyrolysis oil and diesel blend, Energy Reports, 9, 12, 87–92.

G. Maitlo, I. Ali, H.A. Maitlo, S. Ali, I.N. Unar, M.B. Ahmad, D.K. Bhutto, R.K. Karmani, S. ur R. Naich, R.U. Sajjad, S. Ali, M.N. Afridi, 2022, Plastic Waste Recycling, Applications, and Future Prospects for a Sustainable Environment, Sustainability (Switzerland), 14, 18, 11637.

I. Fahim, O. Mohsen, D. Elkayaly, 2021, Production of fuel from plastic waste: A feasible business, Polymers (Basel), 13, 6, 915.

J. Nyika, M. Dinka, 2022, Recycling plastic waste materials for building and construction Materials: A minireview, Materials Today Proceedings, 62, 6, 3257–3262.

M.I. Jahirul, M.G. Rasul, D. Schaller, M.M.K. Khan, M.M. Hasan, M.A. Hazrat, 2022, Transport fuel from waste plastics pyrolysis – A review on technologies, challenges and opportunities, Energy Conversion and Management, 258, 115451.

M.S. Qureshi, A. Oasmaa, H. Pihkola, I. Deviatkin, A. Tenhunen, J. Mannila, H. Minkkinen, M. Pohjakallio, J. Laine-Ylijoki, 2020, Pyrolysis of plastic waste: Opportunities and challenges, Journal of Analytical and Applied Pyrolysis, 152, 104804.

P.T. Williams, E.A. Williams, 1999, Interaction of plastics in mixed-plastics pyrolysis, Energy and Fuels, 13, 1, 188–196.

R. Palos, A. Gutiérrez, F.J. Vela, M. Olazar, J.M. Arandes, J. Bilbao, 2021, Waste Refinery: The Valorization of Waste Plastics and End-of-Life Tires in Refinery Units. A Review, Energy and Fuels, 35, 5, 3529–3557.

S. Honus, S. Kumagai, O. Němček, T. Yoshioka, 2016, Replacing conventional fuels in USA, Europe, and UK with plastic pyrolysis gases – Part I: Experiments and graphical interchangeability methods, Energy Conversion and Management, 126, 1118–1127.

T. Maqsood, J. Dai, Y. Zhang, M. Guang, B. Li, 2021, Pyrolysis of plastic species: A review of resources and products, Journal of Analytical and Applied Pyrolysis, 159, 105295.

Z. Jin, D. Chen, L. Yin, Y. Hu, H. Zhu, L. Hong, 2018, Molten waste plastic pyrolysis in a vertical falling film reactor and the influence of temperature on the pyrolysis products, Chinese Journal of Chemical Engineering, 26, 2, 400–406.

Flavio Manenti, Gintaras V. Reklaitis (Eds.), Proceedings of the 34th European Symposium on Computer Aided Process Engineering / 15th International Symposium on Process Systems Engineering (ESCAPE34/PSE24), June 2-6, 2024, Florence, Italy
 http://dx.doi.org/10.1016/B978-0-443-28824-1.50193-9

Modelling Natural Gas Dehydration by Adsorption under High CO_2 Conditions

Yuri Alves[a], Felipe R. Pinto[a], Felipe C. Cunha[a], Argimiro R. Secchi[a], Dárley Melo[b], Amaro G. Barreto Jr.[a]*

[a]*Postgraduate Program in Chemical and Biochemical Process Engineering – EPQB, Universidade Federal do Rio de Janeiro, Brazil*

[b]*Petrobras - Research, Development, and Innovation Center - CENPES, Rio de Janeiro, Brazil*

amaro@eq.ufrj.br

Abstract

This study aims to gather information on high-pressure gas dehydration, intending to model, compare, and simulate breakthrough curves, evaluating their performance in a binary mixture of H_2O/CO_2. Our approach considers the presence of other components in calculating the water fugacity in the gas phase under high pressure. The water adsorption process using zeolite 4A under high-pressure conditions is simulated, and the results are meticulously compared. The findings underscore the significance of this consideration, revealing differences of up to 24 hours compared to models that overlook this factor.

Keywords: adsorption, natural gas dehydration, modelling, high pressure.

1. Introduction

Natural gas conditioning aims to remove impurities such as water (H_2O), carbon dioxide (CO_2), nitrogen (N_2), hydrogen sulphide (H_2S), and other contaminants. In this regard, there is a need for some treatment or conditioning processes to ensure compliance with industry specifications, safety standards, and transportation of natural gas (NG). Among these contaminants, water in gas streams can pose a significant challenge to the primary stages of natural gas processing. Thus, moisture removal is crucial to prevent two common problems in high-pressure and low-temperature gas streams: hydrate formation and corrosion.

Adsorption dehydration emerges as a viable option and is widely employed when there is a requirement to achieve very low levels of water vapour content (1 ppm) in large gas flows. In this context, solid desiccants such as zeolites, silica gel, and alumina are preferred for natural gas dehydration. The adsorption operation is carried out through cyclic processes with two main steps: an adsorption step (in which water molecules are retained by the adsorbent) and regeneration step (in which water molecules are removed from the adsorbent). The adsorbent regeneration can be achieved through temperature swing adsorption (TSA) or pressure swing adsorption (PSA). TSA-based processes appear to be the most viable alternative for water vapour removal in gas streams for offshore oil industry operations under high-pressure conditions.

Berg et al. (2019) reviewed adsorptive processes used in industrial natural gas processing and concluded that TSA is an established and essential process, but thermodynamic and kinetic principles still need to be fully understood. More recently, Cavalcante and Pessoa (2023) presented a simulation study regarding the effects of adsorbent aging. However, in addition to high-pressure operations, a high CO_2 content can also become a challenge in some oil and gas exploration fields. In this context, the state-of-the-art phenomenological modelling of TSA processes has seldom explored such field operation conditions (Gholami et al., 2010).

TSA process modelling requires a deep understanding of adsorption equilibrium and the transport of components in the porous media. In this scenario, experimental adsorption equilibrium data for CO_2 are available in the literature in a wide range of pressures and temperatures for several adsorbents. However, such data are scarce for water vapor, and existing data are in sub-atmospheric conditions for a few temperatures and adsorbents (Wynnyk, 2019; Wilkins et al., 2021).

Therefore, this work aims to develop a theoretical/computational model to simulate the natural gas dehydration process. In the obtained simulations, the feed stream consists of a mixture containing water and CO_2 at a temperature of 40 °C. Two molar fractions of water were used in the feed stream: 7.1×10^{-4} at 1 bar and 1.4×10^{-5} at 50 bar, with both cases corresponding to a concentration of 36.8 mmol/m³ of water. The adopted approach considers the impact of increasing pressure on calculating water fugacity in the gas phase. For this purpose, the Peng-Robinson equation of state is employed to consider this effect. The main goal of this study is to deepen the understanding of the effects of water vapor adsorption in the presence of CO_2 at high pressure through the analysis of breakthrough curves obtained from modeling that utilizes the Peng-Robinson equation of state.

2. Methods

2.1. Mathematical modeling

The mathematical description of a fixed bed adsorption process encompasses principles of mass, energy, and momentum conservation coupled with thermodynamic models. The solution to this problem involves the numerical resolution of a system of partial differential equations (PDEs) for each adsorption and regeneration stage sequentially, with appropriate boundary conditions to reflect the sequence of steps in each cycle of an interconnected column system. In this study, the focus is on understanding the adsorption operation in a single column. The simulation of the adsorption column considered the following hypotheses: constant mass and heat transfer coefficients, negligible pressure drop, constant superficial velocity, mass transfer of components between fluid and solid phases described by the Linear Driving Force (LDF) model, and the Peng-Robinson equation of state for the bulk phase.

Additionally, the numerical resolution of the PDE system was performed by the finite difference method in the axial coordinate, and numerical integration was performed using DASSLC (Differential-Algebraic System Solver in C) for Backward Differentiation Formula (BDF) in the temporal coordinate. The EMSO software was utilized to implement and solve the model (Soares and Secchi, 2003). Given the principles of adsorption, the basic equation to describe the dynamics of a fixed bed is derived from an infinitesimal mass balance per component in the gas phase:

$$D_{z,i}\frac{\partial^2 C_i}{\partial z^2}+\frac{\partial (uC_i)}{\partial z}+\frac{\partial C_i}{\partial t}+\left(\frac{1-\epsilon}{\epsilon}\right)\rho_s\frac{\partial \bar{q}_i}{\partial t}=0 \tag{1}$$

In which, $D_{z,i}$ is the effective axial dispersion coefficient, C_i is the concentration of component i in the fluid phase, u is the fluid velocity, ε is the bed void fraction, ρ_S is the density of the adsorbent, and $\bar{q}_i$ is the average concentration in the adsorbed phase. For the mass balance in the solid phase, the Linear Driving Force (LDF) model is presented:

$$\frac{\partial \bar{q}_i}{\partial t} = k_i(q_i^* - \bar{q}_i) \tag{2}$$

In which, k_i is a global coefficient of mass transfer resistance, and q_i^* is the concentration of species *i* in the adsorbed phase in equilibrium with the concentration of the fluid phase. There are various proposals for the calculation of the coefficient k_i depending on the dominant resistance type in the system. Equation 3 describes the energy balance in the gas phase:

$$-\lambda_L \frac{\partial^2 T_g}{\partial z^2} + \rho_g C_g \frac{\partial (u T_g)}{\partial z} + \rho_g C_g \frac{\partial T_g}{\partial t} + \left(\frac{1-\epsilon}{\epsilon}\right) h_f a_s (T_g - T_s) + \frac{4 h_w}{\epsilon d_{int}} (T_g - T_w) = 0 \tag{3}$$

wherein λ_L is the effective axial thermal dispersion, T_g is the temperature of the gas, T_s is the temperature of the solid, T_w is the temperature of the wall, ρ_g is the density of the gas, C_g is the heat capacity of the gas, h_f is the heat exchange coefficient between gas and adsorbent, a_s is the ratio of external surface area to volume of the particle, h_w is the coefficient of internal convection heat transfer between the gas and the column wall, and d_{int} is the internal diameter of the column. Finally, the energy balances in the solid phase and on the wall of column are given by Eqs. 4 e 5:

$$\rho_s C_s \frac{\partial T_s}{\partial t} = h_f a_s (T_g - T_s) + \sum_{i=1}^{n} (-\Delta H_i) \frac{\partial \bar{q}_i}{\partial t} \tag{4}$$

$$\rho_w C_w \frac{\partial T_w}{\partial t} = h_w a_w (T_g - T_w) + U a_a (T_\infty - T_w) \tag{5}$$

wherein C_s is the heat capacity of the adsorbent, H_i is the enthalpy of adsorption of component *i*, C_w is the heat capacity of the column wall, ρ_w is the density of the column wall, a_w is the ratio of the internal surface area to volume of the column wall, *U* is the overall external heat transfer coefficient, a_a is the ratio of the external surface area to volume of the column wall, and T_∞ is the ambient temperature.
The initial and boundary conditions are the following:

	Mass balance	**Energy balance**
t = 0:	$C_i = 0, \ \bar{q}_i = 0$	$T_g = T_i^0, T_s = T_i^0, T_w = T_\infty$
z = 0:	$D_{z,i} \frac{\partial C_i}{\partial z} = u_0 [C_i - C_i^0]$	$\lambda_L \frac{\partial T_g}{\partial z} = \rho_g C_g u [T_g - T_g^0]$
z = L:	$\frac{\partial C_i}{\partial z} = 0$	$\frac{\partial T_g}{\partial z} = 0$

Table 1 provides information regarding the fixed bed considered for simulation, along with some properties treated as constants. Further constitutive equations of the model are presented by Braun (2019).

Table 1 - Column parameters

Bed length (L)	0.5 m	Thermal conductivity (k_w)	17 W/m/K
Bed diameter (d_{int})	0.038 m	Heat capacity (C_w)	500 J/kg/K
Bed specific mass (ρ_w)	8000 kg/m³	Bed void fraction (ϵ)	0.42
Volumetric flow (Q)	0.5 m³/h		

2.2. *Adsorption isotherm*

Proper modelling of the adsorption isotherm is crucial for evaluating the type of adsorbent and understanding the behaviour of beds containing porous materials. This study employed a Langmuir-type model for water adsorption on zeolite. The pressure information has been replaced by the fugacity of the component in the isotherm model to adapt the modelling to high-pressure and high CO_2 content conditions.

$$q_i^* = n^\infty \frac{K f_i}{1 + K f_i}, \qquad where \quad K = K_0 \exp\left(-\frac{\Delta H}{RT}\right) \tag{6}$$

Although the isotherm model considers both components for adsorption, the water's equilibrium constant, *K*, is significantly higher than that of CO_2. This reflects the greater affinity of water for the adsorbent, resulting in a situation where there is minimal competition for adsorption sites. Water molecules have a stronger tendency to displace CO_2 molecules and occupy the available sites. Therefore, we assume that only water is being adsorbed. Lastly, parameter estimation employed a hybrid procedure that combines a nondeterministic method, such as Particle Swarm Optimization (PSO), with a deterministic Newton-like method.

3. Results and Discussion

From the experimental equilibrium data presented in Wynnyk (2019), parameters were obtained to construct the water adsorption isotherm at temperatures of 298, 323, 348, 373, and 398K. The obtained parameters are presented in Table 2. It is important to emphasize that the estimation was performed using the entire set of experimental data, and Figure 1 illustrates the fit of the modified Langmuir model.

Table 2 - Estimated parameters for Langmuir isotherm model

Parameter	4A
n^∞(mol/kg)	13.3
K_0(1/bar)	7.14×10^{-4}
ΔH(J/mol)	4.158×10^{-4}

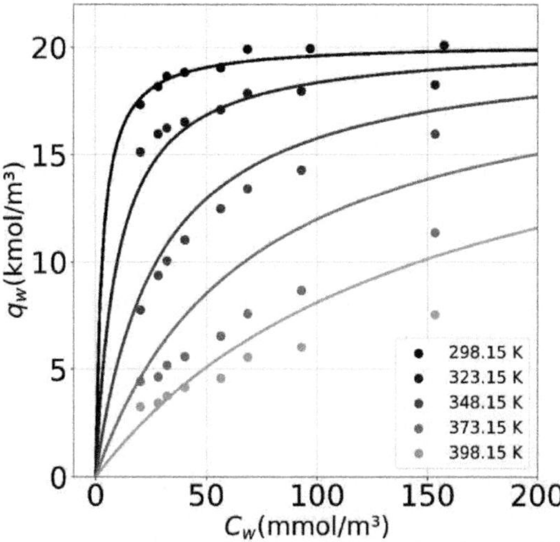

Figure 1 - Calculated adsorption isotherms for water vapor adsorption on zeolite 4A at different temperatures. Experimental data are represented by markers (Wynnyk, 2019).

Using the estimated parameters for water adsorption on zeolite 4A, a series of simulations were conducted to evaluate a fixed-bed adsorption column. Based on data obtained at low pressures, the model was developed for application over a broader range, considering the pressure effect on the fugacity of each component in the mixture that forms bulk phase. Consequently, breakthrough curves were obtained at 1 bar and 50 bar pressures. Figure 2a displays the critical results obtained.

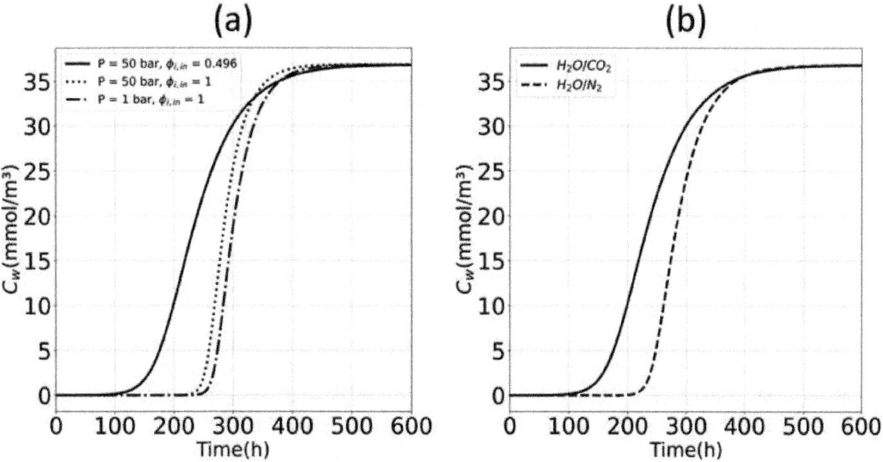

Figure 2 - (a) Breakthrough curves at 313K H2O/CO2 in different conditions (b) Breakthrough curves at 40 °C and 50 bar for H2O/N2 and H2O/CO2 mixtures

In Figure 2a, it is possible to observe three breakthrough curves at different pressures, each associated with distinct fugacity coefficients in the feed, given that $f_i = x_i\,\phi_i\,P$, and ϕ_i is a function of P and x_i, causing f_i to vary along z and t. The difference between the solid curve, representing breakthrough at high pressure considering the pressure effect,

and the dashed curve, also at high pressure assuming the fugacity coefficient is equal to 1 (i.e., ideal gas), is approximately 24 hours. Under industrial operating conditions, this time difference could mean a significant cost increase. Another observed effect is the increase in pressure when considering the fugacity coefficient as 1. Thus, precise calculation becomes evident when dealing with water adsorption at high pressures.
To demonstrate the effect of fugacity in the mixture, Figure 2b compares the breakthrough curves when feeding the column with H_2O/N_2 and H_2O/CO_2 mixtures under high-pressure conditions (50 bar). It can be observed that bed saturation occurs more rapidly when CO_2 is present in the gas stream. This is attributed to the lower fugacity coefficient for water in the H_2O/CO_2 mixture, which is 0.49, compared to the H_2O/N_2, which is 0.75.

4. Conclusion

A computational model was developed to simulate natural gas dehydration at high pressure in the presence of CO_2, using experimental data of zeolite 4A available in the literature. The model generated relevant breakthrough curves, and the results highlighted the crucial importance of calculating the fugacity coefficient in the operation time of the process. This consideration can lead to differences of up to 24 hours compared to models that do not consider this factor. A common area for improvement in the literature is using low-pressure data, extrapolating to high pressure with a correction only in the isotherm parameters, neglecting the correction in fugacity. As demonstrated in this work, this approach can lead to prediction errors, resulting in higher operational costs. Therefore, the findings and information provided by the computational model contribute significantly to an enhanced understanding of natural gas dehydration processes.

5. Acknowledgements

The authors gratefully acknowledge Conselho Nacional de Desenvolvimento Científico e Tecnológico (CNPq), Fundação de Amparo à Pesquisa do Estado do Rio de Janeiro (FAPERJ), Brazil, Coordenação de Aperfeiçoamento de Pessoal de Nível Superior (CAPES), Brazil, and Petrobras-ANP (Agência Nacional do Petróleo) for the financial support.

References

Berg, F., Pasel, C., Eckardt, T., & Bathen, D. (2019). Temperature Swing Adsorption in natural gas processing: A concise overview. ChemBioEng Reviews, 6(3), 59-71.

Braun, F. E. (2019). Modelagem e otimização de projeto de unidades de desidratação de gás natural por adsorção. MSc Dissertation. Federal University of Rio de Janeiro, Brazil.

Gholami, M., Talaie, M. R., & Roodpeyma, S. (2010). Mathematical modeling of gas dehydration using adsorption process. Chemical Engineering Science, 65(22), 5942-5949.

Cavalcante, C. J., & Pessoa, P. de A. (2023). Modeling and simulation of an industrial adsorption process of dehydration of natural gas in 4A molecular sieves. Results in Engineering, 18, 101144.

Soares, R. D. P., & Secchi, A. R. (2003). EMSO: A new environment for modelling, simulation and optimisation. In Computer Aided Chemical Engineering, Vol. 14, pp. 947-952. Elsevier.

Wilkins, N. S., Rajendran, A., & Farooq, S. (2021). Dynamic column breakthrough experiments for measurement of adsorption equilibrium and kinetics. Adsorption, 27(3), 397-422.

Wynnyk, K. G. (2019). High-pressure Adsorption Equilibria Aimed at Optimizing Sour Gas Conditioning. Thesis Phd. University of Calgary, AB, Canada.

Flavio Manenti, Gintaras V. Reklaitis (Eds.), Proceedings of the 34th European Symposium on Computer Aided Process Engineering / 15th International Symposium on Process Systems Engineering (ESCAPE34/PSE24), June 2-6, 2024, Florence, Italy
 http://dx.doi.org/10.1016/B978-0-443-28824-1.50194-0

Haber-Bosch process alternatives for the production of green ammonia

João Leitão[a], Catarina G. Braz[b], Henrique A. Matos[a]

[a] Centro de Recursos Naturais e Ambiente, Instituto Superior Técnico, Universidade de Lisboa, Av. Rovisco Pais 1, 1049-001 Lisboa, Portugal

[b] Industrial Process and Energy Systems Engineering (IPESE), École Polytechnique Fédérale de Lausanne, Lausanne, Switzerland

henrimatos@tecnico.ulisboa.pt

Abstract

This work focuses on the simulation with *Aspen Plus V11* of a conventional Haber-Bosh (HB) and an absorbent-enhanced HB process (AE-HB) to produce green ammonia. Both simulations can be divided into three separate parts, the hydrogen synthesis, through water electrolysis, the nitrogen production, accomplished with a cryogenic air separation unit, and the ammonia synthesis loop, which can be absorbent-enhanced or not.

To evaluate the energy requirements of these production processes, an energy analysis was performed for each simulation and further heat integration was explored using *Aspen Energy Analyzer*.

Keywords: Haber-Bosch, green ammonia, water electrolysis, heat integration, Aspen Plus.

1. Introduction

Climate change is one of the largest problems of the next decades and countries are starting to be legally obliged to tackle it. The European Parliament has adopted the European Climate Law, in which the EU must reduce net greenhouse gas emissions by at least 55 % by 2030 and achieve climate neutrality by 2050.

Ammonia is a vital compound in the agricultural industry due to its large application in nitrogen-based fertilisers. More recently, it has been considered a promising hydrogen carrier, due to its low pressure and temperature storage conditions combined with its high volumetric hydrogen content, 121 kg H2/m3, which is almost two times higher than liquid hydrogen. Which is why it's seen as a key player in achieving the decarbonization goals set by the European Union.

The most common ammonia production pathway is the Haber-Bosch process, accounting for over 1 % of total carbon emissions, emphasizing the need for its carbon footprint minimization.

With this in mind, the development and optimization of large-scale green ammonia production processes are of the utmost relevance to ensure green ammonia can substitute current ammonia synthesis processes and help decarbonise some of the biggest GHG emitting industries.

One of the current challenges in green ammonia production is reducing its energy consumption, where the separation of ammonia by absorption is seen as a possible alternative. Absorption requires elevated temperatures, unlike separation by condensation, which requires cryogenic temperatures, eliminating the necessity to use so much energy in the cooling of the reactor effluent.

2. Methodology

The development of a large-scale green ammonia production plant was simulated in *Aspen Plus V11*, with three main process sections. The hydrogen synthesis through alkaline water electrolysis, the nitrogen production, in a cryogenic air separation unit, and the ammonia synthesis loop, which can be carried out with absorption or without. A green NH_3 production of 200 kt/y was set as a production goal, meaning that 35.5 kt/y of green H_2 and 164.5 kt/y of N_2 are necessary.

The air separation unit was adapted from a model developed by Amorim (2023), whilst the hydrogen production section was simulated using an electrolyser model imported from *Aspen Custom Modeler*, which was adapted from the work of Amores *et al* (2021).

Regarding the energy analysis of the process, *Aspen Energy Analyser* was used to retrieve the energy consumption values of each process section and to perform heat integration when necessary.

3. Results

3.1. Nitrogen production

Focusing first on the nitrogen production section, a cryogenic Air Separation Unit (ASU) was chosen as the appropriate method due to its prevalence in the industry and elevated capacity, which will be required throughout this process. The flowsheet for this section is represented in Figure 1.

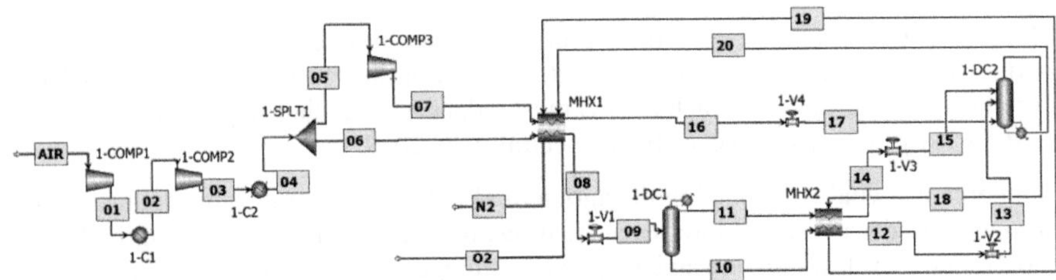

Figure 1 - Flowsheet of the ASU section.

Multiple sensitivity analyses were performed on the different equipment in order to reach the best conditions that maximize N_2 production and purity, with the final results being shown in Table 1.

Table 1 – Main parameters of the ASU.

Parameter	ASU
Total N_2 flow (kt/y)	163.6
N_2 purity ($\%_{wt}$)	99.1
Process yield (%)	99.3

The two-column design for the ASU proved to be satisfactory, with the N_2 flow produced being 0.5 % below the desired value, while the nitrogen purity obtained is acceptable regarding ammonia production.

3.2. Hydrogen production

The next step towards green ammonia production is the hydrogen synthesis section. Alkaline water electrolysis was chosen as the appropriate technology for water electrolysis since it is well-documented, with low costs, and the most common process to produce green hydrogen. The H_2 production flowsheet is represented in Figure 2.

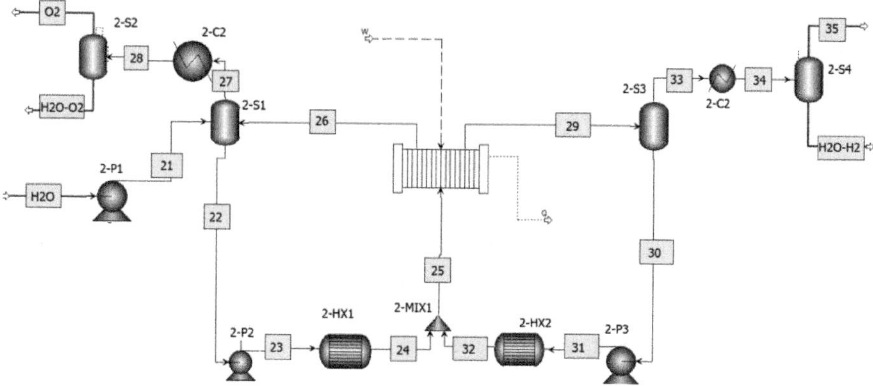

Figure 2 - Flowsheet of the AWE.

The electrolyser model was defined by specifying four different parameters – fraction of heat lost to surroundings, pressure, number of cells and area of each cell. To control the hydrogen flow that was produced, the power of the electrolyser also had to be defined. Different simulations were performed to obtain the best electrolyser conditions, and the results for the hydrogen production section are shown in Table 2.

Table 2 - Main parameters and results of the H_2 production section

Parameter	AWE	Result	AWE
Fraction of heat lost	0.1	Total H_2 flow (kt/y)	34.9
Pressure (bar)	6.7	H_2 purity (%wt)	99.2
Number of cells	770	HTO (%))	1.5
Area of each cell (m^2)	3.1	Energy efficiency (%)	72.4
Power (MW)	200	Faraday efficiency (%)	88.4

The results obtained for the H_2 production are satisfactory, with the flow being 1.6 % below desired and the purity being acceptable for NH_3 production. It is important to mention the Hydrogen to Oxygen (HTO) diffusion rate being lower than 2 % since HTO's higher than this value can lead to explosive mixture.

3.3. Green ammonia production

The final step to complete the large-scale green ammonia production plant is the ammonia synthesis loop, shown in Figure 3.

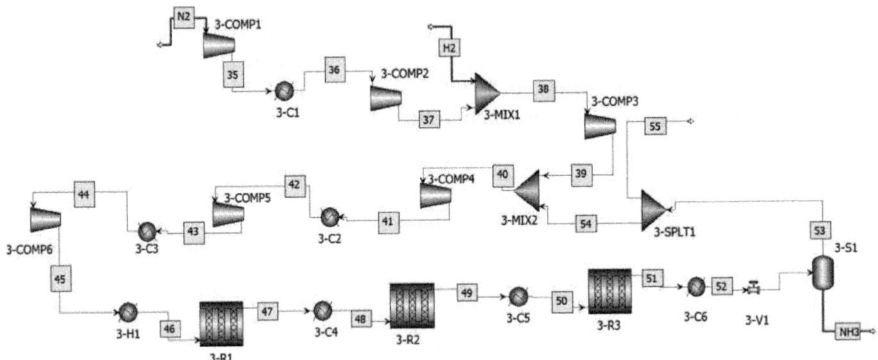

Figure 3 - Flowsheet of the HB process.

An alternative to this process was also developed, the absorbent-enhanced HB process (AE-HB), where the separation of ammonia occurs by absorption instead of condensation, using $MgCl_2$ as an absorbent, as represented in Figure 4.

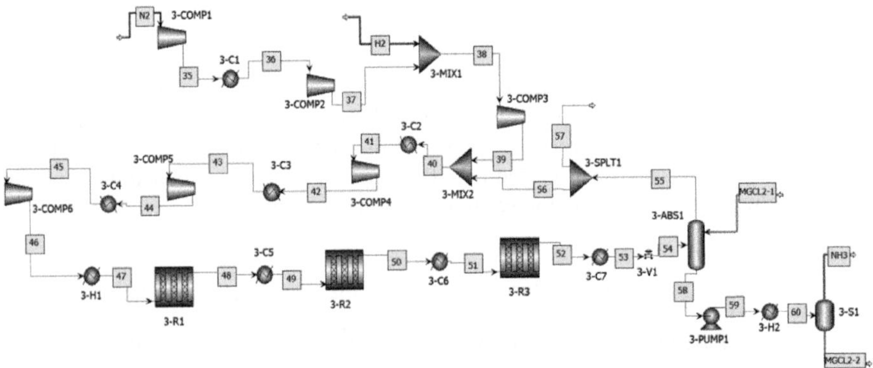

Figure 4 - Flowsheet of the AE-HB process.

The results for both simulations are presented in Table 3. It is clear that the HB process obtained satisfactory results, with high purity and conversion values, and a production 5 % below its goal. As for the AE-HB process, the absorption process led to too many inefficiencies which not only affected the final product purity but also its total production.

Table 3 – Main parameters for the HB and AE-HB processes.

Parameter	HB	AE-HB
Total N_2 flow (kt/y)	190.9	178.1
NH_3 purity (%wt)	99.7	90.7
NH_3 conversion (%)	97.0	90.4

3.4. Energy consumption

An energy analysis was performed for each section of the process mentioned previously, with the results being shown in Figure 5.

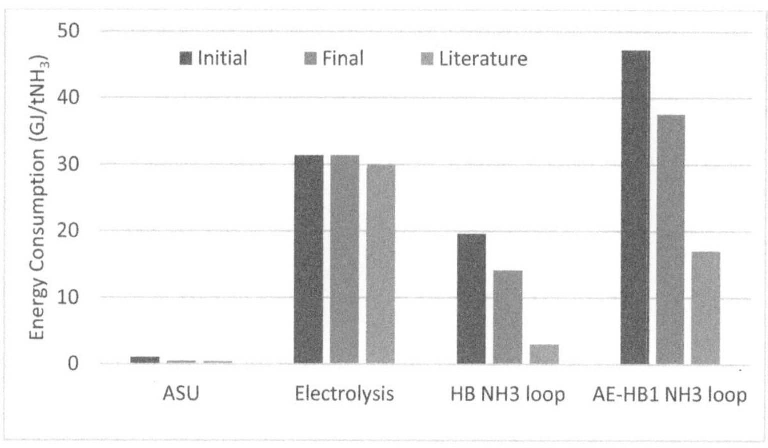

Figure 5 - Energy consumption values for the different production processes, with initial, final and literature values from left to right.

The energy results show that the nitrogen and hydrogen production processes are comparable to those practised in real production plants, whereas the synthesis loops have accentuated differences regarding the literature values. The changes between the initial and final values for the ASU are related to enhancements in the utility usage in the process, whereas the synthesis loops' initial and final differences are related to the heat integration performed for those processes. Furthermore, although heat integration proved to be successful for the synthesis loops, (it significantly reduced the heat consumption of these processes) they are still quite distant from literature values. This could be explained by inefficiencies related to steam utilization and poor use of the purges in the process since they are not burned to save energy. However, the energy consumption differences for both the synthesis loops could also be related to the large scale of this process, since the literature considers that energy consumption scales linearly, which may not be the case for processes with such scale.

4. Conclusions and Future Work

In this work, large-scale HB and AE-HB processes were simulated. High flowrates of nitrogen and green hydrogen were successfully obtained withpurity and conversion values similar to the literature. Nonetheless, more studies need to be performed on maximizing efficiency in these processes, particularly regarding large-scale alkaline water electrolysis. Good conversion and purity values were also obtained for the HB synthesis loop, while for AE-HB, more studies are necessary.

The specific energy consumption values of both the HB and the AE-HB process simulations are far from the literature values, meaning that further studies on the process variables and improvements in energy integration are needed.

References

A. Amorim, "Modeling and design of the calcium-looping process for carbon capture,", 2023, IST, Lisboa, Portugal.

E. Amores, M. Sánchez, N. Rojas, and M. Sánchez-Molina, "Renewable hydrogen production by water electrolysis," in Sustainable Fuel Technologies Handbook, Elsevier, 2021, pp. 271–313.

K. H. R. Rouwenhorst, A. G. J. Van Der Ham, G. Mul, and S. R. A. Kersten, Renew. Sustain. Energy Rev., vol. 114, p. 109339, Oct. 2019

Flavio Manenti, Gintaras V. Reklaitis (Eds.), Proceedings of the 34th European Symposium on Computer Aided Process Engineering / 15th International Symposium on Process Systems Engineering (ESCAPE34/PSE24), June 2-6, 2024, Florence, Italy
 http://dx.doi.org/10.1016/B978-0-443-28824-1.50195-2

Overcoming the challenges of dynamic systems in steady-state simulations: the use of meta-modeling as a surrogate for complex kinetic models

Andrew M. Elias,[a,b,*] Carina L. Gargalo,[a] Cristiane S. Farinas,[b] Krist V. Gernaey[a]

[a]PROSYS, Dept. of Chemical and Biochemical Engineering, Technical University of Denmark, Søltofts Plads, Building 228 A, 2800 Kgs. Lyngby, Denmark.
[b]Embrapa Instrumentation, Rua XV de Novembro 1452, 13560-970, São Carlos, SP, Brazil.
andrewmilli@gmail.com

Abstract

Steady-state simulators are typically used for designing and optimizing industrial processes and techno-economic analysis. However, there are instances where dynamic phenomena play a crucial role in the process and cannot be overlooked. Certain unit operations, such as batch reactors, inherently exhibit dynamic behavior. To accurately capture the response of these systems under varying plant operating conditions, they must be modeled dynamically. Integrating a dynamic model into a full plant for steady-state simulation presents a significant challenge, regardless of whether the simulator concept is sequential or equation-oriented. A potential strategy to alleviate the computational load of integrating a dynamic model into a whole plant's steady-state simulation involves assuming a fixed and predetermined conversion for these reactors. However, such simplifications often result in a loss of accuracy and predictive capability, especially when assessing operational flexibility. Moreover, in some instances, the reaction time for batch operations could be a critical factor to consider in the overall plant design or optimization process. A potential solution for this challenge could be using surrogate models as substitutes for specific dynamic models, with time factoring in as an extra input for the meta-model. This work put this method into practice in an equation-oriented simulator (EMSO), applying a Kriging meta-modeling technique, where the meta-model replaced the kinetic model for fungi cultivation. In conclusion, this study explores the use of the metamodeling technique to replace complex kinetic models. It lays the groundwork for future research and potential scientific breakthroughs.

Keywords: Surrogate model, Kriging, submerged fermentation.

1. Introduction

Chemical plants have high production volumes and energy demands, which makes process modeling essential for enhancing their output. A small improvement in the process can have a significant impact on the overall performance. Despite the advances in computing science and the faster speed of computer processors that enable detailed dynamic simulations, steady-state modeling remains the most common method for full plant design and optimization (Seider et al., 2009).

Some unit operations, such as batch reactors, have dynamic behavior by nature. Dynamic modeling is necessary to capture how this kind of system reacts to different operating conditions of the plant. One way to reduce the numerical complexity of linking a dynamic model to a steady-state simulation of a whole plant is by assuming a fixed and predetermined conversion for these reactors. However, these simplifications usually result in loss of accuracy and prediction ability when the plant needs to operate under different conditions. Furthermore, in some cases, the reaction time for those batch operations could be a crucial factor to consider in the whole plant's design or optimization (Bechara et al., 2016).

Equation-oriented process simulators tackle the system of equations concurrently. While they benefit processes with numerous recycle streams, this approach hinders the adoption of strategies to address local convergence issues. Specifically, it prevents the inclusion of ad hoc algorithms within the models of specific process units (referred to as "modules" in sequential modular simulators) (Smith, 2005). A sequential simulator could allow the integration of the original dynamic model into the whole simulation, but this would increase the solver's computational cost, simulation time, and convergence difficulty. For equation-oriented simulators, the direct integration of the dynamic model into the steady-state simulation is even more challenging. A potential solution to avoid this problem is to use a surrogate model that mimics the dynamic model to be integrated. This strategy was used to replace a CFD simulation (Partopour and Dixon, 2016), to mimic a kinetic model of enzymatic hydrolysis (Furlan et al., 2016), and to establish Surrogate Assisted Optimization (Carpio et al., 2017).

Meta-modeling simplifies complex dynamic kinetic models, reducing time, cost, and computational effort in steady-state simulation. It provides flexibility for exploring various scenarios, enhances decision-making processes, and improves predictive performance. It offers detailed solutions, captures high-level mechanisms with simpler rate expressions, and delivers robust, reproducible results. It presents an efficient, flexible, and understandable approach to dealing with complex dynamic kinetic models (Carpio et al., 2018).

This article proposes a Kriging meta-model to replace the dynamic model of a *Trichoderma reesei* fermentation reactor. The meta-model keeps the original dynamic response of the system by adding the processing time as an extra input to the Kriging meta-model. This simple strategy improves the accuracy of the meta-model, while still having low computational cost.

2. Methodology

2.1. Simulator

The EMSO simulator (Environment for Modeling Simulation and Optimization), which was used in this work, is equation-oriented. This simulator has an internal object-oriented modeling language that enables to add new models into its internal library. Furthermore, it is possible to add plug-ins for running calculations that are not compatible with the equation-oriented approach; and new solvers can be linked as dynamic libraries as well.

2.2. Kinect model

The dynamic model of the submerged fermentation reactor was simulated in EMSO using the kinetic model described by Velkovska et al. (1997). The model was based on four main points: (i) there are two types of mycelia: primary and secondary; (ii) only the secondary mycelia produce cellulase; (iii) the cellulase binds to the cellulose particles as a catalyst; and, (iv) the cellulose becomes less reactive as it is converted.

The kinetic model yields three output variables: biomass concentration (S), microorganism concentration (X), and biomass conversion into microorganisms. The fermentation reaction time was selected as the input variable for building the Kriging meta-model.

The fermentation reactor model can be broken down into the following steps:

1. **Medium Addition**: The reactor cultivation medium is gradually added until it fills 99 % of the reactor's operating volume.
2. **Inoculation**: The inoculum is introduced, filling the entire operating volume of the reactor.
3. **Batch Stage**: During this stage, the substrate is consumed, leading to the formation of primary and secondary mycelia.
4. **Discharge**: The reactor volume is completely emptied.
5. **Cleaning**: The reactor undergoes a cleaning process.
6. The cycle then returns to step 1.

The reactor's volume is determined through mass balances, considering the Height/Diameter ratio of the tank (which is set to 2). Additionally, the energy consumed during agitation is calculated by the diameter of the impeller, agitator rotational speed, and friction factor.

2.3. Kriging meta-model

Kriging meta-models are popular for replacing complex non-linear models because they can accurately interpolate even with relatively small data sets. This work used Universal Kriging, Eq. (1), which is one of several types of Kriging meta-models.

$$\hat{y}(x) = \mu(x) + z(x) \tag{1}$$

where the Kriging prediction at the point x is $\hat{y}(x)$, which consists of a regression model $\mu(x)$ (a kind of variable mean) and a stationary random function $z(x)$ (stochastic process) with zero mean.

A first-order polynomial was used for the regression model ($\mu(x)$), and a Gaussian correlation for the random function ($z(x)$).

2.4. Procedure for the surrogate model fitting and validation.

The detailed dynamic model was implemented in EMSO, the Python-EMSO communication interface was used to build the response surface, and MATLAB code was

used to automate and validate the Kriging fitting process. The procedure is based on (Carpio et al., 2018).
(a) *Input data*: the number of input and output variables; the lower and upper bounds of input variables; the number of design points for validation and initial fitting; the incremental step for the number of design points for fitting at each iteration; and the accuracy criterion.
(b) *Design of Simulations (DoS)*: Latin Hypercube Sampling (LHS) was used to select the input data set for validating the meta-model with the dynamic model simulations.
(c) *Dynamic model simulations to obtain validation I/O data set*: The dynamic simulation with all the input variable combinations was performed from step b, to get the output variables for validation.
(d) *Design of Simulations for meta-model fitting*: Similar to step b, an LHS method is utilized to select the input data set that will be used to simulate the dynamic model, specifically to fit Kriging models.
(e) *Dynamic model simulations to obtain a fitting I/O data set.*: All the input variable combinations obtained during the DoS in step d are fed into the dynamic simulation. The simulation then produces the output variables that best fit the model.
(f) *Kriging meta-model fitting*: The fitting I/O dataset is provided to the DACE software (developed by (Lophaven et al., 2002)), which is a freeware MATLAB toolbox used for fitting the Kriging meta-model.
(g) *Calculate the Kriging prediction for the validation Input data*: All the input variable combinations intended for validation purposes are fed into the Kriging meta-model. The model then provides predictions for the output variables.
(h) *Compare the Kriging prediction to the validation Output data*: In this step, the accuracy criterion is calculated by comparing the Kriging prediction for the validation dataset with the dynamic model response. If the accuracy criterion is not met, the number of design points for meta-model fitting is increased (considering the incremental step specified in Step 1).

After estimating the final Kriging parameters in MATLAB, the meta-model was implemented in EMSO.

3. Results and discussion

The quantitative results of the evaluation of the Kriging meta-model, built with 30 design points, are shown in Table 1. To evaluate the metamodel's ability to predict, 10 data points were used.

Table 1 - The quantitative results of the Kriging meta-model evaluation, derived from the detailed dynamic model, are juxtaposed with predictions made by the Kriging meta-model.

Parameters	Values		
	Conversion	S*	X*
Correlation coefficient (r)	0.99998	0.99998	0.99997
Mean absolute error	0.00039	0.00750	0.00425
Maximum absolute error	0.00101	0.01928	0.01087

*Biomass concentration (S) and microorganism concentration (X)

It was observed that, with a small set of input data, low absolute deviations were obtained, as can be seen in Table 1. Worth noting is that the quantitative results demonstrate the Kriging meta-model's successful substitution of the rigorous dynamic model within the validity region. However, for a deeper understanding, consider the qualitative results of the meta-model evaluation depicted in Fig. 1.

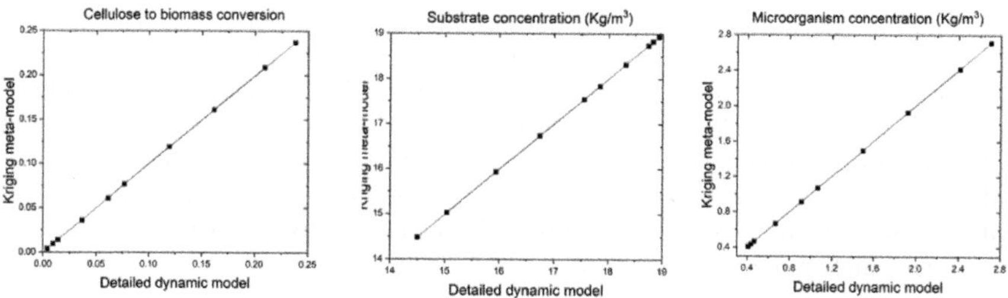

Figure 1 - Qualitative results of the Kriging meta-model evaluation with 10 validating points.

Figure 1 illustrates the close to ideal alignment between the meta-model response and the detailed dynamic model outcomes across a comprehensive range of output models. It has been confirmed that, for the chosen variables in constructing the metamodel, a mere 30 data points were sufficient to yield curves with coefficients of determination exceeding 0.9999. Figure 2 presents the substrate (S) and biomass (X) process dynamics built from the metamodel added to the EMSO process simulator.

The behaviour of the variables over time can observed from Figure 2. The error bars are nearly invisible, given that the maximum absolute error for each output variable is extremely low. The computation time required by the meta-model in one simulation of the fermentation reactor was approximately 0.0001 s using a Ryzen 7 7745HX @ 3.60 GHz laptop machine, a very significant improvement over the computation time required for the original model.

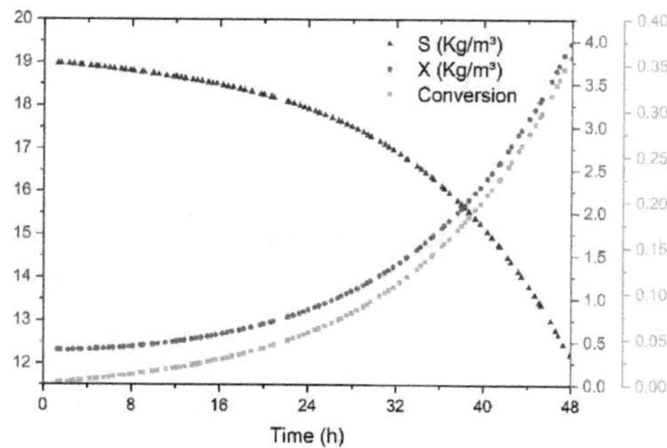

Figure 2 – Microorganism production kinetics of *Trichoderma reesei.* Biomass concentration (S), microorganism concentration (X), and biomass to microorganisms'

conversion as a function of time. The error bars are almost invisible due to the low maximum absolute error.

4. Conclusions

A methodology for integrating dynamic models into steady-state simulations was introduced in this work, primarily for optimization or design objectives. The approach entails replacing dynamic models with Kriging meta-models, incorporating time as an additional input variable to the meta-model. This methodology facilitates the creation of simplified models that closely approximate the outcomes of detailed dynamic models within the desired accuracy range for feasible operating conditions. The developed model will be employed in subsequent projects within a biorefinery framework. This approach will enable a more precise application of global sensitivity analysis, uncertainty assessment, and optimization techniques.

Acknowledgments

The authors are grateful for the financial support provided by: (i) Fundação de Amparo à Pesquisa do Estado de São Paulo (FAPESP, grants #2016/10636-8, #2020/15450-5, and #2022/10900-8; and, (ii) Novo Nordisk Foundation-funded Sustain4.0: Real-time sustainability analysis for Industry 4.0 (NNF0080136).

References

Bechara, R., Gomez, A., Saint-Antonin, V., Schweitzer, J.-M., Maréchal, F., 2016. Methodology for the optimal design of an integrated first and second generation ethanol production plant combined with power cogeneration. 214, pp. 441–449, Bioresour Technol.

Carpio, R.R., Furlan, F.F., Giordano, R.C., Secchi, A.R., 2018. A Kriging-based approach for conjugating specific dynamic models into whole plant stationary simulations. 119, pp. 190–194, Comput Chem Eng.

Carpio, R.R., Giordano, R.C., Secchi, A.R., 2017. Enhanced Surrogate Assisted Global Optimization Algorithm Based on Maximizing Probability of Improvement, in: Computer Aided Chemical Engineering. pp. 2065–2070, Elsevier.

Furlan, F.F., de Andrade Lino, A.R., Matugi, K., Cruz, A.J.G., Secchi, A.R., de Campos Giordano, R., 2016. A simple approach to improve the robustness of equation-oriented simulators: Multilinear look-up table interpolators. 86, pp. 1–4, Comput Chem Eng.

Lophaven, S.N., Nielsen, H.B., Søndergaard, J., 2002. DACE - A Matlab Kriging Toolbox, Version 2.0.

Partopour, B., Dixon, A.G., 2016. Computationally efficient incorporation of microkinetics into resolved-particle CFD simulations of fixed-bed reactors. 88, pp. 126–134, Comput Chem Eng.

Seider, W.D., Seader, J.D., Lewin, D.R., Widagdo, S., 2009. PRODUCT DESIGN PRINCIPLES AND PROCESS Synthesis, Analysis, and Evaluation, Third Edit. ed. John Wiley & Sons, Hoboken, NJ.

Smith, R., 2005. Chemical process design and integration. John Wiley & Sons, Chichester.

Velkovska, S., Marten, M.R., Ollis, D.F., 1997. Kinetic model for batch cellulase production by Trichoderma reesei RUT C30. 54, pp. 83–94, J Biotechnol.

Flavio Manenti, Gintaras V. Reklaitis (Eds.), Proceedings of the 34th European Symposium on Computer Aided Process Engineering / 15th International Symposium on Process Systems Engineering (ESCAPE34/PSE24), June 2-6, 2024, Florence, Italy
 http://dx.doi.org/10.1016/B978-0-443-28824-1.50196-4

An Ionic Liquid Mixture Design for CO_2 Capture through Bayesian Optimization and Molecular Dynamics Simulation

Dulce María de la Torre-Cano[a], Miguel Angel Gutiérrez-Limón[a*], Antonio Flores-Tlacuahuac[b], Mauricio Sales-Cruz[c]

[a]*Departamento de Energía, Universidad Autónoma Metropolitana-Azcapotzalco, Av. San Pablo 420, Ciudad de México, 02128, México*

[b]*Escuela de Ingeniería y Ciencias, Tecnológico de Monterrey, Campus Monterrey, Ave. Eugenio Garza Sada 2501, Monterrey, N.L, 64849, México*

[c]*Departamento de Procesos y Tecnología, Universidad Autónoma Metropolitana – Cuajimalpa, Av. Vasco de Quiroga No. 4871, Ciudad de México, 05348, México.*

**magl@azc.uam.mx*

Abstract

CO_2 emissions into the atmosphere have become a global concern in recent years. The amount of CO_2 generated in post-combustion processes has deserved the attention of the international scientific community. Thus, a variety of processes have emerged that try to address this problem from different points of view, such as the traditional absorption process that uses some type of amine as a solvent. Several other alternatives have been tried to solve the problems presented by this process. One of these alternatives consists of using ionic liquids as solvents in the CO_2 absorption process. An important characteristic of ionic liquids is that their vapor pressure is very low, which makes them practically non-volatile. The task of designing ionic liquids for this purpose has gained interest in recent years. In previous work, our group designed ionic liquids using a computer-aided molecular design methodology, posing the problem as a MINLP problem. (Valencia-Márquez, et. al. 2017), (Silva-Beard, et. al. 2022). In this work, we use Molecular Dynamics Simulation (MDS), to calculate the capacity of absorption of a mixture of ionic liquids and propose an approach of experiments guided by Bayesian optimization to find an optimal mixture of ionic liquids that maximizes the amount of CO_2 captured. The results suggest that following the procedure proposed it is possible to reduce the number of numerical experiments and therefore, the CPU time.

Keywords: Bayesian Optimization, Molecular Dynamic Simulation, Ionic Liquids, CO_2 Capture.

1. Introduction

A current global challenge is the growth of greenhouse gases (GHG), coming mainly from the burning of fossil fuels and industries. GHG emissions have been increasing since the Industrial Revolution and have not yet reached their peak (Friedlingstein et al., 2022). All this leads to an increase in temperature on the planet, the thawing of the poles and other typical problems derived from global warming. Carbon capture and storage (CCS) is considered the most practical option for reducing greenhouse gases. CO_2 can be used to improve oil processes or as a raw material in some industries. The most studied and used CO_2 capture is precombustion because it can be adapted to existing facilities, modifying only the final part of the process (Figueroa et al., 2008).

Current post-combustion technologies use amines to capture CO_2; however, these solvents have some drawbacks such as high volatility and corrosion in the treatment units, so it is required to monitor the concentration and solvent flow. This is why in recent years new alternatives have been studied to carry out this task, such as ionic liquids (ILs).

2. Problem Statement

2.1. Ionic Liquids

Ionic liquids (IL) are considered potential materials for CO_2 capture. These are a mixture of a cation and an anion. Given the large number of mixtures, each IL can present unique properties. ILs have negligible vapor pressure, that is, they are liquid at high temperatures, have a low melting point and have high chemical and thermal stability. The solubility of CO_2 in ionic liquids can occur both in chemical and physical absorption, with a lower cost in desorption for the first case. (Jia et al., 2022).-Investigations on absorption of gases in ionic liquids by Molecular Dynamics Simulation have been carried out with pure ionic liquids and the absorption results have not been very efficient. On the other hand, artificial intelligence has become very popular in recent years. They use some algorithms to predict things, but for all that they must implement some hyperparameters to get better results. These parameters are difficult to decide which ones are good, for this reason they sometimes use Bayesian optimization to guide their search and predict better. Therefore, in this work we aim to evaluate the absorption of CO2 in a mixture of ionic liquids with Molecular Dynamic Simulation. Our experiments are guided by Bayesian optimization to find the optimal combination for maximum CO_2 absorption.

3. Methodology

3.1 Molecular Dynamic Simulation

Molecular dynamics simulation (MDS) is a computational tool that analyzes the behavior of atoms which are treated as particles moving under the influence of classical mechanics. It explains the behavior of fluids and materials at an atomistic level. The software used in this work is LAMMPS (Large-scale Atomic/Molecular Massively Parallel Simulator). Verlet algorithm was used to predict velocities and positions of atoms. To calculate the properties, it is necessary to calculate the forces involved within a molecule, known as the force field. This force field is made up of bonding and non-bonding interactions. On the one hand, on the bonding side we have the forces arising from dihedral twisting, bond stretching and bond bending. And the non-bonding forces consist of the Lennard Jones potential and the Coulomb potential. Table 1 shows the list of ionic liquids found in the literature that have higher solubility in CO_2.

Table 1 Ionic liquids investigated (*Ionic liquids chosen)

Ionic liquid or mixture	Solubility CO_2 (mole fraction)	Henry´s constant CO_2 (MPa)	Source
[BMIM][BF6]	0.013-0.017		(Blanchard et al., 1999)
[BMIM][PF6]*		8-10	(Lim et al., 2009).
[EMIM][B(CN)4]	0.135		(Babarao et al., 2011)
[EMIM][SCN]*		16.2-90.9	(Liu et al., 2021)
[EMPyr][bFAP]		1.74	(Jia et al., 2022b)
[MIM][TF2N]* / [MIM][MeSO4]	0.3660		(Silva-Beard et al., 2022b)

Factors that influence the absorption of CO_2 have been found, to mention some such as the presence of Fluorine and nitrile in the anion, the longer chains in the cation have a

greater absorption capacity. That said, the ionic liquid from Silva's research work was chosen and the cation was modified with a longer chain to have better absorption.
Ionic liquids that appear to be good candidates for further absorption are [BMIM][TF2N] and [EMIM][SCN]. Another ionic liquid mixture tested was [BMIM][TF2N] and [BMIM][PF6]. The MDS solves Newton's equation, in this way we can obtain speed, position and different properties, we only need the force field. The methodology consists of obtaining the Henry constant with MDS and using Bayesian Optimization as a tool to guide us to find a concentration of ionic liquids that achieves the highest CO_2 absorption. The procedure will stop until a maximum of the function is found. See Figure 1.

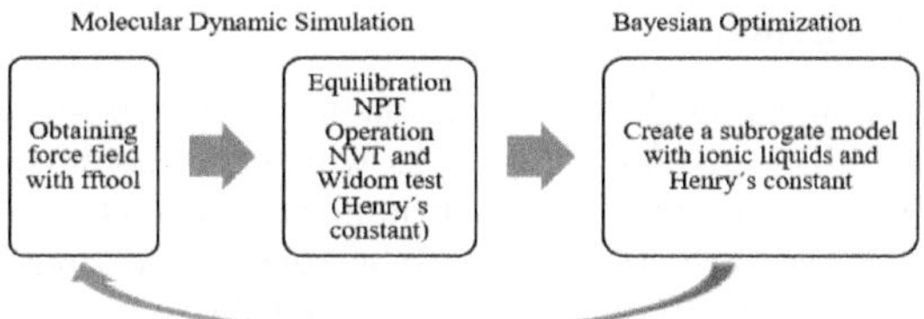

Figure 1 Metodology of this work

The CL&P force field (Canongia, Lopes & Pádua, 2012) was selected and constructed based on the OPLSAA model that has been calculated especially for ionic liquids. The initial configurations for the molecular dynamics simulation were obtained with fftool and PACKMOL software.

3.2 Solubility and Henry´s constant

MDS can further help to understand the interactions between CO_2 and ILs at the atomic and molecular level, providing insight into the mechanism of CO_2 uptake in ILs. The solubility of CO_2 in ILs is an important factor in determining the CO_2 uptake capacity of ILs. ILs with higher CO_2 solubility can absorb more CO_2 molecules, making them more effective for CO_2 capture. (Jia et al., 2022). The Widom test particle insertion scheme has been used to determine the solubility of small molecules in different systems with good agreement with experimental results in both cases (Hossain et al., 2019). Henry's constant can be calculated by Widom insertion, where the excess chemical potential is calculated by the following equation:

$$\mu^{ex} = \mu - \mu^{ideal} = -kT \ln\left(\frac{< V \exp(-\beta V_g) >_{NPT}}{< V >_{NPT}} \right) \quad (1)$$

where μ^{ex} is excess chemical potential and V_g is the energy experienced by a "ghost" particle that interacts with the rest of the molecules in the system. V represents the volume of the system, while k and T denote the Boltzmann constant and the temperature, respectively. The Henry´s constant of a solute in a solvent, H, is obtained by the following equation:

$$H = \rho RT \exp(\beta\mu^{ex}) \quad (2)$$

3.3 Bayesian Optimization

Bayesian optimization (BO) is a technique used to find the best hyperparameter configuration in ML models. It relies on probabilistic methods and Bayes' theorem to guide the search efficiently. BO provides a principled method for making decisions under uncertainty. The objective of BO is to find the global minimum or maximum of a black-box objective function, min X∈F(X). The function F is said to be a black-box function because its explicit functional form is unknown. However, it is assumed that information about the function can be obtained by evaluating it at points in its domain X. However, such evaluations are assumed to be expensive. Therefore, the goal of BO is to minimize F with as few evaluations of the black box function as possible (Močkus, 1975). BO constructs a surrogate (i.e., approximate) function for the objective function and quantify the uncertainty in that surrogate function using a Bayesian machine learning technique, Gaussian process regression, and then use an acquisition function defined from this surrogate function to decide where to sample (Frazier, 2018).

4. Results and Discussion

For the MDS, each atom within the molecule was first identified with an ID, as shown in Figures 2 and 3. In MDS, one normally works with zmat coordinates where the bond length, bond angle and dihedral angle of each atom were generated with its ID, the zmat for each anion and cation of the IL mixture. Subsequently, the force field was obtained with zmat and fftool and Packmol. Finally, the script for the Lammps simulation was configured. The Lennard Jones parameters for the interactions between atoms of different molecules are calculated using the Lorentz-Berthelot combination rules given by Eqs. 3 and 4.

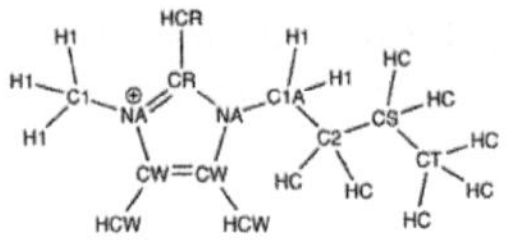

Figure 2 1-butyl-3-methylimidazolium (C4C1im+)

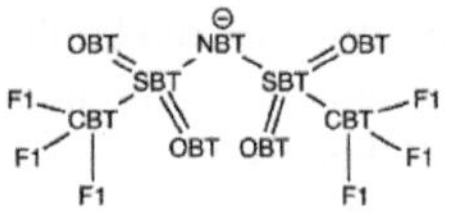

Figure 3 Bis(trifluoromethane)sulfonimide (TFSI- or NTF2-)

$$\sigma_{ij} = \frac{(\sigma_{ii} + \sigma_{jj})}{2} \quad (3)$$

$$\varepsilon_{ij} = (\varepsilon_{ii}\varepsilon_{jj})^{1/2} \quad (4)$$

In this work a force field validation was performed with the selected ionic liquids by calculating the density with the MDS, this was done with the NPT and NVT assemblies. The results are shown in Table 2.

Table 2 Validation of the force field with the density, every simulation was run with 50 molecules, and the mixture was run with 50 molecules of ionic liquid and 5 molecules of CO_2.

	[EMIM][SCN]$^-$	[BMIM][NTF2]$^-$	[BMIM][NTF2]$^-$/CO_2
ρ (g/cm^3) Experimental	1.113	1.444	1.4345
ρ (g/cm^3) MDS	1.131684	1.4149018	1.395161
Error	1.95%	1.74%	2.70%

The excess chemical potential at 298 K and 1 atm was obtained by inserting molecules known as Widom, and then the Henry's constant and Solubility were calculated. The mole fraction of the molecules is a variable that will be modified as indicated by the BO.

The BO was performed in Python with the "bayesian_opt" library with Gaussian processes and the acquisition function "expected improvement" (Fernando Nogueira, 2014). The limits were set between 0 and 1 for the concentration of ionic liquids. BO conducts the experiment and constructs the surrogate function until the maximum point of Henry's constant is known. Bayesian optimisation suggests strategic points by using Gaussian processes and maximising the acquisition function and thus reducing the search space. This is how the surrogate function is constructed. The BO algorithm will stop until the maximum point of the function is known. Figures 4 and 5 show iteration #4 of the

BO, with an expected improved acquisition function. The combinations of ionic liquids suggested by the BO and tested in the MDS are shown in Table 3. The two groups that were tested in MSD show that the pure liquid [BMIM][NTF2]- has a greater Henry's constant, that is, a greater solubility and therefore a greater absorption of CO2 in this mixture of ionic liquids.

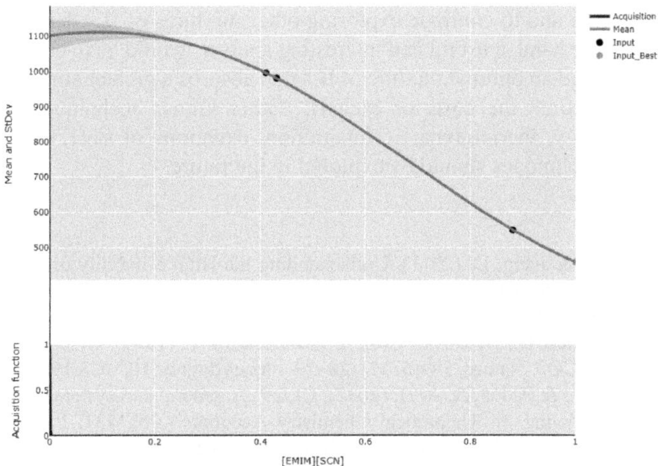

Figure 4 Iteration #4 of Bayesian Optimization with [BMIM][NTF2]$^-$ and [EMIM][SCN]$^-$

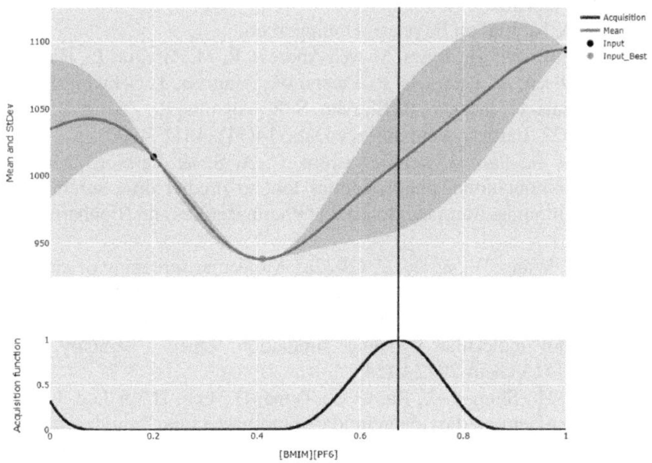

Figure 5 Iteration #4 of Bayesian Optimization with [BMIM][NTF2]$^-$ and [BMIM][PF6]$^-$

Table 3 Combination of IL'S suggested by Bayesian Optimization and tested using MDS.

[EMIM][SCN]$^-$	[BMIM][NTF2]$^-$	Henry's constant (atm)	[BMIM][PF6]$^-$	[BMIM][NTF2]$^-$	Henry's constant (atm)
0.43	0.57	980.34	0.41	0.59	937.95
1.00	0.00	458.37	1	0	738.1
0.41	0.59	995.3	0.2	0.8	1014.4
0.88	0.12	549.5	0.67	0.33	850.02
0.00	1.00	1368.14	0	1	1094
0.23	0.77	1159.13	0.11	0.89	1053.62

5. Conclusions

MDS and BO are useful tools in different fields, such as chemical engineering and ML, on their own. The simultaneous use of these has shown to be useful for the problem posed in this work. From the results, it has been demonstrated that pure IL [BMIM][NTF2] is a good CO_2 absorber. The methodology used and the results obtained motivate us to continue in this line and to continue exploring other mixtures of ILs that produce better results. On the other hand, a useful and interesting analysis would be to consider the costs of ILs in order to find an optimal mixture of ILs that absorbs a greater amount of CO_2 and also takes into account the costs of each IL. Other known techniques make use of solvation free energy, thermodynamic integration, equations of state, etc. to calculate solubility. These techniques should be explored in the future.

References

Babarao, R., Dai, S., & Jiang, D. (2011). Understanding the High Solubility of CO 2 in an Ionic Liquid with the Tetracyanoborate Anion. The Journal of Physical Chemistry B, 115(32), 9789–9794. https://doi.org/10.1021/jp205399r

Blanchard, L. A., Hancu, D., Beckman, E. J., & Brennecke, J. F. (1999). Green processing using ionic liquids and CO2. Nature, 399(6731), 28–29. https://doi.org/10.1038/19887

Canongia Lopes, J. N., & Pádua, A. A. H. (2012). CL&P: A generic and systematic force field for ionic liquids modeling. In Theoretical Chemistry Accounts (Vol. 131, Issue 3, pp. 1–11). Springer New York LLC. https://doi.org/10.1007/s00214-012-1129-7

Figueroa, J. D., Fout, T., Plasynski, S., McIlvried, H., & Srivastava, R. D. (2008). Advances in CO2 capture technology-The U.S. DOE's Carbon Sequestration Program. International Journal of Greenhouse Gas Control, 2, (1), 9–20.

Frazier, P. I. (2018). A Tutorial on Bayesian Optimization.

Friedlingstein, P., O'Sullivan, M., Jones, M. W., Andrew, R. M., Gregor, L., Hauck, J., Le Quéré, C., Luijkx, I. T., Olsen, A., Peters, G. P., Peters, W., Pongratz, J., Schwingshackl, C., Sitch, S., Canadell, J. G., Ciais, P., Jackson, R. B., Alin, S. R., Alkama, R., Zheng, B. (2022). Global Carbon Budget 2022. Earth System Science Data, 14(11), 4811–4900.

Hossain, S., Kabedev, A., Parrow, A., Bergström, C. A. S., & Larsson, P. (2019). Molecular simulation as a computational pharmaceutics tool to predict drug solubility, solubilization processes and partitioning. European Journal of Pharmaceutics and Biopharmaceutics, 137, 46–55.

Jia, X., Hu, X., Su, K., Wang, W., & Du, C. (2022a). Molecular screening of ionic liquids for CO_2 absorption and molecular dynamic simulation. Open Chemistry, 20(1), 379–387.

Jia, X., Hu, X., Su, K., Wang, W., & Du, C. (2022b). Molecular screening of ionic liquids for CO2absorption and molecular dynamic simulation. Open Chemistry, 20(1), 379–387. https://doi.org/10.1515/chem-2022-0154

Lim, B.-H., Choe, W.-H., Shim, J.-J., Ra, C. S., Tuma, D., Lee, H., & Lee, C. S. (2009). High-pressure solubility of carbon dioxide in imidazolium-based ionic liquids with anions [PF6] and [BF4]. Korean Journal of Chemical Engineering, 26(4), 1130–1136. https://doi.org/10.1007/s11814-009-0188-5

Mahurin, S. M., Lee, J. S., Baker, G. A., Luo, H., & Dai, S. (2010). Performance of nitrile-containing anions in task-specific ionic liquids for improved CO2/N2 separation. Journal of Membrane Science, 353(1–2), 177–183. https://doi.org/10.1016/j.memsci.2010.02.045.

Močkus, J. (1975). On bayesian methods for seeking the extremum (pp. 400–404). https://doi.org/10.1007/3-540-07165-2_55.

Nogueira, F., Bayesian Optimization: Open source constrained global optimization tool for Python, 2014, https://github.com/fmfn/ByesianOptimization.

Silva-Beard, A., Flores-Tlacuahuac, A., Rivera-Toledo, M., (2022) Computers and Chemical Engineering,157, 107622.

Valencia-Marquez, D., Flores-Tlacuahuac, A., Vazquez-Medrano, R. (2017) Journal of Cleaner Production, 168, 1652-1667.

Flavio Manenti, Gintaras V. Reklaitis (Eds.), Proceedings of the 34th European Symposium on Computer Aided Process Engineering / 15th International Symposium on Process Systems Engineering (ESCAPE34/PSE24), June 2-6, 2024, Florence, Italy
 http://dx.doi.org/10.1016/B978-0-443-28824-1.50197-6

A systems approach to model nonconventional streams applied to biocrude production from hydrothermal liquefaction

I. Aslanoglou[a], K. Anastasakis[b], C Michalopoulos[a], E. Marcoulaki[c] & A. Kokossis[a,*]

[a]*National Technical University of Athens, Greece*
[b]*Aarhus University, Denmark*
[c]*National Center for Scientific Research "Demokritos", Greece*
[*]*akokossis@mail.ntua.gr*

Abstract

This work proposes a systems approach to model and characterize non–conventional streams, applied to the Hydrothermal Liquefaction (HTL) of sewage sludge towards biocrude. Biocrudes are complex mixtures involving a great many number of compounds, and this introduces challenges in their characterization and the HTL process modelling. For the development of suitable representations and property models for the HTL input/output streams, we create a mathematical model, and solve it using four different optimization algorithms. The optimization is based on experimental data found in the literature, mapping the quantitative and qualitative characteristics of different feedstocks and product streams (organic substrate, reactor inlet and biocrude) and byproducts. Results reveal the most efficient models in terms of their prediction accuracy and convergence speed.

Keywords: Hydrothermal Liquefaction, biocrude, sewage sludge, property modelling, nonconventional stream characterization, optimization

1. Introduction

Fuels derived from biomass are efficient, sustainable and cost-effective alternatives to fossil fuels and they are increasingly used to reduce the carbon emissions (Liu et al., 2021). Biofuels typically originate from nonconventional feedstocks processed through nonconventional processes. Their production involves advanced thermochemical or biochemical processing, e.g. transesterification, gasification, pyrolysis, fermentation etc. (Lin & Lu, 2021). There are several challenges in the design, efficiency and operation of these process, since it is particularly hard to characterize such highly heterogeneous mixtures of chemicals of diversified composition and origin. The thermodynamic, physical and transport properties depend on the feedstock, and it is required to carry out expensive experiments for the selection of the best process conditions, and apply heuristics e.g. for process integration. Due to lack of accurate simulation models it is impossible to scale up these processes and create commercial and business promise for novel biofuel production technologies.

This work considers the HTL of sewage sludge towards biocrude and proposes a systems approach to address the above challenges. HTL (or hydrous pyrolysis) is among the processes that can be used to convert wet biomass into biofuels. It operates at high pressure (10–25 MPa) and moderate temperature (280 °C–370 °C), and uses the water as the reaction medium and catalyst. HTL can accommodate diversity of organic substrates as potential feedstocks; process feedstocks with high humidity or water content; wide range of process conditions and organic content in product streams; and potential to upgrade locally or centrally. After upgrade, the resulting biocrude can be used as a liquid fuel alternative. The total processing cost of the HTL and the upgrade processes is very competitive, but depends strongly on the process performance (Pedersen et al., 2018).

The HTL process has been widely investigated to understand the mechanism and kinetics at different batch scales of operation. Different types of mathematical models are used to predict product yields and compositions for different biomass and waste feedstocks (Kumar, 2022). However, the biomass feedstock and the resulting biocrudes are complex mixtures involving hundreds or thousands of chemicals. This introduces challenges in their characterization and prediction of basic physical and thermodynamic properties, the available process simulation and optimization technology can be extremely poor, the mass and energy balances are done empirically etc. Therefore, despite the high readiness level of HTL technologies, it is impossible to monitor the process efficiently and adjust the operating conditions according to the processed stream.

The compositions of the processed streams are oftentimes obtained by analytical methods, since the chemical content is critical to predict the stream properties. Gas Chromatography – Mass Spectrometry (GC-MS) is one of the most popular method to obtain data on the presence and the quantity of different organic compounds. Zhu et al. (2017) relied on GC–MS data to predict the composition of the bioliquid outlet stream, and validated their model using elemental balances. Taghipour et al. (2022) used biocrude GC–MS data combined with fractional distillation data and applied multi-objective optimization to improve the prediction accuracy of the density and the Boiling Point Temperature (BPT) curve. Yu et al. (2023) considered the HTL of municipal solid waste and analyzed the effect of operating conditions and waste to water ratio on the mass and energy yield. Machine learning has recently gained attention for accurate and efficient biofuel process modelling (Jeon et al., 2023), and Gopirajan et al. (2021) applied ML-based optimization to improve the process-specific yield and the quality of the product.

In view of the difficulty to apply conventional systems methods, this work proposes data modelling and optimization to predict the quantitative and qualitative composition of the biomass inlet, the biocrude and the upgraded biocrude streams. Section 2 presents the proposed models, section 3 reports the obtained results for HTL of sewage sludge towards biocrude and discusses the potential of the models, and section 4 concludes this work.

2. Methodology

This work integrates diversified sets of experiments, and combines them with first-principle based models to produce reliable representation of the involved input-output streams. For a systems description of the problem, we consider that given are the:

- Experimental data
- Process operations: reaction, downstream separation
- Feedstock/product streams: substrate, reactor inlet, biocrude, byproducts
- Background data (first-principle based)
- Set of compounds, conventional thermodynamics, unit operations

and we need to optimally determine:

- Chemical representation: minimum set of suitable components and composition: discrete variables
- Surrogate models: suitable adjustments to existing models

The above problem is formulated as a discrete-continuous optimization model:

$$\min_{N, x_n, y_{n,k}} f = \sum_{n}^{N} \sum_{k}^{K} \left(\frac{\hat{y}_{n,k} - y_{n,k}}{\hat{y}_{n,k}} \right)^2 \tag{1}$$

Where N is the set of measuremens, with n in N, K is the set of properties, $\hat{y}_{n,k}$ denote the experimental data, $y_{n,k}$ are the first-principle based data: $y_{n,k} = g(x_n, p_k)$, x_n is the mass fraction of n, and p_k denotes the value of property k.

For the processing of sewage sludge using HTL, the model is configured for each one of the following streams: the biomass inlet, the biocrude and the upgraded biocrude. Each of these streams is expected to contain a different set of compounds. The model parameters and the model constraints differ between streams, but they can be easily adjusted to address any similar problem. Each stream is associated with a subset of properties and different contraints apply. The properties in the K set generally include:

- biochemical composition of proteins, lipids, carbohydrates, lignin, etc.: $bc = \sum_n^{N_{bc}} x_{bc_n} / \sum_n^N x_n$, $\sum_n^N x_n = a,\ 0 \leq x_n \leq 1$, where a is the total organic content of the feedstock ($a = 1$ for biomass)
- elemental composition of C, H, O, N, P, etc. $ec = \sum_n^N((Ar_i \cdot N_{n,i})/(MW_n \cdot N))$, where Ar_i is the atomic weight of the respective element i, MW_n is the molecular weight of compound n.

Additional constraints apply for the boiling point (BP) temperature distribution {bpd} of the biocdude streams:

- compositions per BP fraction: $\sum_n^{N_i} x_n \leq a_i, \forall N_i = \{n \epsilon N: BP_n \leq T_i\}$, where a_i is the sum of compositions in fraction I, BP_n is the BP temperature of component n, and T_i is the cut point temperature of fraction i.

The resulting mixed-integer nonlinear programming (MINLP) problem is solved using four open-source algorithms: two evolutionary (firefly algorithm (FA) and particle swarm optimization (PSO)) and two deterministic algorithms (sequential quadratic programming (SQP) and least squares optimization (LS)).

3. Model comparison results and discussion

The prediction model of section 2 is applied here to the biomass input, the biocrude and the upgraded biocrude steams. The problem considered here for sewage sludge invloves 165 component candidates, BP range: 20-750 °C and MW range: 45-700. Since the composition of sewage sludge can radically differ depending on its origin, we create an extensive dataset of experimental literature data, to map the diversity of quantitative and qualitative characteristics of different feedstocks, product streams and byproducts.

The prediction model is trained and tested on this dataset, using the four optimization algorithms of section 2. The performance of the four resulting models depends on their capacity to predict the stream compositions and properties. Table 1 reports the results obtained from the four algorithms for each stream, and their relative deviations (green) from the experimental values (blue). The experimental values shown on the table include the stream elemental and biochemical (shown here as component groups) compositions, and property values. HHV denotes the Higher Heating Value of the fuel, which increases from biomass, to biocrude and to upgraded biocrude, as expected. SSRD denotes the sum of the squares of the relative deviations likewise to the objective function of Eq. (1). The table also reports the overall statistics for each stream and the total SSRD per algorithm. Note that, the upgraded biocrude contains 60 % fuel and has density 1048 kg/m^3. An important assumption to be reconsidered in the future is that biocrude is not solid-free.

Table 1: Optimization results: deviations from target values

Stream		x_n, p_k	$\hat{x}_n, \hat{p}_k$	SQP		FA		LS		PSO	
Biomass	Carbon	54.20	52.36	3.40%	52.84	2.52%	52.26	3.57%	51.97	4.12%
	Hydrogen	7.30	7.43	1.77%	7.40	1.43%	7.32	0.31%	7.50	2.70%
	Oxygen	34.20	36.85	7.73%	36.69	7.29%	37.32	9.11%	37.22	8.84%
	Nitrogen	3.60	3.248	9.78%	2.944	18.2%	2.963	17.7%	3.204	11.0%
	proteins	15.77	17.42	10.4%	17.89	13.4%	17.84	13.2%	17.52	11.1%
	H/C	40.58	42.66	5.13%	42.41	4.51%	42.25	4.12%	42.73	5.29%
	lipids	13.06	13.45	3.00%	13.37	2.34%	13.47	3.11%	13.46	3.09%
	Lignin	25.10	26.47	5.46%	26.34	4.94%	26.44	5.33%	26.29	4.73%
	HHV	24.51	23.71	3.24%	23.92	2.40%	23.68	3.39%	23.54	3.94%
	SSRD			0.0355		0.0629		0.0648		0.0423
Biocrude	Carbon	74.67	74.46	0.28%	76.22	2.08%	75.38	0.95%	75.44	1.03%
	Hydrogen	10.30	10.57	2.67%	9.96	3.33%	10.70	3.92%	11.13	8.10%
	Oxygen	11.30	12.29	8.76%	11.99	6.13%	11.30	0.04%	11.01	2.56%
	Nitrogen	2.76	3.046	10.4%	2.200	20.3%	2.993	8.43%	2.611	5.41%
	HHV	33.20	33.10	0.30%	33.88	2.04%	33.49	0.88%	33.50	0.92%
	SSRD			0.0191		0.0469		0.0088		0.0103
Upgraded biocrude	Carbon	86.20	85.41	0.92%	85.84	0.42%	85.39	0.94%	85.04	1.35%
	Hydrogen	13.00	13.56	4.31%	12.30	5.35%	13.50	3.86%	13.86	6.64%
	Oxygen	0.70	0.777	11.0%	0.992	41.7%	0.849	21.3%	0.867	23.8%
	Nitrogen	0.10	0.111	11.1%	0.701	601%	0.111	11.0%	0.084	15.5%
	HHV	38.06	37.71	0.94%	37.93	0.36%	37.70	0.95%	37.54	1.38%
	SSRD			0.0264		36.353		0.0590		0.0856
Total	Minimum			0.28%		0.36%		0.04%		0.92%
	Quartile1			2.22%		2.21%		0.95%		2.63%
	Median			4.31%		4.51%		3.86%		4.73%
	Quartile3			9.27%		10.4%		8.77%		8.47%
	Maximum			11.1%		601%		21.3%		23.8%
	SSRD			0.0810		36.46		0.1326		0.1382

According to the results, there is particularly good match between the experimental data and the predicted biocrude compositions/properties for SQP, LS and PSO. For all algorithms, the majority of observed deviations lie around 3-4 % and is generally below 10 %. Only in the case of FA on upgraded biocrude we observe high deviations on the predicted values for most of the components, elements and HHV, and unacceptably high deviations in the compositions of O and especially N (these account for 0.8 % of the mixture). The average error per parameter is 6.06 %, 6.56 %, 7.49 % and 59.01 % for SQP, LS, PSO and FA, respectively. Looking at the total SSRDs for all algorithms and each stream, SQP is the best option to model the biomass and upgraded biocrude, and LS is the best for biocrude.

Another critical metric beyond compositions is the fit of the obtained BP curves to the experimental data for biocrude. Figure 1 shows the curves for biocrude without (up) and with (down) upgrade. Note that, the quality of the upgraded product is superior since it has higher HHV. Again, we observe excellent match of experimental data for the deterministic methods and PSO, and a good amount of desired fractional cuts.

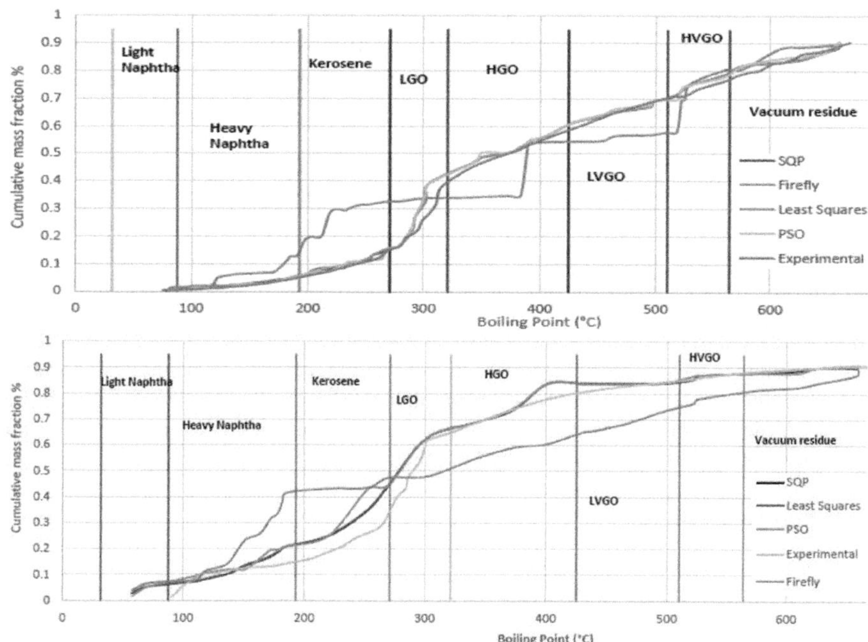

Figure 1: Experimental data and predicted biocrude (without / with upgrade) BP curves

The developed models allow us to explore changes in the operation as a function of variations, investigate process and energy integration opportunities, and improve process performance and energy efficiency. The convergence speed is also very important for real-time process control. SQP is the fastest for upgraded biocrude with execution time 9.1 s, followed by 40 s for PSO and over 67 s for LS and FA. This particularly low convergence speed indicates that SQP might also be a very good candidate for real-time applications. Therefore, based on its overall performance, SQP is found to be the most accurate, reliable and fast optimization option for this case study.

The predicted stream compositions and properties can be used as input to simulation software within a complete simulation package that will be validated on existing HTL pilots. Accurate simulations will certainly facilitate the development of reliable scale-up/down models for HTL and other novel processes, the assessment of uncertainties, and the conduction of techno-economic analyses for different business cases with potential lower cost for efficient resource utilization and biofuel production.

4. Conclusions and future work

Biocrude can be produced from a variety of resources and unless properly characterized, this valuable product stream would be unable to enter conventional refineries either as a drop-in fuel or, alternatively, as an intermediate feedstock to upgrade.

This work proposes a systems approach to model and characterize non–conventional streams, applied to the HTL of sewage sludge towards biocrude. For the development of suitable representations and property models for the process input/output streams, we build an MINLP model and solve it with four different optimization algorithms (SQP, PSO, FA and LS). The objective function is expressed as the sum of squares of relative differences between the known data and the model predictions. The modeling of physical processes (e.g. distillation) relies on the physical properties of the input streams (e.g. the BP temperatures of the stream components), and data quality is important to obtain reliable models. The proposed approach is generic and systematic; therefore, it can be suitable to represent and characterize a wide range of nonconventional streams typically encountered in biomass/biofuel processes.

Preliminary results for the biomass inlet and the biocrude (with and without upgrade) using the SQP, PSO and LS algorithms appear very promising. The prediction accuracy is very good (0.3-11 % for SQP), while the predicted chemical compositions are reasonable and consistent with literature data. Additionally, the SQP execution time is adequately low to consider online implementation for real-time process control.

Future work involves the reconsideration of assumptions, and the expansion of the components dataset to extend the model applicability. We also wish to investigate improvements in terms of the algorithm implementation, to increase accuracy and speed, and generally extend the capabilities of the implemented tools. Our work will enable more accurate process simulations, therefore a more efficient and reliable study of HTL and other novel processes to improve biofuel production.

5. Acknowledgements

This project is implemented within the framework of the National Recovery and Resilience Plan "Greece 2.0" and financed by the European Union (NextGeneration EU).

6. References

Gopirajan, P.V., Gopinath, K.P., Sivaranjani, G. and Arun, J., 2021. Optimization of hydrothermal liquefaction process through machine learning approach: process conditions and oil yield. Biomass Conversion and Biorefinery, pp.1-10. https://doi.org/10.1007/s13399-020-01233-8

Jeon, P.R., Moon, J.H., Olanrewaju, O.N., Lee, S.H., Ling, J.L.J., You, S. and Park, Y.K., 2023. Recent advances and future prospects of thermochemical biofuel conversion processes with machine learning. *Chem. Engineering J.*, p.144503. https://doi.org/10.1016/j.cej.2023.144503

Kumar, R., 2022. A review on the modelling of hydrothermal liquefaction of biomass and waste feedstocks. *Energy Nexus*, 5, p.100042. https://doi.org/10.1016/j.nexus.2022.100042

Lin, C.Y. and Lu, C., 2021. Development perspectives of promising lignocellulose feedstocks for production of advanced generation biofuels: A review. Renewable and Sustainable Energy Reviews, 136, p.110445. https://doi.org/10.1016/j.rser.2020.110445

Liu, Y., Cruz-Morales, P., Zargar, A., Belcher, M. S., Pang, B., Englund, E. et al., 2021. Biofuels for a sustainable future. *Cell*, 184(6), 1636-1647. https://doi.org/10.1016/j.cell.2021.01.052

Pedersen, T. H., Hansen, N. H., Pérez, O. M., Cabezas, D. E. V. and Rosendahl, L. A., 2018, Renewable hydrocarbon fuels from hydrothermal liquefaction: A techno-economic analysis. Biofuels, *Bioproducts and Biorefining*, 12(2), 213-223, https://doi.org/10.1002/bbb.1831

Taghipour, A., Ramirez, J., Rakhmetova, O. and Rainey, T.J., 2022. A method for HTL biocrude simulation using multi-objective optimisation and fractional distillation. *Computers & Chemical Engineering*, 157, p.107600, https://doi.org/10.1016/j.compchemeng.2021.107600

Yu, D., Guo, J., Meng, J. and Sun, T., 2023. Biofuel production by hydro-thermal liquefaction of municipal solid waste: Process characterization and optimization. *Chemosphere*, 328, p.138606. https://doi.org/10.1016/j.chemosphere.2023.138606

Zhu, Y., Biddy, M.J., Jones, S.B., Elliott, D.C. and Schmidt, A.J., 2014. Techno-economic analysis of liquid fuel production from woody biomass via hydrothermal liquefaction (HTL) and upgrading. *Applied Energy*, 129, 384-394. https://doi.org/10.1016/j.apenergy.2014.03.053

Flavio Manenti, Gintaras V. Reklaitis (Eds.), Proceedings of the 34th European Symposium on Computer Aided Process Engineering / 15th International Symposium on Process Systems Engineering (ESCAPE34/PSE24), June 2-6, 2024, Florence, Italy
 http://dx.doi.org/10.1016/B978-0-443-28824-1.50198-8

Assessment of low-carbon alternative fuels in maritime integrated with CCS on board

Nefeli Roufogali,[a] Konstantinos A. Pyrgakis,[a] Antonis C. Kokossis[a]

[a]*School of chemical engineering, National Technical University of Athens, Iroon Polytechneiou 9, GR-15780, Athens, Greece*
akokossis@mail.ntua.gr

Abstract

This work uses PSE methods for screening, simulation, integration, and analysis of low-carbon fuels in maritime along with options for CCS on board. The efficiencies of conventional fuels (HFO, diesel) were addressed in front of alternative fuels (methanol, LNG, H2, biocrude) to investigate energy and fuels savings considering the potentials of process and energy integration and cogeneration that uses available heat from flue gases and the engine in new engine designs of ROPAX ships. The accounted energy demands include shaft work, electricity and heat respectively used for propulsion, the engine room, and the hotel. Alternative fuels could improve economic performance of shipping by 10% (LNG)-340% (Methanol). Energy integration of the ship's hot/cold streams could reduce fuels costs by up to 10%, while CCS on board could yield CO2 emissions reduction in the range of 40% (cryogenic)-80% (MEA adsorption).

Keywords: marine engines; ROPAX; integration; CCS; LNG, methanol, H2, biocrude

1. The need for low-carbon fuels in maritime

Maritime produces ≈3% of GHG emissions, while shipping holds 80% of global trade (Faber et al., 2020). Most vessels currently use HFO or MDO bringing them in front of stringent emission regulations set by the International Marine Organization (IMO), which requires short- and long-term strategies to reduce GHG emissions. Key goals for 2030 include GHG emissions reduction by 20% and reduction of CO2 emissions per transport work by at least 40% (compared with 2008 levels). The goal of IMO is to achieve net-zero GHG emissions, as soon as possible within this century, which necessitates significant efficiency improvements to follow business-as-usual operations (Gibbs et al., 2014). These goals require drastic changes from conventional operations and the use of low-carbon fuels taking advantage of design (fuels and integration) and technology (engines and CCS) innovations on board. Still, sustainability of alternative fuels is also strongly affected by cost-effective upstream chemistries to valorize bio-based sources (Pyrgakis et al., 2016; Pateromichelakis et al., 2022). Fuel replacement is the promising long-term solution. Since novel fuels and engine systems are at lower TRLs and the bunkering systems for alternative fuels are underdeveloped, then energy integration and CCS on board can facilitate short- and mid-term scenarios. This work examines the performance of alternative low-carbon fuels, integration patterns and CCS on board.

2. Background of alternative fuels, designs, and technology options

Shipping needs to drastically reduce emissions of any kind requiring changes in fuels, equipment, and operation practices to reach IMO's targets. This requires testing of various alternative options and degrees of freedom towards cost-effective shipping decarbonization. LNG is the most attractive and market competitive alternative to HFO and MDO by holding high energy density and meeting the needs for SOx and NOx limits; however, LNG is challenged by high cooling demands and volumes for storage (−163 °C). Bio-based and synthetic LNG constitute an even more promising alternative for further emissions reduction. Other high trended bio-based and low-carbon fuels include methanol (MeOH); biocrude from pyrolysis or liquefaction of biomass; and hydrogen. MeOH holds adequate energy density, while green sourcing needs to be considered. Hydrogen is the most promising option for maritime decarbonization (zero-carbon emissions), but lacks cost-efficient production, sourcing, and requires high-cost infrastructures. Biocrude is attractive, but remains at low TRL featuring instability, equipment corrosion, and low mixture compositions. Overall, sourcing, seasonality, price volatility, and divergence from marine standards are vital challenges for new fuel entries. Other options to drive emissions reduction involve direct intervention on existing operations in terms of process intensification by setting goals to optimally valorize available heat across ship and by appropriately integration with current energy demands, eventually reducing fuels consumption in the main engines and the boiler/heaters. Besides classical pinch analysis, there are several state-of-the-art process-to-process energy integration approaches to facilitate optimality in energy savings and applied utilities (Pyrgakis and Kokossis, 2019). Moreover, electricity cogeneration using steam turbines is another option to reduce loadings of auxiliary engines. The updated Turbine Hardware Model of Pyrgakis and Kokossis (2020) was used for estimation of the cogeneration potential. Such options are feasible for short-term strategies, but are challenged by re-engineering of existing mechanical, electronic and control systems.

Carbon capture and storage (CCS) on board is another option for CO2 emissions reduction. Different technologies and designs could be adapted to the specific needs and conditions of various industries including maritime. CO2 absorption with amine solutions (e.g., MEA) is the most mature and efficient technology for CO2 capture, though is challenged by utilities costs, and demands for compressing CO2 captured in vapor phase. Cryogenic distillation is another, also mature, option based on physical processing and is adaptable to various conditions. The high energy cost for CO2 condensation is the main challenge. Thus, a potential to use it in LNG ships can be justified, since cryogenic storage of LNG offers a viable source of cold energy enabling CO2 liquefaction and lower energy penalties for CCS and short-term storage on board. The captured CO2 could be deposit at port and be integrated with other energy carriers' supply chains and industries.

The above fuel, design and technology options have been examined to investigate best combinations that achieve highest economic and environmental performance in ROPAX ships. The analysis takes for granted the known and fixed energy demands of a ROPAX reference ship (150 m length, 1200 passengers) including propulsion, electricity and heat for hotel and auxiliary operations. This work systematically screens the performance of each fuel, design and CCS option considering variations in the engine cylinder design and operating conditions. Marine engines using alternative fuel were simulated and their demands were integrated with the vessel's streams to identify highest potentials for fuels savings considering, at the same time, process, and energy integration of CCS on board.

3. Screening, analysis, and design methodology

The approach involves 3 analysis steps to systematically assess the economic, technical, and environmental performance of alternative fuels, when used alone or combined with conventional fuels. The steps are:

(1) Quick and robust screening: 6 conventional (diesel, HFO) and alternative (MeOH, H2, biocrude, LNG) fuels were examined by means of mathematical modelling considering an equation system to describe combustion kinetics; fuels and flue gas properties; mass and energy balances; and cylinder operations. The model receives user-defined inputs for the cylinder operating conditions (fuel inlet pressure and temperature and Air Fuel Ratio-AFR) and design (compression ratio, bore and height) and fuel prices. The model returns as output the cylinder's mass and energy balances, fuel conversion, energy efficiencies, power output, torque, fuel consumption, and CO2 emissions.
The analysis focused on the impact of the engine operations on the energy, economic and environmental performance. This approach was also considered for different compatible fuels mixtures (conventional with alternative) to assess trade-offs in economic and environmental performance. Overall, the aggregated results were used to map and rank the overall performance of single and mixed fuel alternatives.
(2) Engine simulation and process integration: Using the results of step (1), the analysis deepened in the engine design developing flowsheets and simulations based on the use of each fuel and type of engine in the basis of ROPAX ships energy demands. The simulations involved the engine cylinders, the turbochargers, the fuel feeding system (storage, pressurization, heating, vaporization), and flue gases production. The simulations were performed in ASPEN plus and the detailed mass and energy balances were calculated and used to estimate the reference energy savings from utilization of hot streams (engine, lubricating oil, and scavenge air) with cold streams of the ship, which include steam and calorifier energy production, fuel, and auxiliary heating processes across ship. The distribution of the reference fuel combustion energy among all above ship operations (including propulsion, shaft work for electricity production, the heater and energy losses) was mapped ringing the bell for process intensification across ship. A great potential of available energy was identified in energy losses in hot flue gases (>290 °C depending on the type of fuel) and the circulating cooling water (heat rejected to the sea heat sink) used for cooling the engine, the lubricating oil and the scavenge air. Both heat sources could be used to save fuel used for heat production (through integration) and fuel used for electricity production (through cogeneration). The composite curves of the reference scenarios were calculated revealing the integration, cogeneration and fuel savings potentials in the heater and ME/AE engines.
(3) Carbon Capture and Storage on board: The produced flue gases were further considered for Carbon Capture and Storage (CCS) on board through two alternative technologies: MEA absorption (MEA-CCS) and Cryogenic distillation (Cryo-CCS). In the case of MEA-CCS, both kinetic and equilibrium reactions among MEA-CO2-H2O as well as an absorber-stripper system were considered with appropriate integration of the energy intensive heating of absorbed CO2 and cooling of recycled MEA. The energy intensive Cryo-CCS requires delicate design adapted to the specific conditions and composition of flue gas to ensure sustainable CCS. Reference designs (Songolzadeh et al., 2014) regularly include (i) water condensation, (ii) high pressure compression (up to 80 bar) (iii) partial removal of air content and (iv) cryogenic distillation for sharp separation of CO2-air. High pressures enable lower dew points of CO2, which return lower electricity demands for chilling. However, high pressure compression of flue gas with low CO2 content (4-8% w/w) is not a sustainable option. This is outcome of using high AFRs in maritime to ensure full fuel consumption in the cylinder. The high compression power results in high electricity demands and fuel consumption in auxiliary engines producing extra CO2 emissions; almost equivalent to the CO2 that is captured by Cryo-CCS. This raises concerns about using lower AFR to favor CO2 capture, but lower LNG consumption results in either high CH4 emissions (25 times higher than CO2) or

high energy costs to recover unconverted CH4. Under these conditions, CCS in LNG-ROPAX is re-engineered by bypassing compression and taking advantage of the viable cold energy from LNG storage to partially liquefy CO2 from flue gases. Short-term CO2 storage on board requires multistage compression and condensation of vapor CO2 in MEA-CCS, while liquefied CO2 (Cryo-CCS) can be pumped and stored at lower cost.
4) CCS design versus energy integration efficiencies: The analysis involves fixed streams of the ship and variable streams from CCS process that need to be appropriately designed to ensure the maximum feasible energy savings and CO2 capture efficiencies. Thus, the whole ship energy demands were continuously inspected through the integration graph of composite curves to ensure sustainable operation and CCS. The inspection of composite curves guided the flowsheeting and operating conditions of CCS, holding the target of CO2 emissions reduction by at least 40% (IMO goals for 2030).

4. Results

4.1. Screening alternative fuels

The kinetic models of Aronowitz et al. (1979), Konnov et al. (2019) and Frassoldati et al. (2009) were used, respectively, for the combustion of MeOH, H2 and CH4. The polynomial equation and parameters from ASPEN plus v.12 were used to model heat capacity of fuels, air and flue gases, while a 4-stroke diesel engine cycle was considered to model the temperatures, pressures, volumes and energy balances in the cylinder. The full cylinder model was implemented at various operations of real-life engines (Table 1). The impact of alternative fuels and operating conditions (AFR, compression ratio, fuel inlet temperature and pressure) on energy and economic performance (torque-T [Nm] to fuel consumption-Price [€/hr]) were investigated. Indicatively, Figure 1 (left) presents trade-offs between various economic (T/Price) and energy efficiencies (n_{actual}) at different operating conditions and engine designs. Figure 2 also maps the economic performance vs CO2 emissions at best condition identified for each type of engine.

Table 1 Design specification of cylinders of addressed marine engines.

Fuel type	Diameter/Height	kW/RPM
MeOH	0,32/0,4	470/700; 580/750
H2 *and* H2-Diesel	0,128/0,157	740/1900; 750/2100
Biocrude *and* Biocrude-HFO	0,225/0,3	130/750; 150/900
Diesel *and* MeOH -Diesel	0,31/0,43	485/700; 600/750
LNG *and* H2-LNG	0,31/0,43	420/650; 520/700

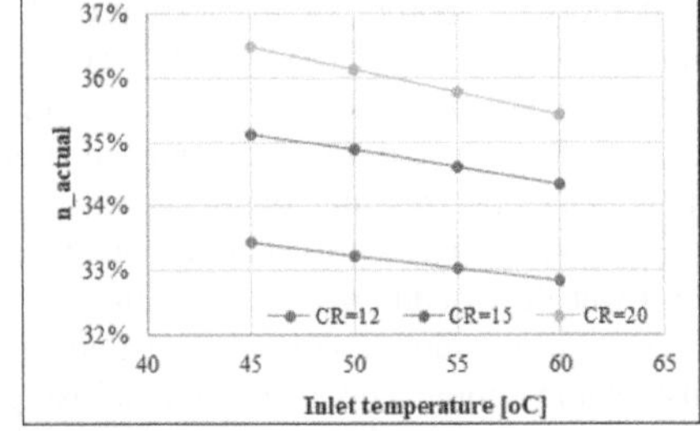

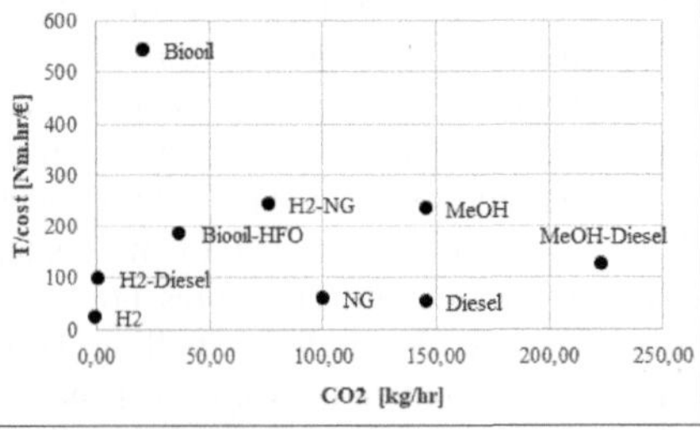

Figure 1 Energy efficiencies vs temperature and compression ratio in MeOH engines (left); map of economic-environmental performance of addressed marine fuels (right).

4.2. Engine simulation and process integration

The process flowsheets of engine operations and fuel management (vaporization, pressurization and/or heating) were developed and simulated in Aspen plus (Figure 2) resulting in the detailed mass and energy balances across engine. All thermal data were extracted and used for the energy analysis and detection of the maximum feasible energy savings, while electricity cogeneration was also considered.
Figure 3 presents the composite curves of a MeOH, LNG, and HFO engines revealing the potential for full integration of ship's heating demands with available energy from the engine (producing hot water at 350 °C) and hot flue gases (≥190 °C).
In HFO-ROPAX, all steam production and Thermal Oil Heater demands can be covered by the engine's available heat and the flue gases economizer reducing HFO consumption by ≈1.5%. Steam production using energy form the engine, scavenge air and flue gases can be used for 940 kW of cogeneration further reducing fuel consumption in auxiliary engines by 3%. Similar integration patterns in MeOH engines can reduce heating demands and fuel consumption from 3600 to 3200 kg/hr (10%), while the cogeneration of 585 kW could cover 30% of the hotel and engine room ventilation demands. In LNG-ROPAX, fuel savings from energy integration can reduce LNG consumption by 14%, while 44 kg/hr are further saved by cogeneration, resulting in total fuel savings at ≈17%.

4.3. Carbon Capture and Storage on board

CCS on board was investigated and appropriately integrated within ROPAX ships. Both MEA- and Cryo-CCS technologies were tested in HFO, MeOH and LNG ships. The process flowsheets of each CCS technology and storage stages have been developed in ASPEN Plus. Prior CCS, cooling of flue gases (at 40-50 °C) and water condensation were considered reaching 4-8% w/w CO2 content. Such low CO2 contents raise the energy penalty in CCS and requires delicate design and adaptation of CCS conditions to appropriately match and/or cover chilling demands with waste cold energy of effluent air streams. The design of MEA-CCS followed a typical structure from literature (Songolzadeh et al., 2014). In contrast, Cryo-CCS needed to be appropriately tuned (temperatures, pressures and flowsheet) to ensure energy fitting with the ship's streams.
MEA-CCS most fits to HFO and MeOH ships. MEA-CCS required 5060 kW to capture CO2 (7.4% w/w) from 166 tn/hr of HFO-based flue gases reaching 85% CO2 capture efficiency. In MeOH ships, MEA-CCS required 3591 Kw to capture CO2 (6.2% w/w) from 73.5 tn/hr flue gases reaching 81% CO2 capture. In Cryo-CCS, the use of flue gases compression (80 bar) resulted in additional fuel consumption equivalent to 70-80% of the fresh fuel consumption. Instead, the solution was to bypass compression and directly condense CO2 at atmospheric pressure and higher temperatures (−145 to −155 °C) matching with the cold energy for LNG vaporization and heating (−163→40 °C). The condensed AIR-CO2 mixture is next pumped (80 bar) and driven to cryogenic distillation to recover pure CO2. This strategy resulting in the lowest feasible Cryo-CCS demands (4.23 MJ_{elec}/kg of captured CO2) and in the highest CO2 emissions reduction (40%).

5. Conclusions

A preliminary screening of alternative fuels performance highlighted biocrude, LNG and MeOH from economic and environmental perspectives. However, biocrude still lacks maturity and stability in use (asphaltenes precipitation and corrosion) and needs additives to enable use at concentrations. Instead, LNG and MeOH are best alternatives used alone or in mixtures. MeOH ships appear a higher integration and cogeneration potential than LNG and HFO, but methanol's lower heating value requires larger fuel flows and CO2

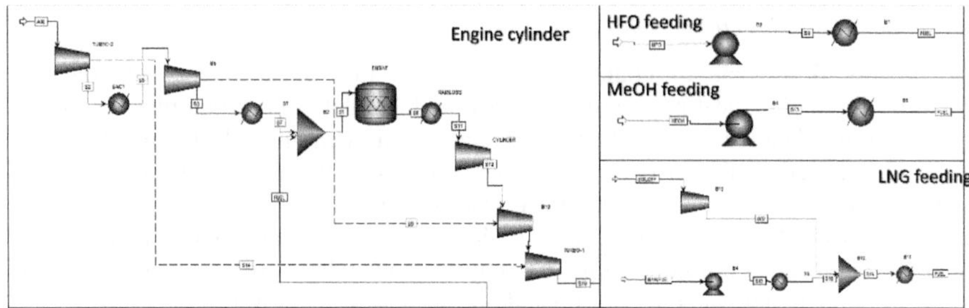

Figure 2 Process flowsheets of cylinder and fuel handling simulates in ASPEN Plus

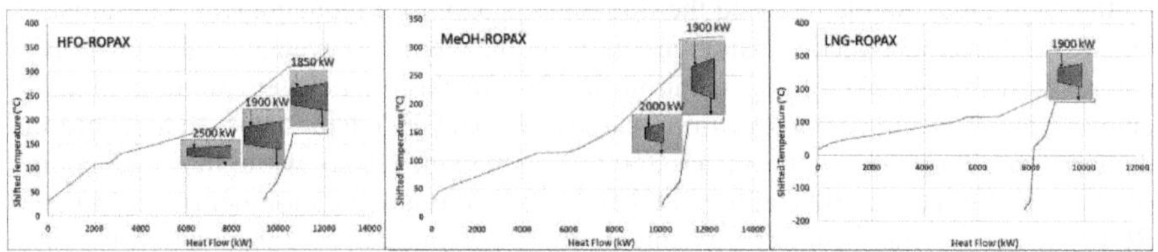

Figure 3 Composite curves of integrated ship's demands.

emissions. CCS on board appears feasible reaching CO2 capture efficiencies of up to 80% using MEA-CCS and 40-50% Cryo-CSS, the latter better fits with energy profiles of LNG ships. Moreover, mixing of appropriate fuels, energy integration and cogeneration facilitated fuel savings by up to 10% compared with current practices in ROPAX.

Acknowledgments

The project is implemented within the framework of the National Recovery & Resilience Plan "Greece 2.0" and has been financed by the European Union (NextGeneration EU).

References

Aronowitz, D., Santoro, R.J., Dryer, F.L., Glassman, I., 1979. Kinetics Of The Oxidation Of Methanol: Experimental Results Semi-Global Modeling And Mechanistic Concepts. Symposium on Combustion, 17, 1, 633-644

Faber, J., et al., 2020. Fourth IMO GHG Study 2020. IMO, London SE1 7SR

Frassoldati, A., Cuoci, A., Faravelli, T., Ranzi, E., Candusso, C., Tolazzi, D., Simplified kinetic schemes for oxy-fuel combustion. S4FE 2009

Gibbs, D., Rigot-Muller, P., Mangan, J., Lalwani, C., 2014. The role of sea ports in end-to-end maritime transport chain emissions. *Energy Policy*, 64, 337–348

Konnov, A.A., 2019. Yet another kinetic mechanism for hydrogen combustion. Combustion and Flame, 203, 14–22

Pateromichelakis, A., Psycha, M., Pyrgakis, K., Maréchal, F., Kokossis, A., 2022. The use of GVL for holistic valorization of biomass. Computers & Chemical Engineering, 164, 107849

Pyrgakis, K.A., de Vrije, T., Budde, M.A.W., Kyriakou, K., López-Contreras, A.M., Kokossis, A.C., 2016. A process integration approach for the production of biological iso-propanol, butanol and ethanol using gas stripping and adsorption as recovery methods. BEJ, 116, 176-194.

Pyrgakis, A., Kokossis, A.C., 2019. A Total Site Synthesis approach for the selection, integration and planning of multiple-feedstock biorefineries. C&CE, 122, 326-355

Pyrgakis, K.A., Kokossis, A.C., 2020. Total Site Synthesis: Selection of Processes to Save Energy and Boost Cogeneration. Computer Aided Chemical Engineering, 48, 1345-1350

Songolzadeh, M., Soleimani, M., Ravanchi, M.T., Songolzadeh, R., 2014. Carbon Dioxide Separation from Flue Gases: A Technological Review Emphasizing Reduction in Greenhouse Gas Emissions. 2014, ID 828131

Flavio Manenti, Gintaras V. Reklaitis (Eds.), Proceedings of the 34th European Symposium on Computer Aided Process Engineering / 15th International Symposium on Process Systems Engineering (ESCAPE34/PSE24), June 2-6, 2024, Florence, Italy
 http://dx.doi.org/10.1016/B978-0-443-28824-1.50199-X

Facilitating the Shift Toward an Environmentally Friendly Plastic Waste Management Economy through Mathematical Optimization

Oluwadare Badejo,[a] Borja Hernández,[ab] Marianthi G. Ierapetritou.[a*]

a Department of Chemical and Biomolecular Engineering, University of Delaware, 150 Academy Street, Newark, Delaware 19716, USA.
b TECNUN Engineering School, University of Navarra, Manuel Lardizabal Ibibildea 13, San Sebastian 20018, Spain.
mgi@udel.edu

Abstract

This work presents a multiperiod mixed integer linear programming (MILP) problem for planning the decarbonization of plastic waste management. The problem includes multiple plastic waste management technologies, transportation modes, technology location, and number of facilities for planning the decarbonization transition in the East Coast of the United States. The optimization problem is solved considering two type of decarbonization policies: a tax based policy, and a carbon cap policy. The former, reduces the emissions by 34%, which is not sufficient to meet the decarbonization agreements. This requires a carbon cap policy approach that promotes the use of sustainable technologies (mechanical recycling, chemical recycling, hydrocracking); instead of upcycling technologies that generate valuable products, e.g., upcycling of plastic wastes to lube oils and aldehydes through pyrolysis.

Keywords: Plastic waste management decarbonization, plastic upcycling, planning, mathematical programming.

1. Introduction

Plastic waste, with 400 million metric tons produced yearly, has become a critical environmental issue. After its first use, most of this plastic is landfilled without generating any value. Only 9% of the plastic waste is mechanically recycled, and 16% is incinerated (OECD, 2022). However, mechanical recycling degrades plastic waste, limiting its infinite recycling(Dogu et al., 2021; Larrain et al., 2021). Alternatively, chemical recycling and upcycling have appeared as solutions to this problem. Chemical recycling has been performed in two ways: through a solvent-precipitation process or with thermochemical processing. In solvent-precipitation, monomers are separated from mix plastic waste streams(Walker et al., 2020), and recovered with intact properties. Thermochemical recycling employs pyrolysis produce olefins that can be cracked to increase the content of light olefins (ethylene or propylene) that are finally polymerized (Larrain et al., 2021; Somoza-Tornos et al., 2020). Upcycling consists of the use of plastic waste for generating high-value products. This may involve different thermochemical techniques like gasification to produce hydrogen, hydrothermal liquefaction and hydrocracking to produce fuels, hydrogenolysis for lube oil production, or pyrolysis that produces a mixture of paraffins, aromatics, and olefins(Li et al., 2022). In particular, olefins can be upgraded to valuable products like lube base oils, plastics, or aldehydes.

Among all these options, the technology and the product generated have been demonstrated to be critical contributors in plastic waste treatment's emissions and economic performance (Hernández et al., 2023). However, the recommended process for each product is dependent on the desired trade-off between economics and environmental objectives. Upcycling technologies can generate significant value from plastic waste and can be alternatives to mechanical or chemical recycling. The recommendations from the superstructure/process design point of view have been extended to strategic supply chain level (O. A. Badejo et al., 2023; Erickson et al., 2023). The supply chain design has selected the same technologies: upcycling methods for economic objectives and mechanical recycling for environmental objectives (O. Badejo et al., 2023). The electrification of the transportation also showed that under environmental objectives upcycling technologies are implemented in more areas and manage higher fraction of plastic waste. However, a high penetration of them increases the emissions compared to mechanical recycling with increased global warming potential (GWP).

This increase in the GWP may put climate agreements at risk and prevent maintaining temperature increase below 1.5 °C. To avoid this increase in the GWP, it is therefore necessary to implement decarbonization policies that promote recycling technologies instead of upcycling ones. However, there is a need for a systematic assessment of the roadmap of the technologies and timeline to achieve the required objectives posed by global treaties. To propose such a roadmap, deciding the technologies, location, transportation methods, and when to implement them, in this work, we propose using mathematical programming to formulate and solve this problem. The novelty of this work lies in integrating an optimization strategy with a decarbonization approach, which targets net-zero emissions by 2050.

2. Methodology

A multiperiod mixed-integer linear programming (MILP) model is developed to determine the decarbonization roadmap for the East Coast of the United States. The optimization reproduces the market dynamics to increase the profit extracted from plastic waste with the environmental policies introduced as constraints. More details of the framework are given in the subsequent subsections.

2.1. *Description of the proposed optimization framework.*

We consider a three-echelon supply chain as a graph network $\mathbb{G}(n, e)$. The supplier nodes are the county centers, facility nodes are the potential facility locations, and the consumer nodes are the refineries and the cities to take in the final products. The edges are transportation networks connecting the nodes; they transfer materials from one node to another. Each edge has two modes corresponding to electrical and conventional transportation. The network is structured such that at every time period t, commodity flows from node n to n', through a transportation mode m. The flow quantity $Q(k, n, n', m, t)$ captures commodity movement involving raw materials r and products p, with collection cost φ_n, for raw materials. Flows incur cost $\alpha(m)$ and emissions $\beta(m)$. Facilities transform commodities with yield $\gamma(k, k')$, operating cost $c(\tau)$, and emissions $e(\tau)$. Storage at facilities has cost $\hbar(k)$. The optimization goal is to determine facility location, technology type τ, and capacity ℓ, optimal commodity flows and inventory, and the required transportation modes.

2.1.1. Model Formulation

The set of equations for each node includes the continuity, flow, and conservation equations. Each supplier node represents a county, where the capacity is limited to the maximum amount of plastic generated in the county. At the potential facility nodes, decisions determine the selection of facility location, type, and capacity; these are implemented with a piecewise formulation, equations (1a) – (1g).

$$\sum_{\tau} y(n,\tau,\ell,t) \leq 1 \; \forall n \in F, \ell \in L, t \in T \tag{1a}$$

$$\sum_{\ell} y(n,\tau,\ell,t) \leq 1 \; \forall n \in F, \tau \in T, t \in \mathrm{T} \tag{1b}$$

$$\sum_{\tau,\ell} y(n,\tau,\ell,t) \leq 1 \; \forall n \in F, \tau \in T, t \in \mathrm{T} \tag{1c}$$

$$cL(\ell-1) \times y(n,\tau,\ell,t) \leq cap(n,\tau,\ell,t) \leq cL(\ell) \times y(n,\tau,\ell,t) \quad \forall n \in F, \tau \in T, \ell \in L, t \in \mathrm{T} \tag{1d}$$

$$\mathfrak{f}cap(n,\tau,t) = \sum_{\ell} cap(n,\tau,\ell,t) \; \forall n \in F, \tau \in T, t \in \mathrm{T} \tag{1e}$$

$$\sum_{\mathcal{k}} Q^{T}(k,\tau,n,t) \leq \mathfrak{f}cap(n,\tau,t) \; \forall n \in F, \tau \in T, t \in \mathrm{T} \tag{1f}$$

$$\sum_{k} Inv(k,n,t) \leq \mathfrak{I}nvcap(n,t) \times \sum_{\tau,\ell} y(n,\tau,\ell,t) \quad \forall n \in F, t \in \mathrm{T} \tag{1g}$$

Equations $(2a)$ – $(2d)$ computes the costs and emissions at each node and arc. Equations (2a) and (2b) compute node and transportation mode operating costs. Equations (2c) and (2d) calculate node and transportation mode emissions. The technology costs implemented have been reduced with linear and piecewise linear approaches from our previous work (O. Badejo et al., 2023).

$$\mathcal{n}cost(n,t) = \sum_{\tau,\ell} y(n,\tau,\ell,t) \times \mu(\tau,\ell) + \sum_{\mathcal{k},n',m} \varphi(n) \times Q(k,n,n',m,t) + \sum_{\tau} c(\tau) \times Q^{T}(\tau,k,n,t) + \sum_{\mathcal{k}} \mathcal{h}(k) \times Inv(k,n,t) \quad \forall n,t \tag{2a}$$

$$\mathcal{m}cost(m,t) = \sum_{n,n'} \mathfrak{f}c(m) \times ntrucks(n,n',m,t) + \sum_{\mathcal{k},n,n'} c(m) \times Q(k,n,n',m,t) \quad \forall m \in M, t \in T \tag{2b}$$

$$\mathcal{n}Emm(n,t) = \sum_{(k,\tau)} e(\tau) \times Q^{T}(k,\tau,n,t) \quad \forall n \in N, t \in T \tag{2c}$$

$$\mathcal{m}Emm(m,t) = \sum_{k,n,n'} \beta(m) \times Q(k,n,n',m,t) \quad \forall m,t \tag{2d}$$

Facilities and transportation fleet decarbonization investments are allowed in each period (Eqs. 3a–3d). Eq. (3a) calculates period investments, including technology and facility costs. Eqs. (3c)–(3d) compute the residual amount and include it in the next 'period' budget. Two objectives are considered: profit and total emissions.

$$Investment(t) = \sum_{n,\tau,\ell} y(n,\tau,\ell,t) \times \mu(\tau,\ell) + \sum_{n,n',m} \mathfrak{f}c(m) \times ntrucks(n,n',m,t) \; \forall t \in T \tag{3a}$$

$$Investment(t) \leq EffBudget(t) \; \forall t \in T \tag{3b}$$

$$Res(t) = EffBudget(t) - Investment(t) \; \forall t \in T \tag{3c}$$

$$EffBudget(t) = Budget(t) + Res(t-1) \; \forall t \in T \tag{3d}$$

The profit is shown in $(4a)$, and the emissions in $(4b)$.

$$profit = \sum_{\mathcal{k},n,n',m,t} \mathcal{pr}(p(k)) \times Q(p(k),n,n',m,t) - \sum_{n,t} \mathcal{n}cost(n,t) - \sum_{m,t} \mathcal{m}cost(m,t) \; \forall m,t \tag{4a}$$

$$\mathcal{E}mm(t) = \sum_{n} \mathcal{n}Emm(n,t) + \sum_{m} \mathcal{m}Emm(m,t) \; \forall t \in T \tag{4b}$$

To solve the multi-objective problem, we cast the problem to a single objective by implementing the environmental policy as a constraint. In this way, we achieve the environmental objective while maximizing the profit of the entire network. This is explained in the next section.

2.1.2. Implementation of CO_2 Policies as Constraints.

Decarbonization policies are integrated as constraints in the multiperiod optimization model. The first policy involves CO_2 taxes, penalizing plastic waste treatment based on the GWP of the management technology. The penalty term is added to the objective function Eq. (5a) as $\mathcal{C}^{tax}(t)$ representing penalties on emissions. Carbon tax policies are defined in the range of \$10/ton$_{CO2}$ to \$50/ton$_{CO2}$, with an extrapolation through the years given by the estimated increase in the gross domestic product per person.

$$Obj = profit - \sum_{t} \mathcal{C}^{tax}(t) \times \mathcal{E}mm(t) \quad (5a)$$

The second decarbonization policy adopts carbon cap policies, setting an annual emission limit that gradually decreases towards a final target at the last period. A new constraint, Eq. $5(b)$, is included to ensure annual emissions stay below the specified target. The carbon cap target is set as a reduction of 50% in the Global Warming Potential (GWP) for 2030 as defined in the Paris Agreement(Chamas et al., 2020; New UN' 'roadmap' shows how to drastically slash plastic pollution | UN News, 2023).

$$\mathcal{E}mm(t) \leq Target\mathcal{E}mm(t) \ \forall t \in T \quad (5b)$$

2.1.3. Case study

The MILP problem is applied to design the decarbonization roadmap for the plastic waste industry, evaluating three scenarios: (i) the first one considers no action on the system and aims to maximize the profit; (ii) the second case is using a carbon tax policy, and (iii) the third one considers a carbon cap policy with a constant reduction every year so the system can meet the 50% 'emissions' reduction by 2030.

3. Results

3.1 *Computational analysis*

The optimization models were solved using GAMS/CPLEX on a PC with an Intel Core i7-10510U, 2.30GHz, and 16GB RAM. The algorithm was set to terminate at 10% optimality gap or 1000 seconds.

3.2 *Economic and environmental results of the system.*

For the no-action case, the problem was solved to an 8% optimality gap, focusing on profit maximization and identifying 35 locations primarily employing pyrolysis and mechanical recycling. This approach, illustrated in Figure 1(a), processed 20 million metric tons of plastics annually, yielding a substantial \$80 million profit. The high GWP of 2.7 kg$_{CO2}$/kg$_{Plastic}$ reflected the reliance on conventional transportation modes over the 3-year investment period. Under the carbon tax scheme, Figure 1(b), the problem reached a 4% optimality gap, with penalties influencing technology distribution across 32 locations. Incorporating electric transportation modes and emphasizing pyrolysis in lubricant oil production contributed to a reduced \$62 million profit. The lower GWP of 1.8 kg$_{CO2}$/kg$_{Plastic}$ reflects the system's response to carbon taxes compared to the no-action case. In the context of the carbon cap scenario, Figure 1(c), the solution achieved a 7.5% optimality gap. Technologies such as pyrolysis, hydrocracking, and mechanical recycling were strategically distributed across 30 locations over a 5-year investment period, processing 21 million metric tons annually. The resulting profit of $39 million and a lower GWP of 1.3 $kg_{CO2}/kg_{Plastic}$ was due to further decarbonization and stringent temporal environmental limits.

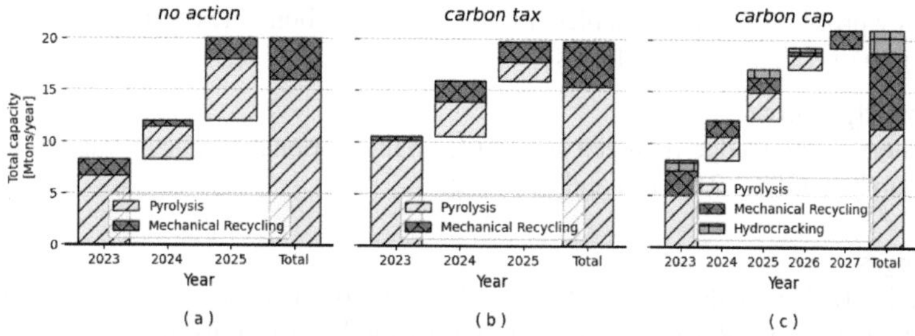

Fig 1: Temporal investment technologies; (a) no action; (b) carbon tax; (c) carbon cap

Comparing the operational outcomes, the results indicate that the carbon tax policy proves more profitable, while the carbon cap policy demonstrates greater potential for reducing carbon emissions. It is crucial to recognize that these policies operate from distinct perspectives: the carbon tax aims to incentivize stakeholders (consumers, manufacturers, and other actors) to minimize emissions and avoid penalties, making stakeholders the driving force behind emission reductions. Conversely, the carbon cap approach establishes emission goals, with stakeholders determining the cost of achieving those goals. This fundamental difference is evident at the operational level, as illustrated in Figure 2(a)-(c). Fig. (2a) demonstrates higher profits with a carbon tax scheme, albeit showing a temporal decline due to annual tax increases. In contrast, Fig. (2b) depicts the carbon cap's emission temporal decline, signaling effective emissions reduction through technology choices. Overall results (Fig 2c) indicate the carbon tax's profitability, while the carbon cap successfully achieves decarbonization agreements, reducing emissions to less than 70%.

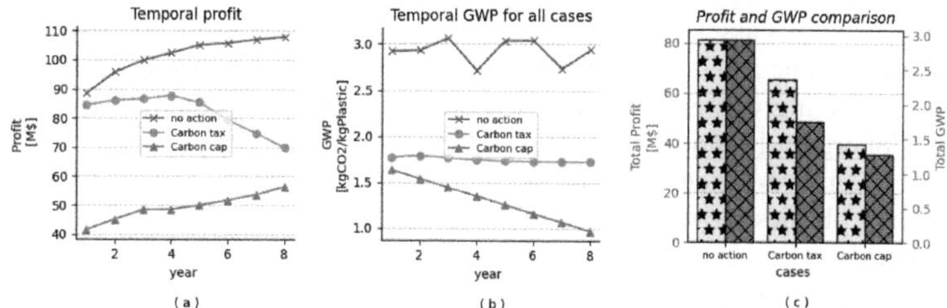

Fig 2: Operational results; (a) temporal profit profile; (b) temporal GHG profile; (c) overall profit and GHG

4. Conclusions

This work has presented a framework for designing the decarbonization roadmap for the plastic waste industry. The novelty lies in integrating an optimization strategy with a pragmatic decarbonization approach aligned with the Paris Agreement, targeting a 50% reduction in current emissions by 2030 and net-zero emissions by 2050. The framework is based on developing a multiperiod MILP optimization problem that is solved by employing two types of policies: carbon tax and carbon cap policies. The comparison of the two policies shows that the carbon cap is more effective in reducing emissions than carbon tax and it promotes the introduction of sustainable plastic waste management practices. The technologies included in this management are mechanical recycling, hydrocracking, and chemical recycling through pyrolysis. On the other hand, carbon tax policies are less effective in promoting sustainable technologies, with a significant fraction of plastic waste diverted to the upcycling of plastic waste to other chemicals through pyrolysis. Future work will integrate a carbon trading scheme to boost carbon cap policy profitability. This enables trading surplus carbon between technologies while adhering to overall carbon cap limits.

Acknowledgments
The authors acknowledge financial support from the National Science Foundation, award numbers OIA – 2119754 and 2217472.

References

O. Badejo, B. Hernandez, DG. Vlachos M. Ierapetritou. Design of supply chains for Managing Plastic Waste: A Case Study for Low Density Polyethylene. Available at SSRN 4516671 2023.

A. Chamas, H. Moon, J. Zheng, Y. Qiu, T. Tabassum, JH Jang et al. Degradation Rates of Plastics in the Environment. ACS Sustainable Chem Eng. 2020; 8: 3494-511. https://doi.org/10.1021/acssuschemeng.9b06635

O. Dogu, M. Pelucchi, R. Van de Viver, PHM Van Steenberge, DR D'Hooge, A. Cuoci et al. The chemistry of chemical recycling of solid plastic waste via pyrolysis and gasification: State-of-the-art, challenges, and future directions. Progress in Energy and Combustion Science 2021;84:100901. https://doi.org/10.1016/j.pecs.2020.100901.

E. Erickson, J. Ma P. Tominac, H. Aguirre-Villegas, V. Zavala. Evaluating the Economic and Environmental Benefits of Deploying a National-Scale, Thermo-Chemical Plastic Waste Upcycling Infrastructure in the United States 2023. https://doi.org/10.26434/chemrxiv-2023-96xng

B. Hernandez, P. Kots, E. Selvam, DG Vlachos, MG Ierapetritou. Techno-Economic and Life Cycle Analyses of Thermochemical Upcycling Technologies of Low-Density Polyethylene Waste. ACS Sustainable Chem Eng 2023;11:7170–81. https://doi.org/10.1021/acssuschemeng.3c00636.

M. Larrain, S. Van Passel, G. Thomassen, B. Van Gorp TT Nhu, S. Huysveld et al. Techno-economic assessment of mechanical recycling of challenging post-consumer plastic packaging waste. Resources, Conservation and Recycling 2021;170:105607. https://doi.org/10.1016/j.resconrec.2021.105607.

H. A. Li H. Aguirre-Villegas, R.D. Allen, X. Bai, C. Benson, G.T. Beckham, et al. Expanding plastics recycling technologies: chemical aspects, technology status and challenges. Green Chemistry 2022;24:8899–9002. https://doi.org/10.1039/D2GC02588D

New UN' 'roadmap' shows how to drastically slash plastic pollution | UN News. 2023. https://news.un.org/en/story/2023/05/1136702 (accessed May 26, 2023).

ECD. Global Plastics Outlook: Policy Scenarios to 2060. Paris: Organisation for Economic Co-operation and Development; 2022.

A.Somoza-Tornos A. Gonzalez-Garay, C. Pozo, M. Graells, A. Espuña, G. Guillén-Gosalbez, Realizing the Potential High Benefits of Circular Economy in the Chemical Industry: Ethylene Monomer Recovery via Polyethylene Pyrolysis. ACS Sustainable Chem Eng 2020;8:3561–72. https://doi.org/10.1021/acssuschemeng.9b04835.

TW. Walker, N. Frelka, Z. Shen, AK. Chew, J. Banick, S. Grey, et al. Recycling of multilayer plastic packaging materials by solvent-targeted recovery and precipitation. Science Advances 2020;6:eaba7599. https://doi.org/10.1126/sciadv.aba7599.

Flavio Manenti, Gintaras V. Reklaitis (Eds.), Proceedings of the 34th European Symposium on Computer Aided Process Engineering / 15th International Symposium on Process Systems Engineering (ESCAPE34/PSE24), June 2-6, 2024, Florence, Italy
 http://dx.doi.org/10.1016/B978-0-443-28824-1.50200-3

Optimal Loading of Porphyrin in Porphyrin@$Bi_{12}O_{17}Cl_2$ heterojunction: Application in Photocatalysis

Osemeikhian Ogbeifun [a*], Shepherd M. Tichapondwa[a], Evans M. N. Chirwa[a]

[a]*Water Utilization and Environmental Engineering Division, Department of Chemical Engineering, University of Pretoria, Pretoria, 0002, South Africa*
**osemeikhianosi@yahoo.com*

Abstract

The recombination of photogenerated electrons (e^-) and holes (h^+) and under-utilisation of the visible light spectrum (>420 nm) are significant challenges in photocatalysis involving $Bi_{12}O_{17}Cl_2$. In this study, the photocatalytic efficiency of $Bi_{12}O_{17}Cl_2$ was significantly enhanced in the fabrication of novel porphyrin@$Bi_{12}O_{17}Cl_2$ heterostructure photocatalyst. Aggregated porphyrins have emerged as photosensitisers in light-dependent applications like photocatalysis. The excellence of porphyrin is fully harnessed when combined with inorganic photocatalysts such as $Bi_{12}O_{17}Cl_2$ to form organic-inorganic junctions, thereby enhancing the visible light absorption, charge separation and transport in the material. Various amounts of aggregated rod-shaped 5,10,15, 20-Tetrakis (4-carboxyphenyl) porphyrin (0.02% wt., 0.1% wt., 0.4% wt., 1% wt. and 10% wt.) were coupled to $Bi_{12}O_{17}Cl_2$ and the optimum loading of porphyrin in terms of photocatalytic efficiency was determined for Porphyrin@$Bi_{12}O_{17}Cl_2$ heterostructure. The photocatalytic degradation efficiency of Porphyrin@$Bi_{12}O_{17}Cl_2$ was tested on Rhodamine B dye as a representative pollutant. The highest and lowest performances were reported for 1% wt. and 10% wt. of porphyrin loading in $Bi_{12}O_{17}Cl_2$, respectively, representing 3.1 and 0.5 times increases compared to pure $Bi_{12}O_{17}Cl_2$. The findings offer a new option for improving the photocatalytic performance of $Bi_{12}O_{17}Cl_2$ through photosensitisation and heterojunction strategies for use in numerous photocatalysis applications.

Keywords: $Bi_{12}O_{17}Cl_2$, aggregated porphyrin, photosensitisation, heterostructure, charge recombination, photogenerated

1. Introduction

$Bi_{12}O_{17}Cl_2$ is an attractive semiconductor photocatalyst with comparatively low bandgap energy, visible light or infrared activity (Chen *et al.*, 2013). With these properties, $Bi_{12}O_{17}Cl_2$ is a choice material for mitigating environmental contamination via photocatalytic degradation technology. However, a drawback to applying $Bi_{12}O_{17}Cl_2$ in photocatalytic technology is the quick recombination of photogenerated charge carriers (e^- and h^+) as fast as they are produced. (Passi and Pal, 2022). This phenomenon limits the capacity of the material to degrade target contaminants oxidatively (Zheng *et al.*, 2018). To enhance the photocatalytic degradation ability of $Bi_{12}O_{17}Cl_2$, various strategies have been employed, including heterojunction fabrication (Bi *et al.*, 2016), ion doping

(Yang *et al.*, 2022), plasmon resonance effect (Zhang *et al.*, 2017), solid solution (Zhang *et al.*, 2020) and photosensitization effect (Ye *et al.*, 2014).

The photosensitization strategy, which is the focus of this study, involves applying a photosensitizer such a porphyrin, to photocatalysts to increase visible light utilization. Porphyrin is a group of organic molecules made of four pyrrole rings that are linked with methine bridges to form a planer macrocyclic structure known as porphyrin ring (Araki *et al.*, 2013). Porphyrin strongly absorbs visible light, producing a photochemical reaction (Joseph and Haridas, 2020), that generates triplet (activated state) that can oxidize contaminants in the medium (Neves *et al.*, 2019). When porphyrin is irradiated, excited electrons move from highest occupied molecular orbital (HOMO) to the lowest unoccupied molecular orbital (LUMO) (Moshari *et al.*, 2016). The LUMO electrons are transferred and injected into the conduction band (CB) of the host material, bringing about the separation of holes and electrons, boosting photocatalytic performance (Zhang *et al.*, 2017).

In this study, self-assembled rod-shaped 5,10,15, 20-Tetrakis (4-carboxyphenyl) porphyrin was prepared and anchored to $Bi_{12}O_{17}Cl_2$. The photocatalytic activity of the surface modified- $Bi_{12}O_{17}Cl_2$ was evaluated by measuring the degradation of Rhodamine B under visible light. The optimum composition of porphyrin in the composite and their photocatalytic efficiency was determined.

2. Method

2.1. Synthesis of $Bi_{12}O_{17}Cl_2$

$Bi_{12}O_{17}Cl_2$ was synthesized by dissolving 4.84 g (0.01 mol) of Bi $(NO_3)_3{\cdot}5H_2O$ in 25 mL of acetic acid solution (acetic acid: H_2O 2:1 v/v) with stirring for complete dissolution. Next, 3.2 g (0.01 mol) of cetyltrimethylammonium chloride (CTAC) was dissolved in 25 mL of deionized water and added to the nitrate solution. The resulting solution was stirred for 30 min. The pH was then adjusted to 13 using a 10M NaOH solution. After an additional 30 min of stirring, the reaction mixture was subjected to microwave treatment (1000 W; 2450 Hz) for 10 min at atmospheric pressure. The resulting product was collected by centrifugation, washed several times with ethanol: water, and dried in an oven at 60 °C for 18 h.

2.2. Synthesis of aggregated porphyrin

In a typical synthesis, 0.04 g of porphyrin powder was dissolved in 0.5 mL of 0.2 M NaOH (referred to as the host solution). The “guest’ solution was prepared by dissolving 0.036 g of Cetyltrimethylammonium bromide (CTAB) in 10 mL of 0.01 M HCl. The guest solution was quickly injected into the host solution with vigorous stirring for 30 min in the dark. The resulting precipitate referred to as Porph was collected by centrifugation at 9,000 rpm for 10 min and washed with deionized water several times to remove the surfactant.

2.3. Synthesis of Poprhyrin@$Bi_{12}O_{17}Cl_2$

The preparation of $Bi_{12}O_{17}Cl_2$ containing 0.02% wt., 0.1% wt., 0.4% wt., 1% wt., and 10 % wt. porphyrin was carried out as follows: 0.2 g of as-synthesized BOC was added to 20 mL of methanol containing a certain amount of Porph (0.04 mg, 0.2 mg, 0.8 mg, 2 mg, and 20 mg). The mixture was sonicated for 5 min and then stirred at 60 °C in the dark to completely volatilize the methanol. The resulting materials were collected and washed with water to remove unattached porphyrin and were labelled as *x*%Porph@BOC (0.02%Porph@BOC, 0.1%Porph@BOC, 0.4%Porph@BOC, 1%Porph@ BOC and 10%Porph@BOC), where *x* represents the weight percentage of Porph in BOC.

Scheme 1. shows the synthesis of $Bi_{12}O_{17}Cl_2$, aggregated porphyrin and Poprhyrin@$Bi_{12}O_{17}Cl_2$ heterostructure.

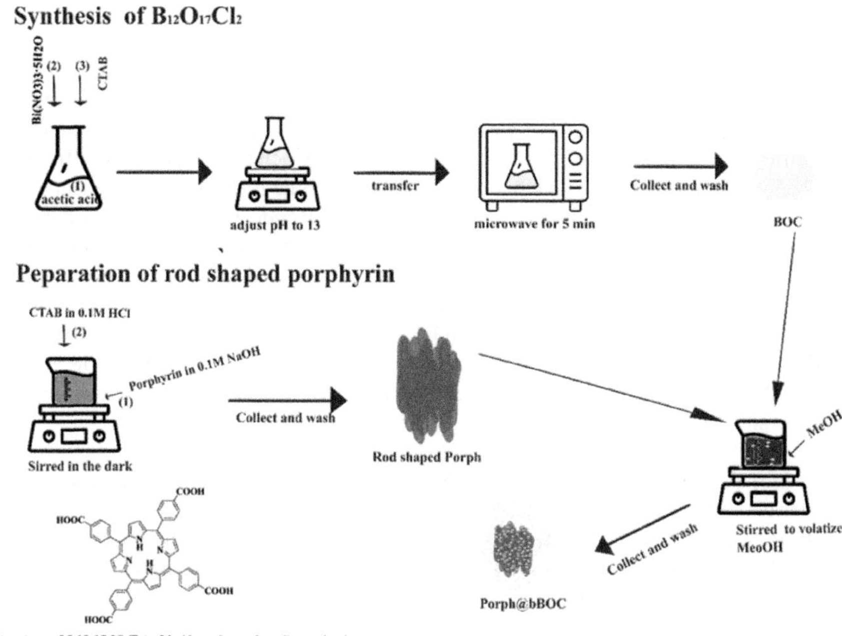

Scheme 1. Synthesis of aggregated porphyrin, $Bi_{12}O_{17}Cl_2$ and Porph@BOC. and structure of 5,10,15,20-Tetrakis (4- carboxyphenyl) porphyrin

3. Results and discussion

Degradation studies were conducted at room temperature (25°C) on Rhodamine B as a representative contaminant using the synthesised materials described from the preceding section. In doing that, 60 mL of 20 mg L^{-1} of Rhodamine B dye was placed in a 100 mL-beaker reactor, and 0.025g of photocatalyst material was added to the solution. The mixture was stirred in the dark for 3 h to achieve adsorption-desorption equilibrium. The solution was then irradiated for 4 h 30 min with visible light from six 16W fluorescent tubes (OSRAM, Germany) having a total intensity of 6300 lux. To monitor the degradation of Rhodamine B, 2 ml of aliquots were withdrawn at 0.5 h intervals. The photocatalyst particles were separated using a centrifuge and the absorbance of the remaining dyes solution were measured with a spectrophotometer at 553 nm absorbance. The concentration of Rhodamine B was calculated from the equation of the standard curve. Photolysis experiments were also performed in the absence of photocatalyst to differentiate photolysis from photocatalysis reaction. The percentage degradation was calculated from the following equation:

$$\frac{Co - Ct}{Co} \times 100\%$$

where C_0 and C_t are the initial concentration and concentration at time of Rhodamine B. From Fig. 2(a), after 120 min of irradiation of light, the degradation efficiency of Rhodamine B on BOC, Porph, 0.02%Porph@BOC, 0.1%Porph@BOC, 0.4%Porph@BOC, 1%Porph@BOC and 10%Porph@BOC were reported to be 31.1%, 16.5%, 41.8%, 52.4%, 60.9%, 71% and 23.6%, respectively. Among the modified materials, 1%Porph@BOC performed the best with an efficiency of 71% while, 10%Porph@BOC was the least performing material with an efficiency of 23.6% efficiency, which is less than that of BOC with an efficiency of 31.1%. At the end of the photocatalytic degradation experiment (4.5 h), 82.6% degradation efficiency was achieved on 1%Porph@BOC. It was also demonstrated that photolysis did not contribute significantly to the removal of Rhodamine B and only achieved a removal efficiency of 3.5% by light irradiation. The kinetics of Rhodamine B degradation was determined from the data obtained in the degradation study to be a pseudo-first-order kinetic equation. First-order kinetic $-\text{in } C/C_o = kt$ where C_0 and C are the initial and final concentrations of Rhodamine B, *k*, the rate constant, and *t*, the time, was used to fit the experimental data. The linear curve in Fig. 2(b) confirmed the pseudo-first kinetic. The R^2 values for 0.02%Porph@BOC, 0.1%Porph@BOC, 0.4%Porph@BOC, 1%Porph-@BOC, 10%Porph@BOC and BOC were found to be 0.9566, 0.97107, 0.97808, 0.99063, 0.97548, 0.94701, 0.97018, respectively. Overall, the degradation of Rhodamine B on 1%Porph@BOC was 3.1 times faster than on pristine BOC.

Fig. 2(c) shows a gradual increase in photocatalytic degradation of Rhodamine B on the materials in the following order: 0.02%Porph@BOC < 0.1%Porph@BOC < 0.4%Porph@BOC < 1%Porph@BOC. This shows that 1% wt. porphyrin-loaded material is the best-performing material. As observed from Fig. 2(c), there was a sharp decrease in the photocatalytic degradation at 10%Porph@BOC. The decrease in the photocatalytic activity of 10%Porph@BOC was caused by blockage of active sites on $Bi_{12}O_{17}Cl_2$ surface and low light penetration in the reaction solution at high porphyrin dose in 10%Porph@BOC.

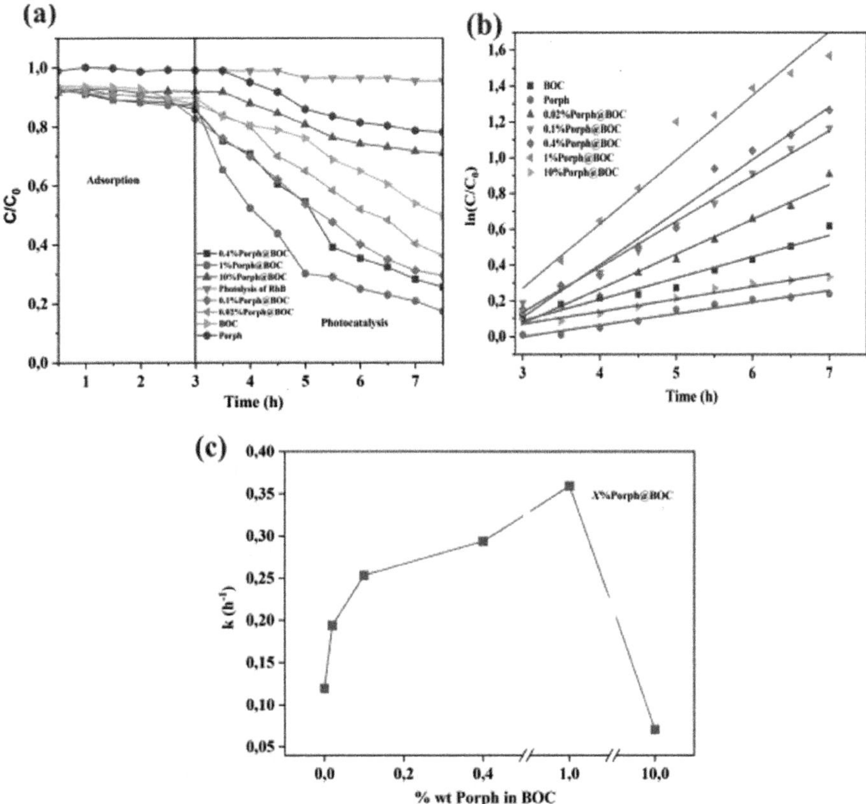

Fig. 2. (a) Photocatalytic degradation of Rhodamine B on *x*%Porph@BOC. **(b)** Rate constants of Photocatalytic degradation of Rhodamine B on *x*%Porph@BOC materials. **(c)** Percentage weight of aggregate porphyrin, x, in BOC versus kinetic rate constant, k, of degradation of Rhodamine B.

4. Conclusions

The photocatalytic efficiency of porphyrin@ $Bi_{12}O_{17}Cl_2$ heterostructure was tested at various porphyrin loading of 0.02%, 0.1%, 0.4%, 1%, and 10% w/w. The optimum porphyrin dose in the composite to achieve the highest degradation efficiency of Rhodamine B was determined as 1% w/w, which is 3.1 times higher than that of pure $Bi_{12}O_{17}Cl_2$. The enhanced performance was attributed to the synergy between the anchored porphyrin and $Bi_{12}O_{17}Cl_2$. However, at the highest dose of 10%w/w porphyrins, a deterioration of the photocatalytic activity was observed due to blockage of active sites on $Bi_{12}O_{17}Cl_2$ surface and low light penetration on the reaction solution. Two phenomena were found to be crucial to the photocatalytic activity of the composite: $Bi_{12}O_{17}Cl_2$ surface area and the photosensitisation effect of porphyrin. Therefore, it is essential to strike a balance between these effects to harness the synergy between porphyrin and $Bi_{12}O_{17}Cl_2$ in porphyrin@ $Bi_{12}O_{17}Cl_2$ composite to achieve optimum performance. The optimum activity achieved with 1% wt. porphyrin in porphyrin@ $Bi_{12}O_{17}Cl_2$ provided for adequate exposure of active sites on the surface of $Bi_{12}O_{17}Cl_2$ for the photodegradation of Rhodamine B, while still benefiting from porphyrin's photosensitisation effect.

References

Araki, K, Yang, D-H, Wang, T, Selyanchyn, R, Lee, S-W & Kunitake, T (2013) "Self-assembly and imprinting of macrocyclic molecules in layer-by-layered TiO2 ultrathin films" *Analytica Chimica Acta*, 779 72-81

Bi, C, Cao, J, Lin, H, Wang, Y & Chen, S (2016) "BiOI/Bi12O17Cl2: A novel heterojunction composite with outstanding photocatalytic and photoelectric performances" *Materials Letters*, 166 267-270

Chen, L, Huang, R, Xiong, M, Yuan, Q, He, J, Jia, J, Yao, M-Y, Luo, S-L, Au, C-T & Yin, S-F (2013) "Room-Temperature Synthesis of Flower-Like BiOX (X═Cl, Br, I) Hierarchical Structures and Their Visible-Light Photocatalytic Activity" *Inorganic Chemistry*, 52 (19), 11118-11125

Joseph, M & Haridas, S (2020) "Recent progresses in porphyrin assisted hydrogen evolution" *International Journal of Hydrogen Energy*, 45 (21), 11954-11975

Moshari, M, Rabbani, M & Rahimi, R (2016) "Synthesis of TCPP–Fe3O4@S/RGO and its application for purification of water" *Research on Chemical Intermediates*, 42 (6), 5441-5455

Neves, CMB, Filipe, OMS, Mota, N, Santos, SAO, Silvestre, AJD, Santos, EBH, Neves, MGPMS & Simões, MMQ (2019) "Photodegradation of metoprolol using a porphyrin as photosensitizer under homogeneous and heterogeneous conditions" *Journal of Hazardous materials*, 370 13-23

Passi, M & Pal, B (2022) "Recent advances on visible light active non-typical stoichiometric oxygen-rich Bi12O17Cl2 photocatalyst for environment pollution remediation" *Journal of Environmental Chemical Engineering*, 10 (3), 107688

Yang, Y, Zeng, Y, Jin, T, Zhang, X, Teng, H, Wang, S & Chen, H (2022) "Construction of oxygen vacancy on Bi12O17Cl2 nanosheets by heat-treatment in H2O vapor for photocatalytic NO oxidation" *Journal of Materials Science & Technology*, 123 234-242

Ye, L, Su, Y, Jin, X, Xie, H & Zhang, C (2014) "Recent advances in BiOX (X = Cl, Br and I) photocatalysts: synthesis, modification, facet effects and mechanisms" *Environmental Science: Nano*, 1 (2), 90-112

Zhang, M, Bi, C, Lin, H, Cao, J & Chen, S (2017) "Construction of novel Au/Bi12O17Cl2 composite with intensive visible light activity enhancement for contaminants removal" *Materials Letters*, 191 132-135

Zhang, Z, Liu, H, Xu, J & Zeng, H (2017) "CuTCPP/BiPO4 composite with enhanced visible light absorption and charge separation" *Journal of Photochemistry and Photobiology A: Chemistry*, 336 25-31

Zhang, Z, Zhao, Y, Shen, J, Pan, Z, Guo, Y, Wong, PK & Yu, H (2020) "Synthesis of 1D Bi12O17ClxBr2−x nanotube solid solutions with rich oxygen vacancies for highly efficient removal of organic pollutants under visible light" *Applied Catalysis B: Environmental*, 269 118774

Zheng, J, Chang, F, Jiao, M, Xu, Q, Deng, B & Hu, X (2018) "A visible-light-driven heterojuncted composite WO3/Bi12O17Cl2: Synthesis, characterization, and improved photocatalytic performance" *Journal of Colloid and Interface Science*, 510 20-31

Flavio Manenti, Gintaras V. Reklaitis (Eds.), Proceedings of the 34th European Symposium on Computer Aided Process Engineering / 15th International Symposium on Process Systems Engineering (ESCAPE34/PSE24), June 2-6, 2024, Florence, Italy
 http://dx.doi.org/10.1016/B978-0-443-28824-1.50201-5

Process intensification opportunity for reactive-extractive distillation: A new configuration for ternary azeotropic separation

Zong Yang Kong,[a] Yu-Ying Chen,[b] Juan Gabriel Segovia-Hernández,[c] Hao-Yeh Lee[b,*]

[a]*Department of Engineering, School of Engineering and Technology, Sunway University, Bandar Sunway 47500, Selangor, Malaysia*

[b]*National Taiwan University of Science and Technology, Department of Chemical Engineering, No.43, Keelung Rd., Sec.4, Da'an Dist., Taipei City 106335, Taiwan*

[c]*Universidad de Guanajuato, Campus Guanajuato, División de Ciencias Naturales y Exactas, Departamento de Ingeniería Química, Noria Alta s/n, 36050, Guanajuato, Gto, Mexico*

haoyehlee@mail.ntust.edu.tw

Abstract

A common problem in all intensified reactive-extractive distillation (RED) systems, like the dividing-wall double column RED (DW-DCRED), is the inability to provide energy savings, which sets it apart from conventional distillation systems. To address this limitation, we propose a new alternative configuration, i.e., an extractive-reactive distillation (ED-RD) by rearranging the column sequence in the original RED system. The ED-RD offers potential cost savings of up to 4 % and its corresponding intensified configuration, i.e., the dividing-wall ED-RD (DW-ED-RD), was able to provide significant energy and cost saving up to 21 and 26 %, respectively, in contrast to the limitations observed in conventional RED systems. This reflects the potential intensification opportunity of the proposed configuration for azeotropic separation.

Keywords: Reactive-extractive distillation, Ternary azeotropic mixture, Process Intensification, Energy-saving, Resource conservation

1. Introduction

The hybrid reactive-extractive distillation (RED) has garnered substantial attention as an innovative hybrid method, which combines chemical reaction and azeotropic separation into a single unit operation. Such method first appeared in 2020 in the form of a triple-column RED (TCRED) (Su et al., 2020), and soon afterward, a double-column RED (DCRED) was proposed in subsequent studies, streamlining the process from three columns (Wang et al., 2021). In comparison to the conventional extractive or pressure-swing distillation, the hybrid RED has been proven to provide significant improvement in the energy consumption and cost (i.e., total annual cost (TAC)) by at least half. Since the introduction of TCRED and DCRED, the field has witnessed a growing body of research. A comprehensive review of these RED studies can be found in literature for those interested (Kong et al., 2022b, 2022a). Moreover, some studies have explored the combination of RED with other process intensification (PI) techniques, such as dividing-wall (Liu et al., 2022) and side-stream (Yang et al., 2023), to maximize energy recovery. Nonetheless, a notable challenge present in all the existing intensified studies on RED is the absence of demonstrated energy savings in comparison to DCRED (Yang et al., 2023,

2022). This contrasts with intensified studies on conventional distillation, where significant reductions in energy consumption (e.g., up to 30 %) have been reported through intensified configurations that eliminate remixing effects. Remixing effect arises when the distillate product of the subsequent column reaches its peak purity in the prior column and then decreases. This signifies that the component is not collected at its maximum purity level, which necessitate extra energy to purify the component again. This clarifies why the remixing effect is commonly linked to increased energy consumption in the process. For example, Yang et al. (2022) worked on the dividing-wall DCRED (DW-DCRED) and demonstrated that despite the lower TAC and CO_2 emission achieved, these advantages were traded-off by increased energy consumption when compared to the DCRED. This paper endeavors to investigate an alternative configuration whose intensified counterpart holds potential for conserving energy. Just as TCRED and DCRED marked the initiation of RED studies, this work lays the foundation for more comprehensive research on its application in ternary azeotropic mixture separation.

2. Methodology

2.1. Process configuration for base case

Figure 1(a) shows the DCRED process reproduced from Zhang et al. (2021) for the separation of tetrahydrofuran (THF), ethanol (Eth), and water. It was selected as base case since it is one of the earliest works on RED. The first column is a reactive-extractive distillation column (REDC) where the fresh feed enters at 100 kmol h^{-1}. The water reacts with the externally injected ethylene oxide (EO), resulting in the formation of ethylene glycol (EG) according to **Eq. (1)**. The produced EG is subsequently used as solvent for the azeotropic separation in the same column. Note that the quantity of the externally injected EO is equivalent to that of water to facilitate complete water removal. In addition to the produced EG, extra EG is introduced into the REDC to ensure an adequate supply of solvent for the azeotropic separation. The distillate from the REDC is expected to achieve a THF purity of 99.6 mol%. The remaining mixture (Eth + EG) proceeds to the solvent regeneration column (SRC), where Eth of 99.6 mol% is obtained as the distillate, and EG of 99.92 mol% is recovered as the bottom product. The regenerated EG is cooled before recycled back to the REDC and any surplus solvent is purged from the system.

$$EO + Water \rightarrow EG$$

$$r_1\left(\frac{mol}{s * cm^3}\right) = 3.15 \times 10^9 exp\left(\frac{-9547}{T}\right) x_{water} x_{EO} \quad (1)$$

Figure 1(b) shows the DW-DCRED modified from the base case (**Figure 1(a)**). In the DW-DCRED, the initial SRC containing 10 stages is integrated with the REDC, forming the upper section of the DW-DCRED. This results in an increase in the number of stages for the SRC from 10 to 60 and the elimination of the reboiler at the bottom of the SRC. This integration approach aligns with similar methodologies applied in prior research (Wu et al., 2013) and the objective is to identify potential energy consumption savings directly from the TAC. The removal of the original SRC reboiler due to integration necessitates the introduction of a vapor-liquid interconnection flowrate between the left and right side of the column (separated by the dividing wall). This leads to a portion of water and EO originally in the left side of the column to escape to the right side before a complete reaction according to **Eq. (1)** occurs, which significantly impacts product purity. To rectify this issue, it is necessary to effectively distribute the reaction throughout the entire DW-DCRED. Such an approach has not been explored in previous studies on intensified RED. From **Figure 1(b)**, the total reboiler energy consumption of the DW-

DCRED amounts to 1120 kW, marking a 6 % increase compared to the base case. Such observation is consistent with prior research, which suggests that intensified DCRED typically do not yield energy savings (Yan et al., 2022; Yang et al., 2022), even after it has been optimized.

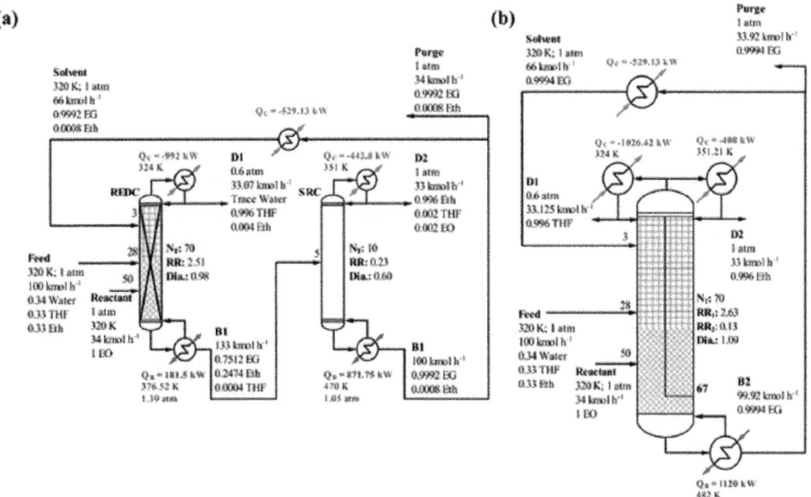

Figure 1. The separation of THF, Eth, and water using **(a)** DCRED reproduced from Zhang et al. (2021) and **(b)** the intensified DW-DCRED.

2.2. Process simulation and evaluation

The simulations were carried out using Aspen Plus V12.1. The fresh feed flowrate, composition, and thermodynamic package were maintained at the same value as the base case, allowing for a fair and consistent comparison. Here, note that the DCRED from previous work was not subjected to optimization and the study relied on a "Rule of Thumb" approach to determine the total stages of distillation columns. This approach was designed to ensure that the number of stages was equivalent to or fewer than those in their reference base cases, thus facilitating fair economic performance comparisons. In this study, we follow a similar methodology because our objective is to introduce an alternative conceptual design. The rest of the design parameters (i.e., feed stage location) are manipulated individually to attain the minimum energy consumption. Note that our new configuration already exhibits a lower TAC than the previous DCRED, even before process optimization (further detailed results will be provided in **Section 3.1**). The performance of the newly proposed process is evaluated using both the total reboiler energy consumption and economic indicators (TAC). The TAC is calculated using **Eq. (2)**, following the approach of Douglas (1988)'s textbook.

$$\text{TAC} = \frac{\text{Total capital cost (TCC)}}{\text{Payback period (3 years)}} + \text{Total operating cost (TOC)} \tag{2}$$

3. Results and discussion

3.1. Proposed hybrid extractive-reactive configuration

Figure 2 shows the proposed ED-RD, featuring an inversion in the ED and RD sequence compared to the DCRED (**Figure 1(a)**). The first column serves as an extractive distillation column (EDC) where fresh feed, accompanied by the EG solvent, is introduced into the EDC, yielding a high-purity THF distillate. The residual mixture proceeds to the second column, acting as a reactive distillation column (RDC) for further separation. In the RDC, the water undergoes hydration reaction with externally added EO (**Eq. (1)**). This reaction effectively eradicates the azeotrope, ensuring that all the water is completely converted. Eth is collected as the distillate while the generated EG retrieved from the bottom is conveniently cooled and recycled back to the EDC, mirroring the base case procedure. The TAC of the ED-RD is approximately \$0.52 million per year, signifying a notable 4 % decrease in TAC in contrast to the DCRED. This reduction primarily stems from a 22 % decrease in the TCC due to the utilization of fewer stages in the proposed setup. The TOC for the ED-RD is only marginally higher than the base case, even though there is a 22 % increase in energy consumption within the ED-RD configuration. This is predominantly attributed to the primary use of cost-efficient low-pressure (LP) steam in the EDC, as opposed to the base case, which heavily relies on pricier high-pressure (HP) steam in the SRC. Also, the second column in the DCRED required nearly five times more energy than the first column while in the ED-RD, this energy difference is less pronounced due to the absence of simultaneous reaction and azeotropic separation. Note that the ED-RD already demonstrates a lower TAC even before process optimization, emphasizing its superiority over the previous DCRED. Consequently, optimization of the process will likely amplify the advantages of this innovative configuration (Giuliano et al., 2015).

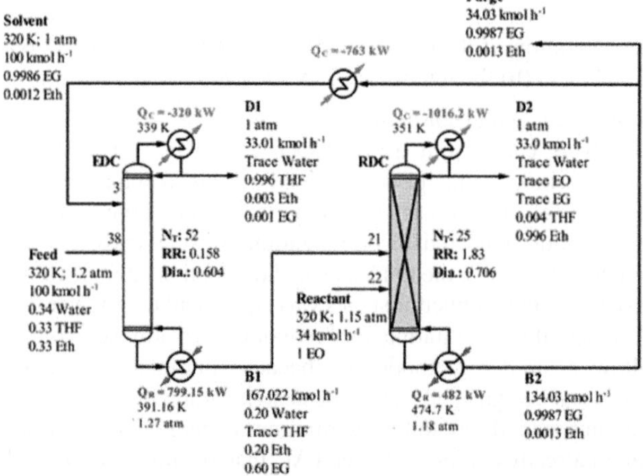

Figure 2. The proposed ED-RD configuration for the ternary azeotropic separation of THF, Eth, and water.

3.2. Dividing-wall double column extractive-reactive configuration

Figure 3 illustrates the intensified dividing-wall double column extractive-reactive distillation (DW-ED-RD), with a TAC of approximately \$0.40 million per year, marking a significant 23 % reduction compared to the proposed ED-RD. This reduction primarily results from the decrease in energy consumption of about 35 %. Such tremendous decrease in energy consumption was attributed to the exceptional ability of DW-ED-RD to eliminate the remixing effect, which sets it apart from the TC-DCRED, where remixing is not eliminated (**Figure 4**). Also, both in DW-ED-RD and DW-DCRED systems, the reaction zone is distributed throughout the column for the complete reaction of **Eq. (1)**. However, what makes the DW-ED-RD even more intriguing is that having the reaction zone throughout the column enhances EO hydration more than in DW-DCRED, as reflected by the higher product purities achieved (99.9 mol%), surpassing the specified requirement of 99.6 mol%. We consider this an acceptable outcome, given that it attains a higher product quality with a lower energy consumption and a lower TAC.

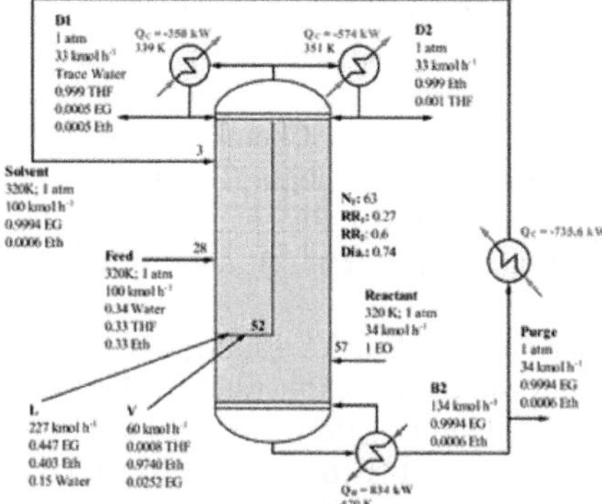

Figure 3. The intensified DW-ED-RD configuration for the ternary azeotropic separation of THF, Eth, and water.

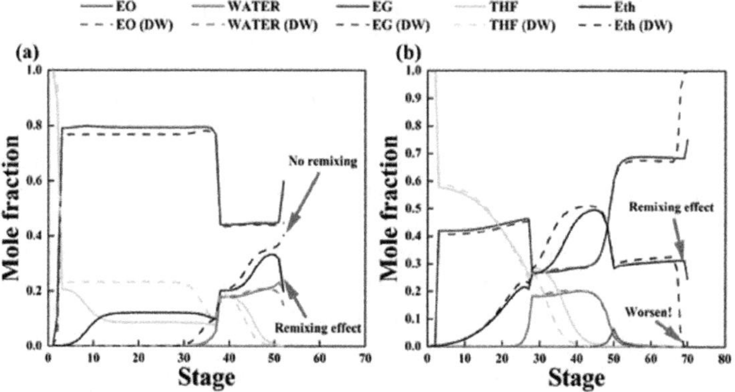

Figure 4. The composition profile of **(a)** newly proposed ED-RD/DW-ED-RD and **(b)** DCRED/DW-DCRED.

4. Conclusion

This research introduces an innovative configuration for RED by altering the column sequence, resulting in an ED-RD configuration. The primary aim is to explore potential PI opportunities, addressing the existing challenge of achieving energy savings in intensified RED processes. The ED-RD configuration proposed in this work provides a 4 % reduction in the TAC compared to the traditional DCRED. Moreover, the intensified DW-ED-RD configuration outperforms the ED-RD configuration by achieving a remarkable 23 % reduction in TAC. Overall, the DW-ED-RD configuration demonstrates an impressive 21 % reduction in total reboiler energy consumption and a 26 % decrease in TAC compared to the base case. This reflects its potential for substantial energy and cost savings through PI, presenting a viable alternative to the conventional DCRED.

5. References

Douglas, J.M., 1988. Conceptual design of chemical processes. McGraw-Hill.

Giuliano, A., Poletto, M., Barletta, D., 2015. Process design of a multi-product lignocellulosic biorefinery, in: 12th International Symposium on Process Systems Engineering and 25th European Symposium on Computer Aided Process Engineering. Elsevier, Copenhagen, pp. 1313–1318.

Kong, Z.Y., Sánchez-Ramírez, E., Yang, A., Shen, W., Segovia-Hernández, J.G., Sunarso, J., 2022a. Process intensification from conventional to advanced distillations: Past, present, and future. Chemical Engineering Research and Design 188, 378–392. https://doi.org/https://doi.org/10.1016/j.cherd.2022.09.056

Kong, Z.Y., Sunarso, J., Yang, A., 2022b. Recent progress on hybrid reactive-extractive distillation for azeotropic separation: A short review. Frontiers in Chemical Engineering 4.

Liu, J., Yan, J., Liu, W., Kong, J., Wu, Y., Li, X., Sun, L., 2022. Design and multi-objective optimization of reactive-extractive dividing wall column with organic Rankine cycles considering safety. Sep Purif Technol 287, 120512. https://doi.org/https://doi.org/10.1016/j.seppur.2022.120512

Su, Y., Yang, A., Jin, S., Shen, W., Cui, P., Ren, J., 2020. Investigation on ternary system tetrahydrofuran/ethanol/water with three azeotropes separation via the combination of reactive and extractive distillation. J Clean Prod 273, 123145. https://doi.org/https://doi.org/10.1016/j.jclepro.2020.123145

Wang, C., Zhuang, Y., Liu, L., Zhang, L., Du, J., 2021. Design and comparison of energy-saving double column and triple column reactive-extractive hybrid distillation processes for ternary multi-azeotrope dehydration. Sep Purif Technol 259. https://doi.org/10.1016/j.seppur.2020.118211

Wu, Y.C., Hsu, P.H.C., Chien, I.L., 2013. Critical assessment of the energy-saving potential of an extractive dividing-wall column. Ind Eng Chem Res 52, 5384–5399. https://doi.org/10.1021/ie3035898

Yan, J., Liu, J., Ren, J., Wu, Y., Li, X., Sun, T., Sun, L., 2022. Design and multi-objective optimization of hybrid reactive-extractive distillation process for separating wastewater containing benzene and isopropanol. Sep Purif Technol 290, 120915. https://doi.org/https://doi.org/10.1016/j.seppur.2022.120915

Yang, A., Kong, Z.Y., Sunarso, J., 2023. Design and optimisation of novel hybrid side-stream reactive-extractive distillation for recovery of isopropyl alcohol and ethyl acetate from wastewater. Chemical Engineering Journal 451, 138563. https://doi.org/https://doi.org/10.1016/j.cej.2022.138563

Yang, A., Su, Y., Sun, S., Shen, W., Bai, M., Ren, J., 2022. Towards sustainable separation of the ternary azeotropic mixture based on the intensified reactive-extractive distillation configurations and multi-objective particle swarm optimization. J Clean Prod 332. https://doi.org/10.1016/j.jclepro.2021.130116

Zhang, Y.R., Wu, T.W., Chien, I.L., 2021. Intensified hybrid reactive-extractive distillation process for the separation of water-containing ternary mixtures. Sep Purif Technol 279. https://doi.org/10.1016/j.seppur.2021.119712

Flavio Manenti, Gintaras V. Reklaitis (Eds.), Proceedings of the 34th European Symposium on Computer Aided Process Engineering / 15th International Symposium on Process Systems Engineering (ESCAPE34/PSE24), June 2-6, 2024, Florence, Italy
 http://dx.doi.org/10.1016/B978-0-443-28824-1.50202-7

An Intensified-Integrated Supercritical Extraction-Vacuum Distillation-Reactive Distillation Process to produce Phytosterols, Glycerol and Ultra-Clean Biodiesel from Crude Vegetable Oils

Eduardo S. Pérez-Cisneros[a]* , Verónica Rodríguez-López[b] , Ricardo Morales-Rodriguez[c] , Edgar I. Murillo-Andrade[a]

[a]*Universidad Autónoma Metropolitana – Iztapalapa, Departamento de Ingeniería de Procesos e Hidráulica, San Rafael Atlixco No. 186, Colonia Vicentina, Delegación Iztapalapa, 09340 Ciudad de México, México*

[b]*Universidad Autónoma del Estado de Morelos, Facultad de Farmacia, Av. Universidad 1001 Chamilpa, Cuernavaca, Morelos, México*

[c]*Departamento de Ingeniería Química, Universidad de Guanajuato, Noria Alta s/n, 36050, Guanajuato, Gto., México*

espc@xanum.uam.mx

Abstract

A novel intensified-integrated supercritical extraction (ScE)-vacuum distillation (VcD)-reactive distillation (RD) process to produce phytosterols (β-sitosterol and stigmasterol), glycerol and ultra-clean biodiesel from crude vegetable oils has been developed. The integrated process consists of two main sections: i) a supercritical extraction - vacuum distillation section, whereby using CO_2 and a CO_2-CH_3OH mixture as supercritical fluids, the separation of triglycerides from phytosterols, phyto-glucoside compounds and fatty acids (FFA) is carried out. Further, the separation of phytosterols, phyto-glucoside compounds and the FFA by VcD is performed; ii) a second section where a RD column is used to perform the triglycerides transesterification reactions to produce ultra-clean biodiesel and glycerol. The effect of several operating conditions on the different process sections has been analysed. It was found that the operating pressure and the feed ratio of CO_2/CH_3OH mixture fed to the ScE column were the key variables to modify the phytosterols concentration produced in the first section. The methanol to triglyceride flow ratio in the RD section determines the complete conversion to produce a high-quality ultra-clean biodiesel.

Keywords: intensified-integrated process, phytosterols production, reactive distillation.

1. Introduction

Vegetable oils contain compounds in minor amounts that affect their quality and nutritional value, for example, phytosterols, tocopherols, waxes are some of the minor composition components in vegetable oils. Phytosterols are plant sterols that have structural and biological functions like cholesterol. They have been shown to have protective properties against various chronic diseases such as cardiovascular, hepatoprotective, diabetes and cancer. Regarding cancer prevention, it has been claimed that a diet rich in phytosterols can reduce the risk of cancer by 20% (Ju *et al*, 2004). Despite these health beneficial characteristics of phytosterols in the vegetable oils, these oils have been used to produce biofuels. Sterol glucosides (SGs) occur naturally in vegetable oils and fats in the acylated form. During the biodiesel conversion process, they are converted to nonacylated SGs. It has been found the presence of SGs in biodiesel, and it has been determined that these SGs contribute to flowability problems in biodiesel and biodiesel blends (Lee *et al*, 2007). Due to the high melting point of SGs and its insolubility in biodiesel or diesel fuel, SGs can essentially be considered "dispersed fine solid particles" in biodiesel. These dispersed SG particles may also promote the crystallization of other compounds. Therefore, a process to eliminate SGs in the production of biodiesel fuel and at the same time to produce the high health value phytosterols should be considered. The objective of the present work is to develop an intensified-integrated supercritical extraction (ScE)-vacuum distillation (VcD)-reactive distillation (RD) process to produce phytosterols (β-sitosterol and stigmasterol), glycerol and ultra-clean biodiesel from crude vegetable oils. Since CO_2 is one of the most popular species to perform the extraction of valuable compounds from vegetable oils, the developed process in this work could be integrated with a CO_2 capture process (Sofia et al., 2015) with environmental improvement.

2. Methodology

In order to develop the integrated-instensified process two aspects are considered: i) determination of the required thermodynamic properties and ii) the integration of the different sections of the process.

2.1. Thermodynamic properties prediction of the complex mixture

To perform the simulation of the intensified-integrated process, a crude vegetable oil (Palm oil) with the following composition has been considered: triolein (0.488172 % wt.), tripalmitin (0.465289), oleic acid (0.044125), β-sitosterol (0.0004), stigmasterol (0.0001), α-tocopherol (0.001), β-carotene (0.0005), acylated β-sitosterol glucoside (0.00036), β-sitosterol glucoside (0.000055). Thus, the thermodynamic properties of the above mixture are required. Due to the lack of information about the thermodynamic properties of sterols and SGs compounds, it is necessary to use a group contribution method to calculate such properties. Figure 1(a) shows the generalized phytosterols molecule, where it can be observed that the radical (R) make the difference between cholesterol, β-sitosterol and stigmasterol. Figure 1 (b) shows the β-sitosterol glucoside molecule, where it is important to note the presence of OH and CH_2OH radicals and oxygen bonds. With this molecule´s information, the thermodynamic properties were calculated using the computational tool ProPred (Constantinou and Gani, 1994). Due to space restriction, Table 1 only shows some of the predicted thermodynamic properties of β-sitosterol, stigmasterol and β-sitosterol glucoside. It should be noted that the values of the thermodynamic properties of sterols and β-sitosterol glucoside are quite different.

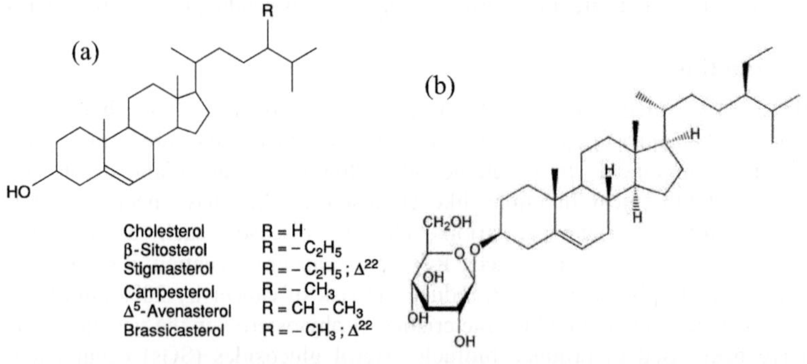

Figure 1. (a) Generalized phytosterol molecules and (b) β-sitosterol glucoside molecule

Table 1. Calculated thermodynamic properties using ProPred

Parameter	Units	β-Sitosterol	Stigmasterol	β-Sitosterol-Glucoside
MW		414.715	412.7	576.858
w		1.05429	1.0631	0.0913968
Tb	K	778.05	778.05	1456.81
Pc	atm	11.054	11.23	8.14
Tc	K	953.05	953.65	1977.11

2.2. The intensified-integrated ScE-VcD-RD process

Figure 2 shows the optimal ScE-Vc flowsheet section obtained after intensive simulation to produce pure triglycerides at the bottom of the super critical extraction column and the separation of the phyto-sterols from the FFA at the vacuum distillation column. It was found that 30 equilibrium stages for the super critical extraction column and 10 stages for the vacuum distillation at P= 0.05 atm were required. To obtain the optimal ScE-Vc flowsheet section it was necessary to vary, first, the operating pressure of the ScE column from 5 to 40 atm and, monitoring the amount of triglyceride at the top of the column and secondly, the amount of CO_2/methanol ratio (from 0 to 10) fed to the SCE column was adjusted, observing the purity of the triglycerides at the bottom of the column. Also, for the Vc distillation column the operating pressure was modified (from 1 to 0.02 atm) and the purity of the FFA at the top of the column was checked. It should be pointed out that PURGE1, PURGE 2 and SEP equipments can be considered as specific membranes to separate the residual CO_2 streams.

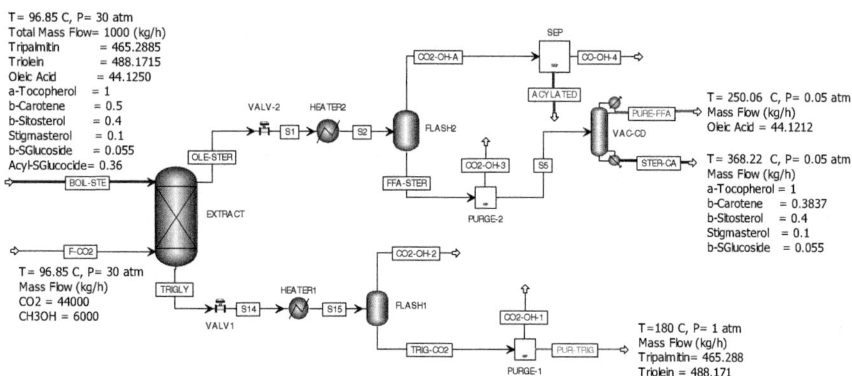

Figure 2. Optimal ScE-Vc flowsheet section obtained after intensive simulation. Stream PUR-TRIG is cooled to 70 C and sent to the second section.

Figure 3 shows the optimal RD section after intensive simulation to produce ultra-clean biodiesel and glycerol. In order to obtain the optimal RD flowsheet section, it was necessary to vary the number and location of the reactive stages monitoring the triglyceride conversion and the biodiesel purity. For the CD-GLYCE conventional column the number of stages was adjusted observing the purity of glycerol produced. It should be mentioned that 20 equilibrium stages for the RD column at P= 1 atm (reactive stages from 4 to 18) were needed to achieve a full conversion of the triglyceride mixture to biodiesel.

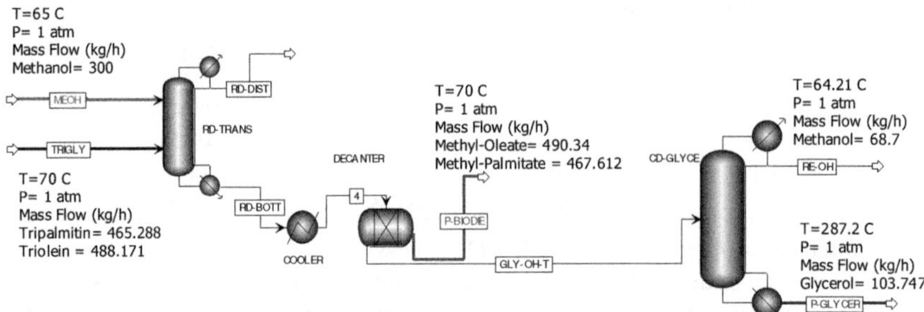

Figure 3. Optimal RD flowsheet section obtained after intensive simulation.

3. Results and discussion

The final simulation results for each optimal flowsheet sections were obtained by using Aspen-Plus V 10.0 with the RK-Aspen Equation of State for super critical extraction and vacuum distillation and NRTL-RKS model for the reactive distillation process.

3.1. ScE-Vc section: Production of pure triglycerides and phyto-sterols

Table 2 shows the simulation results for the ScE-VcD section to produce pure triglycerides and the separation of phytosterols from FFA. It can be noted from Table 2 that the stream PUR-TRIG only contain triolein and tripalmitin. Also, from Table 2 it can be noted that streams PURE-FFA and STER-CA contain only oleic acid at 250 C and sterols, part of carotene and the non-acylated glucoside at 368 C, respectively. Figure 4 shows the liquid composition profile for the VcD column and it can be observed that at the top of the column the oleic acid composition is 1 (pure) and at the bottom a mixture of sterols, carotene and non-acylated glucoside are obtained.

Table 2. Simulation results of the integrated-intensified ScE-VcD section. Calculations were performed using RK-Aspen Equation of State

				Material				
Steam Name	**Units**	**BOIL-STE**	**F-CO2**	**OLE-STER**	**TRIGLY**	**PUR-TRIG**	**PURE-FFA**	**STER-CA**
From				EXTRACT	EXTRACT	PURGE-1	VAC-CD	VAC-CD
To		EXTRACT	EXTRACT	VALV-2	VALV1			
Stream Class		CONVEN	CONVEN	CONVEN	CONVEN	CONVEN	CONVEN	CONVEN
Phase		Liquid Phase	Vapor Phase	Liquid Phase	Liquid Phase	Liquid Phase	Liquid Phase	Liquid Phase
Temperature	C	96.85	96.85	96.7451	96.85	180	250.074	368.218
Pressure	atm	30	30	30	30	1	0.05	0.05
Molar Vapor Fraction		0	1	0	0	0	0	0
Average MW		775.878	42.1219	42.149	156.9	845.526	282.467	446.843
Mass Flows	kg/h	1000	50000	49751	1249.01	953.46	44.1212	1.93867
Mass Fractions								
B-SITOST		0.0004	0	8.04E-06	1.41E-129	0	8.38E-20	0.206327
OLEIC-AC		0.044125	0	0.000886917	1.18E-115	0	1	2.28E-05
STIGMSTE		0.0001	0	2.01E-06	7.87E-132	0	1.53E-20	0.0515819
TRIPALMI		0.465289	0	5.63E-10	0.372527	0.488	0	0
TRIOLEIN		0.488172	0	1.78E-13	0.390848	0.512	0	0
CO2		0	0.88	0.878742	0.225549	0	0	0
B-SG		5.50E-05	0	1.11E-06	6.02E-10	0	3.52E-47	0.0283676
ACYL-SG		0.00036	0	7.24E-06	1.79E-69	0	0	0
A-TOCOPH		0.001	0	2.01E-05	4.26E-127	0	2.70E-20	0.5158190
B-CAROTE		0.0005	0	1.00E-05	9.85E-09	0	9.25E-12	0.197882
CH3OH		0	0.12	0.120323	0.0110759	0	0	0

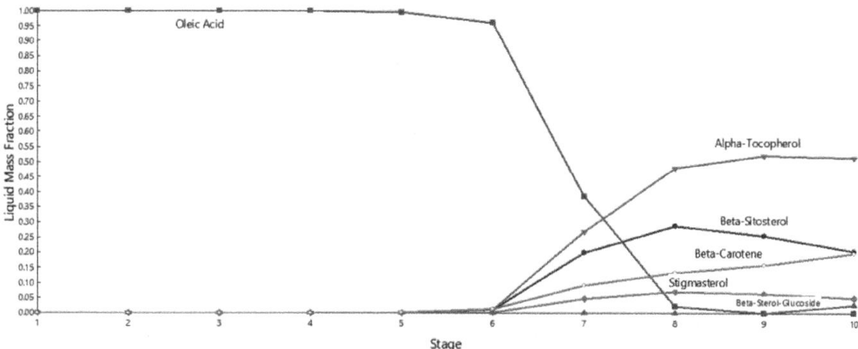

Figure 4. Liquid composition profile of the vacuum distillation column

3.2. RD section: Production of ultra-clean biodiesel and glycerol

For the RD section, the reaction kinetics for the conversion of triglycerides to biodiesel were taken from Dosin et al. (2006). Table 3 shows that the bottom stream RD-BOTT is concentrated (mass fraction) in biodiesel (methyl oleate and methyl palmitate) with little amounts of methanol and glycerol at 115 C, while at the top of the RD column pure methanol is obtained and it can be recycled to the ScE column in the first section. After cooling and decanting the RD-BOTT stream pure biodiesel is produced and the residual glycerol and methanol are separated in a conventional distillation column.

Figure 5a shows the liquid composition profile (mass fraction logarithmic plot) of the RD column. It can be noted that at the top of the column pure methanol is obtained and at the bottom of the RD column a mixture of methyl oleate, methyl palmitate, glycerol and methanol is obtained.

Table 3. Simulation results of the RD section. Calculations were performed using NRTL-RKS model.

				Material				
Steam Name	**Units**	**MEOH**	**TRIGLY**	**RD-BOTT**	**RD-DIST**	**P-BIODIE**	**P-GLYCER**	**RE-OH**
From				RD-TRANS	RD-TRANS	DECANTER	CD-GLYCE	CD-GLYCE
To		RD-TRANS	RD-TRANS	COOLER				
Stream Class		CONVEN	CONVEN	CONVEN	CONVEN	CONVEN	CONVEN	CONVEN
Phase		Liquid Phase	Liquid Phase	Liquid Phase	Liquid Phase	Liquid Phase	Liquid Phase	Liquid Phase
Temperature	C	65	70	115.632	64.2006	70	287.205	64.2122
Pressure	atm	1.3	1	1	1	1	1	1
Average MW		32.0422	845.526	163.745	32.0422	283.186	92.0947	32.0697
Mass Flows	kg/h	300	953.459	1140.5	112.955	958.005	103.747	78.7521
Mass Fractions								
TRIOLEIN		0	0.512	0	1.15E-35	0	0	0
METHANOL		1	0	0.0689592	1	0	4.08E-08	0.998681
GRYCEROL		0	0	0.0910568	2.24E-32	0	1	0.00131886
METHY-OL		0	0	0.42998	3.85E-36	0.51189	0	0
TRIPA-01		0	0.488	6.73E-20	1.05E-35	0	0	0
METHY-PA		0	0	0.410004	3.21E-29	0.48811	0	0

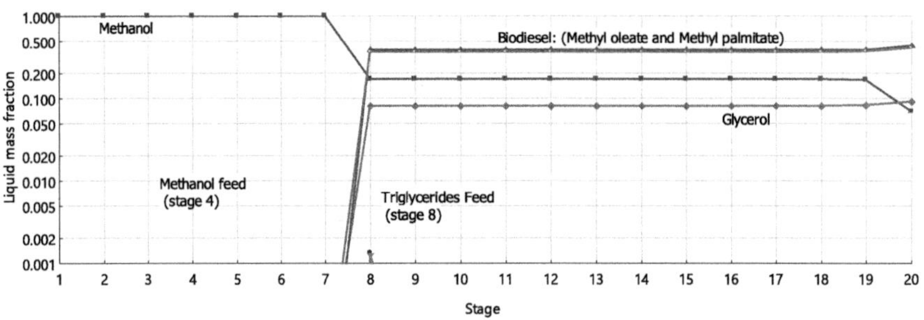

Figure 5a. Liquid composition profile for the reactive distillation column.

4. Conclusions

A novel intensified-integrated ScE-VcD-RD process to produce phytosterols (β-sitosterol and stigmasterol), glycerol and ultra-clean biodiesel from crude vegetable oils has been developed. A CO_2-CH_3OH mixture was used as supercritical fluid for the separation of triglycerides from phytosterols, phyto-glucoside compounds and fatty acids (FFA). It was found that for 1000 Kg/h of vegetable oil fed To the ScE Column an amount of 50 times of the supercritical fluid mixture was required to fully separate the triglycerides in a 30 equlibrium stages ScE column at 30 atm. Further, the separation of phytosterols, SGs compounds and FFA by a 10 equilibrium VcD colum is performed at 0.05 atm. It should observed that part of the β-carotene is eliminated in the ACYLATED stream. In the RD column second section the triglycerides transesterification reactions to produce ultra-clean biodiesel and glycerol using a 20 equilibrium stages RD column. Such 20 equilibrium stages with 15 reactive stages were needed to fully convert the triglycerides present in the vegetable oil. It should br pointrd out that the Sc fluid mixture CO_2-CH_3OH can be recycled from the FLASH1 and FLASH2 in the ScE-VcD section and methanol can be recycled to the RD column in the Rd section. Future work is planned to consider the economical and energy evaluation of the integrated-intesified process and also, to incorporate a section of CO2 capture for environmental improvement.

References

Leonidas Constantinou and Rafiqul Gani, 1994, New group contribution method for estimating properties of pure compounds, AIChE Journal, Vol. 40, 1697-1710.

TF Dossin, M.F. Reyniers, RG Berger, GB Marin. Simulation of heterogeneously MgO-catalyzed transesterification for fine-chemical and biodiesel industrial production. Appl Catal B: Environ 2006;67:136–48.

Young H. Ju, Laura M. Clausen, Kimberly F. Allred, Anthony L. Almada, and William G. Helferich, 2004, β-Sitosterol, β-Sitosterol Glucoside, and a Mixture of β-Sitosterol and β-Sitosterol Glucoside Modulate the Growth of Estrogen-Responsive Breast Cancer Cells In Vitro and in Ovariectomized Athymic Mice, Nutrition and Cancer, 1145-1151.

Inmok Lee, Lisa M. Pfalzgraf, George B. Poppe, Erica Powers and Troy Haines, 2007, The Role of Sterol Glucosides on Filter Plugging, Biodiesel Magazine, April 6, 1-4.

D. Sofia, A. Guliano, M. Poletto, D. Barletta, 2015, Techno-Economic Analysis of Power and Hydrogen Co-Production by an IGCC Plant with CO2 Capture Based on Membrane Technology, Computer Aided Chemical Engineering, Vol. 37, 1373-1387.

Flavio Manenti, Gintaras V. Reklaitis (Eds.), Proceedings of the 34th European Symposium on Computer Aided Process Engineering / 15th International Symposium on Process Systems Engineering (ESCAPE34/PSE24), June 2-6, 2024, Florence, Italy
 http://dx.doi.org/10.1016/B978-0-443-28824-1.50203-9

Techno-economic evaluation of novel dual-function reactor for direct air capture applying superstructure optimisation

Meshkat Dolat[a], Melis S. Duyar[a,b], Michael Short[a,b*]

[a] *School of Chemistry and Chemical Engineering, University of Surrey, Guildford, Surrey GU2 7XH, United Kingdom.*

[b] *Institute for Sustainability, University of Surrey, Guildford, Surrey GU2 7XH, United Kingdom*

m.short@surrey.ac.uk

Abstract

This study introduces Dual Function Materials (DFM) technology within the context of direct air capture (DAC) and incorporates it into a superstructure optimisation framework for optimal flowsheet development. A comparative assessment against an established DAC process, temperature vacuum swing adsorption (TVSA), underscores the potential operational and economic advantages of DFMs. The application of superstructure optimisation reveals critical determinants, including the reactor geometry, mass and heat transfer parameters, and the equilibrium CO_2 capacity of the sorbent-catalyst, as crucial for evaluating the feasibility of DFMs in relation to TVSA. Apart from hydrogen production, the operational cost is significantly impacted by the pressure drop in the adsorption section, with reactor/contactor size and quantity primarily constrained by pressure drop rather than adsorption rates.

Keywords: Superstructure optimisation, Direct air capture, CO_2 utilisation, Techno-economic analysis, Dual function material.

1. Introduction

Direct air capturing (DAC) as a potential solution to the majority of non-location specific greenhouse gas emitters faces unique techno-economic challenges, mainly handling extremely low CO_2 concentrations. In response, there are different technologies available, among which temperature vacuum swing adsorption (TVSA) has found to be the most energy efficient capturing solution, which is backed by substantial research literature, and has been steadily gaining momentum in commercial implementation (Sabatino et al., 2021). Numerous studies emphasize the environmental risks and uncertainties of storing CO_2 (Faruque Hasan et al., 2022), prompting a shift toward exploring carbon utilisation. One sustainable approach involves catalytic conversion of captured CO_2 into products like synthetic natural gas using green hydrogen known as power-to-gas (PtG).

In this context, Dual Function Material (DFM) technology has emerged as a promising solution. In this novel approach proposed by Duyar et al. (2015) CO_2 selectively adsorbs on an alkaline or alkaline earth element acting as sorbent and undergoes in-situ hydrogenation assisted by a noble metal without requiring energy-intensive intermediate CO_2 sequestration processes. The continuous operation occurs consecutively in four parallel trains of reactors due to the 4-staged process: in one stage CO_2 is contacted with the DFM until saturation occurs. In the second stage, the reactor is purged with an inert gas and consequently, hydrogen is injected, leading to the release and transport of the chemisorbed CO_2 to the neighbour metal site where the methanation process occurs. The process is re-commenced after purging the reactor.

To systematically evaluate the operability and techno-economic potential of the DFM technology and understand its behavior within a broader context encompassing crucial technologies upstream and downstream, a comparative framework is necessary.

Superstructure optimisation employs mathematical models and optimisation algorithms, to systematically identify the most suitable process flowsheets based on a defined set of objective functions (Bertran et al., 2017). Superstructure optimisation serves as an effective approach to explore and determine the optimal process route when various process layouts or technology options are available for a specific product synthesis, or there is a need of "selection" among a various range of feedstocks and/or range of prospect products. While superstructure optimisation studies have been dominant in sub-systems (Chen & Grossmann, 2017), there are very few studies applying superstructure optimisation approach in the synthesis of PtX processes covering the utilisation of CO_2. Uebbing et al. (2020) employed a superstructure optimisation approach to investigate the methanation of CO_2 obtained from a biogas plant. Kenkel et al. (2021) have developed an open-source python-based tool, to model superstructures with the optimisation performed using Pyomo. In their case study, they investigate methanol synthesis from CO_2 hydrogenation under various hydrogen production and carbon capture scenarios. Up to now, no prior research has undertaken an evaluation of the techno-economic aspects of various DAC technologies within the superstructure framework. Furthermore, the DFM process has not been considered as a potential option for CO_2 capture and utilisation in any optimisation study so far. This study aims to systematically compare the performance of the DFM process versus the TVSA technology taking into account the pivotal downstream and upstream process layers leveraging the superstructure optimisation framework.

2. Methodology

The superstructure and building block process units are modelled in Pyomo, as an open-source Python-based platform for further integration into future studies and taking the benefit of utilisation of other relevant packages and models from prior works. Also, the whole superstructure and unit models are formulated as a mixed-integer nonlinear program (MINLP), with the objective function set to minimise the total annual cost of the project. The formulations follow a generic format. According to Figure 1(a) in the unit model, $x_{k,c}$ (kmol/s) represent the molar flow of component c in stream k. Each stream k encompasses lumped properties (Θ) such as pressure (p) and temperature (T) as well as individual properties of each component c (such as specific heat, molecular weight, etc.). In the superstructure representation Figure 1(b), where there are several operation units available in a process layer U_{layer} (bounded between two nodes), the selection will be made by the means of binary variables y_u which ensure that the inlet and outlet streams of the chosen unit match the inlet and outlet streams of the adjacent nodes.

$$x_{k,c} = \sum_{u \in U_{layer}} \sum_{c \in C} x_{outlet\ u,c}\, y_u \tag{1}$$

$$\Theta_k = \sum_{u \in U_{layer}} \Theta_{outlet\ u}\, y_u \tag{2}$$

$$\sum_{u \in U_{layer}} y_u = 1 \tag{3}$$

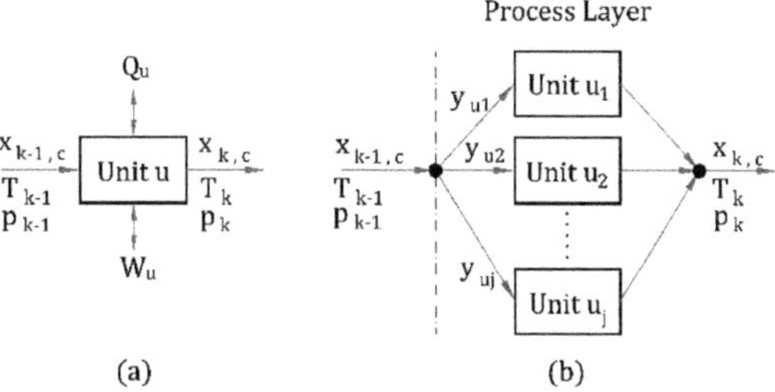

Figure 1: (a) Schematic of a process unit model consisting of inlet-outlet material stream with heat-power demand/output. (b) Schematic superstructure representation of units in a process layer.

The link between the inlet and outlet material and energy streams of a unit is achieved through the mathematical model of the unit which performs the mass and energy balance related to that specific unit and also calculates the operational and capital cost pertained to the mass and energy flow inside the system.

To ensure a standardised approach to equipment cost evaluation, a general costing procedure for equipment has been adopted, based on procedure proposed by Towler & Sinnott (2021). The technology (or equipment) capacity (or size) is determined by the model and the pertinent costing parameters are derived from the relevant tables in the reference. The minimum and maximum equipment size in the cost estimation table serves as a constraint during the optimisation process. This constraint balances the choice between scaling up the size and increasing the number of equipment units.

3. Case study

According Figure 2, the case study includes a superstructure encompassing the DFM and TVSA as two main CO_2 capturing and utilisation route along with the integration of various fans, hydrogen production and steam generation technologies. Centrifugal Backward Curved Fan (CBCF), Centrifugal Straight Radial Fan (CBSRF) and Vane Axial Fan (VAF) are the options available for the air-intake technologies. Alkaline (AEL), proton exchange membrane (PEMEL), and high-temperature solid oxide (SOEL) electrolyzers are the H_2 production options. Depending on the outlet H_2 temperature and the hydrogenation step requirements in either the Sabatier reactor or the DFM reaction stage, a furnace may be required. There are also options available to select the desired level of steam generation (low, medium, high pressure saturated steam). The TVSA route includes four different types of solid sorbents named as APDES-NFC, Tri-PE-MCM 41, MIL-101(Cr) PEI-800 and Lewatit VP OC 106 with isotherm and physical parameters reported by Sabatino et al. (2021).

A base case model is prepared to accommodate a capturing rate of 10,000 tonnes CO_2 per year, aligned with the recent industrial capacity benchmarks in this field. Bbase case model is realised by initialising the model degrees of freedom, which include both continuous and binary variables, with arbitrary yet feasible values. For the base case, 20 CBCFs are considered as the selected fans and AEL (with furnace) is considered as the hydrogen production unit. TVSA with 8,874 kg APDES-NFC sorbents is the initial capturing route, with the Sabatier reactor as the compulsory downstream reaction option. In each of the 4-trained processes, there are 15 contactors each with 2m diameter and 3m length (9.42 m^3 size). Finally, heat integration through high pressure steam generation is considered. The resultant pressure drop in the columns is 3,712 Pa leading to a

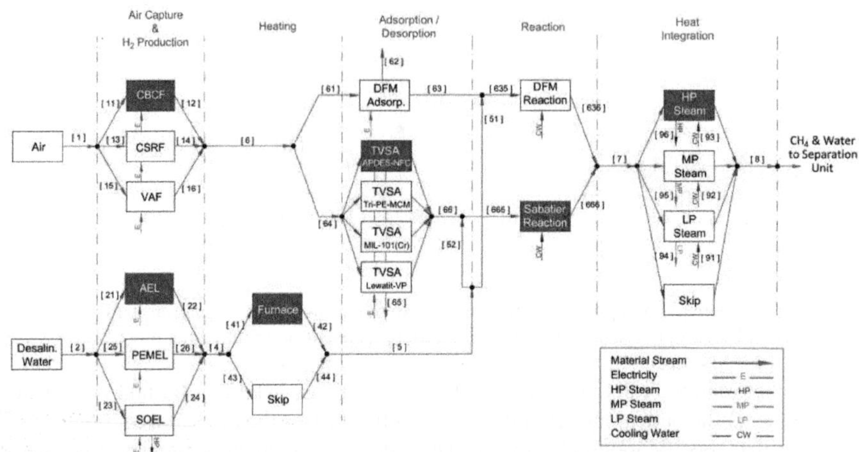

Figure 2: Superstructure presentation of DAC integrating TVSA/Sabatier reaction vs DFM technology routes. The base case units are highlighted.

requirement of 2,984 kW fan power. The resultant operational and capital costs of the process are reported in Table 1.

4. Results and discussions

The superstructure model was solved using the BARON solver accessible through integrating GAMS as an external solver. The result of the superstructure optimisation is shown in Figure 3 with economic metrics listed in Table 1. According to the results, the VAF and SOEL are selected as air-intake and hydrogen production units respectively. The DFM technology is selected as the optimal route for CO_2 adsorption and hydrogenation and the steam generation through LP-steam is found as the best heat integration scenario for exploiting the reactor's products thermal energy. Also, as the hydrogen is supplied through the high temperature SOEL, the furnace was not selected.
The optimised flowsheet halves the TAC of the plant compared to the base case. This substantial decrease is primarily attributed to the significant 55% decrease in the operational cost. The decrease in OPEX is primarily due to the transition from AEL to SOEL, despite the higher purchase cost of the SOEL technology. The noticeable 61% increase in CAPEX has minimal impact on this positive trend which is expected due to the fact that such processes are energy intensive rather than being highly affected by capital investments. Also, due to the fixed production rate (26 $kmol_{CH4}$ /h) the only change in revenue (slight 0.32 % increase) is attributed to earnings from the low-pressure steam generation level.
The transition from 20 CBCF units to 3 VAF units in the fan technology had a profound impact on the process economy, leading to a significant reduction of nearly 84% in electrical consumption (466 kW) and 60% reduction in total capital expenditure of air-intake unit. This transformation was closely related to the improvement in the pressure drop in the downstream reactors of the DFM unit, which stands at 580 Pa, well below the 2500 Pa threshold of the VAF. This improvement enabled the utilisation of VAF as suitable options for low-pressure air-intake.
To accommodate this change, the diameter of the reactors increased from 2m to 4m while decreasing their length from 3m to 1m, working within the defined optimisation bounds. These adjustments were crucial, as they significantly impacted the pressure drop.

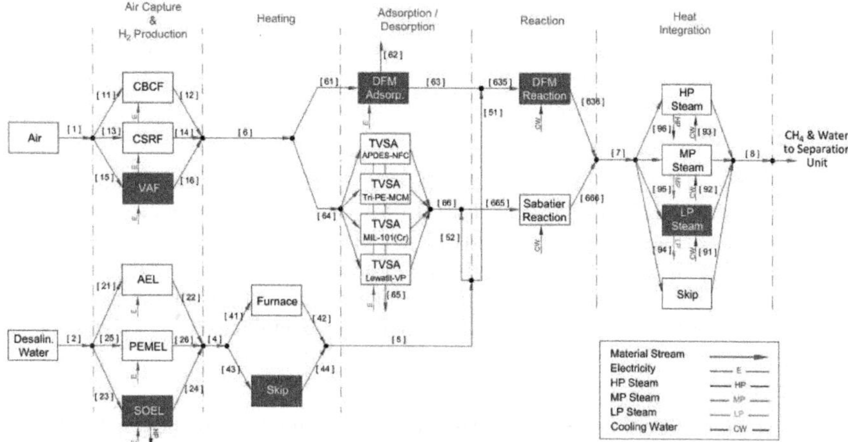

Figure 3: The optimised flowsheet showcasing the selected units leading to minimum TAC.

Notably, the number of sections decreased from 15 to 8 units. Below this threshold, the pressure drop and fans' operational costs increased. Conversely, exceeding this level leads to a considerable rise in purchased equipment costs, which, when multiplied by 4 to account for all four trains, affects the overall process economy.

The current DFM process assumes isothermal adsorption capacity at elevated temperatures (350°C), resulting in a significantly lower equilibrium capacity compared to amine-functionalised sorbents or MOFs in the TVSA route, by about an order of magnitude. This leads to a requirement of 16,244 kg of catalysts (twice as much as required for solid sorbents in TVSA). Despite this substantial difference and a non-industrialized cost of approximately \$272/kg for a DFM catalyst, nearly 18 times higher than reported for solid sorbents like MIL-101 (Sinha et al., 2017), DFMs demonstrate cost superiority. This is attributed to the fact that the size and number of reactors are mainly dictated by pressure drop limitations rather than adsorption rates. Additionally, the heat-intensive TVSA process imposes a high operational cost on the plant economy, a cost that can be mitigated by the DFM process with negligible external heat demand.

The selected adsorption columns have the potential to accommodate additional sorbent loadings and increase adsorption rates, as the chosen reactor size (12.6 m^3 reactors) exceeds the necessary catalyst containment volume by about 2.5 m^3. This results in an extra total volume of 80 m^3 for the entire 4 trains, indicating significant potential for elevating CO_2 concentration through scenarios such as integrating point source capturing. It's noteworthy that the optimised DFM route is closely followed by the optimum TVSA route (in terms of minimised TAC), indicating room for further improvement in operational performance.

Table 1: Economic metrics of the base-case and the optimised case

Description	Variable	Base-Case	Optimised
Total annual cost	*TAC (\$)*	32,632,516	16,016,557
Total annualise capital cost	*CAPEX (\$)*	2,056,203	3,308,706
Total operating cost	*OPEX (\$)*	32,444,606	14,582,117
Total revenue	*Revenue (\$)*	1,868,293	1,874,266

The DFM process will undergo further study in the non-isothermal mode, automatically increasing its CO_2 capacity rate, reducing catalyst weight, and associated capital costs. Furthermore, ongoing material enhancements aim to further augment CO_2 uptake.

5. Conclusions

Despite its lower CO_2 capacity and a more expensive catalyst, DFM is shown to being a more cost-effective DAC technology than TVSA (3,260 $\$/t_{CO2}$ per year) indicating a promising future for development. This is potentially achievable through enhancing uptake capacity via low-temperature adsorption and material design. Additionally, the research highlights the crucial impact of reactor geometry on air-intake performance, subsequently affecting fan energy consumption and the overall cost of DAC projects.

References

Bertran, M. O., Frauzem, R., Sanchez-Arcilla, A. S., Zhang, L., Woodley, J. M., & Gani, R. (2017). A generic methodology for processing route synthesis and design based on superstructure optimization. *Computers & Chemical Engineering*, *106*, 892–910. https://doi.org/10.1016/J.COMPCHEMENG.2017.01.030

Chen, Q., & Grossmann, I. E. (2017). Recent Developments and Challenges in Optimization-Based Process Synthesis. *Https://Doi.Org/10.1146/Annurev-Chembioeng-080615-033546*, *8*, 249–283. https://doi.org/10.1146/ANNUREV-CHEMBIOENG-080615-033546

Duyar, M. S., Treviño, M. A. A., & Farrauto, R. J. (2015). Dual function materials for CO2 capture and conversion using renewable H2. *Applied Catalysis B: Environmental*, *168–169*, 370–376. https://doi.org/10.1016/J.APCATB.2014.12.025

Faruque Hasan, M. M., Zantye, M. S., & Kazi, M.-K. (2022). *Challenges and opportunities in carbon capture, utilization and storage: A process systems engineering perspective*. https://doi.org/10.1016/j.compchemeng.2022.107925

Kenkel, P., Wassermann, T., Rose, C., & Zondervan, E. (2021). A generic superstructure modeling and optimization framework on the example of bi-criteria Power-to-Methanol process design. *Computers & Chemical Engineering*, *150*, 107327. https://doi.org/https://doi.org/10.1016/j.compchemeng.2021.107327

Sabatino, F., Grimm, A., Gallucci, F., van Sint Annaland, M., Kramer, G. J., & Gazzani, M. (2021). A comparative energy and costs assessment and optimization for direct air capture technologies. *Joule*, *5*(8), 2047–2076. https://doi.org/10.1016/J.JOULE.2021.05.023

Sinha, A., Darunte, L. A., Jones, C. W., Realff, M. J., & Kawajiri, Y. (2017). Systems Design and Economic Analysis of Direct Air Capture of CO2 through Temperature Vacuum Swing Adsorption Using MIL-101(Cr)-PEI-800 and mmen-Mg2(dobpdc) MOF Adsorbents. *Industrial & Engineering Chemistry Research*, *56*(3), 750–764. https://doi.org/10.1021/acs.iecr.6b03887

Towler, G., & Sinnott, R. (2021). Chemical Engineering Design: Principles, Practice and Economics of Plant and Process Design. *Chemical Engineering Design: Principles, Practice and Economics of Plant and Process Design*, 1–1027. https://doi.org/10.1016/B978-0-12-821179-3.01001-3

Uebbing, J., Rihko-Struckmann, L., Sager, S., & Sundmacher, K. (2020). CO2 methanation process synthesis by superstructure optimization. *Journal of CO2 Utilization*, *40*, 101228. https://doi.org/https://doi.org/10.1016/j.jcou.2020.101228

Flavio Manenti, Gintaras V. Reklaitis (Eds.), Proceedings of the 34th European Symposium on Computer Aided Process Engineering / 15th International Symposium on Process Systems Engineering (ESCAPE34/PSE24), June 2-6, 2024, Florence, Italy
 http://dx.doi.org/10.1016/B978-0-443-28824-1.50204-0

Synthesis of heat-integrated distillation sequences considering vapor recompression under the constraint of fossil energy consumption

Fangjun Ye [a], Yiqing Luo [a,b,c,*], Shengkun Jia [a,b], Xigang Yuan [a,b,c]

[a] *School of Chemical Engineering and Technology, Tianjin 300350, China*

[b] *Chemical Engineering Research Center, Tianjin 300350, China*

[c] *State Key Laboratory of Chemical Engineering, Tianjin 300350, China*

luoyq@tju.edu.cn

Abstract

Distillation has been the most widely used separation technology in chemical and petrochemical industries. Typically, they only use energy as separating agent which are mainly provided by fossil fuel combustion with high carbon emissions. Therefore, it is of great significant to study an efficient distillation sequence synthesis method that considers the use of low-carbon green electricity to completely or partially replace traditional fossil energy. In this study, a method of synthesizing heat-integrated distillation sequences using electricity via the vapor recompression (E-HIDSs) under fossil energy constraints is proposed based on stochastic optimization. By introducing heat pumps driven by electricity during the optimal synthesis, the opportunity of heat integration among columns is greatly increased, thereby minimizing fossil energy consumption in reboilers. The example case of separating five-component alkane mixture shows that the proposed method in this study can obtain the corresponding optimal solution under the constraint of fossil energy consumption at different levels.

Keywords: fossil energy constraint, vapor recompression, heat integration, distillation sequence synthesis, stochastic optimization

1. Introduction

It's widely recognized that the use of fossil energy is the main cause of the greenhouse effect. Fossil fuel combustion accounts for more than 75% of greenhouse gas emissions and nearly 90% of CO_2 emissions (United Nations, 2023). Distillation is a very common separation process in the chemical industry. However，it has low thermodynamic efficiency and its main source of energy comes from the burning of fossil fuels (Sholl et al, 2016). Hence, both the amount and intensity of carbon emissions generated by distillation are at high levels. It has been shown that distillation sequence synthesis is an effective means to achieve distillation system optimization. Researchers often take the economic index represented by the total annual cost (TAC) as the objective function, represent different distillation configurations by matrix method (Shah et al, 2010), super structure (Caballero et al, 2001), binary tree-based method (Zhang et al; 2018, 2021), and use deterministic algorithm or stochastic optimization algorithm to solve the synthesis problem. In this research area, the search domain of the distillation sequences continues to expand progressively. On the one hand, it has evolved from considering only sharp separation in the early stages (An et al, 2009), then to allowing partial intermediate components to exist in non-sharp separation (Wang et al, 2016), and finally to realizing expression of all intermediate components in non-sharp separation (Aggarwal et al, 1990; Shah et al, 2010; Zhang et al, 2021). On the other hand, more and more efficient energy-saving technologies have been considered in the distillation sequence synthesis, such as heat integration (An et al, 2009), thermal coupling (Amminudin et al, 2001), intermediate heat exchangers (An et al, 2008), and heat pumps (Yuan et al, 2021). With the increasing pressure on carbon emissions in the chemical industry, researchers must carefully consider the limits of fossil energy consumption in distillation sequences synthesis. An effective strategy is to continuously apply green electricity derived from renewable sources such as solar energy, wind energy, and biomass energy to effectively substitute for traditional fossil fuels in the distillation sequence synthesis.

The simultaneous consideration of vapor recompression and heat integration is one of effective approaches to reduce distillation column energy consumption, that is, by consuming a small amount of electricity, the total energy consumption is greatly reduced through heat integration. As shown in Figure 1, the vapor from the column top is compressed by a compressor, then the vapor with higher temperature and pressure exchanges heat with the liquid in the reboiler at the bottom of the column. After the heat exchange, the vapor is cooled down and depressurized by a throttle valve, and finally is partially withdrawn as a product or refluxed into the column. This technology, often referred to as a heat pump, is commonly used in distillation system with a single column (Felbab et al, 2013) or known column sequence structures (Wang et al, 2020). In a distillation sequence, there are more opportunities for heat integration due to the presence of more reboilers and more top vapors existing in the sequence. Nevertheless, simultaneous optimization distillation sequence with non-sharp separation, heat integration structure, heat pump setting, as well as operation parameters such as column pressure which is the most critical parameter affecting compressor setting and heat integration, is not a trivial work. It's necessary to effectively deal with the very difficult problems of superstructure expression, model formulation and optimization of multi-component separation system. Therefore, to realize the optimal design of distillation system by vapor recompression-based heat integration, this study proposes a stochastic optimization-based method for E-HIDSs under the constraint of fossil energy consumption to confine or even eliminate the usage of traditional fossil fuel.

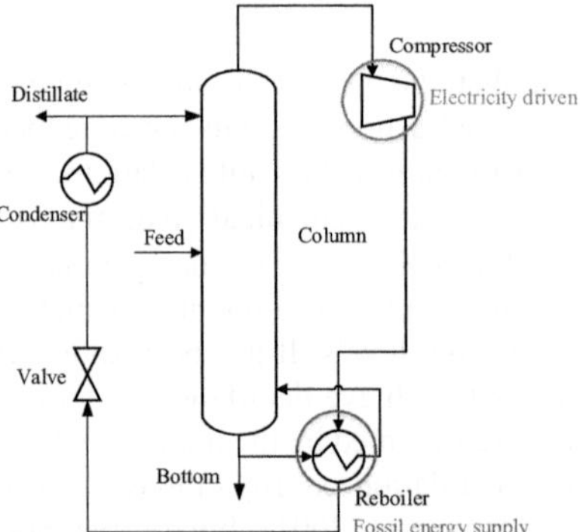

Fig. 1 Heat pump structure in a single column

2. Problem formulation

2.1. Problem description

Given a non-azeotrope mixture of N components (N≥3), the objective is to synthesize an optimal sharp or non-sharp E-HIDS to obtain N pure components with the minimum TAC under the constraint of fossil energy consumption. To reasonably decrease search space complexity, only basic distillation configurations with N-1 columns are considered in the synthesis (Giridhar et al, 2010). Additional assumptions and specifications for the problem are as follows:

(1) Compressors are driven by green electricity.

(2) Hot utilities needed are all generated from the combustion of fossil energy.

(3) Cooling water as cold utility doesn't consume fossil energy or electricity.

(4) The prices of refrigerants are determined by the amount of electricity used to produce them.

(5) The minimum temperature approach for hear integration is set to 10K.

2.2. Representation of E-HIDSs structure

This study adopt the binary tree coding strategy developed in our previous work (Zhang et al, 2021) to represent any sharp or non-sharp distillation sequences structure. The present or absence of a vapor recompression structure in the distillation sequence is represented by variable CR which is compression ratio of a compressor defined by Yuan et al (2022a, 2022b). As shown in Eq. (1), p_c and p_i represent the compressor outlet pressure and inlet pressure, respectively.

$$\mathrm{CR} = \frac{p_c}{p_i} \tag{1}$$

2.3. Evaluation method for fossil energy consumed

In distillation sequences, the level (grade) of hot utilities used in each column are often not identical, in order to accurately evaluate the amount of fossil energy consumed, this study introduces the standard coal equivalent to measure the amount of fossil energy consumption of distillation sequences. The specific expressions are shown in Eq. (2).

$$K_{coal} = \sum_{k=1}^{M} S_k Q_k \leq C_{sce} \tag{2}$$

where K_{coal} is the amount of standard coal consumed by an E-HIDS. Q_k represents the amount of hot utility of level k $(k = 1,2,\dots,M)$. S_k represents the amount of standard coal per unit heat of fossil energy of level k, which can be calculated according to the national standard document (Chinese government, 2014). C_{sce} indicates the upper limit of fossil energy consumption, i.e., the upper limit of standard coal equivalent consumption.

2.4. Implicit MINLP formulation

In this study, stochastic optimization strategy is used to optimize the synthesis of multicomponent distillation sequences. Therefore, the synthesis problem can be expressed by an implicit MINLP model, as shown in Eq. (3). The objective function C_{cost} is the minimal TAC of an E-HIDS, which is the function of distillation sequence $\{Tree\}$ represented by an array of binary integer variables [Zhang et al, 2021; Yuan et al, 2022a], the operating pressure in each column $(\boldsymbol{p})$, the recovery of light and heavy critical components in each column $(\boldsymbol{\xi}_{LK}, \boldsymbol{\xi}_{HK})$, the compression ratio (**CR**), the ratio of the actual reflux ratio to the minimum reflux ratio $(\boldsymbol{r})$, and the preheat temperature rise in the preheater $(\boldsymbol{\Delta T_{pre}})$. Symbolic equation $CSS\,(\{\boldsymbol{Tree}\}, scp) = 0$ conducts random generation of all feasible column sequence structures, and scp refers to the sequence coding parameter for evolving $\{Tree\}$ [Zhang et al, 2021; Yuan et al, 2022a]. T_{out}^{k}、T_c^k and T_d^k are defined as the compressor outlet temperature, the critical temperature of the compressed stream, and the dew point temperature for separation task k, respectively. K is the set of separation tasks in a distillation sequence.

$$\begin{aligned}
&\min C_{cost}(\{Tree\},\boldsymbol{p},\xi_{LK},\xi_{HK},\boldsymbol{CR},\boldsymbol{r},\boldsymbol{\Delta T_{pre}}) \\
&s.t.\ K_{coal}(\{Tree\},\boldsymbol{p},\xi_{LK},\xi_{HK},\boldsymbol{CR},\boldsymbol{r},\boldsymbol{\Delta T_{pre}}) \le C_{sce} \\
&CSS\ (\{\boldsymbol{Tree}\},scp) = 0 \\
&T_d^k \le T_{out}^k \le T_c^k \quad k \in K
\end{aligned} \tag{3}$$

3. Optimization framework

This study adopts the simulated annealing-particle swarm optimization (SA-PSO) method [Zhang et al; 2018, 2021; Yuan et al, 2022a] to solve the MINLP problem of synthesizing E-HIDSs. An improvement is made for the PSO where the penalty function is added to the objective function to deal with the additional constraint on fossil energy consumption. Thus the value of particle fitness function φ is the summation of TAC and Penalty. The improved synthesis framework of E-HIDSs based on the improved SA-PSO algorithm is shown in Fig. 2. In the outer layer, the SA algorithm is used to optimize the distillation sequence structure. In the inner layer, the improved PSO algorithm is used to optimize the operating parameters for a given sequence. Thus, the discrete variables ($\{\boldsymbol{Tree}\}$) and continuous variables ($\boldsymbol{p}, \boldsymbol{\xi}_{LK}, \boldsymbol{\xi}_{HK}, \boldsymbol{CR}, \boldsymbol{r}, \boldsymbol{\Delta T}_{pre}$) can be optimized under the constraint of fossil energy consumption simultaneously.

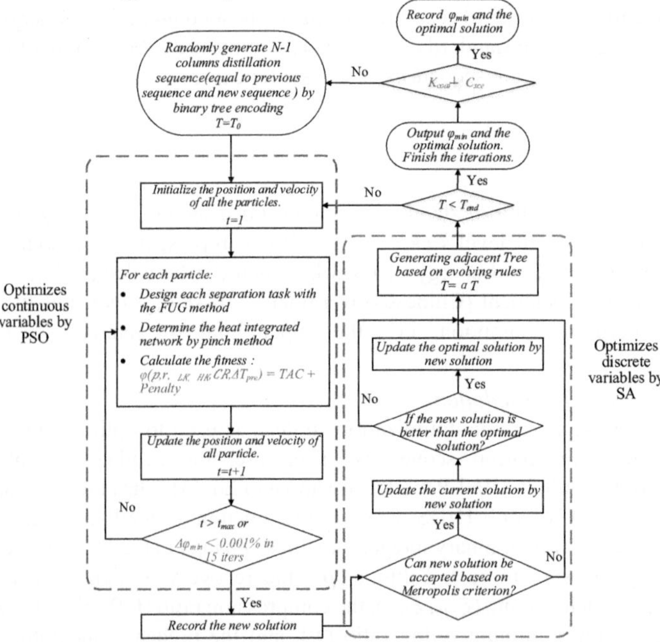

Fig. 2 The improved synthesis framework of E-HIDSs based on SA-PSO algorithm

4. Case Study

To verify the effectiveness of the proposed method, a five-component alkane separation example (propane, i-butane, n-butane, i-pentane, and n-pentane) which was addressed by Yuan et al [2022b] is studied for synthesizing E-HIDSs. The amount of standard coal consumed by the optimal distillation sequence structure (without considering constraint of fossil energy consumption) in the literature [Yuan et al, 2022b] is equivalent to 1865.59 kg ce/h. Thus, the upper limit of C_{sce} is set to 1,865.59 kg ce/h in the present optimization. To understand the influence of different level constrains on the optimal results, in this study, six values in the upper and lower bounds of C_{sce} are separately used as the constraints for hot utility consumption when synthesizing optimal distillation sequence under each constraint. Note that, due to the limitation of the compressor outlet temperature ($T_d^k \leq T_{out}^k \leq T_c^k$), there will be no feasible solution when C_{sce} is less than or equal to 665.59 kg ce/h. From the results synthesized under the constraint of fossil energy consumption, it can be found when the constraint become tighten, the optimal distillation sequence structure may change. However, there are also cases when the distillation sequence structure remains unchanged and the constraints are still satisfied by optimizing the continuous variables. It is worth noting that in order to accommodate the tightening constraint, the settings for vapor recompression are gradually increase so that the opportunities for heat integration (both the number of heat integration and the depth of heat matching) in a distillation system are increased accordingly.

As with most engineering problems, there is a trade-off between economic cost and environmental benefits (e.g. fossil energy consumption) in distillation sequence synthesis. Fig. 3 shows the relationship of TAC and standard coal consumption (K_{coal}) of the optimal solutions under different constraints of C_{sce}, The red and blue curve refers to K_{coal} and TAC, respectively. The two curves in the figure show significant mutual constraints. TAC shows a monotonically increasing trend with a cumulative increase of 41.93%, while K_{coal} shows a monotonically decreasing trend with a cumulative decrease of 53.67%. Fig. 4 shows the hot utility (Q_{heat}) and electricity (Q_{elec}) consumed in the optimal distillation sequence under different constraints of C_{sce}, where the red and green curve refers to hot utility and electricity, respectively. As the constraints on fossil energy consumption tighten, heat integration opportunities increase due to more vapor recompression is used, resulting in the reduction of hot utilities (i.e., fossil energy consumption) consumed in the reboilers. As a result, the two curves show significant mutual constraints. Electricity consumption shows a monotonic increasing trend, with a cumulative increase of 5658.41%. While hot utility consumption shows a monotonically decreasing trend with a cumulative decrease of 53.67%. In this process, there is a significant substitution relationship between electricity consumption and heat energy consumption (i.e., fossil energy consumption) in the optimal solutions.

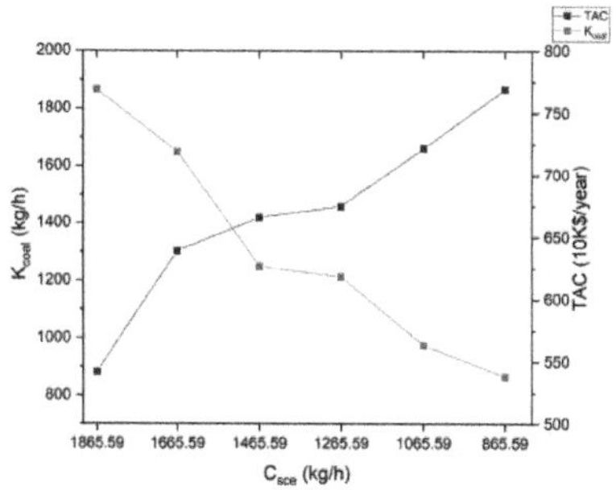

Fig. 3 Relationship between TAC and K_{coal} of the optimal solution under different constraints of C_{sce}

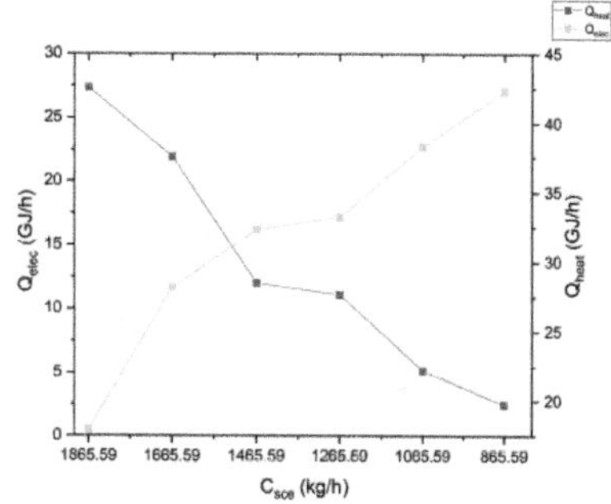

Fig. 4 Hot utility (Q_{heat}) and electricity (Q_{elec}) consumed in optimal distillation sequences under different constraints of C_{sce}

5. Conclusions

In this study, the synthesis method of E-HIDSs considering vapor recompression under the constraint of fossil energy consumption based on the SA-PSO stochastic algorithm is established to pursue the substitution of energy types used in the distillation process. A separation of five-component alkane mixtures is taken as an example to synthesis with the objective of minimum TAC using the proposed method. Results show that the optimal distillation sequence structure and continuous variable parameters under different constraints of fossil energy consumption can be obtained simultaneously.

The relationship of TAC and K_{coal} of the optimal sequences under each constraint shows significant mutual constraints. With the tightening of constraint of fossil energy consumption, electricity consumption and the percentage of electricity in operating costs have been increasing, while hot utility consumption and the percentage of hot utility in operating costs have been decreasing. This demonstrates the feasibility of the idea of "substituting fossil energy with green electricity by considering both vapor recompression and heat integration ". In industry practice, the constraint on fossil energy consumption can be set based on the factory's fossil energy consumption limit or CO_2 emission limit. The optimal distillation sequence is then obtained by the method to drive the energy transition in the distillation process.

References

Aggarwal A, Floudas C. Synthesis of general distillation sequences—nonsharp separations [J]. Computers & Chemical Engineering, 1990, 14(6): 631-653.

Amminudin K A, Smith R, Thong D Y C, et al. Design and optimization of fully thermally coupled distillation columns. Part 1: preliminary design and optimization methodology [J]. Chemical Engineering Research and Design, 2001, 79: 701–715.

An W, Yu F, Dong F, et al. Simulated annealing approach to the optimal synthesis of distillation column with intermediate heat exchangers [J]. Chinese Journal of Chemical Engineering, 2008, 16: 30–35.

An W, Yuan X. A simulated annealing-based approach to the optimal synthesis of heat-integrated distillation sequences [J]. Computers & Chemical Engineering, 2009, 33(1): 199-212.

Caballero J A, Grossmann I E. Generalized Disjunctive Programming Model for the Optimal Synthesis of Thermally Linked Distillation Columns [J]. Industrial & Engineering Chemistry Research, 2001, 40(10): 2260–2274.

Felbab N, Patel B, El-Halwagi M M, et al. Vapor recompression for efficient distillation. 1. A new synthesis perspective on standard configurations [J]. AIChE Journal, 2013, 59(8): 2977-2992.

Giridhar A, Agrawal R. Synthesis of distillation configurations: I. Characteristics of a good search space. Comput. Chem. Eng. 2010, 34, 73–83.

National Development and Reform Commission. Guidelines on Greenhouse Gas Emission Accounting Methodology and Reporting for Petrochemical Enterprises in China [S], 2014.

Sholl D S, Lively R P. Seven chemical separations to change the world [J]. Nature, 2016, 532(7600): 435-437.

Shah V H, Agrawal R. A matrix method for multicomponent distillation sequences [J]. AIChE Journal, 2010, 56: 1759–1775.

United Nations. Climate Action [EB/OL]. https://www.un.org/zh/climatechange/raising-ambition/renewable-energy.

Wang F, Luo Y, Yuan X. A formulation methodology for multicomponent distillation sequences based on stochastic optimization [J]. Chinese Journal of Chemical Engineering, 2016.

Wang N, Ye Q, Ren X, et al. Performance Enhancement of Heat Pump with Preheater-Assisted Pressure-Swing Distillation Process[J]. Industrial & Engineering Chemistry Research, 2020, 59(10): 4742-4755.

Yuan H O, Luo Y Q, Yuan X G. Synthesis of Heat-integrated Distillation Sequences with Mechanical Vapor Recompression by Stochastic Optimization. Computers & Chemical Engineering, 2022a.

Yuan H O. Distillation sequence synthesis based on stochastic optimization for steam recompression energy integration [D]. Tianjin: Tianjin University, 2022b.

Zhang S, Luo Y, Ma Y, Yuan X. Simultaneous optimization of nonsharp distillation sequences and heat integration networks by simulated annealing algorithm. Energy, 2018, 162, 1139–1157.

Zhang S, Luo Y, Yuan X. A novel stochastic optimization method to efficiently synthesize large-scale nonsharp distillation systems [J]. AIChE Journal, 2021, 67(9): e17328.

Flavio Manenti, Gintaras V. Reklaitis (Eds.), Proceedings of the 34th European Symposium on Computer Aided Process Engineering / 15th International Symposium on Process Systems Engineering (ESCAPE34/PSE24), June 2-6, 2024, Florence, Italy
 http://dx.doi.org/10.1016/B978-0-443-28824-1.50205-2

Sustainability Assessments of Styrofoam Waste Recycling for Styrene Monomer Recovery: Economic and Environmental Impact

Eprillia Intan Fitriasari[a], J. Jay Liu*[a]

[a]*Department of Chemical Engineering, Pukyong National University, 48513 Busan, South Korea.*
jayliu@pknu.ac.kr

Abstract

The use of styrofoam has increased in various industries, including packaging and food, leading to a short lifecycle and the generation of large amounts of waste. Styrofoam waste poses a significant problem due to its non-biodegradable nature and the difficulties associated with its processing and disposal. However, there have been efforts to address this issue, including chemically recycling styrofoam waste. In this work, sustainability assessments were conducted to evaluate the economic and environmental performance of chemically recycling styrofoam waste to recover its styrene monomer. Three scenarios were developed based on the feed pretreatment and monomer quality. The process model was performed based on experimental results in simulation software. The outcomes of the process modelling were employed as input data for economic analysis and life cycle assessment. According to the economic analysis results, the scenario for high-quality styrene monomer recovery, with a minimum selling price of $ 1.52/kg, emerged as the most economically viable option. Furthermore, all scenarios demonstrated lower carbon emissions compared to the production of petroleum-based styrene, with scenario 1 being the most environmentally friendly, achieving an 89% reduction in carbon emissions.

Keywords: plastic recycling, techno-economic analysis, life cycle assessment, carbon emissions.

1. Introduction

Over the past decades, global plastic production has soared from 2 million tons in 1950 to 368 million tons in 2019, with an expected doubling in the next two decades (Geyer et al., 2017). Plastic, widely used in diverse applications, has seen increased demand, particularly in packaging, accounting for 39.6% in 2019 (Plastic Europe, 2020). Despite recycling efforts, only 14% of plastic waste is collected, and projections suggest that by 2050, only 27% will be recycled, with most incinerated or landfilled (Geyer et al., 2017). Implementing circular economy principles, particularly through chemical recycling, offers a potential solution to these challenges, aiming to prevent plastic waste and create economic opportunities while reducing environmental impact. At present, mechanical recycling stands as the dominant method. However, its scope is largely limited to retrieving lower-grade products. Chemical recycling, especially catalytic degradation, emerges as a promising alternative to traditional mechanical recycling, producing higher-quality recycled materials and reducing environmental impact. This process aims to recover styrene monomer from styrofoam waste, a crucial step in advancing circular economy goals. However, despite advancements, challenges remain, including economic viability and environmental impact assessment, necessitating comprehensive analyses to ensure the success of these chemical recycling technologies at a global industrial scale. This study conducts in-depth techno-economic and life cycle assessments, critically evaluating the potential of catalytic degradation in creating a sustainable circular economy for styrofoam waste, examining economic viability and environmental friendliness to meet sustainability criteria.

2. Methodology

2.1. Process Description

A process model for recovering styrene monomer from styrofoam waste was developed using Aspen Plus V11. This model served as the foundation for economic analysis and environmental impact assessment. Three scenarios were modeled based on feedstock pre-treatment process and product purity: Scenario 1 – liquefaction in heat as pre-treatment with a target product purity of 95%, Scenario 2 – feedstock dissolution as pre-treatment with a target product purity of 95%, and Scenario 3 – liquefaction in heat as pre-treatment with a target product purity of 99.6%. The process was designed with a feedstock composition derived from the analysis of polystyrene waste, taken from the research detailed by Oh et al (2018). The feedstock was sourced from a local facility that recovers styrofoam waste to pellet, assumed to have undergone initial sorting, shredding, melting, ingot caking and ingot pelleting processes. According to Korea Environment Corporation (2021), the price of recycled polystyrene pellets from styrofoam waste is $ 0.74/kg, which was used as the feedstock cost in the model. We considered 300 kg/h of styrofoam waste pellets as the feedstock, operating for 8,000 h annually. The degradation of styrofoam waste to recover styrene monomer followed the optimal conditions from an experimental study using a base catalyst, as reported by Liu et al (2016). This degradation occured in the reactor, which was modeled as Ryield reactor in the model, yielding 85 wt% of styrene monomer.

The flowsheet illustrating the process flow for modeling three scenarios is depicted in Figure 1. This process is divided into three primary sections: pre-treatment, catalytic degradation, and product separation and recovery. The process initiates with the pre-treatment of the feedstock. Polystyrene pellets and catalyst are blended in a mixer. In Scenario 2, Tetrahydrofuran (THF) is introduced as a solvent into the mixer alongside polystyrene pellets and catalyst, facilitating the dissolution of polystyrene. The mixture undergoes heating to 370°C in pre-heater and HE-1, causing EPS and THF to transform into a gaseous state. Following pre-treatment, the gas mixture and catalyst are introduced into the catalytic degradation reactor (REACTOR), operating at 370°C, 0.08 MPa pressure, and 30 minutes of residence time. A separator (SEP1) is utilized to segregate products from catalysts and solid. The product is conveyed to the product separation and recovery section via a compressor (COMP). Through a sequence of heat exchangers and separators, the products undergo separation for heavy hydrocarbon. Flash-type separators are used to segregate the mixture based on their distinct phases. The product separation procedure start by passing the products through SEP2. SEP3 yields heavy hydrocarbon as the bottom product, sent for wastewater treatment, while light gas is also separated in SEP4 and used for energy recovery. To attain the desired purity level of styrene monomer, the product from separation section undergoes multiple processes depending on the scenario. In Scenario 1, the product is transported to the styrene recovery section, aiming for a 95% purity via distillation in DISTL1. Recovered styrene monomer is obtained as the bottom product, and the top product is recycled to maximize the yield. In Scenario 2, the product goes to DISTL1, which separates the THF from the product achieving 99% of THF to be recycled back to the pre-treatment section. The products is further purified in the DISTL2 to obtain recovered styrene monomer with 99% purity. In Scenario 3, two distillation columns (DISTL1 and DISTL2) are utilized in the product recovery section to achieve styrene monomer at a purity of 99.6%, with the remaining light gases used for energy recovery. The used catalyst is recovered in a separate section using a calcination process at 600°C and by utilizing the produced light gas as fuel.

2.2. Economic Analysis

Initially, the equipment cost is estimated in order to conduct techno-economic analysis. Each equipment cost is determined by factors such as its type, size, capacity, and power or duty, as modeled in Aspen Plus. The catalytic degradation reactor equipment cost was computed using correlations provided by Turton et al (2009), while the cost of other equipment was based on literature from analogous studies in plastic waste processing. The equipment cost is adjusted using the equation:

$$C_n = C_o \left(\frac{CEPCI_n}{CEPCI_o}\right)\left(\frac{Z_n}{Z_o}\right)^n \tag{1}$$

Here, C_n is the updated cost of equipment at the new capacity, C_o is the cost in the baseline year, Z_n is the new capacity, Z_o is the baseline capacity, and n is the scaling exponent. The unit price of other material and utility used in operating cost were sourced from various publications. THF cost is taken from reference at $ 3.28/kg, while the catalyst cost was estimated based on SBA-15 modification at $ 70/kg. Utility expenses, including makeup water, electricity, and natural gas, were obtained from reports by United States Energy Information Administration and National Renewable Energy Laboratory. Total capital investments were calculated following the methodology by Turton et al (2009), which factors in total direct cost (TDC) and total indirect cost (TIDC). The assumptions used for economic analysis is listed in Table 1. Following the computation of all costs, a discounted cash flow analysis is conducted to estimate the minimum selling price (MSP) of recovered styrene monomer at which zero net present value (NPV) is generated for the entire process over a 30-years project life.

Table 1: Assumptions for economic analysis

Parameter	Value
Depreciation year	7 years
Tax rate	20%
Salvage value	0
Project life	30 years
Internal rate of return (IRR)	10%
Plant start-up year	1
Operating hours	8,000 h

2.3. Life Cycle Assessment

Life cycle assessment (LCA) was performed to evaluate the environmental impact of recovering styrene monomer from styrofoam waste. The LCA was conducted according to ISO 14040/44:2006 standard. The goal of this assessment is to compare the carbon emissions of the recovered styrene monomer with conventional styrene derived from fossil-based raw material. The life cycle impact assessment was carried out using SimaPro 9.4.0.2, employing CML-IA baseline 3.07 method. Global warming potential (GWP 100a) was selected as the impact category to measure the carbon emissions. Ecoinvent v3.8 served as the life cycle inventory (LCI) database. The LCI was defined based on material and energy balance results from process modeling, and the functional unit was set at 1 kg of recovered styrene monomer. The LCA was conducted from gate-to-gate, with the system boundary illustrated in Figure 2. The feedstock was assumed to be transported using truck over a distance of 100 km.

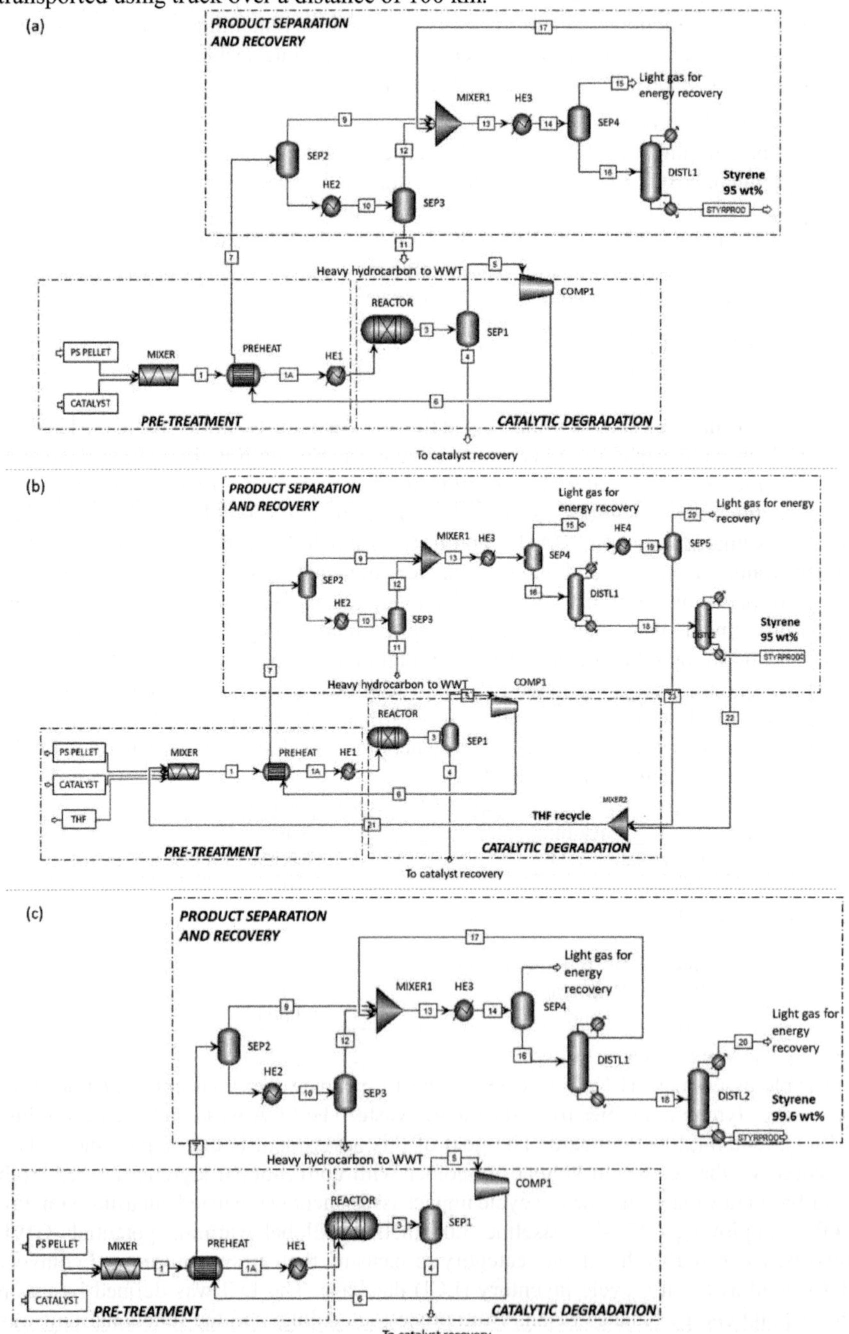

Figure 1: Process flowsheet of styrene monomer recovery from styrofoam waste through catalytic degradation for (a) Scenario 1, (b) Scenario 2, and (c) Scenario 3.

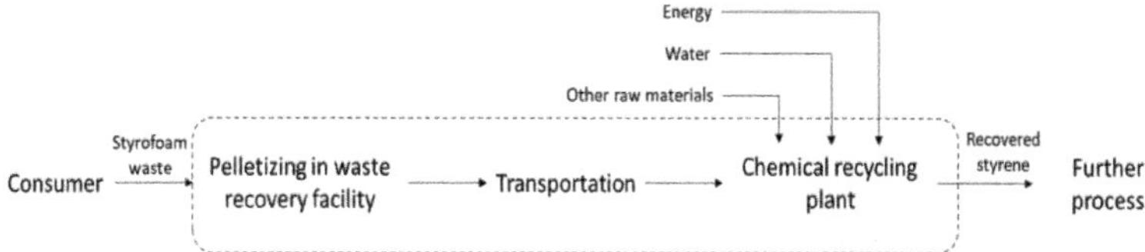

Figure 2: System boundary for LCA

3. Results

The mass and energy balance results from the process simulation are summarized in Table 2. It is evident from the table that Scenario 2 employs THF for dissolution. The optimal ratio between polystyrene and THF solvent is 0.5 to ensure complete dissolution of all polystyrene. Considering a 99% recycling rate, the required amount of THF stands at 3 kg/h. Additionally, with a ratio of 0.02 between catalyst and polystyrene pellets, the process requires a total of 6 kg/h of catalyst. As observed in the table, Scenario 1 demonstrates the highest yield among the scenarios. This can be attributed to the increased possibility of product loss in Scenarios 2 and 3 due to the presence of more separation equipment. Scenarios 2 and 3 necessitate more makeup water because additional columns require increased cooling water for the total condenser. Furthermore, Scenarios 2 and 3 require more steam to meet the heating requirements for the reboiler. The electricity is sourced from the grid, and the heat requirement is fulfilled by natural gas.

Table 2: Mass and energy balance for all scenarios

Parameter	Scenario 1	Scenario 2	Scenario 3
Feedstock			
Polystyrene pellet (kg/h)	300	300	300
THF (makeup) (kg/h)	-	3	-
Catalyst (kg/h)	6	6	6
Products			
Styrene monomer (kg/h)	262	251	248
Utilities			
Makeup water (t/h)	13.38	36.89	87.01
Steam (t/h)	0.11	0.28	0.88
Heat (MMBtu/h)	0.075	0.22	0.075
Electricity (kW)	53.25	53.44	54.37

The results of the economic analysis show the MSP of recovered styrene detailed in Figure 3 (a). The MSP for Scenario 1, 2, and 3 are \$ 1.15/kg styrene, \$ 1.40/kg styrene, and \$ 1.52/kg styrene, respectively, with feedstock cost being the major contributing factor. The conventional styrene price (\$ 0.93/kg styrene) is taken from IHS market (2021). It is evident that Scenario 1 offers the most competitive price in comparison to conventional styrene. However, Scenario 3, with a product purity of 99.6%, may have better market acceptance due to its equivalent purity to conventional styrene. The results of LCA are depicted in Figure 3 (b). As shown in the figure, all scenarios exhibit lower carbon emissions than conventional styrene, with a GWP result of 0.36 kgCO_2-eq/kg styrene, 0.57 kgCO_2-eq/kg styrene, and 0.54 kgCO_2-eq/kg styrene for Scenario 1, 2, and 3, respectively. Scenario 1 shows the lowest carbon emissions, accounting for 89% lower emissions compared to conventional styrene. Notably, the energy requirement contributes significantly to the carbon emissions of recovered styrene monomer from styrofoam waste.

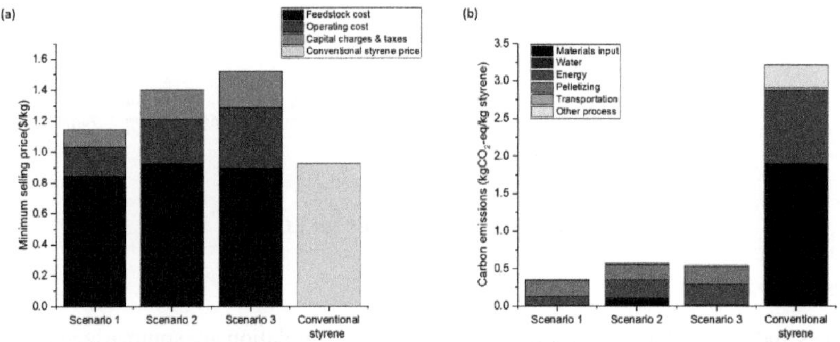

Figure 3: (a) The minimum selling price (MSP) breakdown and (b) carbon emissions breakdown of recovered styrene for all scenario relative to conventional styrene.

4. Conclusions

This study examined the recycling of styrofoam waste to recover styrene monomer using catalytic degradation to address environmental challenges linked to plastic waste. Demonstrated across three scenarios, varying in pre-treatment process and product purity, the TEA reveals Scenario 3, yielding an MSP of \$ 1.52/kg styrene as the most viable option. This pricing aligns with conventional styrene monomer and have advantage similar purity, offering a solution to recycled material quality concerns. The LCA indicates that recovered styrene from styrofoam waste production across scenarios is more environmentally friendly than conventional styrene, with Case 1 showcasing an 89% reduction in GWP result at 0.36 kgCO_2-eq/kg styrene. Energy consumption during styrofoam waste recycling significantly contributes to carbon emissions, suggesting potential avenues for further reduction through renewable energy utilization and lower-temperature degradation catalyst development.

Acknowledgement

This research was supported by Basic Science Research Program through the National Research Foundation of Korea (NRF), funded by the Ministry of Science and ICT (2019R1A2C2084709 and 2021R1A4A3025742). This work was also supported by the Korea Institute of Energy Technology Evaluation and Planning (KETEP) and the Ministry of Trade, Industry & Energy (MOTIE) of the Republic of Korea (RS-2023-00233414).

References

D. Oh, H.W. Lee, Y.M. Kim, Y.K. Park, 2018, Catalytic pyrolysis of polystyrene and polyethylene terephthalate over Al-MSU-F, Energy Procedia, 144,111–117.

PlascticsEurope, Plastics-The Facts 2020: An analysis of European plastics production, demand and waste data, 2021.

R. Geyer, J.R. Jambeck, K.L. Law, 2017, Production, use, and fate of all plastics ever made, Science Advances, 3, 25–29.

R. Turton, R.C. Bailie, W.B. Whiting, J.A. Shaeiwitz, Analysis, Design and Synthesis of Chemical Processes, 2009.

X. Liu, L. Li, X. Song, F. Liu, S. Yu, X. Ge, 2016, Degradation of Polystyrene Using Base Modified Mesoporous Molecular Sieves K2O/BaO-SBA-15 as Catalysts, Catalytic Letters, 146, 1910–1916.

Flavio Manenti, Gintaras V. Reklaitis (Eds.), Proceedings of the 34th European Symposium on Computer Aided Process Engineering / 15th International Symposium on Process Systems Engineering (ESCAPE34/PSE24), June 2-6, 2024, Florence, Italy
 http://dx.doi.org/10.1016/B978-0-443-28824-1.50206-4

Techno-Economic and Life Cycle Assessments of the Utilization of Carbon-Free Energy Sources as an Alternate Fuel in Naphtha Cracker

Eprillia Intan Fitriasari[a], J. Jay Liu*[a]

[a]*Department of Chemical Engineering, Pukyong National University, Busan 48513, South Korea*

jayliu@pknu.ac.kr

Abstract

Ethylene, a key intermediate chemical in petrochemicals, is predominantly produced through naphtha cracking, requiring intense energy inputs at 800°C. This conventional process relies on methane and natural gas combustion, generating carbon emissions. As carbon-free energy sources, green ammonia and hydrogen are potential fuels to address this environmental issue. This study proposes using green ammonia and green hydrogen as alternative fuels in an existing naphtha cracker to cut carbon emissions in South Korea. The Aspen Plus software simulated the proposed processes, and a thorough techno-economic and life cycle assessment evaluated economic feasibility and environmental impact. Economic analysis identified additional production costs, while the life cycle assessment revealed reduced carbon emissions compared to the conventional process. Integrating economic and environmental results, a blend of 50% green hydrogen and 50% methane emerges as a potentially more economically viable solution, with a cost of avoiding carbon at \$148.48/t CO_2.

Keywords: Decarbonization, green ammonia, green hydrogen, techno-economic analysis, life cycle assessments.

1. Introduction

In recent years, the global focus on decarbonizing industrial processes has intensified due to the escalating carbon emissions contributing to global warming and climate change. According to United States Environmental Protection Agency (U.S. EPA) (2021), industries account for 25% of carbon emissions, primarily from fossil fuel combustion. Thiel et al (2020) suggested various approaches to decarbonization, including the use of carbon-free fuels, upgraded heat distribution systems, electrification, and improved heat management technologies. Ethylene (C_2H_4) plays a crucial role as an intermediate chemical in the petrochemical industry worldwide. It is mostly manufactured via naphtha cracking, a process that consumes 26-31 GJ/t C_2H_4, with 65% of the energy focused on the furnace (Ren et al., 2006). This demand is conventionally met by burning methane, leading to carbon emissions. Gu et al (2022) conducted research on electrifying naphtha cracking furnaces to meet energy demand. However, electrification faces challenges, such as higher electricity costs and the need for significant upgrades in electricity transmission and distribution. To overcome these issues, we aim to decarbonize naphtha cracking plant in South Korea by introducing carbon-free fuels—imported green ammonia and domestically-produced green hydrogen. These fuels can directly substitute for fossil fuels without requiring substantial modifications to existing furnace infrastructure, offering a straightforward transition for industries reliant on traditional fuel sources. Additionally, they provide high energy density and easier storage compared to electricity in large-scale industrial operations. We conducted an evaluation focusing on economic performance, carbon emission reduction, and the cost of avoiding carbon across various case studies: Case 1 - utilizing methane (conventional naphtha cracking plant), Case 2a - 100% imported green ammonia, Case 2b - a blend of 50 vol% imported green ammonia and 50 vol% methane, Case 3a - 100% green hydrogen, and Case 3b - a blend of 50 vol% green hydrogen and 50 vol% methane.

2. Methods

2.1. Process Description

The feedstock for this study is naphtha from crude oil refinery. The composition of naphtha consists of n-Paraffins (36.13 wt%), isoparaffins (36.62 wt%), olefins (0.21 wt%), napthenes (21.06 wt%), and aromatics (5.98 wt%) following literature data (Zimmerman and Walzl, 2012). The design capacity for this study is 1,000,000 t/y of ethylene production. The annual feedstock requirement is approximately 3,019,397 t/y of naphtha with an expected 8,406 operating hours per year (96% plant availability). The naphtha cracking plant is modelled in the Aspen Plus V14 process simulator to investigate the material and energy balance for all cases. Peng-Robinson equation of state is used to describe the thermodynamic properties of the components.

- *Case 1: Conventional naphtha cracking plant*

  Figure 1 illustrates the simplified process flow diagram of the naphtha cracking plant. The naphtha cracker furnace operates at 359.19 t/h of naphtha and 179.59 t/h of steam, achieving a 0.5 steam-to-naphtha ratio. Split into convection and radiation sections, the furnace preheats the feed in the convection zone without initiating reactions. The radiation section maintains an 800°C temperature and 1 atm, providing heat for cracking through fuel combustion, modeled in an RStoic reactor. Yield data is sourced from Zimmerman and Walzl (2012). After rapid quenching at 350°C, heavy hydrocarbons are removed using a primary fractionator, and further cooling eliminates residual heavy hydrocarbons. A multistage compression system raises gas pressure to 40 bar. At the intermediate compressor stage, a drying unit (molecular sieve column) and an acid gas removal unit (caustic wash unit) operate under high pressure. Refrigeration system drops the gas stream's temperature to -95°C. Distillation columns separate light fractions from heavy fractions, producing highly pure ethylene and propylene. Light gas are separated in the de-methanizer then directed to pressure swing adsorption to separate methane and hydrogen, with methane used as furnace and boiler fuel, and hydrogen directed to the deacetylenizer. The de-ethanizer separates acetylene, ethane, and ethylene, converted in the deacetylenizer to ethylene, further distilled via a C2-splitter. The de-propanizer purifies C3+ components, while the C3-splitter recovers valuable propylene. The debutanizer further separates C4 materials, C5 materials, and aromatics. A steam cycle integrated into the plant produces and distributes steam. Heat from the quenching process is used for feed steam and power generation.

- *Case 2: Imported green ammonia*

  In Case 2, imported green ammonia serves as an alternative fuel to replace methane. The combustion of fuel is modeled in two scenarios: (a) 100 vol% green ammonia and (b) 50 vol% green ammonia+50 vol% methane. Any remaining methane is assumed to be marketed as byproduct. The imported green ammonia is assumed to be stored in a refrigerated ammonia storage vessel for 14 days. The tip of naphtha cracking furnace is modified to allow access of green ammonia as fuel. Green ammonia is combusted with excess air in the furnace. De-NOx unit is installed to remove the NOx emission from ammonia combustion. The De-NOx unit utilizes selective catalytic reduction (SCR) technology and is designed by assuming the amount of NOx on flue gas is 250 ppm. In this study, green ammonia is imported from Australia, with production and the transportation processes based on literature data (Akhtar et al., 2021). The transportation involves shipping the green ammonia from Western Australia to the Busan port in South Korea, covering a distance of 7,161 km using semi-refrigerated and fully refrigerated gas carriers. Upon arrival at the South Korea port, the green ammonia is transferred to the naphtha cracking plant via a 5 km pipeline.

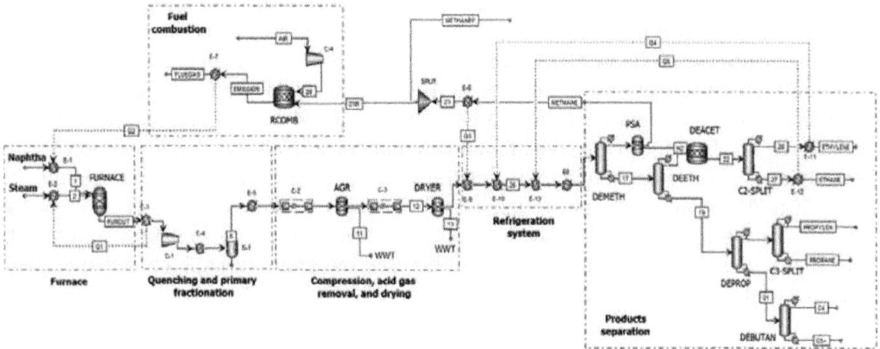

Figure 1: Process flow diagram of naphtha cracking plant

- *Case 3: Green hydrogen*

  In Case 3, green hydrogen is employed as an alternative fuel. The green hydrogen is generated through water electrolysis powered by solar PV power plants at a centralized location in South Korea, following procedures outlined in literature (Akhtar et al., 2021). Fuel combustion is modeled in two scenarios: (a) 100 vol% green hydrogen and (b) 50 vol% green hydrogen+50 vol% methane. Any remaining methane is assumed to be sold as byproduct of the naphtha cracking plant. The produced green hydrogen is then transported via pipeline to the naphtha cracking plant, covering a distance of 100 km. The hydrogen is assumed to be stored in naphtha cracking plant using pressurized storage vessel at 700 bar with storing time 3 days.

2.2. Economic Analysis

Based on the process design and simulation, we can identify additional equipment and operating cost for Case 2 and Case 3. To calculate the capital expenditure (CAPEX) of additional equipment, the nth plant analysis was employed to perform the economic analysis of the process. CAPEX were determined by employing fundamental chemical engineering cost computation methods (CEPCI and scaling coefficients). Data from reference is used to calculate the additional operating cost (OPEX) based on the material and energy balance results. In Case 2, the additional CAPEX includes a furnace tip modification, estimated at 10% of the furnace price ($19.61 MM), a green ammonia storage vessel cost assumed at $0.81/kg NH_3 (Nayak-Luke at al., 2021), and a DeNOx unit costing $58.5 MM (Jiang et al., 2020). The OPEX of Case 2 encompasses additional costs of $0.609/kg for green ammonia (IHS Markit, 2023), $0.056/kg for shipping it from Australia to South Korea (Akhtar et al., 2021), $149/t NH_3/y for the refrigeration system (Nayak-Luke et al., 2021), and $0.491/t-flue gas for DeNOx operating costs (Jiang et al., 2020). In Case 3, the additional CAPEX comprises a furnace tip modification (10% of the furnace price, \$19.61 MM) and green hydrogen vessel storage estimated at \$460/kg H_2 (Nayak-Luke et al., 2021). For the OPEX of Case 3, an extra cost of \$17.32/kg is required for green hydrogen (Akhtar et al., 2021).

2.3. Life Cycle Assessments

Life cycle assessment (LCA) represents a systematic method to assess a product's or process's environmental impacts within a specified system boundary. The LCA, conducted according to the ISO 14040/44:2006 standard methodology, encompassed the entire life cycle from cradle to gate. Life cycle impact assessment calculations were executed using SimaPro 9.4.0.2 software, employing the CML-IA baseline 3.07 method. Global warming potential (GWP) is selected as the representative impact category to calculate carbon emissions. Data used for LCA simulation was sourced from Ecoinvent v3.8 and other publications. According to Akhtar et al (2021), the GWP result for green ammonia and green hydrogen in South Korea are 0.144 kg CO_2-eq/kg NH_3 and 5.35 kgCO_2-eq/kg H_2, respectively. The functional unit considered was the production of 1 kg of ethylene. The system boundary is illustrated in Figure 2. The naphtha was assumed to be transported from petroleum refinery at a distance of 5 km. The life cycle inventory (LCI) of naphtha cracking center was obtained from process simulation results. The electricity generated in the process would be used internally in naphtha cracking plant. The co-products were allocated based on their mass.

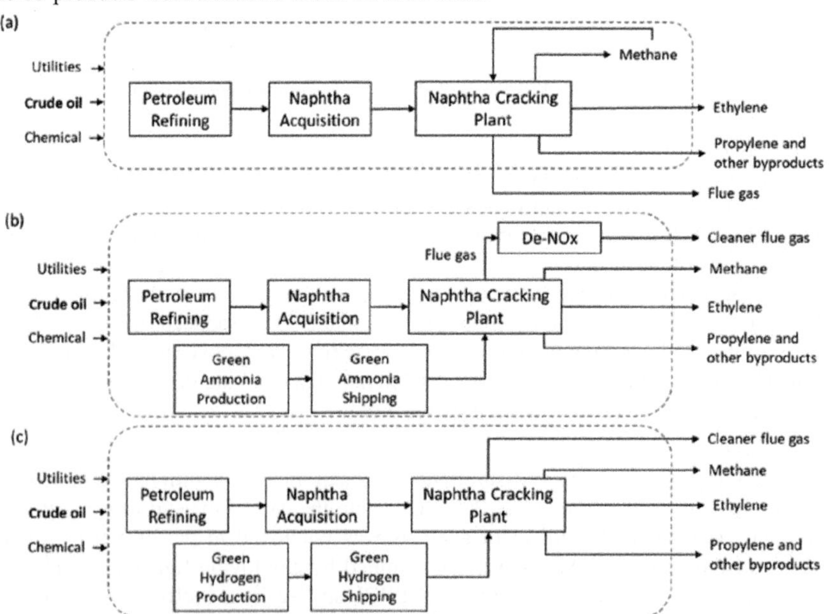

Figure 2: System boundary of cradle to gate LCA for naphtha cracking plant (a) Case 1, (b) Case 2, and Case 3.

2.4. Cost of Avoiding Carbon

To ensure cost competitiveness with the conventional 100% methane-based fuel naphtha cracking plant, the costs of avoiding carbon for Case 2a, Case 2b, Case 3a, and Case 3b were calculated using the following equation:

$$Cost\ of\ avoiding\ carbon = \frac{(Total\ annual\ additional\ cost/ethylene\ capacity)}{Carbon\ emissions\ of\ base\ case\ -\ Carbon\ emissions\ new\ case} \quad (1)$$

To calculate the total annual additional cost, the additional CAPEX is divided by the plant's life, assumed to be 30 years. The additional annual CAPEX is thereby determined. The total annual additional cost is then obtained by summing up the additional annual CAPEX and OPEX.

3. Results

Initially, the Aspen Plus software was used to develop the process simulation model for the standard naphtha cracking plant. Validation of this simulation involved comparing its results to data from a typical naphtha cracking plant (Ren et al., 2006). Ethylene and propylene are the primary products, accounting for 33.20% and 14.62% yields, respectively. The plant's total energy consumption stands at 3,546 GJ/h, with 64.8% consumed by the naphtha cracking furnace. Analyzing the furnace's energy needs helps determine the necessary alternative fuel amount for each case. Green hydrogen in Case 3 has the lowest flow rate among methane and green ammonia, owing to its higher heating value, while green ammonia exhibits the highest flow rate. In Case 2 and Case 3, any remaining methane, resulting from energy needs met by imported green ammonia and green hydrogen, is treated as a by-product. Electricity is generated in the plant and is assumed to be utilized internally. The major material and energy balance were described in Table 1.

Table 1: Major material and energy balance in naphtha cracking plant.

Parameter	Case 1	Case 2a	Case 2b	Case 3a	Case 3b
Feedstock					
Naphtha (kg/h)	359,195	359,195	359,195	359,195	359,195
Product					
Ethylene (kg/h)	118,962.90	118,962.90	118,962.90	118,962.90	118,962.90
Propylene (kg/h)	52,381.06	52,381.06	52,381.06	52,381.06	52,381.06
Methane (kg/h)	-	56,801.95	42,601.46	56,801.95	45,441.56
Ethane (kg/h)	13,204.01	13,204.01	13,204.01	13,204.01	13,204.01
Propane (kg/h)	6,701.56	6,701.56	6,701.56	6,701.56	6,701.56
Butanes (kg/h)	32,749.06	32,749.06	32,749.06	32,749.06	32,749.06
Fuel oil (C5+) (kg/h)	77,481.61	77,481.61	77,481.61	77,481.61	77,481.61
Fuel consumption					
Methane (kg/h)	17,697	-	14,200	-	13,916
Green NH_3 (kg/h)	-	65,000	13,878	-	-
Green H_2 (kg/hr)	-	-	-	7,374	1,595

Economic analyses were conducted to determine the additional unit ethylene production costs. Case 1 serves as the base case for the naphtha cracking plant. Figure 3 (a) displays the additional CAPEX and OPEX results for Case 2 and Case 3. In this comparison, Case 3a incurred the highest CAPEX, totalling \$ 263.83 MM, while Case 3b has the lowest CAPEX at \$ 72.44 MM. This significant difference is influenced by the quantity of green hydrogen consumed in Case 3a and Case 3b, as well as the high cost associated with hydrogen storage vessels. The economic analysis also indicates that Case 3a demonstrated the highest OPEX at \$ 1,073.55 MM, whereas Case 2b demonstrated the lowest OPEX at \$ 83.48 MM. The substantial difference arises from the considerably higher domestic-centralized production cost of green hydrogen, approximately 26 times more expensive than green ammonia. Figure 3(b) presents the LCA results for each case, revealing carbon emissions of 1.49 t CO_2-eq/t C_2H_4 for Case 1, 0.91 t CO_2-eq/t C_2H_4 for Case 2a, 0.99 t CO_2-eq/t C_2H_4 for Case 2b, 1.15 t CO_2-eq/t C_2H_4 for Case 3a, and 0.97 t CO_2-eq/t C_2H_4 ethylene for Case 3b. Notably, Case 2a emerges as the most environmentally friendly alternative, reducing carbon emissions by up to 0.58 t CO_2-eq/t C_2H_4. By integrating the economic analysis and LCA results, the cost of avoiding carbon were calculated. The result reveals that Case 2a, 2b, 3a, and 3b have cost of avoiding carbon at \$ 640.31/t CO_2, \$ 148.48/t CO_2, \$ 3,187.51/t CO_2, and \$ 464.11/t CO_2, respectively. The findings indicate that Case 2b has the lowest cost of reducing carbon emissions, positioning it as the most cost-effective strategy for reducing emissions among other cases.

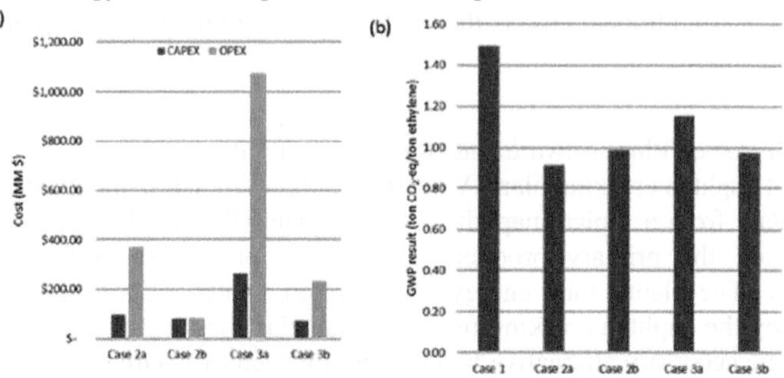

Figure 3: (a) Additional CAPEX and OPEX in Case 2 and Case 3, (b) GWP results of all cases.

4. Conclusions

In this study, we proposed green ammonia (Case 2) and domestic-produced green hydrogen (Case 3) as alternative fuels for decarbonizing a South Korean naphtha cracking plant. Alongside the conventional process (Case 1), each alternative had a 50 vol% fuel blending scenario. Using Aspen Plus, we modelled process designs to analyze material and energy balances, aiding techno-economic and LCA evaluations. The integration of economic analysis and LCA results facilitated the calculation of cost of avoiding carbon. Regarding the LCA results, all the proposed cases demonstrated the potential to reduce carbon emissions in naphtha cracking plant. Overall, considering the cost of avoiding carbon emissions, Case 2b emerges as a more cost-effective approach for curbing carbon emissions, suggesting its viability as a more economically sound solution for emission reduction. Future work aims to explore more decarbonization strategies for naphtha cracking plants.

Acknowledgements

This research was supported by Basic Science Research Program through the National Research Foundation of Korea (NRF), funded by the Ministry of Science and ICT (2019R1A2C2084709 and 2021R1A4A3025742). This work was also supported by the Korea Institute of Energy Technology Evaluation and Planning (KETEP) and the Ministry of Trade, Industry & Energy (MOTIE) of the Republic of Korea (RS-2023-00233414).

References

G.P. Thiel, A.K. Stark, 2021, To decarbonize industry, we must decarbonize heat, Joule, 5, 3, 531-550.

H. Zimmermann and R. Walzl, 2012, Ethylene, Ullmann's Encyclopedia of Industrial Chemistry, Vol. 13, 465-529.

K. Jiang, H. Yu, L. Chen, M. Fang, M. Azzi, A. Cottrell, K. Li, 2020, An advanced, ammonia-based combined NOx/SOx/CO_2 emission control process towards a low-cost, clean coal technology, Applied Energy, 260, 2020, 114316.

J. Gu, H. Kim, H. Lim, 2022, Electrified steam cracking for a carbon neutral ethylene production process: Techno-economic analysis, life cycle assessment and analytic hierarchy process, Energy Conversion and Management, 270, 116256.

M.S. Akhtar, R. Dickson, H. Niaz, D.W. Hwang, J.J. Liu, 2021, Comparative sustainability assessment of a hydrogen supply network for hydrogen refueling stations in Korea-a techno-economic and lifecycle assessment perspective, Green Chemistry, 23, 9625-9639.

R.M. Nayak-Luke, C. Forbes, Z. Cesaro, R. Bañares-Alcántara, K.H.R. Rouwenhorst, 2021, Techno-Economic Aspects of Production, Storage and Distribution of Ammonia, Techno-Economic Challenges of Green Ammonia as an Energy Vector, Academic Press, 191-207.

T. Ren, M. Patel, K. Blok, 2006, Olefins from conventional and heavy feedstocks: Energy use in steam cracking and alternative processes, Energy, 31, 425–451.

Flavio Manenti, Gintaras V. Reklaitis (Eds.), Proceedings of the 34th European Symposium on Computer Aided Process Engineering / 15th International Symposium on Process Systems Engineering (ESCAPE34/PSE24), June 2-6, 2024, Florence, Italy
 http://dx.doi.org/10.1016/B978-0-443-28824-1.50207-6

Optimization of the catalytic cracking process and biodiesel coproduction supply chain considering seasonal factors

Wenhui Zhang[a], Yiqing Luo[a,b*], Xigang Yuan[a, b]

[a] *Chemical Engineering Research Center, School of Chemical Engineering and Technology, Tianjin University, Tianjin 300350, China*

[b] *State Key Laboratory of Chemical Engineering, Tianjin University, Tianjin 300350, China*

luoyq@tju.edu.cn

Abstract

The growing demand for energy is driving the vigorous development of renewable energy. Biodiesel reduces harmful greenhouse gases while also providing high-quality performance. As the existing production of biodiesel is not enough to meet the huge fuel market, it is urgent to adopt new production methods to expand production. This study proposes a new collaborative production supply chain model, which integrates the catalytic cracking process in traditional petrochemical production with the biodiesel production process to increase production and the conversion of biomass feedstock to gasoline products. A mixed integer nonlinear programming (MINLP) model of the integrated supply chain of biodiesel and petroleum is developed. The integrated biodiesel and petroleum supply chain makes better use of petrochemical plant idle capacity, and minimizes total annual costs and improves energy supply reliability. Considering the uncertainty of biomass supply, the amount of biomass supply is subdivided by 12 months to improve the reliability of the supply data. A real case in the U.S. state of Illinois is studied. The results show that the seasonal cooperative production supply chain model will respond to the environmental changes in advance, and there are corresponding changes in the model structure.

Keywords: Supply chain, Biodiesel, Seasonal factors

1. Introduction

The intensification of global economic activities has led to a continuous increase in energy demand (Ghelichi et al., 2018). At the same time, environmental issues such as the depletion of fossil fuels and global warming make the development of alternative energy sources imminent (Jun Inumaru, 2021, Serpilkılıç depren, 2022). Today's biodiesel is a reliable, high-performance fuel that works in any diesel engine without modifications. Biodiesel reduces harmful greenhouse gases while also delivering high-quality performance (Marquardt et al., 2010; Omar Ellabban et al., 2014). Widespread use and high demand for biomass fuels are driving research to more systematically design and optimize the entire bioenergy supply chain (Yue et al., 2014, Daoutidis et al., 2013). Conventional petrochemical plants have some unutilized capacity. Compared to a traditional single supply chain, coupling the bio-diesel supply chain with the petrochemical supply chain (Tong et al., 2014b). It can minimize carbon emissions and improve the robustness of the supply chain network while maximizing production efficiency (U.S. department of energy, 2013).

As existing biodiesel production is not sufficient to meet the huge fuel market, and at the same time, the large investment required for biorefineries may lead to unaffordable production costs and biofuel prices, there is an urgent need to adopt new production methods to expand production.(Espinoza Pérez et al., 2017) In this study, a novel process was used to integrate the biodiesel supply chain with the traditional petrochemical supply chain, co-processing the reduced pressure gas oil (VGO) and bio-oil produced by pyrolysis to reduce biofuel costs through existing refinery infrastructure such as fluidized catalytic cracking (FCC) and HDT processes. The process uses 10% bio-oil and 90% vacuum gas oil to produce gasoline and diesel at the same time (Wu et al., 2020).
One of the key challenges in the operation of biofuel supply chains is the seasonality of biomass supply. The production of soybean biomass is seasonal, and soybeans in Illinois are usually planted in the spring and harvested in the fall (ILSoybean, 2023b; USDA, 2010). Seasonality leads to inconsistent biodiesel production, which adversely affects the efficiency of the biodiesel refinery (Sheel et al., 2021). Some studies have analyzed the seasonal fluctuations of biomass supply (Huang et al., 2014; Omar Ellabban et al., 2014; Tong et al., 2014a; Xie et al., 2014; Yue et al., 2014), but most of the existing studies focus on rough seasonal differences or abstract the supply into fuzzy numbers, and the research on the differences in supply months is still blank.
In this work, we construct an integrated supply chain network. Given the seasonality of biomass supply, the seasonality of fuel demand, the reverse of the seasonality of gasoline and diesel demand, and the fact that the supply of crude oil does not vary with the season, these characteristics create new problems for supply chain optimization. In this study, the time is divided into months, and the mixed integer nonlinear model is used for optimization. In this system, soybeans are used to produce biodiesel. The work takes into account the geographical distribution and moisture content of biomass, as well as the location and size of bio-refineries and petrochemical refineries, and the different conversion pathways. Optimize the design and siting of the pre-treatment plant, optimize the network structure of the supply chain, and optimize the proportion of different conversion paths.

2. Problem background

The superstructure of supply chain considered in this study is shown in Figure 1, where biomass collected (i) are transported to pretreatment centers (j). The biomass is processed into bio-oil in the pretreatment plant (j), and then are transported to a bio-refinery (k) for processing into biodiesel, or to a petrochemical refinery (m) in the catalytic cracking process for further co-processing with vacuum gas oil to produce gasoline and diesel. Vacuum gas oil (o) can also be processed directly in petrochemical refineries to produce gasoline and diesel. Bio-refined products can be mixed with petrochemical products. Finally, diesel and gasoline are shipped as products to customers where there is demand.

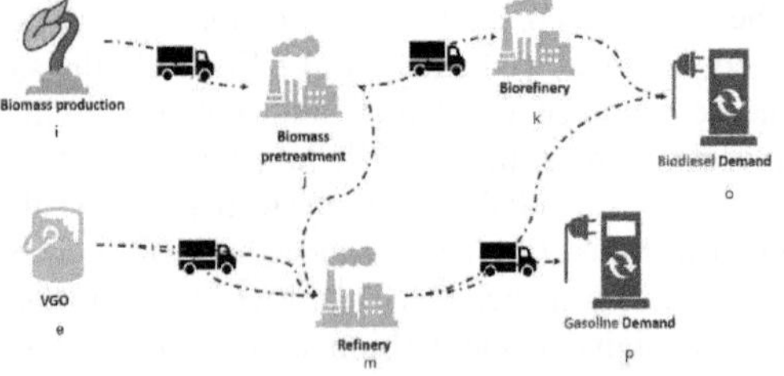

Figure 1. Supply chain network structure

In order to reflect data fluctuations in the real supply chain, the biomass supply is divided into 12 sub-intervals on a monthly basis, and the 12 sub-intervals are allocated respectively according to the fluctuations of the actual monthly biomass production data on the NSDA. Given where the demand points are, where the biomass feedstock is, the potential locations of pretreatment plants, biorefineries and petrochemical refineries, as well as the product demand and biomass output of each region and the population of each county, the aim is to optimize the number and location of pretreatment plants, biodiesel refineries and petrochemical refineries, and selection of conversion paths, so that minimize annual economic costs by optimizing supply chain network structure. The transportation distance and transportation cost in the supply chain network system can be calculated based on geographical location (Brummelen, 2013). The following assumptions were taken into account in establishing the mathematical model:

a) The locations and processing capacities of both petrochemical refineries and bio-refineries are known.
b) The processing costs at different stages of the production process are known and directly proportional to the amount of processing.
c) The fixed cost of constructing a facility is known.
d) A petrochemical refinery can process both diesel oil and VGO by using the co-production process of catalytic cracking.
e) The ratio of feedstock produced through the co-production is fixed and must be put into production in the form of 1 part bio-oil and 9 parts vacuum gas oil.

3. Mathematical model

The mathematical model is developed to minimize the total annual cost (TAC), which includes the construction cost of plants, transportation cost between nodes, storage cost and processing fees for each node. The objective function:

$$F = Min(CostT + CostP + CostS + CostF) \tag{1}$$

Where, CostT indicates the cost incurred in the transportation process within the supply chain, CostP represents the expenses of processing, CostS represents the cost of warehousing, CostF indicates the fixed cost of constructing factories.

The cost of transportation is directly proportional to the distance and the amount of goods being transported.

$$CostT = \sum_{t\epsilon T}\left[\sum_{i\epsilon I}\sum_{j\epsilon J} c_{ij} \times d_{ij} \times q_{ijt} + \sum_{j\epsilon J}\sum_{k\epsilon K} c_{jk} \times d_{jk} \times q_{jkt} + \sum_{k\epsilon K}\sum_{o\epsilon O} c_{ko} \times d_{ko} \times q_{kot} + \sum_{j\epsilon J}\sum_{m\epsilon M} c_{jm} \times d_{jm} \times q_{jmt} + \sum_{k\epsilon K}\sum_{m\epsilon M} c_{km} \times d_{km} \times q_{kmt} + \sum_{m\epsilon M}\sum_{o\epsilon O} c_{mo} \times d_{mo} \times q_{mot}\right] \tag{2}$$

The cost of production and storage is calculated by multiplying the quantity by the unit cost. The fixed cost of factory construction is obtained by multiplying the number of factories to be built by the unit fixed construction cost. A detailed description of each variable and constraint is not given for space reasons.

$$CostP = \sum_{t\epsilon T}\left[\sum_{j\epsilon J} CJU \times A_{jt} + \sum_{k\epsilon K} CKU \times A_{kt} + \sum_{m\epsilon M} CMU \times A_{mt} + \sum_{m\epsilon M} CMU \times A_{mmt}\right] \tag{3}$$

$$CostS = \sum_{t\epsilon T}\left[\sum_{j\epsilon J} CJS \times S_{jt} + \sum_{k\epsilon K} CKS \times S_{kt} + \sum_{m\epsilon M} CMS \times S_{mt} + \sum_{m\epsilon M} CMS \times S_{mmt}\right] \tag{4}$$

$$CostF = \sum_{j\epsilon J} f_j \times Y_j + \sum_{k\epsilon K} f_k \times Y_k + \sum_{m\epsilon M} f_m \times Y_m + \sum_{mm\epsilon MM} f_{mm} \times Y_{mm} \tag{5}$$

4. Case studies and data results

In this supply chain network, location and capacity data for biomass production and refineries in Illinois comes from the official website of the U.S. Energy Information Administration (EIA). The locations of ten biomass points, four crude oil points, seven potential pretreatment plants, seven potential petrochemical refineries, four diesel demand points and four gasoline demand points were selected based on geographic location. Consider storage for pretreatment plants, biorefineries and petrochemical refineries. The MINLP models for all cases are encoded in Lingo 18.0.

As can be seen from the supply chain network in Figure 1, there are three production lines in the network. The production Line 1 is the biomass raw material through the pretreatment plant to produce bio-oil, the bio-oil is transported to the biodiesel refinery to produce diesel, and then transported to the diesel demand point. The production Line 2 is to mix the bio-oil produced by the biomass with the VGO in a certain proportion and then transport to a catalytic cracking petrochemical refinery to produce gasoline and diesel, which are finally transported to the demand point. The production Line 3 is the production of gasoline and diesel by catalytic cracking of VGO directly, and the two products produced are transported to the point of demand.

Seasonality can have an impact on annual costs. Taking into account seasonality, the corresponding annual total costs are shown in the table below. Considering seasonality, there is only a less increase in annual costs (0.002%). This is because when the supply chain is involved in changes in supply and demand, the cheapest production methods may not be able to meet demand at any given time, or other production lines may need to be mobilized to make up for the impact of supply and demand changes over time. Since the supply of raw materials is basically sufficient, the impact of seasonal fluctuations on annual costs is not obvious. When collaborative production is not considered, the supply chain only runs production Line 1 and production Line 3, and the total annual cost of the non-integrated supply chain is higher than that of the integrated supply chain, as shown in the table below. This shows that collaborative production can reduce the annual cost (0.9%) of this supply chain.

Table 1. Annual costs under different circumstances

Type	Annual Cost (Millions of dollars)
Consider seasonality of raw materials and seasonality of demand	924.38
Do not consider the seasonality of raw materials and demand	924.36
Non-cooperative production model	932.91
Cooperative production model	924.38

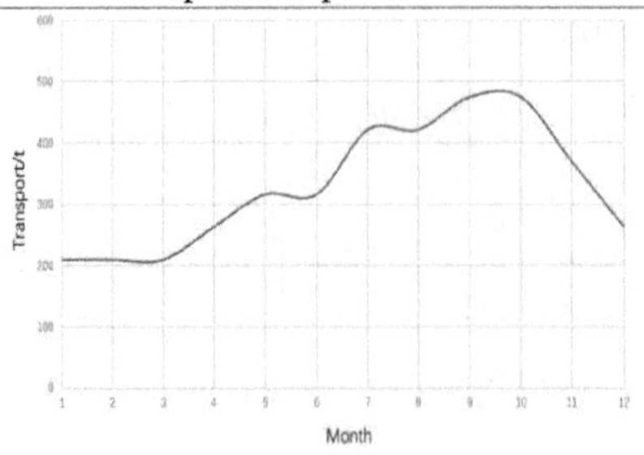

Figure 2. Monthly variation curve of biomass yield

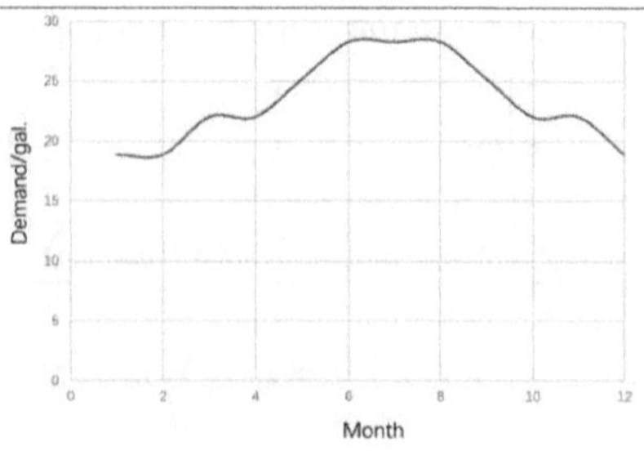

Figure 3. Monthly variation curve of gasoline demand

The supply of biomass is more seasonal, with higher yields generally in autumn. The monthly variation curve of biomass yield is shown in Figure 2. The demand for gasoline is higher in the summer, and the demand curve with month is shown in Figure 3. The rest of the supply and demand are more stable and are not considered in this case. The number of raw materials transported by each production line in different months is shown in Figure 4.

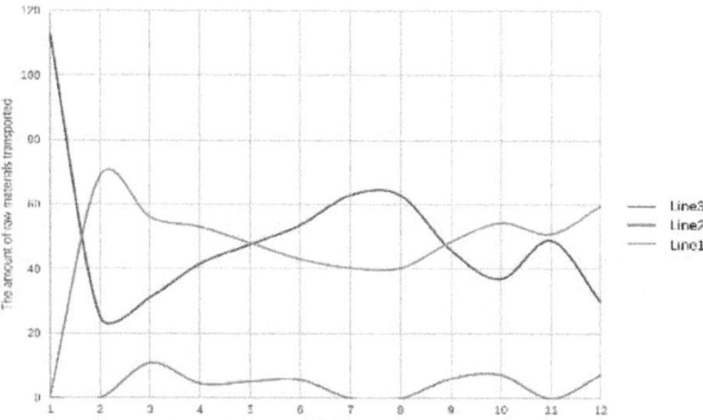

Figure 4. The number of raw materials transported by each production line in different months

As can be seen from Figure 4, at the beginning of the year, due to the low yield of biomass and the long processing cycle (pretreatment is required before it can be put into production), Line3 became the mainstream of production proportion. With the increase in the output of biomass raw materials and the smooth processing of pretreatment links, the biomass production capacity has been increased, and in February, March, April and May, Line1 has become the production line with the largest supply of raw materials. At the same time, the mixed collaborative production Line 2 also gradually occupies a certain production share, and the production share is limited because the economic advantage of this production mode is not as good as that of the traditional model. Since then, the demand for gasoline has increased one after another, and the production capacity of Line1 has not been enough to meet market demand, so Line3 has the highest conversion rate of gasoline, and has once again become the mainstream of production. After September, the demand for gasoline has decreased, and the proportion of production of two production lines with biomass as raw material Line 1,2 has increased. In both cases, the number and location of factories in each node are the same, which indicates that in this model, the addition of seasonality does not affect the optimal structure of the supply chain.

5. Conclusion

This study proposes a new collaborative production supply chain model, which integrates the catalytic cracking process in traditional petrochemical production with the biodiesel production process to increase production and realize the conversion of biomass feedstock to gasoline products. In this paper, a mixed integer nonlinear programming (MINLP) model is proposed to optimize the network model of the integrated supply chain of biodiesel and petroleum. An integrated biodiesel and petroleum supply chain that makes better use of petrochemical plant idle capacity, minimizes total annual costs, and improves energy supply reliability. In order to deal with the complexity and uncertainty of the actual biodiesel supply chain, the biomass supply variance is subdivided into 12-

month sub-intervals to improve the reliability of the supply data. The goal is to keep annual operating expenses to a minimum as low as possible. Consider a real case in the U.S. state of Illinois. Co-production can reduce the cost of the supply chain, which is much more environmentally friendly due to the addition of biomass feedstocks. The addition of seasonality adds a small amount to the annual cost of the system, but allows the supply chain to better regulate transportation and distribution at different times. When there is seasonality, the system will optimize the supply chain network structure according to the demand of different months, and change the contribution of each production line. However, the addition of seasonality does not affect the optimal structure of this supply chain system.

References

Z. Ghelichi, M. Saidi-Mehrabad, M.S. Pishvaee, A stochastic programming approach toward optimal design and planning of an integrated green biodiesel supply chain network under uncertainty: A case study, Energy. 156 (2018) 661–687.

S. Depren, Energy consumption and environmental degradation nexus: A systematic review and meta-analysis of fossil fuel and renewable energy consumption, Ecol. Inform. 70 (2022) 101747.

J. Inumaru, Fossil fuels combustion and environmental issues, Adv. Power Boil. (2021) 1–56.

O. Ellabban, enewable energy resources: Current status, future prospects and their enabling technology, Renew. Sustain. Energy Rev. 39 (2014) 748–764.

W. Marquardt, A. Harwardt, M. Hechinger,, The biorenewables opportunity - toward next generation process and product systems, AIChE J. 56 (2010) 2228–2235.

D. Yue, F. You, S.W. Snyder, Biomass-to-bioenergy and biofuel supply chain optimization: Overview, key issues and challenges, Comput. Chem. Eng. 66 (2014) 36–56.

P. Daoutidis, A. Kelloway, W.A. Marvin, S. Rangarajan, A.I. Torres, Process systems engineering for biorefineries: new research vistas, Curr. Opin. Chem. Eng. 2 (2013) 442–447.

K. Tong, F. You, G. Rong, Robust design and operations of hydrocarbon biofuel supply chain integrating with existing petroleum refineries considering unit cost objective, Comput. Chem. Eng. 68 (2014) 128–139.

U.S. department of energy, Replacing the Whole BarrelTo Reduce U.S. Dependence on Oil, (2013).

A.T. Espinoza Pérez, M. Camargo, P.C. Narváez Rincón, M. Alfaro Marchant, Key challenges and requirements for sustainable and industrialized biorefinery supply chain design and management: A bibliographic analysis, Renew. Sustain. Energy Rev. 69 (2017) 350–359.

L. Wu, Y. Yang, T. Yan, Y. Wang, L. Zheng, K. Qian, F. Hong, Sustainable design and optimization of co-processing of bio-oil and vacuum gas oil in an existing refinery, Renew. Sustain. Energy Rev. 130 (2020) 109952.

ILSoybean, Home, Ill. Soybean Assoc. (2023). https://www.ilsoy.org.

USDA, Field Crops Usual Planting and Harvesting Dates, (2010).

A. Sheel, Y. p. Singh, V. Nath, Issues of biodiesel supply chain for public sector transportation in India, Int. J. Bus. Perform. Supply Chain Model. 12 (2021) 27–43.

Y. (Eric) Huang, Y. Fan, C.-W. Chen, An Integrated Biofuel Supply Chain to Cope with Feedstock Seasonality and Uncertainty, Transp. Sci. 48 (2014) 540–554.

K. Tong, M.J. Gleeson, G. Rong, F. You, Optimal design of advanced drop-in hydrocarbon biofuel supply chain integrating with existing petroleum refineries under uncertainty, Biomass Bioenergy. 60 (2014) 108–120.

F. Xie, Y. Huang, S. Eksioglu, Integrating multimodal transport into cellulosic biofuel supply chain design under feedstock seasonality with a case study based on California, Bioresour. Technol. 152 (2014) 15–23

G.V. Brummelen, Heavenly Mathematics: The Forgotten Art of Spherical Trigonometry, Princeton University Press, 2013.

Flavio Manenti, Gintaras V. Reklaitis (Eds.), Proceedings of the 34th European Symposium on Computer Aided Process Engineering / 15th International Symposium on Process Systems Engineering (ESCAPE34/PSE24), June 2-6, 2024, Florence, Italy
 http://dx.doi.org/10.1016/B978-0-443-28824-1.50208-8

Analyzing a Database of Digitalized Process Flowsheets to Extract Relevant Initialization Structures for Evolutionary Process Synthesis Methods

Jean-Marc Commenge*, Andres Pina-Martinez

Université de Lorraine, CNRS, LRGP, F-54000 Nancy, France
jean-marc.commenge@univ-lorraine.fr

Abstract

Process synthesis using evolutionary methods, based on the iterative application of mutation operators, requires to initialize the method by one or a set of process structures. Appropriate initialization might reduce computation times by providing first proposals that reduce the number of mutations to reach optimal structures, in terms of units and connectivity. This work demonstrates how to identify, from a given database of flowsheets, the most-central flowsheets that might play a pivotal role in the evolutionary approach. Three centrality criteria (outcloseness, betweenness and pagerank) are combined in a Pareto analysis to ensure centrality and diversity of the initial population.

Keywords: process synthesis, flowsheet, database, evolutionary distance, centrality.

1. Introduction

The energy transition requires certain chemical processes to be redesigned to adapt to sustainable operation (biobased inputs, intermittency, decentralized production, etc.) and new processes to be created from scratch, increasing the need for fast, or even automatic, process synthesis methods. These methods have considerably evolved from heuristics-based to mathematical-programming based optimization (leading often to MINLP problems): by reducing the influence of prior knowledge and expert bias, evolutionary approaches enlarge the scope of attainable structures, but may be resource demanding to converge to optimal structures. Evolutionary approaches differ in the way they integrate the evolutionary feature, either by including a genetic algorithm in the optimization of a proposed population or superstructure (Koch et al., 2007; Skiborowski et al., 2015), or by applying mutation operators to evolving process structures (Wang et al., 2015; Neveux, 2018). In all cases, proper initialization with unbiased complex process structures should enable accelerate convergence while enlarging the explored domain.

To identify appropriate initialization structures, a database of digitalized process flowsheets has been created, which enables to visualize statistical distributions of these processes with respect to their number of units and streams, that directly relates to process engineering strategies such as process integration and intensification. Analysis of mutations operators enables to define a semi-distance between structures: the flowsheet distribution can then be studied according to centrality criteria. Three centrality criteria are computed (outcloseness, betweenness and pagerank) yielding to a Pareto front ensuring diversity and relevance of selected structures. This work presents the database of digitalized flowsheets, the main features of their statistical distributions, the computation of the evolutionary distance and the most central process flowsheets with respect to the centrality criteria.

2. Database of digitalized flowsheets

2.1. General features

The database used for this analysis contains 767 flowsheets, digitalized from 278 papers published since 2006. They include 9971 units (including process inputs and outputs) and 10721 streams. For each flowsheet, the database provides an entry name, the number of streams, unit operations, process inputs, outputs and units among a list of 23 types (Absorber, Compressor, Cyclone, Distillation, etc.). The ordered list of units, with meaningful prefixes and numbers to distinguish duplicate units, is provided as well as the incidence matrix: each column corresponds to a unit, and each line to a stream with values -1 or +1 to identify upstream or downstream units respectively. Additional data include the flowsheet image, keywords, species and the scientific reference. Among the 9971 units, all 23 types of units are present despite a large domination of 1263 heat exchangers, 1173 distillation columns and 818 mixers compared to only 4 filters, 5 dryers and 9 mills.

2.2. Statistical distribution of the flowsheet's population

Figure 1 presents projections of the population as a function of the number of process inputs and outputs (left) and number of streams and unit operations (right). Grey-shaded areas indicate impossible zones: except 6 cycles which possess no input or output, a process with a non-null number of inputs (resp. outputs) must contain a non-null number of outputs (resp. inputs). Also, a process with a number of units larger than the number of streams plus one is not feasible. In Figure 1 (left), despite a mode corresponding to 2 inputs and 2 outputs with 131 structures, the distribution is asymmetric with a medoid corresponding to 2 inputs and 3 outputs. This large number of process outputs with respect to the inputs might result from the vast literature dedicated to separation processes. Despite the large number of inputs/outputs of some flowsheets, up to a total of 16, almost 90 % of them exhibit less than 4 inputs and 4 outputs.

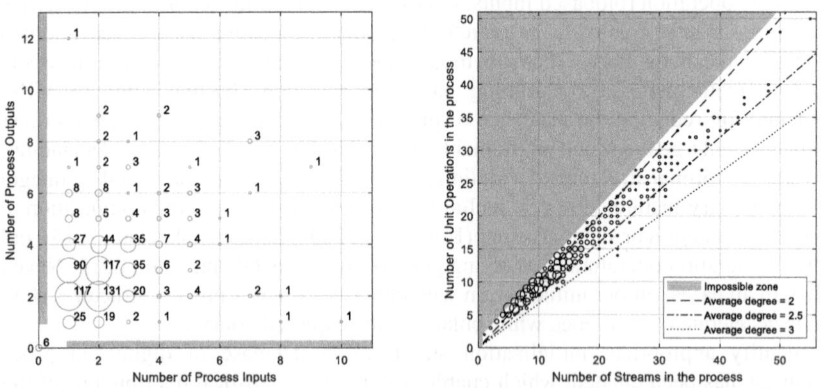

Figure 1: Projections of the distribution of digitalized flowsheets as a function of the number of process inputs and outputs (left) and number of streams and unit operations (right).

In Figure 1 (right), the distribution ranges from a single stream (Neveux et al., 2018) up to a complex power-to-liquids process with 55 units and 50 streams (Gao et al., 2022), with a dense core around 10 units and 10 streams. The distribution shape is governed by the average degree of the process graphs. In a graph representing a process, the degree of a vertex (process unit) is the number of edges (process streams) adjacent to this vertex.

The average degrees of the processes range from 1 (single stream) up to 3.28, with a global average of 2.16. Only a few dozen processes exhibit an average degree above 2.5, whereas the majority lies between 2 and 2.5. Despite these low average degrees, some processes contain highly-connected units, mainly multi-fluid heat exchangers, with an individual degree up to 12.

3. Evolutionary methods, mutations and evolutionary distance

3.1. Evolutionary methods, mutations and their impact on process structures

Evolutionary methods based on step-wise modifications of process structures by application of mutation operators mainly consider insertion and removal of units, and streams permutations (Wang et al., 2015; Neveux, 2018). In the present work, these operators are parameterized with respect to the degree of the inserted/removed units, and a new operator consisting in merging one input and one output is added (Table 1). For each operator, Table 1 indicates its impact on the total number of inputs and outputs, the number of streams and number of units. For example, inserting a distillation column of degree 3 (D = 3) increases the number of inputs and outputs by one unit, whereas the numbers of streams and units increase by two.

Table 1: Impact of the application of various mutation operators on the total number of process inputs and outputs, number of streams and number of units. D denotes the degree of a unit.

Mutation operator	$N_{inputs} + N_{outputs}$	$N_{streams}$	N_{units}
Permute stream connections	=	=	=
Add a Dth-degree unit ($D \geq 2$)	$+D-2$	$+D-1$	$+D-1$
Remove a Dth-degree unit ($D \geq 2$)	$+D-2$	-1	$+D-3$
Merge one input and one output	-2	-1	-2

3.2. Definition and computation of an evolutionary (semi-)distance

The evolutionary distance used to select the most appropriate process structures for initialization is defined as the minimum number of mutations to be performed to transform a given process structure P_{source} into another given process structure P_{target}, under a set of authorized mutations, excluding stream permutations. Being given two structures P_{source} and P_{target} with their lists of units and incidence matrices, the computation of the distance $d(P_{source}, P_{target})$ includes the following steps:

1. List all units (except inputs and outputs) and corresponding degrees in the source and target structures,
2. Compare the number of inputs and outputs and number of streams of structures to calculate the required increments $\Delta_{Inputs + Outputs,req}$ and $\Delta_{streams,req}$,
3. Identify all units (with type and degree) that are not common to both structures,
4. Initialize actual increments $\Delta_{Inputs+Outputs}$ and $\Delta_{streams}$ and $d(P_{source},P_{target})$ to 0,
5. Update actual increments $\Delta_{Inputs + Outputs}$ and $\Delta_{streams}$ according to Table 1, and increase the distance $d(P_{source}, P_{target})$ by one unit for all necessary mutations:
    a. Remove all not-common units included in the source structure,
    b. Add all not-common units missing in the target structure,
6. Merge one input and one output of the target structure as many times as required (and accordingly increase the distance $d(P_{source}, P_{target})$ by one unit) so that $\Delta_{Inputs+Outputs}$ and $\Delta_{streams}$ be equal to $\Delta_{Inputs + Outputs,req}$ and $\Delta_{streams,req}$.

This computation sequence provides a measurement of the difference between structures, more specifically a semi-distance: indeed, whereas identity and positivity conditions are obvious, the symmetry condition is not satisfied: d(P_{source}, P_{target}) is not always equal to d(P_{target}, P_{source}). The triangle inequality has been checked on 60 million triplets (P_1, P_2, P_3). This lack of symmetry slows down the computation of the distance matrix and hinders some post-treatment methods. When necessary, a real distance can be defined by averaging d(P_{target}, P_{source}) and d(P_{source}, P_{target}).

Figure 2 (left) presents the distribution of evolutionary distances between all couples of process structures in the database. Whereas 480 couples exhibit a null distance, indicating the presence of similar processes in the database that only differ by their connections, the average distance is about 17.5 mutations, confirming the diversity of the flowsheets. The maximum distance is as large as 70, demonstrating that even large flowsheets can include radically different units in terms of type or connectivity. The shape of the distribution does not enable to identify any significant structure (clusters, gaps, etc.) in the population.

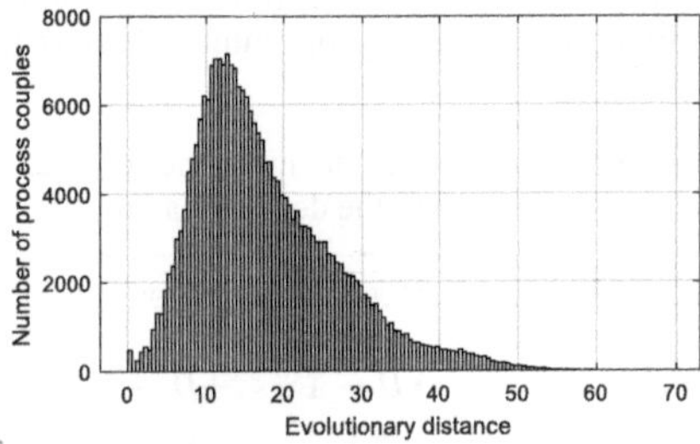

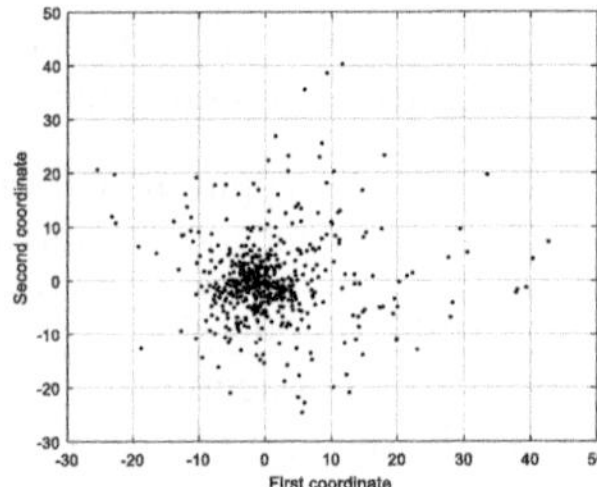

Figure 2: Distribution of evolutionary distances (left) and visualization of the population of flowsheets by 2D multi-dimensional scaling (right).

A 2D multidimensional scaling (MDS) is presented in Figure 2 (right) (Aggarwal, 2015). MDS is a projective method for dimensionality reduction that optimizes a distribution of points (here on a plane) that exhibit a distance matrix similar to the original data. Despite its projective character, this view confirms the lack of structure in the population, that looks like a gaussian distribution. The maximum distance between the points on the far right and those on the far left, about 70, is coherent with the distance distribution.

4. Analysis of most-central flowsheets

The population of flowsheets can be considered as a graph whose nodes are the process structures and whose edges are weighted by the distance between structures. To identify flowsheets that might be relevant for initialization of evolutionary approaches, three centrality criteria are computed for the database flowsheets (Aggarwal, 2015):

- Outcloseness measures how many mutations are required to access any other structure j from a structure i. Centrality is maximal when the sum of distances is minimal, explaining the use of the inverse of the sum of distances as:

$$J_{outcloseness}(i) = \frac{1}{\sum_{j \neq i} d(i,j)} \tag{1}$$

- Betweenness measures how often each process structure appears on a shortest path between two other structures in the population. For structures s and t, the total number of shortest paths between them is denoted N_{st}, and the number of shortest paths including the structure i is denoted $n_{st}(i)$:

$$J_{betweenness}(i) = \sum_{s,t \neq i} \frac{n_{st}(i)}{N_{st}} \tag{2}$$

- Pagerank measures the probability of presence at the node i of the graph of flowsheets during a random walk through this graph. At each node in the graph, the next node is chosen from all downstream nodes with a probability inversely proportional to their evolutionary distance. The pagerank can be interpreted as the average time spent at each node during this random walk.

Figure 3 presents the centrality criteria for all structures as a function of their numbers of streams and units. Structures of interest possess maximal values of the criteria. All criteria exhibit similar trends, with a decrease as a function of the number of streams and units. Betweenness is the most discriminatory whereas outcloseness and pagerank have similar shapes. Large structures mainly exhibit low centrality but exceptions exist: some large processes with up to 48 units exhibit medium centrality. According to outcloseness and betweenness, best structures are small including less than 5 streams/units, whereas pagerank favors structures with 6 to 10 streams/units, indicating that a compromise might be necessary to ensure relevance and diversity of the initialization.

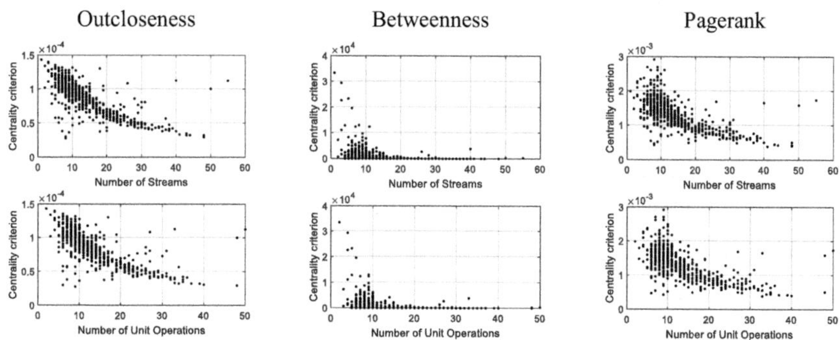

Figure 3: Evolutions of the three centrality criteria for all structures in the database as a function of their numbers of streams and unit operations.

To consider all criteria, a multi-objective analysis is performed in the 3D space composed by the criteria. Projections in Figure 4 highlight with circles the 20 non-dominated structures according to the three criteria. The similar trends observed in Figure 3 reduce the number of Pareto structures while maintaining diversity of their central character. Only 8 circles (with overlap) are visible in Figure 4 confirming the presence of similar structures (subject to stream permutations).

Figure 5 presents the process flowsheets of the 8 different types observed along the Pareto front. Except inputs and outputs, they only contain distillation columns, mixers and splitters. The simplest one is the single stream (most central structure with respect to single-objective optimization of outcloseness), and the most complex includes three columns with a recycle stream (most central structure with respect to single-objective optimization of pagerank).

Despite the surprising absence of heat exchangers in the optimal solutions (most frequent unit type in the database), the dominating presence of distillation columns in the database might be a bias that favors this unit type: reduction of the database should be considered on a case by case basis to fit to case studies specifications.

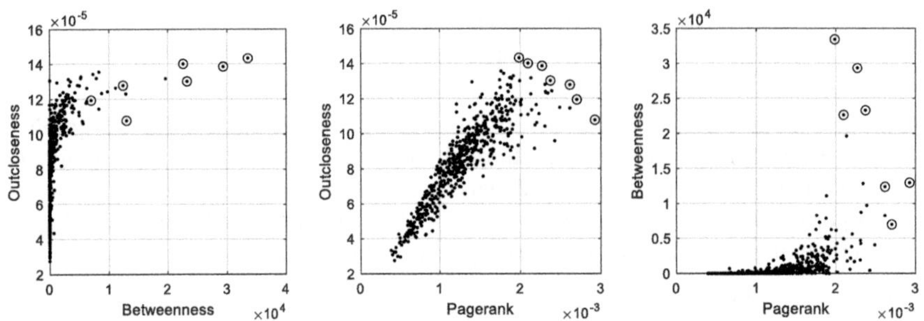

Figure 4: Projections of the database structures over the planes of the three-dimensional space of the three criteria. Circles indicate the structures on the Pareto front.

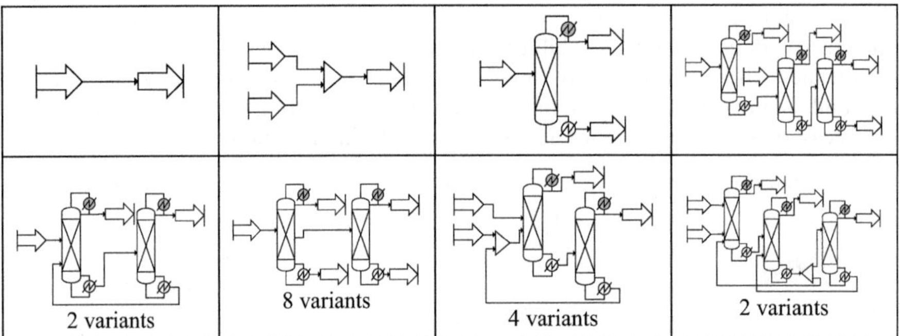

Figure 5: Visualization of the 8 different types of process structures on the Pareto front.

5. Conclusions

Analysis of a flowsheets database enabled to identity 8 types of process structures (and their variants by stream permutation) that are the most central with respect to three centrality criteria (outcloseness, betweenness and pagerank). This pivotal position among the population of flowsheets makes them relevant for initialization of evolutionary approaches for process synthesis, while ensuring some diversity of the initialization. Effective impact of this initialization on the complete process synthesis computation still needs to be quantified as well as the possible introduction of biases.

References

C. Aggarwal, 2015, Data Mining – the textbook, Springer.

R. Gao, L. Zhang, L. Wang, X. Zhang, C. Zhang, K.-W. Jun, S. K. Kim, H.-G. Park, Y. Gao, Y. Zhu, T. Zhao, H. Wan, G. Guan, 2022, A comparative study on hybrid power-to-liquids/power-to-gas processes coupled with different water electrolysis technologies, Energy Conversion and Management, 263, 115671.

C. Koch, F. Cziesla, G. Tsatsatonis, 2007, Optimization of combined cycle power plants using evolutionary algorithms, Chemical Engineering and Processing, 46, 1151-1159.

T. Neveux, 2018, Ab-initio process synthesis using evolutionary programming, Chemical Engineering Science, 185, 209-221.

M. Skiborowski, M. Rautenberg, W. Marquardt, 2015, A hybrid evolutionary-deterministic optimization approach for conceptual design, Ind. Eng. Chem. Res., 54, 10054-10072.

L. Wang, P. Voll, M. Lampe, Y. Yang, A. Bardow, 2015, Superstructure-free synthesis and optimization of thermal power plants, Energy, 91, 700-711.

Flavio Manenti, Gintaras V. Reklaitis (Eds.), Proceedings of the 34th European Symposium on Computer Aided Process Engineering / 15th International Symposium on Process Systems Engineering (ESCAPE34/PSE24), June 2-6, 2024, Florence, Italy
 http://dx.doi.org/10.1016/B978-0-443-28824-1.50209-X

Robust Scheduling of Energy Systems Under Forecasting Uncertainty – A Multi-Parametric Optimization Approach

Rahul Kakodkar[a,b], Dustin Kenefake[a,b], Harsh Shah[a,b], Iosif Pappas[c], C. Doga Demirhan[d], Mete Mutlu[d], Xiao Fu[c], Efstratios N. Pistikopoulos [a,b,*]

[a]*Artie McFerrin Department of Chemical Engineering, Texas A&M University, 3122 TAMU, College Station, TX 77843, USA*

[b]*Texas A&M Energy Institute, Texas A&M University, 1617 Research Pkwy, College Station, TX 77845, USA*

[c] *Shell Technology Center, Shell Global Solutions International B.V., Amsterdam, Netherlands*

[d] *Shell Technology Center, Shell International Exploration and Production Inc., Houston, TX*

*stratos@tamu.edu

Abstract

Energy systems are affected by uncertainty at many scales; in the short term, scheduling energy systems with a high penetration of renewables can be challenging owing to the intermittency of solar and wind. Predictive frameworks can provide some insight through forecasts of weather and demand patterns. However, the forecasts themselves can introduce uncertainty. Nevertheless, methods exist to quantify the distribution and spread of forecasting error. To this end, we present a framework which leverages from quantified forecasting error to generate robust schedules at varying levels of conservativeness that is tunable by the decision-maker. Here the problem is cast as a multi-period robust optimization problem, then the robust deterministic equivalent is generated wherein our uncertainty in forecast is parameterized resulting in a multi-parametric formulation of the robust energy scheduling problem. This allows for an explicit representation of not only the robust schedule decisions, but also the exact relationship between the cost and forecasting uncertainty. The framework is demonstrated on a robust energy system scheduling problem involving a wind farm with uncertain availability and small modular nuclear reactor for power generation, and lithium-ion batteries for energy storage.

Keywords: forecasting, optimal scheduling, robust programming, multi-parametric optimization

1. Introduction

Renewable solar and wind energy has been proposed as an alternative energy source to support the push towards decarbonization. However, solar and wind are both available intermittently which presents a significant challenge in terms of planning and scheduling of energy systems (Kakodkar et al., 2022). It becomes important for decision makers to be aware of, even hedge against, the uncertainties that systems are affected by. In the multiscale multiperiod approach variabilities such as renewable intermittency, resource demand, costing parameters for resources and technology are treated through the consideration of time-series data at various scales (Zhang and Grossman, 2019) (Demirhan et al. 2020). Renewable intermittency is captured through historical weather data such as wind speed, solar irradiance, cloud cover, etc. While such frameworks provide considerable insight into integrated design and scheduling, resulting networks do not necessarily guarantee robustness.

Forecasting of weather-related phenomena and demand can be helpful to schedule the dispatch of power. However, the actual realizations can differ considerably from forecasts. To an extent, it is possible to estimate the uncertainty in predictions via methods such as Monte Carlo Dropout (MCD) which provides a more robust estimate of predictions by quantifying uncertainty or confidence. This allows quantitative insight into the extent of predictive error which decision makers can utilize to hedge against uncertainty in predictions. Such risk aware approaches can also be applied to determine the trade-off between cost and robustness. Additionally, multi-parametric optimization allows the generation of explicit algebraic solutions as a function of parameters, allowing to generate closed form solutions of optimization problems over a set of parameter realizations; further and more detailed information can be found in (Pappas et al., 2021).

To this end, we propose a multi-parametric optimization methodology that leverages the error bounds of forecasts to allow decision makers to generate the family of parametric robust schedules. The problem is first modelled as a parametric robust scheduling optimization problem, where the range of forecasting realizations is parameterized. This is then transformed into the parametric robust equivalent, which allows for the explicit solution as a function of the uncertainty in the forecast. This is then solved to recover the explicit algebraic relationship between uncertainty and the resulting robust schedule. This methodology is applied to a 24-period scheduling problem of an energy system with the option to meet a constant power demand for hydrogen production through uncertain wind forecasts and dispatchable nuclear energy, with an option for battery storage.

2. Methodology

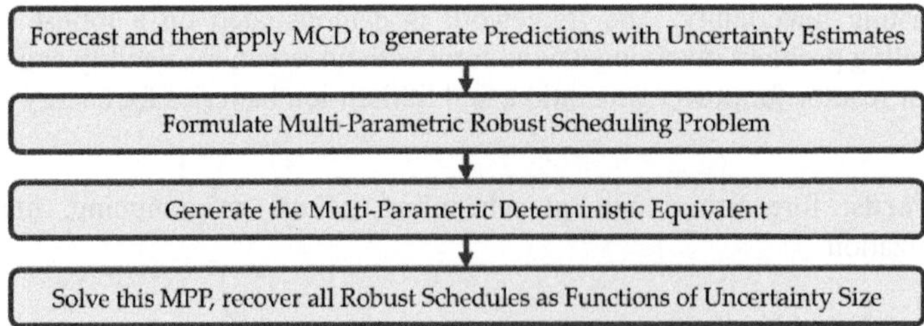

Figure 1: Overview of proposed methodology

The methodology of generating the parameterized set of robust schedules is described in this section. It is a four-step process, firstly the forecast and the forecast uncertainty are quantified, secondly the multiparametric robust scheduling problem is formulated, then this is converted into a deterministic equivalent where the uncertainty set for each forecast is parameterized, finally this is solved to recover the explicit algebraic relationship between uncertainty in the forecasts and the accompanying robust schedule. The overall flow of this methodology is summarized in Figure 1.

Recurrent Neural networks (NN) can be used to predict model outputs when modelling the underlying phenomena is elusive. One such method, Long Short-Term Memory (LSTM) takes time and sequence into account making it especially good at predicting weather patterns. The MCD model is applied during the model training which provides the distribution of the predictions, allowing the error surrounding the predictions to be inferred. This gives us the uncertainty bands around the predictions based on the alpha choice level, which is the chosen level of significance that determines the width of the confidence interval. Figure 2 illustrates these predictions and the confidence intervals surrounding these forecasts at chosen levels (99%, 95%, 90%, 85%).

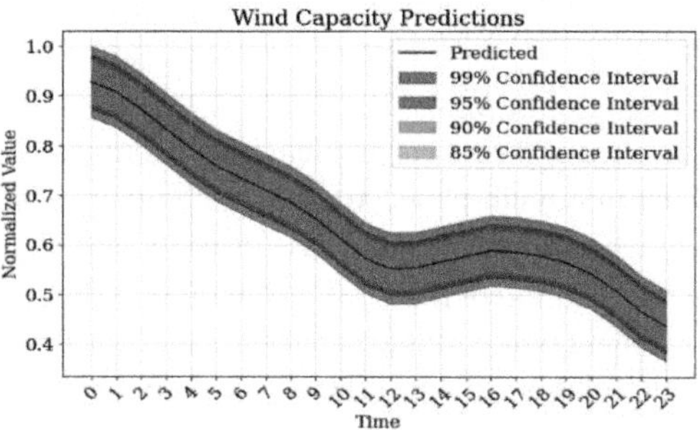

Figure 2. Short term wind forecast with error bounds using LSTM and MCD

A robust scheduling optimization problem is then formulated to model an energy system. The formulation considers consumption (C), inventory (Inv), discharge (S) for resource ($r \in R$), and production levels (P) for processes ($i \in I$) as variables, while Cap^{Pred} is the predicted production capacity for a process in the time period ($t \in T$). The demand is fixed at a constant (D). The associated costs in the objective are purchase cost of resource (C^{purch}) and variable operation cost (V_{opex}). A diminishing cost factor, δ, is applied to prioritize decisions taken earlier in the scheduling horizon. Inventory can be transferred between different periods, which is captured in the inventory balance constraints (7). The range of the uncertainty, $\sigma \cdot \epsilon$, in the prediction is bounded by the parametric variable, θ. By modifying θ, the size of the uncertainty set also changes, and thus the level of robustness. Such that when $\theta = 0$, this is simply the nominal case, where no error is considered in the forecasted variables, Cap^{Pred}. More generally, each uncertainty, ϵ, can be parameterized separately, here we model them together, so that all uncertainties share the same confidence intervals.

$$min \sum_{t \in T} \sum_{r \in R} \delta^t \cdot C^{purch} \cdot C_{r,t} + \sum_{t \in T} \sum_{i \in I} \delta^t \cdot V_{opex} \cdot P_{i,t} \tag{1}$$

$$Inv_{r,t} \leq Cap_{i,t}^{Store-Max} \qquad \forall\, r \in R^{store}, t \in T \tag{2}$$

$$P_{i,t} \leq Cap_{i,t}^{Pred} + \sigma_{i,t}^{i}\epsilon_{i,t}^{i} \qquad \forall\, i \in I, t \in T, \forall\, \epsilon_{i,t}^{i} \in [-\theta, \theta] \quad (3)$$

$$-S_{r,t} \leq -D_{r,t} + \sigma_{r,t}\epsilon_{r,t} \qquad \forall\, r \in R^{sell}, t \in T, \forall \epsilon \in [-\theta, \theta] \quad (4)$$

$$C_{r,t} \leq C^{max}{}_{r,t} \qquad \forall\, r \in R^{purch}, t \in T \quad (5)$$

$$-S_{r,t} + \sum_{i \in I} P_{i,t} \cdot \eta(i,r) = 0 \qquad \forall\, r \in R^{sell}, t \in T \quad (6)$$

$$-Inv_{r,t-1} + Inv_{r,t} - \sum_{i \in I} P_{i,t} \cdot \eta(i,r) = 0 \qquad \forall\, r \in R^{store}, t \in T \quad (7)$$

$$C_{r,t} + \sum_{i \in I} P_{i,t} \cdot \eta(i,r) = 0 \qquad \forall\, r \in R^{cons}, t \in T \quad (8)$$

The deterministic equivalent of the robust problem is then formulated with the uncertainty in the forecast resulting in a multi-parametric linear program (mpLP). This is done by robustifying constraint 3 by taking the worst-case realization of $\epsilon_{i,t}^{i}$, which is simply $-\theta$ in this case, as shown in eqn. 9 (Ben-Tal and Nemirovski, 1998). This transformation results in a mpLP containing only a single parameter, and thus can be efficiently solved to generate an explicit solution of the schedule as a function of the parameterized uncertainty. Schedules for any choice of robustness can then be generated by varying the θ parameter.

$$P_{i,t} \leq Cap_{i,t}{}^{Pred} - \sigma_{i,t}^{i}\theta \quad (9)$$

3. Case Study and Discussion

We consider a simple energy system as seen in Figure 3, which seeks to meet a constant demand of power for a hydrogen production unit. The demand is met through generation from a wind farm (WF); a small modular nuclear reactor (SMR) is able to supplement power generation at a higher cost, and a lithium ion battery (LiI) is available for energy storage. The demand for power is assumed to be constant, while the availability of wind varies with time periods. An initial inventory of power is provided, where maximum inventory is capacitated.

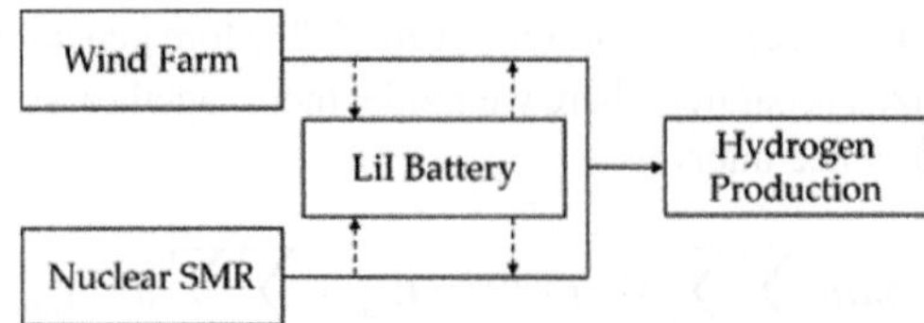

Figure 3. Schematic representation of the considered process

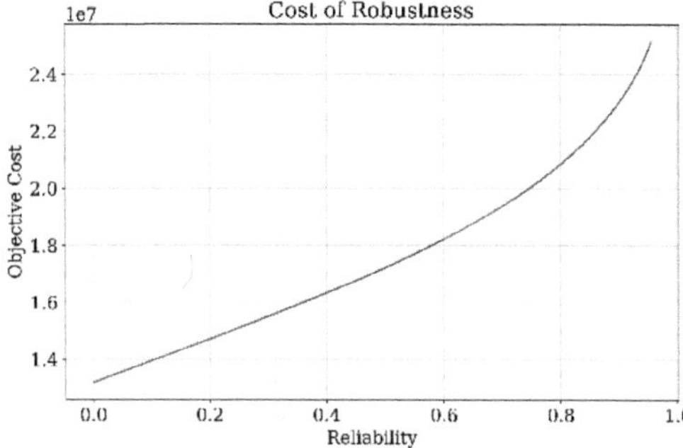

Figure 4. Cost and Reliability Trade-off

LSTM with MCD is used to generate a 24 hour weather forecast with quantified uncertainty. The model is trained on Houston (USA) wind speeds, which serve as a proxy for capacity factors. The model is found to fit well (RMSE: 0.056, MAPE: 2.105, R-squared: 0.971, MDA: 0.663). The wind predictions are used as the parameter $Cap_{i,t}^{Pred}$ with $\sigma_{i,t}^{i}\epsilon_{i,t}^{i}$ representing the range of the uncertainty in forecast. As we do not consider uncertainty in any other process or demand besides WF, we consider $\sigma = 0$ for the rest. The system is modelled in the energiapy python package (Kakodkar and Pistikopoulos, 2023), to generate the initial robust formulation, and the deterministic robust equivalent.

The resultant mpLP is solved to generate the explicit solution containing six critical regions. This was done utilizing PPOPT (Kenefake and Pistikopoulos, 2022), a general purpose multi-parametric optimization solver, using the geometric algorithm. The solution is obtained within 0.5 seconds. The size of the uncertainty set, θ, captures varying degrees of robustness, and the associated schedules are generated along with the objective cost. A comparison of costs over different levels of robustness allows the determination of the cost of robustness as shown in Figure 4.

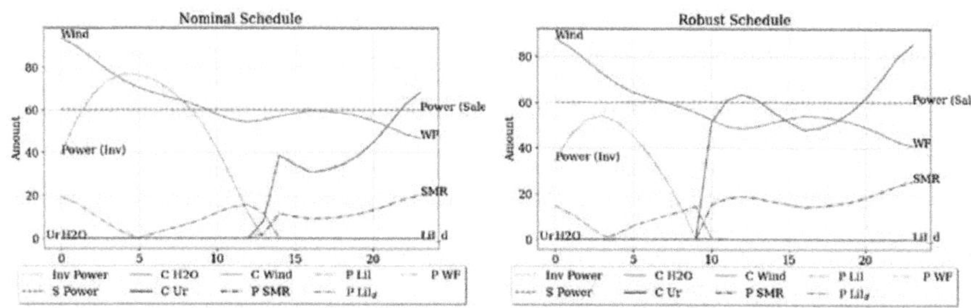

Figure 5. a) Schedule for nominal case study without considering uncertainty b) Robust schedule immunizing against 95% of uncertrainty realizations

The objective cost of the scheduling solution is plotted for two standard deviations ($\theta = 2$) which covers a 95% confidence interval. Further, schedules can be generated for any choice of θ. Figure 5a, shows the schedule for the nominal case, i.e. $\theta = 0$. The robust schedule (Figure 5b), for a 95% confidence interval, maintains a lower inventory level as compared to the nominal case. This is due to the expectation of a lower wind forecast which leads the system to rely on more expensive dispatchable power (SMR). In contrast, the nominal schedule utilizes a larger inventory sourced through wind production; nuclear power is also utilized relatively later in the planning horizon.

4. Conclusions and Future Directions

A risk-aware framework for the scheduling of energy systems under uncertainty was proposed, where the level of robustness is parameterized. Given that the explicit robust solution is found as a function of the uncertainty, it can be used to determine cost optimal schedules under varying degrees of robustness at a given time step. The cost v. reliability curve for schedules was produced, in this case showing a nonlinear relationship between reliability and cost. One of the robust schedules was compared to the nominal solution to visualize the effect of introducing robustness into the scheduling problem. The robustness levels were found to prefer more expensive dispatchable sources of power to uncertain renewables. This in turn affects the inventory levels which are lower for the robust scenario. The system was modelled and optimized in the energiapy and PPOPT python packages respectively. In future iterations, the framework will be augmented to include discrete decisions resulting in robust multi-parametric mixed integer linear programs (mpMILPs), an increase in the size of the energy system that is being analysed, operational constraints such as ramping constraints for dispatchable energy sources, and uncertainty in demand realizations alongside intermittency of renewables, and multiple locations.

5. Acknowledgements

We would like to thank Shell Plc., the Texas A&M Energy Institute, and the Artie McFerrin Department of Chemical Engineering for their generous support and funding.

References

R. Kakodkar, G. He, C. D. Demirhan, M. Arbabzadeh, S. G. Baratsas, S. Avraamidou, and D. Mallapragada, 2020, A review of analytical and optimization methodologies for transitions in multi-scale energy systems., Renewable and Sustainable Energy Reviews, 160, 112277.

Ben-Tal, A., & Nemirovski, A. (1998). Robust convex optimization. Mathematics of operations research, 23(4), 769-805.

Zhang, Q., Martín, M., & Grossmann, I. E. (2019). Integrated design and operation of renewables-based fuels and power production networks. Computers & Chemical Engineering, 122, 80-92.

Demirhan, C. D., Tso, W. W., Powell, J. B., Heuberger, C. F., & Pistikopoulos, E. N. (2020). A multiscale energy systems engineering approach for renewable power generation and storage optimization. Industrial & Engineering Chemistry Research, 59(16), 7706-7721.

Kenefake, D., & Pistikopoulos, E. N. (2022). Ppopt-multiparametric solver for explicit mpc. In Computer Aided Chemical Engineering (Vol. 51, pp. 1273-1278). Elsevier.

Kakodkar, R., & Pistikopoulos, E. (2023, November). Energiapy-an Open Source Python Package for Multiscale Modeling & Optimization of Energy Systems. In 2023 AIChE Annual Meeting. AIChE.

Pappas, I., Kenefake, D., Burnak, B., Avraamidou, S., Ganesh, H. S., Katz, J., ... & Pistikopoulos, E. N. (2021). Multiparametric programming in process systems engineering: Recent developments and path forward. Frontiers in Chemical Engineering, 2, 620168.

Flavio Manenti, Gintaras V. Reklaitis (Eds.), Proceedings of the 34th European Symposium on Computer Aided Process Engineering / 15th International Symposium on Process Systems Engineering (ESCAPE34/PSE24), June 2-6, 2024, Florence, Italy
 http://dx.doi.org/10.1016/B978-0-443-28824-1.50210-6

Optimal Design of Heat Pump Assisted Distillation Sequences

José A. Caballero,[a*] Juan A. Labarta,[a] Zinet Mekidiche-Martínez[a]

[a]*Inttitute of Chemical Process Engineering, University of Alicante. Carretera de S. Vicente s.n. 03690, Alicante, Spain*
caballer@ua.es

Abstract

This study demonstrates enhanced distillation sequence efficiency achieved through the simultaneous optimization of column sequences and various heat integration methods, including thermal couples, direct integration (reboiler-condenser heat exchange), and assisted integration via vapor recompression and bottom flashing cycles. The model applied to the separation of a 4-hydrocarbon mixture, reveals a substantial reduction in total utility costs (hot, cold, and electricity) compared to the top-performing non-heat integrated alternative (fully thermally coupled distillation sequence), achieving a remarkable 78% reduction.

In alignment with the "Roadmap to Achieve Net Zero Emissions by 2050," the proposal to electrify distillation sequences is introduced to replace non-renewable utilities with electricity. Despite cost increases, the optimal electrified solution remains competitive with the best non-heat integrated alternative. However, in sequences involving challenging separations, the most effective solution may necessitate electricity as the sole utility.**Keywords**: Distillation, Vapor Recompression, Electrification, Bottom Flashing, Heat Integration.

1. Introduction

Energy consumption in the industrial sector constitutes approximately one-third of the global energy used, reaching 156 EJ (1.56 10^{20}J) in 2020 and is projected to reach 207 EJ in 2050 (IEA, 2022). Within this sector, chemical and petrochemical industries account for 20-30%. For example, the European Union recorded 21.5% in 2021 (Eurostat), which is around 2.159 EJ. Distillation is the predominant method used for approximately 90 to 95% of all separations and purification processes. This means that distillation contributes to around 40-60% of the energy consumption in chemical and petrochemical industries (Sholl & Lively, 2016).

There are many alternatives to increase the energy efficiency of distillation, such as direct heat integration, thermally coupled distillation (TCD), heat pump-assisted distillation, and multi-effect distillation, etc. (Kruber et al., 2021). Although, ongoing advancements in distillation yield substantial energy and cost savings, fossil fuels remain the primary energy source for distillation.

However, a transformative shift is currently underway, as highlighted in the "Roadmap to Achieve Net Zero Emissions by 2050" (NZE scenario) (IEA, 2022). In this NZE scenario, electricity is set to play a central role in thc global energy landscape, with renewables growing fourfold by 2030. Key milestones include 50% low-emission electricity by 2025, advanced economies' electricity sector achieving net-zero emissions by 2035, and 40% of industrial energy being electric by 2040. The plan aims for 50% of heat demand met by heat pumps by 2045 and 90% renewable-sourced electric energy by 2050, aligning with Industry 4.0's goal of transitioning from fuel to electrified processes. In this work, we present a comprehensive superstructure for generating optimal distillation sequences that simultaneously considers all the possible heat integration alternatives such as thermal couples, direct condenser-reboiler heat integration, and vapor recompression/bottom flashing between different condenser/reboilers not necessarily in the same column.

The objectives are twofold. Firstly, we strive to minimize the overall cost associated with the distillation process. Simultaneously, we aim to maximize the utilization of electricity. We demonstrate that, in certain scenarios, these objectives are not conflicting; however, a substantial compression cost may result in an excess cost for the electrification process.

2. Synthesis of heat pump assisted distillation sequences.

The problem we are dealing with can be stated as follows. Given is a zeotropic N component mixture, we want to separate the individual components using distillation columns considering simultaneously the possibility of thermal couples, direct heat integration (e.g. reboiler-condenser heat exchange), and indirect heat integration through vapor recompression of the vapor before entering the condenser or bottom flashing of the liquid previous to the reboiler. The objective is twofold, to minimize the total annual cost and to significantly decrease the reliance on hot utilities derived from fossil fuels, effectively electrifying the chemical industry.

The initial phase involves the creation of a comprehensive superstructure encompassing all relevant alternatives. For this purpose, we utilize a superstructure exhibiting intermediate characteristics bridging the gap between the State Task Network and State Equipment Network formalism (Yeomans & Grossmann, 1999). The generation process is as follows:

- First, we generate all the possible sub-mixtures (States) excluding final products. For example, in a 4-component mixture, these are ABCD, ABC, BCD, AB, BC, and CD (components named with capital letters ordered by decreasing relative volatilities). For each state, we then generate all potential separation tasks. For instance, for the initial ABCD mixture, tasks include A/BCD, AB/BCD, AB/CD, ABC/BCD, ABC/CD, and ABC/D. Each separation task can be conceptualized as a "pseudo-column," comprising rectifying and stripping sections where components to the left of the slash move to the distillate, those to the right go to the bottoms, and those on both sides are optimally distributed between distillate and bottoms. For instance, in the ABC/CD separation, B is the light key, D is the heavy key, and C is distributed between the distillate and bottom streams. It is important to note that when the sequence of states is fixed, the sequence of separation tasks is entirely determined.
- According to Caballero & Grossmann (2006) and Giridhar & Agrawal (2010), the search space must be formed by 'regular configurations' (sequences of tasks/ states that can be reordered in exactly N-1 columns). So, we must include a set of logical relationships that ensure only regular configurations. See Caballero & Grossmann (2006) for a comprehensive discussion on this topic.
- The connection between two different states can be through a thermal couple, a condenser (reboiler), a vapor recompression (VR) at the top of a column, or a Bottom Flashing (BF). (See Figure 1a, 1b)
- In the case in which two separation tasks generate the same state, these two columns can be stacked to form a single column. In general, it is necessary to increase the reflux (or boil-up) in one of those columns to compensate for the imbalance in flows in the

connection. Alternatively, it is possible to use a condenser/reboiler at that point to compensate for the flow imbalance (Caballero & Grossmann, 2014). This second approach has the advantage of increasing the possibilities for heat integration (Navarro et al., 2013) and it is the approach followed in this work. (See Figure 1c)

To promote direct heat integration, we must allow the distillation columns to operate at different pressures (and therefore different temperatures in the condenser and reboiler). But there are some constraints. Two columns connected by a thermal couple, or two stacked columns must be at the same nominal pressure. Besides, to avoid very different diameters in different sections of the columns all the streams entering a distillation column are assumed to be saturated liquid.

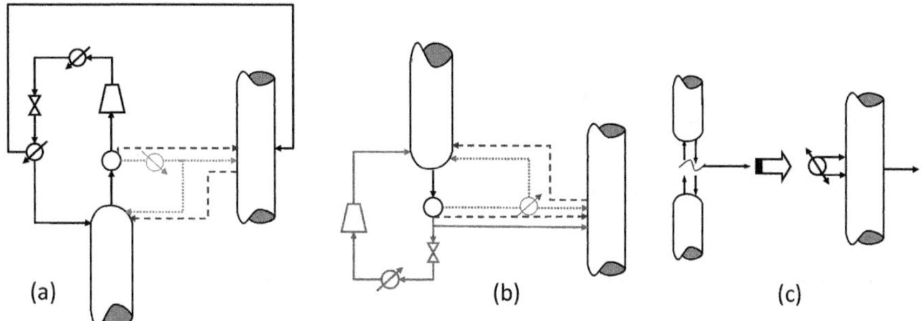

Figure 1. Alternatives for the connectivity between columns. a) The rectifying section of a task includes a condenser (small dotted line, in green), a thermal couple (dotted magenta lines), and Vapor Recompression (continuous lines in blue). b) Stripping section: reboiler (small dotted line in orange, thermal couple (dotted magenta lines), and Bottom Flashing (continuous line in red). c) Stripping and rectifying section sharing a common state.

Heat integration encompasses all the condensers, reboilers, coolers in VR, heaters in BF, as well as all heaters/coolers required to obtain saturated liquid in the feed points to columns and to address the vapor/liquid imbalance in stacked columns. Heat integration is simultaneously optimized with the operating conditions of the rest of the system (separation sequence, column pressures, pressure change in compressors, etc.) using pinch analysis (Duran and Grossmann, 1986)

3. Case Study

To exemplify the capacities of the proposed approach we examine the separation of an equimolar mixture of 4 hydrocarbons (n-pentane, n-hexane, n-heptane, n-octane). Table 1 presents the data for the example.

The distillation columns were simulated using the Fenske-Underwood-Gilliland (FUG) shortcut. The relative volatilities exhibit some pressure dependence and were computed rigorously using the Peng Robinson equation of state at the conditions of the feed at each column, employing Aspen-HYSYS™ as a thermodynamic properties server. The rest of the operations including compressors and valves in vapor recompression and bottom flashing cycles, pumps, and all heat transfer operations (condensers, reboilers, and feed conditioning) were also rigorously calculated using Aspen-HYSYS™ as a thermodynamic server.

The optimization includes the cost of energy, the main equipment (columns, compressors, compressor drivers, and pumps), and an estimation of the heat transfer equipment assuming a vertical heat transfer approach. (Smith, 2016) However, the actual structure of the heat exchanger network is calculated a posteriori using a sequential approach (Biegler et al., 1997).

Table 1. Data for the example.

Components	Composition (mol fraction)		
n-pentane	0.25	Feed Flow	200 kmol/h
n-hexane	0.25	Feed Pressure	100 kPa
n-heptane	0.25	Feed Temperature	25 ºC
n-octane	0.25		
Cold Utilities	Cost (\$/kW·y)	**Hot Utilities**	Cost (\$/kW·y)
Water	10.19	HP Steam	509.76

Electricity 800 \$/kW·y
Interest = 10% in 10 years
Cost estimation based on correlations by (Turton et al., 2018)
Thermodynamics Peng Robinson (default Aspen-HYSYS parameters)
ΔT_{min} in Heat Exchanger Network: 10 ºC
Isentropic Efficiency in compressors: 75%
Nominal Pressure in columns between [100 – 1000] kPa
Minimum pressure after a valve: 10 kPa

The optimal separation sequence consists of a set of separation tasks, where the light and heavy key components are determined by their extreme volatilities (ABC/BCD - AB/BC – BC-CD – A/B – B/C – C/D) but unlike what might be expected if all columns were maintained at the same nominal pressure, in which we would get a fully (or almost) thermally coupled configuration, the optimal solution takes advantage of a large number of heat integration opportunities, Notably, only a thermal couple connects the bottoms of separation ABC/BCD with the feed of separation BC/CD. Additionally, a VR cycle emerges, replacing the condenser in the separation task AB/BC.

The existence of a Thermal Couple allows us to go a step further and reduce by one the total columns by introducing an internal wall. Figure 2(a) shows the optimal configuration using three distillation columns. Figure 2(b) shows the intensified counterpart and Figure 2(c) shows the heat exchanger network.

The total annualized cost of the best solution is \$1.235 10^6 per year, with approximately 61% attributed to operating costs (mainly utilities). For the sake of comparison, the total cost of hot utilities in the fully thermally coupled configuration is \$1.337 10^6/y. that is 77% more than the total utilities in the proposed solution.

Adhering to the recommendations outlined in the «Roadmap to Achieve Net Zero Emissions by 2050» which advocates for electrifying the chemical industry, it becomes possible to identify an optimal sequence where hot utilities are not employed (not presented due to space constraints). In this scenario, the total annualized cost rises to \$1.721·10^6/y, an increase of approximately 39%, but remains competitive with the best non-heat integrated sequence.

It is worth remarking, that difficult separations tend to favor the presence of VR / BF configurations because the difference in temperatures is relatively small and therefore the compression work is also reduced. In those cases, it is even possible that the best configuration does not include non-renewable utilities.

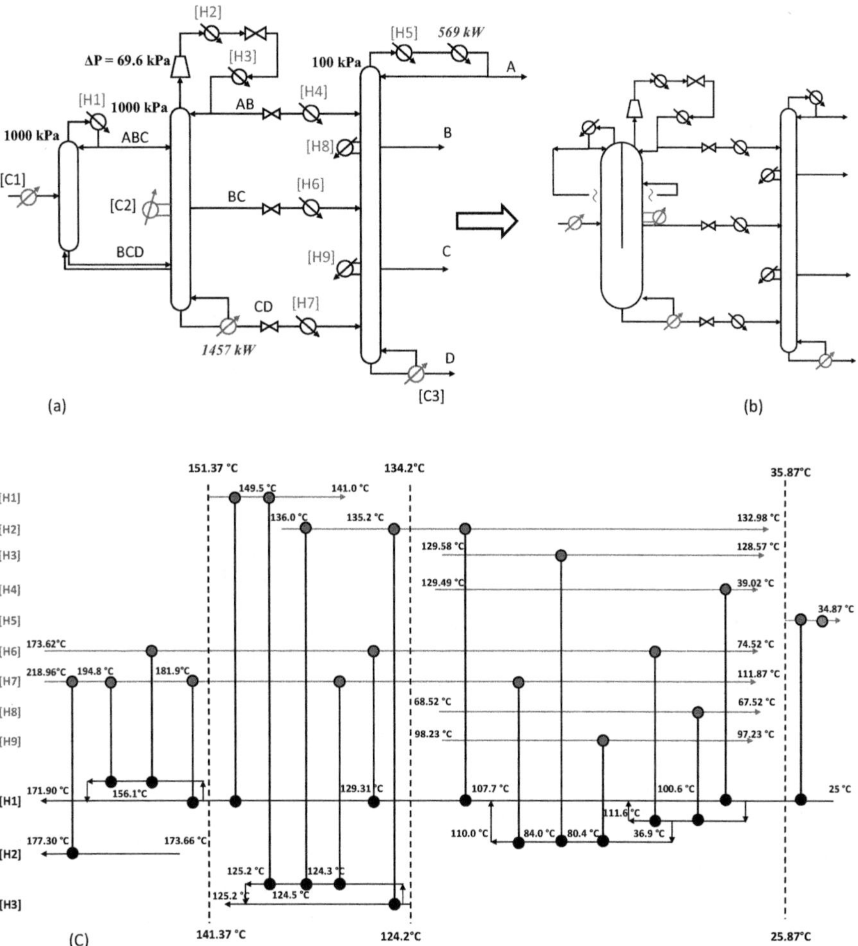

Figure 2. Best solution obtained. a) Regular configuration (N-1 columns) A: n-pentane, B: n-hexane, C: n-heptane, D: n-octane. In square brackets is a code to identify the streams in the Heat Exchanger Network. b) Thermodynamically equivalent intensify sequence. Columns 1 and 2 are merged in a Divided Wall Column. c) Heat Exchanger Network.

4. Conclusions

In this work, we have shown that it is possible to increase the efficiency of distillation sequences by concurrently optimizing the column sequence and exploring various heat integration alternatives, such as, thermal couples, direct integration (reboiler–condenser heat exchange), and assisted heat integration by the use of vapor recompression cycles using the vapor from the top of the separation sequences and bottom flashing by expanding the liquid before entering the reboiler.

The model was exemplified through the separation of a 4-hydrocarbon mixture, showcasing a significant reduction in total utility costs (encompassing hot, cold, and electricity) compared to the most effective non-heat integrated alternative—a fully

thermally coupled distillation sequence. For the presented example, this reduction reached an impressive 78%.
In the spirit of the "Roadmap to Achieve Net Zero Emissions by 2050" electrifying the distillation sequence is proposed to eliminate the use of non-renewable utilities, substituting them with electricity. Despite the associated cost increase, the optimal solution remains competitive with the best non-heat integrated alternative. However, this is not necessarily always the case. In sequences with some difficult separations, the best result might include electricity as the sole utility.

Acknowledgments

The authors acknowledge financial support from the «Ministerio de Ciencia e Innovación», Spain, under project PID2021-124139NB-C21, and to the «Conselleria de Innovacion, Universidades, Ciencia y Sociedad Digital of the Generalitat Valenciana», Spain, under project PROMETEO/2020/064.

References

Biegler, T.L., Grosmmann, I.E., Westerberg, A.W., 1997. Systematic Methods of Chemical Process Design. Prentice Hall PTR., Upper Saddle River, NJ. USA.

Caballero, J.A., Grossmann, I.E., 2006. Structural Considerations and Modeling in the Synthesis of Heat-Integrated−Thermally Coupled Distillation Sequences. Ind. Eng. Chem. Res. 45, 8454–8474.

Caballero, J.A., Grossmann, I.E., 2014. Optimal synthesis of thermally coupled distillation sequences using a novel MILP approach. Comput. Chem. Eng. 61, 118–135.

Duran, M.A., Grossmann, I.E., 1986. Simultaneous optimization and heat integration of chemical processes. AIChE J. 32, 123–138.

Giridhar, A., Agrawal, R., 2010. Synthesis of distillation configurations: I. Characteristics of a good search space. Comput. Chem. Eng. 34, 73.

International Energy Agency (IEA)., 2022. World Energy Outlook. https://www.iea.org/reports/world-energy-outlook-2022

Kruber, K.F., Grüters, T., Skiborowski, M., 2021. Advanced hybrid optimization methods for the design of complex separation processes. Comput. Chem. Eng. 107257.

Navarro-Amorós, M.A., Ruiz-Femenia, R., Caballero, J.A., 2013. A new technique for recovering energy in thermally coupled distillation using vapor recompression cycles. Aiche J. 59, 3767–3781.

Sholl, D.S., Lively, R.P., 2016. Seven chemical separations to change the world. Nature 532, 435–437. https://doi.org/10.1038/532435a

Smith, R., 2016. Chemical Process Design and Integration, 2nd edition, John Wiley & Sons. West Sussex, United Kingdom.

Turton, R., Shaeiwitz, J.A., Bhattacharyya, D., Whiting, W.B., 2018. Analysis, Synthesis, and Design of Chemical Processes. 5th edition. Prentice Hall.

Yeomans, H., Grossmann, I.E., 1999. A systematic modeling framework of superstructure optimization in process synthesis. Comput. Chem. Eng. 23, 709–731.

Flavio Manenti, Gintaras V. Reklaitis (Eds.), Proceedings of the 34th European Symposium on Computer Aided Process Engineering / 15th International Symposium on Process Systems Engineering (ESCAPE34/PSE24), June 2-6, 2024, Florence, Italy
 http://dx.doi.org/10.1016/B978-0-443-28824-1.50211-8

Scaling Up and Down Power-to-Methane Facilities with CO_2 Capture: Towards Modular Design

Diego Santamaría, Antonio Sánchez, Mariano Martín

Department of Chemical Engineering, University of Salamanca, Plz Caidos 1-5, 37008, Salamanca, Spain
mariano.m3@usal.es

Abstract

The scale-up and down of synthetic methane production from H_2 and CO_2 captured is evaluated towards modular design. Hydrogen is obtained from water splitting using renewable energy (wind or solar). For the carbon capture, three technologies are compared: absorption with amines, PSA system and membranes. In addition, two reactors for methanation reaction are considered: isothermal multitubular and adiabatic multi-bed. The combination of all of them results in six different alternatives. Each design is optimized to maximize the methane production. The investment cost and operation cost are evaluated at different CO_2 treatment capacities. The results show that processes with isothermal mulitubular reactors are more profitable than processes with multi-bed reactors. Among processes with isothermal mulitubular reactors there are some differences: for low scales carbon capture by membrane technology is the most profitable option, at medium scales PSA is the most economical and for large scales, the absorption system seems better option, as expected. From a production of 50 kg/h of CH_4 equivalent to the CO_2 treatment of the annual emission of an oil tanker that spends 390 h at the sea, the minimum sale price of methane stabilises at around 40 $/MMBTU. While today, this price is not competitive, in 2022 it could be competitive, as the methane price reached 70.04 $/MMBTU in the European market.

Keywords: Methanation, CO_2 utilization, renewable energy, modular design.

1. Introduction

Methane is one of the most important fuels and raw materials, reaching an annual consumption of almost 4,000 billion cubic meters worldwide in 2022 (Institute Energy, 2023). Methane has traditionally been obtained by extracting natural gas from fields. However, reserves are not only limited, but it may also suffer supply disruptions due to political instabilities. To reduce its effect, synthetic methane production by methanation using carbon dioxide (CO_2) and hydrogen (H_2) as raw materials is one of the most promising ways (Davis & Martín, 2014). This process can generate a clean renewable energy carrier by avoiding the use of a limited resource while reducing greenhouse gas emissions from industrial processes and fossil fuel combustion. The sustainability of the process lies in the origin of the H_2, and the CO_2 used. The hydrogen is obtained from an electrolyzer that runs on renewable electricity (from wind and solar energy). The CO_2 comes from industrial residual gases and to be used it must be captured and separated from other gases. There are different technologies such as: absorption, adsorption, cryogenics, chemical-looping combustion (CLC) and membranes (Olajire, 2010). The three most widely used (absorption, adsorption, and membrane) are considered together with two different types of methanation reactors (isothermal multitubular and adiabatic multi-bed) are studied at different scales. In this work, the various proposed alternatives are subjected to a mathematical optimization followed by a techno-economic analysis. The source of CO_2 is considered from 230 t/y to 130,000 t/y.

2. Methodology

The methodology presents a process level analysis to systematically compare the six different settings to determine the most profitable process at different scales. The settings are created by the combination of the three alternatives for CO_2 capture (absorption, adsorption, and membranes) and two designs of methanation reactors (isothermal and multi-bed), see Figure 1.

2.1. Process design: technology scaling

All alternatives are modeled using a combination of mass and energy balances, thermodynamic equilibria, experimental data, and rules of thumb. They start from the same feed and are optimized to maximize methane production and minimize costs. The processes are optimized by solving an NLP for each one and all six have the same objective function, eq (1):

$$OBJ = Max(P_{CH_4} \cdot CH_4 - Cost_{utilites} - Cost_{CO_2 separation}) \quad (1)$$

2.2. Process description

The process can be divided into four subsections: CO_2 capture, hydrogen production, methane production and methane purification. Each subsection is described below.

2.2.1. CO_2 Capture

Three technologies for CO_2 capture are evaluated: absorption, adsorption, and membranes.
Absorption. It takes place via amines. From previous work (Martín-Hernández et al., 2020), the amine suggested is diethanolamine (DEA). Two columns are needed, the first one is the absorption column where the gases are brought into contact with the amine. Then, CO_2 rich amine stream, it is heated, and introduced into the second column. It is a stripping column where the CO_2 is desorbed from the amine, obtaining a pure CO_2 stream. The amine is recycled to the first column and mixed with new amines to make up for losses. This model is formulated based on first principles and industrial data.
Adsorption. A PSA system is used. The gases are fed to a zeolite 13 X bed (Martín-Hernández et al., 2020) where CO_2 is captured in the bed whereas nitrogen can cross the bed mostly. Langmuir solid-gas adsorption isotherm is used to model it.
Membranes. The configuration consists of a single-stage compressor train, two membranes for CO_2 separation and a mixer, where the fresh stream and the permeate of second membrane is mixed. The permeate of first membrane, which is rich in CO_2, is fed into a mixer and the retentate is introduced into a second membrane. The permeated of the second membrane is discharged into the atmosphere whereas the retentate is returned to the mixer. To model this system data of permeability and selectivity of membrane are used.

2.2.2. Hydrogen production

This subprocess begins with a PEM electrolyzer where oxygen and hydrogen are produced from water. The oxygen is dried, compressed and finally stored in a tank. The first step of hydrogen line is also water reduction with a phase separator. Next, as the hydrogen stream contains traces of oxygen, it is fed into a deoxygenation reactor to remove them, but water is produced. Finally, to achieve a pure hydrogen, the stream must be dried with a zeolites bed. At this point, hydrogen can be mixed with the captured CO_2 to produce methane.

2.2.3. Methane production

The hydrogen, CO_2 and the recirculation stream are introduced in a mixer. Next, the gases mixture is compressed to reach the methanation reactor conditions. There are two possibilities for choosing a type of methanation reactor: multitubular isothermal and multi-bed adiabatic. The isothermal reactor aim is to try to keep the temperature unchanged whereas the multi-bed reactor operates adiabatically and the heat exchangers between the bed reduce the temperature.

The reactions for methane production are as follows and their constants are modelled with equilibrium constants.

$$CO + 3H_2 \rightleftarrows CH_4 + H_2O \tag{2}$$

$$CO_2 + H_2 \rightleftarrows CO + H_2O \tag{3}$$

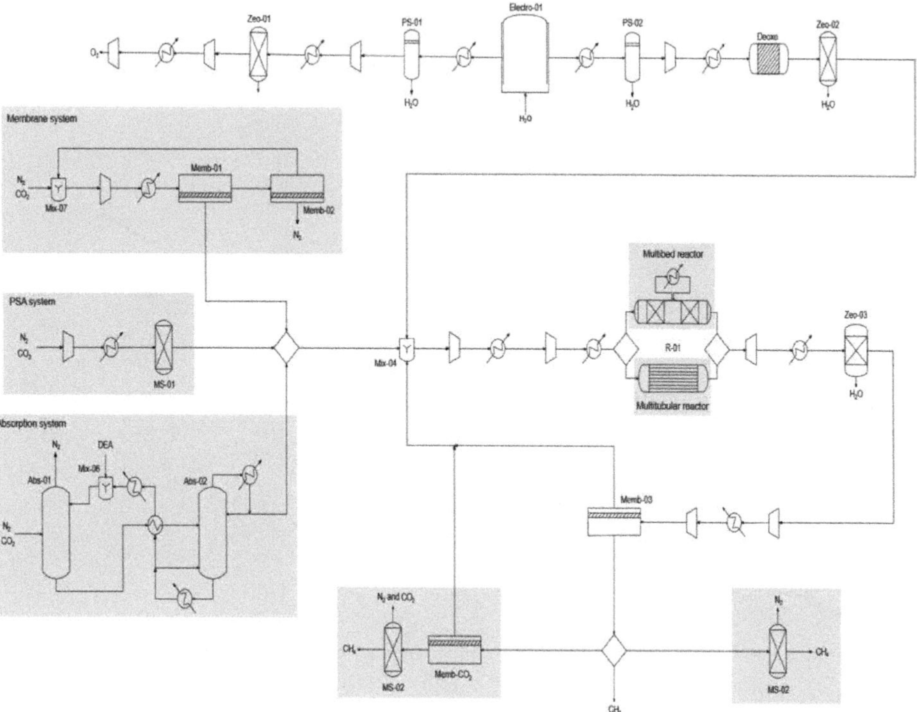

Figure 1. Process flowsheet. The colored areas correspond to the different alternatives for carbon capture, methanation reactors or purification stages.

2.2.4. Methane purification

The purification is a key stage because legislation requires methane with a purity over 95 % to be introduced in the natural gas network. The outlet stream of the methanation reactor is dried and finally a membrane separates the hydrogen from the other gases. Up to this point, the purification stage is the same for all alternative processes, but some of them need an extra stage because there are other components, which must be separated. When the carbon capture is performed with a PSA system or a membranes system and the methanation is performed in a multi-bed reactor, the output reactor stream contains methane and hydrogen, but also CO_2 and nitrogen. After the separation of water and hydrogen, CO_2 and N_2 are also removed. CO_2 is separated from the other gases by a membrane, and it is recirculated to the reactor and nitrogen is removed by a PSA system and it is released into the atmosphere. When the carbon capture is performed a membranes system and the methanation is performed in a tubular reactor, the reactor output flow is composed of methane, hydrogen and nitrogen. After hydrogen removal, only nitrogen must be removed, and this is also done by a PSA system.

2.3. Scale-up/down method

The cost of the units depends on its production capacity. The scale up coefficient changes from unit to unit. The factorial method is used to estimate the investment cost from the units cost (Sinnott & Towler, 2019). Each equipment has a characteristic variable that indicates the range in which it can operate. If the characteristic variable of an equipment exceeds this range, another unit must be installed in parallel (Sánchez & Martín, 2018). To perform the scale analysis, different points of CO_2 treatment capacity of the plant been chosen.

3. Results

This section shows the scale effect on investment and production cost. In addition, the comparison between different processes is also shown.

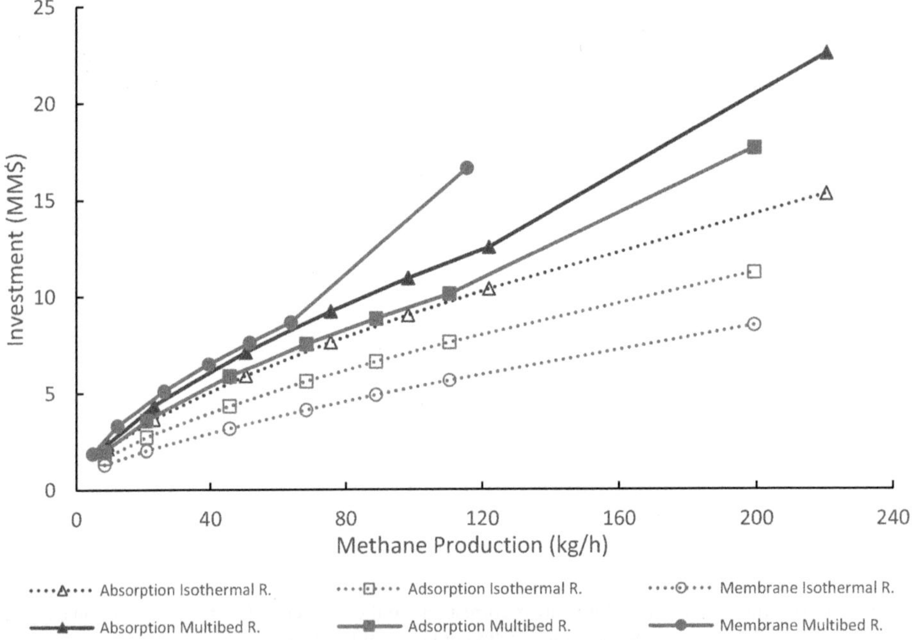

Figure 2. Investment for the different process to produce methane.

In Figure 2, the equipment investment cost of each technology proposed for different methane production capacity is represented. The best ratio between investment cost and methane production is achieved in processes with isothermal reactors, as a higher conversion rate is reached. Note that only at small scales close to isothermal operation can be achieved. As the processes are very similar to each other, the difference in investment cost is located in the carbon capture stage. Among process with the isothermal reactor, carbon capture using membrane technology shows the lowest investment cost.

In general, the processes with muti-bed reactors require a higher investment cost than processes with isothermal reactors. The multi-bed reactor with CO_2 capture by PSA requires the least investment to this type of reactors. At low scales, when the capture is done with membrane technology or absorption systems, the investment is very close. However, when the methane production excess 70 kg/h absorption is more economical than membranes.

The evolution of the production cost at different methane production capacities can be seen in Figure 3. The unit of production cost is \$/MMBTU because it is the most common unit in the US methane market. The processes using an isothermal reactor show lower production costs. Although, their production costs are very similar, it is possible to determine which is the most profitable at each point of methane production. At low scales, membrane technology is de most suitable process up to a capacity of 100 kg/h of CH_4. This can be equivalent, for example, to the treatment of the annual emissions of a general cargo ship spending 3688.66 h at the sea (*EMSA\THETIS-MRV*, 2023). For a capacity between 100 kg/h of CH_4 and 950 kg/h of CH_4 (may correspond, for example, to the treatment of annual emission of a hospital with a surface area of 200000 m^2 such as the University Hospital of Salamanca) (García-Sanz-Calcedo, 2019), PSA technology is the most economic and for larger scales, the absorption system seems better option.

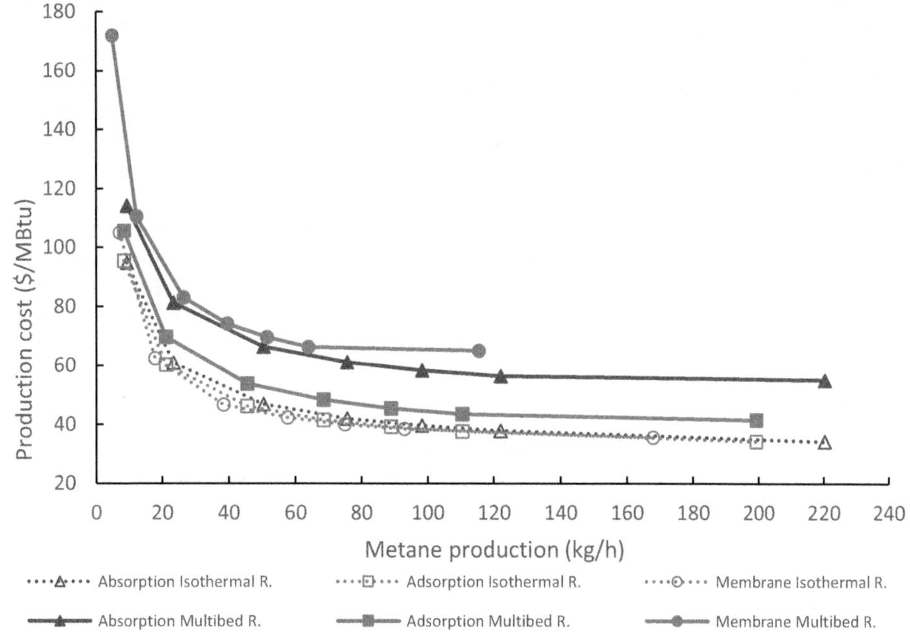

Figure 3. Production cost of methane of each process at different scale.

The processes with multitubular reactors have a higher production cost. On the one hand, as it can see in Figure 2, the investment is higher for these processes. On the other hand, utilities costs are decisive for the production cost. Process with PSA has the lowest utilities costs and therefore a lower production cost is possible.

The results show that the sale price of the obtained methane is around 40 \$/MMBTU and it does not reach a competitive level. However, the prices obtained are much lower compared to the European methane market in 2022 which was 70.04 \$/MMBTU.

4. Conclusions

An evaluation of six different configurations to producing synthetic methane by a renewable route is presented. Hydrogen is obtained from a PEM electrolyzer while carbon dioxide is obtained by capturing industrial emissions or fossil fuel combustion. Three technologies for carbon capture are analyzed: absorption, PSA system and membranes system while two types of reactors are analyzed: isothermal multitubular and multibed adiabatic. It is important to indicate that although the methanation process in the multitubular reactor is supposed to occur isothermally, achieving this situation is difficult.

The units of the six configurations are modelled and optimized using first principles, thermodynamics equilibria and rules of thumb. Then, the investment and production cost are estimated, and the scaling study is developed.

The processes with isothermal reactors have a lower investment and production cost than multi-bed rectors and it is possible to differentiate which configuration is the most profitable, but the maximum size of such reactor is yet to be defined. Depending on the CH_4 production capacity the most suitable carbon capture technology changes. For low capacities up to 100 kg/h of CH_4 membranes are the technology of choice. For a capacity between 100 kg/h of CH_4 and 950 kg/h of CH_4, PSA technology is the most economical and for larger scales, the absorption system seems to be the best option. The methane production capacity can be translated into CO_2 treatment capacity. A methane production capacity of 100 kg/h of CH_4 may correspond to the treatment of the annual CO_2 emissions of a general cargo ship spending 3688.66 h at the sea (*EMSA\THETIS-MRV*, 2023) while a production capacity of 950 kg/h of CH_4 may correspond to of a hospital with a surface area of 200,000 m^2 such as the University Hospital of Salamanca (García-Sanz-Calcedo, 2019).

The minimum sale price of methane stabilises at around 40 \$/MMBTU, when its capacity is sufficient to treat the annual emission of a tanker ship spending an annual emission of an oil tanker spending 390 h and producing 50 kg/h of CH_4. In 2023, this price is not yet competitive, but in 2022 it could be competitive, as the methane price reached 70.04 \$/MMBTU on the European market.

Acknowledgments

This work was supported by the Regional Government of Castilla y León (Junta de Castilla León) and by the Ministry of Science and Innovation MICIN and the European Union NextGenerationEU / PRTR (H2MetAmo project - C17.I01.P01.S21).

References

Davis, W., & Martín, M. (2014). Optimal year-round operation for methane production from CO2 and water using wind energy. *Energy*, *69*, 497–505. https://doi.org/https://doi.org/10.1016/j.energy.2014.03.043

EMSA\THETIS-MRV. (2023). https://mrv.emsa.europa.eu/#public/emission-report

García-Sanz-Calcedo, J. (2019). Study of CO2 emissions from energy consumption in Spanish hospitals. *Vibroengineering Procedia*, *26*, 46–51. https://doi.org/https://doi.org/10.21595/vp.2019.20965

Institute Energy. (2023). *Statistical Review of World Energy*.

Martín-Hernández, E., Guerras, L. S., & Martín, M. (2020). Optimal technology selection for the biogas upgrading to biomethane. *Journal of Cleaner Production*, *267*, 122032. https://doi.org/https://doi.org/10.1016/j.jclepro.2020.122032

Olajire, A. A. (2010). CO2 capture and separation technologies for end-of-pipe applications–A review. *Energy*, *35*(6), 2610–2628. https://doi.org/https://doi.org/10.1016/j.energy.2010.02.030

Sánchez, A., & Martín, M. (2018). Scale up and scale down issues of renewable ammonia plants: Towards modular design. *Sustainable Production and Consumption*, *16*, 176–192. https://doi.org/10.1016/j.spc.2018.08.001

Sinnott, R., & Towler, G. (2019). *Chemical engineering design: SI Edition*. Butterworth-Heinemann.

Flavio Manenti, Gintaras V. Reklaitis (Eds.), Proceedings of the 34th European Symposium on Computer Aided Process Engineering / 15th International Symposium on Process Systems Engineering (ESCAPE34/PSE24), June 2-6, 2024, Florence, Italy
 http://dx.doi.org/10.1016/B978-0-443-28824-1.50212-X

A hierarchical selection and decision matrix for energy-efficient intensified distillation technologies

Qing Li,[a] Ana Somoza-Tornos,[a] Anton A. Kiss[a*]

[a]Department of Chemical Engineering, Delft University of Technology, Van der Maasweg 9, Delft, 2629 HZ, The Netherlands
A.A.Kiss@tudelft.nl

Abstract

Distillation is widely used for separation in chemical industries, but accounts for a half of operational costs and 40% of the energy usage due to its low energy efficiency. Process intensification could effectively enhance the energy efficiency and reduce the energy requirement of the distillation processes by integrating unit operations or functions. However, there is no general methodology that enables to choose the best intensified distillation technologies among all available choices for a given separation task. This study generates a conceptual de-composed selection and decision approach by first identifying the process bottlenecks and intensification targets, and then select the most promising intensified techniques via a selection framework and decision matrix based on the identified bottlenecks and intensification targets. Two separation cases are illustrated to demonstrate the developed methodology, and the outcomes are verified with conceptual designs reported in the literature.

Keywords: Distillation; process intensification; energy efficiency; process optimization

1. Introduction

Distillation is the most widely used separation technology in chemical industries. However, because of its relatively low thermodynamic efficiency, distillation accounts for around half of the operational costs of chemical plants (Kiss et al., 2012). To reduce the operational costs as well as the capital costs, advanced distillation techniques based on process intensification (PI) principles are considered highly competitive in terms of enhancing the energy efficiency and economic performance. However, matching suitable intensified distillation techniques – such as heat pump assisted distillation (HPAD), heat integrated distillation (HIDiC), membrane assisted distillation, high gravity (HiGee) distillation, cyclic distillation (CyDist), thermally coupled distillation systems (TCD), dividing wall column (DWC), extractive distillation and azeotropic distillation – with given separation tasks based on a wide range of application cases (e.g., a variety of mixtures, a wide range of feed flowrates and concentrations, and different products purities) remains a crucial problem. Currently, to the best of our knowledge, there is only one paper that developed a framework for choice of intensified reaction equipment (Commenge and Falk, 2014), but no general methodology that allows the selection of the most promising PI technologies for different fluid separation tasks, and screening the PI opportunities for process design becomes a challenge.

To address this decision-making problem, this work is the first to develop a knowledge-based methodology that provides a list of most promising intensified distillation techniques for given separation tasks via a novel PI matrix. The first step of the methodology consists in analyzing the given separation task in terms of selection criteria (e.g., volatile difference between key components, the type of separation tasks, feed and product flow, product specifications at different target purity levels, operating pressure, reboiler duty and its temperature level, reflux ratio, heat of vaporization). Subsequently, the methodology relates the selection criteria to process bottlenecks and promising intensified distillation techniques, through a connection matrix, in order to effectively address the identified bottlenecks. Finally, each selected techniques are scored and the potential solutions are compared against the task specifications.

The PI matrix proposed in this work aims to yield a short list of appropriate solutions to be designed and economically assessed, proposing a screening framework for separating binary and ternary mixtures in order to make a rapid selection at an early stage, applying to both ideal and non ideal separation systems. Two case studies related to methanol-water and benzene-toluene-xylene mixture (BTX) separation are carried out to illustrate the application of the proposed methodology. The proposed CAPE methodology may also help reduce the search space before carrying out rigorous optimization for the synthesis and design of the distillation.

2. Problem statement

The selection of promising intensified distillation techniques among possibilities (i.e., heat pump assisted distillation, HIDiC, membrane assisted distillation, HiGee, cyclic distillation, thermally coupled distillation systems, DWC, extractive distillation and azeotropic distillation) is challenging for given tasks (e.g., variety of mixtures, a wide range of feed flowrates and concentrations, and different products purities). This work develops a decision matrix to select promising intensified distillation technologies before carrying out detailed process design, based on the different separation bottlenecks and intensified targets, aiming to provide a generate user-friendly and easy-to-understand selection method.

3. Results and discussion

This section describes the proposed research approach and supporting case studies. Two case studies of industrial relevance are used to demonstrate the application of the new approach: non-ideal binary separation (methanol-water), and an ideal ternary mixture, benzene (B)/toluene (T)/xylene (X) separation.

3.1. Key benefits and disadvantages of the intensified distillation technologies

Table 1 lists the intensified distillation techniques considered in this study, including intensification targets, features, key advantages and disadvantages of each technology. Binary and ternary separation are defined base on the number of products.

3.2. Identification of limitations and criteria

For a given separation task, three sets of data are first extracted: the basis of the tasks (feed composition, key components and separation requirements), thermodynamics and kinetics, as shown in Figure 1. Next, the following steps show the proposed approach.

Step 1. Special components identification in the mixture: The non-condensable components, which result in low condenser temperature; components with the risk of solidification (freezing); thermo-sensitive components, e.g., thermal denaturation, polymerizing or decomposing are identified by following the high level questions, which are proposed in Figure 1, as well as the recommended distillation techniques.

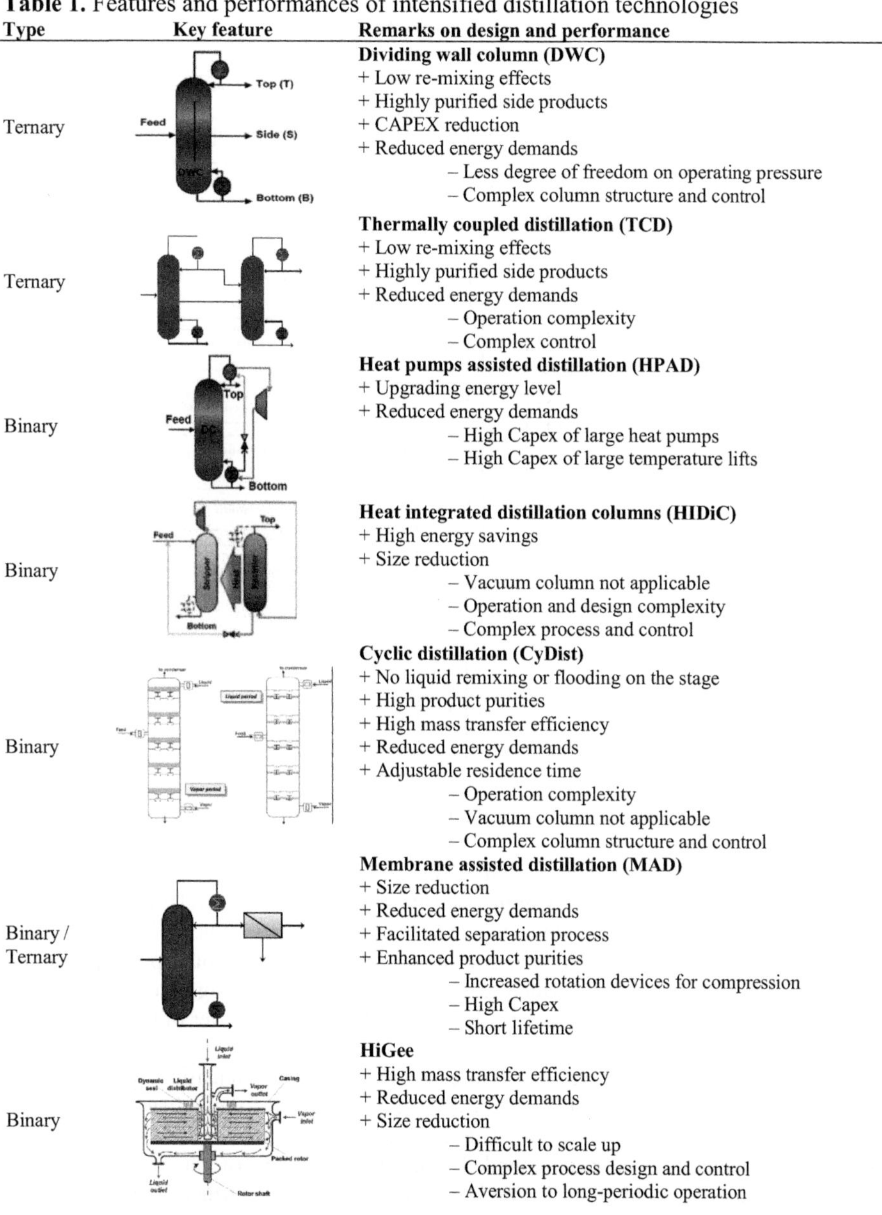

Table 1. Features and performances of intensified distillation technologies

Type	Key feature	Remarks on design and performance
Ternary	Feed; Top (T); Side (S); Bottom (B); DWC	**Dividing wall column (DWC)** + Low re-mixing effects + Highly purified side products + CAPEX reduction + Reduced energy demands – Less degree of freedom on operating pressure – Complex column structure and control
Ternary		**Thermally coupled distillation (TCD)** + Low re-mixing effects + Highly purified side products + Reduced energy demands – Operation complexity – Complex control
Binary	Feed; Top; Bottom	**Heat pumps assisted distillation (HPAD)** + Upgrading energy level + Reduced energy demands – High Capex of large heat pumps – High Capex of large temperature lifts
Binary	Feed; Top; Bottom	**Heat integrated distillation columns (HIDiC)** + High energy savings + Size reduction – Vacuum column not applicable – Operation and design complexity – Complex process and control
Binary		**Cyclic distillation (CyDist)** + No liquid remixing or flooding on the stage + High product purities + High mass transfer efficiency + Reduced energy demands + Adjustable residence time – Operation complexity – Vacuum column not applicable – Complex column structure and control
Binary / Ternary		**Membrane assisted distillation (MAD)** + Size reduction + Reduced energy demands + Facilitated separation process + Enhanced product purities – Increased rotation devices for compression – High Capex – Short lifetime
Binary		**HiGee** + High mass transfer efficiency + Reduced energy demands + Size reduction – Difficult to scale up – Complex process design and control – Aversion to long-periodic operation

Step 2. Phase equilibrium limitation identification: separations are categorized as azeotropic mixture and very close boiling point mixture separation ($\Delta T_b \leq 10°C$); close boiling point mixture separation ($10°C < \Delta T_b < 20°C$); and (near)ideal mixture separation ($\Delta T_b \geq 20$ °C) based on the normal boiling point difference (ΔT_b) and relative volatilities (RV). High heat of vaporization, high recovery or high purity products can also lead to high energy requirements even for (near)ideal mixture separations.

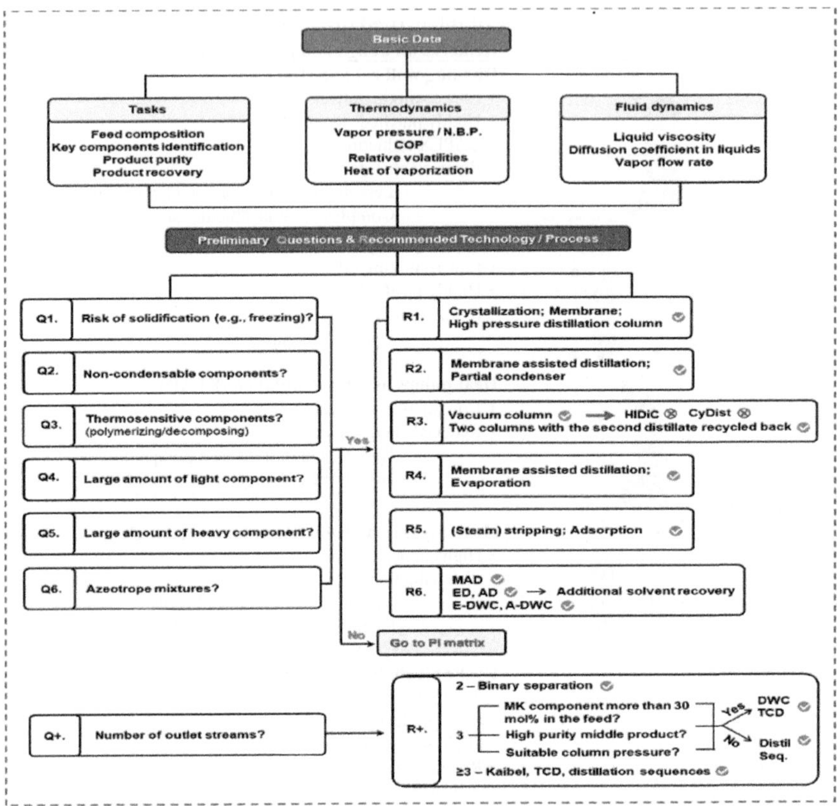

Figure 1. Conceptual framework of the intensified distillation techniques selection

Step 3. Mass transfer limitation identification:
Mass transfer could be limited by high viscosity (dimensionless correlating to Reynolds number), which causes difficulties to create turbulence and achieve high gas/liquid interface; low liquid phase diffusion coefficient leads to inefficient vapor liquid mass transfer; high vapor flow rate, which leads to liquid foam, flooding, and liquid mixing on the tray; and low vapor flow rate could also limit the mass transfer of the separation.

The criteria from Step 2 and Step 3 are composed in an intensification matrix for advanced distillation technologies, as shown in Figure 2. The column lists the advanced distillation technologies, and the row lists the decision criteria. The check mark means the specific technology is recommended when meeting the criteria; the exclamation mark represents the technology is good to be considered, but further check is needed; while a cross mark represents the technology is not good to be used according to that specific criteria. No marks means the criteria is not relevant to the decision of the specific technology. Taking the first column as an example, if $\Delta Tb \leq 10°C$, conventional column is possible to achieve the separation requirement, while further check of the reflux ratio and the energy requirement are needed, HPAD and HIDiC are recommended, cyclic distillation is not applicable in this case. With this intensification matrix, both the relevance (i.e., whether the criteria has an influence on the selection of the specific technique), and the recommendation level of the techniques are suggested.

	ΔT_b <10°C	10-20°C	20-60°C	>60°C	RV 1.01-1.15	High Heat of Vaporization	Vacuum operation	High recovery	High purity	High viscosity	Low diffusion coefficient	High minimum reflux ratio
ConvDist	!	!	✓	✓	⊗		✓	✓	✓			
HPAD	✓	✓	!	!	!	✓	!	✓	✓			
HIDiC	✓	✓	!	!	!	✓	⊗	✓	✓			
CyDist	✓	✓	✓	✓	✓		⊗	✓	✓		✓	✓
MAD	!	!			!	✓		✓	✓	⊗		
HiGee	⊗	!	✓	✓	⊗		✓			✓	✓	
ED/AD	✓	!			✓			✓	✓			✓
DWC	⊗	!	✓	!	⊗		✓	✓	✓			✓
TCD	⊗	!	✓	!	⊗		✓	✓	✓			✓

Figure 2. Process intensification matrix for advanced distillation technologies

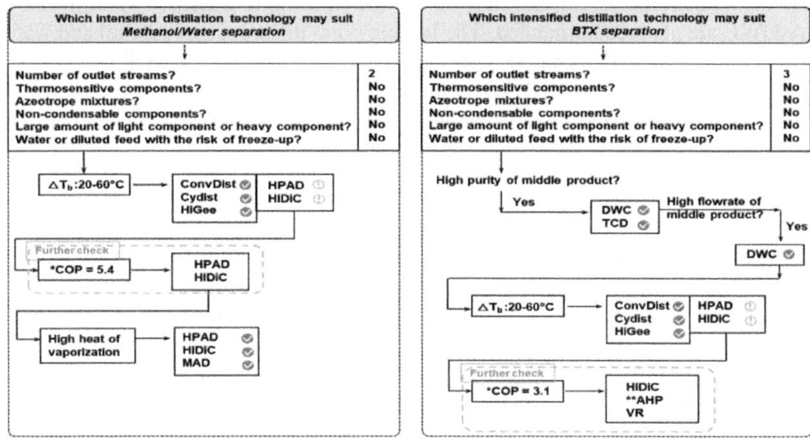

Figure 3. Decision making approach and outcomes for methanol/water separation (left), and BTX separation (right)

3.3. Case study: Methanol-water separation

Feed consists of 69.81 mol% methanol and 30.19 mol% water (Shahandeh et al., 2015), N.B.P. difference 35.3 °C (N.B.P water 100 °C, methanol 64.7 °C), RV 3, heat of vaporization methanol 1273.4 kJ/kg, water 2265.6 kJ/kg. Methanol product purity 99.99 mol%, recovery 99.98%, RRmin 0.87 (under atmospheric pressure), and it is a large scale separation with the capacity of 1,100 ktpy feed. As shown in Figure 3 left, HIDiC and heat pumps are recommended for methanol water separation, cyclic distillation and membrane assisted distillation are promising, and conventional distillation column can also achieve the separation target. This is also inline with the reports from literature (Shahandeh et al., 2015; Pribic et al., 2006; Pătruţ et al., 2014). However, note that although HiGee distillation is also recommended and there are also research on this (Wang et al., 2011), HiGee is limited by the difficulty to manufacture large-size high-speed rotator. The annual production capacity is usually smaller than 10 ktons. Practically, most cases are running with the annual scale less than 5 ktons.

3.4. Case study: Benzene (B)/Toluene (T)/Xylene (X) separation

The feed consists of 33.3 mol% benzene, 33.4 mol% toluene and 33.3 mol% m-xylene (Gupta and Kaistha, 2015), ΔTb = 59.0°C (N.B.P.: benzene 80.1°C; toluene 110.7 °C and m-xylene 138.4 °C), $RV_{B/T}$=2.39, $RV_{T/X}$=2.19. Heat of vaporization: benzene 395.9 kJ/kg; toluene 365.1 kJ/kg; m-xylene 347.0 kJ/kg. The purities of BTX products are 99.0 mol%, and the recoveries are 99.8%, 98.0 %, and 99.1 %, respectively. The RRmin of B/TX separation is ~1.90, and 1.92 for T/X separation. The viscosity (cP at 20°C) are 0.652, 0.590 and 0.620. As shown in Figure 3 right, dividing wall column is recommended for BTX separation, and by checking the coefficient of performance (COP), heat pumps could also be applied. These recommendations are supported with the studies about DWC (Gupta and Kaistha, 2015), HIDiC (Iwakabe et al., 2006), and heat pump assisted DWC (Chew et al., 2014).

3.5. Case study: Ethanol-water separation

In case of the ethanol-water separation there is a binary azeotrope (95.63 wt % ethanol) that must be taken into account. For Q6, the answer is yes, thus membrane separation, extractive distillation, azeotropic distillation are recommended to break the azeotrope. Due to the additional solvent that may be needed (leading to a ternary system) E-DWC and A-DWC are also recommended. The boiling point difference of ethanol and water is 22 °C, so HPAD and HIDiC can be considered upon further checks. COP is 16 (Tr=100, Tc=78 °C) in this case, thus HPAD is highly recommended (Luo et al., 2015), while using HIDiC for the ethanol-water separation has been also reported (Ponce et al., 2015).

4. Conclusions

The newly proposed decision making framework based on the intensification matrix is useful to make rapid and reliable selection of most promising distillation techniques at an early stage for fluid separation tasks. The features and performances of intensified distillation technologies are assessed and exploited to support the intensification matrix. The two industrially relevant case studies successfully demonstrate the use of the proposed methodology and the results align with the PI techniques reported in the literature. This screening could act as a decision making tool in the pre-selection stage of our recently reported work (Li et al. 2023) regarding the synthesis and optimisation of advanced energy integration distillation techniques.

References

Chew, J.M., Reddy, C.C.S. and Rangaiah, G.P., 2014. Improving energy efficiency of dividing-wall columns using heat pumps, Organic Rankine Cycle and Kalina Cycle. Chemical Engineering and Processing: Process Intensification, 76, pp.45-59.

Commenge J.M., Falk L., 2014, Methodological framework for choice of intensified equipment and development of innovative technologies, Chemical Engineering and Processing: Process Intensification, 84, 109-127

Gupta R., Kaistha N., 2015, Role of nonlinear effects in benzene-toluene-xylene dividing wall column control system design, Ind. Eng. Chem. Res., 54, 9407-9420

Iwakabe, K., Nakaiwa, M., Huang, K., Nakanishi, T., Røsjorde, A., Ohmori, T., Endo, A. and Yamamoto, T., 2006. Energy saving in multicomponent separation using an internally heat-integrated distillation column (HIDiC). Applied thermal engineering, 26(13), pp.1362-1368.

Kiss A.A., Landaeta S.J.F., Ferreira C.A.I., 2012, Towards energy efficient distillation technologies–Making the right choice, Energy, 47, 1, 531-542

Li Q., Finn A. J., Doyle S. J., Smith R., Kiss A. A., 2023, Synthesis and optimization of energy integrated advanced distillation sequences, Separation and Purification Technology, 315, 123717.

Luo, H., Bildea, C.S. and Kiss, A.A., 2015. Novel heat-pump-assisted extractive distillation for bioethanol purification. Industrial & Engineering Chemistry Research, 54(7), pp.2208-2213.

Pătruţ, C., Bîldea, C.S., Liţă, I. and Kiss, A.A., 2014. Cyclic distillation–Design, control and applications. Separation and Purification Technology, 125, pp.326-336.

Ponce, G.H.S.F., Alves, M., Miranda, J.C., Maciel Filho, R. and Maciel, M.R.W., 2015. Using an internally heat-integrated distillation column for ethanol–water separation for fuel applications. Chemical Engineering Research and Design, 95, pp.55-63.

Pribic P., Roza M., Zuber L., 2006, How to improve the energy savings in distillation and hybrid distillation-pervaporation systems, Separation science and technology, 41, 2581-2602.

Shahandeh, H., Jafari, M., Kasiri, N. and Ivakpour, J., 2015. Economic optimization of heat pump-assisted distillation columns in methanol-water separation. Energy, 80, pp.496-508.

Wang, G.Q., Xu, Z.C. and Ji, J.B., 2011. Progress on Higee distillation—Introduction to a new device and its industrial applications. Chemical engineering research and design, 89(8), pp.1434-1442.

Flavio Manenti, Gintaras V. Reklaitis (Eds.), Proceedings of the 34th European Symposium on Computer Aided Process Engineering / 15th International Symposium on Process Systems Engineering (ESCAPE34/PSE24), June 2-6, 2024, Florence, Italy
 http://dx.doi.org/10.1016/B978-0-443-28824-1.50213-1

Multi-Objective Optimization Approach for Enhancing Flexibility of a Pharmaceutical Tableting Process

Ilias Bouchkira[a,b], Brahim Benyahia[c,*]

[a] *E2S UPPA, LaTEP, Universite de Pau et des Pays de l'Adour, Pau, France.*

[b] *Laboratoire Réactions et Génie des Procédés, Université de Lorraine, Nancy, France.*

[c] *Department of Chemical Engineering, Loughborough University, Epinal Way, Loughborough, LE11 3TU, United Kingdom.*

b.benyahia@lboro.ac.uk

Abstract

In the field of process engineering, the flexibility index has emerged as a cornerstone for ensuring production adaptability and resilience in the face of volatile and unpredictable market demand. This paper introduces a novel approach, leveraging multi-objective optimization techniques, to enhance flexibility, with a focus on meeting the rigorous quality requirements of the pharmaceutical industry. A pharmaceutical tableting process, renowned for its tight regulatory and quality requirements, precision, and adaptability, serves as a model to validate the proposed methodology. Two crucial operating parameters, lubrication rate and solid fraction, are identified as Critical Process Parameters (CPP), with the tablet tensile strength and hardness being the Critical Quality Attributes (CQA). Through multi-objective optimization, the approach transcends traditional univariate methods, offering a holistic perspective to simultaneously optimize quality and flexibility alongside conventional key performance indicators. Preliminary findings reveal the identification of a robust Design Space, characterized by specific combinations of lubrication rate and solid fraction, ensuring exceptional tableting performance even in the presence of uncertainties. This research pioneers a more resilient and adaptive manufacturing landscape, offering pharmaceutical and related industries a groundbreaking opportunity to optimize processes and mitigate risks in an ever-changing and uncertain operating environment.

Keywords: Flexibility Analysis, Multi-Objective Optimization, Design Space, Critical Quality Attributes, Tableting Process.

1. Introduction

In the ever-evolving landscape of process engineering, the pursuit of flexibility has become a cornerstone principle, vital for ensuring the adaptability and resilience of industrial processes in the face of volatile and often unpredictable market demand of modern production (Floudas et al. 2001). This concept of flexibility analysis and the exploration of design space have gained significant importance within the realm of chemical engineering (Campbell et al. 2022). They provide a means to enhance not only the quality and precision of manufacturing processes but also their adaptability to evolving conditions and requirements.

This paper presents a groundbreaking approach to augmenting flexibility in industrial processes, leveraging the power of multi-objective optimization techniques. Through a compelling case study within the pharmaceutical sector, this research introduces an innovative methodology that has the potential to improve process design and operation, with a specific focus on meeting the stringent quality requirements in pharmaceutical production.

The pharmaceutical tableting, a domain where quality, precision, and adaptability are of paramount importance, serves as a demonstrator for this proposed methodology. In this context, the research narrows its focus to two pivotal operating parameters: the lubrication rate and solid fraction, both selected as Critical Process Parameters. Complementing these inputs is tablet tensile strength, identified as model Critical Quality Attribute (Bouchkira and Benyahia, 2023).

The main novelty of the proposed approach is the utilization of multi-objective optimization, which transcends the limitations of traditional, single objective optimization methods (Benyahia et al. 2010). This methodology offers a more comprehensive perspective, considering both quality and flexibility alongside the conventional key performance indicators. Preliminary findings from this research are promising, as they systematically identify the primary operating region, often referred to as the "Design Space" in a polygonal shape, which differs from the classic approach that results in a Box-shape. This region is characterized by specific combinations of the lubrication rate and solid fraction, and it remarkably sustains exceptional tableting performance even in the presence of significant uncertainties. This underscores the robustness and adaptability of the pharmaceutical tableting process, setting a precedent for other industrial applications.

2. Model and method

2.1. Lubrication model

In tablet press, tensile strength is a very important Critical Quality Attributes (CQA) which requires tight monitoring and effective control. This CQA can be related to the solid fraction in the tablets (sf) and the powder lubrication extent (k). Several mathematical models can be used to capture tablets' tensile strength amongst which are those developed by Kushner and Moore (2010) and Pitt et al. (1988) given by

$$\frac{ts}{ts_{sf=0.85,0}} = (1-\beta) + \beta\exp(-\gamma k) \tag{1}$$

Where $ts_{sf=0.85,0}$ is the initial tensile strength at 0.85 solid fraction, γ is the lubrication rate constant of the blend, and β is the total fraction of tensile strength that can be lost due to lubrication. To avoid dependence on the initial solid fraction, the following empirical equations were introduced:

$$ts_{sf=0.85,0} = a_1\exp(b_1(1-sf)) \tag{2}$$

$$\beta = a_2(1-sf) + b_2 \tag{3}$$

The resulting model captures the impact of two main factors or inputs namely the solid fraction sf and lubricant extent k, and involves a vector of five unknown parameters to ($\theta = [a_1(MPa);\ b_1(-);\ a_2(-); b_2(-), \gamma\ (dm^{-1})]$), whose values were taken from Cenci et al., 2022.

2.2. Multi-objective optimization-based Design Space

The approach utilizes a multi-objective optimization technique aiming to enhance the quality and performance of tablet production. The objective is to find an optimal set of parameters (Design Space) that balance the tensile strength of the tablets with other criteria. In this work, solid fraction and lubrication extent are considered. As shown in the figure below, the main purpose is to find the maximized variation ranges $[Sf^N - \delta.\Delta Sf;\ Sf^N + \delta.\Delta Sf]$ and $[k^N - \delta.\Delta k\ ; k^N + \delta.\Delta k]$, respectively for solid fraction and lubrication extent, that can be allowed during the tableting process, and that would deliver the targeted tablet tensile strength with minimum uncertainty, i.e., min $[T_s - T_s^{obj-}; T_s + T_s^{obj+}]$.

In the scheme below, Sf^N and k^N are nominal values of solid fraction and lubrication extent. ΔSf and Δk are operating errors or uncertainties, δ (in the classic design space approaches i.e., box-based); $\delta_{i,j}$ (in this work) are flexibility factors to be optimized to determine the optimal design space as stated by Floudas et al. 2010. The novelty in the proposed approach is that unlike the box-based approaches which are characterized by the same δ resulting in a single-optimization problem, in this work, each corner is characterized by a specific $\delta_{i,j}$ which gives more flexibility but results in a muti-objective optimization problem. We consequently aim to determine the coordinates of the optimal design space given by A, B, D and D. The targeted optimal design space is shown in figure 1. The corresponding multi-optimization problem is formulated by equation 4.

The constraints on the solid fraction and lubrication extent can be transformed to the matrix notation below (equation 5).

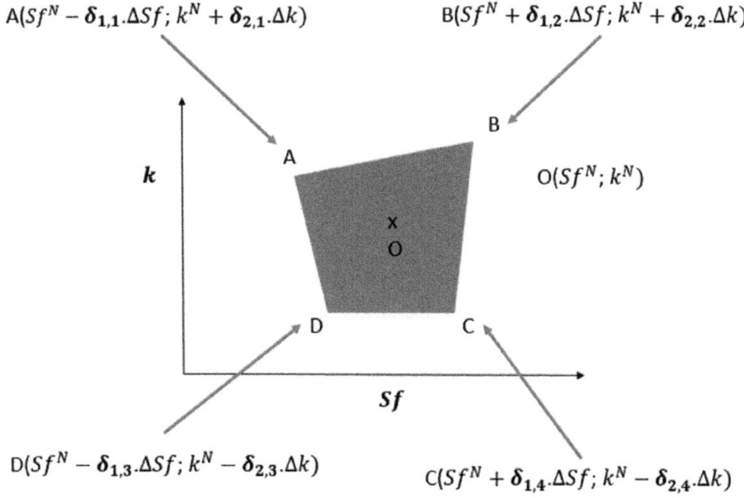

Figure 1. General representation of the optimal Design Space.

$$\min_X \boldsymbol{F} = [f_1, f_2, -f_3]^T$$
$$f_1 = -T_s + T_s^{obj-}, f_2 = T_s - T_s^{obj+}, f_3 = -\sum_{i,j} \delta_{i,j}$$

Subject to: (4)

$$Sf \leq min_i(Sf^N + \delta_{1,i}.\Delta Sf)$$
$$Sf \geq max_i(Sf^N + \delta_{1,i}.\Delta Sf)$$
$$k \leq min_i(k^N + \delta_{2,i}.\Delta k)$$
$$k \geq max_i(k^N - \delta_{2,i}.\Delta k)$$
$$X = [Sf, k, \vec{\delta}]$$

In this work, the proposed multi-objective optimization problem is solved using a genetic algorithm within MATLAB which is a gradient-free global optimization solver. Here, a Pareto front of 200 solutions was identified, and the selection criterion described in the following section was considered to identify the best optimal solutions.

$$\begin{bmatrix} -1 & 0 & -\Delta Sf & 0 & 0 & 0 & 0 & 0 & 0 & 0 \\ 0 & -1 & 0 & -\Delta k & 0 & 0 & 0 & 0 & 0 & 0 \\ 1 & 0 & 0 & 0 & -\Delta Sf & 0 & 0 & 0 & 0 & 0 \\ 0 & 1 & 0 & 0 & 0 & -\Delta k & 0 & 0 & 0 & 0 \\ 1 & 0 & 0 & 0 & 0 & 0 & -\Delta Sf & 0 & 0 & 0 \\ 0 & 1 & 0 & 0 & 0 & 0 & 0 & -\Delta k & 0 & 0 \\ -1 & 0 & 0 & 0 & 0 & 0 & 0 & 0 & -\Delta Sf & 0 \\ 0 & -1 & 0 & 0 & 0 & 0 & 0 & 0 & 0 & -\Delta k \end{bmatrix} \cdot \begin{bmatrix} Sf \\ k \\ \delta_{1,1} \\ \delta_{2,1} \\ \delta_{1,2} \\ \delta_{2,2} \\ \delta_{1,3} \\ \delta_{2,3} \\ \delta_{1,4} \\ \delta_{2,4} \end{bmatrix} \leq \begin{bmatrix} -Sf^N \\ -k^N \\ Sf^N \\ k^N \\ Sf^N \\ k^N \\ -Sf^N \\ -k^N \end{bmatrix} \quad (5)$$

2.3. Selection criterion

As the resolution of the multi-objective optimization problem results in a Pareto front with several optimal solutions, it is essential to select the best optimal solution. Several decision aiding approaches exist in the literature among which, the Multi-attribute Utility Theory (MAUT). However, as we are interested in maximizing the area of the flexibility region, the selection criterion in this work is based on comparing the resulting area values with each optimal solution, and to choose the one that provides more flexibility as the best solution. The Shoelace formula is used to find the area of the polygons given the coordinates of its vertices. For a quadrilateral with coordinates (x_1, y_1), (x_2, y_2), (x_3, y_3), and (x_4, y_4). The Shoelace formula is given by

$$A = \sum_{i=1}^{n} A_i = \frac{1}{2}\sum_{i=1}^{n} (y_i + y_{i+1})(x_i - x_{i+1}) \quad (6)$$

3. Results and discussion

Six different scenarios are simulated and discussed in this section. Indeed, The investigation into tablet formulation scenarios sheds light on the intricate relationship between the formulation parameters and tablet tensile strength. The scenarios conducted offer insights into the sensitivity and impact of variations in solid fraction Sf^N, lubrication extent k^N, uncertainties in these parameters (ΔSf and Δk), and the objective range for tensile strength (T_s^{obj-} and T_s^{obj+}) on the tablet's flexibility and overall quality. The initial scenario (Scenario 1) served as a reference point for subsequent variations. Scenario 2, altering the nominal values of solid fraction and lubrication extent (from 1.2;0.8 to 1.0;1.0), showcased the system's sensitivity to these parameters. This sensitivity underscores the crucial role of solid fraction and lubrication extent in determining tablet tensile strength. Furthermore, it highlights the necessity for precise and robust control and consideration of these parameters in formulation design to achieve desired tensile strength characteristics.

Scenarios 3 and 4 introduced uncertainties ΔSf and Δk in solid fraction and lubrication extent, respectively. The contrast between these scenarios revealed that uncertainty in lubrication extent Δk contributed more significantly to the tablet's quality than uncertainty in solid fraction ΔSf. This finding emphasizes the need for a more in-depth understanding and control of lubrication extent to ensure consistent tablet quality.

The subsequent scenarios, altering the objective range for tensile strength, provided intriguing results. Scenario 5, with a broader objective range, exhibited a higher flexibility region compared to Scenario 6. This outcome suggests that a wider range for acceptable tensile strength leads to a more flexible formulation space. A broader acceptable range enables a wider set of formulation parameters while still meeting the critical quality attributes of the tablets, offering more leeway in the design of pharmaceutical formulations.

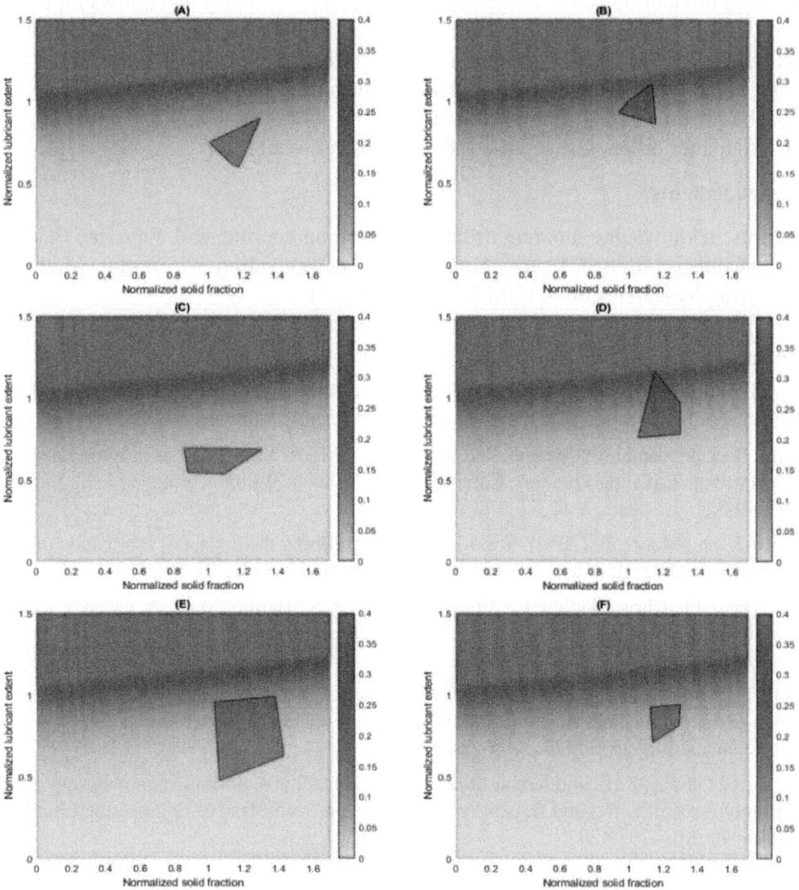

Figure 2. Deign Space for six scenarios. (A-F) correspond to Scenarios (1-6) respectively.

Table 1: Summary of the proposed six different scenarios.

	Sf^N	k^N	ΔSf	Δk	T_s^{obj-}	T_s^{obj+}
Scenario 1	1.2	0.8	0.1	0.1	0.1	0.32
Scenario 2	1.0	1.0	0.1	0.1	0.1	0.32
Scenario 3	1.2	0.8	0.15	0.1	0.1	0.32
Scenario 4	1.2	0.8	0.1	0.15	0.1	0.32
Scenario 5	1.2	0.8	0.1	0.1	0.05	0.45
Scenario 6	1.2	0.8	0.1	0.1	0.15	0.2

4. Conclusion

This research advances process engineering methodologies by employing multi-objective optimization to reconcile quality and flexibility in pharmaceutical manufacturing. The study analyses six scenarios to comprehensively explores the pharmaceutical tableting process, assessing the impact of different formulation parameters on tablet tensile strength and manufacturing flexibility. Scenario 5 stands out for its superior flexibility, introducing a broader objective range ($\boldsymbol{T_s^{obj-}}$ = 0.05, $\boldsymbol{T_s^{obj+}}$ = 0.45) that allows for a more extensive set of formulation parameters, while achieving desired tensile strength objectives. This broader flexibility region demonstrates the importance of defining a wide acceptable range for tensile strength in manufacturing design. While the current Design Space is based on a four-vertices polygon, future works will explore extending the approach to higher orders for increased robustness and reliability.

Acknowledgements

The authors acknowledge funding from the UK Engineering and Physical Sciences Research Council (EPSRC), for Made Smarter Innovation – Digital Medicines Manufacturing Research Centre (DM2), EP/V062077/1.

References

Benyahia, B., Latifi, M.A., Fonteix, C., Pla, F. (2010). Multicriteria dynamic optimization of an emulsion copolymerization reactor. Computer Aided Chemical Engineering 28, 457-462.

Bouchkira, Ilias, and Brahim Benyahia. "Multi-Objective Model-based Design of Experiments of Pharmaceutical Tableting Process." Computer Aided Chemical Engineering. Vol. 52. Elsevier, 2023. 349-354.

Kushner IV J., and Moore, F. (2010). Scale-up model describing the impact of lubrication on tablet tensile strength. International Journal of Pharmaceutics 399(1-2), 19-30.

Cenci, F., Bano, G., Christodoulou, C., Vueva, Y., Zomer, S., Barolo, M., ... & Facco, P. (2022). Streamlining tablet lubrication design via model-based design of experiments. International Journal of Pharmaceutics, 614, 121435.

Campbell, T., Rielly, C. & Benyahia, B. (2022). Digital design and optimization of an integrated reaction-extraction-crystallization-filtration continuous pharmaceutical process. Computer Aided Chemical Engineering, 51, 775-780.

Floudas, C. A., Gümüş, Z.H., and Ierapetritou, M.G. (2001). Global optimization in design under uncertainty: feasibility test and flexibility index problems. Industrial & Engineering Chemistry Research, 40(20), 4267-4282.

Flavio Manenti, Gintaras V. Reklaitis (Eds.), Proceedings of the 34th European Symposium on Computer Aided Process Engineering / 15th International Symposium on Process Systems Engineering (ESCAPE34/PSE24), June 2-6, 2024, Florence, Italy
 http://dx.doi.org/10.1016/B978-0-443-28824-1.50214-3

Hybrid Artificial Intelligence-based Process Flowsheet Synthesis and Design using Extended SFILES Representation

Vipul Mann,[a] Mauricio Sales-Cruz[b], Rafiqul Gani,[c,d,e] Venkat Venkatasubramanian[a,*]

[a]*Columbia University, New York 10027, USA*
[b]*Universidad Autónoma Metropolitana-Cuajimalpa, Ciudad de México, México*
[c]*PSE for SPEED Company, DK-2920, Charlottenlund, Denmark*
[d]*The Hong Kong University of Science and Technology (Guangzhou), China*
[e]*Széchenyi István University, 9026 Győr, Hungary*

Abstract

Process flowsheet synthesis and design involves simultaneously solving several problems, including determining the unit operations and their sequence, underlying reactions and reaction stoichiometry, downstream separation design and operation parameters, sustainability factors, and many more. Naturally, this results in a large amount of data being associated with a given process flowsheet that captures the relevant process context and should be readily accessible. This data is useful for solving related problems both using data-driven and process knowledge-based methods. A hierarchical framework, called the extended SFILES (or eSFILES), proposed recently stores this information using a combination of text-based, graph-based, and ontology-based representations. Here, we provide details on a prototype software for automated flowsheet representation and generation across various levels in the eSFILES framework. The underlying methods include a novel flowsheet grammar, a set of inferencing algorithms, and interfacing with a commercial process simulator facilitating rigorous flowsheet simulation.

Keywords: process design, flowsheet modeling, artificial intelligence, computer-aided flowsheet synthesis

1. Introduction

A central problem in process systems engineering is to efficiently convert raw materials to desired products, which involves evaluating the correct sequence of unit operations, their design, and optimization of associated operations, also known as the process synthesis and design problem. The problem becomes computationally complex due to the various decisions to be made at each stage. To mitigate the challenges associated with this, we recently reported a multi-level flowsheet representation and generation framework, called extended SFILES (or eSFILES), that could be used to efficiently solve flowsheet synthesis and design problems using hybrid artificial intelligence (AI) methods (Mann et al., 2024), (Mann et al., 2023b). The eSFILES framework represents flowsheet information at varying granularity using three levels with a base level 0. At level 0, flow diagrams are represented as purely text-based SFILES strings (Bommareddy et al., 2011), (D'Anterroches, 2005), (Tula et al., 2015). At level 1, SFILES grammar and inferencing algorithms, are used to construct a flowsheet hypergraph explicitly representing flow-diagram connectivity. At level 2, specifications needed for material and energy balance calculations are introduced, and their simulation results with simple models are also added using annotated flowsheet hypergraphs. Finally, at level 3, a process ontology is connected with the annotated flowsheet hypergraph to include design and operation parameters and simulation results with rigorous models.

In this work, we present details on an automated tool for representing process flowsheets using the eSFILES representation. The developed parser (software tool) comprises an extensive set of inference algorithms that allow for the conversion of flowsheet representations at a given level to any other level in the framework. Moreover, it also interfaces with commercial process simulators and process generators. Algorithms underlying the parser include – a novel flowsheet grammar that formally defines syntax rules, flowsheet hypergraph generation and inference algorithms, text-based flowsheet representation generation, rigorous process simulation with integration with commercial process simulators, and so on. The prototype program enables the development of hybrid AI systems that efficiently blend domain knowledge with data-driven techniques (Mann et al., 2023a), (Venkatasubramanian & Mann, 2022). We envision the parser would accelerate the development of fast, efficient, and consistent solutions for flowsheet-related problems, that result in hybrid AI systems as opposed to purely data-driven approaches (Vogel et al., 2022) (Hirtreiter et al., 2022).

2. Extended SFILES representation

The extended SFILES (eSFILES) representation involves representing flowsheets across four levels (levels 0, 1, 2, and 3) with varying degrees of process knowledge. At the core of the eSFILES representation lies the concept of process-atoms and process-bonds from the SFILES representation, the concept of annotated hypergraphs with process-atoms represented as hyperedges and process-bonds represented as nodes, and a novel flowsheet grammar that is combined with inferencing algorithms to facilitate automated parsing and interconversion across multiple representation levels. To illustrate the multi-level eSFILES framework, consider a simple four-component separation task as shown in Figure 1a where four components A, B, C, and D enter the first distillation column and they need to be separated into pure component streams. Details of other more complex examples can be obtained from the authors.

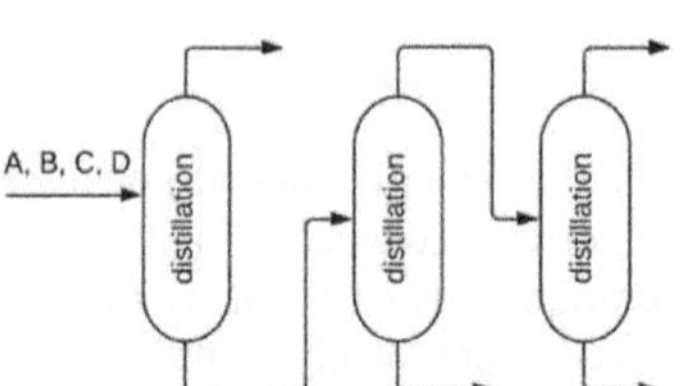

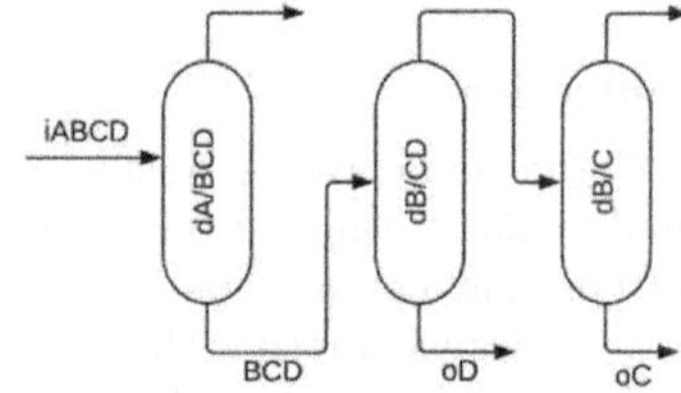

Figure 1. (a) Process flow diagram (b) Process-atoms and process-bonds

2.1. Level 0: Text-based SFILES representation

The process-atoms and process-bonds corresponding to the given process flow diagram are shown in Figure 1b with dA/BCD, dB/CD, and dB/C representing the three distillation columns with top and bottom streams separated by '/'. The process-bonds are the raw input stream iABCD, output streams oA, oC, oB, and oC, and the intermediate streams are BCD and BC. The purely text-based representation comprising eSFILES level 0 representation is given by, (iABCD)(dA/BCD)(oA)(dBC/D)(oD)(dB/C)(oB)(oC)

2.2. Level 1: Hypergraph-based representation

Level 1 represents the connectivity between process-atoms explicitly using a flowsheet hypergraph with process-bonds (ABCD, A, BCD, BC, D, B, C) as nodes and process-atoms (D1, D2, D3) as hyperedges as shown in Figure 2a. The graph-based representation is numeric in nature and could be easily combined with graph-theoretic methods to perform superstructure optimization, flowsheet enumeration, and so on.

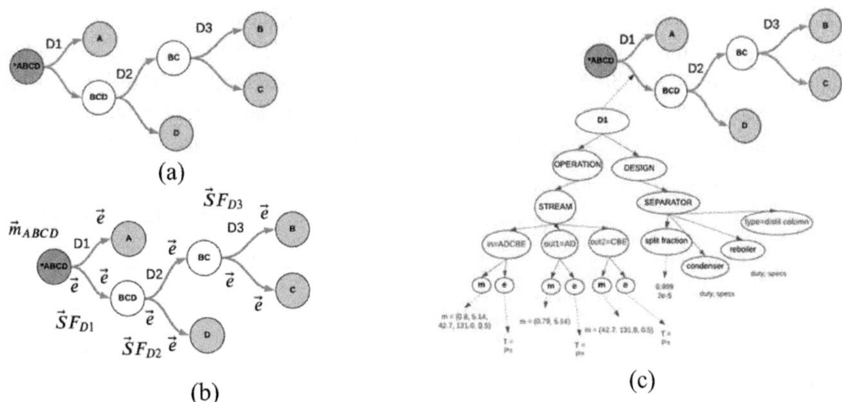

Figure 2. (a) level 1 representation (b) level 2 representation (c) level 3 representation

2.3. Level 2: Annotated flowsheet hypergraph

Level 2 represents additional flowsheet context such as material and energy balance information using node-edge paired annotations in the hypergraph, thus allowing for multiple annotations for the same node connected to different hyperedges. These annotations include component flow rate (s) m_i for streams, split fraction SF_j for each separator, and temperature T and pressure P for each stream entering or leaving the process-atom, as shown in Figure 2b. This representation facilitates the use of simple models for material and energy balance calculations.

2.4. Level 3: Process ontology-connected flowsheet hypergraph

Level 3 represents information on design and operation parameters using a custom-built process ontology connected to the hypergraph via hyperedges (see Figure 2c). Each hyperedge (process-atom) is connected to the instantiated process ontology where the relevant design and operation information are organized hierarchically as classes, subclasses, and properties with process-atom as the main class. This representation is used for rigorous flowsheet calculations using commercial process simulators.

For further details on various levels of the eSFILES framework with additional examples of reactors, recycle streams, and so on, the reader is referred to (Mann et al., 2024).

3. Automatically parsing and generation of eSFILES representation

The primary objective of the developed flowsheet parser is the conversion of the base level, i.e., level 0 of the flowsheet representation to level 1 automatically, and further generation of higher-level representations (levels 2 and beyond) by interfacing with commercial process simulators. This requires inferring the underlying process-atoms, process-bonds, recycle streams, sequence and connectivity patterns, and the input/output streams in the process. While the level 0 string representation, in principle, contains this information, a formal set of rules, heuristics, and algorithms are required to achieve this automation, namely, flowsheet grammar and a set of inferencing algorithms described in the following sections.

3.1. Flowsheet grammar

The flowsheet grammar defines the set of rules that formalize the structure of the text-based representation and is characterized by a set of symbols and recursive rules that could be applied systematically to generate grammatically valid SFILES strings. Formally, it consists of – S, a designated start symbol; $\sum$, the set of terminal symbols; N, the set of non-terminal symbols; and R, the set of syntax rules of the form $A \rightarrow \beta$, where A is a non-terminal symbol and β could either be a terminal symbol (from $\sum$) or a non-terminal symbol (from N). A subset of the developed grammar rules is listed in Table 1. The corresponding grammar symbols are – S: SFILES, N: {i,A,B,C,D}, $\sum$: {PA, PG, EQUIPMENT, INLET, OUTLET, SEP, ...}, and R: R_{1-20}. The hierarchical grammar tree corresponding to the SFILES string for the four-component separation is shown in Figure 3 below. For a complete list of the developed flowsheet grammar and additional examples of grammar trees, please refer to (Mann et al., 2024).

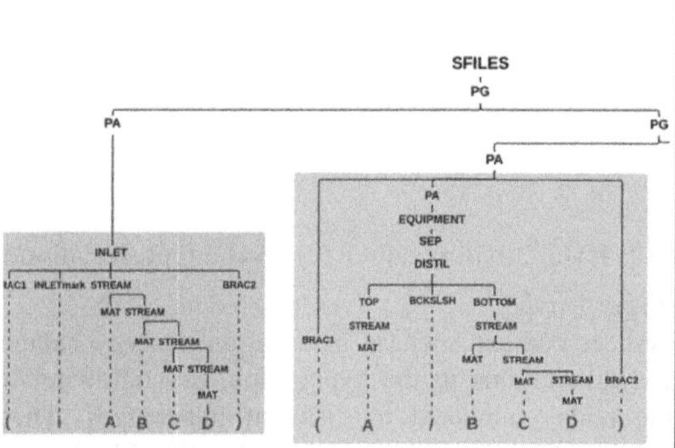

Figure 3: Partially shown grammar syntax tree with inlet and distillation hierarchy

Table 1: A subset of the developed SFILES grammar rules

Rule	Grammar syntax rules
R_1	SFILES → PG
R_2	PG → PA PG | PA
R_4	PA → BRAC1 PA BRAC2
R_6	PA → INLET | OUTLET | EQUIPMENT
R_8	INLET → BRAC1 INLETmark STREAM BRAC2
R_9	OUTLET → BRAC1 OUTLETmark STREAM BRAC2
R_{10}	EQUIPMENT → SEP
R_{11}	SEP → DISTIL
R_{12}	DISTIL → TOP BCKSLSH BOTTOM
R_{13}	TOP | BOTTOM → STREAM
R_{14}	STREAM → STREAM MAT | MAT
R_{15}	MAT → A | B | C | D
R_{16}	BRAC1 → (
R_{17}	BRAC2 →)
R_{18}	BCKSLSH → /
R_{19}	INLETmark → i
R_{20}	OUTLETmark → o

3.2. Inferencing algorithms

3.2.1. Grammar parsing

Given a SFILES string for a process flowsheet, a hierarchical grammar syntax tree indicating additional structural information on the flowsheet string is generated as shown in Figure 3. The grammar rules are generated by providing the complete set of grammar rules (similar to those given in Table 1) to natural language parsers like ChartParser in the NLTK library in Python. The ChartParser uses dynamic programming to efficiently parse a given string and generates a tree structure for each string subsequence using the provided set of grammar syntax rules. For invalid strings, the grammar tree would not be generated, resulting in a parsing error. Thus, the generation of such hierarchical trees facilitate automated syntax checking for SFILES strings.

3.2.2. Inferring process-atoms and process-bonds

In the grammar tree, all the process-atoms and process-bonds are identified by extracting subtrees from the parent tree by filtering them on intermediate node labels. For instance, the inlet, outlet, and recycle streams are identified by extracting subtrees with labels 'INLET', 'OUTLET', and 'RECYCLE'; for intermediate streams, subtrees with label 'STREAM' AND parent labels not in ['INLET', 'OUTLET', 'RECYCLE'] are extracted; the individual materials are identified as subtrees with parent node 'MAT'; separators correspond to subtrees with label 'SEP' and their type is the immediate child node label such as 'DISTIL'; the top and bottom streams, reactor reactant and product streams, and so on are identified based on similar grammar tree-based inferencing.

3.2.3. Inferring connectivity

Connectivity is inferred based on tree-distance between subtrees identified for each process-atom. For computing the distance, the root node for each subtree is represented as a sequence of integers based on whether a given node is on the left or right of the parent node, with an additional integer for each level of depth. For instance, the position of subtree with node 'SEP' in Figure 3 would be represented as (0,1,0,1,0,0). The grammar structure and the SFILES string structure by design is such that adjacent process-atoms are connected together linearly. Each process-atom would have a left-connectivity and right-connectivity, unless they are input or output streams that just have right-connectivity and left-connectivity, respectively. The nearest left and right subtrees are identified based on tree distances, to identify the left connection and right connection of a given process-atom. Since we have information on the top/bottom or reactant/product streams from the grammar tree, the output of the left process-atom automatically becomes one of the inputs of the current process-atom. This also allows performing material balance-based sanity checks while inferring connectivity.

3.2.4. Additional information for level 2

For levels 2 and 3, additional information needs to be input by the user or generated using intelligent design methods similar to those proposed in Tula et al. (2015). For level 2, the information on material and energy balance calculations is required. This information could be obtained from flowsheet generators. The input to such flowsheet generators is the level 1 flowsheet hypergraph and the process context (design goals, etc.) and the output is the information required for simple material and energy balance calculations stored as node-edge labels as shown in Figure 2b. The level 2 representations are used for performing mass and energy balance calculations using simple models.

3.2.5. Additional information for level 3

For level 3, additional information such as the design and operation parameters are required to perform process flowsheet simulations. This information is obtained from commercial process simulators and stored as an instantiated ontology connected to the process-atom hyperedge as shown in Figure 2c. The connection between the eSFILES framework and process simulators is enabled by using the keyword file to translate the possibly different nomenclature between the two systems. Such keyword files have a unique variable name for each piece of information required to simulate the process, and thus, allow information flow between level 3 representation and process simulator input and output. For instance, a snippet of the interfacing between eSFILES level 3 and process simulators such as Pro II is shown in Figure 4. These keywords are mapped to our developed process ontology and connected to the flowsheet hypergraph, facilitating information exchange between the two systems required for rigorous simulations.

4. Conclusions

An automated software tool for performing hybrid AI-based process flowsheet synthesis and design using a multi-level hierarchical flowsheet representation and generation framework called extended SFILES (or eSFILES) has been presented. The developed software tool allows automated interconversion of flowsheet representations at various levels in the eSFILES framework with varying degrees of process flowsheet information. The level 0 (base level) text-based flowsheet representation is converted to level 1 flowsheet hypergraph using a flowsheet grammar combined with tree-based inferencing algorithms to infer unit operations, streams, and connectivity between them. The level 2 and level 3 representations are generated using the level 1 representation and interfacing with process simulators and generators using keyword files. A custom-built process ontology map stores the information from keyword files and is connected to the hypergraph containing relevant information for each process-atom, thus facilitating information sharing between the two systems. The development of the prototype software would aid in the further development of hybrid AI systems that not only leverage process knowledge-based methods but also take advantage of the computational benefits of data-driven methods, thereby allowing reliable, efficient, and rapid process development.

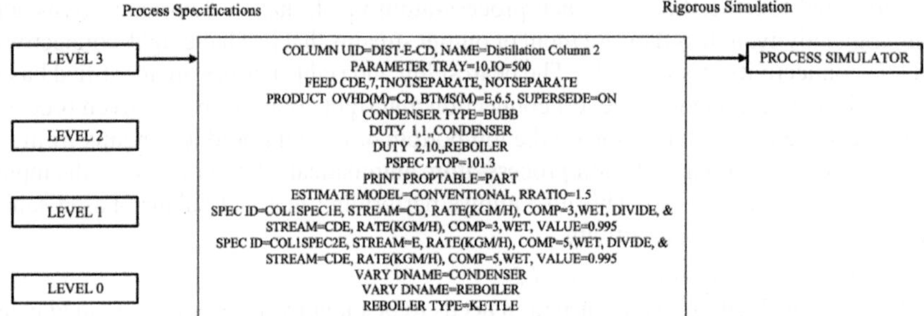

Figure 4: Interfacing between level 3 and commercial process simulators

References

Bommareddy, S., Eden, M. R., & Gani, R. (2011). *Computer Aided Flowsheet Design using Group Contribution Methods* (pp. 321–325). https://doi.org/10.1016/B978-0-444-53711-9.50065-1

D'Anterroches, L. (2005). *Process flowsheet generation & design through a group contribution approach.* [CAPEC], Department of Chemical Engineering, Technical University of Denmark.

Hirtreiter, E., Balhorn, L. S., & Schweidtmann, A. M. (2022). *Towards automatic generation of Piping and Instrumentation Diagrams (P&IDs) with Artificial Intelligence.* http://arxiv.org/abs/2211.05583

Mann, V., Gani, R., & Venkatasubramanian, V. (2023a). Group contribution-based property modeling for chemical product design: A perspective in the AI era. *Fluid Phase Equilibria, 568.* https://doi.org/10.1016/j.fluid.2023.113734

Mann, V., Gani, R., & Venkatasubramanian, V. (2023b). Intelligent Process Flowsheet Synthesis and Design using Extended SFILES Representation. In *Computer Aided Chemical Engineering* (Vol. 52, pp. 221–226). Elsevier B.V. https://doi.org/10.1016/B978-0-443-15274-0.50036-6

Mann, V., Sales-Cruz, M., Gani, R., & Venkatasubramanian, V. (2024). eSFILES: Intelligent process flowsheet synthesis using process knowledge, symbolic AI, and machine learning. *Computers & Chemical Engineering, 181*, 108505. https://doi.org/10.1016/j.compchemeng.2023.108505

Tula, A. K., Eden, M. R., & Gani, R. (2015). Process synthesis, design and analysis using a process-group contribution method. *Computers & Chemical Engineering, 81*, 245–259. https://doi.org/10.1016/J.COMPCHEMENG.2015.04.019

Venkatasubramanian, V., & Mann, V. (2022). Artificial intelligence in reaction prediction and chemical synthesis. *Current Opinion in Chemical Engineering, 36*, 100749. https://doi.org/10.1016/j.coche.2021.100749

Vogel, G., Balhorn, L. S., & Schweidtmann, A. M. (2022). *Learning from flowsheets: A generative transformer model for autocompletion of flowsheets.* http://arxiv.org/abs/2208.00859

Flavio Manenti, Gintaras V. Reklaitis (Eds.), Proceedings of the 34th European Symposium on Computer Aided Process Engineering / 15th International Symposium on Process Systems Engineering (ESCAPE34/PSE24), June 2-6, 2024, Florence, Italy
 http://dx.doi.org/10.1016/B978-0-443-28824-1.50215-5

Progressive Hedging Decomposition for Solutions of Large-Scale Process Family Design Problems

Georgia Stinchfield[a], Jean-Paul Watson[b], Carl D. Laird[a*]

[a] *Carnegie Mellon University, Pittsburgh, Pennsylvannia 15201, USA*

[b] *Lawrence Livermore National Laboratory, Livermore, California 94550, USA*

**claird@andrew.cmu.edu*

Abstract

Rapid, wide-scale deployment of green process systems, such as carbon capture and water desalination systems, is essential for combatting climate change. Methods relying on traditional design or modularity fail to capture the benefits of both economies of numbers and economies of scale. We propose a *process family design* approach, which designs a collection of related processes while simultaneously exploiting opportunities for common elements. In previous work, we explored different optimization formulations to solve this problem. In this work, we develop a decomposition approach to tackle larger problems efficiently. We consider a water desalination case study, which is too large to solve within a reasonable timeframe with the full discretization formulation. We instead exploit the block-angular structure of the full discretization formulation to decompose and solve the problem implicitly using Progressive Hedging (PH). We use the open-source Python package mpi-sppy to execute PH which allows us to leverage parallelization and a HPC cluster to further improve solution time.

Keywords: Decomposition, Process Design, Parallelization, Water Desalination.

1. Introduction

Some challenges faced in climate change-related process systems engineering rely on rapid, wide-scale, and tailored deployment of a particular chemical process. For example, a promising solution for addressing the rapid depletion of bodies of freshwater is to deploy water desalination systems to purify alternative water sources. Currently, common design approaches either focus on economies of scale (traditional design) or economies of numbers (modular design), but both have their drawbacks. In previous work, we introduced a process family design strategy that combines features of both approaches. We have demonstrated process family design via several case studies (Stinchfield et al., 2023). However, for very large-scale problems, computational time is still prohibitive. In this paper, we develop a decomposition approach based on the Progressive Hedging (PH) algorithm (Rockafellar and Wets, 1991) and demonstrate efficient parallel scalability on high-performance computing architectures using the open-source package mpi-sppy (Knueven et al., 2023).

In past work, we introduced a mathematical model for solving a discretized version of the process family design problem (Stinchfield et al., 2023 and Chen et al. 2022). This model considers two sets of discrete decision variables. The first set of variables selects which unit module designs are included in the process platform from a set of candidate options; the second set of variables determines which of these unit module designs are assigned to each variant. In this work, we exploit a parallelized PH algorithm to solve large-scale process family design problems. PH is a well-known algorithm traditionally used to solve stochastic programming problems. PH works as a heuristic in the context of models with discrete decision variables, but as of recently provides gap-closing capabilities. Further, PH can address discrete variables at any stage in the problem structure. While our problem is not a two-stage stochastic programming problem, it shares a mathematically equivalent block-angular structure, so PH can be directly leveraged. We decompose our problem by process variant, treating the discrete platform unit module design variables as "first-stage" variables (in stochastic programming terminology) and the discrete assignment of unit module designs to variants as second-stage. A large-scale case study on water desalination is then solved via PH using mpi-sppy (Knueven et al., 2023) on a multi-node HPC using Gurobi© as the sub-problem solver (Gurobi Optimization, 2023).

2. Background

Our process family design strategy was first inspired by *product* family and platform design, which has documented success in a variety of applications found in the automotive, aircraft, and technology industries (Simpson et al., 2014). Given a set of product variants, product family design creates a platform of common components that are shared across variants, optimizing the remaining elements uniquely. We map this approach to process systems engineering by viewing *product* variants instead as *process* variants; this differs from common design approaches by introducing customization and standardization simultaneously. Traditional engineering aims to exploit economies of scale, with unique designs for each variant. Manufacturing one-off designs is significantly more expensive and time consuming compared to mass manufacturing of standardized components. In contrast, modular design derives cost savings and shortened timelines from economies of numbers through standardization of manufacturing. However, the designs offered are significantly less flexible and typically result in sub-optimal operating conditions. In process family design, we simultaneously design the platform of shared unit modules along with each of the process variants in the family. This approach enables trade-offs between both customization and standardization. In this way, we aim to optimally exploit economies of scale and economies of numbers simultaneously.

3. Problem Statement

The goal is to produce a process system design for a set of process variants V (a complete set of designs forms the process family, $\mathcal{F}$) using a set of standardized unit module designs (from the process platform, $\mathcal{P}$). Each *process variant* is defined by all requirements the variant must meet along with the defining characteristics of the deployment site. The *process system architecture* defines the necessary *unit module types* required to construct the process system, denoted by the set M. For example, a refrigeration system might have a set of unit module types comprised of an evaporator, compressor, condenser, and valve. A unit module type is general; a *unit module type design* specifies all necessary information to build a particular instance of a unit module type. For a variant v to have a complete *process variant design*, there must be a fully specified unit module design, $\mathbf{d}_{v,m}$, for each unit module type $m \in M$. In addition, the combination of unit module designs must be feasible, meaning it satisfies all requirements and characteristics of the process variant.

The unit module types M are separated into the set of common unit module types C and unique unit module types U (where $M = C \cup U$ and $C \cap U = \emptyset$). A *process platform* contains a number of unit module designs for each common unit module type $c \in C$. Building this platform introduces standardization by using common unit module types $c \in C$ for each of the process variants. A *process family* is a complete set of process variant designs where each of the common unit module types have designs sourced from the process platform, and the unique unit module types have their respective designs independently determined. The goal is to simultaneously optimize all the process variants, the platform of common unit module designs, and assign common unit module designs for each $c \in C$ from the platform for all variants V, and determine designs for all unique unit module types $u \in U$ for all variants V.

4. Solution Approach

4.1. Optimization Formulation

In previous work, a discretization approach was proposed for this process family design problem (Stinchfield et al., 2023). We develop a set of *candidate unit module designs* $\hat{\mathbf{d}}_{c,l}$ for all common unit module types $c \in C$. We identify each candidate unit module design using the label l; the set of all labels is denoted by L_c. For each possible *combination of candidate unit module designs* (which is exactly one candidate unit module design $\hat{\mathbf{d}}_{c,l}$ for each $c \in C$) and process variant conditions, we perform an optimization of the system model. This optimization determines the unique unit module designs $\mathbf{d}_{v,u}$, operating conditions $\mathbf{o}_v$, feasibility $\mathbf{i}_v$, and total annualized cost of the system p_v. The set $a \in A_v$ captures all feasible alternatives for variant v. The binary decision variable $z_{c,l}$ determines which candidate common unit module types will be included in the platform. A second decision variable $x_{v,a}$ indicates whether alternative $a \in A_v$ is selected for variant v. The optimization formulation for this approach is shown in (1).

$$\min_{x,z} \sum_{v \in V} w_v \sum_{a \in A_v} p_{va} x_{va} \tag{1a}$$

$$\text{s.t.} \quad \sum_{l \in L_c} z_{c,l} \le N_c \qquad \forall c \in C \tag{1b}$$

$$\sum_{a \in A_v} x_{v,a} = 1 \qquad \forall v \in V \tag{1c}$$

$$x_{v,a} \le z_{c,l} \qquad \forall v \in V, a \in A_v, (c,l) \in Q_a \tag{1d}$$

$$z_{c,l} \in \{0,1\} \qquad \forall c \in C, l \in L_c \tag{1e}$$

$$0 \le x_{v,a} \le 1 \qquad \forall v \in V, a \in A_v \tag{1f}$$

Here, the weight w_v of variant v represents the expected sales. The objective (1a) is to minimize the total weighted cost of designing all variants $v \in V$. In (1b), we constrain the number of designs allowable in the platform via N_c (where $|N_c| \le |L_c|$) to enforce specified levels of standardization. In (1c), we ensure only one alternative is selected for each variant $v \in V$. Due to favorable properties of the presented formulation, we can relax $x_{v,a}$ to be between 0,1 in (1f), and (under mild assumptions) this variable will converge to binary at optimality due to similarities to the classic P-median formulation.

4.2. Decomposition and Solution Strategy

Given the significant size of the problem, we use PH decomposition, typically for stochastic programming problems, for efficient solution (Rockafellar and Wets, 1991). Stochastic programs have a block angular mathematical structure, which is favorable for decomposition because most of the variables can be separated into disjoint sets of variables, y_s, that only appear in the constraints of the associated subproblem s. The remaining variables x prevent the optimization problem from being perfectly separable as they appear in two or more of the subproblems. To decompose via PH, we create a copy of every complicating variable, denoted as x_s, in each sub-problem $s \in S$. The PH algorithm then iteratively solves subproblems to $x = x_s$ for all $s \in S$; these equality constraints are referred to as *non- anticipativity* constraints in the explicit (i.e., full) form of the problem. PH exploits this structure by solving the decomposed sub-problems separately (a step that is trivially parallelizable) by first relaxing the non-anticipativity constraints. To ensure all complicating variables are ultimately non-anticipative, PH penalizes deviations from the first-stage variable average at each iteration by incorporating a linear and proximal penalty term into the sub-problem objectives. PH updates a weight vector after solving all sub-problems at iteration k that informs the penalization terms of the magnitude of deviation from the disaggregated complicating variables $x_s^{(k)}$ and their average $\bar{x}^{(k)} = \sum_{s \in S} \frac{1}{\mathbb{P}(s)} x_s^{(k)}$; $\mathbb{P}(s)$ represents the probability, or "weight", of scenario s. In addition, PH utilizes the parameter ρ to control the magnitude of penalization for deviations.

While our process family design problem is not a stochastic program, it shares the characteristic block-angular structure. In our case, we form sub-problems corresponding to subsets of the variants $v \in V$. This is feasible because the variable $x_{v,a}$ is only dependent on a variant and the associated alternative set $a \in A_v$. The complicating (i.e., first-stage) variables are $z_{c,l}$, which specify what common unit module designs should be offered in the platform; the values of these variables clearly must be equivalent across subproblems. PH thus allows us to solve smaller subproblems rather than attempting to solve the overall formulation (1) with every variant and candidate unit module design considered concurrently. Additionally, using the open-source Python package mpi-sppy (Knueven et al., 2023) allows us to perform the PH algorithm in parallel with incumbent finders and lower bounding capabilities.

5. Case Study and Results

To demonstrate the proposed decomposition approach, we consider the problem of designing a large family of desalination systems for high salinity produced water. We use an equation-oriented model written in Pyomo (Bynum et al., 2021) that was developed as a part of the PARETO framework (Drouven et al., 2022). This system is made up of a single-effect evaporation unit coupled with a single-stage adiabatic compressor. Produced water enters the shell side of the evaporator to be split into a vapor stream and concentrated brine stream. The adiabatic compressor converts the vapor stream into superheated steam. Exiting the compressor there is a minimum recycle line for consideration of design flow operation. The superheated steam provides the heat of evaporation. Finally, the condensation is removed as a freshwater stream.

For this case study, we define each variant by the flow rate of salt water and the concentration of salt. Salt concentrations of produced water sites across multiple Texas water basins are documented in the PARETO project, and only salt concentrations between 20 g/kg and 150 g/kg were included. Flowrates considered were between 0.1 kg/s and 1 kg/s (55 to 500 bbls/day). Additionally, all the unit module types in the system (evaporator and compressor) were selected to be commonly designed. We selected 20 candidate unit module designs for each common unit module type. For the evaporator, we design for heat exchange area and for the compressor, we design for the flow rate.

We solved this process family design for a desalination system requiring 10,897 variants. We constrained the number of unit module design options available in the platform to three evaporator designs and three compressor designs (i.e., $N_c = 3$ for all $c \in C$). The optimal platform selected evaporator area designs of $20\ m^2$, $80\ m^2$ and $220\ m^2$ and compressor flow designs of 0.35 kg/s, 0.6 kg/s and 0.95 kg/s. The combination of common unit module designs assigned to each variant is captured in Figure 1.

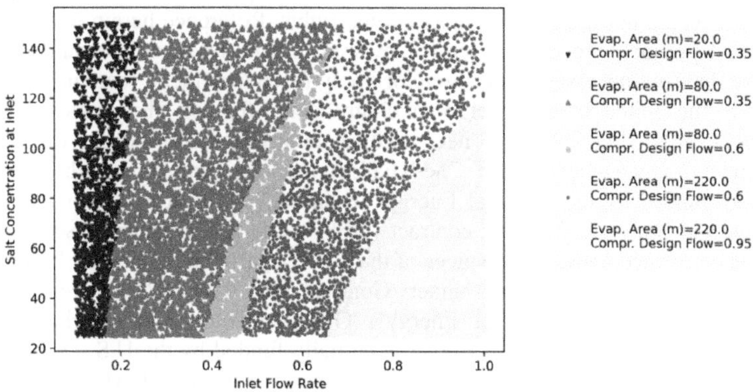

Figure 1. Process Family of the Water Desalination Case Study

The selected alternative (i.e., the combination of common unit module designs selected from the platform) is identified by the element in the legend.

Using mpi-sppy (Knueven et al., 2023), this problem was decomposed into 99 subproblems (with approximately 100 variants per subproblem) and solved using 99 parallel processes. We used a default rho value (**ρ**) of 50 and limited Gurobi© to a maximum of 16 threads per process. We calculated lower bounds using the Frank-Wolfe progressive hedging spoke (fwph) and searched for incumbents using the xhatshuffle spoke. Results were obtained on the Quartz HPC cluster at Lawrence Livermore National Laboratory using 30 nodes. Each node has two 18-core Xeon E5-2695 processors (2.1 GHz) and 128 GiB of RAM. We ran PH for a maximum of 25 iterations, which took approximately 5 hours. The algorithm terminated with a 1.399% optimality gap.

6. Conclusions

We demonstrated the proposed decomposition approach for solving a large-scale process family design problem on a case study of water desalination for produced water. We were able to design 10,897 process variants simultaneously. For comparison, attempting to solve the same problem using formulation (1) without decomposition achieved a 47.8% gap after six hours of Gurobi© solve time. For future work, PH convergence can be improved by tuning the penalization parameter, ρ. Watson and Woodruff (2011) suggest heuristics for constant ρ values, but they depend on objective costs associated with the complicating variables; our problem does not follow this assumption. Incorporating a gradient-based update to ρ values after each iteration of the algorithm is a promising step that could improve the time needed to reach convergence.

7. Disclaimer and Acknowledgements

This project was funded by the U.S. Department of Energy, National Energy Technology Laboratory an agency of the United States Government, through a support contract. Neither the United States Government nor any agency thereof, nor any of their employees, nor the support contractor, nor any of their employees, makes any warranty, express or implied, or assumes any legal liability or responsibility for the accuracy, completeness, or usefulness of any information, apparatus, product, or process disclosed, or represents that its use would not infringe privately owned rights. Reference herein to any specific commercial product, process, or service by trade name, trademark, manufacturer, or otherwise does not necessarily constitute or imply its endorsement, recommendation, or favoring by the United States Government or any agency thereof. The views and opinions of authors expressed herein do not necessarily state or reflect those of the United States Government or any agency thereof. The NETL support contractor's contributions to this work were funded by the National Energy Technology Laboratory under the Mission Execution and Strategic Analysis contract (DEFE0025912) for support services. This work was performed under the auspices of the U.S. Department of Energy by Lawrence Livermore National Laboratory under Contract DE-AC52-07NA27344 and was supported by the Department of Energy's Office of Electricity's Advanced Grid Modeling (AGM) program. This effort was partially funded by the U.S. Department of Energy's Institute for the Design of Advanced Energy Systems (IDAES) supported by the Office of Fossil Energy and Carbon Management's Simulation-Based Engineering/Crosscutting Research Program.

References

B. Knueven, et al., 2023, "A Parallel Hub-and-Spoke System for Large-Scale Scenario-Based Optimization Under Uncertainty" Mathematical Programming Computation, 15, pp. 591-619.

Gurobi Optimization, LLC, 2023, "Gurobi Optimizer Reference Manual".

G. Stinchfield, et al., 2023, "Optimization-Based Approaches for Design of Chemical Process Families using ReLU surrogates", in Proceedings of 2023 Foundations of Computer-Aided Process Operations (FOCAPO) and Chemical Process Control (CPC) Conference

J.P. Watson and D.L. Woodruff, 2011, "Progressive Hedging Innovations for a Class of Stochastic Mixed-Integer Resource Allocation Problems", Computational Management Science (8), pp. 355-370.

M.G. Drouven, A.J. Calderon, M. A. Zamarripa, and K. Beattie, 2022, "Pareto: An Open-Source Produced Water Optimization Framework", Optimization and Engineering, pp. 1–21.

M.L. Bynum, G.A. Hackebeil, W.E. Hart, C.D. Laird, B.L. Nicholson, J.D. Siirola, J.-P. Watson, and D.L. Woodruff, 2021, "Pyomo – Optimization Modeling in Python", Springer.

R.T. Rockafellar and R.J. Wets, 1991, "Scenarios and Policy Aggregation in Optimization under Uncertainty", Mathematics of Operations Research, Vol. 16, pp. 119–147.

T.W. Simpson, J. Jiao, Z. Siddique, and K. Holtta-Otto, 2014, "Advances in Product Family and Product Platform Design", Springer, Vol. 1.

Z. Chen, et al., 2022, "Optimization-Based Design of Product Families with Common Components", Computer Aided Chemical Engineering, pp. 91-96.

Flavio Manenti, Gintaras V. Reklaitis (Eds.), Proceedings of the 34th European Symposium on Computer Aided Process Engineering / 15th International Symposium on Process Systems Engineering (ESCAPE34/PSE24), June 2-6, 2024, Florence, Italy
 http://dx.doi.org/10.1016/B978-0-443-28824-1.50216-7

Constructing a Knowledge Graph for Automated HAZOP Analysis

Zhiyuan Li,[a] Jinsong Zhao [a,b*]

[a]*State Key Laboratory of Chemical Engineering, Department of Chemical Engineering, Tsinghua University, Beijing 100084, China*

[b]*Beijing Key Laboratory of Industrial Big Data System and Application, Tsinghua University, Beijing 100084, China*

jinsongzhao@tsinghua.edu.cn

Abstract

Hazard and Operability (HAZOP) analysis is widely acknowledged as a prominent approach for conducting process hazard analysis. In order to enhance the efficiency of the HAZOP analysis process, several approaches have been proposed in the past few decades to automate the HAZOP analysis. Nevertheless, only a limited number of them have been successfully incorporated into practical chemical processes. This paper presents a novel automated approach for conducting HAZOP analysis, utilizing a comprehensive knowledge graph. The knowledge graph integrates relevant data on processes, equipment, streams, chemicals, and the outcomes of HAZOP analysis. A reasoning model named CompGCN is introduced to predict missing links within a knowledge graph, ultimately aiming to facilitate the automation of HAZOP analysis. In the experimental section, the deep desulfurization process was selected as a case study, and a knowledge graph consisting of 2988 entities, 72 relationships, and 7867 facts was constructed. The reasoning result over the knowledge graph shows the validity of this approach, and helps to discover the hidden relationships between possible risk causes and consequences.

Keywords: HAZOP analysis, Knowledge graph, Graph neural network, Deep desulfurization process

1. Introduction

The Hazard and Operability Study (HAZOP) is a systematic and essential approach used to analyze potential process hazards during the planning or design stage. The heavy dependence on experiential knowledge in the manual process hazard analysis leads to a lack of consistency in the quality of HAZOP reports. In recent decades, many researchers have proposed various automated HAZOP systems. The automated HAZOP system mainly consists of three key components, namely system modeling, knowledge representation, and reasoning engine. The categorization of systems can be based on their reasoning engine, which includes rule-based, model-based, case-based, and process-history-based systems (Single et al., 2019). The advanced HAZOP systems integrates models with case-based reasoning, such as PHASuite (Zhang et al., 2005), PetroHAZOP (Zhao et al., 2009), and KROSA (Daramola et al., 2013). These systems reuse the knowledge derived from previous HAZOP studies and exhibit promising potential for the analysis of hazardous scenarios. However, the progress of these systems is being hindered by the lack of integration between system modeling and knowledge representation.

In this paper, a HAZOP knowledge graph is proposed to effectively integrate system modeling with safety knowledge. Furthermore, automated HAZOP analysis is performed by reasoning over the knowledge graph. The schema of the knowledge graph, and methodology for knowledge graph construction and reasoning were introduced in Section 2. In Section 3, the deep desulfurization process was chosen as a case study. We validated the effectiveness of our reasoning method and derived new knowledge from the existing knowledge graph. The conclusions drawn from our findings are presented in Section 4.

2. Methodology

Figure 1 provides an overview of the process involved in developing a knowledge graph. Firstly, the extraction of triples that represent the relation between two entities from process safety information was conducted. Subsequently, an integration framework was utilized to align entities across various knowledge sources. Based on the existing graph, we further discovered unmined relationships using knowledge graph reasoning techniques. By predicting the relations between deviations and analysis results, the ultimate goal of automating HAZOP analysis could be achieved.

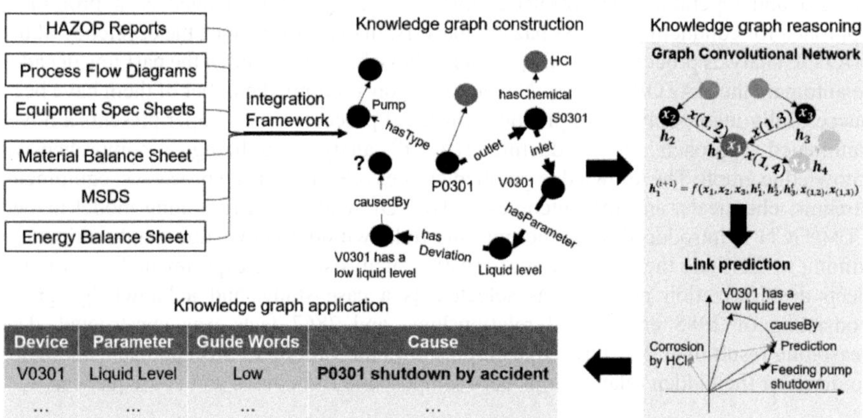

Figure 1. An overview of knowledge graph construction, reasoning, and application in HAZOP analysis.

2.1. Ontology Design

To define the types of entities and relationships in the HAZOP knowledge graph, an ontology was developed in a top-down manner, as illustrated in Figure 2. By defining the ontology, we aim to enhance data quality and combine process system information and HAZOP analysis results into a unified knowledge graph. The process system consists of discrete nodes, each of which contains information about the equipment, streams, and their connections. The safety knowledge relates to structured results of the HAZOP analysis, which include parameter, deviation, reason, consequence and preventions.

2.2. Methodology for Knowledge Graph Construction

As previously stated, the HAZOP knowledge graph serves as a representation of process system and safety knowledge. Therefore, the selection and integration of diverse knowledge sources is highly important. To acquire knowledge about process systems, the interconnections among important equipment components were derived from Process Flow Diagrams (PFDs). Subsequently, the tables related to equipment, chemicals, or streams were transformed into a graph structure. To obtain knowledge regarding safety, we utilized named entity recognition (NER) to extract crucial information about chemicals or equipment from HAZOP reports, the results of the HAZOP analysis were then imported into a graph database. Finally, we integrated the information into a comprehensive knowledge graph for HAZOP analysis. Figure 3 presents an integration framework for the knowledge graph. We started by dividing the process system into nodes and then used stream or equipment ID to align entities from various sources, such as the PFDs, material balance sheets, and Material Safety Data Sheets (MSDSs).

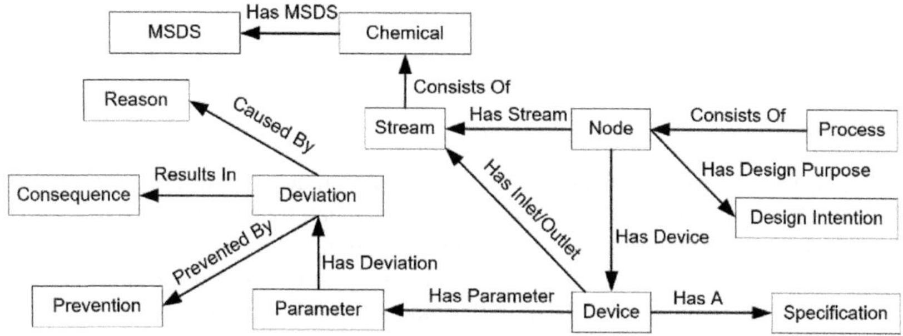

Figure 2. An ontology model of the HAZOP knowledge graph.

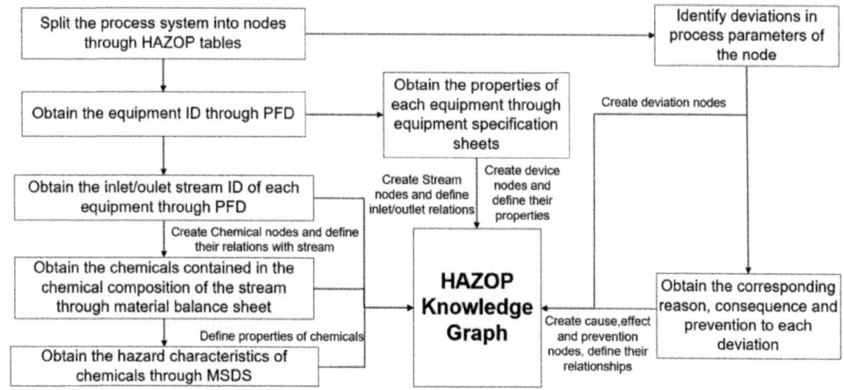

Figure 3. An integration framework for the HAZOP knowledge graph.

2.3. Methodology for Knowledge Graph Reasoning

Knowledge graph reasoning aims to infer unknown facts based on existing facts in the graph. This method can be applied to estimate the causes and consequences of deviations in process parameters. Knowledge graph reasoning can be categorized into four distinct categories: rule-based reasoning, embedding model-based reasoning, Convolutional Neural Network (CNN)-based reasoning, and Graph Convolutional Network (GCN)-based reasoning. In contrast, GCN-based reasoning aggregates the message from neighboring nodes to obtain an updated embedding for the central node. This enables a more comprehensive description of the central node features. By combining scoring functions derived from embedding models or CNN-based models, GCN-based reasoning has shown superior performance in link prediction tasks.

In this paper, the COMPGCN model (Vashishth et al., 2015) is used to represent relations and entities as vectors and combine their representations using vector subtraction, multiplication, or circular-correlation. Besides conventional relationship types, this model also has the capability to represent reverse and self-loop relationship types.

3. Case study

In this section, deep desulfurization, an essential component of petroleum processing technologies, is chosen as a case to develop a knowledge graph for automated HAZOP analysis. The process of deep desulfurization is crucial for maintaining the quality of oil products. Hydrogen sulfide is also widely acknowledged as the main occupational hazard in the petrochemical industry. Moreover, the process of burning this substance results in the formation of sulfur oxides, which are the main cause of acid rain. Therefore, HAZOP analysis is essential for ensuring the reliability of the deep desulfurization process design.

3.1. Implementation of Knowledge Graph

We have collected a total of 19 design works focused on deep desulfurization processes, each containing process flow diagrams, material balance tables, energy balance tables, equipment selection tables and HAZOP tables. Additionally, we provided MSDS for the chemicals used in the process. Then, a comprehensive knowledge graph was constructed by the integration framework. The graph contains a total of 2988 entities, 72 types of relationships, and 7867 facts, as described in Table 1. Since HAZOP reports only analyze production or storage devices with significant hazards, we selected 13 types of equipment for analysis. These include pumps, compressors, heat exchangers, reactors, distillation towers, absorbers, furnaces, gas-liquid separators, electrolytic tanks, reflux drums, buffer tanks, storage tanks, and molecular sieve dehydrators.

Table 1. A description of the HAZOP knowledge graph.

Entities									**Relations**	**Facts**
Chemical	Equipment		Stream	Parameter	Cause	Effect	Prevention			
	Name	Type								
36	133	13	165	37	909	700	995		72	7867

For sentences in HAZOP reports, the BERT-CRF (Bidirectional Encoder Representations from Transformers-Conditional Random Field) framework is chosen as a solution for NER to extract entities such as equipment names, chemicals, and equipment IDs. We also manually annotated 599 sentences that describe the chemical process to validate the feasibility of this method. The experimental results are shown in Table 2. The performance in identifying the entity type 'Equipment ID' is superior. The reason is that the equipment ID follows a standardized format and typically consists of no more than 6 characters. However, the identification of entities such as chemicals and equipment names can be challenging due to the use of abbreviations and aliases.

Table 2. Performance of BERT-CRF in the named entity recognition task evaluated on descriptive texts of chemical processes. F_1 is defined as the harmonic mean of precision and recall.

Entity type	Precision	Recall	F_1
Chemical	0.842	0.865	0.853
Equipment	0.866	0.882	0.874
Equipment ID	**0.988**	**0.977**	**0.982**

In the case of deep desulfurization process, a total of 199 chemicals, 33 equipment ID and 684 equipment names were extracted from HAZOP reports. Figure 4 presents an example of the results. After identifying the equipment ID mentioned in the sentence, we can determine that E0302 has been identified as the equipment related to the root cause of a low feed liquid level in E0303. The included link in the figure has the potential to enhance machine understanding of the intricacies involved in human reasoning.

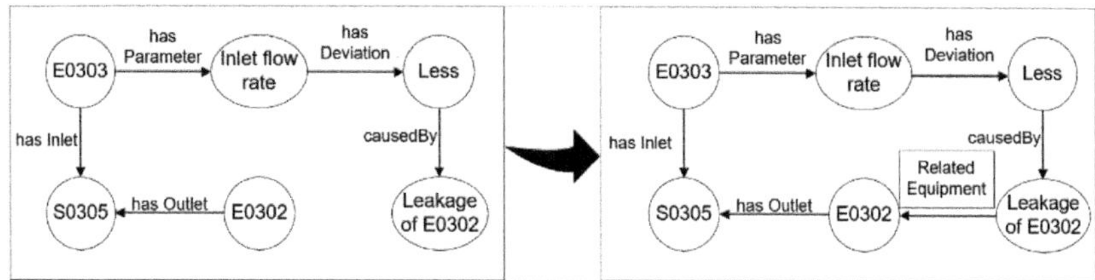

Figure 4. A demonstration of the effect of named entity recognition.

3.2. Results of Knowledge Graph Reasoning

The COMPGCN model was used in this section to predict links on the HAZOP knowledge graph. To evaluate the algorithm's reliability, we partitioned the facts in the original knowledge graph into a training set and a test set, and we attempted to reconstruct the facts in the test set using the facts in the training set. To adapt to the automated HAZOP analysis task, we specifically curated a test set consisting of 715 facts that include the relations 'causeby', 'resultsin', and 'preventedby'. The training set comprised a total of 7152 facts. We compared the performance differences of the COMPGCN model by employing three different scoring functions (TransE, Distmult, ConvE) and three different approaches for combining entity and relationship representations (vector subtraction, multiplication, circular-correlation). The results are shown in Table 3, where 'MR' denotes the mean rank of the triples in prediction results, 'MRR' denotes the mean reciprocal ranking of the triples, and 'Hits@K' denotes the average percentage of the positive triples ranked in the top-K positions.

Table 3. Performance of COMPGCN in link prediction task evaluated on HAZOP knowledge graph.

Score function	Composition operator	MR	MRR	Hits@1	Hits@3	Hits@10
TransE	Sub	232.39	0.030	0.021	0.022	0.027
	Mult	232.49	0.029	0.021	0.021	0.025
	Corr	232.48	0.029	0.021	0.021	0.025
DistMult	Sub	49.07	0.479	0.375	**0.547**	0.657
	Mult	49.97	0.446	0.350	0.499	0.634
	Corr	53.62	0.455	0.345	0.523	0.646
ConvE	Sub	44.82	**0.494**	**0.407**	0.543	0.656
	Mult	**35.36**	0.464	0.354	0.529	**0.666**
	Corr	38.81	0.474	0.379	0.527	0.634

It can be observed that the performance of TransE's scoring function is significantly worse. This is because the TransE model is limited to modeling one-to-one relationships, while in HAZOP analysis, it is common to encounter situations where there are multiple causes for a single deviation, in which the TransE model fails to capture. The scoring functions derived from DistMult and ConvE exhibit comparable reasoning effects, and the impact of composition operators on the reasoning effect is not significant. When considering only the top-ranked prediction from the model, approximately 40% of the entities can be correctly predicted. When considering the top ten ranked predictions, it is observed that around 67% of the answer entities can be accurately predicted. We have also noticed that some expected facts have not been included in the knowledge graph. An illustration of the outcomes can be observed in Figure 5, we predicted the reason for reduced or absence of inlet flowrate in reactor R101 based on COMPGCN model. The true label is ranked second in predictions, while the first one is also a valid reason. This fact can be used to complete the original knowledge graph, thereby improving its overall comprehensiveness.

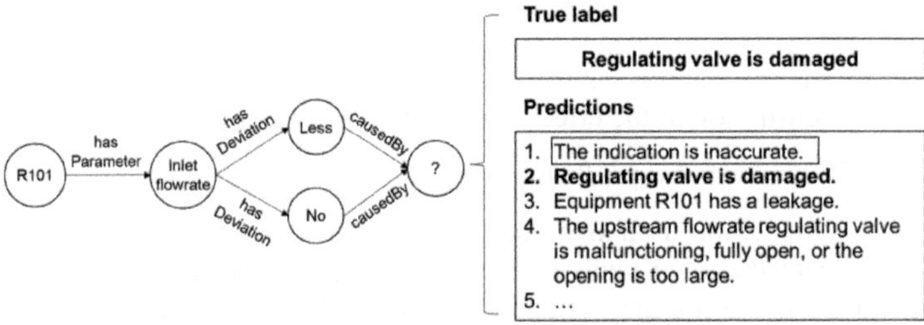

Figure 5. An illustration depicting the outcomes of knowledge graph reasoning.

4. Conclusions

In this paper, we proposed an automated method for constructing and reasoning with a knowledge graph for HAZOP analysis. We first defined the schema of the knowledge graph and outlined the integration framework that facilitated the connection between various knowledge sources. Additionally, a BERT-CRF framework was used to recognize named entities in HAZOP reports. Based on the initial construction of the HAZOP knowledge graph, we utilized knowledge graph reasoning technology, specifically the COMPGCN model, to automate the analysis of causes and consequences related to deviations in process parameters. Our experimental findings indicate that around 67% of the correct responses can be found among the top ten predicted results. This suggests the possibility of using a knowledge graph to implement the automated HAZOP analysis. However, it is important to note that the construction process of the HAZOP knowledge graph did not consider the instrumentation and control information. Therefore, we will further explore the automated extraction of process control information from the P&ID.

References

Single, J. I., Schmidt, J., and Denecke, J. 2019. "State of research on the automation of HAZOP studies". Journal of Loss Prevention in the Process Industries 62 (November): 103952. https://doi.org/10.1016/j.jlp.2019.103952.

Zhao, C., Bhushan, M., and Venkatasubramanian, V. 2005. "PHASuite: An automated HAZOP analysis tool for chemical processes: Part II: Implementation and Case Study". Process Safety and Environmental Protection 83(6): 533-548. https://doi.org/10.1205/psep.04056.

Jinsong Zhao, Lin Cui, Lihua Zhao, Tong Qiu, and Bingzhen Chen. 2009. "Learning HAZOP expert system by case-based reasoning and ontology". Computers & Chemical Engineering 33(1): 371-378. https://doi.org/10.1016/j.compchemeng.2008.10.006.

Daramola, O., Stålhane, T., Omoronyia, I., and Sindre, G. 2013. "Using Ontologies and Machine Learning for Hazard Identification and Safety Analysis". In Managing requirements knowledge: 117-141. https://doi.org/10.1007/978-3-642-34419-0_6.

Vashishth, S., Sanyal, S., Nitin, V., & Talukdar, P. 2019. "Composition-based Multi-Relational Graph Convolutional Networks". In International Conference on Learning Representations (September). https://doi.org/10.48550/arXiv.1911.03082.

Flavio Manenti, Gintaras V. Reklaitis (Eds.), Proceedings of the 34th European Symposium on Computer Aided Process Engineering / 15th International Symposium on Process Systems Engineering (ESCAPE34/PSE24), June 2-6, 2024, Florence, Italy
 http://dx.doi.org/10.1016/B978-0-443-28824-1.50217-9

Distillation Electrification Through Optimal Use of Heat Pumps

Akash Nogaja[a], Mohit Tawarmalani[a,b], Rakesh Agrawal[a]*

[a]*Davidson School of Chemical Engineering, Purdue University, West Lafayette, IN, USA*

[b]*Daniels School of Business, Purdue University, West Lafayette, IN, USA*

**agrawalr@purdue.edu*

Abstract

Decarbonization of the chemical industry necessitates a careful evaluation of the ways in which unit operations are employed. Decarbonizing distillation, which accounts for 90-95% of liquid separations, presents a unique challenge and an opportunity to significantly mitigate chemical sector's carbon emissions on a global scale. Electrification of distillation via the use of vapor compression heat pumps has shown promising results for a variety of binary mixtures. This research explores diverse electrification methods, focusing on Mechanical Vapor Recompression - Heat Pumps (MVR-HP) and delving into the integration of intermediate reboilers/condensers and multi-effect systems. We demonstrate various strategies that reduce energy consumption beyond the simple binary MVR-HP while adhering to CAPEX constraints.

Keywords: Distillation, Heat Pump, Decarbonization

1. Introduction

At the core of chemical and petrochemical sectors, downstream thermal separations play a pivotal role, accounting for a substantial percentage of their energy consumption and operational costs. The most prevalent thermal separation technique, distillation, alone consumes approximately 2.4 Quads per year (energy equivalent to 431 million bbl. of oil) in the United States (Chapas & Colwell, 2007). While distillation systems bolster the global economy, they concurrently contribute substantially to carbon emissions. A 10% reduction in distillation energy consumption has the potential to mitigate CO_2 emissions by approximately 5.3 million tons per year (Environmental Protection Agency, 2008). The aforementioned discussion underscores the imperative need to transition such energy-intensive processes toward more sustainable technologies (Mallapragada et al., 2023).

Traditionally, thermal separations have been reliant on heat generated from the condensation of steam, which, in turn, is primarily produced using fossil fuels. This dependence on fossil fuels as the heat source has been the primary driver of the carbon intensity associated with thermal separations. In our study, we advocate for the transition to electricity as the energy source, with the underlying assumption that the proportion of renewable electricity will witness a substantial increase in the near future (Agrawal & Siirola, 2023). However, our findings reveal that, despite the current economy's reliance on burning fossil fuels for a substantial share of electricity, employing optimally electrified distillation systems remains advantageous compared to traditional steam-driven distillation. In most cases, optimally electrified systems exhibit lower effective fuel consumption, considering both the fuel required for steam generation and electricity production.

Identifying an 'optimally electrified distillation system' using commercial process simulators can prove to be prohibitively complex even for a binary distillation system (Tumbalam Gooty et al., 2021). Heat pumps (HP) are widely acknowledged as one of the most energy-efficient electrification methods, effectively harnessing the heat released at the condenser to power the reboilers (Null, 1976). Various heat pumping technologies, such as mechanical vapor recompression (MVR), bottom flashing, external loop vapor compression, absorption heat pumps, etc., can be the optimal choice depending on the specific application (Kiss & Infante Ferreira, 2016). Moreover, the energy efficiency of such systems can potentially be enhanced by incorporating strategies such as feed pre-heating, intermediate reboilers, multi-effect distillation, and similar process intensification approaches.

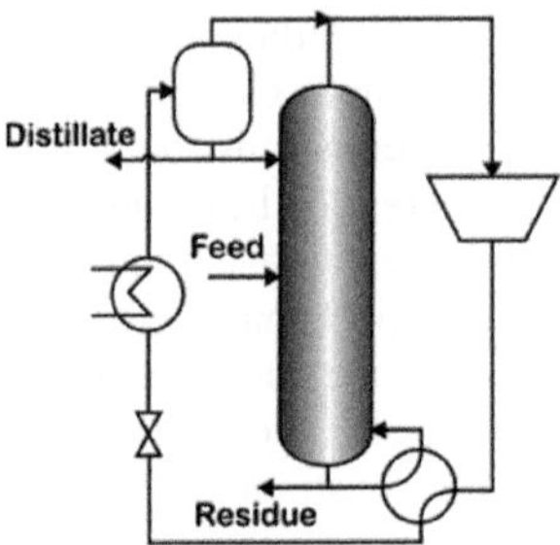

Figure 1: Mechanical Vapor Recompression assisted binary distillation system

The fundamental MVR system for binary distillation is illustrated in **Figure 1**. In this configuration, the overhead vapour is compressed to a higher pressure and subsequently condensed against the boiling liquid in the reboiler. The technology's high coefficient of performance (COP) and extensive applicability render it an attractive choice for electrification. For instance, Chavez Velasco et al. (2021) achieved an impressive COP of approximately 35 for the separation of p/o-Xylene. Assuming a typical power plant efficiency of 50%, the effective fuel consumption is reduced by 20 times compared to steam-driven process. The literature consistently demonstrates the success of MVR for close boiling systems, as exemplified above. In Section 3, titled 'Binary Distillation', we present additional case studies involving mixtures with disparate component boiling points.

To maintain a focused scope, this research specifically delves into MVR-HP, chosen for its widespread applicability. We investigate pathways that reduce effective fuel consumption for binary distillation using simplified models. We rigorously validate our findings across various binary mixtures. Additionally, to further reduce fuel consumption, we consider the use of intermediate reboilers/condensers with HP Assisted Distillation (HPAD). We obtain valuable insights that can help practitioners design optimal heat pump arrangements for binary distillation systems.

Our paper is organized as follows. We first describe our shortcut model and show that it compares well with the detailed ASPEN simulations for binary distillations. Then, we use intermediate heat exchangers to improve the efficiency of HPAD. Finally, to reduce capital expenditure, we use multi-effect distillation that recovers a portion of the energy savings without operating multiple processors.

2. Model Development

Assessment of various binary arrangements for HP systems can prove to be difficult using commercial process simulators. In this section, we develop high fidelity models that can be globally optimized to find the minimum energy consumption. The Underwood equations are employed to calculate the minimum vapor requirement for any ideal split in a distillation column. However, to calculate the heat duties rather than the vapor requirement, we employ simple latent heat transformations discussed by Mathew et al. (2023) -

$$F_i^{LH} = F_i\lambda_i \tag{1}$$

F_i^{LH} is the latent heat variable defining heat flow, F_i is the molar flow and λ_i is the molar enthalpy of vaporization of component 'i' in the feed.

To ensure a positive driving force in the heat exchanger involving condensation of compressed vapor and boiling liquid, we introduce a simple surrogate model (Nogaja et al., 2022)

$$T = \frac{B_{mix}}{A_{mix} + \ln(\rho)} - C_{mix};\ \rho = \frac{P^{ref}}{P}\sum_i \alpha_i x_i \tag{2}$$

The parameters A_{mix}, B_{mix} and C_{mix} are specific to a mixture and are trained using data from experiments or detailed thermodynamic models. The variable ρ captures the thermodynamic state (liquid fraction) of the stream.

To calculate the HP work, we employ a simple Carnot approximation of the isentropic compressor. These equations are combined together in a systematic framework and optimized using Gurobi 9.1 to yield the global minimum energy.

3. Binary Distillation Systems

To validate the constructed simplified model, we apply it to multiple equimolar binary steam-driven and HPAD systems featuring varying component boiling point differences. These flowsheets are also simulated using ASPEN Plus V11, and a comparative study of the shortcut model and the process simulator is illustrated in **Figure 2**. The model demonstrates robust performance for mixtures with close boiling points but exhibits diminishing accuracy as the boiling point differences increase.

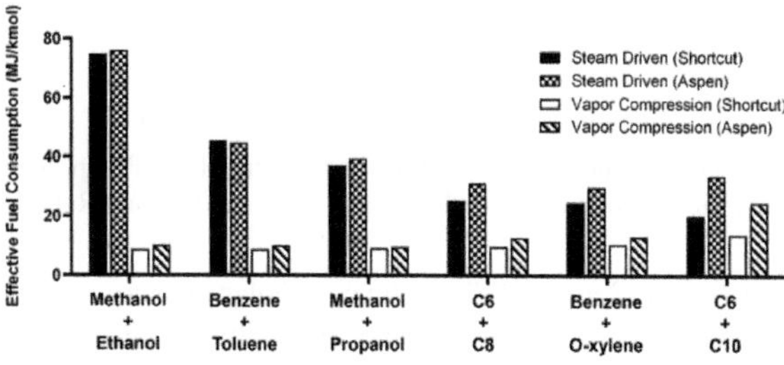

Figure 2: Comparison of shortcut model for binary distillation systems with ASPEN Plus V11. The temperature difference between the components of the mixture increase along the X axis.

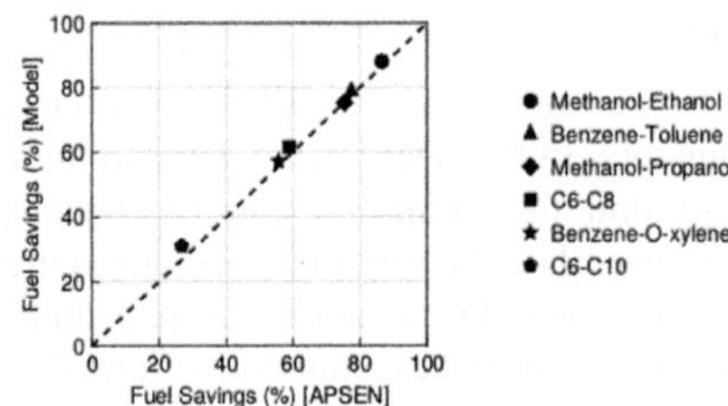

Figure 3: Percent decrease in effective fuel consumption by switching to vapor compression HP

Nevertheless, the shortcut model displays a strong agreement with the percentage reduction in fuel consumption achieved by switching to vapor compression (refer to **Figure 3**). Given that the research's objective is a comparative analysis and identification of lucrative HPAD configurations, the shortcut model offers a reasonable substitute that allows global optimization techniques.

4. Benefits of Intermediate Reboiler / Condensers

Intermediate Reboilers (IR) and Condensers (IC) are recognized for enhancing the exergy efficiency of distillation columns (Agrawal & Herron, 1998). IRs can supply a portion of the energy required by the distillation column at a lower temperature than the reboiler, while ICs can remove heat at a temperature higher than the condenser. However, despite their second law benefits, they do not reduce energy consumption in traditional steam driven distillation systems.

In the context of Heat Pumps, where energy consumption depends on both heat (first law) and temperatures (second law), IRs and ICs present an opportunity for further reducing energy consumption. **Figure 4** depicts the strategies incorporating a heat pump link between (a) the top condenser and IR and (b) IC and bottom reboiler. Note that the heat pump between the top condenser and the bottom reboiler remains active, albeit with a reduced heat load.

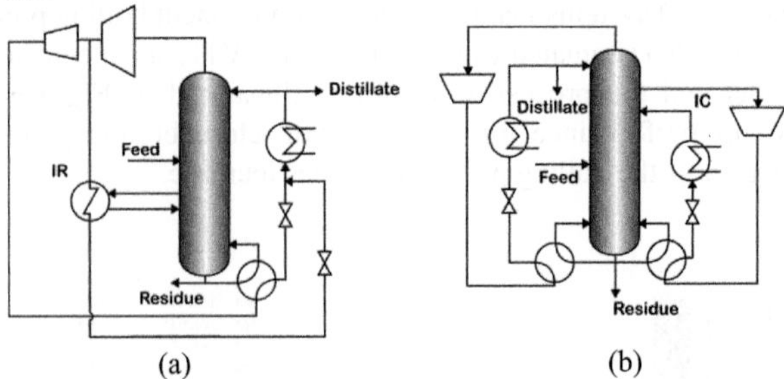

Figure 4: Operational enhancement of Binary Distillation using Heat Pump, featuring Heat Pump integration between (a) Condenser and IR and (b) IC and Reboiler

Taking the example of the Benzene – Toluene equimolar mixture presented in Section 3, the IR assisted HPAD reduces energy demand further by approximately 10% compared to simple HPAD. On the other hand, IC-assisted HPAD decreases energy consumption by approximately 2%. Therefore, while the savings with IR-HPAD are significant, the energy savings with IC-HPAD do not justify the added operational complexity. However, when the feed sis richer in the heavier component, IC-HPAD begins to demonstrate noteworthy energy savings (refer to **Figure 5**). In contrast, IR-HPAD saves more when the feed is richer in the lighter component.

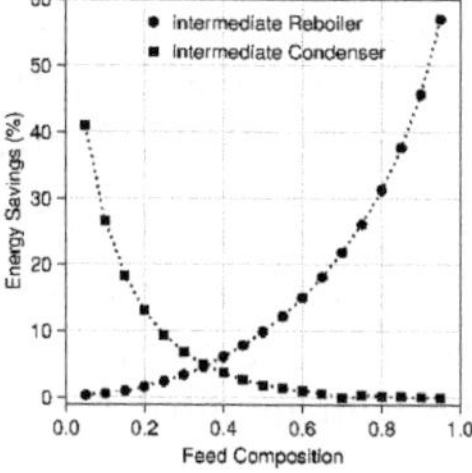

Figure 5: Variation of percent reduction in energy consumption by IR and IC - HPAD as compared to Binary VR-HPAD with feed composition

Although IR/C lead to significant energy savings, they require additional capital expenditure owing to the presence of either a multi-stage compressor (IR-HPAD) or the use of two distinct compressor units (IC-HPAD). To mitigate this concern, we introduce a strategy that utilizes a single compressor but improves the efficiency of MVR-HP.

5. Multi-effect Heat Pump Assisted Distillation (ME-HPAD):

Multi-effect distillation systems are extensively employed to significantly reduce the required heat duty. Introducing heat pumps in multi-effect systems creates two competing effects – the overall heat requirement of the separation system decreases, but at the expense of elevating the pressure and consequently, the temperature of the high-pressure column. The interplay between these two factors determines the energy savings of these systems beyond simple MVR-HP. **Figure 6** shows the proposed ME-HPAD systems. The columns of configuration (a), operating without heat pump and at the same pressure, is theoretically equivalent to IR system. Similarly, configuration (b) is the equivalent of IC. However, increasing the pressure of the HP column limits the energy savings that can be derived from the system.

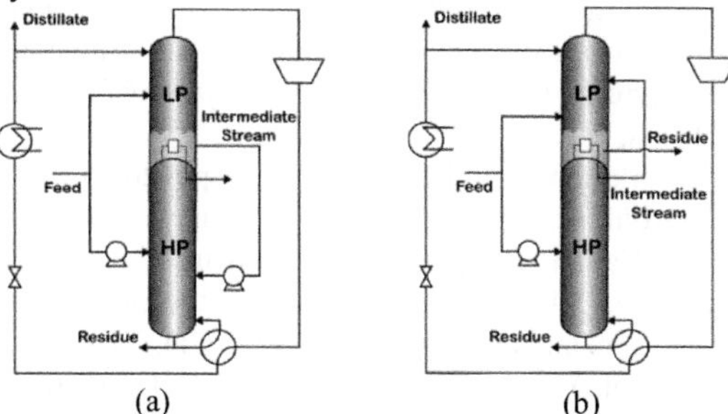

Figure 6: ME - HPAD systems for binary systems. Strategy (a) excels with mixtures having feeds rich in the lighter component, while (b) is preferable for feeds rich in the heavier one.

In the case of the Benzene-Toluene system, with a feed stream comprising of 75% benzene, configuration (a) exhibits an 18% lower energy consumption compared to simple single column MVR-HP. Similarly, for a feed stream with 25% benzene composition, configuration (b) saves 6% energy. For reference, IR (*resp.* IC) presents 26% (*resp.* 9.4%) energy reduction for 75% (*resp.* 25%) benzene composition feeds. Hence, even with a single compressor, ME-HPAD can reduce energy consumption further when compared to a simple single column VRC.

6. Conclusions

Mechanical Vapor Recompression (MVR) offers an energy-efficient strategy for mitigating carbon emissions in binary distillation systems. Our examples demonstrate that, even in the current economy where a significant share of electricity is generated by burning natural gas and other fossil fuels, MVR effectively reduces fuel consumption.

When designing such systems, it is essential not to limit considerations to heat pump links operating solely between the top condenser and the bottom reboiler. Exploring HP links involving intermediate reboilers and condensers can further decrease energy consumption, particularly for feeds with an imbalance in component concentrations.

Nevertheless, IR/IC systems necessitate the operation of at least two compressors. We show that by employing equivalent Multi-Effect Distillation (MED) systems for IR and IC, energy consumption can be reduced. Although the reduction is not as much as with IR/IC - HPAD systems, it remains significant when compared to a simple VRC-HP.

7. Acknowledgements

The authors thank the National Science Foundation under Cooperative Agreement No. EEC-1647722 for funding.

References

Agrawal, R., & Herron, D. M. (1998). Efficient use of an intermediate reboiler or condenser in a binary distillation. *AIChE Journal*, *44*(6), 1303–1315.

Agrawal, R., & Siirola, J. J. (2023). Decarbonization of Chemical Process Industries via Electrification. *The Bridge*, 32–40.

Chapas, R. B., & Colwell, J. A. (2007). *Industrial Technologies Program Research Plan for Energy-Intensive Process Industries*.

Chavez Velasco, J. A., Tawarmalani, M., & Agrawal, R. (2021). Systematic Analysis Reveals Thermal Separations Are Not Necessarily Most Energy Intensive. *Joule*, *5*(2), 330–343.

Environmental Protection Agency. (2008). *Greenhouse Gas Equivalencies Calculator | US EPA*. https://www.epa.gov/energy/greenhouse-gas-equivalencies-calculator

Kiss, A. A., & Infante Ferreira, C. A. (2016). *Heat Pumps in Chemical Process Industry*. CRC Press.

Mallapragada, D. S., Dvorkin, Y., Modestino, M. A., Esposito, D. V., Smith, W. A., Hodge, B.-M., Harold, M. P., Donnelly, V. M., Nuz, A., Bloomquist, C., Baker, K., Grabow, L. C., Yan, Y., Rajput, N. N., Hartman, R. L., Biddinger, E. J., Aydil, E. S., & Taylor, A. D. (2023). Decarbonization of the chemical industry through electrification: Barriers and opportunities. *Joule*, *7*(1), 23–41.

Mathew, T. J., Tawarmalani, M., & Agrawal, R. (2023). Relaxing the constant molar overflow assumption in distillation optimization. *AIChE Journal*, *69*(9).

Nogaja, A. S., Mathew, T. J., Tawarmalani, M., & Agrawal, R. (2022). Identifying Heat-Integrated Energy-Efficient Multicomponent Distillation Configurations. *Industrial and Engineering Chemistry Research*, *61*(37). https://doi.org/10.1021/acs.iecr.2c00870

Null, H. R. (1976). Heat Pumps in Distillation. *Chem. Eng. Prog.*, *58*, 58–64.

Tumbalam Gooty, R., Chavez Velasco, J. A., & Agrawal, R. (2021). Methods to assess numerous distillation schemes for binary mixtures. *Chemical Engineering Research and Design*, *172*, 1–20.

Flavio Manenti, Gintaras V. Reklaitis (Eds.), Proceedings of the 34th European Symposium on Computer Aided Process Engineering / 15th International Symposium on Process Systems Engineering (ESCAPE34/PSE24), June 2-6, 2024, Florence, Italy
 http://dx.doi.org/10.1016/B978-0-443-28824-1.50218-0

Computer-aided Molecular and Process Design (CAMPD) for Ionic Liquid Assisted Extractive Distillation of Refrigerant Mixtures

Ashfaq Iftakher,[a] Rafiqul Gani,[b,c,d] M. M. Faruque Hasan[a,e,*]

[a]*Artie McFerrin Department of Chemical Engineering, Texas A&M University, College Station, TX, USA*

[b]*PSE for SPEED Company, Ordrup Jagtvej42D, DK-2920 Charlottenlund, Denmark*

[c]*Sustainable Energy and Environment Thrust, The Hong Kong University of Science and Technology (Guangzhou), Guangzhou, China*

[d]*Department of Applied Sustainability, Széchenyi István University, Győr, Hungary*

[e]*Texas A&M Energy Institute, Texas A&M University, College Station, TX 77843-3122, USA*

hasan@tamu.edu

Abstract

Computer-aided Molecular and Process Design, CAMPD, is a technique that simultaneously optimizes the choice of materials, such as solvents, and the corresponding process configurations for many chemical separation processes. The technique involves formulating an equation-oriented optimization model representing the overall design problem, which then can be solved in many ways depending on the chemicals involved, the property and process models, and the complexity and size of the problem, among others. Due to the complexity and large-size of the problem, and a lack of predictive property models, we have applied a decomposition-based CAMPD strategy that involves solving a series of subproblems sequentially to reduce the overall search space, thereby reducing the computational burden. We illustrate our strategy through a case study involving the design of ionic liquids (ILs) as solvents for the extractive-distillation based separation of an azeotropic refrigerant mixture, R-410A. Separation of such mixtures is gaining increased interest due to the need to remove, substitute or reuse constituent refrigerant chemicals that have undesirable properties (such as high global warming potential, flammability, etc.). ILs are considered because of their designable properties as functions of their molecular structures. Based on available measured data, group-contribution based predictive property models have been developed and interfaced with the workflow of the proposed strategy. A set of promising ILs have been identified and their performance verified through process simulation.

Keywords: CAMPD, Group contribution, Solvent Design, Process and Product Design, Mathematical Modeling, Optimization

1. Introduction

The systematic identification of optimal materials and processes is often realized through Computer-aided Molecular and Process Design (CAMPD). The influence and importance of the selection of materials on the overall performance of chemical separation processes have been highlighted in the past (e.g., Liu et al., 2018; Iftakher et al. 2023). A typical

CAMPD problem can be formulated as a mixed-integer non-linear programming (MINLP) problem, as shown in Eq. (1).

$$\begin{aligned} \min_{\mathbf{m},\boldsymbol{\eta}} \quad & C(\boldsymbol{\eta},\boldsymbol{p}) \\ \text{s.t.} \quad & \boldsymbol{p} = \boldsymbol{f}(\boldsymbol{m},\boldsymbol{\eta}) \\ & \boldsymbol{s}(\boldsymbol{m}) \leq 0 \\ & \boldsymbol{g}(\boldsymbol{\eta}) \leq 0 \\ & \boldsymbol{h}(\boldsymbol{\eta},\boldsymbol{p}) = 0 \\ & \boldsymbol{m} \in \mathbb{Z}_{+}^{d}, \ \boldsymbol{\eta} \in \mathbb{R}^{n} \times \mathbb{Z}_{+}^{w} \end{aligned} \tag{1}$$

where, the decision variables include both discrete and continuous variables. Molecular design involves finding the optimal values for a set of integer variables ($\boldsymbol{m}$) that represent the building blocks or groups representing the material (solvent). Process design and configuration involves finding the optimal values for a set of process variables ($\boldsymbol{\eta}$) that represents the process design specifications that typically involve a subset of integer variables (e.g., feed location, number of column stages, etc.) and a subset of continuous variables (e.g., solvent flow rate to the extractive distillation (ED) process, reflux ratio, operating pressure, and temperature, etc.). The objective function C minimizes the process operating cost in this example and is subject to a set of constraints. The constraint $\boldsymbol{p}$ involves bounds on thermodynamic and transport properties that are predicted through the molecular structure-property relationships. The constraint $\boldsymbol{s}$ involves a set of molecular structural constraints that ensure that the constructed molecule satisfies atom balance. The constraint $\boldsymbol{g}$ involves process constraints, while the constraint $\boldsymbol{h}$ involves the governing mass and energy conservation of the process.

While the design of organic solvents integrated with separation process design is well-developed (Hostrup et al. 1999, Bardow et al. 2010, Burger et al. 2015, Liu et al. 2018 - to cite a few), the design of ionic liquids (ILs) together with the design of the separation process is relatively new (Song et al. 2018, Chen et al. 2019, Zhou et al. 2021 – to cite a few). Solving CAMPD problems with accurate but computationally expensive property and process models has been a challenge due to the nonlinearity and nonconvexity of these models when ionic liquids are considered as solvents. Also, CAMPD is a multi-scale optimization problem, as it integrates molecular to process level decisions, making it difficult to solve even using the state-of-the-art solvers (Misener and Floudas, 2014).

In this work, we propose a multi-level decomposition framework that decomposes the overall CAMPD into a set of sub-problems, thereby facilitating the optimal/near-optimal design of sustainable, energy-efficient, and cost-effective chemical processes. In particular, we employ the well-known and simple group-contribution (GC) based models together with complex but accurate machine-learning (ML) based models for IL-related property estimations. As both these types of models need measured data, which are not available in sufficient amounts, truly predictive property models, such as the COSMO-based models (Jaschik et al., 2017) are used for generation of gas solubility data needed for design as well as for developing models. The overall optimization model is then decomposed based on the target solvent-process constraints. We illustrate our framework through the solution of an industrially relevant problem, namely the selection of optimal/promising ionic liquid (IL) and the configuration of an ED process for separating

R-410A (50 $wt\%$ – 50 $wt\%$ mixture of R-32 and R-125) refrigerant mixture. ILs are promising solvent candidates due to their high thermal and chemical stability as well as selective gas solubility. However, their design space can potentially be very large due to the likely assignments (combinations) of their anion and cation parts. Also, designing an ED process is highly non-trivial due to the existence of many degrees of freedom. To overcome these challenges, we decompose the CAMPD problem into a series of subproblems to sequentially reduce the overall search space. We first generate a set of structurally feasible ILs (depicted by the outer circle in Figure 1). We then use the developed GC- and ML-based property models (density, viscosity, surface tension and melting point) for ILs and use them to screen the promising IL-candidates based on a set of desired property ranges (depicted by the darker inner circle of Figure 1). Next, we use the developed GC-based gas solubility models and use them to qualitatively identify a reduced number of ILs for selective separation of the R-410A chemicals (depicted by the smallest inner circle of Figure 1). Finally, for the most promising IL, we verify the process performance through rigorous process simulation.

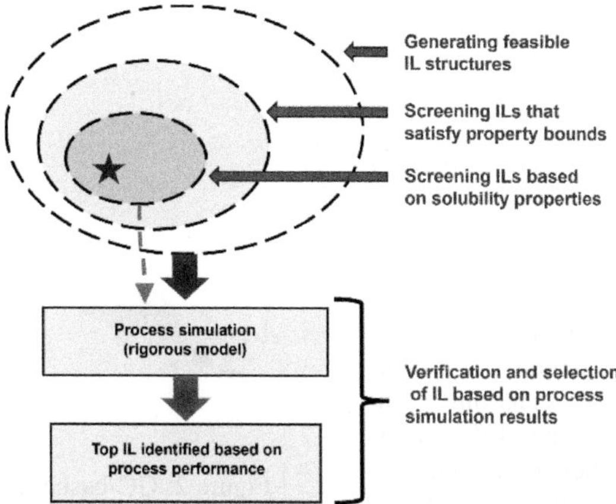

Figure 1: Decomposition of CAMPD for refrigerant separation using ionic liquid

2. Decomposition of CAMPD for Ionic Liquid Design

The solution to the CAMPD is achieved through three sequential steps as illustrated in Figure 1.

2.1. Step 1: Generating structurally feasible IL structures

We first generate a set of feasible IL structures by considering the structural feasibility constraints. Each IL is assumed to be constructed by a cation core, an anion, and an alkyl side chain that is attached to the cation core. For example, 1-butyl-3-methylimidazolium chloride contains an imidazolium cation core, a chloride anion, and a butyl side chain. IL-structural constraints are described in Eq. (2).

$$\sum_{j\in Ca} c_j = 1 \;;\; \sum_{j\in An} c_j = 1 \;; \sum_{j\in Ca\cup Sub}(2-v_j)\cdot c_j - 2 = 0$$
$$LB \le \sum_{j\in Sub} c_j \le UB \qquad (2)$$

where, the first and second constraints ensure that a feasible IL contains only one cation and anion. The third constraint ensures that a feasible IL must satisfy the octet rule, i.e., there must not be any free bonds (Karunanithi et al., 2005). The final constraint provides a bound on the number of groups that can be present in the side chain to ensure generation of a finite number of ILs.

2.2. Step 2: Screening ILs based on pure component and solubility property bounds

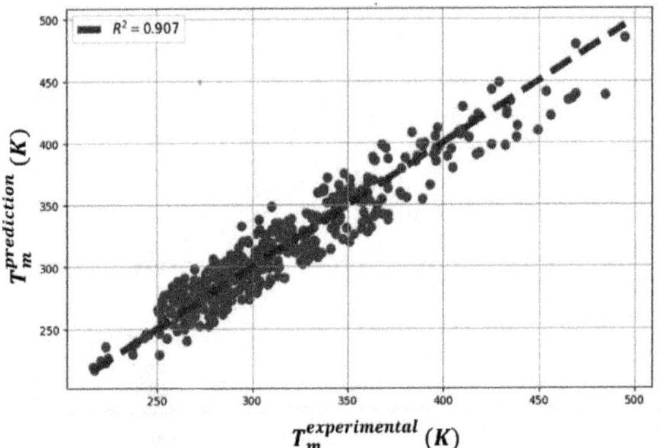

Figure 2: GC-based model for IL melting point

In this step, we screen the ILs (that are generated in Step 1) based on the bounds on viscosity, density, and melting point. Viscosity influences the ED column sizing. Density determines the degree of gas diffusivity in ILs, whereas melting point ensures that the selected IL remains liquid at the operating conditions. To predict these properties, we have developed a GC-based model for melting point (T_m) and trained an Artificial Neural Network with Rectified Linear Unit as activation function (ReLU-ANN) for density (ρ) and viscosity (μ). The limited availability of data along with the high variability (uncertainty) in the dataset makes it difficult to model T_m for ILs. To address this issue, we have carefully collected melting point data for 471 ILs (Paduszynski et al., 2021) and have developed a GC-based model whose performance is shown in Figure 2. For density (31167 temperature and pressure dependent data points) and viscosity (14337 temperature dependent data points), we have achieved good fit for the trained ReLU-ANN model. Regarding mixture properties, we select solubility (and selectivity) as it dictates the degree of selective absorption of refrigerants in IL which are defined in Eq. (3).

$$solubility, S = \frac{1}{\gamma^{\infty}} \quad ; \quad selectivity, S_H^{R32/R125} = \left(\frac{K_{H_{R125}}}{K_{H_{R32}}}\right)_T \tag{3}$$

where, γ^{∞} is the activity coefficient at infinite dilution, and K_H is the Henry's constant measured at a specified temperature and is defined as $= \lim_{x\to 0}\left(\frac{P}{x}\right)$. To capture the selective solubility of ILs towards R-32 or R-125, we predict Henry's constant of R-32 and R-125 in ILs through a GC model.

2.3. Step 3: Process simulation for the set of promising IL-candidates

For the set of screened ILs after Step 2, we perform simulation for the ED process to quantify process performance. We use the Non-Random Two Liquid (NRTL) model. Using the available measured vapor liquid equilibrium (VLE) data, we first regress the NRTL model parameters to compute the activity coefficient (γ). In the absence of sufficient measured data, the predicted Henry's constants through the GC-based model could directly be used to compute the infinite dilution activity coefficient as follows: $\gamma^{\infty} = \frac{K_H}{P^{sat}}$, where P^{sat} is the saturation vapor pressure of the refrigerant.

3. Results for R-410A separation

In Step 1, we generate 710 feasible IL structures that contain 47 cation cores, 48 anion cores and 43 side groups. In Step 2, we then screen the ILs based on the following property bounds: $40\ \mathrm{K} \leq T_m \leq 303\ \mathrm{K}, 900\frac{kg}{m^3} \leq \rho \leq 1600\frac{kg}{m^3}$, $3\ mPa.s \leq \mu \leq 1000\ mPa.s$. From an initial pool of 710 ILs, 315 ILs satisfied the specified property bounds. After that, we further screen the ILs based on mixture properties. Finally in Step 3, among the feasible ILs that satisfy both the pure component properties and the solubility properties, we select a small set of 12 promising ILs as listed in Table 1. The GC model for these ILs also show qualitatively correct trend of solubility and selectivity for R-32 compared to R-125. Also, for these ILs, measured VLE data are available. From the set of promising ILs, we select [EMIM][DCA] to evaluate the process performance. The process configuration is preconceived from our previous work (Monjur et al., 2022). We then simulate the process in Aspen Plus v12 with the objective to achieve high recovery of both R-32 and R-125 (> 99.5 $wt\%$). The simulated process flowsheet is shown in Figure 3. The IL is introduced to the column at 3rd stage while the R-410A mixture is introduced to the column at 15th stage. There are 30 stages in total. 99.5 $wt\%$ R-125 is separated from the top of the ED column. The IL+R-32 stream comes out from the bottom of the column and then is fed to the flash separator. From the top of the flash separator, 99.6 $wt\%$ R-32 is separated, and the IL is recycled back to the ED column. Therefore, highly selective separation of the azeotropic R-410A refrigerant mixture is achieved.

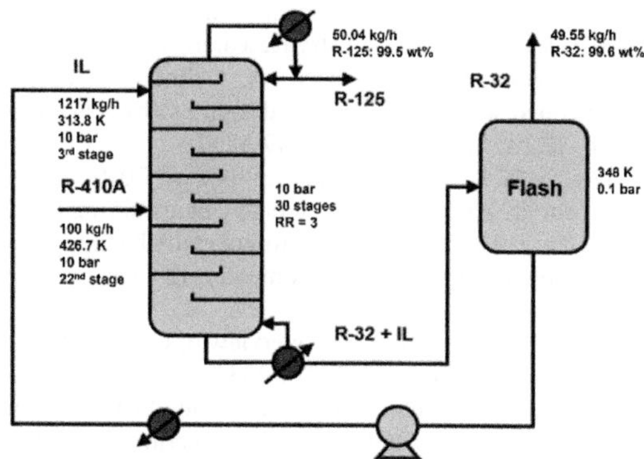

Figure 3: ED process for R-410A separation

Table 1: List of promising ILs with experimental and predicted Henry's constants

ILs	Measured		GC Model	
	$K_{H_{R32}}$	$K_{H_{R125}}$	$K_{H_{R32}}$	$K_{H_{R32}}$
[EMIM][SCN]	4.45	26.96	3.56	37.96
[EMIM][Ac]	2.51	2.89	2.51	2.89
[EMIM][DCA]	***2.91***	***15.79***	***2.79***	***11.93***
[EMIM][OTF]	1.76	3.60	1.98	1.99
[EMIM][TF2N]	1.24	1.32	1.43	0.38
[BMIM][SCN]	2.38	50	3.26	39
[BMIM][DCA]	2.37	9.11	2.49	12.97
[BMIM][BF4]	1.39	6.25	1.57	4.22
[HMIM][BF4]	1.45	3.23	1.27	5.26

[HMIM][OTF]	1.60	2.45	1.38	4.06
[HMIM][TF2N]	1.03	1.52	0.83	2.46
[HMIM][FAP]	0.75	1.32	0.75	1.32

4. Conclusions

We developed a decomposition-based strategy to efficiently solve CAMPD problems focusing on the design of ionic liquid-based solvents for the extractive distillation-based separation of R-410A mixtures. We have developed GC and ML-based models for key IL properties. After generating an initial pool of ILs and subsequently applying property-based constraints, we have identified a set of ILs that show promise for highly selective separation for R-410A with favourable process performance. The simulated process for [EMIM][DCA] shows highly selective separation of both R-32 and R-125, thereby verifying the decomposition-based solution strategy. As a current and future work, we are generating IL-based gas solubility data through the predictive COSMO-sac model to use them as pseudo-measured data to develop GC-based models for a wider application range so that better IL-solvents can be found and to make the applied CAMPD more versatile. Preliminary results have shown sufficient promise to pursue this option.

References

A. Bardow, K. Steur, J. Gross, 2010, Continuous-Molecular Targeting for Integrated Solvent and Process Design, Industrial & Engineering Chemistry Research, 49, 6, 2834-2840

J. Burger, V. Papaioannou, S. Gopinath, G. Jackson, A. Galindo, C. S. Adjiman, 2015, A hierarchical method to integrated solvent and process design of physical CO_2 absorption using the SAFT-γ Mie approach, AIChE Journal, 61,10, 3249-3269

Y. Chen, E. Koumaditi, R. Gani, G. M. Kontogeorgis, J. M. Woodley, 2019, Computer-aided design of ionic liquids for hybrid process schemes, Computers & Chemical Engineering, 130, 106556

M. Hostrup, P. M. Harper, R. Gani, 1999, Design of environmentally benign processes: integration of solvent design and separation process synthesis, Computers & Chemical Engineering, 23, 10, 1395-1414

A. Iftakher, M. S. Monjur, M. M. F. Hasan, 2023, An Overview of Computer-aided Molecular and Process design, Chemie Ingenieur Technik, 95, 3, 315-333

M. Jaschik, D. Piech, K. Warmuzinski, J. Jaschik, 2017, Prediction of gas solubility in ionic liquids using the COSMO-SAC model, Chemical and Process Engineering, 38, 1, 19-30

A. Karunanithi, L.E.K. Achenie, R. Gani, 2005, A new decomposition based CAMD methodology for the design of optimal solvents and solvent mixtures, Industrial & Engineering Chemistry Research, 44, 13, 4785-4797

Q. Liu, L. Zhang, L. Liu, J. Du, A. K. Tula, M. Eden, R. Gani, 2018, OptCAMD: An optimization-based framework and tool for molecular and mixture product design, Computers & Chemical Engineering, 124, 285-301

R. Misener, C. A. Floudas, 2014, ANTIGONE: Algorithms for coNTinuous / Integer Global Optimization of Nonlinear Equations, Journal of Global Optimization, 59, 2-3, 503–526

M. S. Monjur, A. Iftakher, M. M. F. Hasan, 2022, Separation process synthesis for high-gwp refrigerant mixtures: Extractive distillation using ionic liquids. Industrial & Engineering Chemistry Research, 61(12), 4390-4406

K. Paduszynski, K. Klebowski, M. Krolikowski, 2021, Predicting melting point of ionic liquids using QSPR approach: Literature review and new models, Journal of Molecular Liquids, 344, 117631

Z. Song, T. Zhou, Z. Qi, K. Sundmacher, 2018, Systematic method for screening ionic liquids as extraction solvents exemplified by an extractive desulfurization process, ACS Sustainable Chemistry & Engineering, 5 (4), 3382-3389

T. Zhou, R. Gani, K. Sundmacher, 2021, Hybrid data-driven and mechanistic modeling approaches for multiscale material and process design, Engineering, 7 (9), 1231-1238

Flavio Manenti, Gintaras V. Reklaitis (Eds.), Proceedings of the 34th European Symposium on Computer Aided Process Engineering / 15th International Symposium on Process Systems Engineering (ESCAPE34/PSE24), June 2-6, 2024, Florence, Italy
 http://dx.doi.org/10.1016/B978-0-443-28824-1.50219-2

Recycling Rare Earth Elements from End-of-Life Electric and Hybrid Electric Vehicle Motors

Christopher Laliwala, Ana Torres*

Department of Chemical Engineering, Carnegie Mellon University, Pittsburgh 15213, PA, USA

* *aitorres@cmu.edu*

Abstract

The United States is working to decarbonize its electric grid and end-use sectors through a transition to clean energy technologies. However, this transition presents significant challenges, including the reliance on rare earth elements (REEs) to produce these technologies. Therefore, strengthening rare earth supply chains is imperative for the U.S. as it strives to reduce carbon emissions. One approach to enhancing these supply chains is through the extraction of REEs from end-of-life (EOL) products. This study proposes a superstructure-based approach to find the optimal pathway for recovering REEs from the permanent magnets of EOL electric and hybrid electric vehicle (EV and HEV) motors. The superstructure is optimized by maximizing the net present value (NPV) over a 15-year period. To establish the base case optimal result, these projections are used with the assumption that the plant recycles 10 % of all EOL EVs and HEVs in the U.S. each year. The results show that the pathway consisting of automatic disassembly, hydrogen decrepitation, and acid-free dissolution extraction is promising for the recovery of REEs.

Keywords: Recycling, rare earth elements, process design, and optimization.

1. Introduction

The climate crisis poses one of humanity's most significant challenges in the twenty-first century, with the Earth already exceeding pre-industrial levels by 1.1 °C (UNFCCC, 2021). Urgent action is imperative to prevent further escalation, and scientific research emphasizes the need to limit global temperature rise to within 2 °C, preferably 1.5 °C above pre-industrial levels (UNFCCC, 2021). This necessitates prioritizing the decarbonization of energy and our economy by transitioning to clean energy technologies like solar panels, wind turbines, and electric vehicles. In the United States, significant legislative measures, such as the "Bipartisan Infrastructure Law", represent an unprecedented investment of over $430 billion by 2031, targeting reducing carbon emissions across sectors (Steinberg et al., 2023).

Electrification initiatives heavily rely on rare earth elements (REEs). In the global context, most REEs are sourced through mining, with limited to negligible contributions from recycling processes (Smith et al., 2022). Nonetheless, recycling has many advantages compared to conventional mining practices, presenting a pragmatic solution to the environmental concerns associated with the disposal of EOL products. Furthermore, EOL products contain notable concentrations of valuable REEs, such as neodymium, praseodymium, and dysprosium, potentially making them economically attractive as a feedstock. Lastly, recycling processes circumvent potential waste management issues associated with mined feedstocks, as the REEs frequently co-occur with radioactive elements like thorium and uranium in ore deposits (Smith et al., 2022).

In this paper, we develop an optimization-based framework to find the best processing pathway for the recovery of rare earth elements from EOL products. The methodology employed the following steps. Firstly, the projected quantity of REEs available for recycling from EOL EV and HEV motors' Rare Earth Permanent Magnets (REPM) (Blast et al., 2014; Argonne National Laboratory, 2023), along with the projected prices of rare earth oxides (REOs) (Hykawy & Chudnovsky, 2021) over the plant's lifetime were estimated and used to inform the model. Next, a superstructure was constructed containing all possible processing pathways, and the optimal pathway was found by maximizing the net present value (NPV) over a 15-year period, assuming that the plant recycles 10 % of the available EOL EVs and HEVs in the U.S. each year. Finally, a sensitivity analysis was conducted to evaluate the impact of different parameters on the venture's profitability and the optimal processing pathway.

2. Processes for the recovery of REEs from permanent magnets

As schematized in Figure 1, rare earth recycling from permanent magnets comprises four primary processing stages: disassembly, demagnetization, leaching, and extraction. Each stage contains several potential processes, represented as nodes in the superstructure. The naming convention for the nodes is *<stage number, node number>,* where *1* represents the disassembly stage, *2* the demagnetization stage, *3* the leaching stage, and *4* the extraction stage.

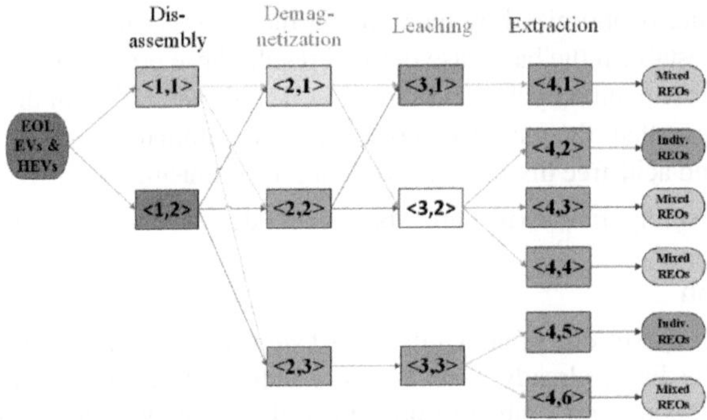

Figure 1. Simplified scheme of the superstructure with processing options for EOL EV & HEV motors' REPM to REOs.

In the disassembly stage, two processes are considered: manual disassembly, where REPMs are removed from EOL vehicle motors by manual labor *<1,1>* (Blast et al., 2014), and automatic disassembly *<1,2>*, which employs robots for automation (Blast et al., 2014). For demagnetization, three processes are explored: hydrogen decrepitation *<2,1>*, involving the reaction of REPM powder with hydrogen gas at 170 °C for 3 hours to produce a demagnetized, friable material (Walton et al., 2015); heating the magnets to 350 °C for 30 minutes followed by milling *<2,2>* (Klemettinen et al., 2021); and heating the magnets to 950 °C for 15 hours to create rare earth oxides and iron oxides followed by milling *<2,3>*, which results in iron precipitation during the subsequent selective leaching process (Vander Hoogerstraete et al., 2014). The leaching stage presents two potential processes: acid dissolution using sulfuric acid *<3,1>* (Lyman & Palmer, 1993), and selective leaching with hydrochloric acid *<3,3>* (Vander Hoogerstraete et al., 2014), which follows high-temperature heating and milling. In selective leaching, iron precipitates as iron(III) hydroxide. Node *<3,2>* is blank and represents skipping the leaching stage.

In the extraction stage, six processes are examined. The first method, hydrometallurgical extraction *<4,1>* (Lyman & Palmer, 1993), precipitates REEs as REE-sodium double salts to separate them from iron. Subsequent steps involve reactions with oxalic acid and calcination to produce mixed REOs, with the iron-containing leachate being treated with ammonium sulfate to precipitate it out of the solution as iron jarosite. The next two processes use supercritical CO_2 to separate REEs from iron (Azimi et al., 2023), with the first process employing solvent extraction (Yoon et al., 2015) for the separation of dysprosium and neodymium followed by oxalic acid precipitation and calcination to produce individual REOs *<4,2>* (Nawab et al., 2022). The second process involves skipping solvent extraction and utilizing oxalic acid precipitation and calcination to produce mixed REOs *<4,3>* (Nawab et al., 2022). In the fourth method, acid-free dissolution extraction *<4,4>*, REPM powder is dissolved in an aqueous solution of copper(II) nitrate, followed by oxalic acid precipitation to produce rare earth oxalates and iron-ammonium oxalates (Chowdhury et al., 2021). The rare earth oxalate precipitates are then filtered from the soluble iron-ammonium oxalates. Finally, the rare earth oxalates are calcined to produce mixed REOs. The fifth and sixth processes follow selective leaching and therefore do not require REE-iron separation. The fifth method involves solvent extraction (Yoon et al., 2015) for dysprosium-neodymium separation followed by oxalic acid precipitation and calcination *<4,5>* (Nawab et al., 2022), while the sixth method directly precipitates the REEs with oxalic acid and calcines them to obtain a mixture of REOs *<4,6>* (Nawab et al., 2022).

3. Optimization problem formulation

To describe the model, mass balance and logical constraints were formulated. The mass balance for a generic node is illustrated in Figure 2 and includes three sequential steps: convergence of inlet flows from different upstream nodes, processing, and separation of outlet flows to different downstream nodes. Components in the feedstock, intermediates, and products were tracked. The specific equations are as defined in Eq. (1-3).

$$\sum_{k=1}^{K^{in}} F_{i,j,k,c,t}^{in} = F_{i,j,c,t}^{in} \qquad \forall i \in I, j \in J_i, c \in C, t \in T \tag{1}$$

$$F_{i,j,c,t}^{out} = a_{i,j,c} * F_{i,j,c,t}^{in} \qquad \forall i \in I, j \in J_i, c \in C, t \in T \tag{2}$$

$$F_{i,j,c,t}^{out} = \sum_{k=1}^{K^{out}} F_{i,j,k,c,t}^{out} \qquad \forall i \in I, j \in J_i, c \in C, t \in T \tag{3}$$

Here, $F_{i,j,c,t}^{in}$ represents the flow of component c entering node $< i,j >$ in year t, and $F_{i,j,c,t}^{out}$ the correspondent outlet flow, $a_{i,j,c}$ is the yield of component c leaving node $< i,j >$, I is the set of all stages in the superstructure, J_i is the set of all nodes in stage i, C is the set of tracked components, and T is the set of all years the plant is in operation. A binary variable $y_{i,j}$ is introduced to model the selection of node $< i,j >$. Logical constraints relating processes at different stages, such as $y_{3,2} = y_{4,2} + y_{4,3} + y_{4,4}$ were added as needed and are not specified here due to limitations in space. Big M constraints relate the flow through a unit to its selection, as shown in Eq. (4), where $M^{i,j}$ represents the maximum inlet flow rate for node $< i,j >$.

$$F^{in}_{i,j,c,t} \leq y_{i,j} * M^{i,j} \qquad i \in I, j \in J_i, c \in C, t \in T \tag{4}$$

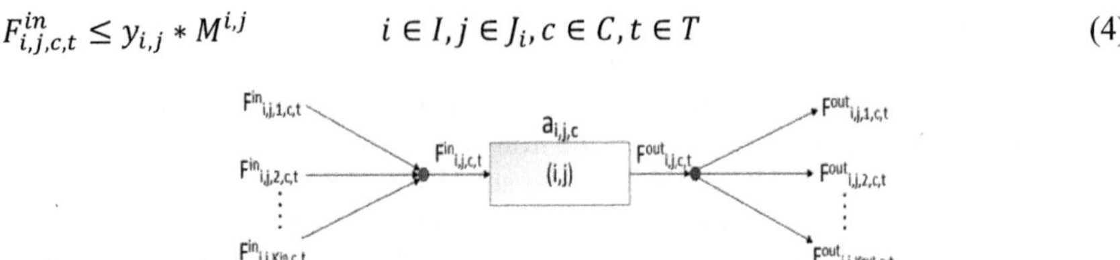

Figure 2. Mass balance for generic node $< i,j > \forall c \in C, t \in T$.

3.1. Objective function

The goal of the optimization problem was to maximize the NPV over the plant's lifetime, as shown in Eq. (5-6) (Seider et al., 2017). Here, CF_n is the cash flow in year n, LT is the plant's life in years, and IR is the interest rate.

$$NPV = \sum_{n=1}^{LT} \frac{CF_n}{(1+IR)^n} \tag{5}$$

$$CF_n = Profit_n - (CAPEX_n + OPEX_n) \tag{6}$$

CAPEX and OPEX calculations for each processing option included in the superstructure were carried out using the methodology described by Seider et al. (2017). When available, costing information and values for the parameters $a_{i,j,c}$ were taken from preliminary techno-economic analyses in the literature. There were cases, such as acid dissolution, selective leaching, hydrometallurgical extraction, oxalic acid precipitation, and solvent extraction, where costing data could not be found in the literature as a consequence of the data being proprietary and the relative immaturity of certain processes. In these scenarios, a process flowsheet was designed, modelled, and simulated in Aspen Plus. The purchased cost of equipment and the cost of utilities were found using Aspen Process Economic Analyzer, after which the methodology described by Seider et al. (2017) was followed to calculate CAPEX and OPEX. In all cases, individual reactions were modelled based on conversions and yields from bench-scale experiments found in the literature. e-NRTL was used to estimate thermodynamic properties, which allowed us to estimate solid precipitation. To preserve the linearity of the model, piecewise linear functions were used to relate costing equations to flow rates. This was done by sampling 6 points spanning the range of flow rates entering the process in the base case.

The MILP optimization problem is then: maximize NPV, subject to Eqs. 1-4, 6, logical relations, and CAPEX and OPEX (linear) relations as a function of the size of the technology. The decision variables are $F^{in}_{i,j,c,t}$, $F^{out}_{i,j,c,t}$, and $y_{i,j}$.

4. Results

The resulting MILP optimization problem was coded in Pyomo and solved using a personal laptop (12th gen i9, 2.50 GHz and 32 GB RAM). The decision variables are the processing options to be included and their sizing. As was mentioned in the Introduction section, the base case assumed that the plant recycles 10 % of all EOL EVs and HEVs in the U.S. each year. The optimal pathway was found to consist of automatic disassembly, hydrogen decrepitation, and acid-free dissolution extraction and resulted in a positive NPV. Among the processing stages, acid-free dissolution extraction dominated CAPEX expenses, accounting for 95 % of the cost, followed by the disassembly step, which accounted for 4 %. Additionally, the acid-free dissolution step also dominated OPEX expenses, accounting for ~99 %. These results suggest the need for focusing on further optimization of the acid-free dissolution process. Next, we found the optimal solution for different plant sizes and the projected REO prices. The results from these analyses can be seen in Figure 3. The NPV was found to be positively correlated to both the plant size and the REO prices, and the optimal pathway never changed. The NPV break-even point was found to occur at ~10 % of the initial estimate for EOL vehicles available for recycling and at ~28 % for the REO prices.

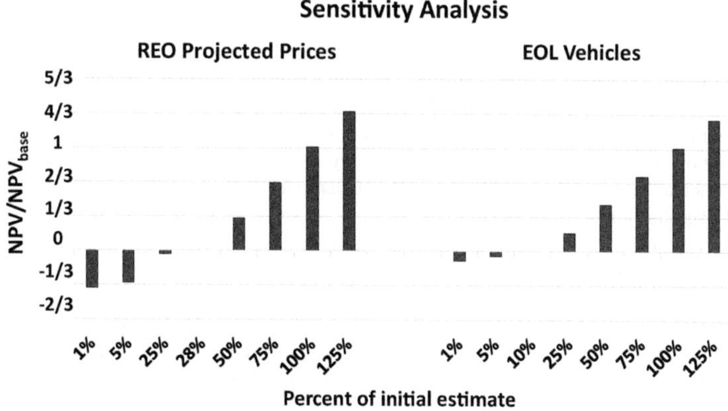

Figure 3. Sensitivity analysis for the product projected prices, and amount of EOL vehicles available for recycling. Values are reported normalized to the base case optimal solution to preserve confidentiality.

5. Conclusions

Superstructure optimization was utilized to define the optimal pathway for recycling REEs from EOL EV and HEV motors' REPM, aiming to maximize the NPV. The study determined that the optimal process consists of automated disassembly, hydrogen decrepitation, and acid-free dissolution extraction. The process was also found to be profitable over a wide range of parameter estimates, suggesting that further investigation to optimize this pathway would be warranted. In particular, acid-free dissolution extraction is indicated as the largest contributor to the optimal pathway, hence supporting the need to further optimize this process.

Acknowledgments

This effort was funded by the US Department of Energy's Process Optimization and Modeling for Minerals Sustainability (PrOMMiS) Initiative, supported by the Office of Fossil Energy and Carbon Management's Office of Resource Sustainability. Neither the United States Government nor any agency thereof, nor any of its employees, nor the support contractor, nor any of their employees, makes any warranty, express or implied, or assumes any legal liability or responsibility for the accuracy, completeness, or usefulness of any information, apparatus, product, or process disclosed, or represents that its use would not infringe privately owned rights. Reference herein to any specific commercial product, process, or service by trade name, trademark, manufacturer, or otherwise does not necessarily constitute or imply its endorsement, recommendation, or favoring by the United States Government or any agency thereof. The views and opinions of authors expressed herein do not necessarily state or reflect those of the United States Government or any agency thereof.

References

Argonne National Lab, 2023, LDV Total Sales of PEV and HEV by Month (updated through May 2023), date accessed: 2023-07-29, URL: https://www.anl.gov/esia/reference/light-duty-electric-drive-vehicles-monthly-sales-updates-historical-data.

G. Azimi, M.E. Sauber, J. Zhang, 2023, Technoeconomic analysis of supercritical fluid extraction process for recycling rare earth elements from neodymium iron boron magnets and fluorescent lamp phosphors, Journal of Cleaner Production, 422, doi: 10.1016/j.jclepro.2023.138526.

U. Bast, R. Blank, M. Buchert, T. Elwert, F. Finsterwalder, G. Hörnig, T. Klier, S. Langkau, F. Marscheider-Weidemann, J.-O Müller, Ch. Thürigen, F. Treffer, T. Walter, 2015, Recycling von komponenten und strategischen metallen aus elektrischen fahrantrieben: kennwort: MORE (Motor Recycling), doi: 10.24406/publica-fhg-297259.

N.A. Chowdhury, S. Deng, H. Jin, D. Prodius, J.W. Sutherland, I.C. Nlebedim, 2021, Sustainable recycling of rare-earth elements from NdFeB magnet swarf: technoeconomic and environmental perspectives, ACS Sustainable Chemistry & Engineering, 9, 15915-15924, doi: 10.1021/acssuschemeng.1c05965.

J. Hykawy, T. Chudnovsky, 2021, Report: Rare Earths, date accessed: 2023-09-21, URL: https://www.stormcrow.ca/wp-content/uploads/2021/03/20210308-Stormcrow-UCore-Initiation-Final.pdf.

A. Klemettinen, A. Żak, I. Chojnacka, S. Matuska, A. Leśniewicz, M. Wełna, Z. Adamski, L. Klemettinen, L. Rycerz, 2021, Leaching of rare earth elements from NdFeB magnets without mechanical pretreatment by sulfuric (H_2SO_4) and hydrochloric (HCl) acids, Minerals, 11, 1374, doi: 10.3390/min11121374.

J.W. Lyman, G.R. Palmer, 1993, Recycling of rare earths and iron from NdFeB magnet scrap, High Temperature Materials and Processes, 11, 175-187, doi: 10.1515/HTMP.1993.11.1-4.175.

A. Nawab, X. Yang, R. Honaker, 2022, Parametric study and speciation analysis of rare earth precipitation using oxalic acid in a chloride solution system, Minerals Engineering, 176, 107352, doi: 10.1016/j.mineng.2021.107352.

W.D. Seider, D.R. Lewin, J.D. Seader, S. Widagdo, R. Gani, K.M. Ng, 2017, Product and Process Design Principles: Synthesis, Analysis and Evaluation – 4th Edition, John Wiley & Sons Inc., New York, USA.

B.J. Smith, M.E. Riddle, M.R. Earlam, C. Iloeje, D. Diamond, 2022, Rare Earth Permanent Magnets: Supply Chain Deep Dive Assessment, U.S. Department of Energy, Washington, D.C., USA.

D. Steinberg, M. Brown, R. Wiser, P. Donohoo-Vallet, P. Gagnon, A. Hamilton, M. Mowers, C. Murphy, A. Prasana, 2023, Evaluating impacts of the inflation reduction act and bipartisan infrastructure law on the U.S. power system, National Renewable Energy Laboratory, Colorado, USA, doi: NREL/TP-6A20-85242.

UNFCCC, 2021, Glasgow Climate Pact, Decision -/CP.26, Glasgow Climate Change Conference, date accessed: 2023-07-27, URL: https://unfccc.int/documents/310475.

T. Vander Hoogerstraete, B. Blanpain, T. Van Gerven, K. Binnemans, 2014, From NdFeB magnets towards the rare-earth oxides: a recycling process consuming only oxalic acid, RCS Advances, 4, 64099-64111, doi: 10.1039/c4ra13787f.

A. Walton, H. Yi, N.A. Rowson, J.D. Speight, V.S.J. Mann, R.S. Sheridan, A. Bradshaw, I.R. Harris, A.J. Williams, 2015, The use of hydrogen to separate and recycle neodymium-iron-boron-type magnets from electronic waste, Journal of Cleaner Production, 104, 236-241, doi: 10.1016/j.jclepro.2015.05.033.

H.-S. Yoon, C.-J. Kim, K.W. Chung, S.-D. Kim, J.R. Kumar, 2015, Process development for recovery of dysprosium from permanent magnet scraps leach liquor by hydrometallurgical techniques, Canadian Metallurgical Quarterly, 54, 318-327, doi: 10.1179/1879139515Y.0000000019.

Flavio Manenti, Gintaras V. Reklaitis (Eds.), Proceedings of the 34th European Symposium on Computer Aided Process Engineering / 15th International Symposium on Process Systems Engineering (ESCAPE34/PSE24), June 2-6, 2024, Florence, Italy
 http://dx.doi.org/10.1016/B978-0-443-28824-1.50220-9

Rule-based Decision Framework for the Digital Synthesis of Optimal Pharmaceutical Processes

Yash Barhate,[a] Daniel J. Laky,[a] Daniel Casas-Orozco,[a] Gintaras Reklaitis,[a] Zoltan Nagy[a*]

[a] *Davidson Schoool of Chemical Engineering, Purdue University, West Lafayette, IN 47907, USA.*

* *znagy@purdue.edu*

Abstract

This study introduces a rule-based decision framework employing PharmaPy for the optimization and rapid in-silico design comparisons of different end-to-end optimal (E2EO) pharmaceutical manufacturing flowsheets. The framework is designed to incorporate hybrid pharmaceutical flowsheets, incorporating unit operations in both batch and continuous modes. The methodology involves the conceptualization and application of heuristic-based synthesis rules on the master superstructure to generate smaller-scale superstructure realizations that can be readily optimized with moderate computational efforts. Lastly, the effectiveness of the framework is demonstrated using a case study, comparing various manufacturing pathways for the synthesis and purification of the anti-cancer drug Lomustine.

Keywords: Process synthesis, Optimization, Pharmaceutical manufacturing.

1. Introduction

The landscape of pharmaceutical manufacturing is undergoing a significant transformation, driven by emerging paradigms such as quality-by-design (QbD) and quality-by-control (QbC). In this rapidly evolving context, model-based digital design tools are essential for informed decision-making in process design and operation due to their in-silico optimization and design comparison capabilities for various unit operations and process flowsheets (Su et al., 2019; Yu et al., 2014). Furthermore, with the ongoing batch-to-continuous transition of the pharmaceutical industry, there is a rising demand for modeling tools capable of flexibly simulating flowsheets with different operating modes such as batch, continuous, or hybrid (incorporating both batch and continuous unit operations). Addressing this need, PharmaPy emerges as a user-friendly, open-source Python-based tool with the capability to configure and simulate various manufacturing setups (Casas-Orozco et al., 2021).

Flowsheet optimization and synthesis are commonly used for comparing and evaluating different manufacturing routes in terms of process efficiency, techno-economic metrics, environmental impact, regulatory compliance, and other relevant factors. Traditional approaches often involve the formulation of a superstructure network, typically solved through mixed-integer nonlinear optimization (MINLP) or generalized disjunctive programming (Chen & Grossmann, 2017). While these equation-oriented methods are frequently applied to simplified models, their effectiveness in optimizing flowsheets modeled with rigorous unit operation models is limited (Navarro-Amorós et al., 2014). Simulation-optimization-based frameworks are used to optimize flowsheets that contain prohibitive complexity for equation-oriented models. However, addressing complex process synthesis problems through a simulation-optimization approach presents challenges, either due to the computational cost associated with exhaustively optimizing each flowsheet or the necessity for specialized interfaces between MINLP optimization algorithms and process simulators (Corbetta et al., 2016).

In this response, this study proposes a rule-based decision process framework for the optimization of end-to-end optimal (E2EO) pharmaceutical manufacturing flowsheets. By applying a set of heuristic process synthesis rules influenced by user preferences, the original process superstructure is systematically condensed into smaller, more manageable sets for subsequent optimization. Thus, this approach reduces the computational cost associated with the optimization of different flowsheets due to the reduction in the search space.

The remainder of the paper is organized as follows: firstly, the rule-based decision framework for the optimal synthesis of pharmaceutical flowsheets is presented. Subsequently, the devised framework is applied in a case study for optimizing various manufacturing pathways to synthesize and purify an active pharmaceutical ingredient (API), Lomustine.

2. Proposed methodology

A generic manufacturing route for producing small-molecule APIs comprises of a few general processing steps: (i) synthesis, (ii) purification, and (iii) isolation. Each of these steps has operating decisions that impact unit performance for a given flowsheet. However, each processing step may be represented with a multitude of different choices that impact what set of operating decisions to make (i.e., desired product, raw materials, complexity of each processing step, unit operations for each step, operating mode of each unit operation, etc.). Each of these decisions impacts the process superstructure. Subsequently, the search space for possible flowsheet alternatives expands exponentially with the increasing number of options (i.e., decision variables) for each decision at each step. Also, in many pharmaceutical processing applications it is desirable to maintain high model fidelity, rendering the aforementioned mixed integer programming frameworks, (Chen & Grossmann, 2017), intractable or insufficient. This presents a substantial computational bottleneck for the optimization of every possible flowsheet within the superstructure using simulation-optimization. Here, a heuristic rule-based synthesis algorithm becomes crucial, enabling the reduction of the superstructure into smaller, manageable sub-structures for optimization with moderate computational efforts.

These synthesis rules are formulated and generalized, considering common commercial and process engineering decision points encountered in pharmaceutical manufacturing. They are systematically organized into five distinct groups: (1) process feasibility rules, (2) regulatory considerations, (3) equipment availability constraints, (4) experience- or knowledge-based rules, and (5) scenario analysis. Regulatory considerations are particularly crucial in pharmaceutical manufacturing to ensure compliance with regulations from agencies such as the FDA. Equipment availability constraints account for practical limitations in manufacturing, ensuring that the synthesis rules are aligned with real-world scenarios. Experience- or knowledge-based rules integrate prior known process knowledge to simplify the synthesis workflow. Finally, scenario analysis rules are designed to facilitate the comparison and optimization of various industrially relevant and interesting manufacturing scenarios, such as end-to-end continuous manufacturing and/or telescoped reaction synthesis, etc. While presenting an exhaustive list of all rules exceed the scope, Table 1 provides illustrative examples from each category, showcasing the flexibility offered by synthesis rules during pharmaceutical flowsheet synthesis.

Table 1: Process synthesis rules with their categories

No.	Category	Example
1	Regulatory aspects	R-1: Isolation of ISO intermediate after Rxn1, increases drug safety
2	Feasibility rules	F-1: For semi-batch reactors, all reactions are assumed to happen in a single reactor
3	Equipment availability constraints	A-1: Batch distillation is not available
4	Scenario Analysis	S-1: End-end continuous manufacturing S-2: Telescoped reaction synthesis
5	Experience or Knowledge-based rules	E-1: Solvent switch is preferred in batch mode of operation. E-2: If reaction 1 is fast and performed in a continuous reactor, avoid batch reactor for performing the next reaction.

From the rule-based knowledge database, a specific set of rules is first selected based on user preferences. These chosen rules are then applied to the comprehensive superstructure, generating small-scale superstructure realizations, as depicted in Figure 1. Configurations violating one or more synthesis rules were systematically excluded from the search space, and only feasible flowsheets were subjected to deterministic optimization. As a result of the explicit formulation of the synthesis rules, arbitrary configurations can be analyzed transparently and systematically, enabling a thorough examination of the superstructure design space.

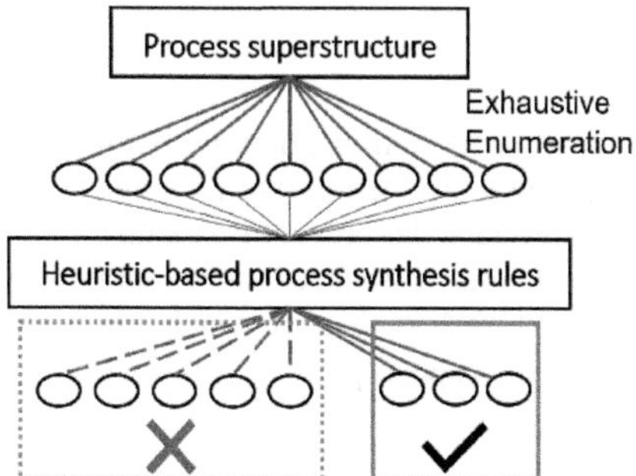

Figure 1: Heuristics reduce the search space of valid superstructure layouts

3. Case Study

In this study, the described methodology is applied to analyze the end-to-end manufacturing of the anti-cancer API, Lomustine. Recent literature highlights ongoing efforts in the development of lab-scale continuous synthesis workflows for Lomustine production (Ewan et al., 2017). This case study aims to supplement these studies by exploring and comparing various manufacturing pathways designed for the synthesis and purification of Lomustine.

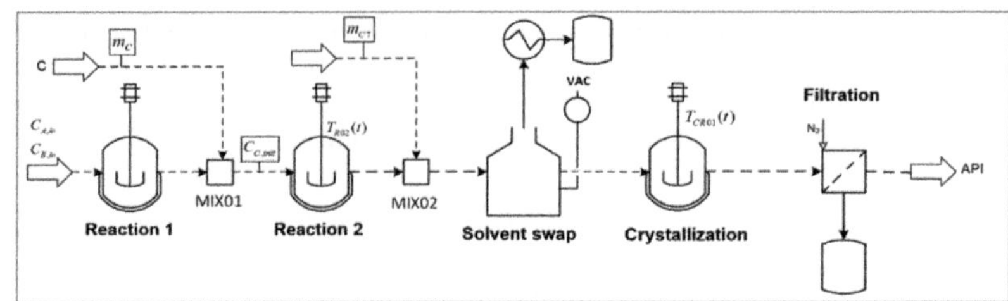

Figure 3: Process-specific superstructure template for Lomustine manufacturing.

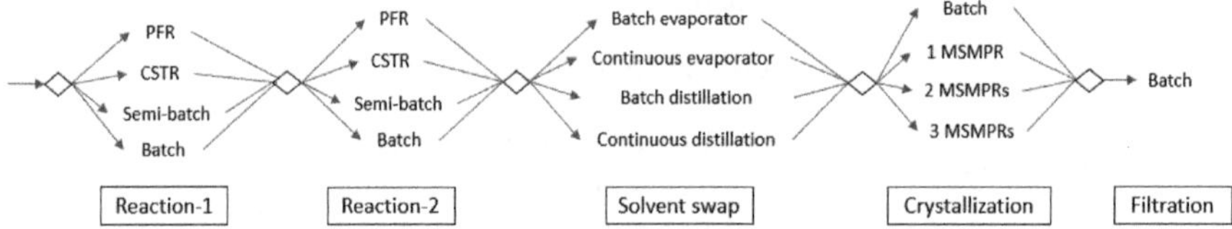

Figure 2: Exhaustive enumeration of possible flowsheet alternatives.

Following the proposed methodology, a process-specific superstructure template was drafted considering the process chemistry as depicted in Figure 3. The manufacturing process encompasses a two-step reaction synthesis carried out in reactors R01 and R02, succeeded by a solvent-switch operation (VAP01), followed by crystallization (CR01) and filtration (F01) processing steps. There are multiple alternative unit operations and operating modes for each step in Figure 3. The comprehensive superstructure, encompassing all potential flowsheet configurations, is depicted in Figure 2. A thorough enumeration of all combinatorically generated flowsheets within this superstructure results in a total of 256 distinct configurations. Process feasibility rule F-1, equipment availability rule A-1, and experience-based rule E-1 were first applied to the above superstructure to screen out disallowed flowsheet configurations. With these rules, the search space narrows down from 256 flowsheets to 40 flowsheets to be optimized.

3.1. Design Problem:

The design problem is formulated as a nonlinear constrained optimization problem (Equation 1) with the dual objectives of maximizing both mass production rate (J_1) and number-based mean crystal size (J_2) of the filtered API product. To prevent premature crystallization in the vaporizer, an inequality constraint was introduced as a path constraint by maintaining the concentration of API ($C_{VAP,API}$) less than or equal to a specified threshold given the fixed operating temperature of the vaporizer ($C_{solub}(T_{VAP})$).

$$\max_{\boldsymbol{x}} \alpha_1 J_1(\boldsymbol{x}) + \alpha_2 J_2(\boldsymbol{x}) \tag{1}$$

$$s.t.\ PharmaPy\ process\ model$$

$$\int_0^{t_f} \left(C_{VAP,API}(t) - C_{solub}(T_{VAP}) \right) \mathrm{d}t < 0$$

$$\boldsymbol{x}_{lb} < \boldsymbol{x} < \boldsymbol{x}_{ub}$$

Table 2: Decision variables used

Unit operations	Variable
Reactor 1	$C_{A/B,in}$ *(mol/L)*, t_{R01}/τ_{R01}, V_{R01}
Reactor 2	$C_{D,in}$ *(mol/L)*, t_{R02}/τ_{R02}
Evaporator	t_{VAP01} *(s)*, *P (bar)*, $R_{C7\|R02}$
Batch Crystallizer	T_1, T_2, T_3, t_{CR01}
MSMPR	T_{CR0n}, τ_{CR0n}

The optimization problem was solved using a simulation-optimization approach. The state variables, inequality constraints, and objective functions were evaluated by using callbacks to the pharmaceutical manufacturing process written in PharmaPy. A mesh adaptive direct search (MADS) algorithm using the Python interface pyNOMAD (Audet et al., 2021) was used to solve the optimization problem. The decision variables($\boldsymbol{x}$) used for the flowsheets are shown in Table 2, where reactor variables one of t_{R01} or τ_{R01} are used for batch or continuous operation respectively.

3.2. Results

Using the optimization framework outlined earlier, all 40 flowsheets were optimized in approximately 63 hours on a MacBook Pro with macOS Catalina 2.6 GHz Quad-core Intel core i7 and 16 GB RAM. A Pareto front (Figure 4) was obtained by solving the dual-objective optimization problem for each possible flowsheet configuration of the process superstructure. Each flowsheet subsequently has optimal operating conditions which lead to varying process outputs, namely crystal size and hourly production. Figure 4A labels each optimal operating output by the first reaction's operating mode (i.e., R01 is batch or continuous). Flowsheet configurations with reactors operating in continuous mode for the first reaction step (R01) show higher production rates compared to batch reactors. Additionally, Figure 4B labels the optimal operating output based on different crystallizer types. Flowsheets employing batch-cooling crystallizers yield larger mean-size crystals than those with MSMPR crystallizers for this case. Therefore, the batch operating mode for the crystallization step is more effective than the continuous mode considering the set of operating constraints given and the flowsheet configurations explored. These insights demonstrate the application of the proposed framework for informed decision-making in selecting optimal operating modes for different manufacturing steps.
Furthermore, to explore the computational benefits of integrating heuristic rules, an additional experience-based knowledge rule (E-2) was added to the original set of rules. This led to the further condensation of the superstructure to a smaller sub-structure of 32 flowsheets instead of 40. Optimizing this refined sub-structure took approximately 47

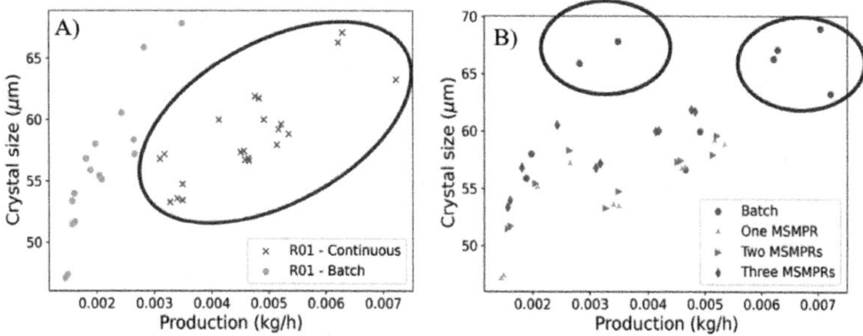

Figure 4: A) Pareto optimal fronts for flowsheets with R01 operating in batch versus continuous modes, B) Pareto front for flowsheets with different types of crystallizers.

hours, resulting in a notable 25% reduction in computational burden underscoring the advantageous impact of incorporating heuristic rules in enhancing the computational efficiency of the optimization process.

4. Conclusions

In this study, a rule-based decision framework for synthesizing and optimizing various end-to-end optimal (E2EO) pharmaceutical manufacturing flowsheets was developed. The framework was applied effectively in a case study focusing on Lomustine production, wherein various manufacturing pathways for the synthesis and purification of the API were analyzed. It was shown that PharmaPy can be used to automate superstructure synthesis and optimization across a wide range of flowsheets featuring unit operations in both batch and/or continuous operating modes. The incorporation of heuristic-based synthesis rules selected based on user preferences facilitated the generation of smaller sub-structure realizations from the original process superstructure. Subsequently, these smaller sub-structures were then optimized using a simulation-optimization framework with significantly reduced computational requirements. The analysis of optimized flowsheets within the Lomustine case study provided valuable insights into selecting optimal operating modes for different unit operations across various manufacturing steps, enhancing overall process efficiency and facilitating informed decision-making.

Acknowledgments

Funding for this work was made possible, by the US Food and Drug Administration (FDA) through grant number U01FD006738. Views expressed herein do not necessarily reflect the official policies of the Department of Health and Human Services; nor does any mention of trade names, commercial practices, or organizations imply endorsement by the United States Government.

References

Audet, C., Digabel, S. Le, Montplaisir, V. R., & Tribes, C. (2021). *NOMAD version 4: Nonlinear optimization with the MADS algorithm*.

Casas-Orozco, D., Laky, D., Wang, V., Abdi, M., Feng, X., Wood, E., Laird, C., Reklaitis, G. V., & Nagy, Z. K. (2021). PharmaPy: An object-oriented tool for the development of hybrid pharmaceutical flowsheets. *Computers and Chemical Engineering*, *153*, 107408.

Chen, Q., & Grossmann, I. E. (2017). Recent Developments and Challenges in Optimization-Based Process Synthesis.

Corbetta, M., Grossmann, I. E., & Manenti, F. (2016). Process simulator-based optimization of biorefinery downstream processes under the Generalized Disjunctive Programming framework. *Computers & Chemical Engineering*, *88*, 73–85.

Ewan, H. S., Iyer, K., Hyun, S. H., Wleklinski, M., Cooks, R. G., & Thompson, D. H. (2017). Multistep Flow Synthesis of Diazepam Guided by Droplet-Accelerated Reaction Screening with Mechanistic Insights from Rapid Mass Spectrometry Analysis. *Organic Process Research and Development*, *21*(10), 1566–1570.

Navarro-Amorós, M. A., Ruiz-Femenia, R., & Caballero, J. A. (2014). Integration of modular process simulators under the Generalized Disjunctive Programming framework for the structural flowsheet optimization. *Computers & Chemical Engineering*, *67*, 13–25.

Su, Q., Ganesh, S., Moreno, M., Bommireddy, Y., Gonzalez, M., Reklaitis, G. V., & Nagy, Z. K. (2019). A perspective on Quality-by-Control (QbC) in pharmaceutical continuous manufacturing. *Computers & Chemical Engineering*, *125*, 216–231.

Yu, L. X., Amidon, G., Khan, M. A., Hoag, S. W., Polli, J., Raju, G. K., & Woodcock, J. (2014). Understanding Pharmaceutical Quality by Design. *The AAPS Journal*, *16*(4), 771.

Flavio Manenti, Gintaras V. Reklaitis (Eds.), Proceedings of the 34th European Symposium on Computer Aided Process Engineering / 15th International Symposium on Process Systems Engineering (ESCAPE34/PSE24), June 2-6, 2024, Florence, Italy
 http://dx.doi.org/10.1016/B978-0-443-28824-1.50221-0

Synthesis, characterization and simulation of thin perovskite films based on calcium titanate ($CaTiO_3$) with possible application in solar modules

Gerardo Hernández-Reyes[a], Guillermo Adolfo Anaya-Ruiz[a], Pascual Eduardo Murillo-Alvarado[a], José Joel Román-Godínez[a], Manuel Salvador Sánchez-Ibarra[a], Alejandra Guadalupe Andrade-Partida[a] and Gabriela Guadalupe Esquivel-Barajas[a*].

[a]Universidad de La Ciénega del Estado de Michoacán de Ocampo. Av. Universidad Sur 3000, Lomas de Universidad, 59103 Sahuayo de Morelos, Michoacán México.
e-mail: ggesquivel@ucemich.edu.mx

Abstract

The continuous growth of the society has promoted the use of fossil fuels to satisfy its needs. In order to reduce the environmental impact generated by these fuels, it is necessary to resort to the use of renewable energies. Such is the case of Solar cells, which are classified into different generations based on their structure, composition and consumer needs. However, these solar cells have a high manufacturing cost. So, the proposal of the present research is to synthesize perovskite-type materials, with ABX_3 composition, because they have had a great boom on the world scene because their photoelectric properties make them attractive for obtaining low-cost and high-quality modules, efficiency as alternatives to monocrystalline and polycrystalline silicon-based solar cells. In this work, calcium titanate perovskite ($CaTiO_3$) was obtained using the Sol-Gel method, resulting in the obtaining of different samples of this perovskite.The sol-gel route is considered because it has been widely reported in the literature, to obtain materials at a nanometric scale, such as glass and ceramics. To do this, a biphasic suspension was obtained from a titanium isopropoxide solution (Sigma-Aldrich) and a sodium hydroxide solution (Merk). Through an aging process at 65°C, the solvent was evaporated, obtaining samples that were subsequently subjected to heat treatment in a muffle (Felisa) at 550°C for 3 hours, finally they were characterized using the scanning electron microscope (SEM), finding high resolution images of the surface of the samples with 100-200nm conglomerates of ($CaTiO_3$), in addition using the Fourier transform (FT-IR), functional groups belonging to this type of perovskite are identified. The results of the samples served as the basis for the simulation process of perovskite in photovoltaic modules.

Keywords: perovskite, calcium titanate perovskite, Sol-Gel.

1. Introduction

It is essential to cover the needs of societies that are in constant development, which causes a dependence on the use of means of transportation that still use fossil fuels as a source, such is the case described by Abhinandan K., *et al* (2021), where mention is made of the burning of fossils and these tend to release large quantities of greenhouse gases (GHG) such as CO_2, CH_4, NO_2, among others, and these cause atrocious effects on the climate. Therefore, it is necessary to identify mechanisms to reduce GHG emissions into the atmosphere from different sectors. At the same time, the development of economic and environmentally friendly energy sources, such as the use of renewable energies to produce and generate electricity, solar energy being a type of clean energy with great potential. According to what was mentioned by (Pinzón C. *et al* 2020), they propose the use of solar cells, which are devices that have the ability to convert energy that originates from solar rays into electrical power. They also mention new technologies in solar cells whose purpose is to have greater energy conversion efficiency and shorter processing time, one of these innovations being perovskite solar cells.

In such a way that the purpose of the present investigation consisted of the synthesis, through the sol-gel route, of the calcium titanate material ($CaTiO_3$), in turn it was characterized by FT-IR and SEM, and a simulation was carried out using the SCAPS-1D software (Burgelman M, *et al* 2020).

2. Perovskites in the development of solar modules

2.1 Semiconductor materials in solar cells

For electron transporting materials, several broad band oxide semiconductors have been studied, such as titanium oxide (TiO_2), Zinc oxide (ZnO) and tin oxide (SnO_2) for their possible application as collectors of electrons for photovoltaic cells. According to Rodriguez R. (2022), he mentions that TiO_2 has proven to be a material with broad advantages such as high chemical stability, low toxicity, it is abundant in the environment and high efficiency. Unlike other broadband semiconductor oxide materials such as ZnO, TiO_2 is resistant to photodegradation when photoexcited.

With the desire to identify technologies that use clean energy, we have chosen to use technologies that use as a cornerstone the use of nanomaterials with photovoltaic benefits. According to Cai M., *et al* (2017), they mention the use of perovskite solar cells (PSC), because at the laboratory level they present efficiencies close to 20% and in the future, they will reach 25%. In turn, Santiago A., *et al* (2021) mention the various components in the precursor solution of the organometallic halide perovskite which can affect the crystallinity of the film, among the components that are used are; $CH_3NH_3MX_3$ (M= Pb o Sn, X= Cl, Br o I). Based on what was described by the authors Amelenan A. et al 2018, they describe that calcium titanate shows dielectric properties with a relative permittivity value of up to 186 and a bandgap of 3.8 to 4.00 eV that can be used as optoelectronic device. In such a way that this material is considered for research as a cornerstone for the proposal to be used in photovoltaic solar modules.

With the above in mind, for the development of this research it was decided to synthesize calcium titanate with the chemical formula $CaTiO_3$, because it is a semiconductor material that has a perovskite-type structure, and whose applications in recent years have focused on taking advantage of the catalytic properties of this material, so the purpose was to synthesize the material by the solgel route, characterize it by SEM and FTIR, culminating with a simulation to identify the arrangement of the layers that make up the photovoltaic module.

3. Metodology

For the development of the research, precursor materials were used, which are from the Sigma-Aldrich brand and the solvents are from the brand golden bell, so that the methodology was divided into three stages.

Stage 1. Material synthesis. 3 stock solutions were prepared, the solutions were; a) first solution, which was called as; Na, contained reagent grade sodium hydroxide homogenized with distilled water, b) the second solution was called: TiO_2OH, which consisted of titanium isoprooxide diluted with isopropyl alcohol in a flask lined with aluminum with the purpose of isolating solar radiation due to the photosensitive properties of titanium dioxide, which was injected with a syringe. and homogenized and c) third solution, called; Ca, which was made up of calcium carbonate ($CaCO_3$), diluted in water. To obtain a $CaTiO_3$ solution, starting with the 1% TiO_2OH solution, a reactor was designed that consisted of a beaker lined with aluminum to which 2 ml of the TiO_2OH solution was added using a pipette, to Subsequently add the Na and Ca solutions, dripping until completing 198ml at a constant stirring of 1400rpm at room temperature until obtaining a 200ml $CaTiO_3$ solution. Afterwards, the mixture was subjected to incubation at 65°C for 2 days in order to obtain evaporation of the solvent. Finally, a heat treatment at 600°C for two hours was applied.

Stage 2. Characterization of the material. For the characterization of the surface of the samples, a scanning electron microscope (SEM), model JEOL JSM-6460LV, was used and in turn the elemental analysis was carried out using X-ray energy dispersion spectroscopy (EDS) and transform infrared spectroscopy. Fourier (FT-IR) Perkin Elmer Frontier model in the 4500-400cm^{-1} region.

Stage 3. Simulation with SCAPS software. In order to have a better understanding of the effect of the effect of different parameters in the performance of the perovskite films. We use a widely computer application called Solar Cell Capacitance Simulator (SCAPS) develop by Professor Marc Burgelman of the university of Gent, Belgium.

4. Results and discussions

The material obtained by the solgel route was characterized by scanning electron microscopy, so that in Figure 1, the micrographs of the material are presented, as well as the EDS analysis, and the distribution of the elements present. In turn, in Figure 1c, you can see a particular size that ranged from 130-30nm.

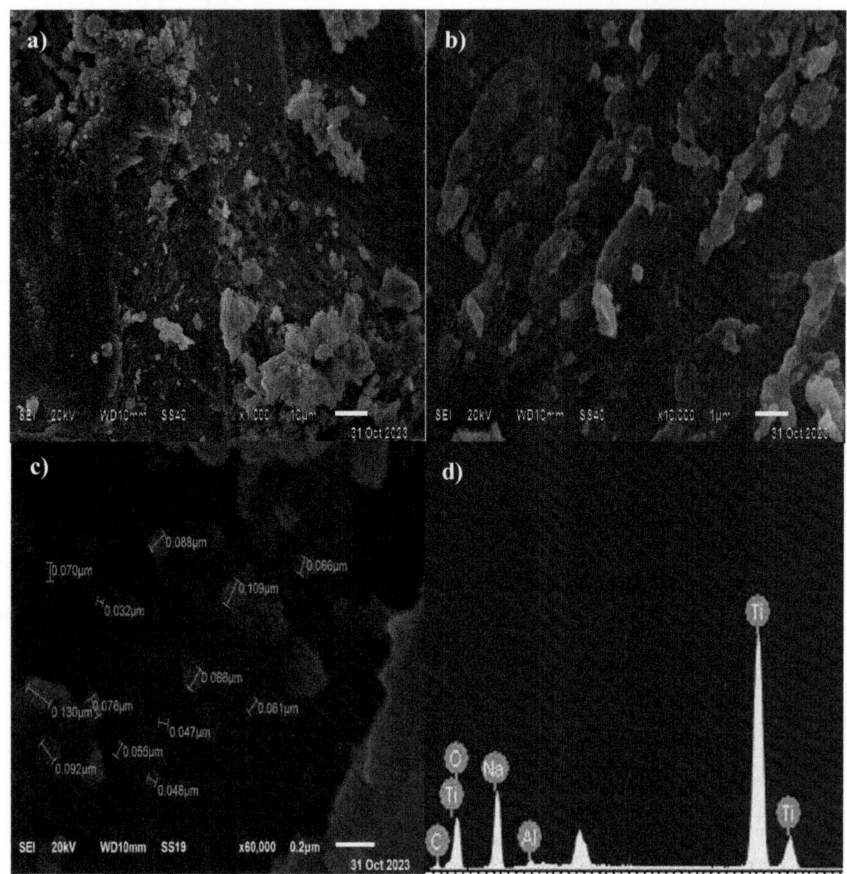

Figure 1. Micrographs taken of the surface of the $CaTiO_3$ composite by scanning electron microscopy, a) 1,000X, b) 10,000X, c) 60,000X and d) EDS analysis of the 60,000X micrograph.

Figure 2 shows the distribution of the elements present on the surface of the material at 60,000X.

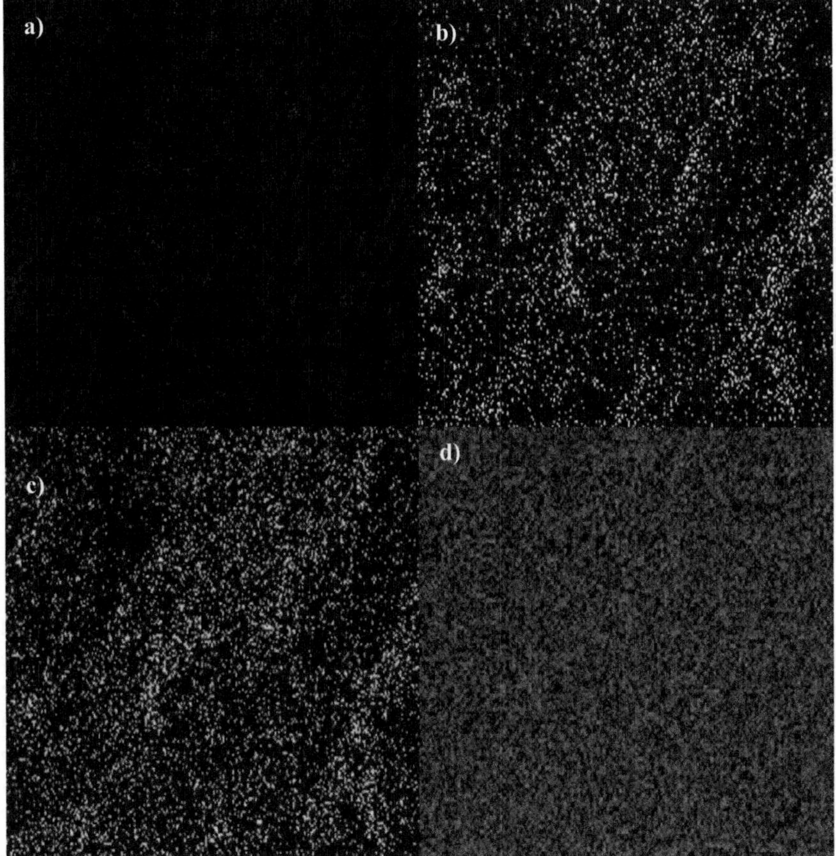

Figure 2. Micrographs taken of the surface of the $CaTiO_3$ a 60 000x.

The infrared spectrum of the $CaTiO_3$ sample is presented in Figure 3a, the FTIR study analysis after calcination temperature at 600 °C was carried out from 4000 to 400 cm^{-1}, respectively. The bands observed between 800-805 and 628 cm^{-1} are assigned to the stretching bands (Ti–O) of titanium in the anatase phase. The peak at 727 cm^{-1} corresponds to stretching (Ti–O–Ti). The peaks observed at 1340 cm^{-1}, 1591 cm^{-1} and 1757 cm^{-1} can be attributed to the stretching (Ti–O) and bridge stretching (Ti–O–Ti) modes. Finally, the broad band in the range of 3600 cm^{-1} to 3200 cm^{-1} can be assigned to the stretching of the hydroxyl group (O–H) located on the surface of the metal oxide nanoparticles.

In Figure 3b, the proposal for the arrangement of the different layers that make up the photovoltaic module is made, considering the perovskite as the last layer.

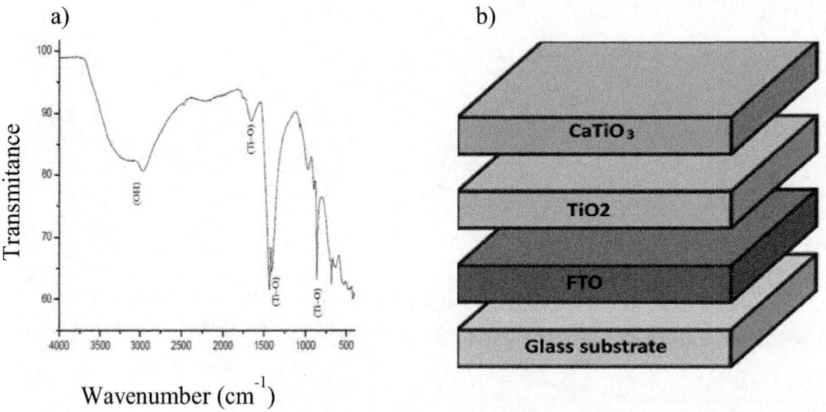

Figure 3. a) FTIR spectrum of the $CaTiO_3$ composite and b) Layer arrangement for photovoltaic module (design of $FTO/TiO_2/CaTiO_3$ device configuration).

5. Conclusions

From the results obtained by the characterization, it is concluded that the values obtained with regard to transmittance correspond to the characteristic functional groups of the $CaTiO_3$ material as reported in the literature. Likewise, the scanning analysis of the scanning electron microscope (SEM) produced high resolution images that ranged from 1000 to 60,000x respectively, in which morphology of agglomerations can be seen on its surface that correspond to the reviewed literature and finally the spectroscopy analysis. Energy disperses analysis (EDS) showed the concentration of elements in the scan of the surface of the material, identifying elements of interest such as titanium.

6. References

Abhinandan Kumar, Pardeep Singh, Pankaj Raizada and Chaudhery Mustansar Hussain (2021) Impact of COVID-19 on greenhouse gases emissions: A critical review. Science of The Total Environment Volume 806, Part 1. Pages 1-2. https://doi.org/10.1016/j.scitotenv.2021.150349.

Amelenan Torimtubun Alfonsina Abat, Cornelia Augusty Anniza Maulana, Eka, and Ernawati Lusi (2018) Affordable and sustainable new generation of solar cells: calcium titanate ($CaTiO_3$) – based perovskite solar cells. Pages 1.2. https://doi.org/10.1051/e3sconf/20186701010

Burgelman M, Nollet P and Degrave S 2000 Thin Solid Films 361–362 527–32

Cai Molang, Yongzhen Wu, Chen Han, Yang Xudong, Qiang, Yinghuai and Han Liyuan (2017) Cost-Performance Analysis of Perovskite Solar Modules. Adv. Sci. Vol 4, DOI: 10.1002/advs.201600269.

Rodríguez Jiménez Rafael Aurelio (2022) Síntesis y Caracterización de Óxido de Titanio usando química verde para su aplicación en celdas fotovoltaicas simuladas por SCAPS-1D. (Tesis de doctorado) Pages 11-26.

Pinzón Carlos, Martínez Nahuel, Casas Guillermo, Alvira Fernando and Cappelletti Marcelo (2020) Evaluación Teórica Del Comportamiento De Celdas Solares De Perovskita Invertida Totalmente Inorgánicas, Avances en Energías Renovables y Medio Ambiente Vol. 24, pp 139-148, 2020 ISSN 2314-1433.

Santiago Mustafat Ana Itzel, Espinosa Roa Arián, González Juárez Edgar, Sánchez Cervantes Eduardo M. (2021) Ingenierías de aditivos en celdas solares tipo perovskita. Ingenierías Vol. 24, No. 90

Flavio Manenti, Gintaras V. Reklaitis (Eds.), Proceedings of the 34th European Symposium on Computer Aided Process Engineering / 15th International Symposium on Process Systems Engineering (ESCAPE34/PSE24), June 2-6, 2024, Florence, Italy
 http://dx.doi.org/10.1016/B978-0-443-28824-1.50222-2

CFD-based Design of Laminated Microdevice with 3D Serpentine Channel for Submillisecond Mixing

Kazuki Okamoto,[a] Heejin Kim,[b] Osamu Tonomura[a]

[a]*Dept. of Chem. Eng., Kyoto University, Nishikyo, Kyoto 615-8510, Japan*
[b]*Dept. of Chemistry, Korea University, Seoul 02841, Republic of Korea*
tonomura@cheme.kyoto-u.ac.jp (O. Tonomura)

Abstract

In chemical synthesis, competition often occurs between reactions of intermediates. The main operation that affects reaction results is mixing, and the control of the mixing time is important. The laminated micromixer with three-dimensional (3D) serpentine channel can achieve residence time in the submillisecond range, allowing control of intramolecular rearrangements not possible with conventional mixers. However, the channel design of this type of mixer is important because the pressure drop increases as the number of bends in the channel increases. In this study, various channel configurations, shapes and sizes were designed, and their mixing performance was evaluated using computational fluid dynamics (CFD) simulation. As a result, a microdevice consisting of a non-alignment confluence section and a mixing channel with two serpentine sections was designed as a laminated mixer. It was shown that the designed microdevice exhibited the mixing performance equivalent to the conventional microdevice for various inlet flowrate ratios and had lower pressure drop than the conventional microdevice. Additionally, the usefulness of the designed microdevice was confirmed through experiments on the anionic Fries rearrangement.

Keywords: CFD-based design, Laminated micromixer, Submillisecond mixing, Process intensification.

1. Introduction

Most functional chemicals are manufactured using batch methods, and a large amount of waste containing organic solvents is discharged, and energy is consumed to dispose of the waste. In recent years, it has been reported that functional chemicals are synthesized with high yield and selectivity using flow methods (Tsubogo et al., 2015). It is expected that the use of such flow methods will increase in the future in place of the batch methods.

Mixing is an important operation for synthesizing target substances using the flow methods, and various mixers have been developed with the aim of achieving rapid mixing (Falk and Commenge, 2010). A mixer can be divided into two sections: a fluid confluence section and a fluid mixing section. The main channel structure of the fluid confluence section is T-shaped or Y-shaped, and the fluid mixing section uses the channel structure in which, for example, the channel diameter is suddenly reduced or the channel is bent. Compared to planar machining, three-dimensional (3D) machining has a possibility of producing a mixer with better mixing performance, but it involves higher machining costs (Chung et al., 2014; Asano et al., 2015). In recent years, a laminated mixer has been reported, which achieves a 3D channel structure by stacking two-dimensionally machined plates (Kim et al., 2016). This type of mixer is attracting attention because it is expected to improve mixing performance while reducing machining costs. The laminated mixer developed in the previous study features 3D serpentine channels and can achieve residence time in the submillisecond range, allowing control of intramolecular rearrangements not possible with conventional mixers. However, the previously developed mixer had the fluid mixing channel with four serpentine sections obtained by stacking six plates, and such complex channel caused high pressure drop. Therefore, in this study, various channel configurations, shapes and sizes were designed with reference to the conventional mixer, and their mixing performance was evaluated using computational fluid dynamics (CFD) simulation.

2. Laminated mixer with 3D serpentine channel

A schematic diagram of the laminated mixer with 3D serpentine channel (Kim et al., 2016) is shown in Fig. 1. At the confluence section, fluid A enters from above perpendicular to the flow of fluid B, which tends to generate vortices. After the two fluids come into contact, the channel at the mixing section is bent four times to promote mixing. Detailed analysis and design optimization of this mixer has not been sufficiently performed so far. In this study, CFD simulation is used to analyze the influence of the channel design of the confluence section and mixing section on mixing performance. The mixing performance is evaluated on the basis of the degree of mixing at the cross section indicated by the red frame in Fig. 1 (corresponding to a mixing time of 0.4 ms). Based on the analysis results, the aim is to design a laminated microdevice with simpler channel structure and lower pressure drop, while having the same mixing performance as the previously reported mixer.

The following constraints were set when designing the microdevice. Excluding the upper and lower cover plates, the number of laminated plates in the previous study was four, but in this study, the maximum number is two. The minimum channel size is 0.2 mm in width and 0.125 mm in height, which were determined based on the previous study. As a design policy of this study, first, the channel shape of the confluence section is investigated so that the kinetic energy of the inflowing fluids is actively utilized for mixing. Next, if a target degree of mixing cannot be achieved by the channel design of the confluence section, the channel shape of the mixing section is further investigated.

In this study, CFD simulations were employed to evaluate the mixing performance. Mathematical model of the microdevice and simulation settings are as follows: the equations used to describe the system are the continuity, Navier–Stokes (pressure and velocity) and the species convection-diffusion equations. In all cases studied, the flow is laminar, while adiabatic conditions are applied at domain boundaries. Compressibility

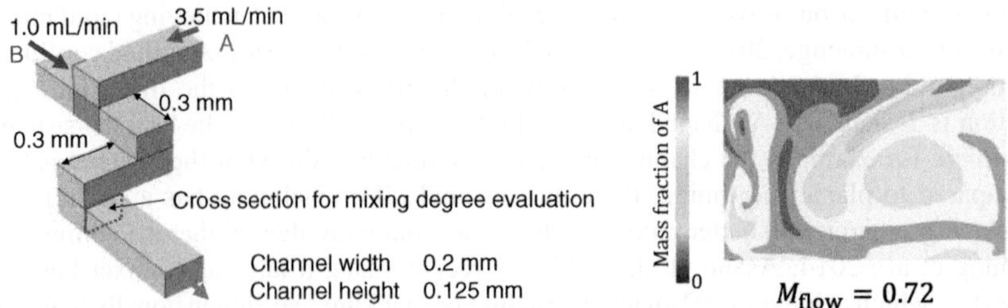

Fig. 1. Previously reported mixer. (Left) schematic diagram and (Right) CFD result.

and slip effects are negligible. Each fluid is supplied in a uniform flow from the inlet, and its physical properties are the same as water (293 K). Unless otherwise stated all simulations were performed in three dimensions. Simulations were performed using ANSYS Fluent. Structured grids were used and the cell size was 2.5μm in all cases. The SIMPLEC method was implemented for pressure-velocity coupling and the spatial discretization was performed using the second order upwind scheme. In addition, M_{flow} calculated by Eq. (1) was used as an evaluation index of the degree of mixing (Malecha and Malecha, 2014). The closer the value is to 1, the higher the mixing performance.

$$M_{flow} = 1 - \frac{\sigma_{flow}}{\sigma_{unmixed}} \tag{1}$$

$$\sigma_{flow} = \sqrt{\frac{\sum F_i(\Phi_i - \bar{\Phi}_{flow})^2}{\sum F_i}} \tag{2}$$

$$\bar{\Phi}_{flow} = \frac{\sum F_i \Phi_i}{\sum F_i} \tag{3}$$

$$\sigma_{unmixed} = \sqrt{\frac{F1F2}{(F1 + F2)^2}} \tag{4}$$

Here, σ_{flow} is the standard deviation of the concentration weighted by the velocity distribution, $\sigma_{unmixed}$ is the standard deviation of the mass fraction when the two fluids are not mixed, $F1$ and $F2$ are the inlet mass flow rates, Φ_i is the mass fraction of a certain component in each grid, and F_i is the flow rate in each grid.

3. Results and discussion

When the previously studied mixer was evaluated using CFD simulation, the concentration distribution on the cross section where the mixing degree was evaluated was as shown in Fig. 1 (right), and the mixing degree, that is M_{flow}, was 0.72. Therefore, the target mixing degree in this study was set to 0.72.

In order to improve the laminated micromixer, first, three types of channel configuration at the confluence section were investigated. As shown in Fig. 2, convective mixing called engulfment flow occurs in all types. Among them, Type C showed the highest mixing performance when mixing at equal flow rates (A: 2.25 mL/min, B: 2.25 mL/min) as well as when mixing at different flow rates (A: 3.5 mL/min, B: 1.0 mL/min). Therefore, Type C was next focused on, and the channel size of the confluence section was investigated with the aim of further improving mixing performance. As a result, the concentration distribution and mixing degree on the cross section indicated by the black frame were as shown in Fig. 3. It was shown that the device Type C with a channel width (W_1) of 0.25 mm at the confluence section had the highest mixing degree when mixing at equal flow rates as well as when mixing at different flow rates. Visualization of the velocity vector in addition to the concentration distribution revealed that when the channel width at the confluence section is small, the formation of vortices is suppressed due to the influence of the wall, and when the channel width is large, stagnation occurs. For these reasons, W_1 = 0.25 seems to have shown the best result. However, the mixing degree has not reached

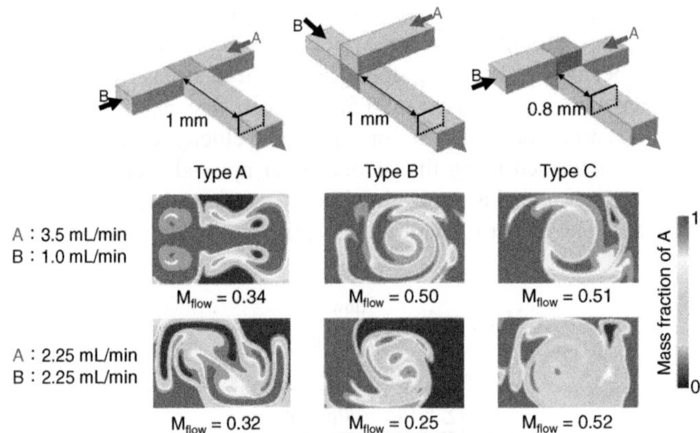

Fig. 2. Effect of channel configuration at the confluence section on the mixing.

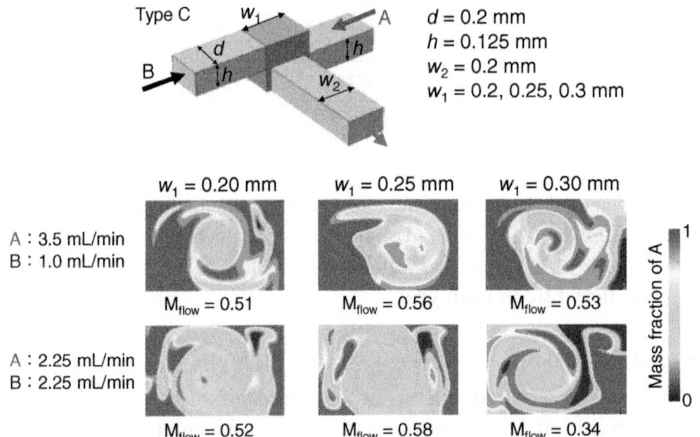

Fig. 3. Effect of channel size at the confluence section on the mixing (Type C).

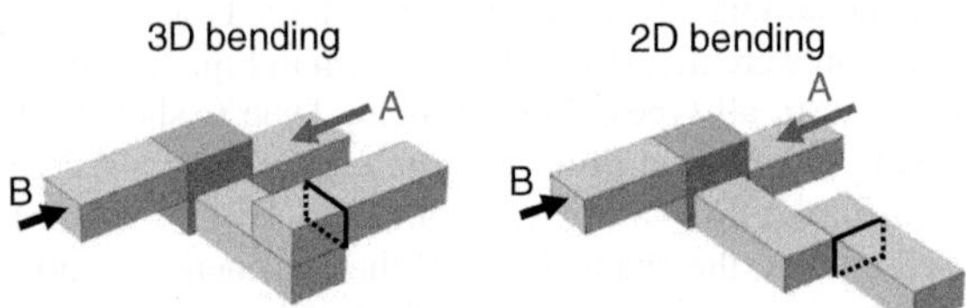

Fig. 4. Type C mixer with 3D bending and 2D bending.

the target value. The main reason for this seems to be that the velocity of the secondary flow at the outlet of the confluence section, which contributed to the promotion of mixing, decreased to about 2/5 times at the cross section where the mixing degree was evaluated.

Table 1. Comparison between proposed and existing mixers.

	Fluid mixing at different flow rates		Fluid mixing at equal flow rates	
	M_{flow} [-]	ΔP [kPa]	M_{flow} [-]	ΔP [kPa]
Proposed mixer	0.73	15	0.72	11
Existing mixer	0.72	31	0.68	28

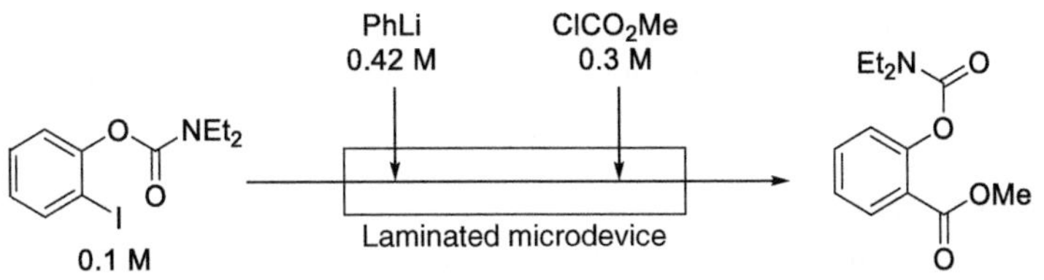

Fig. 5. Experimental verification using anionic Fries rearrangement (Kim et al., 2016).

Therefore, in order to accelerate the secondary flow once again, the channel was bent just before the cross-section for evaluating the degree of mixing. As shown in Fig. 4, two types of channel bending methods were proposed: 3D bending and 2D bending. According to the streamlines obtained from CFD simulations, it was confirmed that 3D bending reduces stagnation and accelerates the secondary flow due to the generation of vortices. As a result, the target mixing degree was achieved. Table 1 summarizes the results of comparing the performance of the mixer with 3D bending proposed in this study and the existing mixer. It was shown that the proposed mixer exhibited the mixing performance equivalent to the existing mixer for various inlet flowrate ratios and had lower pressure drop than the existing mixer.

Additionally, the usefulness of the proposed mixer was confirmed through experiments on the anionic Fries rearrangement, shown in Fig. 5. The proposed mixer was fabricated in one step by stacking and thermally bonding four laser-cut polyimide plates, including two covers for sealing from top and bottom, and was used as R1 and R2 in Fig. 5. As a result of the experiment, the production of by-product was suppressed and the target product was successfully produced selectively, and the result of this study were equivalent to that of the previous study. Furthermore, when the throughput was doubled, leakage was observed with the conventional mixer due to an increase in internal pressure, but with the proposed mixer, the desired product could be selectively obtained without leakage, leading to an increase in production.

4. Conclusions

Micromixers have demonstrated their capabilities in a variety of application fields with the aim of replacing batch synthesis of chemicals with flow synthesis. T-shaped micromixer is one of the typical mixers and can achieve a residence time of a few milliseconds, but in order to further reduce the residence time below milliseconds, it is necessary to devise a micromixer with a smaller internal volume, which requires very sophisticated channel processing techniques. In this study, a laminated microdevice with

3D serpentine channels that can achieve residence times in the sub-millisecond range was featured as an alternative to T-shaped micromixers. Computational fluid dynamics (CFD) simulations are employed to evaluate the mixing performance for various design and operating variables. Based on the evaluation results, a microdevice consisting of a non-alignment confluence section and a mixing channel with two serpentine sections was designed. It was shown that the designed mixer exhibited the mixing performance equivalent to the conventional mixer for various inlet flowrate ratios and had lower pressure drop than the conventional mixer. Additionally, the usefulness of the designed mixer was confirmed through experiments on the anionic Fries rearrangement, a well-known reaction that is often applied to total synthesis of natural products in organic synthesis. Finally, the design of the device in this study involved extensive use of CFD simulations, which have high calculation accuracy but have a heavy computational load. Therefore, improving design efficiency will be a future challenge.

Acknowledgement

This work was partially supported by the Grant-in-Aid for Scientific Research (B) (No. 23H01754) and a project, Development of Continuous Production and Process Technologies of Fine Chemicals, commissioned by the New Energy and Industrial Technology Development Organization (NEDO).

References

S. Asano, T. Maki and K. Mae, 2016, Evaluation of mixing profiles for a new micromixer design strategy, AIChE Journal, 62(4), 1154-1161.

C.K. Chung, C.K. Chang and C.C. Lai, 2014, Simulation and fabrication of a branch-channel rhombic micromixer for low pressure drop and short mixing length, Microsystem technologies, 20(10-11), 1981-1986.

L. Falk and J-M. Commenge, 2010, Performance comparison of micromixers, Chemical Engineering Science, 65, 405-411.

H. Kim, K. Min, K. Inoue, D.J. Im, D.P. Kim and J. Yoshida, 2016, Submillisecond organic synthesis: outpacing Fries rearrangement through microfluidic rapid mixing, Science, 352.6286, 691-694.

Z.M. Malecha and K. Malecha, 2014, Numerical analysis of mixing under low and high frequency pulsations at serpentine micromixers, Chemical and Process Engineering, 35(3), 369-385.

T. Tsubogo, H. Oyamada and S. Kobayashi, 2015, Multistep Continuous-flow Synthesis of (R)- and (S)-rolipram Using Heterogeneous Catalysts, Nature, 520, 7547, 329-332.

Flavio Manenti, Gintaras V. Reklaitis (Eds.), Proceedings of the 34th European Symposium on Computer Aided Process Engineering / 15th International Symposium on Process Systems Engineering (ESCAPE34/PSE24), June 2-6, 2024, Florence, Italy
 http://dx.doi.org/10.1016/B978-0-443-28824-1.50223-4

Global sensitivity Analysis on System Design Parameters of Silver Nanoparticles Production

Ziyi Han[a,b], Heng Yi Teah[c,d], Yasunori Kikuchi[a,c,e]

[a]*Department of Chemical System Engineering, The University of Tokyo, 113-8656 7-3-1 Hongo, Bunkyo-ku, Tokyo, Japan*

[b]*Department of Applied Chemistry, Waseda University, 169-8555 3-4-1 Okubo, Shinjuku-ku, Tokyo, Japan*

[c]*Presidential Endowed Chair for "Platinum society", The University of Tokyo, 113-8656 7-3-1 Hongo, Bunkyo-ku, Tokyo, Japan*

[d]*Waseda Research Institute for Science and Engineering, Waseda University, 169-8555 3-4-1 Okubo, Shinjuku-ku, Tokyo, Japan*

[e]*Institute for Future Initiatives, The University of Tokyo, 113-8656 7-3-1 Hongo, Bunkyo-ku, Tokyo, Japan*

ykikuchi@ifi.u-tokyo.ac.jp

Abstract

This study investigates the environmental impact of silver nanoparticles (AgNPs) synthesis methods, focusing on key system design parameters. Global sensitivity analysis (GSA) is effective in monitoring influences of multiple parameters to a life cycle assessment (LCA) model. In this GSA, alternate silver and energy sources are implemented into the LCA model for AgNPs production by proposing integrated energy and silver scenarios that outline the current and future productions. Our result has highlighted that inherent factors determined by technological options of AgNPs will become increasingly important in the future, envisioning the direction of improvement on the design of AgNPs synthesis routes.

Keywords: silver nanoparticles, life cycle assessment, global sensitivity analysis, green nanomaterials

1. Introduction

Silver nanoparticles (AgNPs) have diverse applications in modern consumer products for antimicrobial, optical, and electrical properties. Developing cleaner syntheses of AgNPs without compromising the functions is desired, as the global AgNP production are increasing (Temizel-Sekeryan & Hicks, 2020). AgNP syntheses can be divided into two categories, wet and dry chemistry. Dry chemistry methods break down bulk silver with external force, usually supported by intensive energy. Wet chemistry methods reduce Ag ions in precursor solution to Ag atoms, often followed by controlled growth of Ag particles with stabilizing agents. There are also emerging biosynthesis methods that exploit biomolecules from plant extracts or microbes for redox reactions. Previous life cycle assessment (LCA) study on AgNP syntheses (Pourzahedi & Eckelman, 2015) revealed that (1) $\geqslant$ 60% of total greenhouse gas (GHG) emissions was attributed to silver source acquisition that depends on reaction yield and silver precursor type; (2) about 20 % was attributed to energy consumption that depends on the choice of the route and the presumed energy efficiency. The environmental impacts from respective reagents, water supply, and direct emissions that differed based on the choice of synthesis method were

trivial. However, changes in external factors such as switching silver sources from primary to secondary, and energy sources from fossil fuels to renewable energy, cannot support the development of AgNP syntheses – the interest of AgNP experimentalists.
Sensitivity analysis is a method to track and simulate parameter changes in the LCA model. Conventional (local) sensitivity analysis is conducted by altering only one parameter at a time on only foreground level. Limitations arise when multiple parameters that affecting background dataset occurred. Global sensitivity analysis (GSA) is proposed (Saltelli et al., 2007), to examine how the LCA output is affected by multiple input uncertainties.

In this study, we intend to clarify the effect of the system design parameters on environmental impact of AgNPs considering the uncertainties of silver and energy sources. We applied GSA to deal with the two parameters simultaneously using integrated silver and energy scenarios, so that the LCA result would be useful in showing the potential improvement in technological choices under some practical scenarios.

2. Method

The goal of this study is to investigate the influence of system design parameters driven by external factors like global energy policies and real-world resource scarcity. We first conduct a prospective LCA of selected AgNP synthesis methods as case studies. We then apply GSA to examine the uncertainty of external factors and demonstrate the value of GSA in the interpretation of LCA results.

2.1. Prospective Life Cycle Assessment

The LCA aimed to evaluate the prospective environmental performance of AgNP production via 11 reported synthesis routes, including five dry chemistry methods (flame spray pyrolysis, arc discharge, and arc plasma (Pourzahedi & Eckelman, 2015; Slotte & Zevenhoven, 2017)), four wet chemistry methods (based on: glucose (Bafana et al., 2018), sodium borohydride (Tolaymat et al., 2010), ethylene glycol, and trisodium citrate (Temizel-Sekeryan & Hicks, 2020) respectively), and two biological methods (using Annona Glabra leaf extract (Amarasinghe et al., 2020), and Rhodococcus (Otari et al., 2012)). Global warming potential (GWP) from IPCC 2013 method was the impact category. Fig. 1 shows the cradle-to-gate system boundary, starting from the acquisition of raw materials to produce necessary reagents, to the reagent production, and ending by the process of producing AgNPs.

The functional unit is defined as 1kg of AgNPs with spherical shapes, and an industrial scale production is assumed.

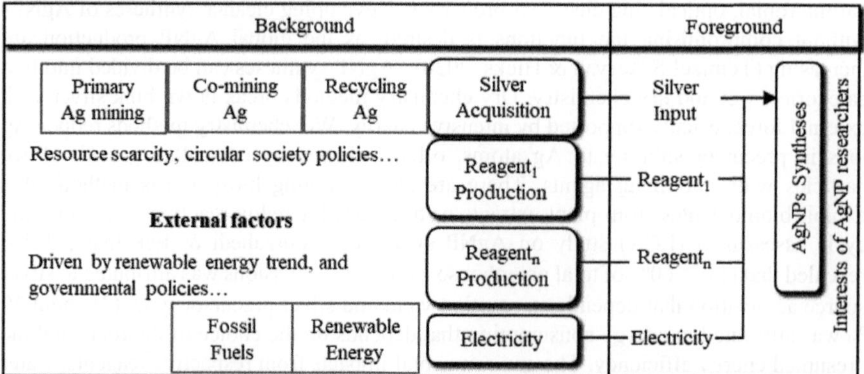

Figure 1. Cradle-to-gate system boundary of prospective LCA for AgNPs synthesis methods

The foreground AgNP inventory, i.e., material and energy required for each AgNP synthesis, is collected from literature. The material input is calculated with stoichiometric relationships, and scaled up from lab to industrial scales, assuming a maximum yield (100 %). The energy input is estimated based on a scale-up framework (Piccinno et al., 2016). The background inventory, i.e., the production of required chemicals, water supply, electricity generation, are obtained from datasheet in ecoinvent Database, version 3.9.1. The region of the rest-of-the-world (RoW), or global (GLO) was selected.

2.2. Global Sensitivity Analysis

The goal of this GSA is to assess the sensitivity of the key system design parameters in LCA modeling. The scope involves energy mix with higher composition of renewable energy and secondary silver source to substitute primary silver mining. Fig.2 describes the framework of GSA and the general calculation procedure.

We first develop the scenarios based on foreseeable near future. The energy plots are inspired by global transition trend towards renewable energy. We set the upper boundary as full enactment of renewable energy equally allocated to wind and solar energy, and the lower boundary as current global energy mix in 2021. An intermediate is selected as the proposed energy mix in 2030 under Announced Pledges Scenario (International Energy Agency, 2022) with 40 % fossil fuel. In both future energy scenarios, heat production by diesel is substituted by biodiesel (Karlsson et al., 2017) with respect to the proportion of renewable energy, but heat from natural gas is unchanged. Regarding resource availability of silver, there are three sources. Primary mining silver is the silver obtained as main product from silver mines, accompanied by other metals from the ore. But primary silver mines are depleting (Silver Institute, 2021), and global silver supply is shifting to co-mining silver, i.e., silver as by-products of mining and refineries of other metals, e.g., gold, copper, lead, and zinc. Recycling silver is a recently essential source of silver from waste x-ray film and waste PV panels. Combining the above scenario settings, four scenarios were set for GSA: (1) Primary silver mining with energy mix in 2021, (2) Co-mining silver with energy mix in 2030, (3) Co-mining silver with 100 % Renewable Energy, and (4) Recycling silver with 100 % Renewable Energy.

Secondly, we adopted the four scenarios to the LCA model by substituting the silver source and energy mix. The energy data in exchange activities of chemicals and water are traced by inventory dataset in ecoinvent at least once, and corresponding impact from different sources are plugged into the model.

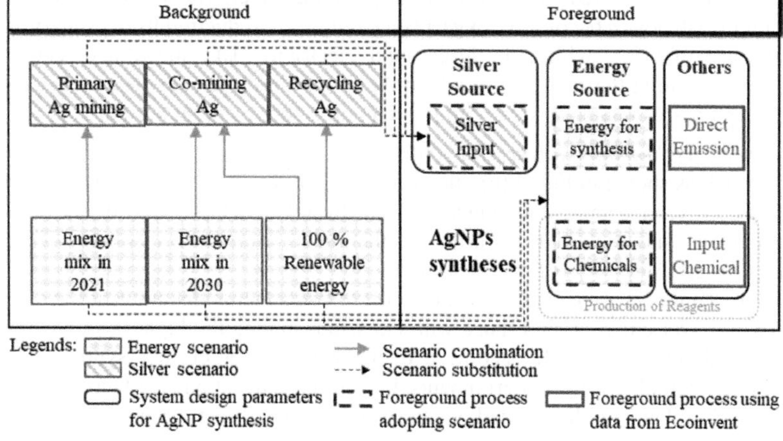

Figure 2. Calculation procedure for global sensitivity analysis of AgNPs.

3. Results and Discussion

Fig. 3 shows the comparison between the average GWP of 3 categories, 11 methods of AgNP synthesis routes among 4 GSA scenarios. The average GWP of each category of methods is taken from the sum of GWP of all methods in the same category divided by the number of the methods. The error bar indicates the range of calculation results. The lower limit of the error bar is the minimum, while the upper limit is the maximum. The emission from silver acquisition in wet chemistry and biosynthesis methods are consistent, as all methods in these two categories use the same silver nitrate precursor, while, in the case of dry chemistry methods, either bulk silver or silver octanoate will be selected as the silver source for the desired method. The "other" factor is inherent among the four scenarios, for it represents the foreground data that are innate in the choices of techniques.

3.1. Scenario 1 (Primary Silver Mining with Global Energy Mix in 2021): Benchmark

Fig. 3 (a) shows scenario 1, representing the upper boundary in GSA. The average overall GWP for dry- and wet- chemistry, and biosynthesis methods are 1190, 859, and 678 kg CO_2-eq, respectively. Silver and energy consumption covered over 90 % of the total GWP for all AgNP methods, conform to the pattern reported by Pourzahedi and Eckelman (2015). But the "other" factor is trivial, suggesting that the selection of AgNP techniques among methods has limited relevance for improving environmental performance.

Specifically, the GWP of silver acquisition peaks at 2399 kg CO_2-eq in dry chemistry category, massively higher than all others. This results from flame spray pyrolysis method. It uses silver octanoate as a unique silver precursor, which is derived from silver nitrate with less than 50 % yield and emits 1014 kg CO_2-eq/kg GHG. Since the production of silver octanoate belongs to the background reagent production, the yield is unlikely to improve under current conditions.

3.2. Scenario 2 (Co-mining Silver with Global Energy Mix in 2030): Near Term

Comparing Fig. 3 (a) and (b), the average for GWP in scenario 2 reduced substantially from scenario 1, with the reduction of 83 % for dry chemistry methods, 74 % for wet chemistry methods, and 88 % for biosynthesis methods regarding 1 functional unit.

The cutback is ascribed to both the reduction in impact factor and the implementation of GSA. The impact of electricity reduced 50%, from 0.72 kg CO_2-eq/kWh in scenario 1 to 0.36 kg CO_2-eq/kWh in this scenario. In addition, 1 kg silver from co-mining emits 48.2 kg CO_2-eq GHG, 92 % reduction from primary mining silver. Without GSA, the impact of co-mining silver will become 382 kg CO_2-eq, only 38 % reduction from primary silver. The absence of GSA, with only foreground electricity data substituted, causes an inconsistency within the scenario, in which AgNP synthesis has adopted energy mix in 2030, but processes related to silver mining maintains to use energy mix in 2021.

3.3. Scenario 3 (Co-mining Silver with 100 % Renewable Energy): Progressive Approach

In scenario 3, as shown in Fig. 3 (c), the average GWP for all three categories continues to decrease. Silver and energy no longer dominate the GWP in this scenario. The emission from energy consumption reduces further, as the impact from electricity is minimized to 0.05 kg CO_2-eq/kWh, 14 % of that in scenario 2.

Moreover, within the wet chemistry category, "other" factor distinguishes the AgNP routes with lower emission and those with emissions among the highest, indicating the technological innovation will become a decisive factor for cleaner syntheses under progressive external resource environments. For instance, the ethylene glycol method has the highest GWP among the 11 methods in scenario 3, the direct reason for which is the reagent consumption like PVP, possessing high inherent environmental impact (328 kg CO_2-eq/kg AgNPs).

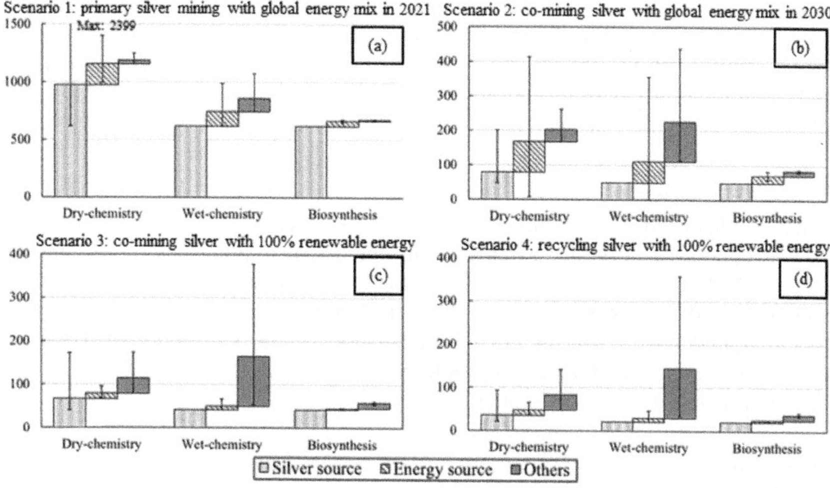

Figure 3. Average Global Warming Potential (unit: kg CO2-eq.) of three groups of eleven reported AgNPs synthesis methods in four proposed scenarios: (a) Primary mining silver with energy mix in 2021, (b) Co-mining silver with energy mix in 2030, (c) Co-mining silver with 100% renewable energy, and (d) Recycling silver with 100% renewable energy.

3.4. Scenario 4 (Recycling Silver with 100 % Renewable Energy): Ideal Sustainability

Scenario 4 represents the lower boundary of GSA. Fig. 3 (d) showed that this scenario has the lowest average GWP and smallest deviation of data among the four. In this scenario, the average portion of "other" factor is even higher, with 52 % in wet chemistry, 30 % in dry chemistry and 35 % in biosynthesis methods. This implies a more complex decision-making process for cleaner AgNP routes, in which the silver and energy source as well as innovations in technological factors are equally important and must be comprehensively considered.

3.5. Discussion

The significance of GSA is highlighted. GSA not only better represents impact factors of silver and energy in alternative scenarios, but also avoiding the inconsistency in the energy mix of foreground and background inventory.

The results also provide insights to evaluate AgNP environmental performance under current and future scenarios. At present, the sources of silver and energy are pivotal to the improvement of AgNP; while, in the future, these two factors become less influential and technical characteristics for a synthesis route, e.g., choices of reagents, are prominent. For dry chemistry methods, their disadvantages in intensive energy input could be relieved to some extent, but the improvement in impacts from silver source like silver octanoate requires further investigation. As for the wet chemistry methods, the factors determined by technology structures have caused distinct performance, making the choices in input reagents more essential, when developing cleaner AgNP syntheses.

4. Conclusions

The incumbent LCA modeling of AgNP syntheses using lab-scale data and current resource plot is insufficient to extend the model into the advancing manufacturing of

AgNPs. This study used global sensitivity analysis based on the trajectory of silver source acquisition and energy generation mix, projecting both foreground and background data, showing the significance of technological innovations considering AgNP productions with better environmental performance in future scenarios, in comparison with current scenario in which silver and energy are the decisive factors. The insights can assist not only laboratory researchers to conceive and design experiment procedures for green synthesis, but also policy makers to better contemplate on this thriving industry.

Acknowledgements

The authors thank Professor Izumi Hirasawa for his special support on the study. This work was conducted in the Research Institute for Social Implementation of Chemical Wisdom, Waseda Research Institute for Science and Engineering. This work was supported by JST SPRING, Grant Number JPMJSP2108. The activities of the Presidential Endowed Chair for "Platinum Society" at the University of Tokyo are supported by Mitsui Fudosan Corporation, Sekisui House, Ltd., East Japan Railway Company, and Toyota Tsusho Corporation.

References

L. D. Amarasinghe, P. A. S. R. Wickramarachchi, A. A. A. U. Aberathna, W. S. Sithara, and C. R. De Silva, 2020, Comparative study on larvicidal activity of green synthesized silver nanoparticles and Annona glabra (Annonaceae) aqueous extract to control Aedes aegypti and Aedes albopictus (Diptera: Culicidae). Heliyon, 6(6), e04322.

A. Bafana, S. V. Kumar, S. Temizel-Sekeryan, S. A. Dahoumane, L.Haselbach, and C. S. Jeffryes, 2018, Evaluating microwave-synthesized silver nanoparticles from silver nitrate with life cycle assessment techniques. Sci. Total Environ., 636, 936–943.

International Energy Agency, 2022, World Energy Outlook 2022, https://www.iea.org/reports/world-energy-outlook-2022

H. Karlsson, S. Ahlgren, M. Sandgren, V. Passoth, O. Wallberg, and P.-A. Hansson, 2017, Greenhouse gas performance of biochemical biodiesel production from straw: soil organic carbon changes and time-dependent climate impact. Biotechnol. Biofuels, 10(1), 217.

S. V. Otari, R. M. Patil, N. H. Nadaf, S. J. Ghosh, and S. H. Pawar, 2012, Green biosynthesis of silver nanoparticles from an actinobacteria Rhodococcus sp. Mater. Lett., 72, 92–94.

F. Piccinno, R. Hischier, S. Seeger, and C. Som (2016). From laboratory to industrial scale: a scale-up framework for chemical processes in life cycle assessment studies. J. Clean. Prod., 135, 1085–1097.

L. Pourzahedi, and M. J. Eckelman, 2015, Comparative life cycle assessment of silver nanoparticle synthesis routes. Environ. Sci. Nano, 2(4), 361–369.

Silver Institute, 2021, World silver survey 2021, https://www.silverinstitute.org/wp-content/uploads/2021/04/World-Silver-Survey-2021.pdf

M. Slotte, and R. Zevenhoven, 2017, Energy requirements and life cycle assessment of production and product integration of silver, copper and zinc nanoparticles. J. Clean. Prod., 148, 948–957.

S. Temizel-Sekeryan, and A. L. Hicks, 2020, Global environmental impacts of silver nanoparticle production methods supported by life cycle assessment. Resour Conserv Recycl, 156.

T. M. Tolaymat, A. M. El Badawy, A. Genaidy, K. G. Scheckel, T. P. Luxton, and M. Suidan, 2010, An evidence-based environmental perspective of manufactured silver nanoparticle in syntheses and applications: A systematic review and critical appraisal of peer-reviewed scientific papers. Sci. Total Environ., 408(5), 999–1006.

Flavio Manenti, Gintaras V. Reklaitis (Eds.), Proceedings of the 34th European Symposium on Computer Aided Process Engineering / 15th International Symposium on Process Systems Engineering (ESCAPE34/PSE24), June 2-6, 2024, Florence, Italy
 http://dx.doi.org/10.1016/B978-0-443-28824-1.50224-6

Intensified biodiesel production from waste palm oil in a plug flow reactor

Barcia-Quimi Andrea F.[a*], Beltran-Borbor Kelly.[a], Piza-Espinoza Angelo[a], Tinoco-Caicedo Diana[a,b]

[a] *Facultad de Ciencias Naturales y Matemáticas (FCNM), Escuela Superior Politécnica del Litoral Ecuador, 090903 Guayaquil, Ecuador.*

[b] *Centro de Energías Renovables y Alternativas (CERA), Escuela Superior Politécnica del Litoral Ecuador, 090903 Guayaquil, Ecuador.*

**abarcia@espol.edu.ec*

Abstract

Biodiesel from waste oil is a promising sustainable alternative to energy supply. Traditionally, this process is carried out in batch reactors, whose reaction times require more than 60 minutes to achieve a maximum yield of 97.6%, according to Narváez et al. (2007). This implies high energy consumption and operating costs for product discharge, cleaning, and running. Therefore, a continuous flow microreactor was designed to intensify the process in a shorter production time under similar operating conditions. Said tubular reactor achieved significant time reduction up to 10 minutes with a yield of 83.33 % and 84.09 % for methanol to oil molar ratios 4:1 and 12:1, respectively. These results were satisfactory compared to the batch yields. The biodiesel quality obtained for both molar ratios was also evaluated under INEN regulations. Those results were within the permissible limits.

Keywords: Waste oil, Tubular reactor, Intensification, Biodiesel

1. Introduction

The increasing energy demand and environmental deterioration over the years have led to the search for sustainable alternatives for energy production. Biodiesel is a promising route to replace fossil fuels as it can be produced from waste oil. This biofuel is an excellent substitute for crude oil-derived diesel, given its similar characteristics in viscosity, energy density, and chain length (Naik et al., 2010). Moreover, its production does not generate toxic waste and does not release polluting gases during combustion (Rodionova et al., 2017). Conventionally, biodiesel synthesis is carried out in batch reactors, as it allows the optimization of operating parameters (Bashir et al., 2022).

These reactors are integrated by a stirred tank that receives a specific concentration of reagents and catalysts to react in a set time. The minimum volume required will depend on the desired production rate and the complete cycle time: reagent loading, heating, reaction, product discharge, and cleaning (Tabatabaei et al., 2019). Despite the simplicity of this reactor, the main drawbacks of the process include operating times over 1 hour, high operating costs, higher energy consumption, higher reagent consumption, non-uniform mixing, and large space requirements (Awogbemi & Kallon, 2022; Zahan &

Kano, 2019). Such shortcomings lead to a rejection in the energy sector towards withdrawing conventional fuels.

Multiple studies have been conducted on different reactor technologies to intensify biodiesel production and solve operational parameter constraints. Researchers are interested in the transition from batch to continuous production. Technologies such as microchannel reactors, continuous stirred tanks, oscillatory flow reactors, and rotating tube reactors promise to improve mass transfer and accelerate reaction rate (Madhawan et al., 2018).

Channels with internal diameters in millimeter ranges characterize the microscale continuous flow reactor. Therefore, mass and heat transfer are inversely related to the dimensions of this cross-section. Thus, this type of technology guarantees a better dissipation of mass and heat since there is a larger contact surface, and the volume and hot spots are minimized (Carlucci, 2022).

As a result, residence times are much shorter than in batch reactors. Tanawannapong et al. (2013) reported 91.7 % conversion of methyl esters in 5 seconds using a 9:1 methanol-to-oil molar ratio and 1 wt % KOH at 65 °C. Baydir & Aras (2022) adapted a 0.8 mm diameter T-type cell mixer inside a 1 mm diameter tubular reactor to obtain 99.8 % Fatty Acid Methyl Esters (FAME) in 2 min residence time using a methanol-oil molar ratio 6:1 and 1 wt. % KOH at 60 °C. Other authors implemented a zigzag structure in microreactors of 240 um hydraulic diameter to achieve 99.5 % FAME conversion in 28 seconds under a 9:1 methanol-oil molar ratio at 56 °C and 1.2 wt. % NaOH (Wen et al., 2009).

Based on the above, using continuous flow technologies is now a challenge that promises to overcome the limitations of the batch reactor and intensify biodiesel production. This paper will present the design and implementation of a microscale plug flow reactor. The reaction yield was compared at different methanol - oil molar ratios (MR) in a batch reactor and the proposed tubular reactor, as well as the effects of virgin and waste cooking oil in the reaction results.

2. Methodology

2.1. Materials

The oil sample used for biodiesel production is refined palm oil from a local distributor, which was previously used to cook fried foods at high temperatures (above 200 °C). Said sample did not require previous treatments and was used as direct feed for the tubular reactor. The acid value of waste cooking oil was 1.16 mg KOH/g according to NTE INEN 38. Methanol (AR grade) was purchased from HaymanKimia. Potassium hydroxide from Merck Co. Ltd. was used to prepare the catalytic solution.

2.2. Reaction conditions

The biodiesel reaction was developed at the upper and lower molar ratios (MR 4:1; MR 12:1), as stated in the latest research by Barcia-Quimi et al. (2023), to reduce methanol consumption during the reaction. KOH concentration was set to 1 wt. % on the mass of palm oil, which was then stirred for 5 minutes with the corresponding methanol to oil molar ratio. The maximum operating temperature (60 °C) reported by the kinetic study of palm oil methanolysis by Narváez et al. (2007) in a batch reactor was adopted in this research. At these conditions, the conversion to methyl esters reaches its maximum after 80 minutes of reaction and 1 wt. % KOH. For the current study, the batch reactor worked for 1 hour under the same operating conditions.

Past research done by Barcia-Quimi et al. (2023) suggests a reaction time of 30 minutes in a batch operation to maximize biodiesel production yield and minimize production costs and carbon footprint. Therefore, the residence time for the proposed tubular reactor must consider this time range so that the solution responds to a viable and cost-effective technology. For this purpose, the molar concentration profile of palm oil ethanolysis by Narváez et al. (2015) was analyzed.

2.3. System description

The reaction was performed in a prototype laboratory-scale tubular reactor. The material availability and its thermal resistance to the reaction temperature of the system were the basis for the selection of the diameter of the channels. Thus, PVC plastic pipes with internal diameters of 4.55 mm and thickness of 0.60 mm were used to transport the reactant fluids and subsequent transesterification. The microchannel length (L) was calculated using Equation 7 after determining the residence time (τ) in min, where v_0 is the feed flow in mL/min and D is the pipe's internal diameter in cm.

$$L = \frac{4\tau v_0}{\pi D^2} \quad (7)$$

The pipeline was arranged in a spiral configuration to promote mass transfer, given the low miscibility between the fatty acids in the oil and methanol, as shown in Figure 1.

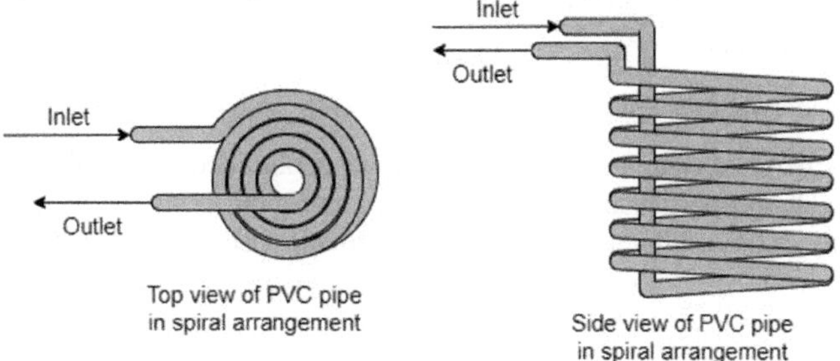

Figure 1. Tubular reactor design drawing.

An inlet-reactor-outlet system was used, in which the reagents must be pre-loaded and pushed by a pumping system to allow mixing of the reagents by turbulence. Figure 2 shows the process flow diagram, including the separation and drying of the biodiesel.

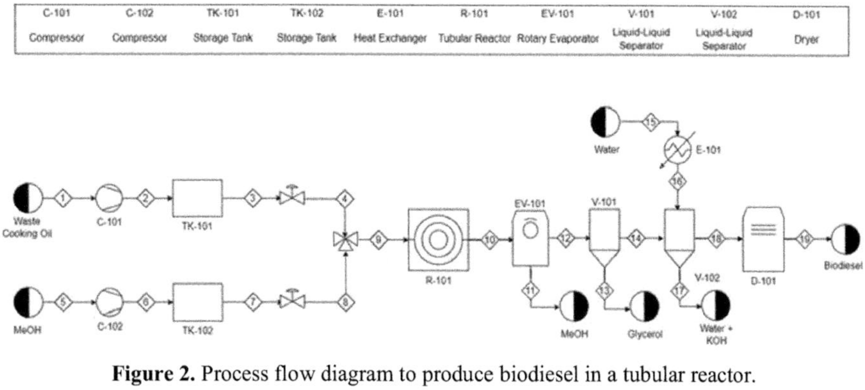

C-101	C-102	TK-101	TK-102	E-101	R-101	EV-101	V-101	V-102	D-101
Compressor	Compressor	Storage Tank	Storage Tank	Heat Exchanger	Tubular Reactor	Rotary Evaporator	Liquid-Liquid Separator	Liquid-Liquid Separator	Dryer

Figure 2. Process flow diagram to produce biodiesel in a tubular reactor.

Waste cooking oil was placed in tank TK-101. Tank TK-102 was filled with catalytic solutions. Compressors C-101 and C-102 were set up as pumping systems. A Welch WOB-L 2534 pressure pump was used for the oil, and a Power 500 aquarium air pump was used for the catalyst.

The pipes used to transport the reagents before entering the reactor were intravenous infusion hoses with their roller flow regulators. Those acted as control valves. A T-shaped micromixer was connected to the reactor piping (R-101). A distillation balloon collected the reaction products at the reactor outlet. The reactor was placed in a water bath at 60 °C.

After transesterification, excess methanol was removed by rotary evaporation (EV-101) at 40 °C and 200 mbar. The mixture was allowed to stand for one day so that glycerol could be separated by decantation (V-101). The biodiesel was washed with distilled water at 50 °C to remove the catalyst. Subsequently, the final product was taken to an oven (D-101) to remove moisture.

2.4. Reaction Yield

The methyl esters in the oil and biodiesel were determined by gas chromatography in different hexane solutions. The methodology reported by Fallon et al. (2007) was followed to prepare the oil samples. The yield (Y %) was calculated as the ratio between the total concentration of the FAMES detected in the chromatographic curve of the biodiesel and the total concentration of the FAMES extracted in the oil.

$$Y\,\% = \frac{[EM]_{Biodiesel}}{[EM]_{oil}}\,x\,100\% \tag{7}$$

2.5. Physicochemical characterization of biodiesel

The physicochemical characteristics of the biodiesel obtained in the tubular reactor were determined. The properties analyzed are cloud point, pour point, acidity, saponification index, density, iodine value, calorific value, kinematic viscosity, and ash content.

3. Results

Figure 3 exhibits the molar concentration profile of the kinetic model of Narváez et al. (2015) adapted to the proposed reactor for MR 4:1 and MR 12:1. As shown in the graph; it is possible to obtain a conversion higher than 80 % TG in the first 5 minutes of reaction under the proposed operating conditions. Considering the limitations of a natural system such as pressure drop, mass and heat transfer limitations, and flow irregularities, a residence time of 10 minutes was estimated. Therefore, a pipe length of 10 meters was calculated.

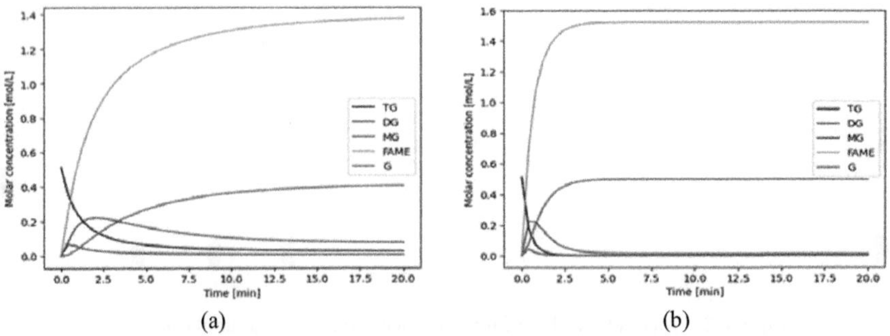

Figure 3. Molar concentration profile of palm oil methanolysis from Narváez et al. (2015) adapted to a tubular reactor at 60 °C and 1 wt. % KOH with (a) RM 4:1 and (b) RM 12:1.

The chromatographic tests reported a higher content of fatty acids in the refined oil than in the waste oil. This could be because the former did not undergo a degradative heating process. Thus, the operating time will be essential to promote the FAME production. On the other hand, the biodiesel from waste oil had satisfactory results due to a lower TG content. Table 1 presents the reaction yields in the batch and tubular reactor.

The batch reactor may be suitable when working with low MR at high TG concentrations since it prioritizes the reaction time. On the other hand, the tubular reactor favors greater contact between molecules due to its high area-volume ratio, which results in a higher yield for an optimal molar ratio. In either case, the tubular reactor continues to be a beneficial option given the significant time minimization of 83.33 %.

Table 1. Results of reaction yields in batch and tubular reactors.

Feedstock	Batch Reactor Yield (%)		Tubular Reactor Yield (%)	
	MR 4:1	MR 12:1	MR 4:1	MR 12:1
Virgin oil	60.37	52.46	55.16	70.26
Waste oil	55.96	81.42	83.33	84.09

Table 2 summarizes the biodiesel characterization results obtained from the tubular reactor at 60 °C with constant volumetric flows and a residence time of 10 minutes for both molar ratios studied. The criteria of the Ecuadorian Technical Norm under which the quality of the product is defined are also indicated.

Table 2. Results of the biodiesel characterization produced in the tubular reactor.

Parameter	Unit	Result		Value range	Normative Reference
		MR 4:1	MR 12:1		
Cloud Point	°C	5	6	-	-
Pour Point	°C	-2	3	-	-
Acidity	wt. %	0.1180	0.1484	≤ 0.5	NTE INEN 2482
Saponification index	mg/g	273.88	258.82	-	-
Density	g/ml	0.8622	0.8594	0.860 – 0.900	NTE INEN 2482
Iodine Value	cg/g	83.4215	83.8945	≤ 120	NTE INEN 2482
Calorific Value	MJ/m3	36 247	37 619	≥ 33 192	ASTM D6751
Kinematic Viscosity	mm2/s	4.1225	3.4933	3.5 - 5	NTE INEN 2482
Ash Content	wt. %	0.022	0.023	≤ 0.025	NTE INEN 2482

These results are all within the specifications of the referenced standards. Therefore, the proposed tubular reactor can produce quality biodiesel in a shorter production time.

4. Conclusions

The operation of a tubular reactor at laboratory scale for the biodiesel production through transesterification of palm oil was successfully tested. It was demonstrated that the millimetric dimensions of the pipe diameter provide a larger contact surface to improve mass transfer and intensify the process. This is because high yields of 83.33 % and 84.09 % corresponding to the MR 4:1 and 12:1 were obtained under the same conditions compared to a batch reactor in a shorter reaction time (10 minutes). Moreover, this biofuel was found to have an acceptable quality according to the characterizations performed under INEN regulations, since the values reported in the experimentation are within the specifications. For future studies, the use of non-toxic catalysts should be explored, so that the reaction runs in an eco-friendly way.

References

Awogbemi, O., & Kallon, D. V. Von. (2022). Application of Tubular Reactor Technologies for the Acceleration of Biodiesel Production. *Bioengineering*, *9*(8), 347. https://doi.org/10.3390/bioengineering9080347

Barcia-Quimi, A. F., Risco-Bravo, A., Alcivar-Espinoza, K., & Tinoco-Caicedo, D. L. (2023). Design of a sustainable biodiesel production process by a multi-objective optimization. *Computer Aided Chemical Engineering*, *52*, 519–524. https://doi.org/10.1016/B978-0-443-15274-0.50083-4

Bashir, M. A., Wu, S., Zhu, J., Krosuri, A., Khan, M. U., & Ndeddy Aka, R. J. (2022). Recent development of advanced processing technologies for biodiesel production: A critical review. *Fuel Processing Technology*, *227*, 107120. https://doi.org/10.1016/j.fuproc.2021.107120

Baydir, E., & Aras, O. (2022). Increasing biodiesel production yield in narrow channel tubular reactors. *Chemical Engineering and Processing - Process Intensification*, *170*(September 2021), 108719. https://doi.org/10.1016/j.cep.2021.108719

Carlucci, C. (2022). An Overview on the Production of Biodiesel Enabled by Continuous Flow Methodologies. *Catalysts*, *12*(7), 717. https://doi.org/10.3390/catal12070717

Madhawan, A., Arora, A., Das, J., Kuila, A., & Sharma, V. (2018). Microreactor technology for biodiesel production: a review. *Biomass Conversion and Biorefinery*, *8*(2), 485–496. https://doi.org/10.1007/s13399-017-0296-0

Naik, S. N., Goud, V. V., Rout, P. K., & Dalai, A. K. (2010). Production of first and second generation biofuels: A comprehensive review. *Renewable and Sustainable Energy Reviews*, *14*(2), 578–597. https://doi.org/10.1016/j.rser.2009.10.003

Narváez, P. C., Noriega, M. A., & Cadavid, J. G. (2015). Kinetics of palm oil ethanolysis. *Energy*, *83*, 337–342. https://doi.org/10.1016/j.energy.2015.02.029

Narváez, P. C., Rincón, S. M., & Sánchez, F. J. (2007). Kinetics of palm oil methanolysis. *JAOCS, Journal of the American Oil Chemists' Society*, *84*(10), 971–977. https://doi.org/10.1007/s11746-007-1120-y

O'Fallon, J. V., Busboom, J. R., Nelson, M. L., & Gaskins, C. T. (2007). A direct method for fatty acid methyl ester synthesis: Application to wet meat tissues, oils, and feedstuffs. *Journal of Animal Science*, *85*(6), 1511–1521. https://doi.org/10.2527/jas.2006-491

Rodionova, M. V., Poudyal, R. S., Tiwari, I., Voloshin, R. A., Zharmukhamedov, S. K., Nam, H. G., Zayadan, B. K., Bruce, B. D., Hou, H. J. M., & Allakhverdiev, S. I. (2017). Biofuel production: Challenges and opportunities. *International Journal of Hydrogen Energy*, *42*(12), 8450–8461. https://doi.org/10.1016/j.ijhydene.2016.11.125

Tabatabaei, M., Aghbashlo, M., Dehhaghi, M., Panahi, H. K. S., Mollahosseini, A., Hosseini, M., & Soufiyan, M. M. (2019). Reactor technologies for biodiesel production and processing: A review. *Progress in Energy and Combustion Science*, *74*, 239–303. https://doi.org/10.1016/j.pecs.2019.06.001

Tanawannapong, Y., Kaewchada, A., & Jaree, A. (2013). Biodiesel production from waste cooking oil in a microtube reactor. *Journal of Industrial and Engineering Chemistry*, *19*(1), 37–41. https://doi.org/10.1016/j.jiec.2012.07.007

Wen, Z., Yu, X., Tu, S.-T., Yan, J., & Dahlquist, E. (2009). Intensification of biodiesel synthesis using zigzag micro-channel reactors. *Bioresource Technology*, *100*(12), 3054–3060. https://doi.org/10.1016/j.biortech.2009.01.022

Zahan, K. A., & Kano, M. (2019). Technological Progress in Biodiesel Production: An Overview on Different Types of Reactors. *Energy Procedia*, *156*(September 2018), 452–457. https://doi.org/10.1016/j.egypro.2018.11.086

Flavio Manenti, Gintaras V. Reklaitis (Eds.), Proceedings of the 34th European Symposium on Computer Aided Process Engineering / 15th International Symposium on Process Systems Engineering (ESCAPE34/PSE24), June 2-6, 2024, Florence, Italy
 http://dx.doi.org/10.1016/B978-0-443-28824-1.50225-8

Rational Function-based Approach for Integrated Ionic Liquid Solvent Selection and Extractive Distillation Process Design

Sahil Sethi,[a] Xiang Zhang,[a,*] Kai Sundmacher[a,b]

[a] *Process Systems Engineering, Max Planck Institute for Dynamics of Complex Technical Systems, Sandtorstr. 1, D-39106 Magdeburg, Germany*

[b] *Chair of Process Systems Engineering, Otto-von-Guericke University Magdeburg, Universitätsplatz 2, D-39106 Magdeburg, Germany*

[*] *zhangx@mpi-magdeburg.mpg.de*

Abstract

The efficacy of an extractive distillation relies significantly on the solvent selection and its detailed process design. Using thermodynamic metrics such as selectivity and capacity at infinite dilution cannot identify the real optimal solvent with minimal process cost. In this work, a novel process-based data-driven approach is developed to screen huge design space of ionic liquid solvents for the separation of ethylbenzene/styrene (et/st). Rational functions were trained with data from quantum chemistry calculations and used as simple surrogates to model vapor-liquid equilibria for facilitating optimal synthesis of extractive distillation processes. Given various process configurations, the real process performance of numerous ionic liquids can be evaluated rapidly. With the strategy of accelerated process synthesis, a multi-level solvent screening framework is adopted. Several ionic liquid solvents are finally identified to compete with the industrial benchmark sulfolane in terms of total annualized cost. This gives promising prospects for improving the efficiency of et/st separation.

Keywords: Ionic liquid solvent screening, extractive distillation, process configuration, surrogate modelling, vapour-liquid equilibrium

1. Introduction

Separation processes contribute substantially to the global energy usage (Sholl et al., 2016). Despite advancements in many separation methods, distillation is anticipated to persist as the primary separation technology for practical uses in the future. Extractive distillation has gained particular attentions for separating close-boiling and azeotropic liquid mixtures. Utilizing an external solvent, namely entrainer, alters the thermodynamic equilibrium of the initial mixture. This makes the original separation more energy-efficient. However, identifying the promising entrainer remains a challenging task due to the huge design space of potential candidates. Traditional methods for solvent screening rely on simple performance metrics (Momoh, 1991) and shortcut process models (Dong, 2018), which cannot find real optimal solvent and the best process performance.

To fill in the above gap, a novel data-driven optimization approach was recently proposed to screen very many organic solvents for the separation of ethylbenzene/styrene (et/st). Rational Function (RF) and Multivariate Polynomial (MP, a subset of RF) were used to approximate complex vapor-liquid equilibria (VLE) to accelerate optimization-based synthesis of extractive distillation processes. This enables to assess the real process performance of a given solvent within a short period of time (e.g., minutes).

Unlike organic solvents, ionic liquids (ILs) possess negligible vapor pressure, which allows to explore various solvent recovery strategies such as simple evaporation and stripping. This offers additional variations for developing efficient extraction distillation technologies. Taking et/st separation as an example, a superstructure-based optimization approach is developed and applied in this work to screen various ILs and recovery strategies. To simplify the thermodynamics, RFs are still trained as VLE surrogates to expedite the optimization. Regarding two process configurations, the real process performance of numerous ionic liquids are evaluated rapidly. At the end, our automated framework finds multiple IL solvents that can compete against sulfolane (i.e., industrial benchmark for et/st separation) in terms of total annualized cost. This presents a promising prospect for enhancing the efficiency of et/st separation.

2. VLE Surrogate Modelling

For the VLE of a 2-component mixture (A and B), six intensive state variables govern the system (i.e., pressure P, temperature T, liquid molar fractions x_A, x_B, and vapour molar fractions y_A, y_B). According to the Gibbs phase rule at a fixed pressure, the degree of freedom in the binary system is equal to 1. Treating x_B as the independent variable, the other four variables can be expressed as functions of x_B. RF surrogate model is trained to correlate T with x_B in Eq. (1.a). MP surrogate model is built to map y_B with (x_B, T) in Eq. (1.b).

$$T_{pred} = \frac{a_m x_B^m + a_{m-1} x_B^{m-1} + \dots + a_1 x_B + a_0}{b_n x_B^n + b_{n-1} x_B^{n-1} + \dots + b_1 x_B + 1} \tag{1.a}$$

$$y_B = \sum_{p=0}^{N} \sum_{q=0}^{N} c_{pq} \cdot x_B^p \cdot T_{pred}^q \tag{1.b}$$

For the instance of styrene/ionic liquid system, its VLE data at two different pressures 1 kPa (very low pressure) and 10 kPa (moderate pressure) can be estimated using COSMO-RS. Specifically, the liquid molar fraction of styrene is treated as an independent variable within [0, 1] and discretized into 100 equal intervals. The corresponding temperatures and vapour molar fractions at equilibrium are computed, resulting into 101 VLE data points. Those data can be directly utilized for surrogate modelling. For many ILs, it was found that the RF models with 1 degree polynomial in numerator and denominator can describe temperature accurately.

Apart from binary mixtures, the VLE of a 3-component mixture (A, B, and S), eight intensive state variables govern the system (i.e., $P, T, x_A, x_B, x_c, y_A, y_B, y_c$) where degree of freedom is 2 at a fixed pressure. Considering x_A and x_B as independent variables, all other variables are expressed as their functions. Similar to binary mixtures, RFs and MPs can be trained for ternary mixtures. For the ethylbenzene/styrene/ionic liquid system, VLE data at 10 kPa is generated using COSMO-RS as well. The liquid molar fractions of ethylbenzene and styrene are set as independent variables and discretized into 100 equal intervals, resulting into 5151 VLE data points. Both RF and MP are found to approximate VLE with great thermodynamic consistency. For many ILs, it was found that RFs for temperature need 3 degree polynomial at numerator and 1 degree polynomial at denominator (Eq. 2.a). MPs for vapor molar fractions needs 4 degree polynomials (Eq. 2.b and 2.c) to achieve desired accuracy.

$$T_{pred} = \frac{\sum_{j=0}^{3} \sum_{k=0}^{3} a_{jk} \cdot x_A^j \cdot x_B^k}{b_{10} \cdot x_A + b_{01} \cdot x_B + 1} \tag{2.a}$$

$$y_A = \sum_{u=0}^{4} \sum_{v=0}^{4} \sum_{w=0}^{4} c_{uvw} \cdot x_A^u \cdot x_B^v \cdot T_{pred}^w \quad (2.b)$$

$$y_B = \sum_{u=0}^{4} \sum_{v=0}^{4} \sum_{w=0}^{4} d_{uvw} \cdot x_A^u \cdot x_B^v \cdot T_{pred}^w \quad (2.c)$$

3. Multi-Level Ionic Liquid Screening Framework

3.1. Screening via Thermodynamic Properties

696 cations and 500 anions covering different families are collected from the Biovera 2020 COSMO Databank resulting in 348,000 possible ILs for screening. COSMO-RS calculations involve two primary steps. Firstly, screening charge density distributions (σ-profiles) for the involved compounds are derived via standard quantum chemical computations. Secondly, the chemical potentials of the involved compounds are quantified based on the obtained σ-profiles to analyze the molecular interactions. This method enables the prediction of activity coefficients in IL-based systems. The calculation of activity coefficients is given by Eq. (3). Selectivity of ILs (i.e., solvent S) at infinite dilution is in Eq. (4) where i and j are ethylbenzene and styrene, respectively. The selectivity of ethylbenzene over styrene should exceed 1 in Eq. (5). To conduct efficient computations, an auxiliary batch-processing program in COSMOthermX (referred to as CT_CREATE) is used to create template input files. Activity coefficients are calculated based on BP_TZVP_20.ctd parametrization in COSMOtherm.

$$\gamma_S^a = exp\left(\frac{\mu_S^a - \mu_i^a}{RT}\right), a \in i, j \quad (3)$$

$$S_S^{\infty,j} = \frac{\gamma_S^{\infty,i}}{\gamma_S^{\infty,j}} \quad (4)$$

$$S_S^{\infty,j} > 1 \quad (5)$$

3.2. Screening via Ionic Liquid Properties

Melting point (T_m) of IL candidates are predicted using the BP_TZVP_21_0106.ctd parametrization in COSMOtherm software (U Preiss et. al, 2010). Since solvent should be in liquid state, Eq. (6) is used as a constraint for screening. In addition, the et/st separation is presumably operated at 10 kPa and ILs are recovered at either 1 kPa or 10 kPa based on the recovery strategies. This can ensure the success of IL recovery and prevent the polymerization of styrene.

$$T_m \leq 315\ K \quad (6)$$

Due to negligible vapor pressure of ILs, it is assumed that ILs are only in liquid form in columns. Since the boiling point of styrene at 10 kPa is 348 K, Eq. (7) is used as the boiling point constraint for ILs.

$$T_b^{10} \geq 368\ K \quad (7)$$

Viscocity (η) is one of the important IL properties and need to be considered from the perspective of practical applications. Here, the COSMO-RS is employed to predict the IL viscosity via a QSPR approach (Eiden et al. 2010) and viscosity is constrained using Eq. (8).

$$\eta < 150\ cP \quad (8)$$

Due to the increasing awareness of potential hazards led by ILs, the assessment of IL toxicity has gained prominence. The evaluation involves predicting the EC50 (half-maximal effective concentration) of ILs against IPC-81, a Leukemia rat cell line. This prediction is executed using two machine learning (ML) models, namely feedforward neural network (FNN) and support vector machine (SVM) in the work of Wang et al., (2021). Adhering to the criteria proposed by the UFT research unit at the University of Bremen, Eq. (9) is adopted as a constraint for the EC50 toxicity.

$$\log(EC50) \geq 2 \tag{9}$$

3.3. Accelerated ED Process Synthesis Using Multiple Recovery Strategies

After the above screening, the real process performance of the remained solvents are accessed. Based on the previous research (Jongmans et. al 2013), simple evaporation at moderate pressure in combination with either additional evaporation at a very low pressure or stripping are considered here for IL recovery. All the binary and ternary VLE data are sampled via the COSMO-RS calculations to train the RF and MP surrogate models. The obtained surrogates are embedded into the process model and the resulted optimization problem is formulated via Generalized Disjunctive Programming (GDP). DICOPT, CPLEX, and CONOPT4 are employed to solve the optimization problems. Embedding VLE surrogates fasten the convergence and do not rely on perfect initializations owing to the reduced non-linearity. In this way, the real promising ILs and the associated solvent recovery strategy can be quickly identified.

3.4. Proximity search for rigorous solution using Aspen Plus

Utilizing the optimal solvent, a local search is conducted by employing genetic algorithm and Aspen Plus to validate the obtained results. The requirement for ethylbenzene and styrene purity and recovery are verified and ensured.

4. Results

Surrogate VLE modelling results in significant simplicity and interpolative accuracy. For [4-mebupy][BF4], Figure (1.a) illustrates the comparison between RF surrogate and the equilibrium temperatures from COSMO-RS. 3rd and 2nd degree polynomials are used in numerator and denominator, respectively. The R^2 score is 0.9981 and the mean absolute error (MAE) is 0.1122, showing the excellent interpolations of the RF model. Similarly, Figure (1.b) is the comparison between MP surrogate and COSMO-RS computations for the vapour mole fraction of styrene. 4th degree MP is trained. The R^2 is 0.9999 and almost negligible MAE shows the excellent interpolation of the MP model to map vapor mole fraction to temperature and liquid mole fractions.

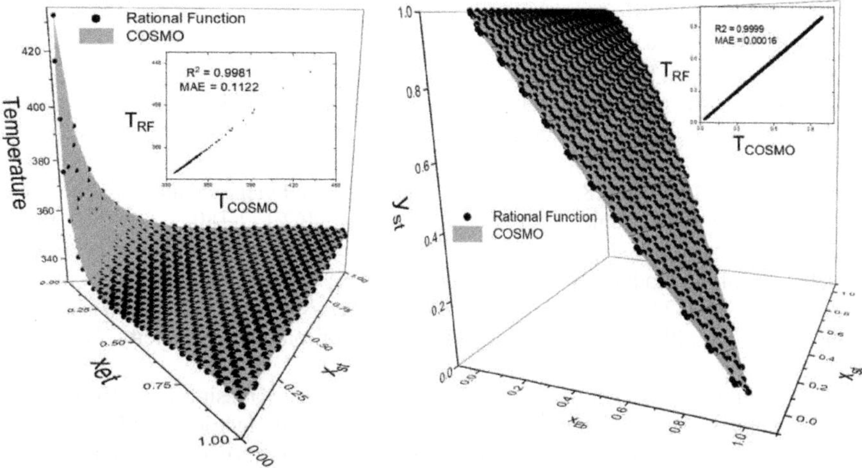

Figure. 1 (a) VLE temperature and (b) styrene vapor molar fraction against liquid molar fractions for ternary system ethylbenzene + styrene + [4-mebupy][BF4] at 10 kPa

Similar calculations for a binary system were performed. Depending on the different configurations, RF models were trained for two different pressures (i.e., 1kPa and 10kPa) as shown in Figure 2.

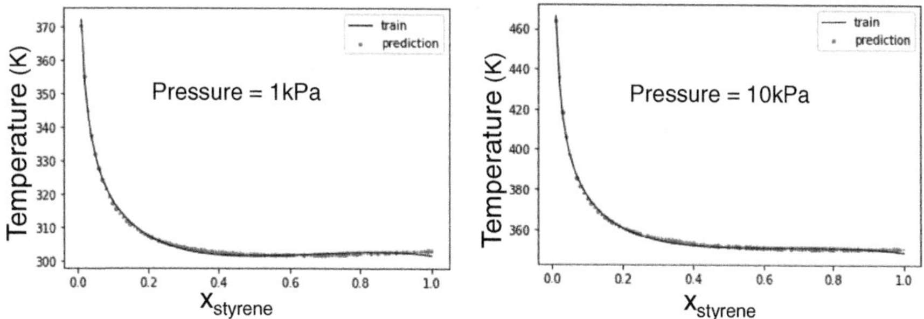

Figure. 2 VLE temperature against liquid molar fraction for the binary system styrene + $[4\text{-mebupy}]^+[BF4]^-$ at (a) 1 kPa and (b) 10kPa

5. Conclusions

This work is an extensions of our recent work for process-based entrainer screening. To explore the huge design space of ionic liquid solvents, a multi-level screening is performed to identify the best solvent and optimal process design including optimal solvent recovery strategy. For expediting process synthesis, rational functions and multivariate polynomials are trained as suitable surrogate models for approximating vapor-liquid equilibrium and ensuring thermodynamic consistency.

References

Sholl D.S. and Lively R.P., 2016. Seven chemical separations to change the world. *Nature*; 532:435-437.

Momoh S.O., 1991. Assessing the accuracy of selectivity as a basis for solvent screening in extractive distillation processes. *Separation Science and Technology*; 26(5):729-742.

Dong Y., Dai C., Lei Z., 2018. Extractive distillation of methylal/methanol mixture using ethylene glycol as entrainer. *Fluid Phase Equilibria*; 462:172-180.

Preiss U., Bulut S., Krossing I., 2010. In silico prediction of the melting points of ionic liquids from thermodynamic considerations: A case study on 67 salts with a melting point range of 337 °C. *The Journal of Physical Chemistry B*; 114:11133-11140.

Wang Z., Song Z., Zhou T., 2021. Machine learning for ionic liquid toxicity. *Processes*; 9:65.

Eiden P., Bulut S., Köchner T., Friedrich C., Schubert T., Krossing I., 2010. In silico predictions of the temperature-dependent viscosities and electrical conductivities of functionalized and nonfunctionalized ionic liquids. *The Journal of Physical Chemistry B*; 115:300-309.

Jongmans M.T.G., Trampé J., Schuur B., Haan de A.B., 2013. Solute recovery from ionic liquids: A conceptual design study for recovery of styrene monomer from [4-mebupy][BF4]. *Chemical Engineering and Processing: Process Intensification*; 70:148-161.

Flavio Manenti, Gintaras V. Reklaitis (Eds.), Proceedings of the 34th European Symposium on Computer Aided Process Engineering / 15th International Symposium on Process Systems Engineering (ESCAPE34/PSE24), June 2-6, 2024, Florence, Italy
 http://dx.doi.org/10.1016/B978-0-443-28824-1.50226-X

Exergy-based optimization for the synthesis of heat pump assisted distillation columns

Mirko Skiborowski[a]*, Kai Fabian Kruber[a]

[a]Hamburg University of Technology, Institute of Process Systems Engineering, Am-Schwarzenberg-Campus 3, 21073 Hamburg, Germany
mirko.skiborowski@tuhh.de

Abstract

While distillation columns are the main unit operation in fluid separation processes, considered versatile, robust, and well-understood, they are also oftentimes framed as energy intensive and potentially inefficient. Heat pumps bear the potential to improve the energy efficiency of distillation processes and simultaneously allow for the electrification of the thermal-driven separation processes. However, the economic viability and potential for energy savings depend strongly on the temperature lift and the compression ratio of the heat pump. Both can be reduced by considering intermediate heat exchangers rather than a full temperature lift from below the top vapor to above the bottoms temperature. Such intermediate heat exchangers may furthermore improve the internal efficiency of the distillation column and thereby improve the overall energy efficiency. The current contribution presents an exergy-based optimization that allows for an improved heat load distribution that can provide significant improvements of the internal efficiency and further enables a conceptual design of heat pump assisted distillation, using vapor recompression to provide the heat loads at the intermediate heat exchangers. The benefits of the approach are illustrated for the separation of a nonideal acetone-water mixture, highlighting the capability to identify unintuitive designs with significant saving potential.

Keywords: conceptual design, distillation, exergy, heat pumps, optimization

1. Introduction

Since distillation columns are not only the most frequently applied fluid separation technology in the chemical industry but also responsible for the majority of the thermal energy demand, they provide substantial improvement potential in the pursuit of a net-zero emissions production by 2050. Heat pumps are considered as one of the most important technologies in the transition to renewable energy sources, which also provide the potential to transform thermally-driven distillation columns to electrically-driven heat pump assisted distillation columns (Kiss et al., 2020). Consequently, heat pumps are considered as key to the desired electrification of the chemical industry. While significant advancements in the performance and applicability range of heat pumps have been made in recent years, the underlying concept and its application to distillation columns had already received considerable attention after the oil crisis in the 1980s (Gopichand et al., 1988).

Yet, a proper set of tools for identifying the best suitable configurations of heat pump assisted distillation is not easily available, despite a variety of publications dealing with the evaluation and optimization of specific process configurations, including the most popular mechanical vapor recompression (VRC) and the most complex internally heat integrated distillation columns (HIDiC). A HIDiC combines the concept of VRC and diabatic distillation, pursuing a continuous heat transfer from the rectifying to the stripping section, by operating the whole rectifying section at an increased pressure. Although this concept bears theoretically huge potential for improving the energy efficiency of the distillation-based separation, it has been shown that comparable energy savings can be achieved by much simpler process configurations, potentially exploiting just a single heat exchanger (Harwardt et al., 2012). Further constraints on the alignment of the temperature profiles present additional limitations for the HIDiC concept (Shenvi et al., 2011). In order to evaluate the potential of heat pump assisted distillation either simplified heuristics, such as sufficiently small boiling point differences (Kiss et al., 2012), dedicated simulation studies by means of commercial flowsheet simulators (e.g. Rix et al. 2023), or more advanced optimization models (Harwardt et al., 2012) can be applied. So far, a simple tool for a quick identification of the best-suited integration of one or multiple heat pumps and a distillation column by means of a quantitative assessment is not available.

In order to overcome this limitation, an exergy-based optimization is proposed, which identifies the most promising locations for intermediate heat transfer to increase the internal efficiency of the distillation column. The resulting locations provide an excellent indication for the proper placement of heat pumps, which is further demonstrated for heat pump assisted distillation employing mechanical VRC. The optimization-based approach is able to identify even unconventional configurations that offer large improvements for the separation of nonideal mixtures and provides a simple tool that can easily be transferred to common process flowsheet simulation software to strategically identify suitable heat pump modifications for the electrification of distillation columns. The application of the method is illustrated for the separation of an acetone-water mixture, considering the full range of feed compositions.

2. Method

The proposed screening approach builds on different calculations and tools to perform a time-efficient evaluation of possible improvements with respect to energy efficiency and the identification and evaluation of a suitable heat pump assisted distillation process. Shortcut-based evaluation of the minimum energy demand (MED) and the vapor compression heat pumps are performed in MATLAB®, while a multi-stage MESH model in GAMS is used for the exergy-based optimization. Finally, a simulation model in Aspen Plus® is used for the validation of the results.

2.1. Evaluation of energy efficiency

The energy efficiency of a separation process is determined in accordance with the description provided by Gooty et al. (2021) as

$$\eta_{sep} = \frac{W_{min}}{W_{sep}}, \tag{1}$$

based on the actual work for the separation (W_{sep}) and the minimum work

$$W_{min} = D(h_D - T_0 s_D) + B(h_B - T_0 s_B) - F(h_F - T_0 s_F), \tag{1}$$

with specific enthalpy (h) and entropy (s) of the products with flowrate (D, B) and feed stream (F) at reference conditions (T_0, p_0). These are taken as 25 °C and 1 atm in the current study. In accordance with the work of Gooty et al. (2021), it is further assumed that product cooling compensates for feed heating, assuming an ideal heat integration with zero exergy losses. The analysis of the energy efficiency therefore focuses on the internal efficiency of the distillation column, which can be calculated from the equivalent exergy of all heat duties provided at vanishing temperature difference and the external efficiency, which considers the actual temperature of the utilities or the power that is required to drive the compressor for the computation of the separation work

$$W_{sep} = \sum Q\left(1 - \frac{T_0}{T}\right) + \sum W_{comp}. \tag{3}$$

2.2. Shortcut screening for energy efficiency rating of simple distillation columns

For an initial evaluation of the energy efficiency of simple distillation columns the minimum energy demand (MED) is analyzed based on the pinch-based rectification body method (RBM) (Bausa et al. 1998). The RBM does not rely on simplifying assumptions like constant molar overflow and constant relative volatility and checks for tangent pinches, which is of special importance for non-ideal systems, such as the investigated acetone-water system.

2.3. Shortcut evaluation of heat pump performance

Based on the heat loads for condensation and evaporation, as well as the composition and temperature of the respective streams an isentropic compression cycle is considered for the evaluation of a possible heat pump implementation. The required compression ratio (CR) is determined by bisection, evaluating the boiling temperature of the compressed stream by individual flash calculations. Enthalpy checks are used to identify the need for an additional supersaturation prior to the compressor. The minimum workload is determined based on an isentropic compression with an efficiency of 80% and mechanical efficiency of 90%. In case the compressed vapor does not provide a sufficient heat load for the evaporation, the remaining heat is provided by an additional steam-heated reboiler. The performance of the heat pump is characterized by the coefficient of performance (COP) and an estimate of cost savings, considering the investment for the compressor with a depreciation of 3 years and an interest rate of 6%, as well as the cost for 3 bar steam (3.3 ct/kWh) and electricity (6 ct/kWh). The equipment costs are estimated for a single stage centrifugal compressor according to Biegler et al (1997).

2.4. Exergy-based optimization for improved energy efficiency

In order to improve both the internal and external efficiency of the distillation column, a multistage MESH model of the distillation column with the possibility of intermediate heating or cooling at dedicated stages in the rectifying and stripping section is optimized in GAMS. The model used for the optimization builds on the model formulation and initialization strategy of Skiborowski et al. (2015) and is optimized for a column with 80 equilibrium stages and possible intermediate heating or cooling at stage 20 or 60 with the objective to minimize the actual separation work ($\min_{Q_i} W_{sep}$).

2.5. Process concept validation

The performance calculations and optimization results are exemplarily validated by rigorous simulation studies in Aspen Plus® based on the included RadFrac and compressor model. The results are evaluated based on the previously computed reboiler duty, reflux ratio, as well as target values for the heat duties of the two intermediate heat exchangers. The latter are achieved by varying the amount of compressed top vapor in both compressors by two design specifications. The RadFrac model is defined in accordance with the optimization model in GAMS, considering 80 equilibrium stages with the feed entering on stage 40 and intermediate heating on stages 20 and 60.

3. Results

In order to illustrate the potential of the proposed exergy-based optimization approach, the separation of the nonideal acetone-water mixture is investigated for varying feed compositions. The thermodynamic model considers the non-random two-liquid (NRTL) activity coefficient model for the liquid phase, the Redlich-Kwong equation of state for the fugacity coefficients of the vapor phase, as well as DIPPR correlations for the specific heat capacities and the heat of evaporation. The respective property model parameters are taken from Skiborowski et al. (2014).

3.1. Shortcut screening for energy efficiency rating

The shortcut-based evaluation of the MED is performed for feed compositions ranging from 2 mol% up to 98 mol% of acetone with an increment of 1 mol%, considering a feed flow rate of 10 mol/s and product purities of 99.5 mol% each. The internal and external efficiency for these separations are determined based on the heat duties and product streams as described in Section 2.1, while the potential for VRC is evaluated based on the isentropic compression cycle as described in Section 2.3. The resulting efficiencies are illustrated in Figure 1 as black, red, and blue solid lines. Obviously, these lines all deviate significantly from the bell-shaped efficiency curves, with maximum efficiencies close to a symmetrical feed composition, that are usually reported for closely ideal systems, as e.g., illustrated in the work of Gooty et al. (2021). This deviation is primarily caused by the tangent pinch in the rectifying section, which controls the MED. While internal efficiencies close to 40% are still feasible for feed compositions with low acetone composition, the internal efficiency drops below 10% for feed compositions above 70 mol% of acetone. More noticeably, external efficiencies for conventional steam heating and wasting the condensation heat to cooling water already drop below 10% at a feed composition of 20% acetone. The energy efficiency of the simple column with VRC is raised considerably, but also drops below 10% for acetone feed compositions above 35 mol%. These VRC applications are also not economically favourable, resulting in considerably increased cost for the 3-year period, which fits to expectations considering the boiling point difference of about 40 K (Kiss et al. 2012). Obviously, simple distillation columns are rather inefficient for this separation, especially for feed compositions that are richer in acetone composition.

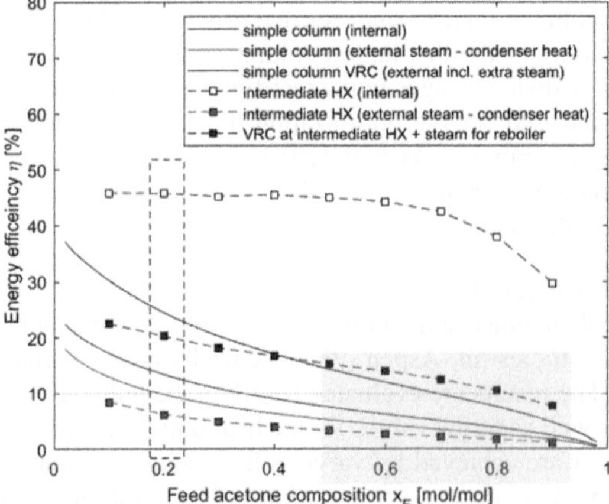

Figure 1: Illustration of the internal and external energy efficiency of simple and complex distillation columns with and without VRC.

3.2. Exergy-based optimization for improved energy efficiency

In order to evaluate the potential for improved energy efficiency by means of intermediate heating, exergy-based optimizations are performed for feed compositions with 10-90 mol% of acetone with increments of 10 mol%. The resulting internal and external efficiencies are also illustrated in Figure 1 as black, red, and blue square symbols, connected by an interpolated dashed line. The intermediate heating enables a substantial increase of the internal efficiency to more than 40% for acetone feed compositions up to 70 mol%. As the improved internal efficiencies are yielded with an increased MED, the respective external efficiencies with steam-based heating drop even below the external efficiencies of the simple column. However, applying VRC for the intermediate heat exchangers, the potential of the increased internal efficiency can be exploited, leading to external efficiencies above the internal efficiency of the simple columns for acetone feed compositions above 45 mol%.

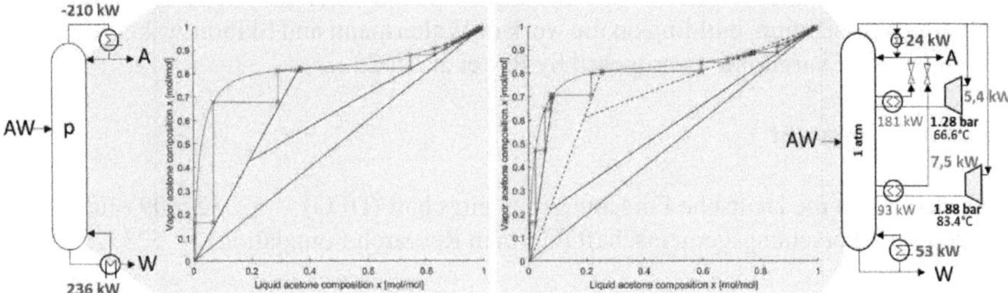

Figure 2: Resulting energy distribution and stage profiles for the simple (left) and complex column with intermediate heat exchangers (right) for a feed with 20 mol% of acetone. Indicated operating lines are approximations based on true stage profiles.

For further elucidation the results of the conceptual design for the simple and complex column are illustrated in Figure 2 for a feed composition with 20 mol% acetone. The simple column requires a reboiler duty of 236 kW, governed by the tangent pinch in the rectifying section. A VRC design with a CR of 3.7 and a COP of 5.5 could compensate most of the heat duty with a power requirement of 36 kW, but would result in a 30% cost increase for the 3-year period. This fits the expectations, given the temperature lift of more than 40 K. In contrast, the complex column with intermediate heat exchangers can compensate for most of the heat requirements by VRC with the intermediate heat exchangers with a cumulative power requirement of only 13 kW. The compressors operate at CRs of 1.3 and 1.9 and yield COP values of 33 and 12, respectively. Both heat pumps enable cost savings within the 3-year period, with 70% and 20% each. Comparing the stage profiles of the simple and complex column, it is apparent that the maximum distance between the operating line and the vapor-liquid equilibrium line is much lower for the complex column, reflecting the reduced exergy losses. A very important aspect in the derived design is that interstage heating is performed in the stripping and the rectifying section. The latter allows for heat integration at a minimum temperature lift but is certainly an extremely unconventional design, or as expressed by Agrawal and Fidkowski (1996) "against the widely accepted, normal distillation practise". The results of the conceptual design are further validated by Aspen Plus® simulations (cf. Section 2.5). The results for the exemplary 20 mol% acetone feed are in excellent agreement, even yielding a slight increase of 2% points in terms of the energy efficiency.

4. Conclusions

The systematic analysis of energy efficiency and exergy-based optimization allow for the derivation of efficient VRC designs with intermediate heat exchangers that can enable external efficiencies above the internal efficiencies of simple distillation columns. The case study highlights the potential to automatically identify unconventional designs, including the illustrated interstage heating in the rectifying section. While we could not find any prominent example of such configurations in publications in the last 20 years, the first indication of such configurations date back to Lynd and Grethlein (1986), who introduced the concept as intermediate heat pumps and optimal side stream return distillation, illustrating the case of a tangent pinch separation for an ethanol-water system. It is probably the most interesting feature of the current approach that it automatically identifies such a rarely known configuration, which obviously contradicts common design heuristics. Future work will extend the method to yield a superstructure-based economic optimization, building on the work of Waltermann and Skiborowski (2019) and exploit pressure variations as proposed by Rix et al., 2023.

Acknowledgement

Gefördert durch die Deutsche Forschungsgemeinschaft (DFG) —523327609 / funded by the Deutsche Forschungsgemeinschaft (German Research Foundation) — 523327609.

References

R. Agrawal, Z.T. Fidkowski, 1996, On the use of intermediate reboilers in the rectifying section and condensters in the stripping section of a distillation column, Ind. Eng. Chem. Res., 35, 2801-2807

L. Biegler, I.E. Grossmann, A. Westerberg, 1997, Systematic methods of chemical process design, Prentice Hall, Hoboken

J. Bausa, R. von Watzdorf, W. Marquardt, 1998, Shortcut methods for nonideal multicomponent distillation: 1. Simple columns, AIChE J., 44 (10) 2181-2198

S. Gopichand, 1988, Heat pump assisted distillation. X: Potential for industrial applications, Int. J. of Energy Research, 12, 569-582

A. Harwardt, W. Marquardt, 2012, Heat-integrated distillation columns: Vapor recompression or internal heat integration?, AIChE J., 58, 12, 3740-3750

T. Kiss, S.J. Flores Landeata, C.A. Infante Ferreira, 2012, Towards energy efficient distillation technologies – Making the right choice, Energy, 47, 531-542

T. Kiss, R. Smith, 2020, Rethinking energy use in distillation processes for a more sustainable chemical industry, Energy, 203, 117788

L.R. Lynd, H.E. Grethlein, 1986, Distillation with intermediate heat pumps and optimal sidestream return, AIChE J., 32 (8), 1347-1359

A. Rix, M. Schröder, N. Paul, 2023, Vapor recompression: An interesting option for vacuum columns?, Chem. Eng. Res. Des., 191, 226-235

A.A. Shenvi, M. Herron, R. Agrawal, 2011, Energy efficiency limitations of the conventional heat integrated distillation column (HIDIC) configuration for binary distillation, Ind. Eng. Chem. Res., 50, 119-130

M. Skiborowski, J. Wessel, W. Marquard, 2014, Efficient optimization-based design of membrane-assisted distillation processes, Ind. Eng. Chem. Res., 53, 15698-15717

M. Skiborowski, A. Harwardt, W. Marquard, 2015, Efficient optimization-based design for the separation of heterogeneous azeotropic mixtures, Comp. Chem. Eng., 34, -51

T. Waltermann, M. Skiborowski, 2019, Efficient optimization-based design of energy-integrated distillation processes, Comp. Chem. Eng., 129, 106520

Flavio Manenti, Gintaras V. Reklaitis (Eds.), Proceedings of the 34th European Symposium on Computer Aided Process Engineering / 15th International Symposium on Process Systems Engineering (ESCAPE34/PSE24), June 2-6, 2024, Florence, Italy
 http://dx.doi.org/10.1016/B978-0-443-28824-1.50227-1

Small-scale ammonia production: a superstructure approach

Alonso Martínez[a], Thien. A. Huynh[b], C. Varela[c], J. Faria[a], E. Zondervan[a]*

[a]*Twente University, Drienerlolaan 5, Enschede 7522 NB, The Netherlands*

[b]*Avebe, Prins Hendrikplein 20, Veendam 9641 GK, The Netherlands*

[c]*Escuela Superior Politécnica del Litoral, km. 30.5 Via Perimetral, Guayaquil, P.O. Box 09-01-5863, Ecuador*

e.zondervan@utwente.nl

Abstract

Ammonia is an important chemical for the energy transition as it can serve as a hydrogen carrier. Small-scale ammonia can be produced from decentralized or waste resources thereby integrating and expanding its use by delivering the product directly to the site of consumption. Nonetheless, the cost of small-scale ammonia is usually higher than large-scale ammonia due to the lack of economy of scale even though new technologies for H_2 and NH_3 synthesis are available. This work presents a superstructure (SE) as a decision-making tool to select the best set of technologies delivering the lowest ammonia cost. The SE is formulated as a mixed-integer linear program (MILP) comparing three different routes: electrolysis, gasification, and thermal decomposition of methane (TDM). The optimal route for a base case of 1000 kg_{NH3}/h is electrolysis with a cost of 1067 \$/t of NH_3. The capital expenditure (CAPEX) of electrolysis and ammonia synthesis, as well as the electricity cost, are the main contributors to this cost. The electrolysis route is the most promising for small-scale ammonia since it envisions the highest potential for cost reduction from lower electrolyzer and electricity prices. Gasification can also become competitive if the price of biomass is low but the cost of carbon capture and storage (CCS) needs to be considered. The TDM route is not suited for small scale due to large CAPEX contribution. The presented tool advances the spread and use of small-scale ammonia.

Keywords: Ammonia, superstructure, optimization, MILP.

1. Introduction

Ammonia has gained interest as an energy storage molecule for renewable hydrogen since it does not require a CO_2 cycle to release H_2. In addition, it has a mature infrastructure in current supply chains (Faria, 2021). Moreover, ammonia can be used to produce electricity in a fuel cell (Jeerh et al., 2021), and it is being researched for direct combustion applications (Kobayashi et al., 2019). Ammonia is produced in large scale plants with capacities of 1200 - 2000 t/d (Appl et al., 2011) using the Haber Bosch process. Large scale production is often centralized around cheap natural gas or coal resources. Therefore, its production is sensitive to disturbances in feedstock prices or disruptions in supply chains caused by geopolitical or environmental conditions. These disturbances can increase transportation costs, carbon footprint and shipping times. Small-scale ammonia production is an alternative to tackle these concerns as it excels at:

- **Flexibility and decentralization**. Ammonia can be produced from renewable energy sources (RES), waste streams (biogas or biomass) or stranded resources (Vrijenhoef,

2017). Since small scale operates at milder conditions, variable loads can be handled, thus enhancing integration with intermittent RES (Rouwenhorst et al., 2020).

- **Supply chain design**. The reduction in transportation distance can lower the price of ammonia in remote locations by 100-150 \$/t (Vrijenhoef, 2017) and the CO_2 emissions. Therefore, localized production improves resilience in current supply chains and reduces the need for storage technologies.

Downscaling the conventional Haber Bosch process is not straightforward as the energy losses and capital expenditures increase as the plant capacity is reduced. Rouwenhorst et al. (2021) evaluated different ammonia synthesis configurations for small scale (3 t/d) based on electrolysis. These configurations included conventional high-pressure Haber Bosch (HB) with condensation, absorbent enhanced Haber Bosch (AEHB) process and a novel single-pass ammonia synthesis where reaction and separation occur in the same vessel. They found that single pass ammonia can be produced at a lower cost than conventional ammonia due to higher conversion of the Ru catalyst supported in activated carbon (AC) and lower cost of the NH_3 synthesis loop. Arora et al. (2016) evaluated the production of 63 t/d of ammonia from biomass employing a Leading Concept Ammonia (LCA) process suited for small scale. The NH_3 cost comes at 1172 \$/t. They also found the biomass price and discount rate are the two major factors influencing the ammonia price. Osorio et al. (2022) performed a sustainability analysis of a novel methane-to-hydrogen-to-ammonia process, which can use either natural gas or biogas as feedstocks. The authors found that the ammonia price cannot compete with current fossil-based ammonia due to low yields. However, future reductions in electricity price and higher energy efficiencies have a great potential to make the process cost competitive. Moreover, selling carbon black as a byproduct is important to make this process economically attractive.

Current studies on small-scale ammonia production preselect the feedstock and ammonia production technologies. However, the integration and synergies between conventional and non-conventional technologies are overlooked. Though one could design several individual processes, this is a time-consuming endeavor. To address these challenges, a superstructure optimization approach is selected. In a SE, all the alternative technologies and feedstocks are compared, and the best possible process layout is chosen according to an objective function that minimizes costs or environmental impact. Superstructures for process synthesis have been developed since 1972. Two relevant superstructure representations are State Task Network (STN) (especially for scheduling operations) and State Equipment Network (SEN). The SE in this work falls within the scope of STN which consists of states and tasks. A state represents the physical condition of a stream while a task represents an operation executed to transit from one state to another (Mencarelli et al., 2020).

2. Problem statement and model formulation

The most relevant assumptions and considerations are:

- The scale of ammonia production has been set between 0 and 50 tpd. This is because the use of stranded energy sources rarely exceeds 20-30 MW (Vrijenhoef, 2017).
- Aggregate models are used to reduce complexity given the number of alternatives.
- Reaction and separation of NH_3 are coupled to resemble a real operation and to eliminate the modelling of recycles.
- Literature is the main source of data. For technical or economic data of a process that is not available, the process is simulated in Aspen Plus to generate such data.

A diagram of the proposed superstructure where forty possible routes are evaluated is shown Figure 1. A description of the different blocks is given in Table 1.

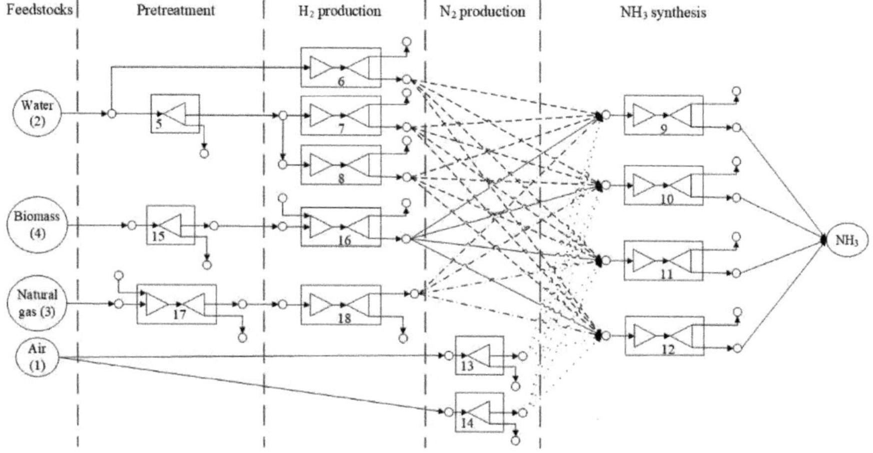

Figure 1. Superstructure for small-scale ammonia production. Triangles pointing to the left represent separation whereas the ones pointing to the right represent reactions. Before the NH_3 synthesis section, dashed lines represent electrolysis based H_2, solid lines gasification based H_2, dash-dot lines TDM based H_2 and dotted lines represent N_2. For number description see Table 1.

Table 1. Technology and index description for blocks in the superstructure.

Block	Index
Deionizer	5
Alkaline electrolyzer (AE)	6
Proton exchange membrane (PEM) electrolyzer	7
Solid oxide electrolyzer (SOEC)	8
High-pressure Fe catalyst w/ condensation	9
Medium-pressure Ru/AC w/absorption	10
Medium-pressure Ru/AC w/condensation	11
Low-pressure Ru/Ba-Ca(NH_2)$_2$/ w/absorption	12
Pressure swing adsorption (PSA)	13
Membrane air separation unit (ASU)	14
Drying	15
Gasification	16
Desulfurization	17
TDM	18

Given a set of technologies for H_2, N_2 and NH_3 production along with different feedstocks (sets and parameters); the SE decides mass flows, technologies and feedstock type (variables); while minimizing the ammonia production cost (objective function). Mass balances per component must be satisfied and a certain ammonia demand is met.

Sets

i	Feedstock or block
k	Chemical component
v	Chemical reaction
u	Utility
b	Breakpoint (used in piecewise linearization)

Parameters		Variables	
$SF_{i,k}$	Separation factor	$\dot{m}^F_{i,k}$	Feed mass flow
$\varepsilon_{v,i}$	Extent of reaction	$\dot{m}^R_{i,k}$	Reactant mass flow
$S_{v,k}$	Stoichiometric coefficient	$\dot{m}^P_{i,k}$	Product mass flow
M_k	Molar mass	y_i	Equipment switch
EC	Bare equipment cost	$x_{i,b}$	Lambda

Objective function

$$AC = \frac{APC}{AP} \tag{1}$$

Constraints

$$EC_i = \sum_{b}^{B} x_{i,b}\, EC_{i,b}\ \forall\, i \tag{2}$$

$$\dot{m}^P_{i,k} = SF_{i,k}\left(\dot{m}^F_{i,k} + \dot{m}^R_{i,k} + \varepsilon_{i,v} S_{v,k} M_k\right)\ \forall\, i\ \forall\, k\ \forall\, v \tag{3}$$

$$y_2 = \sum_{i=5}^{6} y_i \tag{4}$$

$$\dot{m}^P_{2,k} = \sum_{i=5}^{6} \dot{m}^F_{i,k}\ \forall\, k \tag{5}$$

$$\sum_{i=9}^{13} \dot{m}^P_{i,k} = \dot{m}^D_{i,k}\ \forall\, k = "NH_3" \tag{6}$$

The objective function in Eq. (1) is the ammonia cost (AC) which is a function of the annualized plant cost (APC) and the ammonia production (AP) over a year. APC is a function of the Annualized Operating Cost (AOC) and Annualized Investment Cost (AIC). These are ultimately dependent on the equipment cost Eq. (2) and the mass balance Eq. (3). The piecewise- and big-M linearizations have been applied to remove nonlinearities. Each block i has a binary decision variable y_i denoting whether the block is selected or not. This also introduces logic in between sections of the SE. For instance, if water is chosen for H_2 production (block 2 in Figure 1), its flow must be distributed only to the desalination or alkaline electrolysis blocks Eq. (4) and Eq. (5). Finally, a certain ammonia production is enforced in the last section of the SE by Eq. (6). The resulting MILP problem is solved using the Pyomo library within Python. A base case is defined considering data within common ranges. These are: electricity price 30 \$/MWh; biomass price 100 \$/t; natural gas price 0.1905 \$/kg; ammonia production 1000 kg/h; operational hours 8400 h.

3. Results

From Figure 2, the electrolysis route has the lowest NH_3 cost of 1067 \$/t. The major contributors to this cost are the NH_3 production CAPEX, followed by electricity consumption and H_2 production CAPEX. The use of biomass and natural gas has been enforced in separate cases to compare against the best solution.

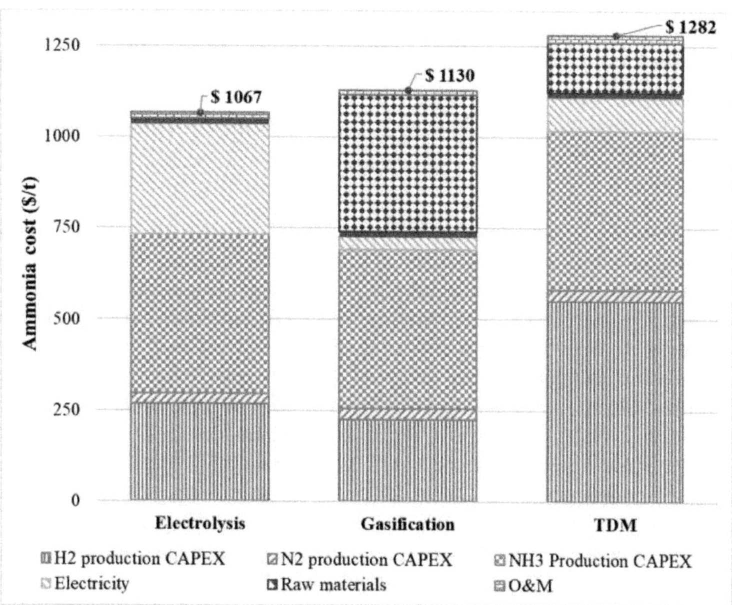

Figure 2. Ammonia cost breakdown for different routes. Electrolysis: indexes 2, 5, 7, 11 and 14 in Figure 1. Gasification: indexes 4, 15, 16, 11 and 14 in Figure 1. TDM: indexes 3, 17, 18, 11 and 14 in Figure 1. O&M: operation and maintenance.

In the case of gasification, the dominating factors are the CAPEX of the NH_3 production section and the cost of biomass. In the case of TDM, the dominating factors are the NH_3 production section and the cost of the pyrolysis reactor. To measure the effect of changes in certain parameters in the ammonia cost, a sensitivity analysis has been conducted (Figure 3). The sensitivity factor S is introduced as the ratio between a change in ammonia price due to a change in a certain parameter. The ammonia price taken as reference for each parameter is that of its corresponding route using the data from the base case.

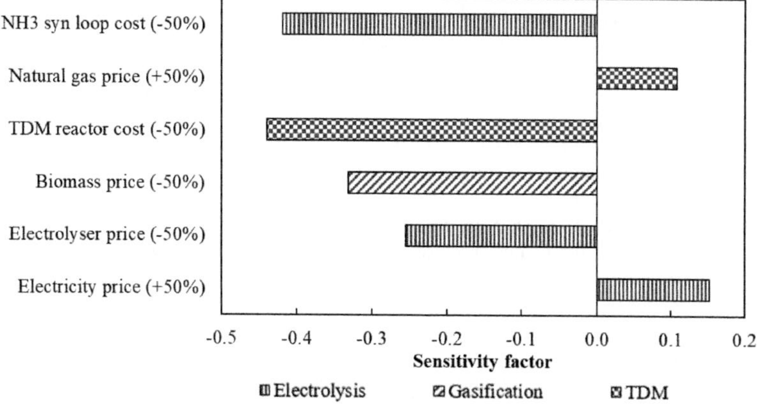

Figure 3. Sensitivity factor.

The cost of the NH_3 synthesis loop has a high impact at low scale. The electrolysis route can reduce costs in terms of electrolyzer type and electricity price. Moreover, O_2 sales could further increase the profitability of this route. Reduction in biomass prices can lower the cost of ammonia in the gasification route. However, CCS is needed to prevent direct CO_2 emissions. The TDM route is more sensitive to the TDM reactor cost than to natural gas prices and thus technological developments should focus in this area.

4. Conclusions

A superstructure to evaluate forty possible routes for small-scale ammonia production was developed as a tool to screen different alternatives and scenarios. Thus, advancing the spread and use of small-scale ammonia. The optimal route for a base case is PEM electrolyzer for H_2 production, a medium pressure HB ammonia synthesis loop using a Ru/AC catalyst with condensation and a membrane ASU. The electrolysis route is the best suited option and has further potential for ammonia cost reduction with lower electrolyzer and electricity prices. Gasification can also become competitive if the price of biomass is low, but the cost of CCS needs to be considered. The TDM route is not suited for low scale due to the large CAPEX contribution. Data collection for the SE remains a time-consuming step. Linearization techniques such as big M and piecewise linear are useful to avoid nonlinearities and reduce problem complexity.
Future work can consider the impact in ammonia price of byproduct valorization (O_2, carbon black, waste). Address the intermittency of RES by including a time index and include the cost of ammonia storage. Downstream processing of ammonia into further value-added products such as H_2 (from NH_3 cracking), electricity (from a fuel cell) and fertilizers.

References

G. Jeerh, M. Zhang, S. Tao, 2021. Recent progress in ammonia fuel cells and their potential applications. Journal of Materials Chemistry A, 9, 727-752.

H. Kobayashi, A. Hayakawa, K. D. K. A. Somarathne, E. C Okafor, 2019. Science and technology of ammonia combustion. Proceedings of the Combustion Institute, 37, 109-133.

J. A. Faria, 2021. Renaissance of ammonia synthesis for sustainable production of energy and fertilizers. Current Opinion in Green and Sustainable Chemistry, 29, 100466.

J. Osorio, K. Van't Veer, N. Long, N. Tran, L. Fulcheri, B. Patil,A. Bogaerts,V. Hessel, 2022. Sustainability analysis of methane-to-hydrogen-to-ammonia conversion by integration of high-temperature plasma and non-thermal plasma processes. Energy Conversion and Management, 269, 116095.

J. P. Vrijenhoef, 2017, Opportunities for small scale ammonia production. Proceedings of the International Fertiliser Society, 801, ISBN 978-0-85310-438-4.

K. H. R. Rouwenhorst, P. M. Krzywda, N. E. Benes, G. Mul, L. Lefferts, 2020.Ammonia, 4. Green Ammonia Production. Ullmann's Encyclopedia of Industrial Chemistry. Wiley-VCH , Wiley Online Library.

K. H. R. Rouwenhorst, A. G. J. Van der Ham, L. Lefferts, 2021. Beyond Haber-Bosch: The renaissance of the Claude process. International Journal of Hydrogen Energy, 46, 41, 21566-21579

L. Mencarelli, Q. Chen, A. Pagot, I.E. Grossmann, 2020. A review on superstructure optimization approaches in process system engineering. Computers & Chemical Engineering, 136, 106808.

M. Appl , 2011. Ammonia, 3. Production Plants. Ullmann's Encyclopedia of Industrial Chemistry. Wiley-VCH , Wiley Online Library.

P. Arora, A. F. A. Hoadley, S.M. Mahajani, A. Ganesh, 2016. Small-Scale Ammonia Production from Biomass: A Techno-Enviro-Economic Perspective. Industrial & Engineering Chemistry Research, 55, 22, 6422-6434.

Flavio Manenti, Gintaras V. Reklaitis (Eds.), Proceedings of the 34th European Symposium on Computer Aided Process Engineering / 15th International Symposium on Process Systems Engineering (ESCAPE34/PSE24), June 2-6, 2024, Florence, Italy
 http://dx.doi.org/10.1016/B978-0-443-28824-1.50228-3

Detailed Design of Shell and Tube Heat Exchangers with Considering Fouling

Yi Cui[a], Chenglin Chang[b], Yufei Wang*[a]

[1]College of Chemical Engineering and Environment, China University of Petroleum, 102249, Beijing, China

[2] School of Chemistry and Chemical Engineering, Chongqing University, 400044, Chongqing, China

Email of the Corresponding Author: wangyufei@cup.edu.cn

Abstract

The shell and tube heat exchanger is a crucial component in the process industry for energy recovery. Its detailed design continues to be a prominent area of research. However, current research models of heat exchangers tend to oversimplify the system, overlooking practical factors, such as fouling. Fouling, being a common and significant factor, is often treated as a constant value during design optimization. This study proposes a method for optimizing the design of heat exchangers by considering fouling variations across multiple operating cycles. The method employs Set Trimming to obtain a comprehensive solution that accounts for the changes in fouling. The design optimization is performed within a specific operating cycle, resulting in an optimal heat exchanger solution for crude oil. Then sensitivity analysis using multiple operating cycles is conducted to identify the most suitable operating cycle and its corresponding heat exchanger design solution for crude oil. The results of the optimization indicate that, within 1-year descaling cycle, the proposed design method successfully reduces the required heat transfer area of the heat exchanger by 2.62%, comparing to the literature value. Through cost optimization, the method identifies the optimal operating cycle for crude oil as 3-year. These findings highlight the potential of the method to enhance heat exchanger performance and decrease refinery expenses.

Key words: Heat exchanger; Fouling; Global optimum; Set trimming.

1. Introduction

The design optimization of heat exchangers, a critical aspect of energy recovery in the industry, continues to be a prominent research area. Commonly employed algorithms for heat exchanger optimization can be broadly categorized into heuristic algorithms and mathematical planning methods.

Heuristic algorithms, such as genetic algorithms (Amini, 2014), simulated annealing algorithms (Khalfe et al., 2011), and particle swarm algorithms (Patel et al., 2010), have been extensively explored in heat exchanger research. In recent years, new algorithms like the imperialist competitive algorithm (Hadidi et al., 2013a), biogeography-based algorithm (Hadidi et al., 2013b), and harmony search algorithm (Turgut et al., 2014) have also been applied to address heat exchanger design problems. Heuristic algorithms offer relatively quick solutions to design problems. However, their limitations include the need for trial and error iterations and parameter adjustments.

In addition, the heat exchanger model often involves nonlinear equations, resulting in a mixed integer nonlinear model (MINLP) when solved using mathematical programming methods. To address this, some researchers have linearized the MINLP model and formulated it as a mixed integer linear programming (MILP) model (Gonçalves and Costa et al., 2016). However, this approach suffers from lengthy solution times and the challenge of model linearization adjustments.

While research on heat exchangers has reached a high level of maturity, many studies simplify calculations by assuming constant values for the physical properties of hot and cold streams during optimization. This undoubtedly reduces the calculations and allows the program to be solved in a short time. However, certain parameters that are considered as constant values in the optimization program may have a huge impact on the design and operation of the heat exchanger in real chemical plant. Fouling is just such a parameter, and its variation during the heat exchanger process is often neglected in current research.

Caputo et al. (2011) investigated the influence of flow velocity on fouling and used genetic algorithm to optimize the heat exchanger, with the total cost as the optimization objective. Costa et al. (2017) used a threshold model to model the fouling resistance value and designed a MILP model to solve the design problem. Comparison with traditional methods with fixed fouling factor showed that this method has the potential reduction of capital cost. Lemos et al. (2018) further explored the relationship between fouling and crude oil type, pressure drop manipulation, and energy integration based on the research of Costa et al. (2017). And then Lemos et al. (2022) employed Set Trimming to design the heat exchanger, considering fouling on both the tube and shell sides, resulting in more realistic outcomes. Among the existing studies on fouling, there is a paucity of research examining the economic cost of heat exchangers during long operating times. Furthermore, there seems to be a scarcity of research specifically focusing on the fouling-cleaning operation cycle.

In this paper, Set Trimming was used to solve the heat exchanger design problem considering the effect of time on the fouling resistance value. Set Trimming is an efficient enumeration algorithm proposed in recent years, which can solve the optimization problem in a short period of time. For a specified operation cycle, the design solution was given with the optimization objective of minimizing the heat transfer area, and the solution of Set Trimming was proved to be more reasonable when compared with the literature values. In addition, a sensitivity analysis of the operating cycle was conducted, using the total cost as the evaluation metric. This analysis aimed to identify the most suitable operating cycle for the given case and consequently provided the corresponding design solution.

2. Model Equations

Without loss of generality, the study in this paper is based on the following assumptions:

(1) the shell of the heat exchanger is E-type. (2) the hot and cold streams are liquids, and no phase changes occur. (3) In addition to the fouling resistance, other physical parameters of the hot and cold streams, such as density, viscosity, etc., are based on the values at the average temperature.

The model of the heat exchanger is given below, and in the description of the optimization model, the parameters that are initially given and do not need to be optimized have the symbol " $\frown$ " at the top.

2.1. Heat Exchanger Model

The shell-side models for the heat exchangers adopts the Kern model, and the tube-side models are from Incropera et al. (2006) and Saunders (1988). In addition to the general shell and tube side model, the tube-side fouling factor is given by equation (1).

$$\frac{dRf_t}{dt} = \hat{\alpha} Re_t^{-0.8} Pr_t^{-0.33} exp(\frac{-Ea}{\hat{R}T_w}) - \hat{\gamma} Re_t^{0.8} \quad (1)$$

where α and γ are model parameters, Re_t and Pr_t are the Reynolds, Prandtl number of tube-side, Ea is the activation energy, R is gas constant, and T_w is wall temperature.

2.2. Bounds

To ensure the validity of the model and the reasonableness of the design solution given by the program, some bounds are added.

The limitations of pressure drop, flow rate, and Reynolds number can be found in the literature (Lemos et al., 2018).

Structural parameters limitations are given by equations (2) and (3), proposed by Hewitt et al. (2008).

$$0.2d_s \leq lbc \leq 1.0d_s \quad (2)$$

$$3d_s \leq L \leq 15d_s \quad (3)$$

where d_s is the shell diameter, lbc is the baffle spacing, and L is the tube length.

Heat transfer area limitations are given by equation (4).

$$A \geq A_{req}\left(1 + A_{exc}\right) \quad (4)$$

where A is the heat transfer area, A_{exc} is the area margin percentage.

2.3. Objective Function

The objective functions involved in this study are as follows, and all of them used in the optimization process are single-objective optimization. The first objective function selected is the heat transfer area. Its calculation is based on equation (5).

$$A = Ntt\ \pi\ d_{t,e}\ L \quad (5)$$

where Ntt is the total number of tubes.

In order to facilitate the comparison of cost reduction in the refinery, the total cost (TC) is selected as another objective function, which is calculated by equation (6)-(9).

$$TC = CA + CP + CC \quad (6)$$

$$CA = af\left(\hat{a}A^{0.8}\right) \quad (7)$$

$$CP = EC\,Hour\left(\frac{m_s\ p_s}{\rho_s\ \hat{\eta}} + \frac{m_t\ p_t}{\rho_t\ \hat{\eta}}\right) \quad (8)$$

$$CC = nFC \quad (9)$$

where CA, CP, and CC are the investment cost, operation cost, fouling-cleaning cost of heat exchanger. af is the annual interest rate, a is the cost parameter of the heat exchanger, EC is the electricity price, $Hour$ is the total operating time of heat exchanger, m_s, ρ_s are the shell-side stream mass flow rate and stream density, m_t, ρ_t are the data of tube-side, η is the motor efficiency, n is the number of fouling-cleaning times, and FC is the cost of a single cleaning operation.

3. Case Study

A case from Lemos et al. (2018) was selected. Detailed data on hot and cold stream as well as design variables can be found in the literature (Lemos et al., 2018). The hot stream fouling factor is 0, and the cold stream fouling factor is calculated according to equation (1). Using Set Trimming for optimization, detailed logic can be found in Costa et al. (2019).

In the optimization process, the following parameters are considered as constants. The thickness of the tube-side is 0.00165 m. A_{exc} in equation (4) equals 0. α in equation (1) equals 0.0002798 $m^2 \cdot K/(W \cdot h)$, γ equals $4.17 \cdot 10^{-13}$ $m^2 \cdot K/(W \cdot h)$, Ea equals 48 KJ/mol, and R equals 8.314 J/(mol·K). af in equation (7) equals 0.264 and a equals 21. EC in equation (8) equals 0.12 $\$ \cdot kWh^{-1}$, *Hour* equals 24,000 h (the heat exchanger has a service life of 30 years and operates 8,000 hours per year.), and η equals 75%. FC in equation (9) equals 2,000 $.

First, the heat exchanger descaling cycle is given as 1 year (8,000 h), the objective function is to minimize the heat transfer are. The design solutions, thermofluid dynamic results are shown in Table (1).

Table 1: Optimization results of heat transfer area

Design solutions		Thermofluid dynamic results	
Total number of tubes	1071	Heat transfer area/m^2	312.58
Tube outer diameter/m	0.019	Tube-side velocity/$m \cdot s^{-1}$	2.29
Tube length/m	4.877	Shell-side velocity/$m \cdot s^{-1}$	0.72
Tube pitch ratio	1.25	Tube-side heat transfer coefficient /$W \cdot (m^2 \cdot K)^{-1}$	2372.24
Tube layout	Triangular	Shell-side heat transfer coefficient /$W \cdot (m^2 \cdot K)^{-1}$	1221.61
Number of tube passes	4	Overall heat transfer coefficient /$W \cdot (m^2 \cdot K)^{-1}$	657.96
Number of baffles	13	Tube-side pressure drop/Pa	75,559.14
Shell diameter/m	0.889	Shell-side pressure drop/Pa	74,074.57
		Tube-side fouling factor/$m^2 \cdot K \cdot W^{-1}$	0.000128

Through the optimization of Set Trimming, the minimal heat transfer area is 312.58 m^2, representing a 2.62% reduction compared to the literature value of 321 m^2, proving the effectiveness of Set Trimming and the models. The reduction in heat transfer area is attributed to the selection of a smaller shell diameter, resulting in a smaller total number of tubes, and the adoption of triangular tube-layout, enabling more heat transfer tubes to be arranged on the same tube sheet area. Corresponding to the reduction of the heat transfer area is the improvement of the pressure drop, both the tube and shell pressure drops are improved to different degrees, 4.95% and 4.76%, respectively. In addition, from the thermofluid dynamic results, the overall heat transfer coefficient is 657.96 $W \cdot (m^2 \cdot K)^{-1}$, which is smaller than the literature value of 692 $W \cdot (m^2 \cdot K)^{-1}$. Nevertheless, this paper gives a smaller value of heat transfer area than the literature because A_{exc} is given to be 0. In the actual calculations, there are still some area margins in both the design solutions given in this paper and the literature. Larger overall heat transfer coefficient in the literature will result in a smaller A_{req}, leading to larger area margins and improved heat exchanger safety and operational flexibility. Despite these differences, it is crucial to emphasize that the design solutions proposed in this paper remain feasible and rational.

Subsequently, a sensitivity analysis of the descaling cycle is performed, assuming a heat exchanger operating life of 30 years and varying descaling cycles from 1 year to 10 years. The optimization is performed with the objective of minimizing the total cost.

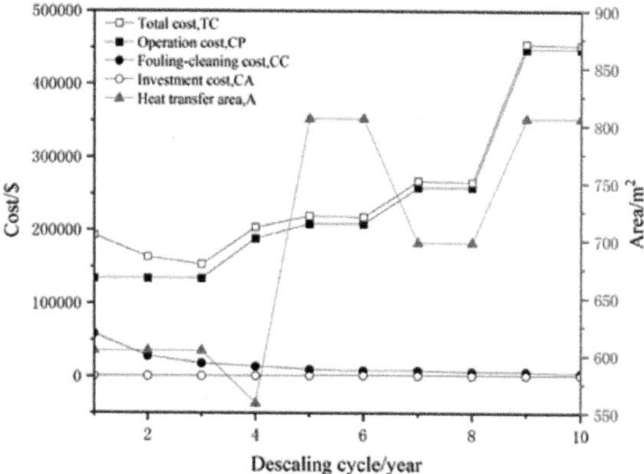

Figure 1: Sensitivity analysis results - based on descaling cycle

Figure 1 shows the results of the sensitivity analysis. It is evident that the minimum total cost is achieved with the 3-year descaling cycle. In terms of the composition of the total cost, the operation cost and the total cost have basically the same trend. As the heat exchanger descaling cycle increases, both the operation cost and the total cost show an upward trend. Conversely, the fouling-cleaning cost is decreasing with the extension of the descaling cycle, and the investment cost of the heat exchanger accounts for less in the total cost.

In terms of the heat exchange area, the program gives consistent results for different descaling cycle conditions. For descaling cycles of 1-year, 2-year, and 3-year, identical heat exchanger design solutions are produced, resulting in equivalent investment and operation cost. However, varying descaling cycles impact descaling cost, with the 3-year cycle resulting in the minimal cost. In the case of a 4-year descaling cycle, the largest tube outer diameter among the 10 cycles reduces the total number of tubes, leading to the smallest heat exchanger area. At the same time, adopting the 6-tube-pass increases tube-side velocity and pressure drop, consequently elevating operation cost and total cost. For descaling cycles of 5-year and 6-year, a set of design solutions is applicable, while 9-year and 10-year cycles correspond to another set. Despite both groups of design solutions providing the same heat transfer area, the longer descaling cycle prompts the latter set to select the 6-tube-pass, resulting in higher operation cost and a notably larger total cost compared to the former set. Descaling cycles of 7-year and 8-year result in a small heat transfer area and high total cost due to factors akin to those observed in the 4-year descaling cycle, including large tube outer diameters and an increased number of tube passes.

4. Conclusion

This paper introduces a novel approach to designing shell and tube heat exchangers, utilizing Set Trimming and incorporating a fouling model for more realistic optimization. When minimizing heat transfer area, the program generates a value 2.6% smaller than the literature value. This results in a higher pressure drop and reduced heat exchanger area margin, but remains within acceptable limits.

Moreover, a sensitivity analysis of the heat exchanger descaling cycle is conducted to minimize total cost, revealing that the 3-year descaling cycle offers optimal cost efficiency. Results indicate that operation cost have a greater impact on total cost, with investment and fouling-cleaning cost comprising a smaller fraction of total cost. However, when different descaling cycles yield identical design solutions, fouling-cleaning cost become the decisive factor. The proposed method is validated by adjusting the objective function and conducting a sensitivity analysis, demonstrating its rationality and superiority. This method has the potential to enhance heat exchanger performance and reduce refinery cost.

References

M. Amini, M. Bazargan, 2014, Two objective optimization in shell-and-tube heat exchangers using genetic algorithm, Applied Thermal Engineering, 69,1-2, 278-285.

A. C. Caputo, P. M. Pelagagge, P. Salini, 2011, Joint economic optimization of heat exchanger design and maintenance policy, Applied Thermal Engineering, 31, 8-9, 1381-1392.

A. L. H. Costa, J. C. Lemos, M. J. Bagajewicz, 2017, Heat Exchanger Design Optimization Considering Threshold Fouling Modelling, Computer Aided Chemical Engineering, 40, 799-804.

A. L. H. Costa, M. J. Bagajewicz, 2019, 110th anniversary: On the departure from heuristics and simplified models toward globally optimal design of process equipment, Ind. Eng. Chem. Res. 58, 18684–18702.

C. D. O. Gonçalves, A. L. H. Costa, M. J. Bagajewicz, 2016, Shell and tube heat exchanger design using mixed-integer linear programming, AIChE Journal, 63, 6, 1907-1922.

A. Hadidi, M. Hadidi, A. Nazari, 2013a, A new design approach for shell-and-tube heat exchangers using imperialist competitive algorithm (ICA) from economic point of view, Energy Conversion & Management, 67, Mar., 66-74.

A. Hadidi, A. Nazari, 2013b, Design and economic optimization of shell-and-tube heat exchangers using biogeography-based (BBO) algorithm, Applied Thermal Engineering, 51, 1-2, 1263-1272.

G. F. Hewitt, 2008, Heat exchanger design handbook, Begell house: New York, United States of America.

F. P. Incropera, D. P. DeWitt, T. L. Bergman, A. S. Lavine, 2006, Fundamentals of Heat and Mass Transfer, 6th ed., John Wiley & Sons: Hoboken, United States of America.

N. M. Khalfe, S. K. Lahiri, S. K. Wadhwa, 2011, Simulated annealing technique to design minimum cost exchanger, Chemical Industry & Chemical Engineering Quarterly, 17, 4, 409-427.

J. C. Lemos, A. L. H. Costa, M. J. Bagajewicz, 2018, Globally optimal linear approach to the design of heat exchangers using threshold fouling modeling, AIChE Journal, 64, 6, 2089-2102.

J. C. Lemos, A. L. H. Costa, M. J. Bagajewicz, 2022, Design of shell and tube heat exchangers considering the interaction of fouling and hydraulics, AIChE Journal,68, 5, e17586.

V. K. Patel, R. V. Rao, 2010, Design optimization of shell-and-tube heat exchanger using particle swarm optimization technique, Applied Thermal Engineering, 30, 11-12, 1417-1425.

E. A. D. Saunders, 1988, Heat Exchangers Selection, Design and Construction, John Wiley & Sons: New York, United States of America.

O. E. Turgut, M. S. Turgut, M. T. Coban, 2014, Design and economic investigation of shell and tube heat exchangers using Improved Intelligent Tuned Harmony Search algorithm, Ain Shams Engineering.

Flavio Manenti, Gintaras V. Reklaitis (Eds.), Proceedings of the 34th European Symposium on Computer Aided Process Engineering / 15th International Symposium on Process Systems Engineering (ESCAPE34/PSE24), June 2-6, 2024, Florence, Italy
 http://dx.doi.org/10.1016/B978-0-443-28824-1.50229-5

Glycerol Valorisation to Glycerol Carbonate: Process Synthesis, Design and Control

Prakhar Srivastava[a],Aayush Gupta[a], Nitin Kaistha[a*]

[a]*Chemical Engineering, IIT Kanpur 208016,India*

[*]*nkaistha@iitk.ac.in*

Abstract

This study outlines a economic process for valorising of glycerol (GLY) to glycerol carbonate (GC) through transesterification with dimethyl carbonate (DMC), generating methanol (MeOH) as a byproduct. The flowsheet, guided by a residue curve map, reveals a pressure-sensitive MeOH-DMC azeotrope exploited through pressure swing for methanol recovery and MeOH-DMC azeotrope recycle. The process incorporates a pressurized reactive distillation (RD) column, followed by three low-pressure distillation columns, with heat integration for enhanced energy efficiency. Optimizing design variables yields an economically optimal steady-state process. Comparative analysis with recent designs—reactive distillation pervaporation (RDPV) and reactive distillation extractive distillation (RDED)—indicates a cost objective reduction of 70% and 24%, respectively. Energy consumption per kilomole of GC product is also reduced by 16% and 10%. The process, easily controlled through a decentralized plantwide system, handles large disturbances, ensuring precise product quality control and smooth flow transitions. This research significantly contributes to the 'green' biodiesel fuel value chain, efficiently transforming glycerol, a biodiesel byproduct, into GC.

Keywords: RD, PSD,Azeotrope,Heat Integration

1. Introduction

Glycerol carbonate (GC) is emerging as a promising avenue to enhance the value of glycerol (GLY), a byproduct resulting from biodiesel production. With biodiesel gaining popularity as a greener alternative to diesel, effective glycerol valorisation becomes crucial for the biodiesel economy. The significance of industrial-grade GC lies in its high market value, attributed to characteristics such as low volatility, low toxicity, high polarity, and biodegradability (H.W. Tan 2013). GC plays a vital role as a raw material for producing polymers, surfactants, and serves as a precursor for glycidol, utilized in pharmaceuticals, cosmetics, plastics, and as an electrolyte in lithium-ion batteries (S. Sahani 2020). The transesterification of glycerol with dimethyl carbonate (DMC) stands out as a highly promising route, ensuring substantial glycerol conversion and GC yield. Under controlled conditions, employing the Zn_4La_1 catalyst, it is recommended to maintain a reactive bed temperature below 140°C to preserve product yield and a DMC to glycerol ratio above 2 to maximize the selectivity.

The development of an economically optimized steady-state design for an industrial-scale plant converting glycerol (GLY) to glycerol carbonate (GC) through transesterification with dimethyl carbonate (DMC) is imperative for advancing the economics of biodiesel manufacturing. In the limited literature on the subject, two distinct approaches come to light: Yu's (Yu 2020) design, incorporating Reactive Distillation with Homogeneous Extractive Distillation (RDED), and Sun et al.'s (Dayu Sun 2022) strategy, which employs Reactive Distillation with a Pervaporation Module (RDPV). Despite both methods presenting reported benefits, Extractive Distillation introduces a third component, impacting product purity and incurring makeup costs. Conversely, pervaporation, a membrane-based technique, introduces challenges like membrane fouling, periodic replacement costs, and the need for electricity-consuming vacuum pumps. These issues, coupled with a lack of control flexibility, suggest that membrane-based techniques like pervaporation should be considered only when distillation proves impractical—a criterion not met in this scenario.

This study introduces a process design based on distillation for the cost-effective production of glycerol carbonate (GC) through the transesterification of glycerol with dimethyl carbonate (DMC). In contrast to existing literature, our design, comprising a reactive distillation (RD) column followed by only three additional columns (a total of 4 columns), proves to be significantly more economical. The article progresses with the synthesis of the process flowsheet, its optimization to minimize the cost objective *J*, and a comparative analysis with existing designs. A plantwide regulatory control structure is then presented and evaluated for its ability to handle throughput and feed composition changes. The conclusion summarizes the key findings and contributions of the study.

2. Process model

Aspen Plus Dynamics serves as the tool for both steady-state and dynamic process modelling in this study. The thermodynamic package and reaction kinetics outlined in the work by Yu

Table 1:Reaction and Kinetics Details

Reaction	Reaction Kinetics
$GLY + DMC \rightarrow GC + 2MeOH$	$r_1 = 1.31 \times 10^{16}\, exp\frac{(-144000)}{RT} x_{GLY} x_{DMC}$
$GC + 2MeOH \rightarrow GLY + DMC$	$r_2 = 6.06 \times 10^{4}\, exp\frac{(-60013)}{RT} x_{GC} x_{MeOH}^2$
$GC \rightarrow GLC + CO_2$	$r_3 = 1.63 \times 10^{9}\, exp\frac{(-113000)}{RT} x_{GC}$

r: rate constant in kmol/kg(cat).s x: liquid phase mole fraction of species
R:kJ/kmol.K

(Yu 2020) are adopted for our simulations. The steady-state design is formulated to achieve a glycerol carbonate (GC) product rate and purity of 10 kmol/h and 99.64 mol%, respectively. Additionally, a methanol (MeOH) co-product purity of 99.5 mol% is targeted. The reaction and kinetic expressions in detailed are given in Table 1 are taken from the Yu (Yu 2020) work. We ensure the fidelity of our simulations by employing the validated binary interaction parameters previously reported by Yu (Yu 2020).

3. Process Synthesis and Design

The synthesis of a proposed process flowsheet relies on utilizing the residue curve map (RCM) for the four primary components in the main reaction: MeOH, DMC, GLY, and GC. The process begins with the reactive zone, aiming to drive the main reaction rightward while suppressing side reactions. This is achieved by executing the reaction in an excess of DMC, with glycerol as the limiting reactant. Reaction kinetics demand a high temperature and pressure in the reactive zone, introducing the heavier reactant (GLY) at the top and the lighter reactant (DMC) at the bottom within the reactive section of the RD column. Examining the vapor and liquid streams from the reactive zone, the high boiling point of GC leads to a GC-free vapor exit stream, composed of DMC, light MeOH by-product, and traces of vaporized GLY. Rectification of this vapor stream yields the HP MeOH-DMC azeotrope as the column

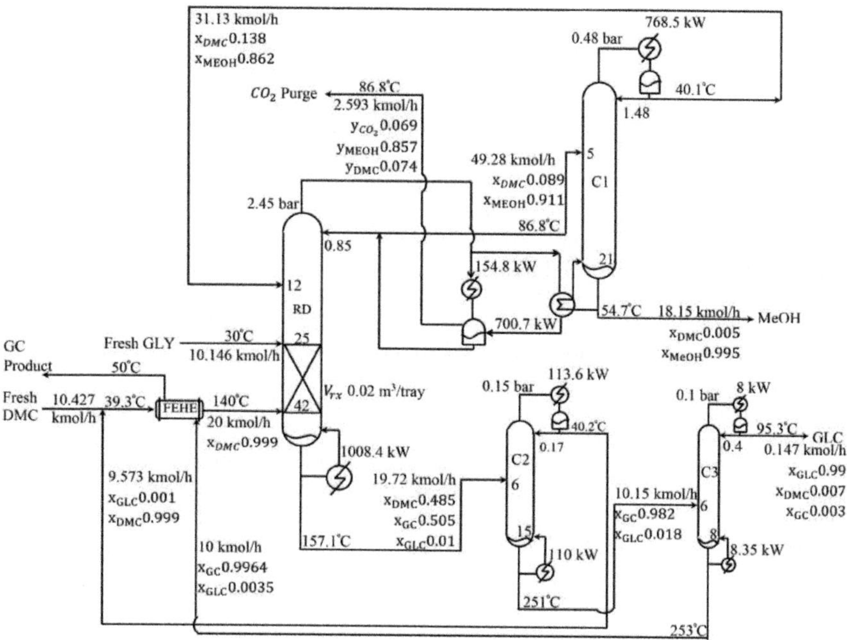

Figure 1:Proposed process with nominal design and operating condition

distillate. On the liquid side, catalyst-loaded reactive trays ensure near-complete conversion of GLY, producing a stream primarily composed of DMC, GC, and Glycidol (GLC). The HP MeOH-DMC azeotrope distillate can undergo separation in a low-pressure column, denoted as C1. The resulting distillate is the LP MeOH-DMC azeotrope, featuring a MeOH mol fraction to the left of the HP azeotrope distillate from the RD column. Utilizing a pressure swing, a straightforward LP distillation process recovers MeOH as the bottom product and the

Table 2:Degree of freedom and Specification

S.N.	Steady State dof	Specification Variable
1.	Glycerol feed rate	TPM
2.	GC product purity (molar basis)	99.64%
3.	MeOH co-product purity	99.5%
4.	GLC Purity	99%
4.	C2 DMC distillate purity	99.9%
5.	C2 DMC bottom purity	10 PPM
6.	RD distillate MeOH mole fraction	0.911
7.	C1 distillate MeOH mole fraction	0.862
8.	RD bottom MeOH purity	1 PPM
9.	Total DMC to fresh feed GLY ratio	2
10.	RD column liquid distillate CO_2 mole fraction	10 PPM
	Design dof	
1.	RD column pressure	2.45 bar
2.	Co-product column (C1) pressure	0.48 bar
3.	C2 column (C2) pressure	0.15 bar
4.	Product column (C3) pressure	0.1 bar
5.	No. of rectifying trays in RD column	24
6.	Location of LP azeotrope stream into the RD	Tray no. 12
7.	No. of reactive trays in RD column	18
8.	No. of trays in C1 column	21
9.	No. of trays in C2 column	15
10.	No. of trays in C3 column	8
11.	FEHE Cooled GC Stream Temperature	50° C

LP azeotrope as the top product, which is recycled to the RD column's rectification zone. The C2 column processes RD column bottoms, recovering GC and GLC in the bottom stream and excess DMC in the top stream, recycled to the RD column after blending with fresh DMC. The C3 column specializes in recovering GLC from the top and GC from the bottom. Adjustments may be needed for exit streams of the side-reaction product CO_2. The essential modification involves incorporating a vapor distillate stream from the RD column to facilitate CO_2 exit from the process. Now, the process flow sheet includes the RD column, followed by C1, C2, and C3 columns.

We aim to achieve a near-optimal economic steady-state design to produce 10 kmol/h of glycerol carbonate with a purity of 99.64 mol%. The processing system under scrutiny possesses 10 steady-state operating degrees of freedom (DOFs) and 11 equipment design DOFs. The specification variables corresponding to these DOFs are detailed in the accompanying Table 2. We wish to adjust the specification variables to minimize an economic cost objective, J, subject to process constraints. J is defined as

$J = \text{TAC} + \text{IMC}$

where the total annualized cost TAC = Total Capital Cost/PBP + Total Operating Cost with the payback period (PBP) taken as 3 years.

The incremental material cost IMC term in J accounts for very slight differences in overall plant material balances of the three flowsheets considered. All flowsheet designs are developed for an identical GC product rate of 10 kmol/h and purity of 99.64 mol%. Also, the MeOH co-product purity is fixed at 99.5 mol%.

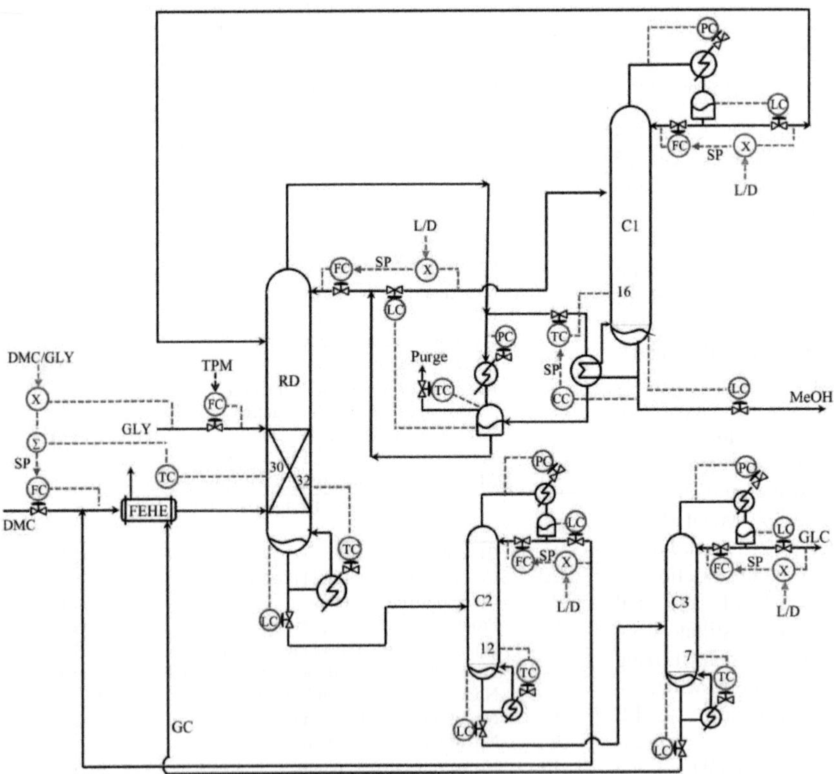

Figure 2: Control Structure of Proposed design

4. Plantwide Control

The evaluation of dynamic controllability for the proposed design involves the development of a conventional decentralized control system, subjected to rigorous dynamic simulations to assess its performance against anticipated principal disturbances. The primary disturbance considered as a flow and composition changes in the throughput manipulator (TPM), with the limiting glycerol reactant fresh feed rate serving as the TPM. Synthesis of regulatory control loops is carried out to effectively close the unit material and energy balances, as well as the overall plantwide material balance, as illustrated in Figure 2. Ensuring stoichiometric balance, the total (fresh + recycle) DMC rate into the RD column reactive zone is maintained in ratio with the fresh glycerol feed rate (TPM). Standard LV control loops are applied across all columns, with the regulation of reflux drum and bottom sump levels achieved through the manipulation of distillate and bottoms rates, respectively. The column pressure is controlled by adjusting the condenser duty. On the RD column, the overhead pressure is managed by manipulating the auxiliary condenser duty, while the condensate temperature is controlled through the manipulation of the vapour distillate rate. Maintaining the RD distillate in proximity to the HP azeotrope involves the maintenance of the reflux rate in ratio with the distillate rate (L/D). To prevent MeOH leakage down the bottoms, the sensitive temperature is controlled. In the MeOH recovery column (C1), the split stream valve on the RD column major overhead vapour is manipulated to regulate a sensitive tray temperature which is in cascade to the MeOH product composition. Finally, on the GC product column (C3), a sensitive tray temperature is controlled by manipulating the reboiler duty.

5. Economic and Sustainability Comparison

The economic and sustainability metrics of the proposed flowsheet design are compared with the existing RD pervaporation (RDPV) flowsheet developed by Sun et al. (Dayu Sun 2022) and the RD extractive distillation (RDED) flowsheet developed by Yu. (Yu 2020) All three flowsheets share the same GC product rate, GC product purity, and MeOH by-product purity, allowing for a consistent comparison. Identical cost correlations and pricing data are used for this analysis. The cost objective J, total energy consumed per kmol GC product, and glycerol

Table 3:Energy and sustainability comparison of different designs

	Proposed	**RDPV**	**RDED**
GLY/kmol GC Product	1.0146	1.0198	1.0265
DMC/kmol GC Product	1.0427	1.0533	1.051
ANI/kmol GC Product	0	0	0.0032
Energy/kmol GC Product	112.67	131.3	124.09
Incremental Material Cost	0	0.0991	0.1332
TAC × 10^6 yr^{-1} ($)	0.5341	0.8099	0.5344
Cost objective (*J*)	0.5341	0.909	0.6666

and DMC reactants consumed per kmol GC product serve as the economic and sustainability metrics. The results, detailed in Table 3, reveal that the proposed process flowsheet design is the most cost-effective, with a 70% and 24% advantage in cost objective J over the RDPV and RDED designs, respectively. Additionally, the total energy consumption per kmol GC product is significantly lower, with advantages of 16% and 10% compared to RDPV and RDED, respectively. Furthermore, the incremental material cost (IMC) for the proposed design indicates superior material utilization efficiency compared to the alternative designs. Notably, the proposed process design outperforms both the RDPV and RDED designs in terms of economic efficiency, energy usage, and material efficiency. It is worth mentioning that RDPV faces the drawback of periodic membrane replacement, while RDED deals with the periodic makeup for the loss of the aniline entrainer in trace amounts in the product streams during sustained continuous operation.

6. Conclusion

In this study, we have successfully synthesized and designed a 4-column flowsheet for the valorisation of glycerol into glycerol carbonate (GC) through transesterification with dimethyl carbonate (DMC). Our proposed process design proves to be notably superior to the existing alternatives, namely RDPV and RDED process designs, in both economic and sustainability metrics. The cost objective J for the alternative flowsheets is higher by 70% and 24%, respectively, compared to our proposed design. Similarly, the energy consumption per kmol GC product is 16% and 10% higher in the alternative designs. While the material utilization efficiency of our proposed design is marginally better, rigorous dynamic simulations affirm its robust controllability. A conventional decentralized control system adeptly manages principal disturbances, ensuring tight control over product quality. This comprehensive design exhibits the potential to significantly enhance the economics of the biodiesel 'green' fuel value chain.

References

Bor-Yih Yu. 2020. "Development of two plant-wide glycerol carbonate production processes: Design, optimization and environmental analysis." *Journal of the Taiwan Institute of Chemical Engineers* 19-25.

Dayu Sun, Lijing Gao, Ruiping Wei, Jin Zhang, Xiaomei Pan, and Guomin Xiao. 2022. "Process design ,economic optimization,and enviromental assesment for production of glycerol carbonate via reactive distillation with pervaporation." *Industrial & Engineering Chemistry* 16552-16564.

H.W. Tan, A.R. Abdul Aziz, M.K. Aroua. 2013. "Glycerol production and its applications as a raw material: A review." *Renewable and Sustainable Energy Reviews* 27: 118-127.

S. Sahani, S. N.Upadhyay, Y. C Sharma. 2020. "Critical review on production of glycerol carbonate from byproduct glycerol through transesterification." *Industrial & Engineering Chemistry Research* 33: 67-88.

Flavio Manenti, Gintaras V. Reklaitis (Eds.), Proceedings of the 34th European Symposium on Computer Aided Process Engineering / 15th International Symposium on Process Systems Engineering (ESCAPE34/PSE24), June 2-6, 2024, Florence, Italy
 http://dx.doi.org/10.1016/B978-0-443-28824-1.50230-1

System optimization of hybrid processes for CO_2 capture

Luca Riboldi,[a,*] Sai Gokul Subraveti,[a] Rubén Mocholi Montañés,[a] Donghoi Kim,[a] Simon Roussanaly,[a] Rahul Anantharaman[a]

[a]*SINTEF Energy Research, 7019 Trondheim, Norway*
luca.riboldi@sintef.no

Abstract

An optimization framework is developed to investigate the techno-economic potential of optimal hybrid process designs for post-combustion CO_2 capture, where a hybrid process involves a combination of different CO_2 capture technologies. System level optimization (i.e., system optimization) is compared with optimizing the capture technologies in sequence (i.e., cascade optimization). The technologies considered to be combined in a hybrid configuration are a vacuum pressure swing adsorption (VPSA) process and a membrane process. Fit-for-purpose models of each of these processes are developed and integrated with a detailed techno-economic analysis (TEA) model to allow CO_2 avoidance cost as a key metric for optimization. The optimization results showed that both system and cascade optimization are able to approach a similar optimal hybrid process design. Cascade optimization obtained a minor improvement in terms of overall cost at the price of a significantly higher computational time. If a stream recycle is implemented, a feature that can reduce the cost of about 1%, system optimization is preferable as the iterative effort required to solve the recycle configuration would lead to an excessively high computational time for cascade optimization.

Keywords: CO_2 capture, optimization, hybrid processes, techno-economic analysis.

1. Introduction

A hybrid process is a combination of different technologies selected to perform a separation process in an efficient manner. When a single technology is used to perform a specific separation process, it is often required to operate at non-ideal conditions. Hence, standalone technologies must normally trade off some efficiency to match the case-specific operating conditions and achieve the targeted separation. Conversely, hybrid processes offer increased flexibility by combining multiple technologies. The underlying idea is to put each technology in the conditions at which its performance is maximized by tailoring the hybrid solution to the given application. Among the most relevant applications for hybrid processes, there is CO_2 capture. There exist several separation technologies to capture CO_2. A multitude of potential hybrid configurations for CO_2 capture has been proposed (Song et al., 2018). Different studies have shown that hybrid processes can fare well with respect to single technologies, for instance reducing the energy consumption (Mat et al., 2019). However, there are also expected disadvantages connected to the implementation of hybrid processes. A key disadvantage concerns the increased complexity of the system. Particularly relevant is the difficulty of identifying the optimal design of the hybrid process.

In this work, we investigate how to identify optimal designs of hybrid processes for CO_2 capture. The importance of design optimization at the system level (i.e., system optimization) is investigated and compared to the more standard practice involving the independent optimization of the single steps of a hybrid configuration (i.e., cascade optimization). To investigate the impact of the different approaches to hybrid process design optimization, a hybrid concept is selected with VPSA and membrane technology.

2. Modelling framework

2.1. Hybrid process

A schematic representation of the VPSA-membrane hybrid process is presented in *Figure 1*. The hybrid configuration consists of a first VPSA step for bulk CO_2 separation and a second membrane step for final CO_2 purification. The hybrid configuration can also involve stream recycle, where the retentate gas from the membrane stage(s) is recycled to the VPSA process.

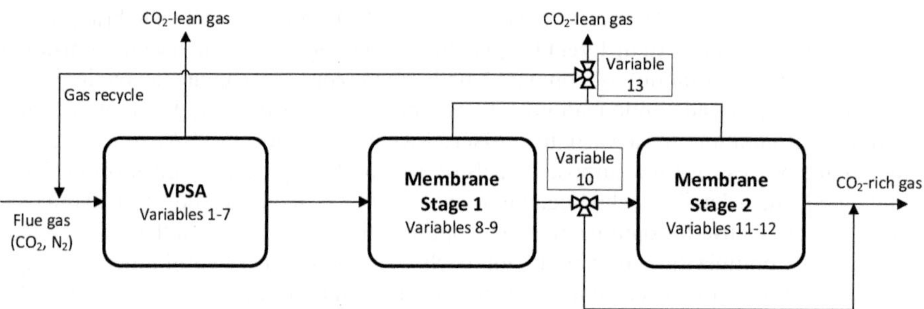

Figure 1. Process scheme of the VPSA-membrane hybrid process.

2.2. Machine learning model of VPSA process

The VPSA process uses an activated carbon as adsorbent material. The rigorous model of the VPSA process is based on a set of partial differential equations as outlined by (Haghpanah et al., 2013). To allow for optimization, an artificial neural networks (ANN) model was developed (the ANN architecture consists of one input layer with 8 decision variables, two hidden layers with 20 neurons each, and an output with one output), trained (using Bayesian regularization with backpropagation algorithm) and validated (using an independent dataset of 600 samples: $R2>0.98$). Previous studies demonstrated very good capabilities of ANNs in predicting the performance of VPSA processes (Subraveti et al., 2019). The VPSA model simulates a 5-step cycle: adsorption (ADS), high-pressure reflux (HR), blowdown (BLO), purge (PUR) and light product pressurization (LPP).

2.3. Membrane multi-stage model

The membrane gas separation step is simulated with an established multi-stage membrane design and optimization framework (Roussanaly et al., 2017). The model represents a mature membrane technology (i.e., MTR Polaris), with the following characteristics: permeance: 5.94 Sm^3/m^2barh, selectivity: 50. One or two membrane stages are simulated depending on the most efficient layout to meet the gas separation requirements.

2.4. Techno-economic analysis model

A techno-economic analysis (TEA) model is integrated into the overall modelling framework. The TEA model, based on the guidelines outlined by (Roussanaly et al., 2021), estimates capital and operational expenditures. The former with a bottom-up approach, the latter based on utilities consumption and standard factors for maintenance and labor.

3. Optimization of the hybrid process

3.1. Optimization problem

The CO_2 capture technologies must treat the industrial flue gas considered and return a product gas stream which: (i) has a CO_2 concentration of at least 95%; (ii) contains at least 90% of the CO_2 originally in the flue gas. Those requirements constitute the CO_2 purity and capture rate constraints of the optimization problem. The objective is to minimize the CO_2 avoidance cost (CAC). The CAC is defined as the ratio between the sum of the annualized cost and the annualized emissions avoided. The process design degrees of freedom are the variables listed in Table 1, for a maximum of 13 optimization variables (see also Figure 1). Variables 11 and 12, referring to the pressure levels of the second membrane stage, are relevant only in the case of a 2-stage membrane layout. Variable 13 is the recovery level of the membrane step. If stream recycle is considered, this parameter can be optimized as it affects the amount of gas that will be recirculated into the VPSA step. Conversely, if there is no stream recycle, the recovery of the membrane step contributes to the final recovery rate of the hybrid process – a process constraint – hence it is determined by the recovery achieved by the VPSA step. The optimizations used a genetic algorithm (GA).

Table 1. Optimization variables and optimization bounds

Variables VPSA	Var. no.	Bounds	Variables Membrane	Var. no.	Bounds Stage 1	Bounds Stage 2
High pressure (bar)	1	1.05 – 3.6	High pressure (bar)	8/11†	1.1 – 50	1.1 – 50
Low pressure (bar)	2	0.01 – 0.5	Low pressure (bar)	9/12†	0.05 – 0.9	0.05 – 0.9
Interstitial vel. BLO (m/s)	3	0.45 – 2.5	No. membr. stages	10	1 – 2	
Interstitial vel. PUR (m/s)	4	0.2 – 1.0	Recovery membr. stages	13‡	0.4 – 0.95	
ADS time (s)	5	100 – 500				
Factor PUR time	6	0.1 – 0.99				
Column size (m)	7	6 – 9				

†These variables apply only when two membrane stages are considered
‡This variable applies only when recycle is considered

3.2. Cascade optimization

Cascade optimization implies that the two capture technologies are optimized in sequence. The industrial gas provides the input conditions for the optimization of the first step – the VPSA process. Optimization variables 1 to 7 are used to determine a design that minimizes the CAC associated with VPSA. A single constraint applies to this case: a target capture rate without stream recycle (different capture rate levels are tested as discussed in the following) or $\geq 90\%$ with stream recycle (as this will make up the entire hybrid process capture rate). The CO_2-enriched gas produced by VPSA is sent to the membrane stage(s). In this case, the relevant optimization variables are 8 to 13. The CO_2 purity constraint ($\geq 95\%$) applies, while a capture rate constraint (subjected to the capture rate achieved from VPSA to ensure meeting the overall requirement $\geq 90\%$) applies only if stream recycle is not implemented. This optimization strategy splits the optimization burden between the two process steps, decreasing the number of variables for each of them – i.e., the search space for the optimal design. On the other hand, it fails to capture the entire system perspective, with the risk that the two optimal solutions for VPSA and membrane steps result in a suboptimal solution for the hybrid process. This is particularly evident when considering VPSA optimization. If the VPSA is optimized independently, the minimum cost would most likely be achieved by designing a process performing the bare minimum separation duty, i.e., lowest allowed CO_2 enrichment and capture rate. However, these conditions are not favorable for the membrane step, with the risk of providing a suboptimal system performance. To account for this, the cascade optimization routine is set up such as to test a matrix of minimum CO_2 purity and capture rate levels at the outlet of the VPSA process:

- 10 VPSA CO_2 purity levels tested, evenly spaced between 30% and 75%
- 4 VPSA CO_2 capture rate levels tested, evenly spaced between 90.5% and 99.5%

This implies that (10X4) 40 optimizations are performed to identify the overall optimum.

3.3. System optimization

System optimization sees the system as a whole and optimized it as such. This implies a single optimization process, including optimization variables 1 to 13 and the two hybrid process constraints on CO_2 purity (i.e., $\geq$ 95%) and capture rate (i.e., $\geq$ 90%). This optimization strategy allows to inherently explore the mutual influences of the two capture technologies and, if successfully implemented, to seek for the system optimum. The disadvantage is that of increased complexity of the optimization problem, which must explore a space that is significantly larger than those from the cascade optimization.

4. Results of process design optimization

The VPSA-membrane hybrid process is designed to capture CO_2 from an industrial flue gas with a volumetric CO_2 concentration of 15%. The gas stream is assumed to be a binary mixture of CO_2 and N_2. The gas flow rate is assumed to be 200 t/h.

4.1. Parameters for optimization

The following key parameters for the GA algorithm were selected for the *cascade optimization*:

- Population size: 30 X number of optimization variables
- Number of generations: 100

And for the *system optimization*:

- Population size: 60 X number of optimization variables
- Number of generations: 200

For *cascade optimization* the selected population size and number of generations showed fit to obtain a good approximation of the optimum. Conversely, a sensitivity analysis had to be performed for *system optimization*. The parameters reported above appear to be a convenient compromise.

4.2. System optimization vs. cascade optimization for baseline hybrid process

Ten runs were performed for both *cascade* and *system optimization* to identify optimal designs of the baseline hybrid process, i.e., not including stream recycle. The obtained results in terms of CAC are summed up in Table 2.

Cascade and *system optimization* obtained similar cost numbers, with similar levels of standard deviation in the results. *Cascade optimization* achieved slightly lower cost figures. However, the difference is minimal (0.3% on average) and arguably negligible. On the other hand, the execution time is, on average, more than 4 times smaller for *system optimization*. The reason is the combination of CO_2 purities and capture rates to be investigated by *cascade optimization*. An a priori knowledge of the system could allow reducing the range of combinations tested, consequently reducing the gap in execution time. However, such a gap will hardly be closed without sacrificing some accuracy.

Table 2. Results of cascade and system optimization for the design of the hybrid process. The results of system optimization include the possibility of stream recycle.

Optimization strategy	Number of runs	CAC* avg (€/t)	CAC* min (€/t)	CAC* max (€/t)	CAC* std. dev. (€/t)	Execution time avg (s)
Cascade (w/o recirc.)	10	56.1	55.4	56.7	0.4	9120
System (w/o recirc.)	10	56.3	55.8	56.9	0.4	2053
System (w/ recirc.)	10	55.7	54.9	56.4	0.5	6882

Objective function (CAC) differs slightly from actual cost (CAC) because of penalty function

The process designs identified by *cascade* and *system optimization* that led to the minimum CAC are outlined in Table 3 for comparison. Very similar designs of the hybrid process are identified. *Cascade* and *system optimization* basically allocated the same separation duty to VPSA, which pre-concentrated CO_2 up to 45-46%. The larger differences can be noted in the pressure levels selected for the first membrane stage. However, this difference led to a minor difference in the overall cost split between the CO_2 capture technologies. All in all, it can be concluded that both optimization strategies approached what is presumably the optimal VPSA-membrane hybrid process design.

Table 3. Selected characteristics of process designs for minimum CAC.

VPSA-membrane hybrid process	Cascade opt. (w/o recirc.)	System opt. (w/o recirc.)	System opt. (w/ recirc.)
Optimized process			
High pressure VPSA (bar)	2.6	2.4	2.5
Low pressure VPSA (bar)	0.3	0.3	0.3
High pressure memb. stg. 1 (bar)	2.0	4.5	1.8
Low pressure memb. stg. 1 (bar)	0.2	0.5	0.2
High pressure memb. stg. 2 (bar)	2.8	2.5	-
Low pressure memb. stg. 2 (bar)	0.8	0.9	-
Performances			
Purity VPSA	45 %	46 %	54 %
Recovery VPSA	97 %	97 %	97 %
Purity memb./hybrid	95 %	95 %	95 %
Recovery memb.	93 %	93 %	81 %
Recovery hybrid	90 %	90 %	97 %
Power VPSA (kW)	7594	7573	10472
Power memb. (kW)	4181	4230	2495
Power hybrid (kW)	11774	11803	12967
CAC VPSA (€/t)	38.8	39.3	46.1
CAC memb. (€/t)	16.6	16.4	8.5
CAC hybrid (€/t)	55.4	55.7	54.7

4.3. System optimization for hybrid process with recycle

Ten additional optimization runs were performed for *system optimization* to identify the optimal design of the hybrid process when implementing stream recycle. *Cascade optimization* was not used in this case as the iterative effort required to solve a recycle configuration would have led to excessive computational time. On the other hand, *system optimization* achieved similar effectiveness in finding the optimum design at reduced execution time, hence it was used. The obtained results are reported in Table 2. *System optimization* with stream recycle slightly decreases the CAC (ca. 1% on average), while at the same time achieves higher CO_2 capture rate (up to 97%, meaning that in this case the related constraint does not limit the optimum). The iterative procedure to solve a system with stream recycle resulted in a more than three-fold increase in execution time.

The process designs identified by *system optimization*, with and without stream recycle, that led to the minimum CAC are outlined in Table 3. The use of stream recycle affects the inlet gas to the hybrid process and, consequently, its optimal process design. The increased CO_2 concentration eases the gas separation duty of VPSA, which can efficiently concentrate CO_2 at higher levels – up to 54% compared to 46% observed without stream recycle. This, together with the increased capital expenditures due to the larger inlet gas flow rate, led to a higher cost associated to the VPSA step – 46.1 against 39.3 €/t. A single stage membrane unit is shown sufficient to perform the final CO_2 purification and the cost of the membrane step is almost halved – 16.4 against 8.5 €/t. Overall, a slight cost decrease (ca. 1 €/t) and higher capture rate was achieved with stream recycle.

5. Conclusions

Two approaches are studied to optimize a VPSA-membrane hybrid process and identify cost-efficient designs. *System optimization* considers the system as a whole and optimized it as such. *Cascade optimization* focuses on one capture technology at a time, meaning that the two are optimized in sequence.

- The two optimization strategies identified a very similar design of the hybrid process that minimizes the cost.
- *System and cascade optimization* achieved basically the same cost figures (0.3% difference on average), but *system optimization* is four times faster.
- Stream recycle leads to a cost reduction of ca. 1 €/t and to a higher CO_2 capture rate. In such case, *system optimization* is the most convenient optimization strategy on the ground of reasonable computational time.

References

R. Haghpanah, A. Majumder, R. Nilam et al. (2013). Multiobjective Optimization of a Four-Step Adsorption Process for Postcombustion CO_2 Capture Via Finite Volume Simulation. Industrial & Engineering Chemistry Research 52, 11, 4249–65.

N.C. Mat & G.G. Lipscomb (2019). Global sensitivity analysis for hybrid membrane-cryogenic post combustion carbon capture process. Int. J. Greenh. Gas Control, 81, 157–169.

S. Roussanaly & R. Anantharaman (2017). Cost-optimal CO_2 capture ratio for membrane-based capture from different CO_2 sources. Chemical Engineering Journal, 327, 618–628.

S. Roussanaly, N. Berghout, T. Fout et al. (2021). Towards improved cost evaluation of Carbon Capture and Storage from industry. Int. J. Greenh. Gas Control, 106, 103263.

C. Song, Q. Liu, N. Ji et al. (2018). Alternative pathways for efficient CO_2 capture by hybrid processes—A review. Renewable and Sustainable Energy Reviews, 82, 215–231.

S. G. Subraveti, Z. Li, V. Prasad, and A. Rajendran. (2019). Machine Learning-Based Multiobjective Optimization of Pressure Swing Adsorption. Industrial and Engineering Chemistry Research, 58, 44, 20412–20422

Flavio Manenti, Gintaras V. Reklaitis (Eds.), Proceedings of the 34th European Symposium on Computer Aided Process Engineering / 15th International Symposium on Process Systems Engineering (ESCAPE34/PSE24), June 2-6, 2024, Florence, Italy
 http://dx.doi.org/10.1016/B978-0-443-28824-1.50231-3

Magnesia-based binders for stabilizing and improving soft soils

Mohamed Harun [a], Abdullahi Abdulrahman Muhudin [b], Umair Ali [a,c], Hammad Raza Khalid [a,c], Asad Hanif [a,c,*]

[a]*Civil and Environmental Engineering Department, King Fahd University of Petroleum and Minerals (KFUPM), Dhahran 31261, Saudi Arabia*
[b]*Architecture and City Design (ACD) Department, King Fahd University of Petroleum & Minerals (KFUPM), Dhahran 31261, Saudi Arabia*
[c]*Interdisciplinary Research Center for Construction and Building Materials, King Fahd University of Petroleum and Minerals, Dhahran 31261, Saudi Arabia*
**Corresponding author:* asad.hanif@kfupm.edu.sa

Abstract

In this work, the improvement and stabilization of soft soils with eco-friendly magnesia-based binders have been reviewed. Magnesia-based binders have gained much attention recently due to increasing environmental protection concerns. Their low environmental impact due to reduced carbon footprint and conservation of resources make them a useful alternative to ordinary Portland cement (OPC) for soil improvement. Further, their intrinsic characteristics, such as rapid setting and hardening without moist curing, are conducive to the rapid improvement of soft soils. In this research, the effects of incorporating reactive magnesia, magnesium oxychloride cement, magnesium, phosphate cement, and magnesium potassium phosphate cement in soils have been studied, and the corresponding influence on the mechanical, microstructural, and durability properties of MgO-solidified soils at different molar ratios, water-to-binder ratios, and curing times have been investigated. The results indicate a great potential and applicability of magnesia-based binders for improving soils under different climate construction environments..

Keywords: Soil stabilization; Reactive magnesia; $MgO/MgCl_2$ ratio; Mechanical properties.

1. Introduction

Soil stabilization refers to the procedure of enhancing the shear strength characteristics of soil, hence augmenting its ability to withstand loads. The use of soil stabilization techniques becomes necessary in cases when the existing soil conditions are unsuitable for supporting structural loads during construction. (Afrin, 2017). Soil stabilization refers to the modification of soil properties by chemical or physical methods with the objective of improving the engineering characteristics of the soil. The primary aim of soil stabilization is to enhance the soil's carrying capacity, resistance to weathering, and permeability(Zaliha et al., 2013). Mechanical stabilization involves the combination of many soil types to enhance the characteristics of the original soil, whilst other approaches include the incorporation of specific additives(Archibong et al., 2020). Chemical stabilization is a well recognized and successful technique used to enhance soil qualities by the incorporation of chemicals into soil matrices. The typical constituents are cement, lime, fly ash, and bituminous material. Commonly used compounds include sodium silicate, acrylamide, N-methylolacrylamide, polyurethane epoxy resins, aminoplasts, phenoplasts, and lignosulfonates, among other substances (Sina Kazemain, 2012). The cumulative results derived from recent research investigations highlight the considerable potential of binders containing magnesia for the purpose of soil stabilization. The use of magnesium oxychloride cement (MOC) has been seen to improve soil compaction and mechanical characteristics, demonstrating early strength benefits that are advantageous for expediting building schedules(Wang et al., 2022). Moreover, the incorporation of waste marble powder into magnesium phosphate cement (MPC) has shown significant enhancements in the load-bearing capacity and shear strength of soils. This approach provides a dual advantage by simultaneously stabilizing the soil and using waste materials(Rai et al., 2020). The use of magnesia-based binders also offers an ecologically sustainable option, so contributing to the reduction of carbon dioxide emissions and energy consumption throughout their manufacturing process(Zhang et al., 2023).

2. Magnesia-based binders

2.1. Magnesium Oxychloride Cement (MOC)

The discovery of magnesium oxychloride cement (MOC) occurred in close proximity to the development of portland cement. MOC pastes consist of a combination of MgO powder or calcined magnesite powder, whereby the primary constituent is MgO, and $MgCl_2$ solutions with specific concentrations within the $MgO\text{-}MgCl_2\text{-}H_2O$ system. The presence of two hydrate phases, namely $5Mg(OH)_2 \cdot MgCl_2 \cdot 8H_2O$ (referred to as the 5 phase) and $3Mg(OH)_2 \cdot MgCl_2 \cdot 8H_2O$ (referred to as the 3 phase), has been established as the primary factors contributing to the solidification and enhanced mechanical properties of magnesium oxychloride cement (MOC)(Dehua and Chuanmei, 1999). Magnesium oxychloride cement has several characteristics that surpass those of Portland cement. The material exhibits a notable level of fire resistance, a low degree of thermal conductivity, a significant resistance to abrasion, as well as notable compressive and flexural strengths. A variety of organic and inorganic aggregates, which may not possess the necessary properties for inclusion in Portland cement concrete, may be effectively used along with oxychloride cement(Dehua and Chuanmei, 1999). MOC has the following chemical equations(Li et al., 2020):

$$3MgO + MgCl_2 + 11H_2O \rightarrow 3Mg(OH)2 \bullet MgCl_2.8H_2O \quad (1)$$

$$5MgO + MgCl_2 + 13H_2O \rightarrow 5Mg(OH)_2\ MgCl_2.8H_2O \quad (2)$$

$$MgO + 2H_2O \rightarrow Mg(OH)_2 \quad (3)$$

2.2. Magnesium Phosphate Cement (MPC)

The formation of magnesium phosphate cements occurs via an acid-base reaction between magnesium oxide (MgO) and a soluble acid phosphate, often an ammonium or potassium phosphate(Walling and Provis, 2016), this reaction results in the creation of a magnesium phosphate salt that has cementitious characteristics, as shown by the following equation:

$$MgO + NH_4H_2PO_4 + 5H_2O \rightarrow NH_4MgPO_4.6H_2O \quad (4)$$

The main reaction product of Magnesium phosphate cement is a well-known crystal called struvite, or magnesium ammonium phosphate hexahydrate, $MgNH_4PO_4.6H_2O$ (Abbona and Boistelle, 1979).

Magnesium phosphate cements (MPCs) function very well because of their quick setting, high early strength, and high adhesive characteristics (Roy, 1988).

2.3. Magnesium potassium phosphate cement (MKPC)

Ammonium gas, a necessary consequence of the process, would, however, produce an unpleasant, sour smell, prompting efforts to replace Ammonium dihydrogen phosphate (ADP) with potassium dihydrogen phosphate (KDP) (Wagh et al., 1999). The KDP-based MPC might be referred to as magnesium potassium phosphate cement (MKPC). The primary reaction product is k-struvite, also known as magnesium potassium phosphate hexahydrate ($MgKPO_4.6H_2O$, MKP)(Air, 2006). MKPC has the following chemical equation(Lu et al., 2016):

$$MgO+KH_2PO_4+5H_2O \rightarrow MgKPO_4.6H_2O \quad (5)$$

2.4. Magnesium-doped cement

The distinctive capacity of reactive magnesium oxide cement (RMC) to effectively capture and retain ambient carbon dioxide (CO2), coupled with its potential to achieve significant strength enhancement, makes it a very appealing substance for sustainable building practices(Khalil et al., 2021). Magnesium oxide (MgO) cements are composed of a combination of Portland cement (PC) and reactive magnesia, with varying amounts determined by their specific intended use. The sustainability benefits of magnesium oxide (MgO) compared to Portland cement (PC) include several factors. Firstly, MgO has the ability to sequester significant amounts of carbon dioxide (CO2). Secondly, it offers considerable durability improvement due to the higher resistance of its hydration and carbonation products in aggressive environments, particularly in situations where reinforcement is absent. Thirdly, MgO exhibits lower sensitivity to impurities, allowing for the utilization of large quantities of waste and industrial by-products. Lastly, MgO has the potential to be fully recycled when used as the sole binder, as its carbonation process generates magnesium carbonates, which are the primary source for producing magnesia (Unluer and Al-Tabbaa, 2013). Table 1 presents physical and chemical properties of raw materials for magnesia-based binders.

Table 1 Physical and chemical properties of raw materials for magnesia-based binders

Compound Name	Appearance	Density (g/cm3)	Molecular Weight
Magnesium Oxide (MgO)	White Powder	3.58	40.3
Potassium Dihydrogen Phosphate (KH_2PO_4)	White powder	2.338	136.09
Ammonium Dihydrogen Phosphate (H_6NO_4P)	White crystals or crystalline powder	1.8	115.03
Magnesium Chloride (Cl_2Mg)	white or colorless crystalline solid	2.32	95.21

3. Soil stabilization by magnesia-based binders

3.1. Compressive strength

Research indicates that magnesia-based binders can enhance the compressive strength of soft soils, crucial for the load-bearing capacity of structures. The unconfined compressive strength (UCS) of such soils is influenced by the H2O/MgCl2 molar ratio and curing time, requiring precise chemical balancing (Liu et al., 2023).Ideal binder compositions have been identified for maximum UCS using methods like response surface methodology (Zhang et al., 2023). Optimal MgO, MgCl2, and H2O levels have been linked to quick early strength gains, beneficial for construction timelines (Wang et al., 2022). The combination of magnesium phosphate cement (MPC) with organic materials like jute fibers has improved soil toughness (Pandey et al., 2022). In sulfate-rich soils, magnesium-based binders with GGBS have exceeded the strength provided by lime (Seco et al., 2017). MgO has also stabilized peat soils effectively, particularly with an optimal OPC to MgO ratio after proper curing (Yacob and Som, 2020). These findings highlight the complex potential of magnesia-based binders for soil stabilization, necessitating customized approaches for different soil types. Table 2 summarizes compressive strength and various properties reported in the literature, while Figure 1 shows the microstructural attributes of such binders.

Table 2 Magnesia based binder soil stabilized properties

Author	Compressive Strength	Other Reported Properties	Remarks
(Liu et al., 2023)	UCS varies with H2O/MgCl2 ratio and curing time	Elastic modulus correlates with UCS; pH value influences stability	Optimal H2O/MgCl2 ratio: 17–20 for MgO/MgCl2 of 3:1–5:1, 29–41 for 6:1–7:1
(Zhang et al., 2023)	Optimal UCS at MgO/MgCl2 of 8.61, MOC content 18%, UCS 2.56 MPa	Water resistance affected by fly ash content	Optimal fly ash content 20.36% for SC of 0.76
(Wang et al., 2022)	Best compressive strength with MgO: MgCl2: H2O at 3.68:1:15	Better durability than traditional cement; poor water resistance	Early strength characteristics with MgO content 5.5%-6%
(Rai et al., 2020)	Max strength 1953.65 kPa with 7.5% MPC, 15% MP at 28 days	Increases MDD and CBR value; reduces Atterberg limits	Improved shear strength with MPC and MP addition
(Pandey et al., 2022)	UCS improves with MPC; max 3.51 MPa at 12% MPC	Enhanced durability with 3 cycles of capillary soaking and drying	UCS further increased to 8.12 MPa with 1% jute fibers at 12% MPC
(Seco et al., 2017)	Improved with PC-8, up to 2–5 MPa, further with GGBS to 11–13 MPa	Reduced swelling; absence of ettringite	PC-8 combined with GGBS performs better than lime-GGBS
(Yi et al., 2016)	MgO-activated GGBS yields higher strength over various periods, >3.5 MPa strength after 3 years with GGBS addition to MgO	Improved permeability; similar C-S-H hydration products	Highest strength with MgO-activated GGBS compared to lime/PC
(Wang et al., 2017)	UCS increases with MgO content and curing time	Soil improvement due to Mg(OH)2 formation	Slight reduction in strength after 28 days noted
(Yacob and Som, 2020)	UCS improved with 50:50 OPC to MgO, achieving 32.97 kPa at 28 days	Significant pH increases towards basicity	Critical role of MgO in stabilization noted with OPC to MgO ratio
(Salem et al., 2020)	CBR value increased by about 1200% with 0.80% nano-MgO	Swelling ratio significantly decreased	Substantial compressive strength improvement with nano-MgO
(Yao et al., 2019)	UCS significantly improved with nano-MgO addition	Ductility and microstructure enhanced; acid attack reduces strength	Optimum nano-MgO content at 15‰ for cement content of 13%
(Seco et al., 2022)	Stabilization with Mg additives comparable to traditional lime	Effective reduction in leaching of sulfate, Ca, Mg, and Cl-	Mg additives with GGBS achieve UCS close to or surpassing traditional cement
(Espuelas et al., 2017)	MgO enhances clay bricks' mechanical properties, comparable to lime	Better water absorption performance with MgO	Fine-tuning MgO levels for optimal brick performance needed
(Yi et al., 2012)	Reactive MgO efficiently activates GGBS, yielding higher strength	Lower permeability with MgO activation	Reactive MgO costlier but yields higher strength than PC

3.2. Density, unit weight, and miscellaneous properties

Utilizing a combination of magnesium phosphate cement (MPC) and marble powder (MP), researchers achieved notable enhancements in soil stabilization. With the application of 7.5% MPC and 15% MP, soils reached a UCS of 1953.65 kPa, increased MDD, and an improved CBR value after a 28-day curing period. These enhancements correlate with a denser soil structure and greater load-bearing capabilities. Additionally, a reduction in Atterberg limits and OMC was observed, suggesting a more stable soil with less moisture sensitivity, conducive to robust engineering applications (Rai et al., 2020). Studies by (Wang et al., 2022), (Yao et al., 2019), and (Yi et al., 2016) highlight that magnesia-based binders enhance the durability of solidified soils. These binders not only confer greater durability than traditional cement in MOC solidified soil, as evidenced by better maintenance of mechanical properties after cycles of capillary soaking and drying, but they also show less environmental impact, with leaching of heavy metals remaining below drinking water standards over a three-year period, except for nickel. Moreover, the swelling behavior of soils is significantly improved upon treatment with magnesium-based binders, with this Study (Seco et al., 2017) showing a marked decrease in natural swelling and better dimensional stability post-immersion compared to lime-treated soils, and Study (Salem et al., 2020) demonstrating that nano-MgO can reduce swelling ratios to just a fraction of untreated soil levels. Study (Yi et al., 2012) reveals that MgO as an activator substantially enhances soil permeability, yielding the lowest values relative to other activators. These findings indicate the efficacy of magnesia-based binders in not only bolstering the structural integrity and environmental soundness of treated soils but also in mitigating swelling and enhancing permeability, thereby reinforcing the suitability of these treated soils for diverse engineering uses.

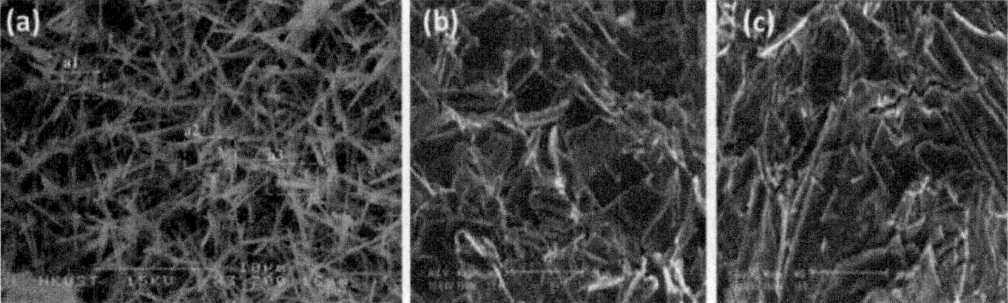

Figure 1 Microstructure of different magnesia-based binders (Ding et al., 2012; Hu et al., 2016)

4. Conclusions

In this work, the improvement and stabilization of soft soils with eco-friendly magnesia-based binders have been reviewed. Magnesia-based binders have exhibited great potential in improving the compressive strength, shear strength, and microstructure of soft soils. In this research, the effects of incorporating reactive magnesia, magnesium oxychloride cement, magnesium, phosphate cement, and magnesium potassium phosphate cement in soils have been studied, and the corresponding influence on the mechanical, microstructural, and durability properties of MgO-solidified soils at different molar ratios, water-to-binder ratios, and curing times have been investigated. The results indicate a great potential and applicability of magnesia-based binders for improving soils under different climate construction environments.

Acknowledgement: The authors acknowledge the project grant # EC231004 from KFUPM titled, ''Development and application of Magnesium Oxychloride Cement for Stabilizing Soft Soils".

References

Abbona, F., Boistelle, R., 1979. J. Cryst. Growth 46, 339–354.

Afrin, H., 2017. Int. J. Transp. Eng. Technol. 3, 19. https://doi.org/10.11648/j.ijtet.20170302.12

Air, B., 2006. United States Patent (19) 3–7.

Archibong, G.A., et al., 2020. a Review of the Principles and Methods of Soil Stabilization. Int. J. Adv. Acad. Res. | Sci. 6, 2488–9849.

Dehua, D., Chuanmei, Z., 1999. Cem. Concr. Res. 29, 1365–1371. https://doi.org/10.1016/S0008-8846(98)00247-6

Ding, Z., et al., 2012. Ceram. Int. 38, 6281–6288. https://doi.org/10.1016/j.ceramint.2012.04.083

Espuelas, S., et al., 2017. Appl. Clay Sci. 146, 23–26. https://doi.org/10.1016/j.clay.2017.05.034

Hu, C., et al., 2016. Constr. Build. Mater. 105, 496–502. https://doi.org/10.1016/j.conbuildmat.2015.12.182

Khalil, A., et al., 2021. Constr. Build. Mater. 308, 125102. https://doi.org/10.1016/j.conbuildmat.2021.125102

Li, K., Wang, Y., Yao, N., Zhang, A., 2020. Constr. Build. Mater. 255, 119381. https://doi.org/10.1016/j.conbuildmat.2020.119381

Liu, W., et al., 2023. Constr. Build. Mater. 393, 132018. https://doi.org/10.1016/j.conbuildmat.2023.132018

Lu, Z., et al., 2016. Constr. Build. Mater. 119, 107–112. https://doi.org/10.1016/j.conbuildmat.2016.05.060

Pandey, A., et al., 2022. Transp. Geotech. 37, 100854. https://doi.org/10.1016/j.trgeo.2022.100854

Rai, P., et al., 2020. Int. J. Geosynth. Gr. Eng. 6. https://doi.org/10.1007/s40891-020-00212-3

Roy, D.M., 1988. U.S. woman Eng. 34, 32–38.

Salem, L.A., et al., 2020. Period. Eng. Nat. Sci. 8, 533–541. https://doi.org/10.21533/pen.v8i1.1210

Seco, A., et al., 2022. Int. J. Pavement Eng. 23, 1840–1850. https://doi.org/10.1080/10298436.2020.1825711

Seco, A., et al., 2017. Appl. Clay Sci. 135, 457–464. https://doi.org/10.1016/j.clay.2016.10.033

Sina Kazemain, 2012. Sci. Res. Essays 7, 2104–2111. https://doi.org/10.5897/sre11.1186

Unluer, C., Al-Tabbaa, A., 2013. Cem. Concr. Res. 54, 87–97. https://doi.org/10.1016/j.cemconres.2013.08.009

Wagh, A.S., et al., 1999. J. Nucl. Mater. 265, 295–307. https://doi.org/10.1016/S0022-3115(98)00650-3

Walling, S.A., Provis, J.L., 2016. Chem. Rev. 116, 4170–4204. https://doi.org/10.1021/acs.chemrev.5b00463

Wang, D., Wang, H., Wang, X., 2017. Mar. Georesources Geotechnol. 35, 878–886. https://doi.org/10.1080/1064119X.2016.1258095

Wang, F., Jin, F., Shen, Z., Al-Tabbaa, A., 2016. J. Hazard. Mater. 318, 302–307. https://doi.org/10.1016/j.jhazmat.2016.07.018

Wang, H., et al., 2022. Adv. Mater. Sci. Eng. 2022. https://doi.org/10.1155/2022/5195450

Yacob, L.S., Som, A.M., 2020. Malaysian J. Anal. Sci. 24, 578–586.

Yao, K., et al., 2019. Constr. Build. Mater. 206, 160–168. https://doi.org/10.1016/j.conbuildmat.2019.01.221

Yi, Y., et al., 2012. Proc., 4th Int. Conf. Grouting Deep Mix. ASCE, Reston, VA 444–453.

Yi, Y., et al., 2016.. Can. Geotech. J. 55, 773–782.

Zaliha, S.Z.S et al., 2013. Aust. J. Basic Appl. Sci. 7, 258–265.

Zhang, H., et al., 2023. Adv. Mater. Sci. Eng. 2023, 1–15. https://doi.org/10.1155/2023/3054786

Flavio Manenti, Gintaras V. Reklaitis (Eds.), Proceedings of the 34th European Symposium on Computer Aided Process Engineering / 15th International Symposium on Process Systems Engineering (ESCAPE34/PSE24), June 2-6, 2024, Florence, Italy
 http://dx.doi.org/10.1016/B978-0-443-28824-1.50232-5

Effective selection of green organics and natural deep eutectic solvents as advanced entrainers by COSMO-RS and group contributions methods for enhanced design of extractive distillation

Dhoni Hartanto[a,b], Boelo Schuur[c], Anton A Kiss[a], André B. de Haan[a,*]

[a]Department of Chemical Engineering, Delft University of Technology, Van der Maasweg 9, 2629 HZ Delft, The Netherlands

[b]Department of Chemical Engineering, Faculty of Engineering, Universitas Negeri Semarang, Kampus Sekaran, Gunungpati, Semarang, 50229, Indonesia

[c]Sustainable Process Technology Group, Process and Catalysis Engineering Cluster, Faculty of Science and Technology, University of Twente, Enschede, The Netherlands.

**a.b.dehaan@tudelft.nl*

Abstract

Green organic entrainers and natural deep eutectic solvents (NADESs) possessing high boiling points and decomposition temperatures, exhibit considerable potential as advanced materials for green entrainers in extractive distillation. However, there is a wide range of solvents to choose from and their properties are only rarely available for use in process design and simulation. The present study aims to assess the selection parameters and examine the performance of and select green organic entrainers and NADESs for the separation of the close boiling mixture methylcyclohexane-toluene. The evaluation carried out was based on selectivity and relative volatility values obtained by using predictive models. COSMO-RS (a unimolecular quantum chemical calculation) was employed to predict the selectivity at infinite dilution, while group contribution methods such as UNIFAC and modified UNIFAC (Dortmund) were used to predict the relative volatility. According to the calculated results, the selectivity appeared a more important selection parameter than the performance index. The relative volatility prediction using the UNIFAC and UNIFAC Dortmund methods exhibits comparable trends to the selectivity results derived from COSMO-RS. However, the use of UNIFAC and modified UNIFAC (Dortmund) in predicting the relative volatility of NADES containing mixtures is limited due to the absence of functional group parameters. This CAPE study reveals that, based on the calculated selectivity (using COSMO-RS) and relative volatility (using UNIFAC, and modified UNIFAC (Dortmund)), most of the proposed green organic entrainers and NADESs exhibit a higher or comparable selectivity and relative volatility as the benchmark entrainers. This confirms the potential of the evaluated green entrainers with higher selectivity and relative volatility to enhance the design of extractive distillation. Therefore, the cost, energy and water consumption, as well as CO_2 emissions in the methylcyclohexane and toluene separation can be reduced.

Keywords: COSMO-RS, group contribution method, green organic entrainers, natural deep eutectic solvents, extractive distillation.

1. Introduction

Distillation is the predominant separation method in the chemical industry due to its numerous advantages (Rico-Ramírez and Diwekar, 2000). However, conventional distillation technology requires high energy consumption, consumes cooling water, incurs considerable costs, and generates significant amounts of CO_2 emissions, particularly when employed for the separation of close-boiling or azeotropic mixtures. Therefore, the utilization of extractive distillation (ED) along with the incorporation of entrainers is frequently employed to overcome the difficulty of the separation. Entrainers can provide interaction with a certain component, hence increasing its relative volatility and thereby facilitating separation. As a result, entrainers can decrease the energy, cost, and water consumption, as well as the emissions of CO_2 in the process. The selection of an entrainer has become a crucial stage in determining the most viable entrainer for the extractive distillation process because the performance of the entrainer determines the design and effectiveness of the extractive distillation process. The most common entrainers used are called conventional organic entrainers such as n-methyl pyrrolidone (NMP) and sulfolane. Nevertheless, these entrainers possess several disadvantages, including volatility, toxicity, lack of environmental friendliness, unsustainability, non-biodegradability, high energy consumption, and prohibition under regulations (George Wypych, 2019). Thus, the search for alternative entrainers that possess more environmentally friendly characteristics has acquired significant interest in recent years. Greener entrainers must exhibit additional features such as sustainability, low or non-toxicity, biodegradability, eco-friendliness, and/or derivates from bio-based materials (Yilmaz and Soylak, 2020). Some of greener entrainers such as ionic liquids, and bio-based entrainers such as Cyrene and glycerol have been studied (Ayuso et al., 2022; Brouwer & Schuur, 2021; and Hartanto et al., 2021). However, industrial-scale utilization of ionic liquids is constrained by their excessive cost, hazardous proclivity, and its limited biodegradability (Costa et al., 2017). In addition, some of bio-based entrainers have limitations due to their low boiling points and/or low decomposition temperatures. In this work, green organic entrainers and NADESs with a high boiling point, a high decomposition temperature, and green characteristic(s) are studied as improved and intensified entrainers. Selection parameters such as selectivity, capacity, and performance index are evaluated. The performance of each entrainers in methylcyclohexane-toluene mixture is examined using selectivity and relative volatility calculated by predictive models. COSMO-RS as a unimolecular quantum chemical calculation, is used to predict the activity coefficient at infinite dilution, while group contributions method such as UNIFAC and modified UNIFAC (Dortmund) is employed to calculate the relative volatility at finite dilution.

2. Methods

2.1. COSMO-RS simulation

The study utilized the COSMOthermX17 program (version C30_1705), which is based on the COSMO-RS concept, to compute the thermophysical properties of individual components and mixtures. Turbomole (version 7.1.1) was employed to optimize new compounds and generate their COSMO files. The COSMO-RS calculation was performed using the BP_TZVP_C30_1701 method with the COMSO density functional theory (DFT) parameterization to estimate the thermophysical properties.

2.2. Group contribution methods (GCMs) simulation

GCMs employ different methodologies for computing molecular interactions compared to COSMO-RS. GCMs are semi-empirical approaches that rely on the optimal binary interaction parameter of the segments obtained from empirical fitting. This study utilizes the original UNIversal Quasichemical Functional-group Activity Coefficients (UNIFAC) and the modified UNIFAC (Dortmund).

3. Results and discussion

3.1. Evaluation of selectivity, capacity, and performance index

As selection parameters, selectivity, capacity, and performance index can be utilized to identify the most efficient entrainer. Selectivity (*S*) stands for the capability of an entrainer to selectively interact with a particular compound over another. Capacity (*C*) refers to the amount of entrainer required for the extractive distillation process. While Performance Index (*PI*) is expressed as the combination of selectivity and capacity (Jiang et al., 2019). The infinite dilution (∞) method, which focuses on the solute-solvent interaction towards pure solvent, can be employed to achieve the maximum effect of interaction. It is crucial to assess the effectiveness of each selection parameter prior to identifying the parameter that can be used as a deciding factor. Figure 1 demonstrates a clear inverse relationship between selectivity and capacity for methylcyclohexane-toluene mixture with the addition of green organic entrainers and NADESs. It shows that increased selectivity results in decreased capacity, and conversely. Therefore, the performance index was examined to combine selectivity and capacity.

The performance index in the methylcyclohexane-toluene mixture exhibits an inverse correlation with selectivity but demonstrates a tendency to align with capacity. Thus, the capacity has a greater impact on the performance index compared to selectivity. It can be inferred that the performance index may exhibit a varying profile in relation to selectivity, or that the capacity depends upon the selectivity value. A higher selectivity value will have a greater impact on the performance index. In order to have a more comprehensive understanding of the extractive distillation performance, it is necessary to conduct further evaluations by process design. This should be done instead of solely relying on the performance index as the sole determinant for selecting an entrainer.

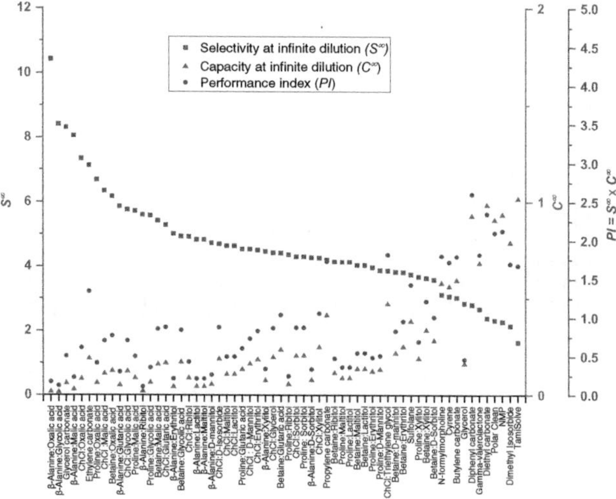

Figure 1. Selectivity, capacity, and performance index prediction of entrainers in methylcyclohexane - toluene mixture at temperature of 400 K.

However, to simulate the process design for all investigated entrainers will take a lot of time and effort. Therefore, this study recommends using selectivity as entrainer selection parameters as it has the most significant effect on the total annual cost calculation. Entrainers with higher selectivity will consistently yield a lower total annual cost and conversely (Momoh, 1991). Some researchers also confirm that selectivity plays a crucial role in determining the selection of entrainer for extractive distillation (Kyle & Leng, 1965; Krummen et al., 2000; Jiménez & Costa-López, 2003; Gutiérrez et al., 2012; and Sun et al., 2019).

3.2. Selectivity for methylcyclohexane-toluene

Selectivity can be calculated from the ratio of the activity coefficient. The activity coefficient at infinite dilution as a representation of the interaction between the solute and solvent is influenced by temperature, which subsequently impacts the selectivity. This study involved the assessment at two temperatures, specifically 293 K and 400 K, to represent conditions of low and high temperature, respectively. In general, the selectivity profiles for both temperatures are similar, as illustrated in Figure 2. However, increasing the temperature will decrease the molecule's interaction, leading to a decrease in non-ideality and hence a decrease in selectivity. This is consistent with the experimental results, which indicate that the activity coefficient at infinite dilution decreases with increasing temperature (Nkosi et al., 2018). For entrainer selection, the selectivity at 400 K is preferred because it more accurately represents the temperature that occurs during extractive distillation. Figure 2 reveals that the toluene-entrainer activity coefficient at infinite dilution is lower than that for methylcyclohexane-entrainer.

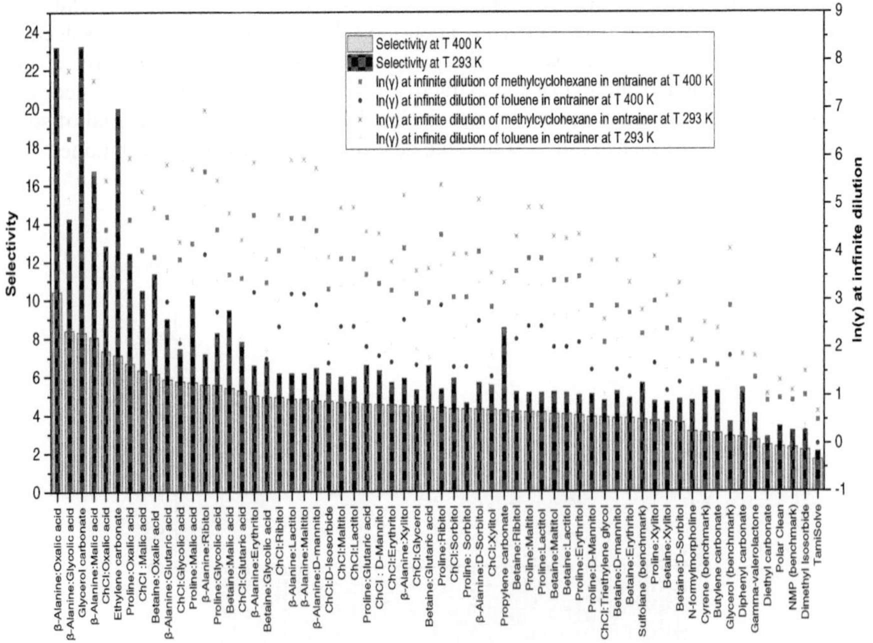

Figure 2. Selectivity prediction of entrainers at different temperatures for methylcyclohexane-toluene mixture and ln(γ) at infinite dilution for methylcyclohexane and toluene in entrainer.

This indicates that the entrainer exhibits more interaction with toluene compared to methylcyclohexane. This figure also demonstrates that the selectivity of nearly all NADESs and green organic entrainers is better or comparable with that of benchmark entrainers, indicating that green organic entrainers and NADESs can be potentially applied to extractive distillation to replace conventional organic entrainers.

3.3. Relative volatility of methylcyclohexane-toluene

Relative volatility predictions were conducted to analyze the separation behavior in the methylcyclohexane-toluene mixture when entrainers were added. This was performed using a real solution at finite dilution to simulate an actual condition in the industrial process. Figure 3 shows the relative volatility of methylcyclohexane-toluene mixture with the addition of green organic entrainers, as predicted by UNIFAC and modified UNIFAC (Dortmund). The relative volatility profile predicted by UNIFAC exhibits a comparable behavior to the results calculated by modified UNIFAC (Dortmund). Furthermore, the relative volatility profile exhibits comparable tendencies with selectivity, as predicted by COSMO-RS. It can be observed that all green organic entrainers enhance the relative volatility, hence enabling the separation of methylcyclohexane from toluene. However, both UNIFAC and modified UNIFAC (Dortmund) models have a limitation because these models are unable to estimate the relative volatility of mixtures when NADESs are added since the required functional group parameters are not available.

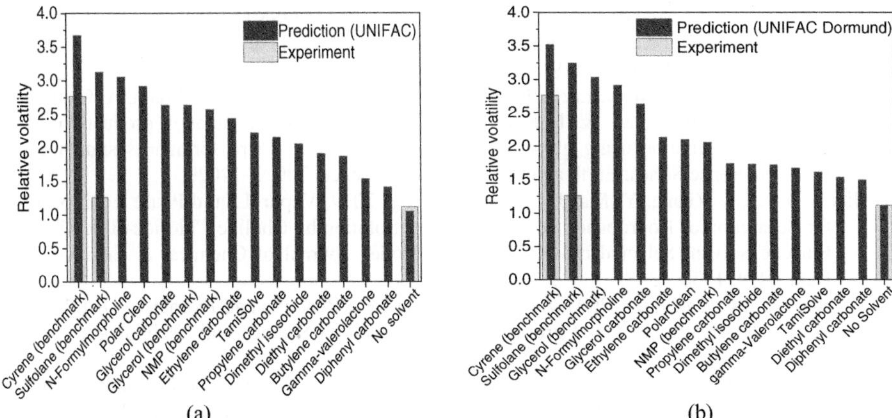

Figure 3. Relative volatility prediction by: (a) UNIFAC and (b) UNIFAC Dortmund for methylcyclohexane (90 mol%) + toluene (10 mol%) mixture with the addition of green organic and benchmark entrainers (Entrainer mass fraction (w_3) = 0.5) at P = 101 kPa. Experimental data obtained from Brouwer & Schuur, 2021.

4. Conclusions

This work showed that selectivity can be chosen as a more significant parameter for selecting an entrainer compared to capacity or performance index. Based on calculated selectivity by COSMO-RS and relative volatility by UNIFAC and modified UNIFAC (Dortmund), most green organic entrainers and NADESs exhibit better or equivalent selectivity and relative volatility performance as the benchmark entrainers in the separation of methylcyclohexane and toluene. However, the UNIFAC and modified UNIFAC (Dortmund) property models cannot be used to predict the relative volatility containing NADESs due to the unavailability of the functional group parameters. The utilization of green organic entrainers and NADESs with higher selectivity and relative volatility can enhance the design of extractive distillation. Hence, it is possible to reduce costs, energy and water consumption, and CO_2 emissions.

Acknowledgements
The authors acknowledge gratitude to the Ministry of Finance, Indonesia through Indonesia Endowment Fund for Education (LPDP) for its financial support in the form of a PhD scholarship for Dhoni Hartanto.

References

M. Ayuso, P. Navarro, C. Moya, D. Moreno, J. Palomar, J. García, & F. Rodríguez, 2022, Extractive Distillation with Ionic Liquids To Separate Benzene, Toluene, and Xylene from Pyrolysis Gasoline: Process Design and Techno-Economic Comparison with the Morphylane Process. Industrial & Engineering Chemistry Research, 61, 6, 2511–2523.

T. Brouwer, and B. Schuur, 2021, Comparison of solvent-based affinity separation processes using Cyrene and Sulfolane for aromatic/aliphatic separations, Journal of Chemical Technology & Biotechnology, 96, 9, 2630–2646.

S. P. F. Costa, A. M. O. Azevedo, P. C. A. G. Pinto, and M. L. M. F. S. Saraiva, 2017, Environmental Impact of Ionic Liquids: Recent Advances in (Eco)toxicology and (Bio)degradability, ChemSusChem, 10, 11, 2321–2347.

E. George Wypych, 2019, Handbook of Solvents: Use, Health, and Environment 3rd ed (G. B. T.-H. of S. (Third E. Wypych (ed.), pp. 1203–1253, ChemTec Publishing.

J. P. Gutiérrez, G. W. Meindersma, & A. B. de Haan, 2012, COSMO-RS-Based Ionic-Liquid Selection for Extractive Distillation Processes, Industrial & Engineering Chemistry Research, 51, 35, 11518–11529.

D. Hartanto, D.S. Fardhyanti, N. Laela, R. Wulansarie, Harianingsih, N. A. C. Imani, A. Chafidz, R. D. Kusumaningtyas, & I. Khoiroh, 2021. Anhydrous tert-butanol production via extractive distillation using glycerol as an entrainer: technical performances simulation. IOP Conference Series: Earth and Environmental Science, 700, 1, 12029.

H. Jiang, D. Xu, L. Zhang, Y. Ma, J. Gao, & Y. Wang, 2019, Vapor–Liquid Phase Equilibrium for Separation of Isopropanol from Its Aqueous Solution by Choline Chloride-Based Deep Eutectic Solvent Selected by COSMO-SAC Model. Journal of Chemical & Engineering Data, 64, 4, 1338–1348.

L. Jiménez, & J. Costa-López, 2003, Solvent Selection for a Reactive and Extractive Distillation Process by Headspace Gas Chromatography, Separation Science and Technology, 38, 1, 21–37.

M. Krummen, D. Gruber, & J. Gmehling, 2000, Measurement of Activity Coefficients at Infinite Dilution in Solvent Mixtures Using the Dilutor Technique, Industrial & Engineering Chemistry Research, 39, 6, 2114–2123.

B. G. Kyle, & D.E. Leng, 1965, Solvent selection for extractive distillation, Industrial & Engineering Chemistry, 57, 2, 43–48.

S.O. Momoh, 1991, Assessing the Accuracy of Selectivity as a Basis for Solvent Screening in Extractive Distillation Processes, Separation Science and Technology, 26, 5, 729–742.

N. Nkosi, K. Tumba, and S. Ramsuroop, 2018, Activity Coefficients at Infinite Dilution of Various Solutes in Tetrapropylammonium Bromide + 1,6-Hexanediol Deep Eutectic Solvent, Journal of Chemical & Engineering Data, 63, 12, 4502–4512.

V. Rico-Ramírez, and U. Diwekar, 2000, Distillation, Multicomponent Distillation (I. D. B. T.-E. of S. S. Wilson (ed.), pp. 1071–1081, Academic Press.

S. Sun, L. Lü, A. Yang, S. Wei, & W. Shen, 2019, Extractive distillation: Advances in conceptual design, solvent selection, and separation strategies, Chinese Journal of Chemical Engineering, 27, 6, 1247–1256.

E. Yilmaz, E., and M. Soylak, 2020, Chapter 5 - Type of green solvents used in separation and preconcentration methods (M. Soylak & E. B. T.-N. G. G. S. for S. and P. of O. and I. S. Yilmaz (eds.) pp. 207–266), Elsevier.

Flavio Manenti, Gintaras V. Reklaitis (Eds.), Proceedings of the 34th European Symposium on Computer Aided Process Engineering / 15th International Symposium on Process Systems Engineering (ESCAPE34/PSE24), June 2-6, 2024, Florence, Italy
 http://dx.doi.org/10.1016/B978-0-443-28824-1.50233-7

Stochastic Technoeconomic Analysis and Optimization of Batch and Continuous Crystallization for Sustainable Pharmaceutical Manufacturing under Supply Delays

Jungsoo Rhim[a,b] , Zoltan Nagy[b]

[a]*Purdue University, Department of Aeronautics and Astronautics Engineering, West Lafayette, IN 47907, USA*

[b]*Purdue University, Department of Chemical Engineering, West Lafayette, IN 47907, USA*

znagy@purdue.edu

Abstract

To better understand the trade-offs between batch and continuous production, a robust technoeconomic cost model to serve as a predictive decision-making tool is necessary. Thus, this study has simulated the annual production cycle for a given active pharmaceutical ingredient (API) at various production volumes for both a batch system and a continuous mixed suspension, mixed product removal (MSMPR) crystallization layout. This was done using PharmaPy, a Python-based modelling tool that was custom-made for pharmaceutical flowsheet analysis. The batch and continuous crystallization configurations are optimized, and the capital expenses (CAPEX) and operational expenses (OPEX) are compared between the two systems. In addition, the environmental sustainability of each system, through the process mass intensity metric (PMI) is analysed. We observed from the results that while the batch system is lower in overall costs, the continuous system shows more potential for expansion. Finally, to better understand each system under stochastic disruption, the optimal results are then simulated in a Monte-Carlo simulation with stochastic delivery delays of varying likelihood and length. With the added decision variable of overstocking considered, we can see that the continuous system, less overstocking is necessary, showing it can serve as a more robust manufacturing option.

Keywords: Technoeconomic Analysis, Industry 4.0, Process Design, Stochastic Optimization, Continuous Manufacturing

1. Introduction

As the field of pharmaceutical manufacturing develops, the application of continuous crystallization techniques as a process intensification method grows more important as it allows for more flexibility and efficiency in drug production, driving a revolution in the pharmaceutical industry (Diab and Gerogiorgis, 2020). However, for new technologies to be successfully implemented, a robust technoeconomic cost analysis is necessary to serve as a decision-making tool for manufacturers. Thus, this paper aims to conduct a preliminary investigation for the comparison of conventional batch crystallizers and mixed suspension, mixed product removal (MSMPR) continuous crystallizers. Additionally, the effect that stochastic disruptions in the form of supply chain delays have on each system are also investigated. For both layouts, the common active pharmaceutical ingredient (API) of paracetamol (PCM), a common analgesic drug, has been selected as the model system. The comparative analysis between the conventional batch crystallization and the MSMPR process is conducted through simulating the annual performance for both systems using PharmaPy, a Python-based simulation tool designed for pharmaceutical flowsheet analysis (Casas-Orozco et al., 2021). The simulation-optimization is conducted with three different annual production volumes and mean crystal size as the key critical quality attribute (CQA). Furthermore, both systems were optimized for minimal costs and environmental impact. This impact was quantified using the process mass intensity (PMI) value of the systems as a quantified metric of environmental sustainability. Then, using the value acquired from the optimized cost case, a simulation of annual production with stochastic delivery delays is optimized for the number of planned deliveries and the required percentage of overstock.

2. Methodology

2.1. Modeled Flowsheets

In this study, the simulation was conducted for just the crystallizer unit operations. The selected API is paracetamol (PCM) and the kinetic parameters for the API have been adapted from Szilagyi et al. (2020). For the batch system, a single unit was set as the default, but extra parallel processes were set as a decision variable, thus allowing for the numbering-up of the batch system as well as scaling-up. For the continuous system, the setup consists of two chained MSMPR crystallizer units to allow for better control of the process. The optimization is conducted with an adaptive Nelder-Mead derivative-free algorithm. For the stochastic analysis, the parameters from the simulation optimized for cost are then applied for a day-by-day simulation of the annual production. For each simulation, the number of deliveries in the year and the percentage of overstocking was selected as a decision variable. Then, for various delivery delay chances and delay amounts, the Monte-Carlo simulation is optimized for minimal costs and minimal stockout with a genetic algorithm 50 times. The summary of the layout is shown in Figure 1. In all cases, crystallizers were modeled with PharmaPy while the optimization algorithms were provided by the SciPy Python library.

2.2. Optimization Formulation

The optimization problem for this study can be written as a nonlinear constrained design problem with the objective function being either the total cost of manufacturing or the sustainability metric, PMI. The mathematical formulation with the constraints can be seen in Equation (1). It should also be noted that to improve the optimizer performance, both the objective function and the constraints were nondimensionalized. Finally, the decision variables of the problem for both the batch and continuous systems are summarized in Table 1.

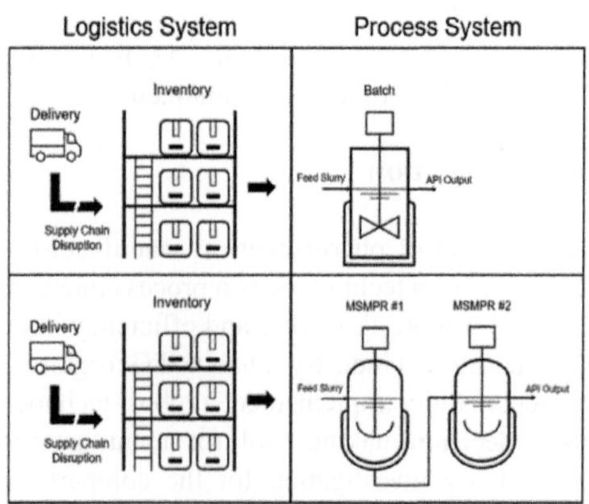

Figure 1 – Schematic summary of the two different setups as well as the stochastic simulation.

$$\min_{x} J(\boldsymbol{x},\boldsymbol{y},\boldsymbol{z})$$
$$\text{s.t.} \quad g_i(x,y,z,u) \leq 0, \qquad \forall i \in I, \tag{1}$$
$$\boldsymbol{x_{lb}} \leq \boldsymbol{x} \leq \boldsymbol{x_{ub}}$$

Table 1 - Description of decision variables for the optimization problems and their bounds.

Variable	System	Description	Bounds
V_{CR}	Batch	Crystallizer Volume	0.1 ~ 7.5 [m³]
t_{CR}	Batch	Cycle Time	10 ~ 720 [min]
n_{CR}	Batch	No. of parallel process lines	1 ~ 3 [lines]
$T_{CR,i}$	Batch	Crystallizer ith Temp. Point	273 ~ 330 [K]
V_{CR01}, V_{CR02}	Cont.	Crystallizer Volume	0.1 ~ 7.5 [m³]
T_{CR01}, T_{CR02}	Cont.	Crystallizer Temp.	273 ~ 330 [K]
H_{ss}	Cont.	Steady state multiplier	1 ~ 100,000
n_d	Stochastic	Number of deliveries per year	1 ~ 24
$OS_{\%}$	Stochastic	Percentage of material overstocking per delivery	0 ~ 100 [%]

For the initial simulation-optimization, there were 5 constraints that were summarized in g_i: mean crystal size, production volume, overall yield, decreasing temperature, and total time. These constraints are summarized in Table 2.

Table 2 - Description of the constraints considered in the problem.

Variable	Description	Constraint
g_1	Mean Crystal Size	$40\ [\mu m] < \bar{L}$
g_2	Production Volume	$PV_{target} < PV_{actual}$
g_3	Overall Yield	$0.9Y_{max} < Y_{actual}$
g_4	Decreasing Temp.	$T_{i+1} \leq T_i$
g_5	Total Time	$t_{total} < 260$ [days]

2.3. Cost Calculations

The costs of manufacturing the API in this study can be categorized as capital expenses (CAPEX) and operational expenses (OPEX). While there are many different methods of estimating these costs, most of the calculations are adapted from Diab et al. (2020). However, it should be noted that for CAPEX, this study uses the equivalent uniform annual cost (EUAC) of the battery limit installation cost. This EUAC equation can be found in literature (Gurnani, 1983). The equation can be seen in Equations (2). Additionally, while there are many different cost drivers for OPEX, for this study, only the material and waste costs are considered. Finally, for the stochastic day-to-day simulation, a daily inventory cost of \$0.01 per kilogram of material was implemented.

$$EUAC = BLIC\left(\frac{i_{rate}(1+i_{rate})^{t_{PL}}}{(1+i_{rate})^{t_{PL}}-1}\right) \tag{2}$$

2.4. Sustainability Metric Calculations

Finally, as previously mentioned, other than cost, the other objective function that was considered was the sustainability of the entire system. While there are many metrics that can be used for this, the metric for this study was the process mass intensity (PMI) (Jimenez-Gonzalez et al., 2011). This metric was chosen over the standard E-factor metric as the PMI metric, which is a ratio of the API produced and the total material used, as that provides a fuller picture as to what material inputs are for a process and not just the waste. The equations for PMI can be seen in Equation (3).

$$\text{PMI} = \frac{total\ mass\ from\ a\ process\ [kg]}{total\ mass\ of\ product\ [kg]} \tag{3}$$

3. Results and Discussion

3.1. Batch vs. Continuous Comparison

From the optimization problem that was described in the previous section, we can then compare the differences in performance as well as cost between the batch and continuous systems. In Figure 2, the CAPEX and OPEX cost drivers have been shown for the different annual production volumes and the different systems. Furthermore, the numerical values from the simulation for the batch and continuous systems can be seen in Table 3 and Table 4, respectively.

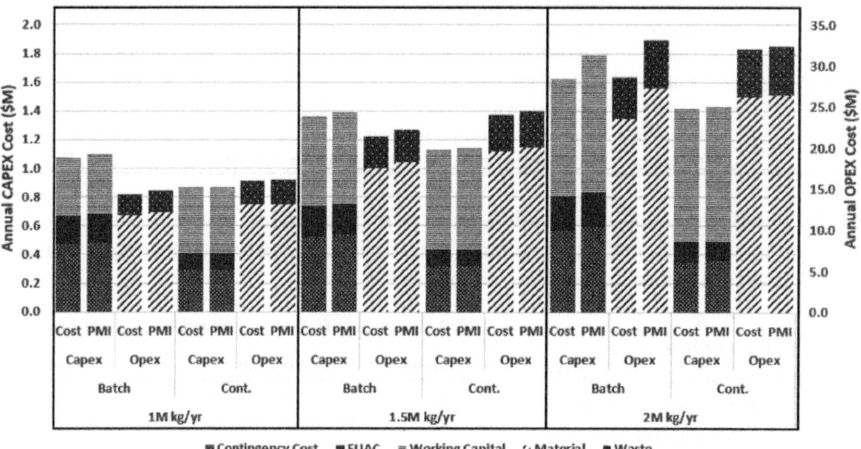

Figure 2 - Annual CAPEX and OPEX comparison for different annual production volumes and objective functions between batch and continuous crystallization units.

From Figure 2, several observations can be made. First, we can see that the CAPEX for the continuous systems is consistently less than the batch counterparts. This is due to the fact that the optimal volume for the MSMPRs are less than the batch crystallizers, even though the batch system always requires two lines. It is important to note that the purpose of the cost model is to serve as a decision-making tool for manufacturers. Thus, from this observation, we can see that a continuous system may be more flexible for a manufacturing line from scratch. However, despite this difference, the overall cost of batch systems is still lower than for continuous production due to lower OPEX costs. However, simply comparing the total cost of the systems does not provide a holistic comparison. While the overall cost may be higher, for all production volume targets, the MSMPR systems were able to produce target volumes in less time, resulting in consistently higher throughput rates. This is reflected in the availability of the crystallizers. In the context of this paper, availability is the ratio of a systems operational period to the total planned production time. As the continuous crystallizers require only a single startup and shutdown period, we can see in Tables 3 and 4 that the continuous systems have higher availability percentage than the batch systems. Thus, from these simulation results, we can see that while batch systems are currently more versatile in existing systems, continuous crystallization systems have potential for scaling up and providing an agile manufacturing alternative. This potential can also be observed when comparing PMI. While the PMI values for the continuous system is generally higher than the batch system, we can see on Table 3 and Table 4 that when optimizing for PMI, the cost difference greatly differs. We can see that while for all cases, the improvement to PMI is less than 1%, the increased cost for the batch system is much higher than that for the continuous system. This can be interpreted as the fact that while the overall PMI for the continuous system may be higher, the cost of improving the system for PMI would be less prohibitive for the continuous system. It should be noted that while the significance of lowering the PMI would be different for each industry on a case-by-case basis, we can observe that for the problem in this study, it is possible for continuous system to show a greater potential for improvement in sustainability.

Table 3 – Numerical results of the batch crystallization setup simulation

	2M kg / yr		**1.5M kg / yr**		**1M kg / yr**	
	Cost Obj.	**PMI Obj.**	**Cost Obj.**	**PMI Obj.**	**Cost Obj.**	**PMI Obj.**
Total	$30,299,710.70	$35,025,675.04	$22,811,463.81	$23,629,527.52	$15,403,923.91	$15,900,095.91
API Made	1999977.11 kg	2328427.96 kg	1500006.076	1556340.47 kg	999996.73 kg	1034675.34 kg
Solvent Used	7313845.94 kg	8479547.28 kg	5472862.24 kg	5674079.24 kg	3654758.21 kg	3773681.50 kg
API Used	2974363.67 kg	3448426.11 kg	2225680.27 kg	2307510.34 kg	1486301.48 kg	1534664.70 kg
Total Time	260.26 days	260.08 days	260.09 days	260.00 days	260.02 days	260.02 days
Throughput	320.187 kg/h	373.024 kg/h	240.304 kg/h	249.409 kg/h	160.246 kg/h	165.798 kg/h
Availability	68.85%	65.65%	73.21%	73.33%	78.59%	78.50%
Cost/Kg	$15.15 /kg	$15.04 /kg	$15.21 /kg	$15.18 /kg	$15.40 /kg	$15.37 /kg
PMI	5.144164E+00	5.122758E+00	5.132341E+00	5.128434E+00	5.141077E+00	5.130446E+00
Cost Change		15.597%		3.586%		3.221%
PMI Change		-0.416%		-0.076%		-0.207%
			Optimal Decision Variables			
V_{CR}	5.893 m³	6.201 m³	5.132 m³	5.209 m³	4.289 m³	4.469 m³
t_{CR}	19510.616 s	17362.060 s	23279.987 s	22704.940 s	30030.870 s	30336.715 s
n_{CR}	2 lines	2 lines	2 lines	2 lines	2 lines	2 lines
$T_{CR,1}$	306.69 K	295.87 K	297.02 K	300.98 K	294.70 K	305.84 K
$T_{CR,2}$	292.24 K	295.87 K	296.19 K	300.95 K	290.49 K	298.39 K
$T_{CR,3}$	273.13 K	273.14 K	273.15 K	273.15 K	273.15 K	273.15 K

Table 4 - Numerical results of the continuous crystallization setup simulation.

	2M kg / yr		**1.5M kg / yr**		**1M kg / yr**	
	Cost Obj.	**PMI Obj.**	**Cost Obj.**	**PMI Obj.**	**Cost Obj.**	**PMI Obj.**
Total	$ 33,546,963.84	$ 33,859,805.92	$ 25,146,755.02	$ 25,717,103.73	$ 16,896,477.54	$ 16,959,178.60
API Made	2000003.58 kg	2020834.54 kg	1500045.79 kg	1534693.85 kg	1001400.91 kg	1006269.14 kg
Solvent Used	8389101.80 kg	8468226.21 kg	6271905.36 kg	6416700.08 kg	4184063.43 kg	4200663.35 kg
API Used	3160355.06 kg	3189758.55 kg	2361312.90 kg	2415827.35 kg	1574916.38 kg	1580915.61 kg
Total Time	210.29 days	258.41 days	226.41 days	231.63 days	163.70 days	174.56 days
Throughput	396.285 kg/h	325.840 kg/h	276.058 kg/h	276.062 kg/h	254.888 kg/h	240.195 kg/h
Availability	99.93%	99.94%	99.93%	99.93%	99.91%	99.91%
Cost/Kg	$16.77 /kg	$16.76 /kg	$16.76 /kg	$16.76 /kg	$16.87 /kg	$16.85 /kg
PMI	5.774718E+00	5.768896E+00	5.755303E+00	5.755237E+00	5.750923E+00	5.745559E+00
Cost Change		0.933%		2.268%		0.371%
PMI Change		-0.101%		-0.001%		-0.093%
			Optimal Decision Variables			
V_{CR01}	2.020 m³	1.653 m³	1.396 m³	1.531 m³	1.288 m³	1.213 m³
V_{CR02}	4.123 m³	3.833 m³	3.068 m³	3.332 m³	2.752 m³	2.821 m³
T_{CR01}	273.00 K	273.00 K	273.00 K	273.00 K	273.00 K	273.00 K
T_{CR02}	273.00 K	273.00 K	273.00 K	273.00 K	273.00 K	273.00 K
H_{ss}	9078.73	11156.65	9774.24	8940.25	7065.28	7534.09

3.2. Stochastic Batch vs. Continuous Comparison

Finally, we simulated the day-to-day operation of batch and continuous process with the obtained optimal parameters. The simulation was then optimized for minimizing cost as well as minimizing the stockouts. From the results in Table 5, we can see that as the chance of delivery delays increased, there was an expected increase in optimal overstocking and less frequent deliveries. However, this was balanced by the inventory cost, thus preventing too much material to be stored. Furthermore, as more and more deliveries delays occurred, the amount of API that could be manufactured for both systems were decreased.

Additionally, we could observe that while both systems required more overstocking, the percentage of overstocking needed for continuous systems was less than for batch systems, demonstrating a potential for a more robust manufacturing process. The percentage difference of overstocking between the two systems can become a significant cost driver as the manufacturing scale increases.

Table 5 - Numerical results for stochastic simulation of batch and continuous processes.

	Delay	**14 days**				**21 days**			
	Delay %	**10%**		**50%**		**10%**		**50%**	
		Value	**STD**	**Value**	**STD**	**Value**	**STD**	**Value**	**STD**
Batch	n_d	21.86	2.44	11.64	3.13	21.66	2.89	11.04	2.96
Batch	$OS_{\%}$	0.230%	0.49%	3.202%	5.87%	0.168%	0.48%	3.529%	10.95%
Batch	**API Made**	2.50E+06 kg	3.61E+04 kg	2.34E+06 kg	1.37E+05 kg	2.48E+06 kg	5.85E+04 kg	2.22E+06 kg	2.16E+05 kg
Batch	**Cost / Kg**	$16.51 /kg	$2.98 /kg	$18.02 /kg	$1.21 /kg	$16.22 /kg	$0.66 /kg	$18.29 /kg	$1.37 /kg
		Value	**STD**	**Value**	**STD**	**Value**	**STD**	**Value**	**STD**
Cont.	n_d	21.78	3.13	12.22	2.48	21.72	2.84	12.06	2.71
Cont.	$OS_{\%}$	0.016%	0.03%	1.939%	6.00%	0.132%	0.39%	2.567%	9.85%
Cont.	**API Made**	3.34E+06 kg	5.18E+04 kg	3.10E+06 kg	1.32E+05 kg	3.34E+06 kg	7.30E+04 kg	2.98E+06 kg	3.40E+05 kg
Cont.	**Cost / Kg**	$17.76 /kg	$0.42 /kg	$19.91 /kg	$1.05 /kg	$17.80 /kg	$0.62 /kg	$20.06 /kg	$1.79 /kg

4. Conclusions

This study defined and solved a simulation-optimization problem for a representative API manufacturing plant. The comparison of batch crystallizers and continuous crystallizers showed the subtle differences the two different methods could have. While the batch method was overall lower in cost and PMI, the continuous method showed better potential for expansion. Additionally, when simulating the systems with the supply chain disruption in a Monte-Carlo simulation, it was shown that while both systems suffered loss in efficiency due to unpredictable delivery delays, the continuous system proved to require less overall material overstocking to prevent stockouts in production. However, it should be noted that these results are with arbitrary parameters and serve as a representative example of a technoeconomic cost model method. The purpose of this study is to show the capabilities of the cost model as a decision-making tool and that it can be applied for any setup and API.

Acknowledgements

This work was supported by the National Science Foundation (NSF) under Grant No. 2229250.

References

Diab, S., & Gerogiorgis, D. I. (2020). No more than three: technoeconomic mixed integer nonlinear programming optimization of mixed suspension, mixed product removal crystallizer cascades for melitracen, an antidepressant API. Industrial & Engineering Chemistry Research, 59(49), 21458-21475.

Casas-Orozco, D., Laky, D., Wang, V., Abdi, M., Feng, X., Wood, E., ... & Nagy, Z. K. (2021). PharmaPy: An object-oriented tool for the development of hybrid pharmaceutical flowsheets. Computers & Chemical Engineering, 153, 107408.

Szilagyi, B., Eren, A., Quon, J. L., Papageorgiou, C. D., & Nagy, Z. K. (2020). Application of model-free and model-based quality-by-control (QbC) for the efficient design of pharmaceutical crystallization processes. Crystal Growth & Design, 20(6), 3979-3996.

Gurnani, Chandan. "Economic analysis of inventory systems." The International Journal of Production Research 21.2 (1983): 261-277.

Jimenez-Gonzalez, C., Ponder, C. S., Broxterman, Q. B., & Manley, J. B. (2011). Using the right green yardstick: why process mass intensity is used in the pharmaceutical industry to drive more sustainable processes. Organic Process Research & Development, 15(4), 912-917.

Flavio Manenti, Gintaras V. Reklaitis (Eds.), Proceedings of the 34th European Symposium on Computer Aided Process Engineering / 15th International Symposium on Process Systems Engineering (ESCAPE34/PSE24), June 2-6, 2024, Florence, Italy
 http://dx.doi.org/10.1016/B978-0-443-28824-1.50234-9

Global system analysis of on-line comprehensive two-dimensional liquid chromatography in gPROMS

Monica Tirapelle*, Dian Ning Chia, Fanyi Duanmu, Maximilian Besenhard, Luca Mazzei, Eva Sorensen

Department of Chemical Engineering, University College London, Torrington Place, London WC1E 7JE, UK
**m.tirapelle@ucl.ac.uk*

Abstract

Process system analysis and consideration of model uncertainty are important toolboxes used by chemical engineers to improve process knowledge, exploit the effect of the most important factors on several output variables, and investigate the inherent uncertainty of model predictions that may arise from uncertainty in input variables and model parameters. These analyses are even more important in regulated environments, where it is crucial to monitor process performance and product quality. In this work, we perform system analysis and model uncertainty analysis of comprehensive two-dimensional liquid chromatography systems that are commonly employed in pharmaceutical analysis, i.e., RPLCxRPLC systems. It is found that ^{1}D flow rate and ^{2}D column length are the main design parameters influencing the feasibility of a design. But most importantly, deviations from the optimal solution due to model uncertainty are shown to be minimal for the case studies considered.

Keywords: Two-dimensional liquid chromatography, in-silico method development, global system analysis, uncertainty analysis, hydrophobic-subtraction model.

1. Introduction

On-line comprehensive two-dimensional liquid chromatography (LCxLC) combines automated coupling of two liquid chromatography columns, ^{1}D (column 1) followed by ^{2}D (column 2), with different selectivities and different designs (Stoll, 2017). In the LCxLC mode, all the fractions of the ^{1}D effluent are transferred through a dual-loop modulation valve to the ^{2}D column such that the components co-eluting from the first dimension (^{1}D) are separated in the second dimension (^{2}D). LCxLC systems are employed in a wide field of applications, including biopharmaceuticals, environmental, food and synthetic polymers due to their high peak capacity (Pirok, et al., 2018b); however, LCxLC design and method development remains a challenging and complex task due to the large number of design variables and the interactions between the columns.

Many methods have been proposed seeking to develop a systematic procedure to replace trial-and-error approaches and one-variable-at-a-time strategies (Bedani, et al., 2012). Among these methods, some are based on the Poppe plot of plate time vs. plate height (Poppe, 1997). These methods have been used to develop most of the protocols available today (Wang, et al., 2006; Schoenmakers, et al., 2006); however, as they are specific to the system considered, they lack generality. Other models use the Pareto-optimality method to find the best combination of parameters given two or more objective functions (Vivó-Truyols, et al., 2010; Sarrut, et al., 2015). In these studies, the objective functions

are *sample-independent*, i.e., the authors focus on optimizing column efficiency and number of plates, but they do not consider parameters such as retention and selectivity. The only *sample-dependent* optimization strategies that have been proposed are by Pirok et al. (2018a) and Tirapelle et al. (2023).
This work applies our shortcut framework (Tirapelle, et al., 2023) for scenario analysis and for evaluation of model uncertainty. The scenario analysis will allow us to improve LCxLC process knowledge and understanding, but more importantly, to explore the design space *systematically*. The uncertainty evaluation allows us to investigate the impact of model inaccuracy on model predictions *quantitatively*. Both investigations are performed with the Global Systems Analysis (GSA) functionality of gPROMS ModelBuilder (Process Systems Enterprise, 2022).

2. Materials and methods

The shortcut model proposed by Tirapelle et al. (2023) consists of a set of analytical equations and relies on the Hydrophobic-Subtraction Model (HSM) (Wilson, et al., 2002; Snyder, et al., 2004) for the prediction of retention factors of different components in different reversed-phase (RP) columns. Due to its simplicity, the shortcut model can predict, in a matter of seconds, the position and band broadening of chromatographic peaks within the two-dimensional separation space of RPLCxRPLC systems. Combined with constraints on modulation time, maximum pressure drops, and minimum number of cuts per peak, the model has been embedded in a two-step framework for in-silico method development and optimization, and has been validated against rigorous numerical simulations based on the equilibrium dispersive model (EDM). However, the impact of model uncertainty and a proper exploration of the design space has yet to be considered and is therefore the focus of this work.
Here, we implement the shortcut model in gPROMS ModelBuilder, version 7.1.1 (Process Systems Enterprise, 2022), and we use the GSA functionality of gPROMS for: 1) *scenario analysis*, to fully exploit the design space and gain insights into RPLCxRPLC performance; and 2) *uncertainty analysis*, to investigate the effect of the main source of model uncertainty on the separation quality. For the uncertainty analysis, we consider the quasi-Monte Carlo method, with quasi-random (Sobol) sequences for sample generation (Process Systems Enterprise, 2022).
Throughout this work, we will consider four key performance indicators (KPIs), namely feasibility, total analysis time, overall separation quality, and number of components overlapping in the 2D chromatogram. For each design, feasibility suggests whether the design is off-spec (feasibility=0) or on-spec (feasibility=1) given the constraints on modulation time and pressure drop. The total analysis time, approximated by the analysis time of the ^{1}D column (Vivó-Truyols, et al., 2010), indicates how long the separation process lasts. Finally, the overall separation quality (Pirok, et al., 2016) and the number of overlaps (Tirapelle, et al., 2023), being both functions of the ^{2}D resolution (Schure, 1997), indicate how good the separation is.

3. Results and discussion

In the following sections, we will discuss the results of scenario (or parametric) analysis and model uncertainty analysis. As case studies, we will consider two of the mixtures used in Tirapelle et al. (2023), consisting of 8 and 16 components, all of which are to be separated. For the 8-component mixture, the columns considered are the Flare C18 (Diamond Analytic) and the Vydac 218MS (Grace/Vydac). For the 16-component mixture, the ZirChrom-PBD (ZirChrom) and the Primesep B (SIELC) columns are used (see Tirapelle et al., 2023 for further information).

3.1. Scenario analysis

As input factors for the scenario analysis, we consider the internal diameter, length, and flow rate of both ^{1}D and ^{2}D columns, as well as sample loop volume and pH pair. The input factors are assumed to have a uniform probability distribution, except for the pH pair, which has a discrete probability distribution. This is because only four combinations of pH pairs are possible for the case studies considered, since the column-selectivity database (Stoll, 2020) provides the column cation-exchange activity at just pH 2.8 and pH 7. The probability of occurrence of each pH pair is 25 %. More information on input factors is summarized in Table 1.

Table 1. Input factors considered in the scenario analysis, with their relative symbol, probability distribution, and range of variability (bounds). Note that the pH pair indicates four possible combinations of pH, in order: (2.8, 2.8)=1, (7.0, 2.8)=2, (2.8, 7.0)=3, and (7.0, 7.0)=4.

Input factor	Symbol	Distribution	Bounds
^{1}D diameter (cm)	d1	Uniform	[0.1, 3.0]
^{2}D diameter (cm)	d2	Uniform	[0.1, 3.0]
^{1}D length (cm)	L1	Uniform	[2.0, 15.0]
^{2}D length (cm)	L2	Uniform	[2.0, 15.0]
^{1}D flow rate (mL/min)	FR1	Uniform	[0.05, 5.00]
^{2}D flow rate (mL/min)	FR2	Uniform	[0.05, 5.00]
Sample loop volume (mL)	LV	Uniform	[0.01, 1.00]
pH pair (-)	pair	Discrete	[1, 4]

Figure 1 shows the resulting parallel plots for the 8-component mixture (top) and 16-component mixture (bottom). In both cases, 20,000 different scenarios are evaluated, of which only 1.34 % and 0.55 % are meeting the specifications (dark blue lines). (These numbers clearly indicate why experimental LCxLC method development is so challenging, if not impossible, and why in-silico procedures are needed.) Interestingly, the top three variables impacting (at 5 % statistical significance) the feasibility of a given design are, in order, the ^{1}D flow rate (mainly characterized by a ^{1}D flow rate smaller than 2 mL/min), ^{2}D column length (smaller than 12 cm) and ^{2}D column internal diameter (smaller than 2 cm). Furthermore, on-spec designs favor larger columns and up to four-fold smaller flow rates in the ^{1}D column compared to the ^{2}D column. Also of interest is the fact that it is most often preferable to operate both columns at low pH. Higher pH values in the ^{1}D column result in longer overall analysis time (not shown here), while operating the ^{2}D column at higher pH reduces the number of feasible solutions (see pH pairs 3 and 4). These results can be used to reduce the range of variability of the parameters in the subsequent optimal design procedure, improving convergence significantly and reducing the solution time for optimization, and thereby improving the accuracy of the resulting designs significantly. This approach will allow users to develop accurate RPLCxRPLC methods systematically and quickly, and to choose the best settings and columns without labor- and material-intensive trial-and-error strategies.

Having considered what design options are practically available, we now discuss how different on-spec designs affect the separation performance. Figure 2 shows the impact of ^{1}D column (left) and ^{2}D column (right) design parameters on overall separation quality and analysis time. The size and intensity of the bubbles refer to the column internal diameter and length, respectively (blue: 8 components; orange: 16 components). With the increase in the number of components, there are fewer on-spec designs available, and there is a significant decline in separation performance. Furthermore, more analysis time is required to achieve good separation quality. If we compare the two panels, we can see that the design of the ^{2}D column is most critical (i.e., the design space is smaller). Note that the impact of each parameter on the separation performance may differ between different samples. The only significant parameters (at 5 % statistical significance) impacting the overall separation quality are pH pair, d1, d2 and FR2 for the 8-component mixture and L2 for the 16-component mixture. This result shows that each parameter may impact the separation performance differently when different mixtures are considered, indicating that *sample-dependent* (or *targeted*) optimization strategies should be preferred over *sample-independent* (or *untargeted*) optimization strategies.

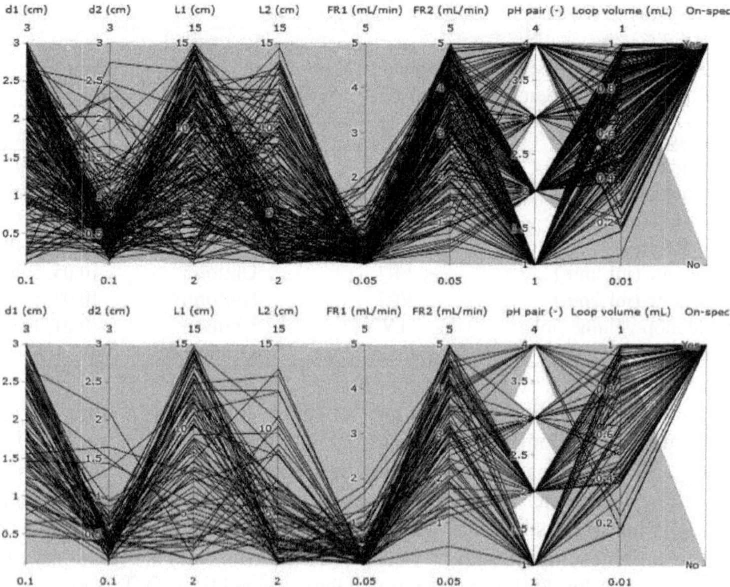

Figure 1. Parallel plots of the different scenarios tested for the 8-component mixture (top) and 16-component mixture (bottom). The dark blue lines refer to the feasible (on-spec) designs.

3.2. Uncertainty analysis

The shortcut model used in this work relies on the Hydrophobic Subtraction Model (HSM) for the prediction of the retention factors. Since the HSM is an empirical model with experimentally measured solute-specific parameters and derived column-specific parameters, it is subjected to inaccuracy. According to Wilson et al. (2002), the HSM model can predict the retention factor ${}^{x}k_i$ of component *i* in dimension *x* with a prediction accuracy of ± 0.7 %. To evaluate how much this uncertainty in ${}^{x}k_i$ values impacts the response factors, and whether this impact jeopardizes the results of the shortcut model, we perform an uncertainty analysis.

For the uncertainty analysis, we consider the mixture of 8 components and the optimal design obtained by Tirapelle et al. (2023). All the ${}^{x}k_i$ values are assumed to follow a normal distribution with mean ${}^{x}\bar{k}_i$ and standard deviation ${}^{x}\sigma_i = 0.007$, while the number of uncertainty scenarios is set to 1000. Figure 3 shows the distributions of each KPI as a function of the uncertainty in the retention factors. The figure shows that the inaccuracy of the model does not impact the feasibility of the method (i.e., all scenarios are on-spec). The uncertainty results in a probability of occurrence of two- and four-component overlapping of 39.8 % and 5.4 %, respectively. However, the distribution of the overall separation quality suggests that the extent of the band overlap is minimal (expected value for the overall separation quality of 0.979); thus, components can still be separated but with a lower yield (i.e., overlapping parts will go to waste or will require reprocessing). This reveals that inaccuracies introduced by the underlying HSM model do not impact the performance of a given RPLCxRPLC system, thus demonstrating that the shortcut model can be safely used for in-silico RPLCxRPLC method development.

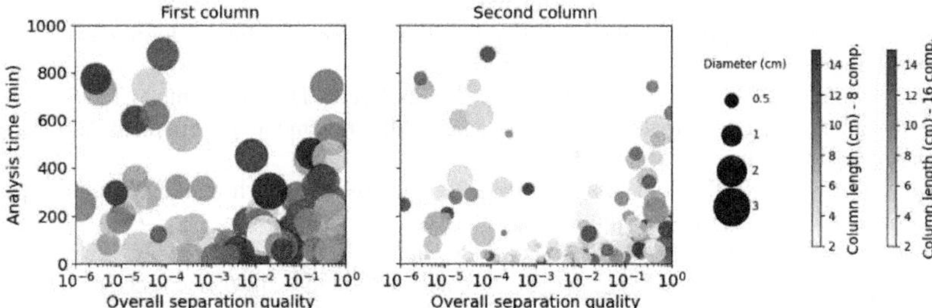

Figure 2. Bubble plot of the overall separation quality vs. analysis time of on-spec designs. The bubble size and color gradient refer to column internal diameter and column length, respectively, for the ^{1}D column (left) and ^{2}D column (right). The blue and orange color-maps refer to the 8-component and 16-component mixtures, respectively.

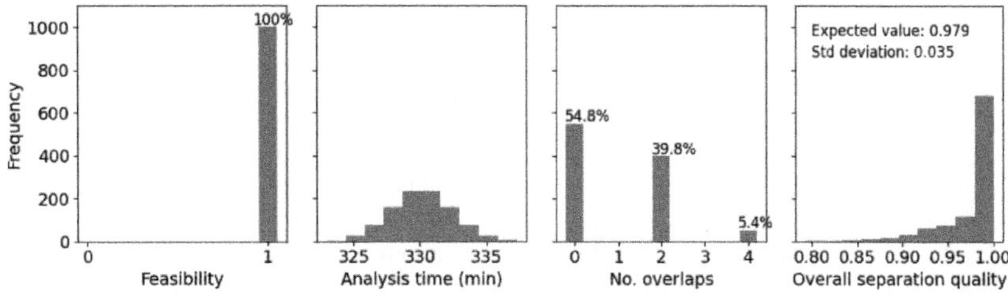

Figure 3. Distribution of feasibility, analysis time, number of overlaps and overall separation quality as a result of uncertainty in the retention factors of the Hydrophobic-Subtraction Model.

4. Conclusions

In this work, we have considered method development and optimization of on-line comprehensive two-dimensional liquid chromatography (LCxLC); in particular, we have demonstrated how global system analysis allows gaining insight into the performance of LCxLC systems and assessing the impact of the main sources of model uncertainty on the responses. Although model uncertainties impact the process performance, variation in the overall separation quality is limited, hence the proposed methodology is robust and permits developing fast and accurate two-dimensional designs.

Acknowledgement

The authors wish to acknowledge the financial support given to this research project by Eli Lilly and Company, and the Engineering and Physical Sciences Research Council (EPSRC), grant code EP/T005556/1.

References

F. Bedani, P. J. Schoenmakers, H.G. Janssen, 2012. Theories to support method development in comprehensive two-dimensional liquid chromatography - A review. Journal of Separation Science, pp. 1697-1711.

B. W. J. Pirok, A. F. G. Gargano, P. J. Schoenmakers, 2018a. Optimizing separations in online comprehensive two-dimensional liquid chromatography. Journal of separation science, 68-98.

B. W. J. Pirok, S. Pous-Torres, C. Ortiz-Bolsico, G. Vivó-Truyols, P. J. Schoenmakers, 2016. Program for the interpretive optimization of two-dimensional resolution. Journal of Chromatography A, pp. 29-37.

B. W. J. Pirok, D. R. Stoll, , P. J. Schoenmakers, 2018b. Recent Developments in Two-Dimensional Liquid Chromatography: Fundamental Improvements for Practical Applications. Analytical Chemistry, pp. 240-263.

H. Poppe, 1997. Some reflections on speed and efficiency of modem chromatographic methods. Journal of Chromatography A, pp. 3-21.

Process Systems Enterprise, 2022. gPROMS ModelBuilder Version 7.1.

G. Qian, A. Mahdi, 2020. Sensitivity analysis methods in the biomedical sciences. Mathematical biosciences, 323, 108306.

M. Sarrut, A. D'Attoma, S. Heinisch, 2015. Optimization of conditions in on-line comprehensive two-dimensional reversed phase liquid chromatography. Experimental comparison with one-dimensional reversed phase liquid chromatography for the separation of peptides. Journal of Chromatography A, pp. 48-59.

P. J. Schoenmakers, G. Vivó-Truyols, W. M. C. Decrop, 2006. A protocol for designing comprehensive two-dimensional liquid chromatography separation systems. Journal of Chromatography A, pp. 282-290.

M. R. Schure, 1997. Quantification of resolution for two-dimensional separations. Journal of Microcolumn Separations, pp. 169-176.

L. R. Snyder, J. W. Dolan, P. W. Carr, 2004. The hydrophobic-subtraction model of reversed-phase column selectivity. Journal of Chromatography A, pp. 77-116.

D. Stoll, 2020. HPLC columns - Column Selectivity Database. Available at: https://www.hplccolumns.org/database/ [Accessed 17 October 2023].

D. R. Stoll, 2017. Introduction to two-dimensional liquid chromatography - theory and practice. Handbook of Advanced Chromatography/Mass Spectrometry Techniques, Elsevier, 227-286.

M. Tirapelle, D. N. Chia, F. Duanmu, M. O. Besenhard, L. Mazzei, E. Sorensen, 2023. In-silico method development and optimization of on-line comprehensive two-dimensional liquid chromatography via a shortcut model, submitted for publication.

G. Vivó-Truyols, S. J. Van Der Wal, P. J. Schoenmakers, 2010. Comprehensive Study on the Optimization of Online Two-Dimensional Liquid Chromatographic Systems Considering Losses in Theoretical Peak Capacity in First-and Second-Dimensions: A Pareto-Optimality Approach. Analytical chemistry, pp. 8525-8536.

X. Wang, D. R. Stoll, A. P. Schellinger, P. W. Carr, 2006. Peak capacity optimization of peptide separations in reversed-phase gradient elution chromatography: fixed column format. Analytical chemistry, pp. 3406-3416.

N. S. Wilson, M. D. Nelson, J. W. Dolan, L. R. Snyder, R. G. Wolcott, P. W. Carr, 2002. Column selectivity in reversed-phase liquid chromatography: I. A general quantitative relationship. Journal of chromatography A, pp. 171-193.

Flavio Manenti, Gintaras V. Reklaitis (Eds.), Proceedings of the 34th European Symposium on Computer Aided Process Engineering / 15th International Symposium on Process Systems Engineering (ESCAPE34/PSE24), June 2-6, 2024, Florence, Italy
 http://dx.doi.org/10.1016/B978-0-443-28824-1.50235-0

Optimal design and sizing of HRES-powered electrochemical microsynthesis system

Weigu Wen, Zhihong Yuan*

State Key Laboratory of Chemical Engineering, Department of Chemical Engineering, Tsinghua University, Beijing 100084, China

**Corresponding author's E-mail: zhihongyuan@mail.tsinghua.edu.cn*

Abstract

Under the context of carbon neutrality, chemical industry, as one of the dominant energy-intensive industries, necessitates high-penetration renewable electricity to reduce the emission of greenhouse gases and pollution. However, the conflict between the rigidity of the industry load and the intermittent nature of renewable energy sources is challenging. Therefore, leveraging microreactors in chemical production powered by renewable electricity, exploiting their flexibility and rapid start-up/shut-down features, has gained attention from academia and industry. This paper formulated a mixed integer linear programming (MILP) encompassing the electrosynthesis system (ESS) design and the corresponding hybrid renewable energy system (HRES). The optimized results reveal the optimal topology of the HRES-powered ESS. As a case study, the proposed model was implemented in the electrosynthesis of tetrabenzylthiuram disulfide (TBzTD) powered by solar and wind energy. The power transmission of the results suggests the flexible operation of microreactors to adapt to fluctuating weather conditions, which emphasizes the pivotal role of advancing electrochemical microreactor technology to facilitate HRES deployment within the electrochemical industry. Furthermore, to achieve competitive production, the technology parameters of the reactors are investigated, and the results imply that the current density and reactor cost are critical parameters, and improving them could dramatically decrease the production cost.

Keywords: HRES, MILP, microreactor, flexibility, TBzTD, mircrosynthesis

1. Introduction

Under carbon neutrality, renewable energy is called to attain clean, sustainable, affordable energy and mitigate greenhouse gas emissions (Papadis and Tsatsaronis, 2020). A rapid transition from conventional fossil energy to renewable energy in multiple sectors, including construction, industry, and transportation, is anticipated, given the current projection for dramatic climate change associated with fossil fuel usage. Within these sectors, chemical industry was the largest energy consumer (Yu et al., 2023). Furthermore, the majority of the energy for the chemical industry is supplied by fossil fuels and coal, causing massive CO_2 emissions. Thus, increasing the renewable energy ratio in the total energy consumption while maintaining profit is urgent for chemical industry.

However, the intermittent nature of renewable energy sources (RES) conflicts with the rigid energy demand of the modern chemical industry. Hybrid renewable energy systems (HRES) incorporating multiple renewable and conventional energy sources are attractive solutions for power system reliability. Extensive research has addressed the fundamental issue of the optimal design and sizing of HRES, considering various renewable resources of the localities, the target users' demands, and the investment with methods including state-of-art MIP solutions, heuristic algorithms, and machine learning (Thirunavukkarasu, Sawle, et al. 2023).

Although researchers explored many topology possibilities of HRES, most of the designs solely considered the characteristics of power sources and omitted the variant needs of the end users, while they have distinct energy consumption profiles. Standard models denote the end users' demands by historical energy consumption data without specific descriptions, leading to the possibility of unbalanced electricity distribution. Furthermore, it is crucial for traditional chemical factories to keep stable operation conditions, and unpredicted loss of power supply is dangerous and unacceptable. Moreover, many chemical processes require high levels of pressure and heat, which are difficult to electrify and incompatible with renewable electricity.

To address the conflicts between conventional chemical processes and HRES, we take the advantage of operational flexibility and rapid start-up/shut-down features of electrochemical microreactors to substitute for traditional industry-scale reactors. Indeed, electrochemical microsynthesis can be operated with high energy efficiency under mild reaction conditions. In other words, the auxiliary units can be easily electrified (Noël and Cao et al. 2019). The flexibility and high electrified levels of the electrochemical synthesis system (ESS) imply a possible route for advancing HRES integration within the chemical industry. However, few have explored the possibility and design methods of combining HRES and ESS. Furthermore, the features of the systems departing from conventional chemical factories need further research. Thus, we formulated an MILP model encompassing the design of the ESS and the corresponding HRES to explore the optimum scale and the system's feasibility. The optimized results reveal the integrated system's topology and energy transmission characteristics.

2. Modeling and Optimization Formulation

2.1. Configuration of HRES-powered ESS

The configuration of the HRES-powered ESS is shown in Figure 1. The system consists of two subdivisions: the energy supply section and the production section. The energy supply part contains PV panels, wind turbines, and battery storage to discharge complementary electricity when necessary. The critical module in production parts is the electromicroreactors that can transmute energy to substances through electrochemical reactions. Other modules, including syringe pumps and electric heaters, are auxiliary chemical engineering units for pumping and heating. The electricity converted by AC/DC or DC/DC converters will be transmitted to the reactors and other units through the DC bus line.

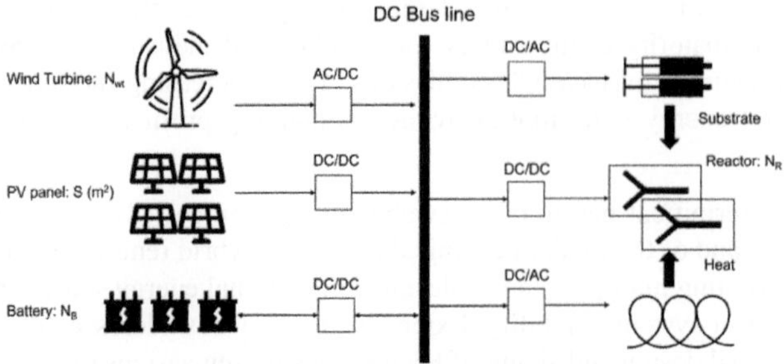

Figure 1. Configuration of HRES-powered ESS

2.2. Module models

The mathematical models of PV panels, wind turbines, and battery storage can be referred to by Maleki and Pourfayaz (2015) and Baruah and Basu (2021). The battery storage system can be charged when surplus energy is generated by PV panels and wind turbines and discharge to compensate for the loss of power supply under concurrent deficiency in solar and wind resources.

The electrochemical microreactors can drive reactions directly engaging electricity in relatively high efficiency under moderate reaction conditions. The flow rates of the reactors can also adjust in a particular range, enabling microreactors to be suitable modules for the HRES-powered ESS. The production output M_{Rec} and the energy input P_{Rec} of the reactors are described in Eq. (1)-(3):

$$P_{\mathrm{Rec}}(t) = N_{\mathrm{Rec}}(t) \times P_{\mathrm{Rec,S}} \tag{1}$$

$$m_{\mathrm{Rec}}(t) = N_{\mathrm{Rec}}(t) \times m_{\mathrm{Rec,S}} \tag{2}$$

$$N_{\mathrm{Rec}}(t) \le N_{\mathrm{Rec,sys}} \tag{3}$$

Where N_{REC}(t) represents the reactors working at time t, $N_{\mathrm{REC,sys}}$ is the total number of reactors set in the ESS. Equation (3) reflects the system's flexibility with which the reactors can be shut down or started up during the time step (1 hour) with little cost, in contrast with traditional reactors. $P_{\mathrm{Rec,S}}$ is the rated power input for one reactor and $m_{\mathrm{Rec,S}}$ is the rated yield, both related to the current density, faraday efficiency and overpotential of the reactors and stable during the period.

2.3. Integration of HRES and ESS

The optimization target is to minimize the annual average construction and O&M cost of the HRES-powered ESS while satisfying the specific market demand for the product, as shown in Eq (4) and (6). The energy supply and the production are integrated through energy balance. Eq. (5) indicates that generated electricity (P_{Gen}) at t should always be larger than the load (P_{L}). In contrast, a strict equation between the generation and load would be costly and unnecessary under various weather conditions. Excess energy can be sold to the grid or dealt with curtailing. The calculation of the cost of modules is listed in Eq. (7), in which om_i represents the O&M cost ratio for each module. CRF refers to the capital recovery factor calculated as $CRF = r(1+r)^n / ((1+r)^n - 1)$. n is the lifetime, and r is the discount rate. c is the construction cost for each unit of the modules, e.g., 1 m^2 PV panel or 1 kWh of battery storage.

$$min\ \mathrm{C}_{\mathrm{tol}} = \sum_i C_{\mathrm{i}} \tag{4}$$

$$P_{\mathrm{Gen}}(t) \ge P_{\mathrm{L}}(t) \tag{5}$$

$$m_{\mathrm{target}} \le \sum_{t=1}^{T} m_{Rec}(t) \tag{6}$$

$$C_i = (1 + om_i) \times CRF \times Capacity_i \times c_i \quad i = \mathrm{PV, WT, EB, Rec, Pum, Heat} \tag{7}$$

Combinations of the target function and module models formulate the optimization model of HRES-powered ESS, which determines the optimum portfolio of electricity generation, storage, transmission, and production. It should be noted that multiple energy sources may be added. The production part can also add more chemical units, such as separation and compression, integrated by energy and substance balance. The optimization model is generally compatible with various energy system topologies and chemical processes.

3. Case Studies and Discussion

3.1. Parameters and data for a case study of Ningbo

The weather data is acquired from ERA5-Land hourly data of Copernicus Climate Change Service (C3S) Climate Data Store (CDS). Ningbo's annual data for 2022 was retrieved. The optimization model was applied to an on-shore wind and solar-powered electrochemical process producing tetrabenzylthiuram disulfide (TBzTD) (Scheme 1), a low-toxicity substitute for wide-used accelerator tetramethylthiuram disulfide (TMTD). The reactors data is based on Zheng and Wang (2022). Although laboratory-scale data are applied here, it is possible to scale up microreactors by juxtaposing electrodes (numbering-up), which maintains efficiency and improves economic feasibility. Thus, we hypothesized that 100 laboratory-level microreactors could be integrated into one industry-scale reactor with minor performance degradation. For comparison, the selling price of TBzTD in China is approximately 3500 \$/t. Average production prices lower than that are considered competitive, which require an annual average construction cost lower than 840,000 \$.

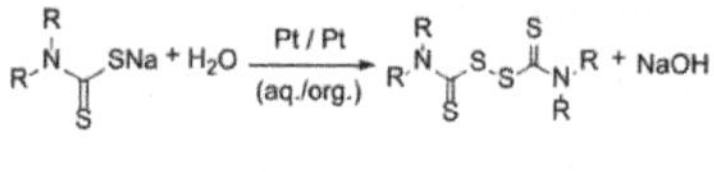

$R_2N{-}C(=S){-}SNa + H_2O \xrightarrow[\text{(aq./org.)}]{\text{Pt / Pt}} R_2N{-}C(=S){-}S{-}S{-}C(=S){-}NR_2 + NaOH$

Scheme 1. Routes of electrosynthesis of thiuram disulfides

3.2. Results

Ningbo is a coastal city in China with abundant solar and wind energy resources. The optimized results of HRES-powered ESS for TBzTD indicate that to fulfill the production target, 24 electrochemical microreactors with corresponding auxiliary units were needed, along with 4197 m^2 PV panel (rated power 120 W/m^2) and three wind turbines (rated power 100 kW). The annual average cost is 1,086,872 \$, which is 4,117 \$/t TBzTD on average (including material cost) compared with 3,500 \$/t selling price in China. The selling price implies that the HRES-powered ESS might be profitable, provided more advanced technology is used (the essential technology parameters are discussed below).

The electricity generation and consumption of modules are derived from the results, and the energy flow on specific days in February is shown in Figure 2. PL represents the reactors' and auxiliary units' consumption in the figure, and Ppv and Pwt represent energy supply. Attributed to the advantages of microreactors, extra flexibility existed in the HRE-powered ESS since reactors can frequently shut down and restart to track the weather conditions and reduce the need for large-scale energy storage, leading to lower construction costs. As in Figure 2(a), when both solar and wind energy were insufficient from 8th to 10th, instead of enlarging the scale of battery storage for stable operations, the production output was dialed down at night and even shut down. Similar flexibility can be observed on the 12th day when the load follows the fluctuation of wind energy (Figure

2(b)). Due to reactors' flexibility, the state of charge (EB in Figure 2) remains nearly constant for over half the period, prolonging the battery lifetime and reducing O&M cost by reducing charge and discharge recycle times.

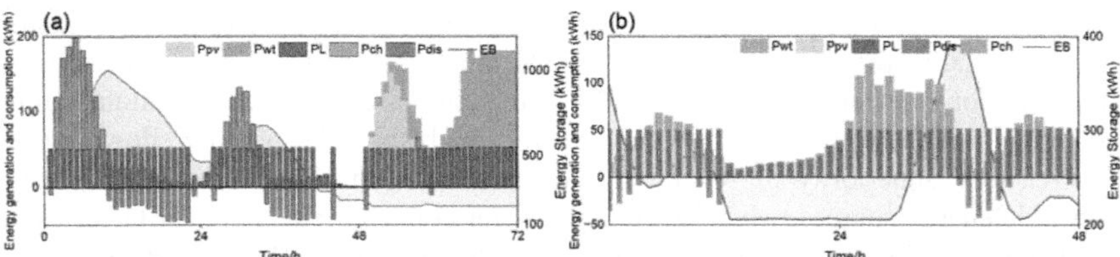

Figure 2. Electricity transmission of the system in February (a) 8th to 10th, (b) 12th to 13th

3.3. Reactor parametric investigation

To assess the crucial reactor parameters for competitive TBzTD production, we analyze the Faraday efficiency (FE), current density, and reactor cost of the electrochemical microreactors and their impact on the average annual cost. Figure 3(a) shows the influence of FE and current density with the cost of reactors set to 20 $/cm^2. Total cost descends rapidly when the current density rises from 1 mA/cm2 to 10 mA/cm2, indicating the paramount impact of current density in this range. When current density exceeds 10 mA/cm^2, the descent is mild, suggesting that current density is less crucial. The ascent of FE shows a more critical impact on the cost with the current density below 10 mA/cm2 than in the high current density situation. This trend is comprehensible for the product of FE and current density represents the efficient current of the main reaction; thus, when the current density is sufficiently high, FE can be lower. The competitive annual average cost marked in the figure (bold dashed line) suggests that under other given conditions, FE higher than 85% and current density larger than 25 mA/cm^2 are requisite.

Figure 3(b) shows the analysis of current density and reactor cost with the FE set to 75 %. The original cost of the reactors (20 $/m^2) is relatively high due to the Pt anode. If the electrode could be replaced by non-noble metal, a dramatic drop in the reactor cost might be expected. Reactor cost significantly impacts current density lower than 10 mA/cm^2 due to many reactors being applied. Along with the increase in current density, reactors' production rate increases and fewer reactors are needed, diluting the impact of reactor cost. Competitive production can be achieved when the reactor cost is lower than 5 $/cm^2 and the current density is higher than 15 mA/cm^2. It can be inferred that the descent of reactor cost is more critical than the improvement of FE with high current density. Furthermore, high FE characterizes electrochemical microreactors. Therefore, future work on electrochemical microreactors should concentrate on improving current density and replacing the noble metal electrode.

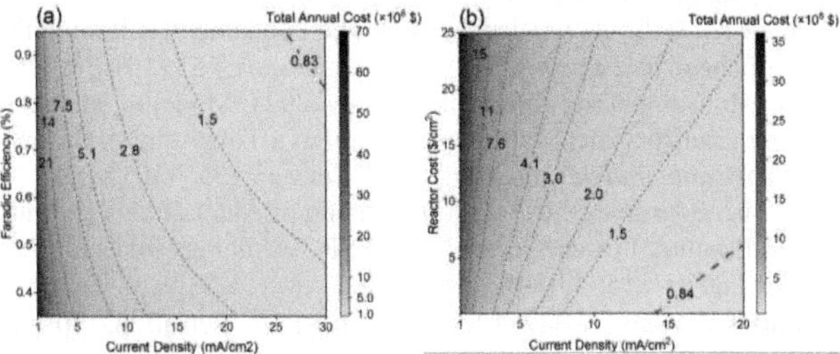

Figure 3. Effects of electrochemical reactor parameters on construction cost. (a) Effect of Faradaic efficiency and current density (b) Effect of reactor costs and current density

4. Conclusion

To address the conflict between the variability of renewable energy sources and the rigidity of load in the chemical industry, we formulated a MILP model to design and optimize HRES-powered ESS, exploiting the flexibility of electrochemical microreactors. The optimization results revealed the optimal topology of the systems that could be referenced for investors and policy-makers. The system's electricity generation, storage, and transmission were acquired for further analysis. The energy flow showed microreactors' superiority of the rapid start-up/shut-down characteristics to adapt to renewable energy sources, which is impractical for conventional chemical factories at a reasonable cost. Current technology is infeasible to sustain a profitable HRES-powered ESS. Thus, we investigated the requisite reactor parameters for the competitive production of TBzTD. Analyses show that current density is the decisive parameter. The current density reaching above 10 mA/cm^2 can dramatically reduce the cost of production, while FE is less crucial considering the already high efficiency of electrochemical microreactors. The cost of the reactors is also significant due to the difficulty of applying Pt electrodes on a large scale. Replacement of the Pt electrodes with non-noble metal can drastically lower the total construction cost, hence the selling price. The analyses imply that future work might focus on raising the current density above 10 mA/cm2 and decreasing the reactor cost to 5 $\$/cm^2$.

Further expansion of the HRES-powered ESS would be explored, including more chemical engineering units and varieties of renewable sources to resemble more complicated practical processes and enhance the adaptation of different sites. Expanding the model will increase the number of variables, resulting in longer CPU time, and oversized models are infeasible for commercial solvers, calling for advanced algorithms for large-scale MILP. In addition, the system's design is based on historical weather data. For installed systems, weather conditions are uncertain due to inaccurate weather forecasts, requesting system operation control under uncertainty to involve the systems' flexibility fully.

References

Papadis Elisa, George Tsatsaronis. 2020. Challenges in the Decarbonization of the Energy Sector. *Energy* 205: 118025.

Zhipeng Yu, Jin Lin, Feng Liu, Jiarong Li, Yuxuan Zhao, Yonghua Song, Yanhua Song, Xinzhen Zhang. 2023. Optimal Sizing and Pricing of Grid-Connected Renewable Power to Ammonia Systems Considering the Limited Flexibility of Ammonia Synthesis. *IEEE Transactions on Power Systems*, 1–18.

Thirunavukkarasu M., Yashwant Sawle, Himadri Lala. 2023. A Comprehensive Review on Optimization of Hybrid Renewable Energy Systems Using Various Optimization Techniques. *Renewable and Sustainable Energy Reviews* 176: 113192.

Noël Timothy, Yiran Cao, Gabriele Laudadio. 2019. The Fundamentals Behind the Use of Flow Reactors in Electrochemistry. *Accounts of Chemical Research* 52 (10): 2858–2869.

Baruah Abhinandan, Mousumi Basu, Deeshank Amuley. 2021. Modeling of an Autonomous Hybrid Renewable Energy System for Electrification of a Township: A Case Study for Sikkim, India. *Renewable and Sustainable Energy Reviews* 135: 110158.

Maleki Akbar, Fathollah Pourfayaz. 2015. Optimal Sizing of Autonomous Hybrid Photovoltaic/Wind/Battery Power System with LPSP Technology by Using Evolutionary Algorithms. *Solar Energy* 115: 471–483.

Zheng, Siyuan, and Kai Wang. 2022. Electrosynthesis of Tetrabenzylthiuram Disulfide via Flow Reactors. *Chemical Engineering Science* 257: 117717.

Flavio Manenti, Gintaras V. Reklaitis (Eds.), Proceedings of the 34th European Symposium on Computer Aided Process Engineering / 15th International Symposium on Process Systems Engineering (ESCAPE34/PSE24), June 2-6, 2024, Florence, Italy
 http://dx.doi.org/10.1016/B978-0-443-28824-1.50236-2

Optimal design of an energy-integrated biogas-powered fuel cell system

Vikram Uday, Sujit Jogwar

Department of Chemical Engineering, Indian Institute of Technology Bombay Mumbai-40076, India

jogwar@iitb.ac.in

Abstract

This paper presents an optimal energy-integrated biogas-SOFC system for renewable electricity generation. It explores the impact of biogas upgradation (CO_2 removal) on the material and energy integration between bio-hydrogen production and subsequent power generation. To this end, optimal design of an upgraded biogas system with partial external/internal reforming and co-generation via steam turbine is considered. With the help of two optimization problems - feed minimization and operating cost minimization, along with energy integration using pinch analysis, an optimal energy-integrated system is developed. The proposed design offers 4.4% improvement in net electrical efficiency over a previously reported design.

Keywords: Process design, optimization, SOFC, heat integration, renewable electricity

1. Introduction

Recent push towards sustainable practices has led to increased activity in the area of renewable power production. Biogas has a key role to play in this context as it serves as a source of renewable hydrogen, which can be subsequently converted into electricity using a fuel cell (Galvagno et al 2013). Thus biogas-based power system consists of two steps – biogas reforming for hydrogen production and electrochemical conversion to generate power. Efficient material and energy integration of these steps is crucial in achieving optimal efficiency of the overall process (Uday and Jogwar, 2023).

Biogas contains significant amount of CO_2 which does not have any fuel value. On the contrary, it promotes dry reforming which can have detrimental effect on the fuel cell anode, it dilutes process streams and thus leads to increased capital and operating cost. To this end, biogas upgradation by CO_2 removal has been proposed in literature (Baldienelli, et al., 2017). Among the available biogas upgradation technologies, membrane separation technology is noted as the most cost-effective (Makaruk et al., 2010). Upgradation via membrane separation requires biogas compression and thus can increase capital and operating cost. However, the existing studies exploring this option lack formal optimization to systematically analyze the trade offs associated with biogas upgradation and energy integration strategy to improve system efficiency.

Motivated by this, we explore the impact of biogas upgradation on the integrated biogas-SOFC system using optimization. Firstly, optimal material integration is achieved by solving a feed minimization problem. The heating and cooling demands of this process are matched using pinch analysis to determine the structure of energy integration. Subsequently, operating cost minimization problem is solved to arrive at the optimal integrated flowsheet. Additional features like cogeneration using steam turbine or micro gas turbine, possibility of pre-reforming or cathode gas recycle are also included in the

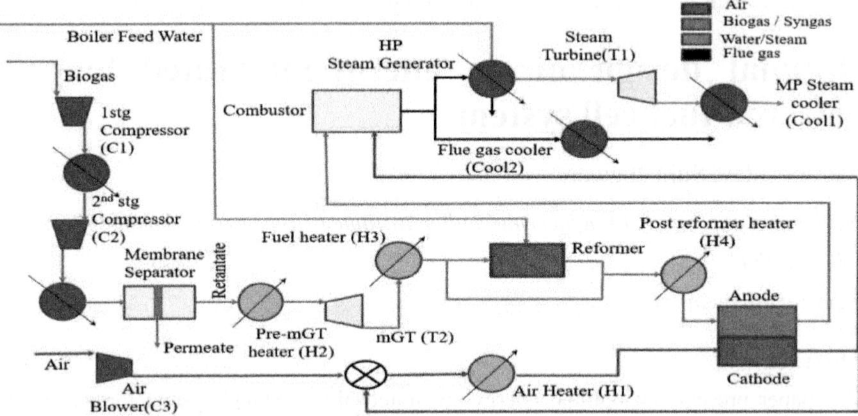

Figure 1: Integrated biogas - SOFC system

design process. The rest of the paper is organized as follows. Section 2 describes the considered system. Section 3 presents the formulation of the two optimization problems. Section 4 presents key results and comparison with the literature design.

2. Process description

The considered process is depicted in Figure 1. Clean biogas is supplied into the process via air blower or a compressor (C3). Biogas is compressed using two compressors (C1) and (C2) with inter-stage and after-stage coolers. The compressed biogas is fed to the membrane separator wherein CO_2 preferentially permeates from the system. The high pressure retentate is expanded over the micro gas turbine (T2) to generate auxiliary power and subsequently sent for reforming. The bypass stream around the reformer controls the relative extents of external and internal reforming. The hydrogen-rich gas from reformer enters the anode section of the SOFC. A part of the cathode exit gas can be recycled back to achieve material and energy integration. The rest of the cathode and anode gas exiting the fuel cell are sent to a combustor. A part of the hot flue gas from the combustor is used to generate high pressure steam, which subsequently generates power through a turbine (T1). The rest of the flue gas can be used to meet heating demands of the process.
The performance of the integrated process is quantified through the net electrical efficiency which is defined as the ratio of the total output electrical power to the thermal energy fed to the system. It is computed using the following equation.

$$\eta_{net-elec} = \frac{P_{SOFC}\ \eta_{DC/AC} + \sum_j W_{turb,j} - \sum_j W_{comp,j}}{n_{feed} LHV_{BG} + Q_{HU}} \quad (1)$$

where P_{SOFC} and W_{turb} refer to power generation via SOFC and turbine, respectively. W_{comp} refers to power consumption by compressors. n_{feed} represents the biogas feed rate, LHV_{BG} represents the heating value of biogas and Q_{HU} represents the hot utility consumption in the process.

3. Optimization problem formulation

The optimal design of the integrated system involves obtaining operating parameters for each of the process units as well as synthesizing the structure of the heat exchanger network (HEN) for energy integration. As these two tasks are inter-connected, a three-step approach is pursued. In the first step, a base case design with material integration is developed by solving a feed minimization. In the next step, the hot and cold streams are extracted from this design and HEN structure is synthesized using pinch analysis. Subsequently, in the third step, the HEN is integrated with the base case design and optimized for minimization of operating cost. The key decision variables and the corresponding trade-offs are given below.

1. SOFC operating pressure (Pr_{SOFC}): High SOFC pressure favors high open circuit voltage and SOFC efficiency, however, it results in increased power consumption in air compressor and lower power production via micro gas turbine.
2. SOFC operating temperature (T_{SOFC}): High SOFC temperature reduces voltage losses in SOFC, requires less airflow to carry exothermic heat and exit gases have high energy integration potential. However, it reduces open circuit voltage and increases hot utility consumption.
3. SOFC Fuel utilization factor (U_f): It represents the fractional conversion of hydrogen via the electrochemical reaction. A high value of U_f increases power generation from the SOFC. However, it leads to increased current density and voltage losses as well as an increase in airflow to maintain SOFC temperature.
4. SOFC Air utilization factor (U_a): It represents the fractional conversion of oxygen in the SOFC. A low value of U_a allows for better heat management in SOFC; however, it results in increased air compression power and dilution at cathode.
5. Reformer temperature (T_{ref}): High reformer temperature results in increased CH_4 conversion and H_2 yield, subsequently leading to high cell voltage and SOFC power generation. However, it also increases the heat load of the reformer and reduces the net electrical efficiency.
6. Reformer S/C ratio (SCR): A high value of SCR increases H_2 yield. However, it also dilutes the anode gas leading to lower open circuit voltage and increased hot utility for steam generation.
7. Reformer bypass fraction (f_{byp}): This fraction controls the extents of external and internal reforming. While external reforming results in high hydrogen partial pressure in the SOFC, it also suffers from increased utility requirements and difficult thermal management in the SOFC. On the other hand, direct internal reforming provides better synergy between endothermic reforming and exothermic electrochemical reactions, but results in lower partial pressure of hydrogen and cell voltage.
8. Flue gas split fraction (f_{split}): This fraction manages the extents of internal energy integration and auxiliary power production via steam turbine. A high fraction going to the steam generator increases turbine power contribution and unloads the SOFC. However, it limits internal energy integration and increases hot utility consumption.
9. Cathode gas recycle fraction (f_{CGR}): A high value of cathode gas recycle fraction reduces the fresh air flow and the corresponding heating and compression loads. However, it causes dilution of cathode gas and reduces cell voltage.

Eq. (2) describes the feed minimization problem. The optimization variables (x) are the decision variables mentioned above. The key equality constraints are material and energy balance equations for each process unit. The key inequality constraint corresponds to net power production and target (P_{target}) matching.

$$\min_{x} n_{feed}$$
$$\begin{aligned} &\text{Subject to: Material and energy balance of each unit} \\ &\qquad P_{target} \leq P_{SOFC} + \textstyle\sum_j W_{turb,j} - \sum_j W_{comp,j} \\ &\qquad x_{min} \leq \text{x} \leq x_{max} \end{aligned} \tag{2}$$

Eq. (3) describes the operating cost minimization problem. Stream split fractions are included as additional decision variables and two set of constraints are included to ensure feasibility of heat transfer. C_{biogas}, C_{HU} and ΔT_{min} represent cost of biogas, cost of hot utility and the minimum approach temperature.

$$\min_{x,s} C_{biogas} n_{feed} + C_{HU} \sum_k Q_{H,k}$$
$$\begin{aligned} &\text{Subject to: Material and energy balance of each unit} \\ &\qquad P_{target} \leq P_{SOFC} + \textstyle\sum_j W_{turb,j} - \sum_j W_{comp,j} \\ &\qquad T_{H,in,j} - T_{C,out,j} \geq \Delta T_{min} \\ &\qquad T_{H,out,j} - T_{C,in,j} \geq \Delta T_{min} \\ &\qquad x_{min} \leq \text{x} \leq x_{max} \end{aligned} \tag{3}$$

Both these NLP problems are formulated on GAMS platform and solved using Baron.

3. Results and discussion

In order to compare with the existing design (Baldienelli et al, 2017), biogas feed composition is taken as 55% CH_4, 35% CO_2 and 10% N_2. A power target of 1402 kW is considered. The solution of the feed minimization problem is given in Table 1. The optimal solution recommends sending only 37% of the upgraded biogas for internal reforming. The SOFC operates at ambient pressure, highest possible temperature and maximum allowed fuel utilization. Similarly, the reformer operates at the highest temperature and minimum SCR. The cathode gas recycle option is not selected as the dilution effects outweigh the integration benefits. As there is no penalty on hot utility consumption, the entire flue gas is used power generation and thus the contribution of SOFC towards the target power is 56%. However, high utility requirement of 6362 kW results in low net electrical efficiency of 17.8%. The corresponding HEN utilizes the heat available with the steam turbine condensate to meet some of the heating demands. This increases the efficiency to 24.4%. In order to determine the energy integration potential of the flue gas, the feed minimization problem was solved without including the steam turbine. The corresponding solution is also presented in Table 1. For this case, the entire heating demands are met by the flue gas and the corresponding net electrical efficiency

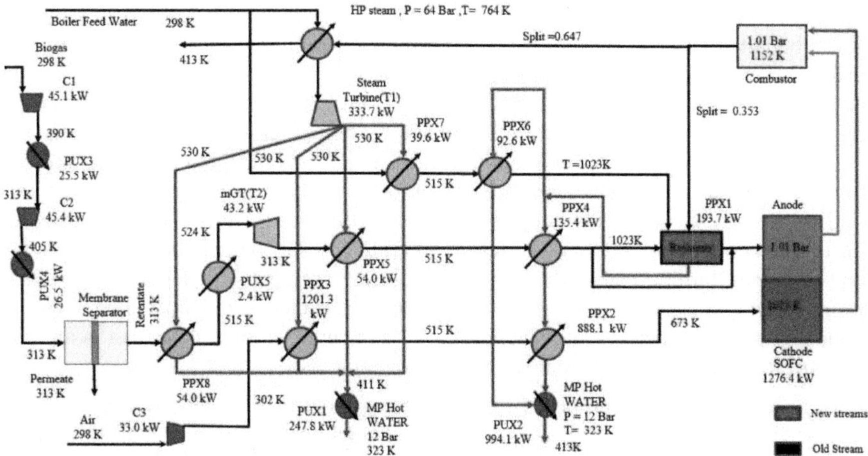

Figure 2: Optimal integrated flowsheet

increases to 41.8%. However, the feed requirement increases by 115%. This suggests that there is an optimal split for the flue gas to achieve a balance between power production.and meeting heat demands. This is essentially exploited by the operating cost minimization problem. The HENs obtained for the first two solutions are merged with to obtained the final energy integration scheme.

Table 1: Details of optimal solutions

Variable	Feed minimization	Feed minimization without Steam turbine	Operating cost minimization
Operating cost ($/y)	6,713,449	3,904,547	2,983,511
$\eta_{net-elec}$(%)	17.8	41.8	54.67
P_{SOFC}(kW)	782.3	1677.3	1276.4
$W_{turb,stm}$ (kW)	782.3	0	333.7
$W_{turb,gas}$ (kW)	26.3	56.5	43.2
W_{comp}(kW)	110.7	164.3	123.7
n_{feed} (mol/s)	3.542	7.608	5.808
n_{air} (mol/s)	291.4	239.7	174.3
n_{BFW} (mol/s)	109.307	3.817	46.29
Pr_{SOFC} (bar)	1.01(LB)	1.01(LB)	1.01(LB)
T_{SOFC} (K)	1073(UB)	1073(UB)	1073(UB)
U_f	.85(UB)	.85(UB)	.85(UB)
U_a	.054	.140	.0.147
T_{ref} (K)	1023(UB)	1023(UB)	1023(UB)
SCR	2(LB)	2(LB)	2(LB)
f_{byp}	0.631	0.459	0.289
f_{split}	1	0	0.647
f_{CGR}	0	0	0

The integrated flow sheet resulting from the cost minimization problem is illustrated in Figure 2. It is worth noting that the key system variables like SOFC temperature and pressure, fuel utilization factor, reformer temperature and S/C ratio approach the same bounds as the feed minimization case. The major deviation is in the flue gas split fraction. It can be noted that 65% of the flue gas is directed for power generation and the rest is utilized to meet the energy demands of the process. The exit of the steam turbine provides preheating duty for some of the cold steams. It is interesting to note that the fraction of upgraded biogas going for internal reforming (71%) has increased as compared to the first design (37%). This helps reduce the heating demand for reforming reactions and thus provides a balance between heat integration and auxiliary power production. In the optimal flowsheet, the SOFC contributes to 91% of the target power. Due to effective heat integration, only 2.4 kW of hot utility is required. The synergy between the SOFC and the steam turbine makes the system largely independent of external heat sources, resulting in a substantial increase in net electrical efficiency (54.7%), along with an optimal operating cost of $2,983,511/y. As compared to the flowsheet with feed minimization, there is 67.5% reduction in the operating cost.

Let us now compare the proposed flowsheet with a reported design (Baldienelli et al, 2017). The reported flowsheet does not include micro gas turbine or a steam turbine. Instead, the combustion is carried out at elevated pressure and the flue gas is expanded over a turbine. Only direct internal reforming is considered and energy integration is implemented in an ad hoc manner. In order to meet the same power target of 1402 kW, the reported process requires 6.1 mol/s biogas feed and results in an operating cost of $3,109,758/y with the net electrical efficiency of 52.5%. It can thus be noted that the proposed design reduces the operating cost by 4.1% and improves the net electrical efficiency by 4.2%. This improvement can be linked to increased auxiliary power production, better coordination between external and internal reforming and efficient energy integration.

4. Conclusions

In this paper, an optimal design for a biogas-based fuel cell system is presented. The option of biogas upgrading is considered and its impact on the overall process design is systematically analyzed through formal optimization. The effect of various design alternatives like external versus internal reforming, cathode gas recycle, auxiliary power production via steam turbine is evaluated and it is shown that the trade-offs associated with these options play a significant role in the synthesis of the optimal flowsheet. Specifically, an optimal value of the extent of pre-reforming and the fraction of flue gas enthalpy used for power generation or energy integration is required to minimize the operating cost or maximize the net electrical efficiency. The synergy between the SOFC and the steam/gas turbine towards meeting power target also results in optimal net electrical efficiency. The proposed design results in 4.1% reduction in operating cost and 4.2% increase in net electrical efficiency as compared to a reported design.

References

A. Baldinelli, L. Barelli, G. Bidini, 2017, Upgrading versus reforming: An energy and exergy analysis of two Solid Oxide Fuel Cell-based systems for a convenient biogas-to-electricity conversion, Energy Conversion and Management, 138, 360-374.

A. Galvagno, V. Chiodo, F. Urbani, F. Freni, 2013, Biogas as hydrogen source for fuel cell applications, International Journal of Hydrogen Energy, 38, 3913–3920.

A. Makaruk, M. Miltner, M. Harasek, 2010, Membrane biogas upgrading processes for the production of natural gas substitute, Separation and Purification, 74(1), 83-92.

V. Uday and S. S. Jogwar, 2023, Optimal design of an integrated biogas-based fuel cell system, Industrial and Engineering Chemistry Research, submitted for publication.

Flavio Manenti, Gintaras V. Reklaitis (Eds.), Proceedings of the 34th European Symposium on Computer Aided Process Engineering / 15th International Symposium on Process Systems Engineering (ESCAPE34/PSE24), June 2-6, 2024, Florence, Italy
 http://dx.doi.org/10.1016/B978-0-443-28824-1.50237-4

Superstructure Modeling of Lithium-Ion Batteries for an Environmentally Conscious Life-Cycle Design

Tomoya Yonetsuka,[a] Ayumi Yamaki,[b] Aya Heiho,[c,d] Yuichiro Kanematsu,[c] Heng Yi Teah,[c] Yasunori Kikuchi[a,b,c*]

[a] *Department of Chemical System Engineering, The University of Tokyo, 7-3-1 Hongo, Bunkyo-ku, Tokyo 113-8656, Japan*
[b] *Institute for Future Initiatives, The University of Tokyo, 7-3-1 Hongo, Bunkyo-ku, Tokyo 113-8654, Japan*
[c] *Presidential Endowed Chair for "Platinum Society", The University of Tokyo, 7-3-1 Hongo, Bunkyo-ku, Tokyo 113-8656, Japan*
[d] *Faculty of Environmental Studies, Tokyo City University, 3-3-1 Ushikubo-Nishi, Tsuzuki-Ku, Yokohama, Kanagawa 224-8551, Japan*
**ykikuchi@ifi.u-tokyo.ac.jp*

Abstract

With the introduction of electric vehicles, mineral resource consumption has increased, and the need for metal recycling has grown. This study aimed to evaluate recycling processes for an environmentally conscious life-cycle design of Li-ion batteries (LiB) by life-cycle assessment (LCA) through a superstructure. There are numerous LiB recycling technologies, and for their organization and comparison, a superstructure was constructed through a literature review, bibliometric analysis, and discussion with process engineers. The superstructure included descriptions of available technologies and processes and could provide designers with potential life-cycle options and design variables to consider. This paper focuses on the end of life of LiB cathodes. Various recycling processes described in the superstructure were selected as cases for LCA, and their environmental performance was evaluated. The environmental impacts of the recycling processes varied. For example, in terms of global warming potential, processes such as furnace roasting and solvent extraction could be potential hot spots. In terms of resource consumption, environmental benefits were observed in all cases, indicating the recycling effectiveness in reducing resource consumption. This study provides information that should be considered in future life-cycle design of LiBs.

Keywords: superstructure, LCA, resource circulation, battery recycling, hydrometallurgy.

1. Introduction

The accelerating adoption of electric vehicles (EVs) made the stable procurement and consumption of metal resources such as Co and Li required for Li-ion batteries (LiBs) challenging. Various types of LiB, including Ni-Co-Al oxide (NCA), Ni-Mn-Co oxide (NMC), and Li-Fe phosphate (LFP) batteries, are in use. The resource consumption of

NMC, which is a common LiB for EVs, is predicted to grow by a factor of more than 15 from 2020 to 2050, emphasizing the need for resource recycling (Xu et al., 2020). The proposed recycling methods for end-of-life (EoL) LiBs include pyrometallurgy and hydrometallurgy or their combinations (Wei et al, 2023). A closed-loop recycling system is required to convert waste into raw materials for the same product. However, there are multiple technical options for metal recycling, and an optimal recycling process should be designed to match the specific conditions. A superstructure would include all available processes (Restrepo-Flórez and Maravelias, 2021), but to the authors' knowledge, a superstructure for LiB cathode recycling has not yet been created. The life-cycle assessment (LCA) of a recycling system using pulsed discharging (Tokoro et al., 2021) has shown that because of the scale of the process there are different environmental impacts and different technologies (Kikuchi et al., 2021). By contrast, detailed analyses of hydrometallurgy have not been conducted. In addition, many recycling technologies for LiBs in the development stage are emerging. If these technologies are implemented in society, the LCA of the system becomes vital information for life-cycle designers (Steubing and Koning, 2021).

In this study, we aimed to evaluate recycling processes for an environmentally conscious life-cycle design of LiBs. The environmental impact of recycling processes for automotive LiBs was assessed using LCA. A superstructure was constructed to illustrate various process combinations that a future LiB life cycle can encompass, including recycling technologies implementable in the development stage. The superstructure was used to visualize the recycling process with a combination of available technologies and was also used to set the cases in the LCA.

2. Methods

2.1. LCA of LiB cathode

The functional unit was set as a 1 kg automotive LiB, NMC111 cathode. Figure 1 presents the life-cycle boundary in this study. The collection and transportation phases are outside the boundary. The recycling targets are Co and Ni; the recovery of Mn and Al is outside the boundary.

Pretreatment includes smelting, roasting, and pulsed discharging, whereas hydrometallurgy involves processes such as acid leaching, solvent extraction, and crystallization. In hydrometallurgy, Co and Ni are recovered as individual elements or sulfate compounds, whereas Li is assumed to be recovered as hydroxides in the cases where pretreatment is different from smelting. Recovered metals are considered to avoid primary material production and therefore have a negative environmental impact in the LCA results (Nordelöf et al., 2019). Direct recycling through pulsed discharging is assumed to recover positive electrode active materials and use them in positive electrode production (Tokoro et al., 2021).

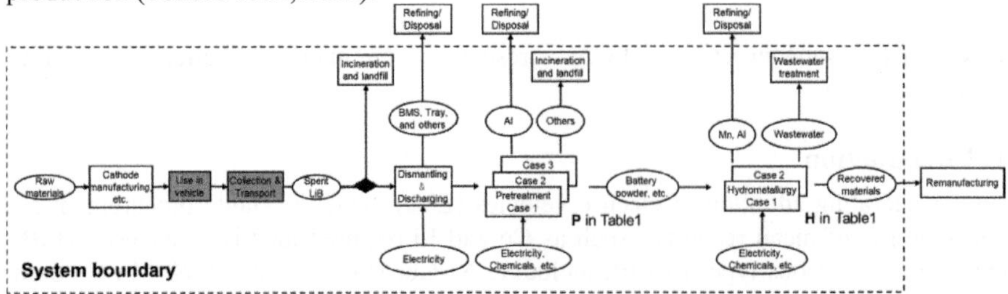

Figure 1 The life-cycle boundary of this study

The inventory data of background processes were extracted from the Inventory Database for Environmental Assessment (IDEA) ver.3.3 (AIST, 2023) and ecoinvent ver.3.8 (ecoinvent, 2021). For the process data, we used a combination of existing LCA papers and papers on the latest recycling technologies. The assessment indicators included five categories: Climate change (LC-GHG), resource consumption (LC-RCP), acidification, carcinogenic human toxicity, and noncarcinogenic human toxicity. Environmental impacts were quantified by the impact assessment method applicable for Japanese ecosystems, i.e., Life-cycle Impact Assessment Method based on Endpoint Modeling2 (Itsubo and Inaba, 2012).

Table 1 Case description, P represents pretreatment and H represents hydrometallurgy.

	Case	A	B-1	C-1	C-2	D-1	D-2	E
	Production	✓	✓	✓	✓	✓	✓	✓
P	**Smelting**		✓					
	Roasting			✓	✓			
	Pulsed discharging					✓	✓	✓
H	**Acid leaching**		✓	✓	✓	✓	✓	
	Solvent extraction		✓	✓	✓	✓	✓	
	Electrowinning		✓	✓		✓		
	Electrodialysis			✓	✓	✓	✓	
	Crystallization			✓	✓	✓	✓	
	Incineration and landfill	✓						
	Recovery of Ni		✓	✓		✓		
	Recovery of NiSO4				✓		✓	
	Recovery of Co		✓	✓		✓		
	Recovery of CoSO4				✓		✓	
	Recovery of LiOH			✓	✓	✓	✓	
	Recovery of PE-sheet (NMC111 oxide)							✓

Seven cases were set up, as shown in Table 1. Case A involves incineration and landfill disposal, B, C, and D involve metal recovery through hydrometallurgy, and E is direct recycling via pulsed discharging. The environmental impacts related to the disposal of waste and wastewater generated from each recycling process are attributed to individual processes. Therefore, in the legend, "incineration and landfill" represents incineration or landfill disposal in the case without recycling (Case A). Case B recovers alloys through smelting in pretreatment, and Li is assumed to be unrecoverable. Case C uses roasting in pretreatment, whereas D uses pulsed discharging. The numbers 1 and 2 indicate differences in the hydrometallurgical process, with 1 considering individual recovery through electrowinning and 2 considering sulfate recovery through crystallization. The metal recovery rates through recycling, regardless of the process, were set according to the European Union (EU) Battery Regulation's minimum targets by 2027, which are 90% for Co, 90% for Ni, and 50% for Li (EU, 2023). In the case of direct recycling (Case E), a recovery rate of 90% was assumed based on experimental results (Tokoro et al., 2021).

2.2. Construction of superstructure for life-cycle design

A superstructure was created to visualize the possible LiB life cycle and serve as a tool for life-cycle design. In this study, the superstructure of the LiB cathode recycling was constructed through a literature review, bibliometric analysis, and discussions.

In the literature review, we extracted technical options related to LiB recycling. At the EoL of LiB, there are options such as incineration/landfill disposal and resource recovery through recycling. The positive electrode recycling process can be categorized into pyrometallurgy, hydrometallurgy, and direct recycling. Pyrometallurgy involves melting, pyrolysis, and roasting (Makuza et al., 2021), whereas hydrometallurgy includes leaching and solvent extraction (Meshram et al., 2014). Additionally, direct recycling is a technology that regenerates positive electrode material without separating it into metal through methods like sintering (Xu et al., 2021).

Bibliometric analysis was used to determine the hot topics in academic papers (Kikuchi, 2017) and to incorporate them into the superstructure. The subject of the analysis was academic papers using both the terms "lithium-ion batteries" and "recycle," published between the years 2016 and 2023. A total of 2,403 papers were retrieved from a web-based literature database, "Web of Science" (Thomson Reuters, 2023). Furthermore, we conducted discussions with process engineers to validate and refine the superstructure.

3. Results and discussion

3.1. Superstructure of LiB cathode recycling

Figure 2 represents a superstructure created for the recycling of LiB cathodes. Pretreatment was categorized into thermal pretreatment, mechanical pretreatment, and chemical pretreatment. In the hydrometallurgical process, acid leaching seems to be inevitable, and subsequent solvent extraction and precipitation steps are selective. Following solvent extraction, metal recovery can be achieved through processes such as electrowinning or crystallization. In addition, multiple methods were proposed for direct recycling from battery powder. Moreover, the results of the bibliometric analysis indicated that the number of studies on re-lithiation using molten salts is increasing.

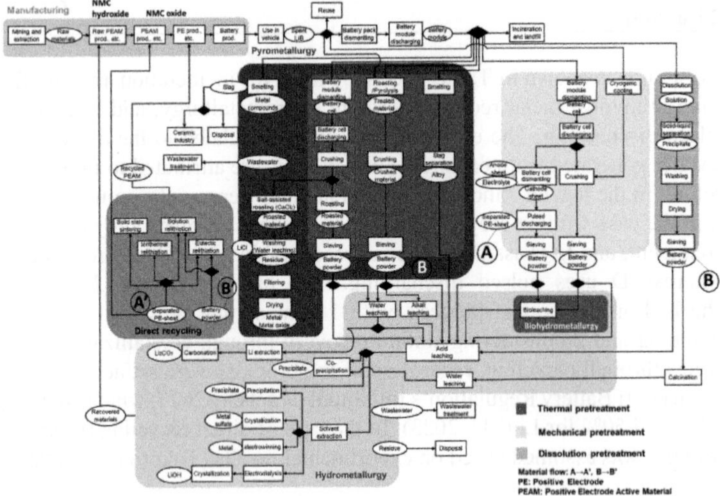

Figure 2 Superstructure of LiB cathode recycling

3.2. LCA of LiB cathode recycling

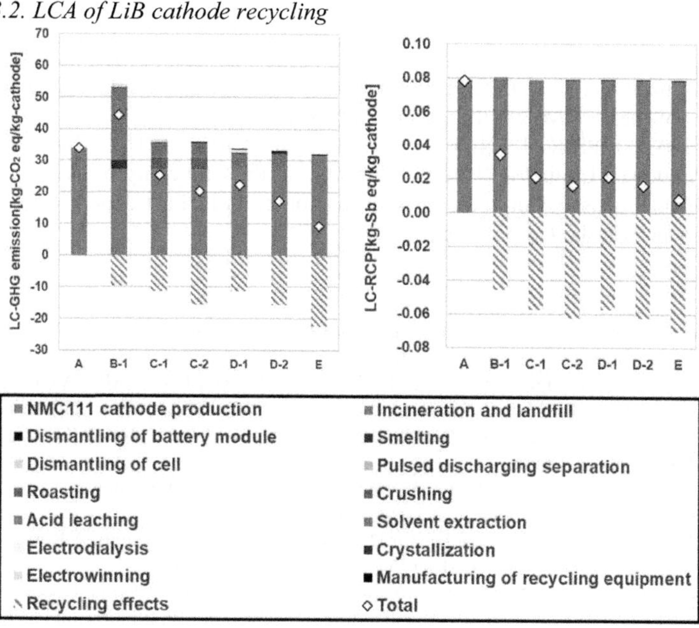

Figure 3 LCA results on LC-GHG and LC-RCP.

The environmental impacts were reduced in all cases compared to A (Figure 3). In terms of LC-GHG emissions, impacts from solvent extraction, roasting, and acid leaching were significant, demonstrating varying environmental impacts from each hydrometallurgical process. However, for LC-RCP, the load of the recycling process was small, and the total resource consumption impact was lower by more than 50% compared to A. Furthermore, comparisons between C-1 and C-2, D-1 and D-2 indicated that the effect of recycling became more significant when recovering as sulfates compared to individual metal recovery at the same recovery rate because the production of metal sulfates has a greater environmental impact. In addition, Case E shows the lowest environmental impact over the entire life cycle. This is because thermal pretreatment and hydrometallurgy can be avoided in this direct recycling process. Acidification and Human toxicity potential showed trends similar to resource consumption. For acidification, the effects of roasting, acid leaching, and solvent extraction were identified. In HTP, the effect of the recycling process was small in both categories, but the effect of equipment manufacturing for pulsed discharging was observed. Overall, recycling reduces the environmental impact of the entire life cycle in all cases in all categories except global warming potential.

4. Conclusions

A superstructure was constructed and a quantitative evaluation was performed using LCA with the aim of designing environmentally conscious recycling processes for LiB. This study systematically organized the LiB recycling processes and presented the varying environmental impacts of some processes, including emerging technologies like pulsed discharging. These LCA results provide valuable information for stakeholders involved in decision-making regarding LiB recycling. Future research should include evaluation of other processes depicted in the superstructure and optimization by setting design variables.

Acknowledgment

This study was financially supported by the New Energy and Industrial Technology Development Organization (NEDO) (Grant number, JPNP21026), This research included the achievements of the JST-MIRAI Program Grant Number JPMJMI19C7, JST COI-NEXT (JPMJPF2003), JSPS KAKENHI Grant Number JP21H03660. The activities of the Presidential Endowed Chair for "Platinum Society" at the University of Tokyo are supported by Mitsui Fudosan Corporation, Sekisui House, Ltd., East Japan Railway Company, and Toyota Tsusho Corporation.

References

Ecoinvent (Swiss Centre for Life Cycle Inventories), 2021. Ecoinvent version 3.8. https://ecoinvent.org/ (accessed 20 November 2023).

European Union, 2023, REGULATION (EU) 2023/1542 OF THE EUROPEAN PARLIAMENT AND OF THE COUNCIL of 12 July 2023 concerning batteries and waste batteries, amending Directive 2008/98/EC and Regulation (EU) 2019/1020 and repealing Directive 2006/66/EC, Official Journal of European Union.

N. Itsubo, A. Inaba, 2012. LIME2 life-cycle impact assessment method based on endpoint modeling. Life-Cycle Assessment Society of Japan, Tokyo, Japan.

Y. Kikuchi, 2017, Simulation-Based Approaches for Design of Smart Energy System: A Review Applying Bibliometric Analysis, J. Chem. Eng. Japan, 50(6) pp. 385–396.

Y. Kikuchi, I. Suwa, A. Heiho, Y. Dou, S. Lim, T. Namihira, K. Mochidzuki, T. Koita, C. Tokoro, 2021, Separation of cathode particles and aluminum current foil in lithium-ion battery by high-voltage pulsed discharge Part II: Prospective life cycle assessment based on experimental data, Waste Manage., 132, 86–95.

B. Makuza, Q. Tian, X. Guo, K. Chattopadhyay, D. Yu, 2021, Pyrometallurgical options for recycling spent lithium-ion batteries: A comprehensive review, J. Power Sources, 491, 229622.

P. Meshram, B. D. Pandey, T. R. Mankhand, 2014, Extraction of lithium from primary and secondary sources by pre-treatment, leaching and separation: A comprehensive review, Hydrometallurgy, 150, 192–208.

National Institute of Advanced Industrial Science and Technology (AIST), Inventory Database for Environmental Assessment (IDEA) version 3.3 (2023/4/15) (2023) https://idea-lca.com/ (accessed 20 November 2023).

A. Nordelof, S. Poulikidou, M. Chordia, F. B. de Oliveira, J. Tivander, R. Arvidsson, 2019, Methodological Approaches to End-Of-Life Modelling in Life Cycle Assessments of Lithium-Ion Batteries, Batteries, 5, 51.

J.-M. Restrepo-Flórez & C. T. Maravelias, 2021, Advanced fuel from ethanol – a superstructure optimization approach, Energy Environ. Sci. 14, 493–506.

B. Steubing, D. de Koning, 2021, Making the use of scenarios in LCA easier: the superstructure approach, Int J Life Cycle Assess., 26, 2248–2262.

Thomson Reuters; Web of Science, 2023, http://wokinfo.com/

C. Tokoro, S. Lim, K. Teruya, M. Kondo, K. Mochidzuki, T. Namihira, Y. Kikuchi, 2021, Separation of cathode particles and aluminum current foil in Lithium-Ion battery by high-voltage pulsed discharge Part I: Experimental investigation. Wast Manage., 125, 58–66.

Q. Wei, Y. Wu, S. Li, R. Chen, J. Ding, C. Zhang, 2023, Spent lithium ion battery (LIB) recycle from electric vehicles: A mini-review, Sci. Total Environ. 866, 161380.

C. Xu, Q. Dai, L. Gaines, M. Hu, A. Tukker, B. Steubing, 2020, Future material demand for automotive lithium-based batteries, Commun. Mater. 1, 99.

P. Xu, D. H. S. Tan, B. Jiao, H. Gao, X. Yu, Z. Chen, 2021, A Materials Perspective on Direct Recycling of Lithium-Ion Batteries: Principles, Challenges and Opportunities, Adv. Funct. Mater., 33, 2213168.

Flavio Manenti, Gintaras V. Reklaitis (Eds.), Proceedings of the 34th European Symposium on Computer Aided Process Engineering / 15th International Symposium on Process Systems Engineering (ESCAPE34/PSE24), June 2-6, 2024, Florence, Italy
 http://dx.doi.org/10.1016/B978-0-443-28824-1.50238-6

Dynamics of dibenzyl toluene hydrogenation and dehydrogenation reactors: design and simulation

Pietro Delogu[a], Elena Barbera[b], Andrea Mio[c,e], Alberto Bertucco[b,d], Maurizio Fermeglia[c,e] *

a. SERICHIM, Italy

b. Department of Industrial Engineering (DII), University of Padova, Italy

c. Department of Engineering and Architecture (DIA), University of Trieste, Italy

d. Centro Studi "Levi Cases" for Energy Economics and Technology, University of Padova, Italy

e. Center for Energy, Environment and Transport Giacomo Ciamician, University of Trieste, Italy

Corresponding Author: maurizio.fermeglia@units.it

Abstract

Long-distance transport and long-term storage of H_2 can be realized with Liquid Organic Hydrogen Carriers (LOHC) based on a two-step cycle: (1) hydrogenation of the LOHC molecule (i.e., H_2 is covalently bound to the LOHC) and (2) dehydrogenation after transport and/or storage. Since the (optimal) LOHC is liquid at ambient conditions and shows similar properties to crude oil-based liquids (e.g. diesel and gasoline), its handling and storage is realized by well-known processes; thus, a stepwise adaptation of the existing crude oil-based infrastructure is technically possible. LOHC show economic advantages compared to compressed H_2 and liquid H_2 for long-term storage/long distance transport applications. The energetic efficiency of the systems depends on the dehydrogenation step. In this paper we will consider the details of thermodynamic and kinetic fundamentals of hydrogenation and dehydrogenation of a typical LOHC, namely Perhydro-Dibenzyl-Toluene. The fundamental chemical equilibrium expressions as a function of temperature and the catalytic kinetic expression for the reaction speed at different conditions are evaluated for the design of a dehydrogenation Continuous Stirred Tank Reactor. A process simulator (Aspen Plus v. 14.1™) is used to simulate the reactor at different operating conditions, focusing on the dynamic response of the reactor to any change in temperature, pressure, and inlet flow rate. The results obtained from the steady state simulation show a good agreement with experimental literature data. The results from dynamic simulation show that the time response of the reactor is compatible with the H_2 production variations needed by fuel cells used for transportation.

1. Introduction

In recent years, liquid organic H_2 carriers (LOHCs) have received a lot of interest as a viable alternative for the efficient, affordable, and secure storage of H_2. Catalytic hydrogenation attaches H_2 to an organic carrier molecule in LOHC systems to produce an H_2-rich storage liquid that mimics a fuel. At room temperature, the latter may be handled and transported utilizing the existing petroleum infrastructure. After that, a catalytic dehydrogenation process is employed for on-demand H2 release at the time and location of energy or H_2 demand. Among the possible LOHC molecules, the dibenzyl toluene (H0-DBT) and the perhydro-dibenzyl toluene (H18-DBT) have achieved

significant interest. DBT is made up of many isomers in both its H_2-rich (HX-DBT) and H_2-lean (H0-DBT) forms. DBT has been used extensively as a heat transfer fluid since the 1960s. [1-4] A H_2 capacity of up to 6.2 weight percent, or a volumetric H_2 content of 56 gH2/L, is provided by the LOHC system H0-DBT/H18-DBT[5]. LOHC, and particularly DBT, show economic advantages compared to compressed H_2 (CGH) and liquid H_2 (LH) for long-term storage/long distance transport applications [3]. Hurskainen et al. [6]. showed the advantages of using LOHC in terms of CAPEX and net H2 payload with respect to GH2 trailers and in terms of lifetime with respect to trucks (table 1).
An example of the possibility of LOHC-based H_2 transport for future international commerce of chemically bonded H_2 is a tanker ship of the Suezmax class that is loaded with H18-DBT. Based on the Lower Heating Value (LHV) of the chemically bonded H_2, its 150,000 metric tons of liquid load would thus contain 9,300 metric tons of H_2, or 309.9 GWh of energy [5]. This indicates that a feasible alternative for the future is LOHC-based transcontinental H_2 trade from wind- or sun-rich regions to industrialized nations that today import a large amount of energy is a realistic option for the future.

Table 1: Comparison of different H_2 carriers [6]: LOHC tanker trailer is 36000 l; GH_2 trailer is 2 x 200 bar steel bottle ISO20 containers; Advanced GH_2 trailer is ISO40 HC 350 bar composite.

	Truck	LOHC tanker trailer	GH_2 trailer	Advanced GH_2 trailer
Investment cost	180 k€	140 k€	530 k€	420 k€
Lifetime	8 years	15 years	15 years	15 years
Fixed O&M		4% of CAPEX	2% of CAPEX	2% of CAPEX
Net H_2 payload		2000 kg (1400 kg net)	400 kg	900 kg
Unloading & loading time		1 h + 1 h	1 h + 1 h	1h + 1 h

The introduction of global emission pricing [7] and growing electricity costs as well as an increase in the demand for electricity (for example, battery vehicle mobility) will make the import of LOHC-bound H_2 appealing already in the short to medium term [3, 8, 9].
The development of the hydrogenation/dehydrogenation equilibrium and kinetic models of the H0-DBT/H18-DBT system is the focus of the current investigation. Understanding equilibrium and kinetic data is essential for sizing of the reversible hydrogenation/dehydrogenation processes. The energetic efficiency of the systems depends on the dehydrogenation step [10]. With the obtained models, the simulation of a Continuous Stirred Tank Reactor (CSTR) for the dehydrogenation process is performed and finally some preliminary results for the dynamic behaviour of the CSTR are shown.

2. The rection schema

H0-DBT is hydrogenated via a sequential, step-by-step process [11]. One outside benzyl ring is hydrogenated to create H6-DBT in the first stage, and the second outer benzyl ring is hydrogenated to form H12-DBT in the second step. The middle ring is hydrogenated to generate H18-DBT in the last and rate-limiting hydrogenation step. The equivalent H6-DBT, H12-DBT, and H18-DBT fractions are made up of the appropriate isomers since H0-DBT is a combination of many of them. The reactions that take place in a catalytic hydrogenation / dehydrogenation reactor of perhydro dibenzyl toluene can be summarized, both from a kinetic and thermodynamic point of view, in three fundamental steps (Figure 1) [8]. Experimental determination of the hydrogenation /dehydrogenation equilibrium of the LOHC system H0/H18 dibenzyl toluene have been recently reported using innovative methods based on 13C-NMR and GC-FID [12]. There are three phases in the system: (1) catalytic solid adsorbing reagents and products.; (2) liquid phase consisting mainly of tricyclic compounds and solubilized H_2 and (3) gaseous phase containing essentially H_2 and tricyclic compounds as a function of their vapor pressure in relation to the composition of the liquid phase and temperature.

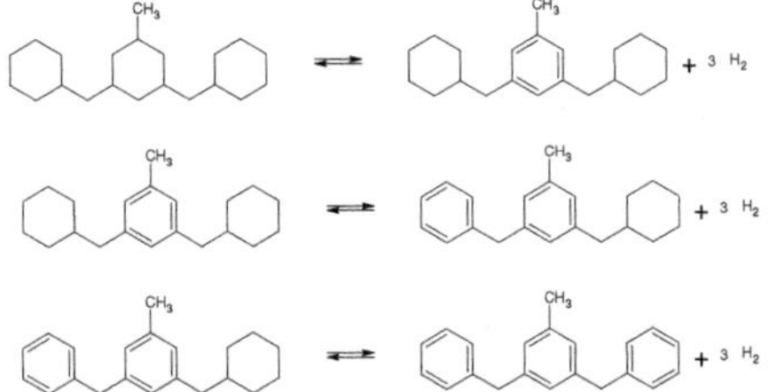

Figure 1: Proposed reaction scheme for hydrogenation and dehydrogenation [8].

It can be assumed, as a first approximation, that phase and adsorption equilibria can be ideal. As a result, chemical equilibrium relationships can be represented by the following expressions:

$K_3 = \frac{c_{L2}^e p_{H2}^3}{c_{L3}^e}$; $K_2 = \frac{c_{L1}^e p_{H2}^3}{c_{L2}^e}$; $K_1 = \frac{c_{L0}^e p_{H2}^3}{c_{L1}^e}$ where $c_{Li}^e = \frac{n_{Li}^e}{V_{liq}}$ is the equilibrium liquid-phase molar concentrations of tricyclic compounds.

The pressure of H_2 is given by the difference between the total pressure and the sum of the partial pressures of the tricyclics:

$$p_{H_2} = P_{tot} - \sum_i P_i^0(T)\frac{n_{Li}^e}{\sum_k n_{Lk}^e} \quad (1)$$

but for sake of simplicity, given the low vapour pressure of these components (about 0.1 bar at a temperature of 290 °C), in the following reference is made only to the H_2 pressure. The kinetics of each of the reactions taking place in the solid phase between the species adsorbed on the catalyst can be described by the following general equation:

$$r_3\left[\frac{moli}{g_{cat}h}\right] = k_3 c_{cat} c_{L3} - k_{-3} c_{cat} c_{L2} p_{H_2}^q \quad (2)$$

and similar for reactions 1 and 2. The exponent is the reaction order for H_2 q. Since the concentration of the catalyst appears in all equations with the same exponent, these can be simplified into the form.

$$r_3\left[\frac{moli}{g_{cat}h}\right] = c_{cat}\left(k_3 c_{L3} - k_{-3} c_{L2} p_{H_2}^q\right) = \frac{m_{cat}}{V_{liq}}\left(k_3 c_{L3} - k_{-3} c_{L2} p_{H_2}^q\right) \quad (3)$$

The material balance of a CSTR reactor is given by:

$$\frac{d\underline{n}}{dt} = \underline{f} - \underline{u} + V_{liq}\,\underline{\underline{v}}^T\,\underline{r} = \underline{0} \quad (4)$$

This form can be employed to all the specific reactions. As far as H_2 is concerned, the overall equation is:

$$\frac{dn_{H_2}}{dt} = f_{H_2} - u_{H_2} + 3m_{cat}\left[\left(k_3 c_{L3} - k_{-3} c_{L2} p_{H_2}^q\right) + \left(k_2 c_{L2} - k_{-2} c_{L1} p_{H_2}^q\right) + \left(k_1 c_{L1} - k_{-1} c_{L0} p_{H_2}^q\right)\right] = 0 \quad (5)$$

Hydrogen pressure and hold-up are related to each other according to the volumes of the phases present in the reactor:

$$n_{H_2} = \frac{p_{H_2} V_{gas}}{RT} \quad (6)$$

Given the similarity of the liquid compounds present in the reactor, they can be assigned a density and an average molecular weight that are the same for all, so that it can be calculated from the volume of liquid N_{tot}

$$N_{tot} = \frac{V_{liq}\bar{\rho}}{\overline{PM}} \quad (7)$$

while the total molar output flow rate must be equal to the sum of the feed flow rates

$$U = \sum f_i \quad (8)$$

The closure constraint at 1 of the summation of molar fractions present in the liquid phase also applies.

Considering now the degree of freedom analysis, we have a total of 19 variables and 9 equations, so the system has 10 degrees of freedom. These can be saturated in various ways, but essentially the variables that could be fixed are feed rates (5), the volumes of the 3 phases (3), H_2 pressure (1), temperature (1), for a total of 10 variables. The parameters of the model consist of the 3 rate constants of the direct reactions, the 3 equilibrium constants for the counter-reactions, and the H_2 pressure exponent. Their estimation has been done starting from the experimental data of Dürr et al [12].

The dependence of the equilibrium constants on the temperature of the three reactions considered has been approximated by the equations.

$$K_i = exp\left(-\frac{\Delta G_r(T)}{RT}\right) \quad (9)$$

$$\Delta G_r(T) = \frac{T}{T°}\Delta G_r(T°) + \Delta H_r(T°)\left(1 - \frac{T}{T°}\right) + \Delta C_p(T - T°) - T\Delta C_p\, ln\frac{T}{T°} \quad (10)$$

whose adaptive parameters are $\Delta G_r(T°)$, $\Delta H_r(T°)$ e ΔC_p. Given the substantial identity of the 3 reactions involved in the model, a single value was used for $\Delta H_r(T°)$ e ΔC_p, while we have identified a specific value of $\Delta G_{ri}(T°)$ for each reaction. The reference temperature was 493 K. Figure 2 shows the comparison between experimental [12] and calculated degree of hydrogenation (DoH) data. It can be seen how the model developed is able to reproduce the available experimental trends and can therefore be used to describe the thermodynamics in the kinetic model of the reaction.

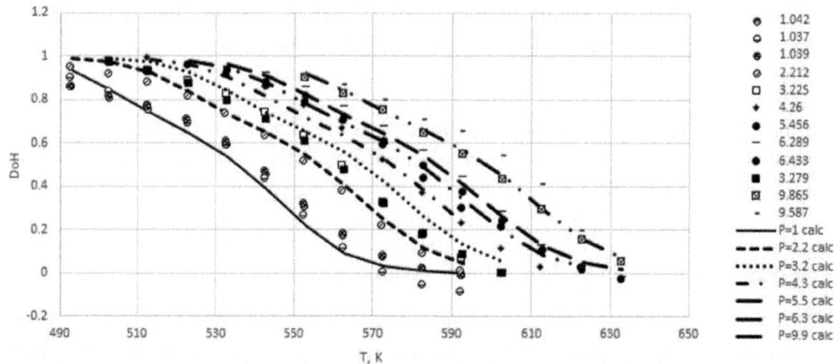

Figure 1: hydrogenation of DBT: experimental and calculated data for DoH.

The best estimation of the parameters of a kinetic model requires the availability of the evolution of the composition of the reactant system under conditions of constant temperature. Jorschick et al. [13] measured data of the composition of the reactants at constant temperature as a function of time. They used Pt on alumina as a catalyst 0.3% by weight at a single concentration of 3 g/100 g, at 30 bar absolute H_2 pressure and temperatures between 201 and 311 °C. They measured the flow of H_2 needed to maintain the pressure constant and calculated the degree of hydrogenation. Using the data of [12] combined with those of [13], we estimated the values of k_i and q.

Figure 3 shows the comparison between experimental values and calculated DoH curves obtained with the equilibrium and kinetic constant derived as reported above and implemented in a batch reactor of Aspen Plus v. 14.1™ process simulator. The results obtained from the simulation show a good agreement with experimental literature data [12,13], thus allowing to state that the reactions implemented in Aspen Plus v. 14.1™ reliably describe the process of interest.

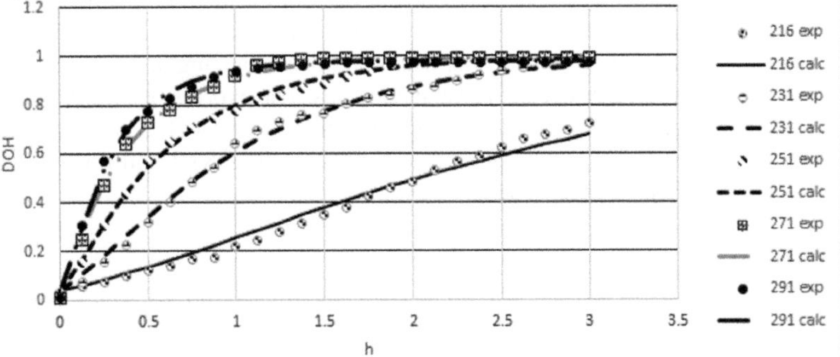

Figure 3: dehydrogenation of DBT: experimental and calculated data for DoH

3. The CSTR process simulation

The output H_2 pressure from the CSTR must be such that it can be fed to a fuel cell (around 4 bar). To obtain a high conversion at this pressure, it is necessary to operate at elevated temperatures, but not to exceed 300 °C, where the decomposition of dibenzyl toluene to volatile compounds become important. A temperature of 291 °C was used in the analysis and consequently it is necessary to supply the heat necessary to raise the temperature of the incoming flow up to 291 °C and the reaction heat. This heat is generated by burning some of the H_2 produced. The heat to be provided for one mole of LOHC is about 38 kcal. The CSTR model available in Aspen Plus v. 14.1™ was used to simulate the dehydrogenation reactions using the equilibrium and kinetic equations developed above. We have also evaluated the transition dynamics of the CSTR between two different power demands. The model calculates the time it takes to reach the new steady state conditions starting from a steady state condition taken as a reference one and the change in the composition of the liquid effluent, taken at the same total molar flow rate as the feed.

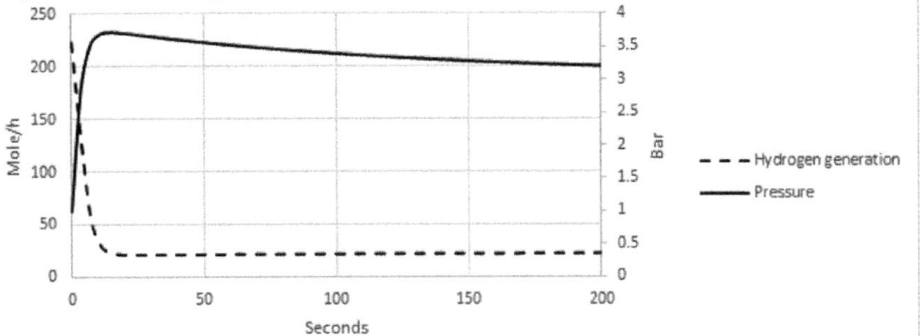

Figure 4: H_2 flow rate (blue) and pressure initial changes (orange) as a function of time.

The time to reach steady state is about 5 seconds. However, this only affects the internal conditions of the reactor, as both the LOHC supply and the H_2 withdrawal are constant from the beginning of the variation. In a first phase, the system produces more of the H_2

withdrawn, and this leads to an increase in pressure; This is then compensated until the steady state is reached. As an example, figure 4 shows the H_2 flow rate and pressure profiles as a function of time for a change in the H_2 request from 10 kW to 100 kW.

4. Conclusions

The main result of this paper is the development of equilibrium and kinetic expressions and parameters from literature experimental data for describing hydrogenation and dehydrogenation of DBT LOHC. All chemical reactions occurring in the processes have been considered, including direct and reverse reactions. The expressions for the reactions' rate developed compare well with the experimental data of DoH. The reactions' rate expression has been used in the simulation of a steady state CSTR and for the dynamic simulation of a transient for the same CSTR.

References

1. P. Preuster, C. Papp, P. Wasserscheid, *Liquid Organic Hydrogen Carriers (LOHCs): Toward a Hydrogen-free Hydrogen Economy.* Accounts of Chemical Research, 2017. **50**(1): p. 74-85.
2. P.M. Modisha, C.N.M. Ouma, R. Garidzirai, P. Wasserscheid, D. Bessarabov, The Prospect of Hydrogen Storage Using Liquid Organic Hydrogen Carriers. Energy & Fuels, 2019.
3. M. Niermann, S. Drünert, M. Kaltschmitt, K. Bonhoff, Liquid Organic Hydrogen Carrier (LOHC) – Techno-economic analysis of LOHCs in a defined process chain. Energy & Environmental Science, 2019.
4. P.T. Aakko-Saksa, C. Cook, J. Kiviaho, T. Repo, Liquid organic hydrogen carriers for transportation and storing of renewable energy–Review and discussion. Journal of Power Sources, 2018. **396**: p. 803-823.
5. N. Brückner, K. Obesser, A. Bösmann, D. Teichmann, W. Arlt, J. Dungs, P. Wasserscheid, Evaluation of Industrially Applied Heat-Transfer Fluids as Liquid Organic Hydrogen Carrier Systems. ChemSusChem, 2014. **7**(1): p. 229-235.
6. M. Hurskainen, J. Ihonen, "Techno-economic feasibility of road transport of hydrogen using liquid organic hydrogen carriers", International Journal of hydrogen energy, Vol. 45 (56), 2020, pagg. 32098-32112.
7. State and Trends of Carbon Pricing 2023, in © World Bank. https://openknowledge.worldbank.org/items/58f2a409-9bb7-4ee6-899d-be47835c838f
8. P. Runge, C. Sölch, J. Albert, P. Wasserscheid, G. Zöttl, V. Grimm, Economic comparison of different electric fuels for energy scenarios in 2035. Applied Energy, 2019. 233: p. 1078-1093.
9. D. Teichmann, W. Arlt, P. Wasserscheid, Liquid Organic Hydrogen Carriers as an efficient vector for the transport and storage of renewable energy. International Journal of Hydrogen Energy, 2012. 37(23): p. 18118-18132.
10. Asif F., Hamayun M.H., Hussain M., Hussain A., M. Maafa I.M., Park Y-K., Performance Analysis of the Perhydro-Dibenzyl-Toluene Dehydrogenation System—A Simulation Study, Sustainability 2021, 13, 6490.
11. G. Do, P. Preuster, R. Aslam, A. Bösmann, K. Müller, W. Arlt, P. Wasserscheid, Hydrogenation of the liquid organic hydrogen carrier compound dibenzyltoluene – reaction pathway determination by 1H NMR spectroscopy. React. Chem. Eng., 2016. 1(3): p. 313-320.
12. S. Dürr, S. Zilm, M. Geißelbrecht, Karsten Müller, P. Preuster, A. Bösmann, P. Wasserscheid, Experimental determination of the hydrogenation/dehydrogenation - Equilibrium of the LOHC system H0/H18-dibenzyltoluene, International Journal of Hydrogen Energy, Volume 46, Issue 64, 2021, 32583-32594, ISSN 0360-3199, https://doi.org/10.1016/j.ijhydene.2021.07.119.
15. H.Jorschick, P. Preuster, S. Durr, A. Seidel, K. Muller, A. Bosmann, P. Wasserscheid, Hydrogen Storage Using a Hot Pressure Swing Reactor. Energy & Environmental Science, 2017.

Flavio Manenti, Gintaras V. Reklaitis (Eds.), Proceedings of the 34th European Symposium on Computer Aided Process Engineering / 15th International Symposium on Process Systems Engineering (ESCAPE34/PSE24), June 2-6, 2024, Florence, Italy
 http://dx.doi.org/10.1016/B978-0-443-28824-1.50239-8

Flexible operation assessment of adsorption-based carbon capture systems via design space identification

Haditya K. Purwanto[a], Steven Sachio[a,b], Adam Ward[a,b], Ronny Pini[a], Maria M. Papathanasiou[a,b]

[a]*Department of Chemical Engineering, Imperial College London, Exhibition Rd, London SW7 2BX, United Kingdom*
[b]*Sargent Centre for Process Systems Engineering, Imperial College London, Exhibition Rd, London SW7 2BX, United Kingdom*
maria.papathanasiou11@imperial.ac.uk

Abstract

Post-combustion CO_2 capture by pressure-vacuum swing adsorption (PVSA) is gaining increasing interest due to the evolving energy landscape and the industry's decarbonization efforts. Within a hybrid energy system composed of conventional fossil-fuel-based power generation balancing renewable electricity sources, PVSA systems must be able to accommodate for transient conditions arising from intermittent operation. In this work, a model-based approach to investigate the operational flexibility of a PVSA unit applied to a 1,000 MW coal power plant is presented. The comparative analysis of two distinct adsorbents reveals a clear trade-off between operability and economics. Specifically, Zeolite-13X exhibits a lower capture cost, while ZIF-36-FRL demonstrates more flexibility in the ranges of high- and low-pressures at which the unit can be operated. The most flexible nominal operating point was successfully identified for each adsorbent using the developed framework, highlighting the importance of incorporating into the design process operational robustness. The latter is represented by a novel metric of normalised space size (NSS). This work demonstrates that significant improvement in NSS can be achieved, while increasing capture cost only marginally. This result highlights that optimal adsorbent selection for CO_2 capture should account for operational flexibility.

Keywords: global sensitivity analysis, design space, pressure-vacuum swing adsorption

1. Introduction

The energy landscape is gradually shifting towards more environmentally friendly and renewable energy sources to substitute conventional fossil-fueled power generation. As a result, a hybrid energy system is emerging that combines both technologies in a load-balancing modality, which ensures a steady supply of power irrespective of the intermittency of renewable resources (Wilkew and Brown, 2022). In this context, fossil fuel combustion methods, extensively used for energy generation, must be redesigned and retrofitted to reduce their carbon emissions. To this end, these technologies can be integrated with post-combustion carbon capture, with amine-based absorption being widely employed on an industrial scale. However, this leading technology faces challenges, including thermal and chemical instability of the solvent.

An alternative approach for post-combustion carbon capture is adsorption, particularly pressure-vacuum swing adsorption (PVSA). While prior research has predominantly focused on developing novel adsorbent materials, the process-level assessment of the same materials presents significant challenges due to high number of design parameters involved (Ward and Pini, 2022). The arising hybrid fossil-and-renewable operation scheme of the energy system also adds complexity, demanding a highly flexible adsorption process design that remains viable under strict output constraints, such as the purity and recovery of CO_2. This scenario calls for an integrated framework to screen adsorbents, encompassing both design performance and operational flexibility considerations (Grossmann et al., 2014).

In this study, an approach that combines global sensitivity analysis with design space analysis (Sachio et al., 2023) for assessing the flexibility and feasibility of the design of a PVSA process for CO_2 capture is presented. This work also contributes to the formulation of a comprehensive adsorbent screening framework that takes into account both performance considerations and the critical aspects of process flexibility and robustness (Pistikopoulos et al., 2021).

2. Computational framework

This study implements a computational framework utilizing the direct sampling method to describe the design space (Sachio et al., 2023). The design space problem is formulated by defining the process model, the relevant input variables (i.e., the process parameters), the key performance indicators (KPIs), and associated constraints. A general flowchart of the methodology applied herein is depicted in Figure 1.

Global sensitivity analysis (GSA) was utilized to determine the most relevant process parameters in design space analysis (Kotidis et al., 2019). In the context of a PVSA process, the KPIs are influenced by various process parameters, broadly categorized into three main groups. First, "design parameters" are decided during the initial design phase and remain fixed throughout its operation. Second, "operational parameters" are expected to remain constant over time but can be adjusted based on the evolving conditions of the

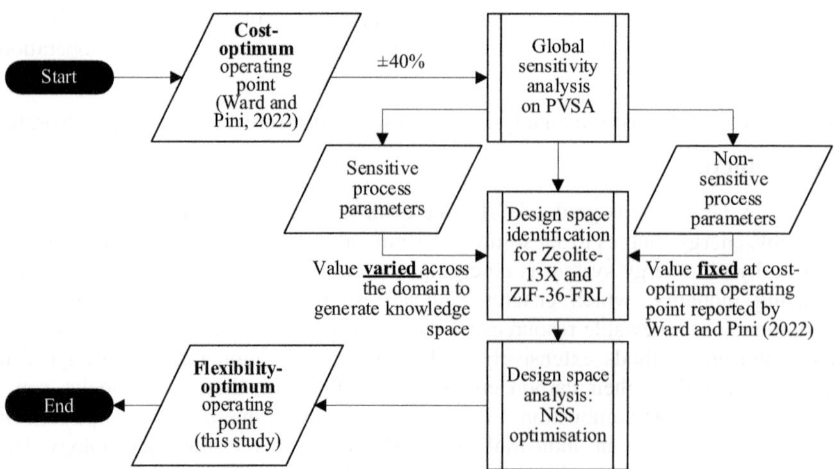

Figure 1. General flowchart of the framework.

PVSA process. Lastly, "material properties parameters" are associated with the physical properties of the adsorbent material employed and remain constant post-design.

Quasi-random Sobol sequence was employed to sample the process model, thereby establishing the knowledge space. Within this space, the design space containing all sample points with feasible output was defined. Subsequently, flexibility regarding prospective optimal operating points within this design space was assessed using a so-called acceptable operating region (AOR). In the context of a three-dimensional scenario, the AOR is visualized as a cuboid. The lengths of the cuboid's edges along each axis reflect the allowable operational range within the model parameter represented by the corresponding axis that guarantee process feasibility. Based on this information, a novel performance index called the normalized space size (NSS) has been applied to quantify and compare process flexibility across various adsorbents at different candidate optimal operating points. The formulation for the NSS is presented in Eq. (1).

$$\begin{matrix}\text{normalized space} \\ \text{size (NSS)}\end{matrix} = \prod_{i\in J}\left(\frac{\text{AOR}_i^{\max}-\text{AOR}_i^{\min}}{\text{UB}_i-\text{LB}_i}\right) \quad (1)$$

Here, J includes all manipulated parameters (i), $\text{AOR}_i^{\max} - \text{AOR}_i^{\min}$ represents the length of the AOR edge along axis i, while UB_i and LB_i are the upper and lower bounds of i.

3. Process model

In this study, a cyclic PVSA operation designed for post-combustion CO_2 capture from a 1,000 MW coal power plant (Ward and Pini, 2022) has been examined. A feed gas mixture composed of 15% CO_2 and 85% N_2 (on a molar basis) available at 298.15 K and 1 bar was assumed. Two distinct adsorbent materials were assessed: Zeolite-13X, a benchmark material for post-combustion carbon capture, and ZIF-36-FRL, known for its high CO_2 adsorption productivity and superior energy efficiency (Khurana and Farooq, 2016). This selection aligns with a previous study comparing their capture costs for industrial-scale application, facilitating a comprehensive extended comparison considering capture costs and operational flexibility of the PVSA unit.

A process model based on a rigorous dynamic simulation of an adsorption column has been employed, capturing non-isothermal and non-isobaric conditions. The process model is constructed through a set of PDEs describing mass, momentum, and energy balance within the column, discretized into 10 volume elements using the finite volume approach. In general, a cyclic PVSA operation is comprised of four stages, repeated cyclically: feed pressurization, adsorption, forward blowdown, and reverse evacuation. During feed pressurization, the column is charged with feed gas, elevating the system's pressure to the desired pressure level, P_H. In the adsorption stage, the CO_2 content of the feed gas is adsorbed into the stationary phase (the adsorbent surface), producing a N_2-rich effluent stream and a CO_2-rich adsorbed phase. In the blowdown stage, the pressure is reduced to the pre-determined level P_I, allowing the bulk gas to be released from the column. In the evacuation stage, the column pressure is further reduced to P_L to produce a high purity CO_2 stream upon desorption of the adsorbed phase.

The performance indicators considered in this study are the CO_2 productivity, CO_2 purity, CO_2 recovery, and CO_2 capture cost. For the latter, a techno-economic analysis by scaling up a single adsorption column to handle industrial-scale flue gas flow rate has been considered. The adsorption column model and the formulation of the KPIs are based on prior research within our group (Ward and Pini, 2022).

4. Results and Discussion

4.1. Global sensitivity analysis (GSA) on PVSA model

For this task, Zeolite-13X, which is widely acknowledged as the benchmark adsorbent for this application, was used as the adsorbent material. To reduce the dimensionality of the problem prior, the single-site Langmuir adsorption model has been chosen to describe the isotherms. For all parameters, the range of uncertainty incorporated for GSA was set at ±40% of the previously reported optimal operating point (Ward and Pini, 2022).

The analysis indicates that "material properties parameters" – more specifically the temperature-dependent adsorption isotherm parameters – play a substantial role in driving the variation of all KPIs. It is noted here that parameters describing the saturation limit of the adsorption isotherm exert the weakest degree of influence, further indicating that the adsorbent bed might not achieve complete saturation during the adsorption step, nor full desorption during the evacuation step — a subject meriting further investigation in subsequent studies. GSA also indicates that "design parameters" primarily affect the capture cost and that "operational parameters" exhibit lower sensitivity relative to the "material properties parameters". Nevertheless, these operational parameters still contribute to process feasibility (CO_2 purity and CO_2 recovery) and affect capture cost. Considering their significance in the PVSA design phase and their impact on these critical factors, they have been included in the design space analysis. The relatively low total sensitivity index values of these parameters underline the relative nature of GSA results: highly influential parameters tend to reduce the sensitivity indices of other parameters.

The result of GSA therefore highlights the importance of prioritizing comparisons between systems that employ different adsorbent materials. However, since the GSA results are not conclusive enough to pinpoint the most influential operational parameters, the three pressure set point parameters (P_H, P_I, and P_L) have been chosen as the manipulated variables in the design space, considering the possible operational disturbances that may occur during PVSA operation. This selection is also motivated by the fact that previous studies in this area have not explored the interaction between these three parameters and their simultaneous effects on the design space of a PVSA.

4.2. Design space analysis on PVSA model

In this analysis, P_H, P_I, and P_L were considered as the manipulated variables, while the other process parameters remained at their nominal operating point as reported by Ward and Pini (2022) using a black-box cost optimization method. For each investigated adsorbent material, a total of 4,096 Sobol sampling points is simulated that yield a minimum CO_2 purity of 95% and CO_2 recovery of 89% (feasibility constraints). The resultant of design spaces of both adsorbents are depicted in Figure 1.

Upon examining the design space visually, it becomes clear that Zeolite-13X exhibits a more constrained design space compared to ZIF-36-FRL, especially for the P_L parameter. This outcome provides a novel perspective on comparing different adsorbents, such as the examined Zeolite-13X and ZIF-36-FRL herein. While Zeolite-13X does indeed offer a lower capture cost compared to ZIF-36-FRL (Table 1), the broader design space of ZIF-36-FRL highlights its enhanced process flexibility. In other words, ZIF-36-FRL's larger design space indicates increased adaptability and robustness in accepting process disturbances and uncertainties in PVSA operation, i.e., the flue gas (feed stream) condition, composition, and flowrate.

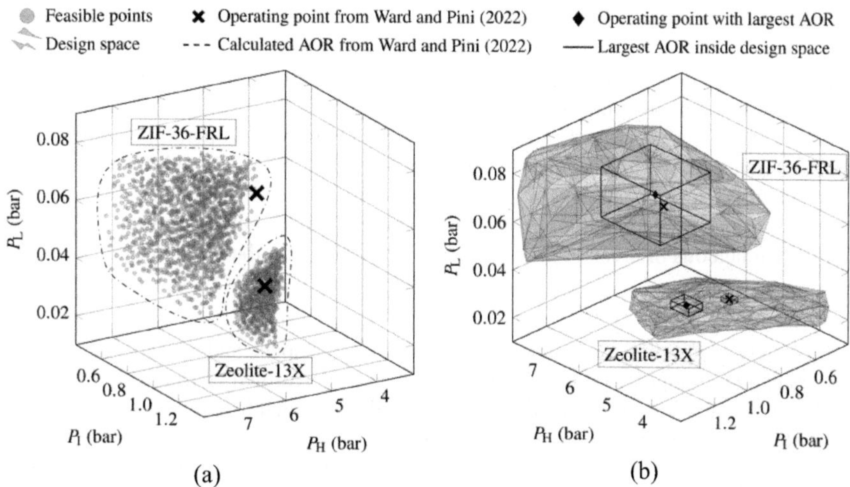

Figure 1. Feasible points (a) and design space analysis (b) of the PVSA process utilising two distinct adsorbents (Zeolite-13X and ZIF-36-FRL).

In line with the NSS definition, an exhaustive search-based optimization algorithm was used to identify the most flexible operating point, representing an operating point with the largest NSS. Surrogate modelling using Gaussian process (GP) was employed to predict the performance index of unexplored points within the design space. The Sobol sampling points were used as the training and test data set to mitigate overfitting of the surrogate model. Compared to artificial neural network (ANN) used in previous study (Sachio et al., 2023), the use of GP opens the possibility of considering the prediction's uncertainty in future studies. Upon assessing the NSS of several operating points within the design space, it is observed that points with a minimal capture cost do not necessarily exhibit optimal flexibility. It should be highlighted that this observation does not imply that an operating point with a higher capture cost will automatically exhibit superior flexibility. The results, in fact, demonstrate that the candidate most-flexible optimal operating point lays within the design space somewhere between the minimum and maximum capture cost. Details of the largest NSS for each adsorbent and their feasible parameters ranges (calculated as relative deviation percentage from the optimal operating point) are available in Table 1. The feasible range of P_H, P_I, and P_L are also illustrated in

Table 1. Feasible ranges of the nominal operating pressure points and the associated KPIs of the PVSA process accounting for operational flexibility (this work) and their comparison against cost-optimal operating points (Literature, Ward and Pini, 2022).

Performance Indicator	Zeolite-13X		ZIF-36-FRL	
	Literature	This Work	Literature	This Work
Feasible range of P_H (bar)	4.72 ± 3.0%	5.28 ± 4.9%	5.52 ± 0.0% [(a)]	6.76 ± 12.5%
Feasible range of P_I (bar)	0.78 ± 2.9%	0.92 ± 4.7%	1.00 ± 0.0% [(a)]	0.78 ± 19.6%
Feasible range of P_L (bar)	0.03 ± 3.0%	0.03 ± 6.0%	0.07 ± 0.0% [(a)]	0.06 ± 18.2%
Normalised space size (NSS)	0.04×10^2	0.26×10^2	0.00	5.61×10^2
CO_2 productivity (mol/m^{3}s)	1.13	1.23	0.92	0.95
Capture cost (USD/tonne)	41.55	44.07	54.46	54.65

[(a)]The reported nominal operating point (Ward and Pini, 2022) is outside the design space

Figure 1(b). These new optimal operating points exhibit a marginal increase in capture cost when compared to the reported operating point in a previous study (Ward and Pini, 2022). It is noted here that the marginal increase in capture cost is compensated by a significant enhancement in process flexibility, as indicated by their corresponding value of NSS. Moreover, it's worth noting that under the proposed operating point, another crucial process performance metric, CO_2 productivity, exhibits a subtle improvement. Consequently, for the studied PVSA system and adsorbent materials, the trade-off between an increase in capture cost and the process performance appears to be almost fully advantageous in favor of process flexibility rather than the CO_2 productivity.

5. Conclusions

In this study, a comprehensive exploration of the design space and operational flexibility of CO_2 capture via post-combustion PVSA has been performed. Through a combination of global sensitivity analysis and design space analysis, valuable insights into the complex interaction between process parameters, performance indicators, and the operational landscape of the system have been gathered. The framework began by utilizing GSA to help justify the choice of process parameters for consideration, thereby reducing the dimensionality of the design exercise. Using this choice of parameters, design space analysis was then conducted. This method successfully mapped out the operating parameter combinations yielding feasible results, given the CO_2 purity and CO_2 recovery constraints. This analysis emphasized the importance of considering not only performance metrics like CO_2 productivity, CO_2 purity, CO_2 recovery, and the capture cost, but also the concept of normalized space size (NSS), which characterizes the flexibility of the operational space around an operating point. Using this technique, the operational robustness of two prominent carbon capture adsorbents, Zeolite-13X and ZIF-36-FRL, has been compared. Despite Zeolite-13X exhibiting a lower capture cost, it was found to possess a more constrained operational flexibility compared to ZIF-36-FRL. This dynamic highlight the complex balance between cost-effectiveness and operational flexibility when selecting optimal adsorbents for CO_2 capture applications.

References

A. Ward and R. Pini, 2022, Efficient bayesian optimization of industrial-scale pressure-vacuum swing adsorption processes for CO_2 capture, *Industrial & Engineering Chemistry Research*, **61**(36), pp.13650-13668.

E.N. Pistikopoulos, Y. Tian, and R. Bindlish, 2021, Operability and control in process intensification and modular design: Challenges and opportunities, *AIChE Journal* **67**, pp. 1-20.

I.E. Grossmann, B.A. Calfa, and P. Garcia-Herreros, 2014, Evolution of concepts and models for quantifying resiliency and flexibility of chemical processes, *Computers & Chemical Engineering*, **70**, 22-34.

M.D. Wilkew and S. Brown, 2022, Flexible CO_2 capture for open-cycle gas turbines via vacuum-pressure swing adsorption: A model-based assessment, *Energy*, **250**, pp.123805.

M. Khurana and S. Farooq, 2016, Adsorbent screening for postcombustion CO_2 capture: A method relating equilibrium isotherm characteristics to an optimum vacuum swing adsorption process performance. *Industrial & Engineering Chemistry Research*, **55**, pp. 2447-2460.

P. Kotidis, P. Demis, C.H. Goey, E. Correa, C. McIntosh, S. Trepekli, N. Shah, O.V. Klymenko, and C. Kontoravdi, 2019, Constrained global sensitivity analysis for bioprocess design space identification. *Computers & Chemical Engineering*, **125**, 558-568.

S. Sachio, C. Kontoravdi, and M.M. Papathanasiou, 2023, A model-based approach towards accelerated process development: A case study on chromatography, *Chemical Engineering Research and Design*, **197**, pp. 800-820.

Flavio Manenti, Gintaras V. Reklaitis (Eds.), Proceedings of the 34th European Symposium on Computer Aided Process Engineering / 15th International Symposium on Process Systems Engineering (ESCAPE34/PSE24), June 2-6, 2024, Florence, Italy
 http://dx.doi.org/10.1016/B978-0-443-28824-1.50240-4

Designing Li-ion Battery Recycling Networks

Pablo Bernal,[a,b] Pablo Miranda,[c] Nathalie Jamett,[a] Francisco Tapia[a,c], Sebastián Herrera-León,[a,b,d*]

[a]*Lithium I+D+i Center, Universidad Católica del Norte, Antofagasta 1270709, Chile*
[b]*Departamento de Ingeniería Química y de Medio Ambiente, Universidad Católica del Norte, Antofagasta 1270709, Chile*
[c]*Departamento de Ingeniería Industrial, Universidad Católica del Norte, Antofagasta 1270709, Chile*
[d]*School of Engineering Science, LUT University, P.O. Box 20, FI-53851 Lappeenranta, Finland*
**Corresponding author at sebastian.herrera@ucn.cl*

Abstract

The transition to electromobility brings a strong demand for lithium-ion batteries that will inevitably result in a large amount of waste in the coming future after these batteries reach their end-of-life. A mixed integer linear program was formulated for designing recycling networks of lithium-ion batteries, comparing the performance of pyrometallurgical and hydrometallurgical recycling processes. The conceptual recycling network proposed consists of three nodes: collection centers, recycling processes, and consumption points. According to the model, the recycling of batteries constitutes 57% of the total cost of the network. In addition, the proposed model only considers the recycling of the cathode material. Therefore, it is crucial to develop recycling networks to process all the battery components efficiently. The proposed model is a valuable tool for designing the supply chain network for recycling Li-ion batteries.

Keywords: Recycling network, lithium-ion batteries, MILP

1. Introduction

Electromobility is an essential driver in the global development of the automotive industry nowadays since modifying energy sources to mitigate the effects of pollution caused by fossil fuel usage is imperative (Ma et al., 2021). According to (Chakraborty and Saha, 2022), 5.6 million electric vehicles (EVs) circulated globally in 2019, and 58% of the world's vehicle fleet will be EVs by 2040. The growing EV manufacturing requires a significant source of electric batteries, such as Lithium-Ion Batteries (LIBs). Raw materials employed to produce LIB, mainly lithium, cobalt, and graphite, are considered critical or strategic supplies, and therefore, one strategy to dampen their demands and final disposal after LIB usage is to recycle LIBs to recover as much of these materials as possible (Rinne et al., 2021).

A significant challenge when recycling LIB is associated with treating the different chemical components of the cathode material. To achieve high recovery rates, designing distinct processes for each type of battery is required (Mossali et al., 2020). According to this context, this work aims to develop an optimization model for designing a LIB recycling supply chain network. As a first approach, the model compares various recycling methods, considering variables such as recovery efficiency and processing costs.

2. Methods

A mixed integer linear programming (MILP) problem is developed to design a recycling network of LIBs. The recycling network comprises three stages: a set of collection facilities, a set of recycling processes, and a set of consumption points. In the first stage, the LIBs are sorted at the collection facilities, and all the LIBs are sent to the recycling plant, where a set of recycling processes is available to recover materials from LIBs. Once the valuable materials from batteries are recovered, they are sold to customers. Note that, to simplify the model, battery waste or residues are considered products; however, all of them are sent to a single specific consumption point named "waste". The following assumptions have been established to streamline the model and simplify its resolution: (1) A period of 1 year is considered; (2) Both collection centers and consumption points are predetermined; (3) Recycling processes, if the model selects it, are installed at the same geographical location, allowing the potential for multiple recycling processes in a single recycling plant; (4) The products obtained from the recycling processes are essentially the chemical elements that constitute the cathode of LIBs; (5) The quantity of LIBs available for recycling was established randomly; (6) The optimization model only considers pyrometallurgical and hydrometallurgical processes, direct recycling processes are not incorporated in this study.

To elucidate the model, various sets were defined as: (1) collection facilities, $H: h \in \{1,2, \ldots, |H|\}$; (2) types of batteries, $I: i\ \{LFP,\ NMC,\ NCA\}$; (3) recycling processes, $J: j \in \{\alpha,\ \beta, \ldots, |J|\}$; (4) products, $K: k\ \{a, b, \ldots, |K|\}$; (5) consumption points, $L: l \in \{1,\ 2, \ldots,\ |L|\}$. Subsequently, the model parameters are detailed in Table 1.

Table 1: Model parameters.

Symbol	Unit	Description
A_j	t	Recycling capacity of each recycling process $j \in J$.
C_j	US$	Fixed operating cost of every recycling process $j \in J$ in the recycling plant.
D_h	km	Distance between each collection center $h \in H$ and the recycling plant.
D_l	km	Distance between the recycling plant and every consumption point $l \in L$.
M_i	$t \cdot battery^{-1}$	Mass of the battery $i \in I$.
Q_{ih}	battery	The available quantity of battery $i \in I$ at the collection center $h \in H$.
T_{kl}	$US\$ \cdot battery^{-1}$	Sale price for the product $k \in K$ in each consumption point $l \in L$
η_{kj}	-	The recovery efficiency of product $k \in K$ in each recycling process $j \in J$.
Φ_{ki}	-	Mass fraction of product $k \in K$ that can be found in each battery $i \in I$.
CP_{ij}	$US\$ \cdot t^{-1}$	The unit cost of processing battery $i \in I$ through the recycling process $j \in J$.
CT_{ih}	$US\$ \cdot battery^{-1} \cdot km^{-1}$	Cost to transport each battery type $i \in I$ from collection point $h \in H$ to the recycling plant.
CT_{kl}	$US\$ \cdot t^{-1} \cdot km^{-1}$	Cost to transport product $k \in K$ from the recycling plant to each consumption point$l \in L$.
N	-	Maximum number of recycling processes that can be selected.

The optimization model minimizes the total cost of the recycling network. To achieve this purpose, an objective function (OF) has been defined considering four terms: (1) cost of recycling, (2) cost of transporting batteries from collection facilities to the recycling plant, (3) cost of transporting products from recycling plant to consumption points, and (4) income from sales. The OF is shown in (1).

$$\min \sum_{i \in I} \sum_{j \in J} Y_{ij} CP_{ij} + \sum_{i \in I} \sum_{h \in H} Q_{ih} D_h CT_{ih} + \sum_{k \in K} \sum_{l \in L} W_{kl} D_l CT_{kl} - \sum_{k \in K} \sum_{l \in L} W_{kl} T_{kl} \quad (1)$$

Moreover, the model has the following constraints:

$$Y_{ij} \leq (\Omega) X_j, \forall i \in I, \forall j \in J \quad (2) \qquad \sum_{j \in J} \Psi_j \leq N \quad (3)$$

$$\sum_{h \in H} Q_{ih} = \sum_{j \in J} Y_{ij}, \forall i \in I \quad (4) \qquad \sum_{i \in I} M_i Y_{ij} \leq A_j, \forall j \in J \quad (5)$$

$$Z_{kj} = \sum_{i \in I} Y_{ij} M_i \Phi_{ki} \eta_{kj}, \forall k \in K, \forall j \in J \quad (6)$$

$$\sum_{j \in J} Z_{kj} = \sum_{l \in L} W_{kl}, \forall k \in K \quad (7) \qquad \Psi_j \in \{0,1\} \quad (8)$$

$$X_{ih} \in \mathbb{N}, \forall i \in I, \forall h \in H \quad (9) \qquad Y_{ij} \in \mathbb{N}, \forall i \in I, \forall j \in J \quad (10)$$

$$Z_{kj} \in \mathbb{Z}^+, \forall k \in K, \forall j \in J \quad (11) \qquad W_{kl} \in \mathbb{Z}^+, \forall k \in K, \forall l \in L \quad (12)$$

Constraints (2) and (3) are logical expressions where $\boldsymbol{\Omega}$ is a sufficiently large number that does not impact the space solution of the model. Constraint (4) implies that all LIBs are being recycled. Constraint (5) establishes that the feedstock LIBs to the recycling plant cannot exceed its capacity. Constraint (6) is a key component of the optimization model because this constraint describes the transformation of LIBs to the products. Constraint (7) defines that all recovered materials are shipped to the consumption points. Finally, constraints (8) to (12) describe the domain of the decision variables.

3. Case study

A case study was generated to validate and apply the proposed model. The case study consists of 5 collection facilities, four recycling processes, three customers, and one waste disposal, as shown in Figure 1. Each process has the same maximum recycling capacity (6,000 t). The processes considered for this conceptual recycling network are based on available recycling technologies to date, encompassing pyrometallurgical and hydrometallurgical methods. Pyrometallurgical processes use high temperatures to recover materials. Generally, this process has three steps: roasting, smelting, and refining. It is important to note that pyrometallurgical processes do not recover lithium. Instead, all of the lithium is directed to the slag for further treatment with another recycling technology. Hydrometallurgical processes consist of separation by components: leaching, solvent extraction, and chemical precipitation. Both types of processes are highly used on an industrial scale. (Li et al., 2023). The literature indicates various processes and recycling products, such as alloys, metals, salts, and hydroxides (Dobó et al., 2023). Details on the recycling efficiency of each process for the respective products are only briefly discussed in the literature. For this reason, in this case study, the efficiencies are defined theoretically based on the type of process and its complexity. The recovery efficiency of these two recycling processes for each product was set to 0.7, except for the recovery of lithium using pyrometallurgical recycling, in which the value was set to 0. Two new recycling processes were introduced: Ad-Hydro, a more sophisticated version of a conventional hydrometallurgical process, and Pyro+Hydro, which combines pyrometallurgical and hydrometallurgical recycling methods. Therefore, given that the two processes mentioned above are more complex than conventional recycling processes the recovery efficiency was set to 0.9 for both processes and each type of product.

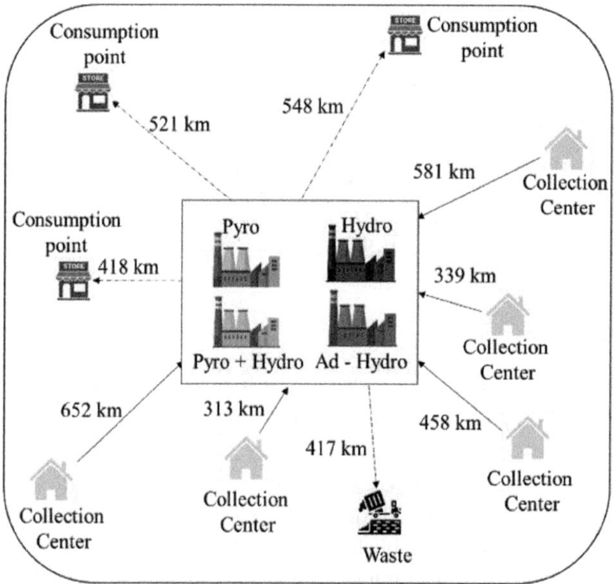

Figure 1: Conceptual recycling network.

Three types of conventional LIBs are considered for this model: NCA, NMC, and LFP. The quantity of LIBs available for recycling is shown in Table 2. The number of LIBs has been generated randomly within a range from 700 to 1,500 batteries. This range of spent lithium-ion batteries is determined based on the current production levels of small-scale recycling industries. Additionally, it considers the emerging lithium battery recycling market (Latini et al., 2022). In this case study, 14,498 LIBs were considered in total.

Additionally, considering that a LIB has 0.365 t unit mass (Wang et al., 2020), there are 5,292 t of LIBs available to recycle in this case study. Moreover, only Li, Co, Ni, and Mn are assumed to be recovered from the cathode material. Gaines et al. (2018) provided the typical mass fraction composition of each battery type. Using this information, the quantity of the mentioned elements for each kind of LIB can be calculated, as detailed in Table 3. The materials not recovered from LIBs are considered waste. The unit transportation cost for transporting batteries from every collection facility to the recycling plant is 8 US$$\cdot$battery$^{-1}\cdot$km^{-1}; furthermore, the unit transportation cost between the recycling plant and every consumption point is 0.12 US$$\cdot$t$^{-1}\cdot$km^{-1} (Li et al., 2018).

On the other hand, Dai et al. (2019) developed a model for estimating the cost of recycling networks, which includes capital and operational costs. The unit recycling costs are detailed in Table 4. Note that the costs for ad-hydro and pyro+hydro are assumed as follows: the costs for ad-hydro are 10% higher than the conventional hydrometallurgical process cost, and the costs for pyro+hydro are calculated as the average of the hydrometallurgical and pyrometallurgical costs. The sale price of Li was defined as 22,769 US$·t^{-1}, 33,420 US$·t^{-1} for Co, 18,284 US$·t^{-1} for Ni, and 5 US$·t^{-1} for Mn (Show The Planet Inc., 2023). On the other hand, products considered waste have a disposal cost of 111.12 US$·t^{-1}; note that the recycling plant must pay to dispose of these waste materials (Reinhart et al., 2023). Two scenarios of this case study were considered to solve the model: the first solves the described model, while the second modifies the OF by eliminating the income for the sales term.

Table 2: Available quantity of each type of battery at each collection center (number of batteries).

Q_{ih}	NMC	NCA	LFP
h_1	1,269	701	901
h_2	946	1,032	767
h_3	1,122	870	1,481
h_4	866	882	801
h_5	1,363	783	714

Table 3: Mass fraction of LIBs components.

Products	NMC	NCA	LPF
Li	0.03	0.02	0.01
Co	0.04	0.03	0.00
Ni	0.11	0.16	0.00
Mn	0.04	0.00	0.00
Waste	0.78	0.79	0.99

Table 4: Unit recycling cost, including capital and operation cost (US$·battery^{-1}).

LIB	Pyro	Hydro	Ad-Hydro	Pyro+Hydro
NMC	2,229	2,118	2,329	2,174
NCA	2,246	2,122	2,335	2,184
LFP	1,166	1,235	1,359	1,201

4. Results

The results are summarized in Table 5. In both scenarios, the cost of recycling comprises 57% of the total cost. Furthermore, considering the data defined in the case study, there is no profit even with the revenue obtained from the sales of the products. The sales amortize only 28% of the total costs. In scenario B, the model chose the cheapest option for recycling, even if it meant recovering less material from the LIBs.

On the other hand, in scenario A, the model chose the best option, recovering the maximum amount of material while using less capital. The recovered materials are sent to the nearest consumption point. In the optimization model, as previously mentioned, only the cathode of LIBs is recycled; therefore, a considerable quantity of materials are not processed; only 12% of the materials that comprise LIBs are recovered. However, it is valuable to highlight that the model may represent several scenarios besides those shown in this document. Further research may be performed by considering scenarios representing potential realizations of public policies, innovation projects, technology development, private initiatives, and cultural changes.

Nevertheless, the proposed model represents a valuable tool for designing the Li-ion batteries recycling supply chain network. Additionally, it is relevant to consider potential scenarios regarding the final destination of the waste generated through all the processes. This is crucial considering the low percentage recuperated from the processed batteries and is highly dependent on the potential scenarios recently mentioned.

Table 5: Case study results

Scenario	RN costs	Recycling process selected	Waste
A	47.0 MM USD	Pyro+Hydro	4,577 t
B	46.5 MM USD	Hydro	4,736 t

5. Conclusions

An optimization model was developed to design recycling networks of LIBs. Based on the data provided, the results only apply to the proposed conceptual recycling network, considering the number of battery types and recovery efficiency. However, the optimization model can be used to assess what recycling process is optimal according to the needs of the user. Continuing research on the recovery efficiencies of today's industrial-scale recycling processes is highly recommended, as there is a lack of information from a technical and scientific perspective. From a chemical and industrial engineering perspective, it is relevant to focus on designing recycling networks that can manage and process all components of LIBs. The proposed model represents a valuable tool for managers and policymakers considering the potentiality of evaluating several potential scenarios regarding potential developments and policies. Consequently, the results obtained are highly dependent on the possible scenarios. Still, it enables considering the consequences of the decisions and developments impacting technologies, efficiencies, and other relevant aspects for designing the Li-ion batteries recycling supply chain network.

References

D. Latini, M. Vaccari, M. Lagnoni, M. Orefice, F. Mathieux, J. Huisman, L. Tognotti, A. Bertei (2022). A comprehensive review and classification of unit operations with assessment of outputs quality in lithium-ion battery recycling. *J. Power Sources 546,* 231979. https://doi.org/10.1016/j.jpowsour.2022.231979

E. Mossali, N. Picone, L. Gentilini, O. Rodrìguez, J. M. Pérez, & M. Colledani (2020). Lithium-ion batteries towards circular economy: A literature review of opportunities and issues of recycling treatments. *Journal of Environmental Management, 264,* 110500. https://doi.org/10.1016/J.JENVMAN.2020.110500

L. Gaines, K. Richa, & J. Spangenberger (2018). Key issues for Li-ion battery recycling. *MRS Energy & Sustainability, 5*(1),* 12. https://doi.org/10.1557/mre.2018.13

L. Li, F. Dababneh, & J. Zhao (2018). Cost-effective supply chain for electric vehicle battery remanufacturing. *Applied Energy, 226,* 277–286. https://doi.org/10.1016/j.apenergy.2018.05.115

L. Reinhart, D. Vrucak, R. Woeste, H. Lucas, E. Rombach, B. Friedrich, & P. Letmathe (2023). Pyrometallurgical recycling of different lithium-ion battery cell systems: Economic and technical analysis. *Journal of Cleaner Production, 416,* 137834. https://doi.org/10.1016/j.jclepro.2023.137834

L. Wang, X. Wang, & W. Yang (2020). Optimal design of electric vehicle battery recycling network – From the perspective of electric vehicle manufacturers. *Applied Energy, 275,* 115328. https://doi.org/10.1016/J.APENERGY.2020.115328

M. Rinne, H. Elomaa, A. Porvali, & M. Lundström (2021). Simulation-based life cycle assessment for hydrometallurgical recycling of mixed LIB and NiMH waste. *Resources, Conservation and Recycling, 170,* 105586. https://doi.org/10.1016/J.RESCONREC.2021.105586

P. Li, S. Luo, L. Zhang, Q. Liu, Y. Wang, Y. Lin, ... & X. Xia (2023). Progress, challenges, and prospects of spent lithium-ion batteries recycling: A review. *Journal of Energy Chemistry.*

Q. Dai, J. Spangenberger, S. Ahmed, L. Gaines, J. C. Kelly, & M. Wang (2019). EverBatt: A Closed-loop Battery Recycling Cost and Environmental Impacts Model. https://doi.org/10.2172/1530874

S. Chakraborty, & A. K. Saha (2022). Selection of optimal lithium-ion battery recycling process: A multi-criteria group decision-making approach. *Journal of Energy Storage, 55.* https://doi.org/10.1016/j.est.2022.105557

Show The Planet Inc. (2023). Daily Metal Prices: Lithium, Cobalt, Nickel, Manganese. https://www.dailymetalprice.com/metalprices.php/

X. Ma, L. Azhari, & Y. Wang (2021). Li-ion battery recycling challenges. *Chem, 7*(11),* 2843–2847. https://doi.org/10.1016/j.chempr.2021.09.013

Z. Dobó, T. Dinh, T. Kulcsár (2023). A review on recycling of spent lithium-ion batteries. *Energy Reports 9,* 6362–6395. https://doi.org/10.1016/j.egyr.2023.05.264

Flavio Manenti, Gintaras V. Reklaitis (Eds.), Proceedings of the 34th European Symposium on Computer Aided Process Engineering / 15th International Symposium on Process Systems Engineering (ESCAPE34/PSE24), June 2-6, 2024, Florence, Italy
 http://dx.doi.org/10.1016/B978-0-443-28824-1.50241-6

Design of Large-scale Industrial Water Networks Based on Multiple Objective Mathematical Programming

Francisco J. G. Patrocínio,[a,b] Ricardo N. Dias,[c] Hugo M. D. Carabineiro,[d] Henrique A. Matos[b] and Nuno M. C. Oliveira,[a*]

[a]CIEPQPF, Dep. Chemical Engineering, University of Coimbra, 3030-790 Coimbra, Portugal

[b]CERENA, Dep. Chemical Engineering, IST, University of Lisbon, 1049-001 Lisbon, Portugal

[c]CQE, IMS, Dep. Chemical Engineering, IST, University of Lisbon, 1049-001 Lisboa, Portugal

[d]Petrogal, S.A., 7520-952 Sines, Portugal

**nuno@eq.uc.pt*

Abstract

Structural optimisation of water networks can be used to generate alternative solutions, providing the basis for the detailed comparison of their relative merits, and a sound framework for environmental footprint reduction. Nonetheless, when based on single-objective optimisation, network degeneracy and modelling simplifications may result in a large number of alternative solutions, ultimately burdening the decision-making process. To overcome this limitation, this work focuses on a multiple objective optimisation strategy applied to the general structural design of industrial water networks.

Keywords: multiple objective optimisation, water network optimisation, decision making, network degeneracy

1. Introduction

The synthesis of process networks through the application of structural optimisation methodologies (based on superstructure concepts) has been widely studied in many engineering design domains with realistic sized problems, including *Industrial Integrated Water/Wastewater Networks* (*IWWNs*; e.g., Patrocínio *et al.* 2022). In complex systems, this framework usually leads to the appearance of alternative degenerated solutions (Faria and Bagajewicz 2010), with distinct topologies and characteristics but with comparable performance, requiring the enumeration of multiple solutions and a detailed posterior analysis step, to identify the final configuration. In some situations, this methodology may prove to be impractical. It also employs structural integer variables, which may complexify the formulation. Problems may be intensively degenerated (or quasi-degenerated) with hundreds of possibilities, where pinpointing an attractive solution can become cumbersome. Also, the search of alternative solutions is a local procedure, heavily leaning on the original result, which may fail to thoroughly explore the feasibility domain. A distinct second group of techniques tries to address these limitations through *Multiple Objective Mathematical Programming* (*MOMP*). The latter incorporates decision-making aspects of the problem during the solution process, directly tracking multiple objectives in the optimization formulation and can produce a more manageable set of interesting solutions. Although the application of these techniques to the optimisation of water networks has been conducted in the past, it regarded smaller specific sections of water networks (e.g., Boix *et al.* 2011). This work considers the design problem of an entire and complete *IWWN* in a *MOMP* aiming for broad, yet tractable, exploration of the feasible domain, supporting the decision on the adopted network.

2. *IWWN* optimisation framework

An *IWWN* model is comprised by a process network superstructure (Figure 1), a set of contaminants or quality indexes, and a flow model expressing the conservation relations. The superstructure includes multiple producer nodes i ($i \in I^{prod}$) and consumer nodes j ($j \in J^{cons}$), accounting for freshwater sources ($FS \subset I^{prod}$), process ($PU \subset (I^{prod} \wedge J^{cons})$) and treatment units ($TU \subset (I^{prod} \wedge J^{cons})$), and effluents ($EF \subset J^{cons}$). All possible node connections are accounted by the superstructure, together with existing flow and concentration (quality) constraints (Karuppiah and Grossmann, 2006, Patrocínio *et al.* 2022).

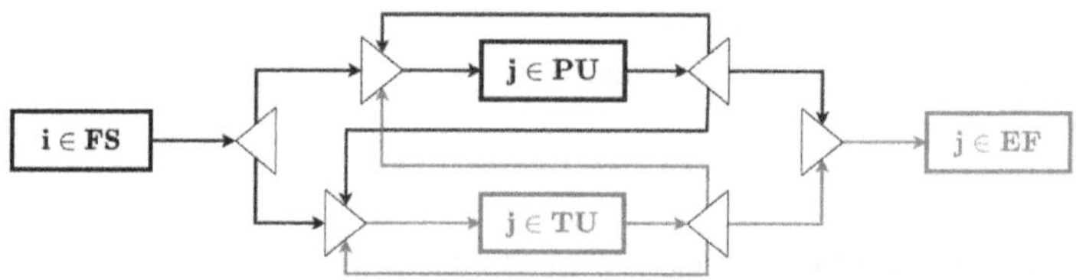

Figure 1 - *IWWN* superstructure.

The usual general mathematical problem formulation corresponds to a mixed integer non-linear program (*MINLP*), generalised in eq. 1. A single objective function (f^{obj}) is minimised, subject to equality and inequality network constraints $g(\mathrm{x},\mathrm{y}) \leq 0$. Relevant constraints in this set are nonlinear, per the bilinearities in the partial contaminant mass balances formulation (i.e., continuous flow variables multiplied by continuous concentration variables). The solution vectors x and y represent continuous variables (in the problem feasibility set X) and binary variables, respectively.

$$\begin{aligned} &\min f^{obj}(\mathrm{x},\mathrm{y}) \\ &\mathrm{s.t.}\, g(\mathrm{x},\mathrm{y}) \leq 0\,, \mathrm{x} \in X, \mathrm{y} \in \{0,1\} \end{aligned} \tag{1}$$

3. Multiple Objective Optimisation

Network optimisation problems can be solved considering multiple different objectives o ($o \in O^{obj}$). Eq. 2 mathematically defines the new *MOMP* problem. The original constraints and variables remain unchanged, although new ones can be introduced to solve this problem. *Pareto Efficiency* is an important characteristic of an *MOMP* solution, and it is achieved if there is no other feasible point in the domain capable of improving at least one of the objectives without deteriorating the others (Ehrgott 2005).

$$\begin{aligned} &\min f_1(\mathrm{x},\mathrm{y}), \dots, f_o(\mathrm{x},\mathrm{y}) \\ &\mathrm{s.t.}\, g(\mathrm{x},\mathrm{y}) \leq 0\;, \mathrm{x} \in X, \mathrm{y} \in \{0,1\} \end{aligned} \tag{2}$$

To apply multiple objective optimisation to *IWWN* synthesis, this work recommends the three-stage strategy illustrated in Figure 2. The *decision maker* (*DM*) intervenes in the first stage to identify the trade-offs in scope. This methodology can be applied to as many different objectives as required. For each trade-off identified in the initial stage, a *MOMP* problem is solved in the second stage, generating alternative Pareto solutions that elucidate the possible compromises within the subset of objectives considered. For simplicity, a larger set of scenarios considering the trade-offs between only 2 objectives can be considered in stage 2, to facilitate the characterisation of the corresponding Pareto surfaces. The last step compiles the results into a *solution pool*, composed by a tractable number of network solutions, spanning the feasibility domain. This tool thus allows a meaningful *a posteriori* comparison of a larger set of solution features, without the need of considerably increasing the problem complexity at stage 2. With the *solution pool* support, the *DM* is supposed to be able to elucidate in detail the relative performance of the solutions identified relative to each individual objective considered and their combination, and therefore produce a final informed choice. If necessary, the procedure can also be extended by incrementally including additional trade-offs in stage 1, and repeating the procedure from the beginning.

Figure 2 - Suggested *MOO* framework.

3.1. MOMP techniques

Hwang and Masud (1979) introduced a broad classification for the different *MOMP* techniques according to the *DM* intervention in the solution process: *no intervention, a priori, interactive,* and *a posteriori*. The latter, particularly relevant when adopting the preconized *IWWN MOO* strategy of Figure 2, can be described as techniques where the *DM* makes a choice, according to some criteria, over a finite subset P^{Pareto} of the *MOMP* solutions (Hwang and Masud 1979). They can be implemented by using an Algebraic Modelling Language (*AML*) or by resorting to metaheuristic procedures, and Pareto fronts (Figure 3) can be identified to visualise the solution trade-offs.

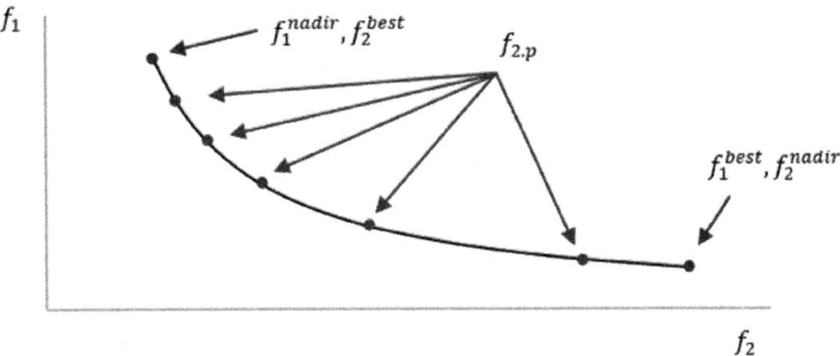

Figure 3 - Pareto front example.

Metaheuristic-based algorithms, inspired by natural processes (e.g. genetic algorithms, simulated annealing) are often employed to solve *MOMP* problems. They focus on the problem domain exploration, although generally lacking a precise characterization of the optimality of the candidate solutions. Only deterministic global optimisation approaches can guarantee *MOMP* efficient solutions. The framework of Mavrotas (2009), using an *AML* compatible formulation and including *a priori* and *a posteriori* techniques, is suitable to produce efficient solutions and was applied to solve the *MOMP* instances of the application example. Supported by Figure 3, for simplicity reasons is limited to the trade-off between two objectives f_1 and f_2, the algorithm description can be enunciated as:

1. The two targeted objectives are ranked in decreasing order of importance (here, we consider f_1 to be more important than f_2). Lexicographic optimisation achieves the objective's *best* and *nadir* points ($f_1^{best}, f_1^{nadir}, f_2^{best}, f_2^{nadir}$, see Figure 3).
2. The interval between these f_2 points is equidistantly partitioned (see Figure 3) to obtain the Pareto candidates $f_{2,p}^{candidate}$ ($p \in \{2,..,card(P^{Pareto}) - 1\}$).
3. f_1 is then minimized using a single objective formulation, utilising the original model constraints as well as the Pareto candidate levels as an additional constraint $f_2(\mathrm{x}) \leq f_{2,p}^{candidate}$. This new program must be solved $card(P^{Pareto}) - 2$ times, for each candidate point. To guarantee Pareto efficiency of all Figure 3 points, global minima and binding constraint objectives must be achieved, for all optimisation instances of the Mavrotas (2009) framework. If efficient, $f_{2,p}^{candidate} = f_{2,p}$ and the optimum of the routine is regarded as $f_1(f_{2,p})$.

The second efficiency condition may not always be met, as f_2 is not considered in the model objective function and alternative, better levels of this objective can occur (such that $f_2(\mathrm{x}) < f_{2,p}^{candidate}$). To address this issue, Mavrotas (2009) slacks the constraint objective ($f_2(\mathrm{x}) + s = f_{2,p}^{candidate}$) and weights the new slack variable s in the objective function. Alternatively, here if for any instance $f_2(\mathrm{x}) < f_{2,p}^{candidate}$, a new program can be solved, minimising f_2 and utilising the global optimum of f_1 as an equality constraint. It is paramount that the new result is a global optimum and will be assumed as $f_{2,p}$.

4. Application example

The generic framework of Figure 2, was applied to the real case scenario of a crude oil refinery *IWWN*. The problem, an extended instance of Patrocínio *et al.* (2022), comprises 6 contaminants, one freshwater source, 23 processes and 6 treatment units, and two effluents. The solution of the single objective *MINLP*, minimising the hourly network expenditure, achieved an objective level of 604.68 €/h with a freshwater intake of 684.21 t/h. This problem displayed over 100 degenerated solutions with almost identical objective levels but with distinct topologies and water footprints. The trade-offs considered were: the *IWWN* hourly expenditure (f_1) *versus* the *IWWN* water footprint (f_2), the *IWWN* hourly expenditure (f_1) *versus* the *IWWN* network complexity (f_3) and the *IWWN* yearly expenditure, accounting for piping capital and the operational cost (f_4) *versus* the environmental impact related to the pipe manufacturing and transport (f_5). The *MOMP* problem was formulated as an *MINLP* and solved using an *AMD Ryzen 7 4800H 16GB RAM* computer and *GAMS 40.3.0*, with the local solver *SBB* proceeded by using the global solver *SCIP*. An optimality gap of 0.001% was imposed in the local step, while *SCIP* was allowed a maximum computing wall clock time of 3 hours.

4.1. f_1 vs. f_2

The f_1 best and f_2 nadir levels are represented by p_1. These levels correspond to the results of the single objective *IWWN MINLP*. Considering the overall result range, the *MOMP* analysis allows a 3.16% (21.65 t/h) decrease in the raw water intake with a global trade-off of increasing 10.32% the hourly network cost (62.4 €/h), as showcased in Figure 4.

4.2. f_1 vs. f_3

The second trade-off scenario concerns the *IWWN* hourly expenditure *versus* the *IWWN* network complexity, expressed as the number of structural connections in the optimal network. Again, the f_1 best level (p_7, f_3 nadir as well) is identical to the single objective *IWWN MINLP* result. The Pareto front of Figure 5 is composed by discrete points (p_7 to p_{13}), due to the nature of the f_3 objective. Here, the network complexity can be decreased by 22% (10 connections less), increasing the hourly network cost by 6.68% (40.24 €/h).

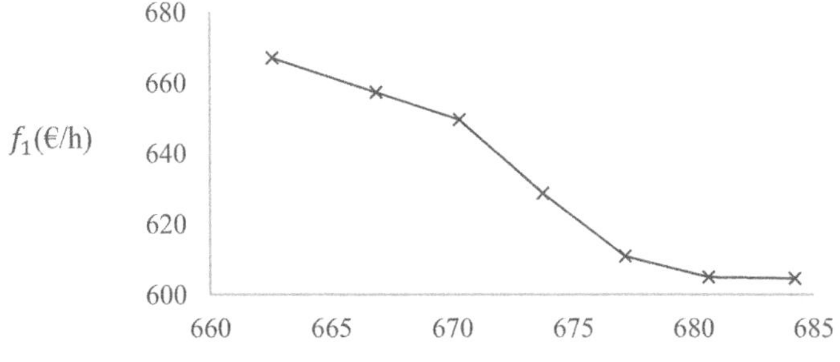

Figure 4 - f_1 vs f_2 Pareto front.

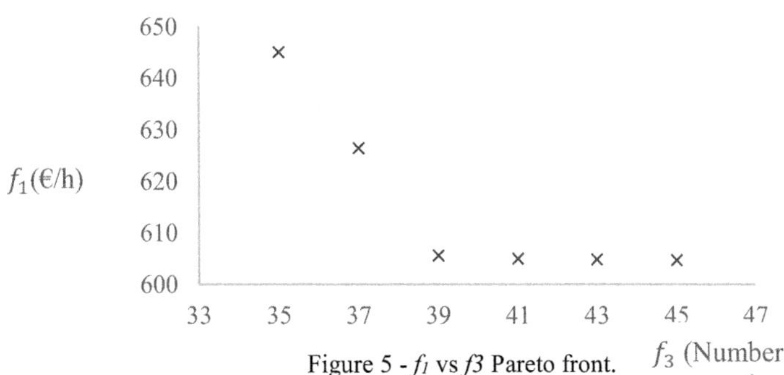

Figure 5 - f_1 vs $f3$ Pareto front.

4.3. f_4 vs. f_5

Pipe cost data was supplied by *INTERFLUIDOS*, and the pipe unitary environmental footprint was extracted from the *SimaPro ecoinvent v3.6* database. Due to the discontinuous nature of the piping items, these parameters were corresponded to the connection flows using the strategy of Patrocínio *et al.* (2023). However, unlike the previous work, a disaggregated *MINLP* could not be applied to account for these discontinuous parameters, due to the size and the complexity of the considered *IWWN* problem. Instead, the pipe expenditure and the pipe environmental footprint were approximated by a linear trend superimposed to the parameters-flow correspondence. The surrogate *IWWN* yearly expenditure (f_4^*) and the surrogate environmental impact (f_5^*) trade-off is displayed in Figure 6. For a 1.53% decrease in the equipment environmental footprint, the yearly network expenditures increase 10.06%. The discontinuity in Figure 6 is due to $f_4^*(p_{17}) \leq f_4^*(p)\,, \forall p | f^{*candidate}_{5,p} \in]4.75 \times 10^5, 4.81 \times 10^5[$, i.e., in the mentioned interval there is no f_4 value better than the level for p_{17}. To obtain the original f_4 and f_5 trade-off, the f_4^* and f_5^* *MOMP* results were converted from surrogate to the original variable space. In the latter, for the studied candidates, p_{16} and p_{19} are the f_5 best and f_4 nadir and f_4 best and f_5 nadir points. The other candidates were disregarded as $\nexists p \in P^{Pareto} | f_{5,p} \in [f_{5,16}, f_{5,19}]$.

With the results of the *MOMP* procedures, 14 relevant solutions were extracted (networks p_7 and p_{13} are the same, and only p_{16} and p_{19} result from the f_4 vs. f_5 analysis). Although obtained from distinct *MOMP* routines, these solutions span and characterise the relevant compromises reachable in the feasible domain, and can be finally compared in light of the trade-offs expressed.

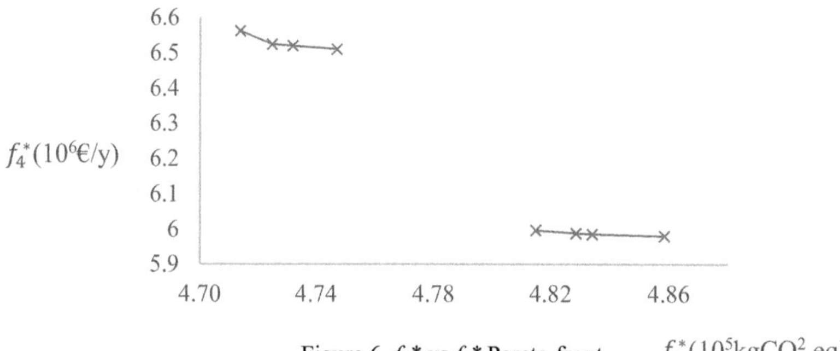

Figure 6 f_4* vs f_5* Pareto front. f_5^*(10^{5}kgCO^2 eq)

Conclusion

Multiple objective optimisation is a suitable and recommended strategy for the solution of *IWWN* design problems. It allows the generation of alternative relevant solutions spanning the entire feasibility domain. Furthermore, the generated networks allow for a pertinent post-processing study of other solution characteristics, whose complexity renders impossible their direct incorporation in the original mathematical models. With the *MOO* support, more thoroughly informed decisions can be made by the DMs.

Acknowledgments: The authors gratefully acknowledge the data provided by Galp Energia, S.A. and INTERFLUIDOS, Lda. Financial support provided by the Ph.D. grant PD/BDE/142833/2018, the CERENA strategic project FCT-UIBD/04028/2020, and the CQE strategic project FCT-UIBD/00100/2020 is also acknowledged.

References

M. Boix, L. Montastruc, L. Pibouleau, C. Azzaro-Pantel, S. Domenech, 2011, A multiobjective optimization framework for Multicontaminant Industrial Water Network Design, J. Environ. Manage., 92, 7, 1802–1808.

M. Ehrgott, 2005, Efficiency and Nondominance, Multicriteria optimization, Springer, 23-64

D. C. Faria, M. J. Bagajewicz, 2010, On the degeneracy of the water/wastewater allocation problem in process plants, Ind. Eng. Chem., 49, 9, 4340–4351.

R. Karuppiah, I. E. Grossmann, 2006, Global optimization for the synthesis of integrated water systems in Chemical Processes, Comput. Chem. Eng, 30, 4, 650–673.

C.-L. Hwang, A. S. Masud, 1979, Multiple objective decision making-methods and applications: A state-of-the-art survey, Springer-Verlag.

G. Mavrotas, 2009, Effective implementation of the ε-constraint method in multi-objective mathematical programming problems, Appl. Math. Comput., 213, 2, 455–465.

F. J. G. Patrocínio, H. M. D. Carabineiro, H. A. Matos, N. M. C. Oliveira, 2022, Water Network Optimisation in Chemical Complexes: A Refinery Case Study, Comput. Aided Chem. Eng. 51 (January), 817–22.

F. J. G. Patrocínio, H. M. D. Carabineiro, H. A. Matos, N. M. C. Oliveira, 2023, Optimal design of water treatment networks: Effluent and piping disaggregated modelling, Comput. Aided Chem. Eng., 949–954.

Flavio Manenti, Gintaras V. Reklaitis (Eds.), Proceedings of the 34th European Symposium on Computer Aided Process Engineering / 15th International Symposium on Process Systems Engineering (ESCAPE34/PSE24), June 2-6, 2024, Florence, Italy
 http://dx.doi.org/10.1016/B978-0-443-28824-1.50242-8

Superstructure-based Optimization for Assessing Defossilization Pathways in Petrochemical Clusters

Michael Tan, [a*] Paola Ibarra-González, [a] Igor Nikolic, [b] Andrea Ramírez Ramírez [c]

[a]*Department of Engineering Systems and Services, Faculty of Technology, Policy and Management, Delft University of Technology, Jaffalaan 5, 2628BX Delft, the Netherlands*

[b]*Department of Multi-Actor Systems, Faculty of Technology, Policy and Management, Delft University of Technology, Jaffalaan 5, 2628BX Delft, the Netherlands*

[c] *Department of Chemical Engineering, Faculty of Applied Sciences, Delft University of Technology, Van der Maasweg 9, 2629 HZ Delft, the Netherlands*

Email corresponding author: m.d.tan@tudelft.nl

Abstract

The petrochemical industry needs to reduce the use of fossil fuel as carbon feedstock to reduce its CO2 emissions. Several alternative carbon sources (ACSs), such as biomass, CO2 and plastic waste are being proposed to replace fossil carbon. As each of these ACS process routes has its tradeoffs, it is essential to identify the defossilization pathways that will have the most significant impact. In this work, a superstructure-based optimization approach is presented that can be used to assess defossilization pathways in existing petrochemical clusters. The small case study shows that CO_2 is a promising ACS to replace fossil fuel as the main carbon source but requires a large amount of green hydrogen and significant modifications to the existing cluster.

Keywords: superstructure, optimization, petrochemical clusters, carbon transition

1. Introduction

To reach the CO_2 emissions goals set out by the European Commission, the petrochemical industry will have to drastically reduce its usage of fossil-based carbon. With this purpose, alternative carbon sources (ACSs), such as biomass, CO_2, and plastic waste, are being investigated. However, their introduction to existing petrochemical clusters is far from straightforward, as it will require the modification of existing processes or the deployment of entirely new processes. Thereby, potentially affecting other processes in a petrochemical cluster due to the significant number of existing material and energy interconnections. Furthermore, each of these ACS processes has its own tradeoffs and limitations. Therefore, it is vital to identify and assess the defossilization pathways that could provide the most optimal transformation of petrochemical clusters.

PSE tools such as superstructure-based optimization have been used for the synthesis and design of new chemical processes. In this approach, a set of alternative equipment or process options is assessed with respect to an objective function. This approach has been used to design new industrial clusters or optimize the exchange network between processes in existing industrial clusters. Kantor et al. (2020) developed a mixed-integer linear programming model for integrating material and energy in industrial clusters. They used single objective functions to determine the ideal network configuration. The authors focused on greenfield applications and, therefore, ignored the existing interconnections that are present in today's petrochemical clusters. However, as processes in petrochemical clusters are interconnected by many material and energy flows, altering such connections due to e.g., replacing processes or flows, can have unforeseen consequences. This could, for instance, result in a shift of emissions from one process to another or from inside the cluster to emissions outside the cluster boundaries due to increased demand on energy or carbon-intensive materials.

This work shows a superstructure-based optimization model that explicitly incorporates interconnections existing in an industrial cluster while assessing different processing routes to replace the source of carbon. This model determines the minimal amount of ACS required to completely replace the fossil-based carbon source and the energy required by the cluster.

2. Method

To set up the model, the chemical processes, utility generation units, available feedstocks, and desired products were defined as nodes (see Figure 1). Besides the nodes, the chemical components and the different energy types in the superstructure were defined as follows: CC is the set of all the chemical components, for instance ethylene, propylene, and methyl tert-butyl ether. CU is the set of set of the utility types, for instance, low-pressure steam, cooling water, electricity. Separate layers were introduced for the material and energy connections in the superstructure, allowing different constraints for each layer to close the respective mass and energy balances. The figure shows that in the material layer, the interconnections between the available feedstocks, process, and utility options, and desired products were explicitly defined using transfer blocks to mimic the existing value chains of a cluster as closely as possible. These transfer blocks distribute the flow of mass between the processes.

Based on Figure 1, mass equations were defined. For each node *b* of the material layer, the total mass of component cc into the node equals all the mass flows of component *cc* into the node:

$$mass_{b,cc}^{In} = \sum_{\substack{i \\ i \in \mathbf{B}, b \neq i}} streams_{i,b,cc}^{Mass} \tag{1}$$

Where, $streams_{i,b,cc}^{Mass}$ stands for the mass flowrate from node *i* to node *b*. It was assumed that the process' input and output scales linearly. For each process, a limiting component was selected that scales the other inputs and outputs of each process. Therefore, the mass flow of a component into a component can then be calculated by:

$$mass_{b,cc}^{In} = mass_{p,cc'}^{In} \cdot X_{b,cc}^{MassIN} \tag{2}$$

Where, $mass_{p,cc'}^{In}$ is the mass flow rate into node p of the limiting component *cc'* and $X_{b,cc}^{MassIn}$ mass flow in a parameter. Based on the mass flow rate into a process node or utility node, the mass flow out of the process node or utility can be calculated by:

$$mass_{p,cc}^{Out} = mass_{p,cc'}^{In} \cdot X_{p,cc}^{Mass} \tag{3}$$

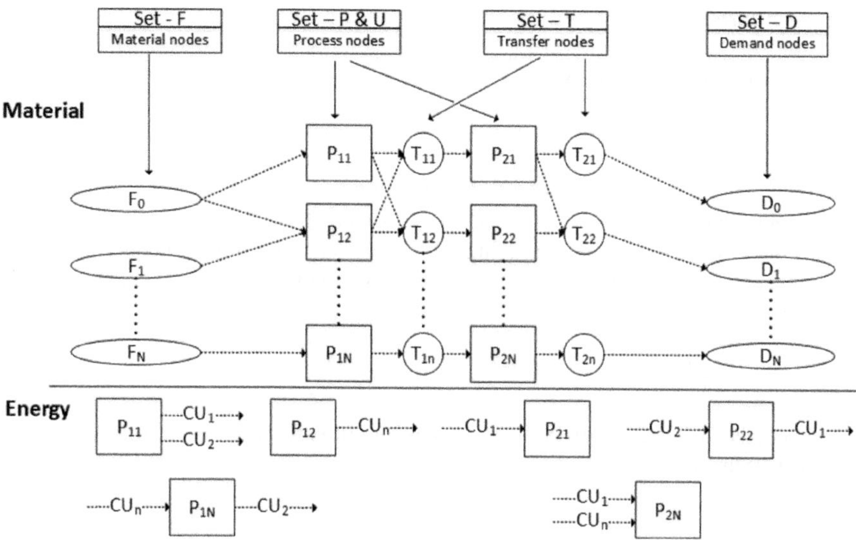

Figure 1

Figure 1: General superstructure representation of the material and energy layers, where F is the set of feed nodes, P is the set of process nodes, U is the set of utility nodes, D is the set of demand nodes, and the set containing all these subsets is B.

Where, $X_{p,cc}^{Mass}$ is the conversion parameter. As there is no reaction in other nodes, the mass flow out is there equal to mass flow in. The mass flowrate between a transfer node t and a node b can thus be calculated by:

$$streams_{t,b,cc}^{Mass} = mass_{t,cc}^{Out} \cdot y_{t,b} \tag{4}$$

Where, $mass_{t,cc}^{Out}$ is the mass flow rate of component cc leaving the transfer node and $y_{t,b}$ is the variable the transfer coefficient that assigns the mass flow rate off each stream leaving the transfer node. For which the following constraint was introduced:

$$\sum_{\substack{b \in B \\ b \neq t}} y_{t,b} = 1 \tag{5}$$

For the other nodes, the mass flow rate between nodes b_1 and b_2 is given by:

$$streams_{b_1,b_2,cc}^{Mass} = mass_{b,cc}^{Out} \cdot S_{b_1,b_2,cc} \tag{6}$$

Where, $S_{b_1,b_2,cc}$ is the separation coefficient, which is a pre-determined parameter based on process simulations that assign the distribution of each component over the outgoing streams. After the definition of the equations of the material layer, the equations for the energy layer were defined. Contrary to the material equations, the available energy connections were not explicitly defined, and the potential connections between nodes can be considered based on the proximity of the other nodes. The energy of type cu supplied by a process or utility node $E_{p,cu}^{D}$is calculated by:

$$E^{D}_{p,cu} = mass^{In}_{p,cc'} \cdot X^{D}_{p,cu} \tag{7}$$

while the energy demanded by a process or utility node is given by:

$$E^{S}_{p,cu} = mass^{In}_{p,cc'} \cdot X^{S}_{p,cu} \tag{8}$$

Where, $X^{D}_{p,cu}$ is the energy demand coefficient of type cu and $X^{S}_{p,cu}$is the energy supply coefficient. These coefficients relate the energy supplied and demanded to the mass flow rate of the limiting component entering the process or utility node, thereby linking the material and energy equations. To solve the energy equation, the energy balance needs to close so:

$$\sum_{i\in\mathbf{B}} E^{D}_{i,cu} = \sum_{i\in\mathbf{B}} E^{S}_{i,cu} \tag{9}$$

To ensure, that that the energy leaving a process or utility node does not exceed the energy supplied by the node:

$$\sum_{j\in\mathbf{B}} streams^{Energy}_{i,j,cu} \leq E^{S}_{i,cu} \tag{10}$$

Finally, to determine the flow of energy between nodes,

$$E^{S}_{i,cu} + \sum_{j\in\mathbf{B}} streams^{Energy}_{j,i,cu} = E^{D}_{i,cu} + \sum_{j\in\mathbf{B}} streams^{Energy}_{i,j,cu} \tag{11}$$

In this paper, for the objective function, the flow of the carbon sources was minimized, and the availability of carbon sources was limited to obtain different optimal configurations.

3. Case study

To illustrate the method, we examine the potential of ACS to defosilize the carbon sources used in the production of ethylene, propylene and MTBE in an existing cluster. With this purpose, an in-house model that mimics part of the Port of Rotterdam was used. The model is described in detail in previous work (Tan et al., 2023). From this model, 10 fossil-based processes, five utility processes, processes, 112 chemical components, and six energy components were taken. Four ACS-based processes were added: biomass to isobutylene via an organosolv route, plastic pyrolysis, CO_2 hydrogenation to methanol, and methanol to olefins (MTO).

Based on the locations in the PoR, the 10 processes were assigned to one of three sites. New ACS-based processes were assumed to be located at the same site as the processes they aimed to replace. Furthermore, the material streams can cross the boundaries of each site, while the energy balance would be solved for each site individually. For each process and utility generation node, the assumption was made that the output linearly scales based on the input. These conversion parameters (e.g. $X^{Mass}_{p,cc}$) were used to linearize the processes were derived based on Aspen Plus simulations of each process. Additionally, the minimal production capacity (defined as the minimal mass of product per year) of each process and utility generation process were limited to a 10% deviation from its base production capacity, while the exiting production capacities in the PoR (e.g., the MTBE process produces 400 kt/y) were set as the upper limit.

For the new ACS-based processes, the production capacity was limited as the vessels involved with these processes are much bigger in size and have a high feedstock demand. Therefore, multiple units of an ACS-based process or combined ACS feedstock (e.g. CO_2 and plastic waste) might be required to replace the current production of a fossil-based product. The petrochemical cluster was required to produce a fixed demand of all the chemicals at the end of each value chain (MTBE, ethylene glycol, and styrene monomer), which was based on the current production levels present in the PoR. Additional demand nodes were added for excess intermediate products (ethylene, propylene, propylene oxide, and tert-butyl alcohol) with no product demand constraint enforced on them. For the energy layer, energy demand and supply nodes were added to each site, representing connections to other processes in the PoR and the electricity grid. These nodes export excess energy from a site and import required energy if the utility processes do not match the demand. The resulting superstructure was implemented as a mixed integer linear programming problem in Pyomo and solved using the Gurobi solver.

4. Results and discussion

The original fossil-based configuration and the optimal configuration of the material layer are shown in Figure 2. The steam that is imported or exported for each configuration is presented in Table 1. The results show that to completely replace the fossil-based naphtha with ACSs, the model selects CO2 as the primary carbon source. This route would require 11 identical CO2 hydrogenation to methanol processes followed by two methanol to olefins plants to replace the fossil-based olefins plant. Therefore, significant modifications to the current cluster are required, requiring a minimum investment of 5.4 billion euros. Furthermore, the CCU route would require 1130 kt/y of green hydrogen.

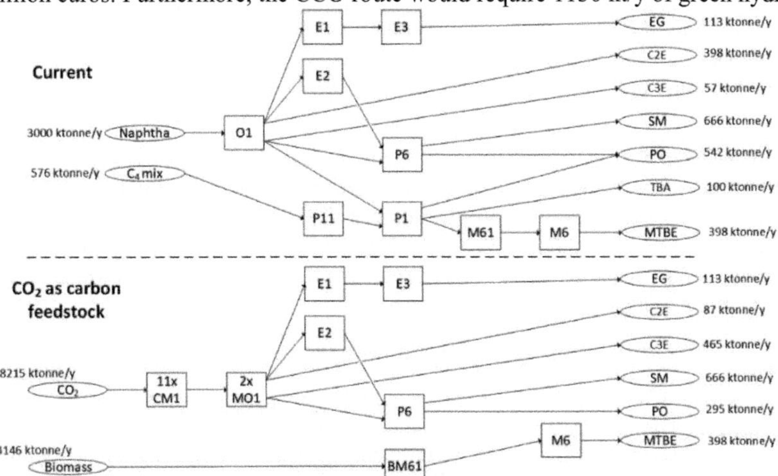

BM61. Biomass to isobutylene via organosolv, CM1. CO2 Hydrogenation to methanol, E1. Ethylene oxide, E2. Ethylbenzene, E3. Ethylene glycol, M6. Methyl tert-butyl ether, M61. Tert-butyl alcohol dehydration, MO1. Methanol to olefins, O1. Olefins, P1. Propylene oxide/Tert-butyl alcohol, P6. Propylene oxide/Styrene monomer, P11. C_4 Isomerization, PO1. Plastic Pyrolysis, C2E. Ethylene, C3E. Propylene, EG. Ethylene glycol, SM. Styrene monomer, PO. Propylene oxide, MTBE. Methyl tert-butyl ether, TBA. Tert-butyl alcohol

Figure 2: The current fossil-based configuration and the optimal CO_2 based alternative configuration

Table 1: Steam imported or exported for each site of the case study

	Fossil naphtha base case	**CO2 as ACS**
Site 1 [TJ/y]	5,792.5	5,792.5
Site 2 [TJ/y]	5,231.2	143,809.8
Site 3 [TJ/y]	-18,713.5	-24,855.3

To completely remove fossil-based carbon as a feedstock, biomass will be used to produce the isobutylene used for the production of MTBE. This will require the isomerization, PO/TBA, and TBA dehydration processes to be removed from the cluster. As a result, there is an overall lower PO production and TBA is no longer exported from the cluster in comparison to fossil-based route. It can also be concluded that using CO2 as a carbon source will result in a larger fraction of propylene product compared to the conventional. This is a result of the larger fraction of propylene produced by the MTO process. Table 1 shows that for the CCU route, there is a significant increase in the demand for steam at Site 2. This is a result of the biomass to isobutylene route via the organosolv process, which requires a very large number of distillation columns with a significant steam demand. This would result in a rise of steam related CO_2 emissions if natural gas were used as the fuel source to generate the required steam.

5. Conclusion

In this work, a superstructure-based optimization model was developed to assess transformation pathways in petrochemical clusters. The model selected CO2 combined with biomass as ACS to completely replace the fossil-based carbon sources. However, this solution would require significant modifications to the existing cluster, potentially resulting in a non-optimal solution. In the next step, we will include minimizing the changes required to the existing petrochemical cluster (in terms of assets, emissions, lands requirements) as objective in multi-objective optimization. The model will also be extended to include the full representative model of the PoR petrochemical cluster (32 chemical processes) and additional ACS-based processes to evaluate the impacts of defossilization in the PoR.

Acknowledgements

This publication is part of the project Unravelling the impacts of using alternative raw materials in industrial clusters (with project number VI.C.183.010) of the research programme Vici DO which is financed by the Dutch Research Council (NWO). The authors would like to thank dr. Mar Perez-Fortes, Inna Stepchuk and Tonny Manalal for their contributions to the in-house and ACS-models.

References

Kantor, I., Robineau, J. L., Bütün, H., & Maréchal, F. (2020). A Mixed-Integer Linear Programming Formulation for Optimizing Multi-Scale Material and Energy Integration. *Frontiers in Energy Research*, *8*(April). https://doi.org/10.3389/fenrg.2020.00049

Tan, M. D., Ibarra-Gonzalez, P., Nikolic, I., & Ramirez, A. (2023). Determining the performance and network properties of petrochemical clusters. In *Computer Aided Chemical Engineering* (Vol. 52). Elsevier Masson SAS. https://doi.org/10.1016/B978-0-443-15274-0.50193-1

Flavio Manenti, Gintaras V. Reklaitis (Eds.), Proceedings of the 34th European Symposium on Computer Aided Process Engineering / 15th International Symposium on Process Systems Engineering (ESCAPE34/PSE24), June 2-6, 2024, Florence, Italy
 http://dx.doi.org/10.1016/B978-0-443-28824-1.50243-X

Optimizing Circular Economy Pathways: Multi-Criteria Decision-Making Tool for Chemical Recycling of Plastic Wastes

Virgil Cabo[a,b], Adrián Pacheco-López[b], Grégoire Léonard[a], Antonio Espuña[b]*

[a]*Department of Chemical Engineering, Université de Liège, Allée de la Chimie B6a, Liège Sart Tilman, 4000, Belgium*

[b]*Department of Chemical Engineering, Universitat Politècnica de Catalunya, Escola d'Enginyeria de Barcelona Est, C/ Eduard Maristany 16, Barcelona 08019, Spain*

**antonio.espuna@upc.edu*

Abstract

The escalating crisis of waste mismanagement underscores the need for innovative treatment strategies, highlighting the inadequacy of conventional evaluation methods in the face of evolving waste management techniques. This study introduces a robust tool applying two decision-making methodologies to an existing multi-objective optimization framework. This framework can assess various waste-to-resource transformation processes, which was applied to the case of mixed plastic waste management within the circular economy. It yielded a set of 16 Pareto optimal recycling pathways according to four competitive objectives. Here, this new decision-making tool is applied to those Pareto solutions using user inputs as weight parameters to systematically rank them according to criteria weighting. Eventually, its capability is tested by a sensitivity analysis, assessing the robustness of solutions.

Keywords: circular economy, multi-criteria decision-making, sensitivity analysis, TOPSIS, PROMETHEE.

1. Introduction

The growing crisis of plastic waste mismanagement presents a complex global challenge characterized by escalating waste accumulation, resource depletion, and extensive environmental degradation. Conventional methods for evaluating the vast array of treatment options for plastic pollution are becoming increasingly insufficient, as highlighted by the continuously evolving landscape of waste management techniques (Chawla et al., 2022). In response, the circular economy paradigm offers a promising shift, focusing on closing material loops and transforming waste into valuable resources. To facilitate this transition towards more sustainable plastic waste management, a comprehensive ontological framework was developed. It was designed to systematically generate and assess various waste-to-resource transformation pathways, optimizing trade-offs between different objectives such as economic viability and environmental impact. Initially, these pathways are pre-assessed based on a global performance indicator, then a superstructure is built, and multi-objective optimization is solved, leading to a set of Pareto optimal solutions (Pacheco-López et al., 2023). However, the existing framework did not address the decision-making (DM) step and had the limitation of analyzing only two criteria simultaneously. To bridge this gap, the tool introduced in this paper integrates two established multi-criteria decision-making (MCDM) methods: TOPSIS (Technique for Order Preference by Similarity to Ideal Solution) (Çelikbilek and Tüysüz, 2020) and

PROMETHEE (Preference Ranking Organization Method for Enrichment Evaluations) (Maity and Chakraborty, 2015). By combining TOPSIS's capacity for straightforward comparative analysis with PROMETHEE's depth in pairwise preference evaluation, the tool achieves a balanced and thorough assessment. The adoption of these methodologies also ensures that the tool's evaluations are methodologically sound, reliable, and transparent. The tool is further enhanced by a sensitivity analysis feature, critically evaluating the robustness of the optimal solutions against uncertainties in the user's criteria weighting. The integration of these DM methods within the ontological framework provides decision-makers with a systematic method to navigate the complex landscape of sustainable recycling and fortifying the application of the circular economy.

2. Methodologies

2.1. Tool description

The tool developed in this work is a Python-based application, providing full compatibility with the existing ontological framework that was partially developed in Python. The system is designed to be user-friendly, efficiently transforming complex datasets into actionable insights. It is structured into three main functional areas:

Data gathering: This step involves importing the decision matrix. The tool captures essential user inputs, including the classification of each criterion as beneficial or non-beneficial and their corresponding weights, and the choice of normalization method.

Data processing: At the core of the tool's analytical capabilities, this section undertakes the necessary mathematical computations as per the selected DM method.

Sensitivity analysis: The sensitivity analysis is designed to evaluate the resilience and reliability of the DM outcomes, especially focusing on the stability of the initially top-ranked solution under uncertain criteria weighting conditions.

Generating weight sets from probability distributions: The sensitivity analysis component of the tool is tailored to account for the variability inherent in DM. User inputs determine confidence intervals for each criterion's weight, which are then used to establish the standard deviations of the corresponding normal distributions. The tool subsequently creates a multitude of unique weight sets by randomly combining these sampled weights across all criteria allowing for an extensive exploration of potential weight variations.

Assessing the stability of the top-ranked solution: Here, the tool determines the frequency with which the initially best-ranked solution maintains its position across various weight scenarios. By applying these diverse weight sets in the DM models, the tool tracks the performance of the initial top solution in each scenario, providing a quantitative measure of its stability.

The sensitivity analysis component is a vital functionality, offering a nuanced understanding of the DM outcomes' robustness. It ensures that the tool not only identifies the optimal solution under given parameters but also evaluates the impact of uncertainties inherent to criteria weighting on this choice.

2.2. Normalization of the dataset

Normalization in MCDM ensures criteria comparability but can introduce biases based on the method used, becoming a crucial choice (Sałabun et al., 2020). The tool employs either min-max or vector normalization to scale all criteria to a uniform range by choice of the user according to data characteristics. The choice of min-max normalization can significantly affect the data distribution in the case of objectives/criteria varying in small ranges. Alternatively, vector normalization maintains the original data distribution, suitable for preserving relative differences.

2.3. TOPSIS

The TOPSIS method is structured to systematically evaluate alternatives based on their similarity to ideal solutions. The steps are as follows:

Weight normalized decision matrix: The process begins by weighting the normalized decision matrix. The values in the normalized matrix are multiplied by the normalized weights for each criterion, reflecting the relative importance as determined by the user.

Determine Utopian and Nadir points: The utopian point is established using the highest values across all criteria, while the Nadir point is based on the lowest values. These hypothetical points represent the most and least desirable outcomes, respectively.

Compute Euclidean distances: Here the Euclidean distances of each alternative from both the utopian and nadir points are calculated. This calculation determines how close or far each alternative is relative to the most and least desirable outcomes.

Evaluate performance and rank alternatives: Performance scores for each alternative are derived from these distances, indicating their relative proximity to the ideal solution. The alternatives are then ranked based on these scores, with the highest-scoring alternative considered the most preferable.

2.4. PROMETHEE

PROMETHEE is a DM method that is based on pairwise comparisons between alternatives, assessing their relative performances based on a set of criteria. The methodology includes the following steps:

Define Preference Function: Preference functions are used to determine the degree of preference between two alternatives for each criterion. While various types of preference functions exist, our tool employs the Gaussian preference function.

Calculate differences in evaluations: For each criterion, the difference in evaluations between each pair of alternatives is computed. These differences form the foundation for assessing preferences between alternatives.

Determine preference values: By applying the Gaussian preference function to the calculated differences, the preference value for each pair of alternatives is calculated.

Compute global preference values: The global preference value for each pair of alternatives is derived by summing the products of the preference values and the weights of the criteria.

Calculate net outranking flows and rank alternatives:

- **Positive and negative outranking flows**: These measures represent the extent to which an alternative is preferred or not over all the others.
- **Net outranking flow**: Calculated as the difference between the positive and negative outranking flows, this value provides the net preference score for each alternative. Alternatives are then ranked based on their net outranking flows.

3. Case study

The case study uses the dataset generated by the ontological framework described in the introduction (Pacheco-López et al., 2023), with a special focus on the chemical recycling of plastic waste. This dataset includes 16 Pareto optimal alternatives, each representing a unique chemical recycling process configuration. These processes include the sorting of plastic wastes, several types of pyrolysis under different temperature conditions, and several separation steps for pyrolytic gas and oil products. The evaluation of these alternatives based on profit, environmental impact on human health (HH), ecosystems, and resources are presented in Table 1. For this study, an objective reduction strategy was applied to the dataset by removing one of the criteria due to the large correlation observed between the environmental impacts on human health and ecosystems. To avoid double

counting an underlying parameter that governs those criteria, the criterion related to environmental impact on human health was arbitrarily chosen for exclusion. This simplification ensures a more accurate and unbiased analysis of the remaining criteria.
The analysis was conducted using both the TOPSIS and PROMETHEE DM methods, with the same weighting maintained between both methods for each criterion to facilitate a consistent comparison. For the same reason, the confidence intervals for the sensitivity analysis were set at ±20% for all criteria and remained constant across the application of both methods. Additionally, in this case, both methods employed min-max normalization.

Table 1. Decision matrix of the chosen Pareto optimal configurations used in the case study (Pacheco-López et al., 2023). HH: Human Health.

Config. number	*Profit (€/h)*	*Impact on HH (DALY/h)*	*Impact on Ecosystems (species·yr/h) ·10^4*	*Impact on Resources (USD2013/h) ·10^-4*
1	566.4	2.474	5.532	4.082
2	2 701.8	2.496	5.576	4.094
3	4 223.2	2.518	5.625	4.124
4	5 381.6	2.539	5.674	4.156
5	6 091.8	2.561	5.720	4.192
6	6 222.0	2.583	5.766	4.214
7	6 271.6	2.605	5.814	4.220
8	6 272.6	2.626	5.862	4.213
9	6 273.6	2.648	5.910	4.205
10	6 274.6	2.670	5.958	4.198
11	5 843.3	2.640	5.890	4.151
12	5 324.8	2.624	5.853	4.103
13	4 575.1	2.606	5.811	4.056
14	3 815.9	2.594	5.785	4.008
15	3 002.1	2.582	5.760	3.961
16	2 227.8	2.571	5.734	3.914

4. Results and discussion

4.1. Multi-criteria decision-making

As shown in Figure 1, the comparative analysis using TOPSIS and PROMETHEE methodologies yielded a consistent set of least favorable alternatives—7, 11, 8, 9, and 10—across both methods. However, the nuance lies in their performance on the profit criterion; while these alternatives score near the upper bound for profit, they suffer significant trade-offs in the other criteria, illustrating a disproportionate balance. This pattern suggests that the methods are robust, particularly in identifying alternatives where an incremental profit gain is offset by larger compromises elsewhere.
For the most viable alternatives, both TOPSIS and PROMETHEE recognized the same top four options, although in a different order, proving the tool's reliability. PROMETHEE's preference for alternative 3 over 16, in contrast to TOPSIS, underscores its capacity for identifying more balanced choices that do not necessarily excel in a single criterion at the expense of others. This reflects a key characteristic of PROMETHEE: the emphasis on relative advantage rather than absolute performance, which can lead to different prioritizations of alternatives compared to TOPSIS.

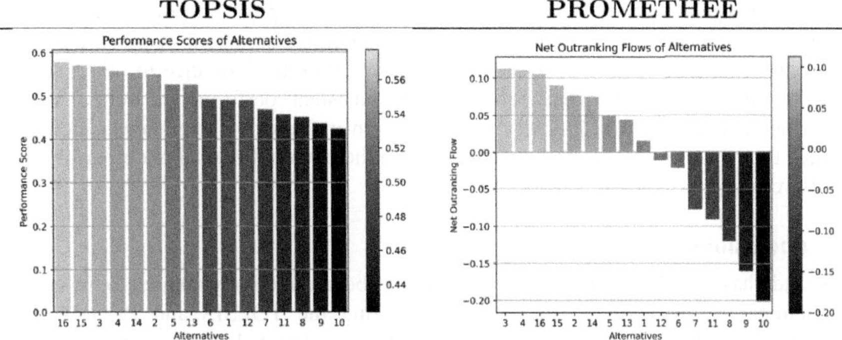

Figure 1: Comparative outcomes of TOPSIS and PROMETHEE methodologies with uniform weighting for each criterion.

4.2. Sensitivity analysis

The sensitivity analysis, conducted with a ±20% uncertainty in the criteria weighting and based on 10 000 generated weight sets, provides a probabilistic understanding of each alternative's robustness within the DM process. The ridgeline plots showing the density distributions of the results for each alternative and both methods are presented in Figure 2. The width of the peaks in the plots is of particular interest; it directly reflects the stability of the alternatives. Narrow peaks denote a high degree of stability, indicating that an alternative's ranking is less sensitive to weight fluctuations. On the contrary, wider peaks suggest greater instability, with the alternative's ranking likely to vary more significantly with changing weights.

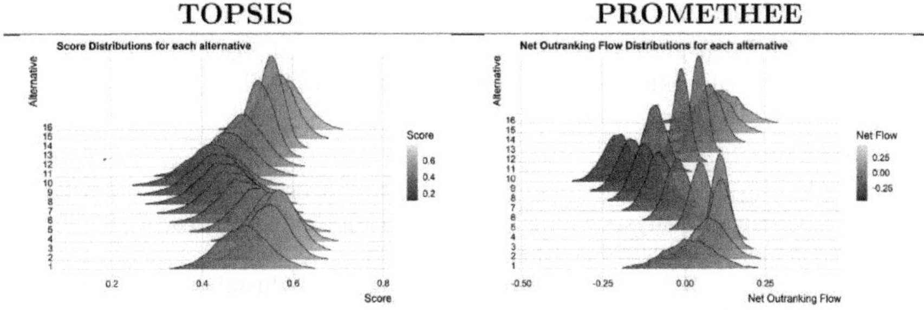

Figure 2: Comparative results from the sensitivity analysis using TOPSIS and PROMETHEE methods with equal weighting and confidence intervals for each criterion.

Numerically, for TOPSIS, the top-ranked alternative 16 maintains its position in 43.23% of the scenarios, signaling a relatively high degree of stability but not complete dominance, while alternative 3 is top-ranked in 19.43% of them. Similarly, in PROMETHEE, alternative 3 remains at the top in 17.92% of the cases, showing that the best solution is more challenged by the other leading alternatives. For instance, alternative 16 is preferred in 41.96% of the scenarios, due to its noticeably wider distribution versus alternative 3. A closer examination of the plots reveals that distributions for alternatives 3 and 4 show clear stability, in contrast to the broader spread for alternatives 15 and 16, suggesting a wider range of performance outcomes for these under varying weights. This difference in variability between the leading solutions, less noticeable in the TOPSIS plot, corroborates the numerical findings that PROMETHEE's top-ranked alternative faces more competition from its contenders. These findings pose a critical decision for stakeholders: choosing an alternative requires a careful assessment between achieving peak performance in certain scenarios at the risk of poor performance in others, versus selecting an option that offers reliable and consistent performance across various scenarios. This decision is guided by the decision-makers risk tolerance, which must balance the pursuit of occasional excellence with the potential cost of underperformance in different circumstances.

5. Conclusions

This study has introduced an MCDM tool that has been effectively applied to the domain of chemical recycling of plastic wastes. Utilizing the TOPSIS and PROMETHEE methods, the tool has evaluated a dataset of 16 Pareto optimal alternatives, illustrating its capability to systematically assess and rank them according to different criteria preference weights. The sensitivity analysis conducted has provided valuable insights into the stability of these alternatives, revealing how their rankings resist the variability in criteria weighting. Looking ahead, one direction for research lies in determining the most suitable weighting of criteria, potentially guided by local sustainability policies and regulatory frameworks. This could ensure that the chosen recycling pathway aligns with specific environmental objectives and legislative requirements. Another direction for future research is the application of the tool to different datasets, possibly within the broader scope of sustainability. The quality of the dataset is critical; accurate and reliable data supports the tool's ability to generate credible recommendations. Finally, enhancing the tool with additional DM methods could provide a wider range of analytical perspectives, making it an adaptable instrument in the pursuit of sustainable solutions.

6. Acknowledgments

Grant CEPI, PID2020-116051RB-I00, funded by MCIN/AEI/10.13039/501100011033 and "ERDF A way of making Europe", by the "European Union".

References

Çelikbilek, Y., Tüysüz, F., 2020. An in-depth review of theory of the TOPSIS method: An experimental analysis. Journal of Management Analytics 7, 281–300. https://doi.org/10.1080/23270012.2020.1748528

Chawla, S., Varghese, B.S., A, C., Hussain, C.G., Keçili, R., Hussain, C.M., 2022. Environmental impacts of post-consumer plastic wastes: Treatment technologies towards eco-sustainability and circular economy. Chemosphere 308, 135867. https://doi.org/10.1016/J.CHEMOSPHERE.2022.135867

Maity, S.R., Chakraborty, S., 2015. Tool steel material selection using PROMETHEE II method. International Journal of Advanced Manufacturing Technology 78, 1537–1547. https://doi.org/10.1007/s00170-014-6760-0

Pacheco-López, A., Gómez-Reyes, E., Graells, M., Espuña, A., Somoza-Tornos, A., 2023. Integrated synthesis, modeling, and assessment (iSMA) of waste-to-resource alternatives towards a circular economy: The case of the chemical recycling of plastic waste management. Comput Chem Eng 175, 108255. https://doi.org/10.1016/j.compchemeng.2023.108255

Sałabun, W., Watróbski, J., Shekhovtsov, A., 2020. Are MCDA methods benchmarkable? A comparative study of TOPSIS, VIKOR, COPRAS, and PROMETHEE II methods. Symmetry (Basel) 12. https://doi.org/10.3390/SYM12091549

Flavio Manenti, Gintaras V. Reklaitis (Eds.), Proceedings of the 34th European Symposium on Computer Aided Process Engineering / 15th International Symposium on Process Systems Engineering (ESCAPE34/PSE24), June 2-6, 2024, Florence, Italy
 http://dx.doi.org/10.1016/B978-0-443-28824-1.50244-1

Supply Chains Design for Sustainability: Addressing Correlated Uncertainty in Life Cycle Inventory

Raquel Salcedo-Diaz*, Florencia L. Garcia-Castro, Rubén Ruiz-Femenia, José A. Caballero

Department of Chemical Engineering, University of Alicante. Ap. Correos 99, E-03080, Alicante. Spain.
raquel.salcedo@ua.es

Abstract

The significance of corporate environmental impact has grown in recent years, driven not only by customer expectations but also by emissions reduction regulations that establish a direct connection between emissions and overall profit. Numerous uncertainties can influence the future performance of a supply chain, underscoring the importance of incorporating them into the initial stages of supply chain design. Decision-makers should possess the necessary information on the influence and repercussions of these uncertainties to optimize network outcomes. While existing literature has explored the impact of uncertain factors such as demand and carbon prices, this study considers specifically uncertainty through Life Cycle Impact Assessment data and the correlation among various parameters.

Keywords: Multi-objective, supply chain management, stochastic modelling, Life Cycle Assessment, correlated uncertainty.

1. Introduction

In recent years, governments have imposed increasingly stringent environmental regulations, elevating the significance of mitigating the environmental impact within supply chains (SC). This study focuses on the Life Cycle Assessment (LCA) as a key metric among various indicators that measure environmental impact. LCA thoroughly analyzes the environmental effects of complete SC, encompassing processes such as raw material extraction, product manufacturing, transportation, and final disposal. The integration of LCA with tools based on multi-objective optimization (MOO), initially proposed by Azapagic and Clift (1999), has gained increasing popularity. This approach treats the environmental aspect as an additional objective rather than an extra constraint in the model. Many studies integrating LCA and MOO predominantly adopt a deterministic approach, concentrating on analyzing the outcome of a single scenario pre-identified as the most probable. This methodology assumes that all parameters are known, and there is no variability among them. While the solution may be optimal for the specified scenario, its performance becomes unpredictable if the parameters deviate from the expected behavior. Consequently, the role of uncertainty has gained prominence in the decision-making process for effective supply chain management. Many key parameters, such as demand and prices, are susceptible to uncertainty, making the precise prediction of future values challenging. This study concentrates on uncertainties within the Life Cycle Inventory (LCI) data obtained from the ECOINVENT database, commonly identified as the primary source of uncertainty in LCA analyses.

To the best of our knowledge, Guillén-Gosálbez and Grossmann (2009) were the first to introduce a robust mathematical programming tool that considers the uncertainty of LCI emissions, using uncorrelated, normally distributed data. In this study, the SC design problem is formulated under uncertainty as a multi-objective stochastic Mixed Integer Linear Program (MILP). The objectives are to maximize profit and minimize environmental impact. The main novelty of this work lies in investigating the influence of the correlation among uncertain LCI emission parameters on the economic and environmental performance of a supply chain.

2. Case study

The proposed model has been applied to the SC structure introduced by Guillén-Gosálbez and Grossmann (2009). The three-echelon European supply chain comprises 7 plants located in Germany (Frankfurt and Leuna), Italy (Mantova), Spain (Tarragona), Poland (Wloclawek), the Czech Republic (Neratovice), and Hungary (Kazincbarcika). Each plant is associated with a warehouse and allows for chemical production using six different technologies. These technologies generate acetaldehyde, acetone, acrylonitrile, cumene, isopropanol, and phenol. The resulting products are distributed and sold across ten European markets situated in Belgium (Brussels), Romania (Pitesti), Germany (Stade), Hungary (Kazincbarcika), Italy (Mantova and Ferrara), the Czech Republic (Neratovice), Spain (Tarragona), Poland (Wloclawek), and Portugal (Sines), in accordance with their respective demands. The interested reader can find the full data describing the supply chain and all constraints in tables 1 to 7 of the original publication by Guillén-Gosálbez and Grossmann (2009).

3. Methodology and mathematical formulation

The goal of this study is to identify a SC design that simultaneously maximizes the expected total Net Present Value (NPV) and minimizes its environmental impact, which is subject to uncertainty. Given are the capacity constraints, the prices of raw materials and final products, a fixed time horizon divided into a set of time periods, a set of possible locations for SC facilities, the investment and operational expenses, as well as the demand. Additionally, the environmental data, subject to uncertainty, is represented through a set of scenarios with assigned probabilities. The approach proposed in this work relies on a two-stage stochastic MILP model, based on that introduced by Guillén-Gosálbez and Grossmann (2009). The model encompasses two types of decision variables. Firstly, the structural decisions encode characteristics of the plants and warehouses, such as their locations, capacities, and the types of installed technologies. The second type of decision variables involves the operational ones, which include the production rate at each plant and in each time period, material flows between plants, warehouses and markets, as well as the amounts of sales of final products. These decisions are made after the uncertainty is revealed and impact operational variables in the model, enabling it to adapt to the new circumstances.

The model consists of three main sets of equations: mass balance equations, capacity constraints, and equations describing the objective functions governing both the economic and environmental performance of the system.

Throughout the manuscript, the subscript p denotes a plant, and the set of plants is denoted P. Similarly, $w \in W$ denotes a warehouse. The chemical products are represented by $j \in J$, and markets by $k \in K$ k. The set of main products for technology $i \in I$ is denoted

$JM_i \subset J$. The time horizon is discretized into a finite number of timesteps, $t \in T$, and scenarios are given by $s \in S$.

3.1. Mass balances and capacity constraints

Mass balances are defined for every node in the supply chain network. In the case of plants, the sum of purchased chemicals and the produced chemicals must equal the quantity transported from the plant, *p,* to the warehouses, *w,* across all time steps and scenarios. The production rate of each technology at each plant, across each time period and scenario, is restricted to be below the corresponding capacity. This capacity is defined by the sum of the previous timestep's capacity and a capacity expansion, which is constrained within specified bounds. For warehouses, in each scenario and at every time step, the inventory at the previous time step, when added to the amount of product transported from the plants, must equal the inventory in the current time period plus the quantity of product sent from the warehouse to the markets. The capacity of a warehouse can also be expanded in each timestep. The quantity of products sold on a market is constrained with a minimum threshold ensuring satisfaction of demand.

3.2. Objective function

The model under study has two objectives. The economic performance, measured in terms of the NPV, is to be maximized, while the quantified environmental performance is to be minimized (eq.(1)).

$$\max_{x,x_s,y} \left[E\left(NPV(x,x_s,y)\right) - WC(x,x_s,y) \right] \tag{1}$$

where *WC* represents the worst case of the environmental impact of the system, x and x_s denote first and second stage continuous variables, respectively, and y are binary variables.

3.2.1. Economic objective function

The NPV(s) is calculated for each scenario $s \in S$ as the sum of the discounted cash flows over all time periods. The expected value of the NPV is then calculated as

$$E\left(NPV\right) = \sum_{s \in S} P\left(s\right) NPV\left(s\right) \tag{2}$$

where $0 \le P\left(s\right) \le 1$ denotes the probability of scenario s.

3.2.2. Environmental impact assessment

In this study, the Global Warming Potential indicator (GWP) was employed to assess the environmental impact. This indicator measures how much one kilogram of a specific greenhouse gas contributes to global warming relative to the emission of one kilogram of carbon dioxide. To quantify the amount of global warming emissions throughout the entire life cycle of the SC, we consider three main sources of emissions: emissions due to the consumption of raw materials; emissions due to transportation of products from plants to warehouses and from warehouses to markets; and emissions due to energy consumption.

$$GWP_{t,s} = \sum_{\substack{p \in P \\ j \in J}} PU_{p,j,t,s} I_{RM\,j} + \sum_{\substack{p \in P \\ j \in J \\ w \in W}} \xi p_{j,p,w,t,s} dp_{p,w} I_{TR} + \sum_{\substack{p \in P \\ j \in J \\ k \in K}} \xi w_{j,w,k,t,s} dp_{w,k} I_{TR} + \sum_{\substack{p \in P \\ i \in I \\ \tilde{j} \in JMi}} F_{p,i,\tilde{j},t,s} EN_i I_{EN} \tag{3}$$

In eq. (3) $PU_{p,j,t,s}$ is the amount of raw materials purchased, I_{RM_j} represents the cumulative life cycle impact assessment (LCIA) associated with the consumption of 1 kg of the corresponding raw material. I_{TR} is the cumulative LCIA associated with the transportation of 1 ton of product over a distance of 1 km, $dp_{p,w}$, $dw_{w,k}$ and $\xi p_{j,p,w,t,s}$, $\xi w_{j,w,k,t,s}$ are the distances and transported flows from plants to warehouses and from warehouses to markets for all timesteps and scenarios, respectively. I_{EN_i} is the cumulative LCIA associated with the consumption of 1 MJ of energy, EN_i denotes the consumption of energy used by each technology *i* and $F_{p,i,\bar{j},t,s}$ the amount of chemical *j* produced at plant *p* with technology *i*. The total GWP is calculated as (eq. (4))

$$GWP_s = \sum_{t \in T} GWP_{t,s}, \quad \forall s \tag{4}$$

3.3. Uncertainty and scenario generation

The LCI and LCIA parameters are obtained from the ECOINVENT database. However, these parameters are uncertain, and the values presented in the database represent their expected values. Analytical information regarding their probability distribution is unavailable. Nonetheless, in accordance with the recommendation by Weidema and Wesnæs (1996), the parameters can be modelled using a lognormal distribution, defined by a location parameter μ and an arithmetic scale parameter σ. This allows for the sampling of uncertain parameters, resulting in a set of scenarios used to address the stochastic SC design problem. The initial step involves utilizing the correlation matrix and standard deviation of the lognormally distributed uncertain parameters to establish a covariance matrix. Subsequently, this matrix, in conjunction with the Monte Carlo technique, is employed to generate samples of normally distributed correlated random variables. The multivariate cumulative density function of the transformed variables is then computed for the impact factors. Finally, the inverse of this multivariate cumulative density function is calculated to assign a probability to each of the generated samples. Scenarios for the stochastic problem are obtained by backtransforming these samples onto the original, lognormally distributed probability spaces. This methodology for handling correlated uncertainty has been employed in previous studies. For instance, Salcedo-Diaz et al. (2020) optimized a water distribution network considering correlated uncertainty in nodes' demand, and Garcia-Castro et al. (2023) addressed the design of SC under correlated uncertainty in energy and carbon prices.

3.4. Solution procedure

The solution to the MOO problem can be depicted through a collection of Pareto points, each of which represents a trade-off between both objectives. To compute these Pareto points, the ε-constraint method is utilized (eq.(5)), transforming the primary problem into a single-objective problem that is solved for different values of the ε-parameter.

$$\begin{aligned} &\max_{x,x_s,y} E\left(NPV(x,x_s,y)\right) \\ &\text{s.t.} \begin{Bmatrix} \text{mass balances} \\ \text{capacity constrints} \\ \text{economic and environmental performance eqs.} \end{Bmatrix} \\ &\text{WC} < \varepsilon \\ &\underline{\varepsilon} \le \varepsilon \le \overline{\varepsilon} \end{aligned} \tag{5}$$

4. Results and discussion

The MILP problem formulated has been implemented in the General Algebraic Modeling System (GAMS) and solved to global optimality using IBMs CPLEX v12.9 optimization algorithm. Given the vast number of scenarios resulting from the consideration of mean values, standard deviation, and correlation among the 35 impact factors in the database, only the five impact factors with the highest contribution to emissions are considered to be correlated and uncertain. These impact factors are carbon dioxide (fossil), carbon monoxide (fossil), dinitrogen monoxide, Methane (biogenic), and Methane (fossil), which are responsible for more than 99% of the total emissions. In each simulation, the correlation between several subgroups of the 5 parameters can either be low, medium, or high. This variability results in distinct correlation matrices for each simulation, serving as input for the sampling algorithm to generate 170 corresponding scenarios. The obtained results reveal a pronounced impact of accounting for correlation among the impact factors on the network's performance. Furthermore, depending on the level of correlation, the economic performance can worsen while maintaining the level of emissions. Therefore, it is crucial to account for correlation among the LCI parameters, as treating them as independent can result in an overestimation of the network's performance. A simulation was conducted to pinpoint the two impact factors whose correlation has the most substantial influence on the overall network performance. The findings reveal that these impact factors are carbon dioxide and fossil methane. Figure 1 displays the Pareto curves obtained without correlation and with a notably high correlation factor of 0.98 between carbon dioxide and fossil methane. It is evident that accounting for correlation between these two impact factors results in a poorer economic performance for a given level of emissions in the network.

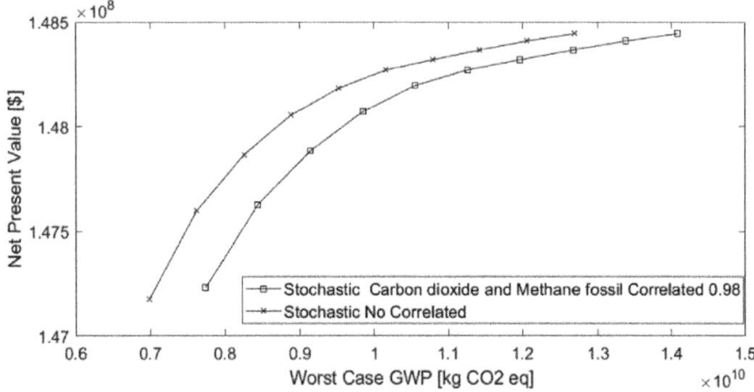

Figure 1. Pareto curve representing the economic and environmental performance of the network without correlation and with high correlation between carbon dioxide and fossil methane.

In a subsequent simulation, a high correlation between these two impact factors was exclusively considered in one component of the global warming potential, namely raw material consumption, transportation, and energy consumption. The outcomes indicate that, as expected, raw material consumption exerts the most significant influence on the overall result, given that the largest proportion of emissions occurs during this stage. Finally, the study examined the dispersion of solutions with and without correlation, considering three values for the σ parameter: 1.7, 1.487, and 1.216. Consistently across all these values, the same trend was observed, that is, the economic performance for a specific GWP is more conservative when considering correlation. Moreover, for lower values of σ, the resulting network is more robust concerning emissions but exhibits a larger variation in economic performance (Figure 2). This suggests that σ, and consequently the dispersion of scenarios, significantly influences the performance of the network.

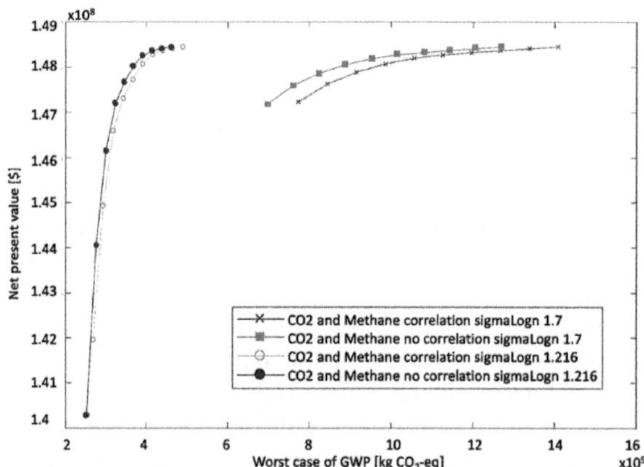

Figure 2. Pareto points for the stochastic model without correlation and with correlations of 0.98 between carbon dioxide and fossil methane for $\sigma = 1.7$ and 1.216, respectively.

In a broad sense, the Pareto optimal set of solutions reveal that SC strategic decisions, encompassing the locations and capacities of its entities, exhibit minimal variations among them. However, differences surpassing a 1% threshold arise in the NPV and GWP due to fluxes between nodes, particularly when accounting for correlations among uncertain parameters that.

5. Conclusions

In this study, the focus is on the design of sustainable SC under correlated uncertainty in the LCI data. The findings reveal that accounting for the correlation between uncertain LCI factors can significantly influence the overall performance of the network. Not considering this correlation may result in a supply chain design that underperforms in potential future scenarios. Introducing correlation among the burdens with the highest contribution to overall emissions is crucial, as precise modelling of these factors is essential. The results emphasize that considering correlation generally leads to more conservative outcomes, implying that the economic performance for a fixed GWP may be compromised. Additionally, the dispersion of scenarios has a substantial impact on the network's performance.

Acknowledments

The authors gratefully acknowledge financial support to the Generalitat Valenciana, Spain, PROMETEO/2020/064 and to the Spanish "Ministerio de Ciencia e Innovación" under project PID2021-124139NB-C21.

References

A. Azapagic and R. Clift. The application of life cycle assessment to process optimisation. Computers & Chemical Engineering, 23(10):1509–1526, 1999.

B. P. Weidema and M. S. Wesnæs. Data quality management for life cycle inventories—an example of using data quality indicators. Journal of Cleaner Production, 4(3):167–174, 1996.

Ecoinvent database. https://ecoinvent.org.

F. L. Garcia-Castro, R. Ruiz-Femenia, R. Salcedo-Diaz and J. A. Caballlero. Sustainable supply chain design under correlated uncertainty in energy and carbon prices. Journal of Cleaner Production 414, 137612, 2023.

G. Guillén-Gosálbez and I. Grossmann. Optimal design and planning of sustainable chemical supply chains under uncertainty. AIChE Journal, 55:99 – 121, 01 2009.

R. Salcedo-Díaz, R. Ruiz-Femenia, J.A. Caballero, and M.A.S.S. Ravagnani, Water Distribution Network Optimization Considering Uncertainties in the Nodes Demands. Computer Aided Chemical Engineering, 48, 1183–1188, 2020.

Flavio Manenti, Gintaras V. Reklaitis (Eds.), Proceedings of the 34th European Symposium on Computer Aided Process Engineering / 15th International Symposium on Process Systems Engineering (ESCAPE34/PSE24), June 2-6, 2024, Florence, Italy
 http://dx.doi.org/10.1016/B978-0-443-28824-1.50245-3

Comparative study of classifier models to assert phase stability in multicomponent mixtures

Lifeng Zhang,[a] Tanuj Karia,[a] Gustavo Chaparro,[a] Kainath Sahebzada,[a] Benoît Chachuat,[a] Claire S. Adjiman[a]

[a]*Department of Chemical Engineering, The Sargent Centre for Process Systems Engineering, Institute for Molecular Science and Engineering, Imperial College London, London, SW7 2AZ, UK*
Corresponding Author: c.adjiman@imperial.ac.uk

Abstract

Asserting phase stability entails the global solution of a nonconvex optimisation problem, typically the tangent plane distance minimisation (TPDM). To improve computational tractability, we propose classifier-based surrogate models to replace the TPDM. We seek models that represent several multicomponent mixtures simultaneously, across various component identities, temperatures, and compositions. We investigate both artificial neural networks (ANN) and support vector machines (SVM) and use Matthew's correlation coefficient (MCC) as performance metric for the corresponding binary classification problems. For SVM models, linear, polynomial, and radial basis function (RBF) kernels are assessed; while for ANNs, the tanh and relu activation functions are investigated. We test the performance of these surrogate models on a set of ternary mixtures that involve ibuprofen and two solvents with fixed or variable temperatures. The results show that ANNs and SVMs can both predict phase stability reliably, with RBF-SVM giving the lowest computational cost.

Keywords: Phase stability, Classifiers, Artificial Neural Network, Support Vector Machines, Multicomponent Mixtures.

1. Introduction

The ability to guarantee phase stability of a multicomponent mixture is critical in chemical manufacturing. Demixing of a multicomponent mixture is detrimental to the performance and safety of a process or product. Phase stability at a given temperature, pressure and composition is often assessed with thermodynamic models during the design phase by minimising the tangent plane distance (Baker et al., 1982). The nonlinear nature of the underlying thermodynamic model renders the optimisation problem nonconvex, which makes it challenging to obtain a global optimum within reasonable runtime, especially in cases where the problem needs to be solved iteratively. Hence, surrogate models that can be used to determine phase stability have been proposed in the literature, such as artificial neural networks (ANN) for a ternary mixture (Schmitz et al., 2006) and support vector machine (SVM) classifiers for mixtures (Gaganis and Varotsis, 2012). However, most studies focus on constructing surrogate models for a specific mixture, which restricts applications in the solvent design field (Lopez-Ramirez et al., 2023).

In this work, we develop surrogate models that can predict phase stability over a wide range of candidate solvents, with a view to substituting the thermodynamic models embedded in solvent design problems. Specifically, ANNs and SVMs are investigated as the basis for classifier models to determine whether a multicomponent liquid mixture is stable (miscible) under given conditions. Section 2 provides a brief introduction to SVMs and ANNs. The methodology is described in Section 3, while the results are presented and discussed in Section 4.

2. Data-driven classifier models

2.1. SVM formulation

Given a training dataset $D = \{(\boldsymbol{x}_1, y_1), (\boldsymbol{x}_2, y_2), ..., (\boldsymbol{x}_N, y_N)\}$ with N points, where $\boldsymbol{x}_i$ denotes the ith feature vector and y_i its corresponding label, the fundamental behind SVMs (Cortes and Vapnik, 1995) is to construct an optimal hyperplane which can separate the positive and negative samplings effectively. The hyperplane can be expressed as follows:

$$\boldsymbol{w}^T \boldsymbol{x} + b = 0 \tag{1}$$

The weights $\boldsymbol{w}$ and biases b in Eq. (1) are determined by solving:

$$\min_{w,b} \frac{1}{2} ||\boldsymbol{w}||^2 + C \sum_{i=1}^{N} \xi_i$$
$$\text{s.t.} \quad y_i(\boldsymbol{w}^T \boldsymbol{x}_i + b) \geq 1 - \xi_i \quad i = 1, \ldots, N \tag{2}$$

where the positive slack variables ξ_i are introduced and penalised in the objective function to allow for a subset of points to be misclassified. The value of the hyperparameter C is important for a good generalisation capability. The features $\boldsymbol{x}_i$ may also be mapped onto a higher-dimensional space via a feature map $\boldsymbol{\varphi}$ which can be a linear kernel for linear classification problems, a radial basis function kernel (RBF) or a polynomial kernel for nonlinear classification problems:

$$K_{\text{rbf}}(\boldsymbol{x}_i, \boldsymbol{x}_j) = \boldsymbol{\varphi}(\boldsymbol{x}_i)\, \boldsymbol{\varphi}(\boldsymbol{x}_j) = \langle \boldsymbol{x}_i, \boldsymbol{x}_j \rangle \tag{3}$$

$$K_{\text{rbf}}(\boldsymbol{x}_i, \boldsymbol{x}_j) = \boldsymbol{\varphi}(\boldsymbol{x}_i)\, \boldsymbol{\varphi}(\boldsymbol{x}_j) = \exp\left(-\gamma |\boldsymbol{x}_i - \boldsymbol{x}_j|^2\right) \tag{4}$$

$$K_{\text{poly}}(\boldsymbol{x}_i, \boldsymbol{x}_j) = \boldsymbol{\varphi}(\boldsymbol{x}_i)\, \boldsymbol{\varphi}(\boldsymbol{x}_j) = \left(\gamma \boldsymbol{x}_i \cdot \boldsymbol{x}_j + r\right)^d \tag{5}$$

where γ, r and d are additional hyperparameters. The solution of the convex optimization problem (2) provides optimal values $\boldsymbol{w}^*$ and b^* as:

$$\boldsymbol{w}^* = \sum_{i=1}^{N} a_i^* y_i \varphi(\boldsymbol{x}_i) \tag{6}$$

$$b^* = y_j - \sum_{i=1}^{N} a_i^* y_i K(\boldsymbol{x}_i, \boldsymbol{x}_j) \tag{7}$$

where a_i^* denotes the optimal Lagrange multiplier for the ith constraint and the label y_j is chosen such that $0 \leq a_j^* \leq C$. The features $\boldsymbol{x}_i$ for whic $a_i^* > 0$ are those lying on the classification boundary and are called support vectors. Finally, the predicted class of a new sample $\boldsymbol{x}$ is given by:

$$f(x) = \text{sgn}(\hat{y}) = \text{sgn}\left(\sum_{i \in N^s} a_i^* y_i K(\boldsymbol{x}_i, \boldsymbol{x}) + b^*\right) \tag{8}$$

where the predicted class $\hat{y}$ of a new sample $\boldsymbol{x}$ is only related to the support vectors $\boldsymbol{x} \in \{\boldsymbol{x}_i \mid i \in \{1, ..., N^S\}\}$ whose subscripts are denoted by N^S, along with the corresponding Lagrange multipliers a_i^*.

2.2. ANN formulation

ANNs are well-known for their ability to approximate complex nonlinear functions. In the context of binary classification, ANNs can provide a probability score for belonging to either of the classes using a softmax function. Given the weight matrix $\boldsymbol{W}_{k\text{-}1}$ and bias vector $\boldsymbol{B}_{k\text{-}1}$, the output $\boldsymbol{m}_k$ of any neurons in hidden layer k can be calculated σ_k as:

$$\boldsymbol{m}_k = \sigma_k(\boldsymbol{l}_k) = \sigma_k(\boldsymbol{W}_{k-1}\boldsymbol{m}_{k-1} + \boldsymbol{B}_{k-1}) \quad \forall k \tag{9}$$

where $\boldsymbol{l}_k = \boldsymbol{W}_{k-1}\boldsymbol{m}_{k-1} + \boldsymbol{B}_{k-1}$. The choice of activation function $\boldsymbol{\sigma}_k$ can have a great influence on the ability to capture nonlinear behaviour. Here, the activation functions tanh and relu are investigated for the hidden layers. The sigmoid function is applied to the output layer to rescale the predictions within [0,1]. These functions are given by:

$$\sigma_{\text{tanh}}(\boldsymbol{l}_k) = 1 - \frac{2}{\exp(2\boldsymbol{l}_k) + 1} \tag{10}$$

$$\sigma_{\text{relu}}(\boldsymbol{l}_k) = \max(0, \boldsymbol{l}_k) \tag{11}$$

$$\sigma_{\text{sigmoid}}(\boldsymbol{l}_k) = \frac{1}{1 + \exp(-\boldsymbol{l}_k)} \tag{12}$$

A loss function L is then minimised to train the ANNs to match the predicted class $\hat{y}_i$ of the samples $i = 1, \ldots, N$:

$$\min_{\boldsymbol{W},\boldsymbol{B}} = -\frac{1}{N}\sum_{i=1}^{N} y_i \ln(\hat{y}_i) + (1 - y_i)\ln(1 - \hat{y}_i) \tag{13}$$

3. Methodology

3.1. Data generation

Classifier surrogates are constructed to predict the phase stability of a liquid phase consisting of a solute (ibuprofen) and a solvent pair (a,b), where a and b are chosen in a set S. Two cases are investigated: In Case 1, the models are trained and used at a fixed temperature of 300 K (Jonuzaj et al., 2016). In Case 2, phase stability is considered over the temperature range 293.15-318.15 K, in which the mixtures exhibit solid-liquid-(liquid) equilibria (Watson et al., 2021). Data are generated from phase equilibria calculations in phasepy (Chaparro and Mejía, 2020) using UNIFAC (Fredenslund et al., 1975). The sizes of the datasets for both Cases are described in Table 1. The solvents considered in Case 1 are methanol, ethanol, 2-propanol, acetone, MIBK, ethylacetate, chloroform, toluene, and water; and in Case 2, water, n-pentane, n-heptane, ethanol, 1-propanol, 1-butanol, 1-pentanol, and acetone. The van der Waals surface area and volume parameters, q_i and r_i, are used to characterize each solvent. The total mole fractions z_i are furthermore included to represent the mixture. Thus $(q_a,q_b,r_a,r_b,z_a,z_b)$ and $(q_a,q_b,r_a,r_b,z_a,z_b,T)$ are used as inputs in Cases 1 and 2, respectively.

Table.1. Description of generated datasets for both case studies

Case	No. solvents	No. solvent pairs	No. samples	Stable: Non-stable	Generation time /s
1	9	36	18,427	86.62%:13.38%	659.98
2	8	56	228,976	82.96%:17.04%	7018.74

3.2. Evaluation of the classifier models

Since the dataset is quite imbalanced, the Matthew's Correlation Coefficient (MCC) (Chicco and Jurman, 2020) is used as the metric for all the models:

$$\mathrm{MCC}=\frac{P_{TP}P_{TN}-P_{FP}P_{FN}}{\sqrt{(P_{TP}+P_{FP})(P_{TP}+P_{FN})(P_{TN}+P_{FP})(P_{TN}+P_{FN})}} \tag{14}$$

where P_{TP} (true positive) and P_{TN} (true negative) denote the number of samples correctly classified as positive (stable) and negative (non-stable), respectively; and P_{FP} (false positive) and P_{FN} (false negative) denote the number of samples incorrectly classified as positive and negative, respectively. The MCC score takes values from -1 to +1, where -1 indicates only false predictions, 0 random predictions, and +1perfect predictions.

3.3. Hyperparameter tuning and model training

Hyperparameter tuning is conducted for each model via Optuna (Akiba et al., 2019). For ANNs, a single hidden layer is used in Case 1, and 3 hidden layers in Case 2. The numbers of neurons are set by Optuna. The dataset is split 80:20 into a training dataset and a test dataset and five-fold cross-validation is conducted on the training dataset, using stratified sampling to ensure consistent distributions of stable and non-stable mixtures in each fold. The selection of hyperparameters is based on achieving the highest average MCC score on the validation datasets. Subsequently, the classifier models are retrained using these optimized hyperparameters. The SVMs are built on scikit-learn v1.3.2 (Pedregosa et al., 2011) and ANNs are built on PyTorch v2.1.0 (Paszke et al., 2019). All the models are trained on Windows11 using Intel(R) Xeon(R) Gold 6226R CPU @ 2.90GHz with 64GB of RAM and NVIDIA RTX A4000 GPU with 16GB of RAM. The GPU is only used in training ANNs.

Table.2. Training and testing results for SVMs

Case	Kernel	$\mathrm{MCC}_{training}$	MCC_{test}	Training time /s	No. support vectors
1	Linear	0.8990	0.8914	2.12	968
	RBF	0.9947	***0.9894***	***0.20***	183
	Poly-2	0.9708	0.9720	0.84	354
	Poly-3	0.9933	0.9848	1.38	98
	Poly-4	***0.9994***	0.9871	3.47	***54***
2	Linear	0.3798	0.3776	774.49	64,297
	RBF	***0.9912***	***0.9864***	***61.19***	4,247
	Poly-2	0.9517	0.9504	468.64	8,195
	Poly-3	0.9735	0.9705	655.62	4,275
	Poly-4	0.9840	0.9813	746.42	***2,839***

4. Results and discussion

The performance of all models is presented in Tables 2 (SVMs) and 3 (ANNs). Polynomial SVMs are denoted by Poly-*d* where *d* denotes the degree. Amongst SVMs, the linear SVM performs worst, with an MCC score of 0.38 in Case 2. The linear SVMs require the largest number of support vectors but this has no impact on model complexity of the decision function. However, this property does not hold for other nonlinear kernels. The RBF-SVM performs quite well in both cases, achieving an MCC score of 0.99 with the shortest training time. It also requires fewer support vectors than Poly-2 in both cases. The performance of polynomial SVMs improves as the degree increases. In Case 1, Poly-4 exhibits a performance comparable to that of RBF, while in Case 2 it requires a larger training time.

With ANNs, the tanh activation function generates models with a higher MCC score than relu. In Case 1, the tanh-ANN has a classification performance comparable to that of the Poly-4 SVM, while the relu-ANN performs similarly to the RBF-SVM. In Case 2, the tanh-ANN is slightly worse than the RBF-SVM, but better than other SVMs. The performance of the relu-ANN is close to that of the Poly-4 SVM. Adding more layers to the ANNs can improve the MCC score, but it does also increase model complexity, especially considering that the training time is already much longer than for SVMs in both cases. One advantage of ANNs over SVNs is that they return a probability of the phase being stable, which is more intuitive than the distance between the input vectors and the classification boundary.

Table.3. Training results for ANNs

Case	Activation function	$MCC_{training}$	MCC_{test}	Training time /s	ANN structure (Nodes per layer)
1	tanh	**0.9977**	**0.9906**	**84.19**	{6,15,1}
	relu	0.9947	0.9871	165.55	{6,17,1}
2	tanh	**0.9883**	**0.9848**	1,394.84	{7,19,17,1,1}
	relu	0.9814	0.9784	**1,096.46**	{7,14,15,8,1}

Fig. 1 illustrates the performance of RBF-SVM with two phase diagrams for the ibuprofen-ethanol-water mixture from Case 2. Here, the larger the value $\hat{y}$ returned by the SVM at a given composition and temperature, the more likely the liquid phase to be miscible, and vice versa. As the temperature increases, the regions of immiscibility (liquid-liquid and solid-liquid-liquid). The RBF-SVM captures this phenomenon with some uncertainty around the exact position of the phase boundary, as shown in dark blue. Similar performance of this classifier is observed for all mixtures, including some mixtures which are always miscible. The typical CPU time to evaluate the miscibility of one composition is 4×10^{-4} seconds and is much faster 2.6×10^{-3} seconds).

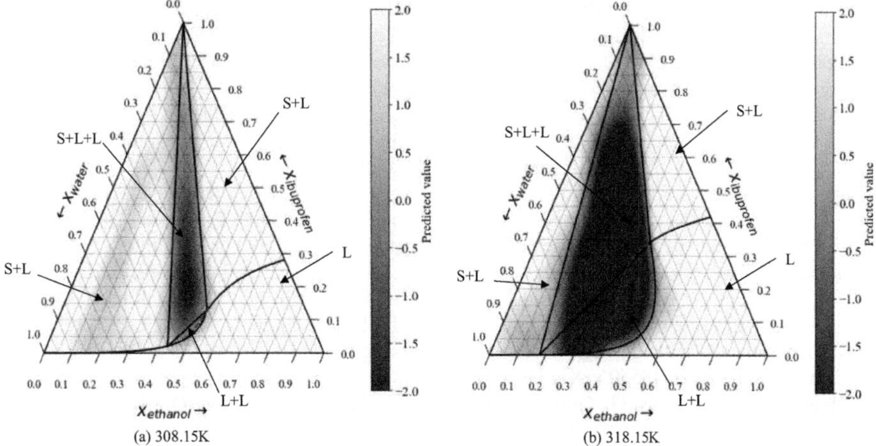

(a) 308.15K (b) 318.15K

Figure 1. Phase diagram for Ibuprofen-Ethanol-Water mixture at (a) 308.15K and (b) 318.15K. The solid curves represent the phase boundaries, while the dashed curve represents a metastable solid-liquid boundary. The color scales represent the magnitude of the RBF-SVM predictions $\hat{y}$ in Eq (8).

5. Conclusion

This paper investigated the potential application of both surrogate SVMs and ANNs to predict the phase stability of multicomponent mixtures. Based on two case studies, several such surrogates achieved good performance with RBF-SVM performing best overall in both MCC score and training time. In addition, considering the number of support vectors,

RBF-SVM was found to offer good potential to be embedded into an optimisation problem without increasing the problem scale significantly. In future work, these models will be used to replace the phase stability constraints in optimisation problems such as solvent design and to investigate the impact on optimization efficiency and solution quality.

Acknowledgement

We gratefully acknowledge funding from the UK Engineering and Physical Sciences Research Council (EPSRC) under grant EP/W003317/1.

Data Statement

Data supporting this article is available by writing to the corresponding author.

References

Akiba, T., Sano, S., Yanase, T., Ohta, T., Koyama, M., 2019. Optuna: A Next-generation Hyperparameter Optimization Framework, in: Proceedings of the 25th ACM SIGKDD International Conference on Knowledge Discovery & Data Mining, KDD '19. Association for Computing Machinery, New York, NY, USA, pp. 2623–2631.

Baker, L.E., Pierce, A.C., Luks, K.D., 1982. Gibbs Energy Analysis of Phase Equilibria. Society of Petroleum Engineers Journal 22, 731–742. https://doi.org/10.2118/9806-PA

Chaparro, G., Mejía, A., 2020. Phasepy: A Python based framework for fluid phase equilibria and interfacial properties computation. Journal of Computational Chemistry 41, 2504–2526.

Chicco, D., Jurman, G., 2020. The advantages of the Matthews correlation coefficient (MCC) over F1 score and accuracy in binary classification evaluation. BMC Genomics 21, 6.

Cortes, C., Vapnik, V., 1995. Support-vector networks. Mach Learn 20, 273–297.

Fredenslund, A., Jones, R.L., Prausnitz, J.M., 1975. Group-contribution estimation of activity coefficients in nonideal liquid mixtures. AIChE Journal 21, 1086–1099.

Gaganis, V., Varotsis, N., 2012. Non-iterative phase stability calculations for process simulation using discriminating functions. Fluid Phase Equilibria 314, 69–77.

Jonuzaj, S., Akula, P.T., Kleniati, P.-M., Adjiman, C.S., 2016. The formulation of optimal mixtures with generalized disjunctive programming: A solvent design case study. AIChE Journal 62, 1616–1633. https://doi.org/10.1002/aic.15122

Lopez-Ramirez, E., Lopez-Zamora, S., Escobedo, S., de Lasa, H., 2023. Artificial Neural Networks (ANNs) for Vapour-Liquid-Liquid Equilibrium (VLLE) Predictions in N-Octane/Water Blends. Processes 11, 2026. https://doi.org/10.3390/pr11072026

Paszke, A., Gross, S., Massa, F., Lerer, A., Bradbury, J., Chanan, G., Killeen, T., Lin, Z., Gimelshein, N., Antiga, L., Desmaison, A., Köpf, A., Yang, E., DeVito, Z., Raison, M., Tejani, A., Chilamkurthy, S., Steiner, B., Fang, L., Bai, J., Chintala, S., 2019. PyTorch: An Imperative Style, High-Performance Deep Learning Library. https://doi.org/10.48550/arXiv.1912.01703

Pedregosa, F., Varoquaux, G., Gramfort, A., Michel, V., Thirion, B., Grisel, O., Blondel, M., Prettenhofer, P., Weiss, R., Dubourg, V., 2011. Scikit-learn: Machine learning in Python. the Journal of machine Learning research 12, 2825–2830.

Schmitz, J.E., Zemp, R.J., Mendes, M.J., 2006. Artificial neural networks for the solution of the phase stability problem. Fluid Phase Equilibria, Proceedings of the Seventeenth European Conference on Thermophysical Properties 245, 83–87.

Watson, O.L., Jonuzaj, S., McGinty, J., Sefcik, J., Galindo, A., Jackson, G., Adjiman, C.S., 2021. Computer Aided Design of Solvent Blends for Hybrid Cooling and Antisolvent Crystallization of Active Pharmaceutical Ingredients. Org. Process Res. Dev. 25, 1123–1142.

Flavio Manenti, Gintaras V. Reklaitis (Eds.), Proceedings of the 34th European Symposium on Computer Aided Process Engineering / 15th International Symposium on Process Systems Engineering (ESCAPE34/PSE24), June 2-6, 2024, Florence, Italy
 http://dx.doi.org/10.1016/B978-0-443-28824-1.50246-5

Design of chemical recycling processes for PUR foam under uncertainty

Patrick Lotz,[a] Luca Bosetti[b], André Bardow[b], Sergio Lucia,[a] Sebastian Engell[a]

[a]*TU Dortmund University, August-Schmidt-Straße 1, 44227 Dortmund, Germany*
[b]*ETH Zurich, Leonhardstrasse 21, 8092 Zurich, Switzerland*
patrick.lotz@tu-dortmund.de

Abstract

Optimization problems in chemical process design involve a significant number of discrete and continuous decisions. When taking into account uncertainties, the search space is very difficult to explore, even for experienced engineers. Moreover, it should be taken into account that while some decisions are fixed at the design stage, other parameters can be adapted to the realization of the uncertainty during the operation of the plant. This leads to a two-stage optimization problem which is difficult to solve. To address this challenge, we propose to combine commercial process simulation software with an evolutionary strategy. This approach is applied to designing a downstream process to isolate valuable products from pyrolysis oil produced by the catalytic pyrolysis of rigid polyurethane foam. The suggested algorithm consistently performed better than a manually designed robust process. Additionally, the analysis of different scenarios provided insight into promising changes in the overall layout of the recycling process.

Keywords: two-stage stochastic optimization, process design, circular economy

1. Introduction

As part of the EU Green Deal, the EU has set the goal of significantly expanding the circular economy of polymers. For rigid polyurethane (PUR) foam which is used for insulation in refrigerators and buildings, there is so far no satisfactory recycling option. One key challenge in the design of a recycling process for PUR is the variety in the composition of the end of life foam. PUR is a composite material that contains several additives, and a variety of recipes are used, depending on the application and manufacturer. The end-of-life products are handled in pretreatment facilities where refrigerators and insulation panels are dismantled and the material is sorted afterwards. This step aims to separate different types of materials, but it is not practical to separate PUR foams with different compositions. The uncertainty regarding the composition of the feed material therefore has to be handled by the chemical recycling plant. The chemical recycling routes that are currently under investigation in the EU project CIRCULAR FOAM are chemolysis and catalytic pyrolysis. Both are followed by a downstream process to separate the components that leave the reaction stage. In this work, the focus is on the downstream processing after catalytic pyrolysis. The pyrolysis step is assumed to be able to function in the presence of variations in the feed composition, but to produce a varying output stream, so that the handling of the uncertainty is transferred to the downstream unit. The task addressed here is to find the optimal design of a downstream processing plant that can handle output streams of the catalytic pyrolysis unit with varying composition such that high purity feed streams for chemical plants, e.g. aniline, are obtained at minimum cost.

In the context of addressing uncertainties in the design of a process, two main approaches can be distinguished. The first involves overdesigning the process to ensure robustness of the process with respect to the uncertainties. The second one is to explicitly consider the uncertainties in the design process. The advantages of the latter were already discussed by Grossmann and Sargent (1978), resulting in a more efficient design compared to overdesigning a process without considering the uncertainty explicitly. In recent years, two-stage stochastic optimization has been applied successfully to design problems under uncertainty in the early phase of conceptual design as shown by Steimel and Engell (2015). The decomposition of design problems for chemical processes in two stages comes naturally. The design parameters are fixed once the plant is built, and thus they constitute the first stage variables. In contrast, the second stage variables, in particular the operating parameters can be adapted to the realization of the uncertainty during operation, e.g. by controlling the properties of the product.

2. Optimization Algorithm

The two-stage stochastic optimization problem for the design of a chemical processes can be formulated as:

$$\begin{aligned} &\min_{x,z} \sum_i w_i f(x,y,z,\theta_i) \\ &s.t.\ h(x,y,z,\theta_i) = 0 \\ &\qquad g(x,y,z,\theta_i) \leq 0 \\ &\qquad x \in \mathbb{R}^a, y \in \mathbb{R}^b, z \in \mathbb{Z}^c, \theta_i \in \mathbb{R}^d, w_i \in [0,1], i = 1,2,\dots,n, \end{aligned} \tag{1}$$

where x is the vector of the continuous operational parameters, y the vector of state variables of the process, z comprises the discrete design parameters and θ_i is the vector of uncertain parameters. The process model and the equality constraints are described by $h(x,y,z,\theta_i)$ and the inequality constraints by $g(x,y,z,\theta_i)$. The uncertainty of the process is considered by optimizing over a set of n scenarios, where each scenario is a different realization of the uncertain variables, θ_i, and the costs of the scenarios are weighted by w_i. Eq. (1) defines a mixed-integer nonlinear program (MINLP). Such MINLP can be solved e.g. by Benders decomposition, see Geoffrion (1972), or by global methods, see Grossmann et al. (1999). In our case, we want to perform the optimization based on the same model and software that are used in the conceptual design in order to realize a seamless workflow and to exploit the capabilities of commercial process simulation software. Urselmann et al. (2011) and Steimel et al. (2015) demonstrated that evolutionary strategies (ES) can solve such problems with embedded simulators or NLP solvers successfully. Such combinations are called memetic algorithms (MA). The ES optimizes the discrete first stage variables and a local solver optimizes the continuous second stage variables. The process simulation software solves the equality constraints $h(x,y,z,\theta_i) = 0$ in Eq. (1) for each scenario. Also, the optimization of the continuous degrees of freedom for the different scenarios is done by the simulation software (see Fig. 1). The advantage of using a process simulation software instead of a custom written model is the ease of model building. Process simulation software comes with a variety of preconfigured models as well as packages for the computation of thermodynamic properties. The use of such software reduces the time to build a process model drastically. This is especially advantageous in the early phase of process design, where different options are explored. The disadvantage is that gradient information may only be available inside the software and cannot be accessed via a custom optimizer. Furthermore, the models may be restricted by the structure of the software and not every custom adaptation may be possible. In previous work by Janus et al. (2019), it has been shown that when employing a process simulation software in combination with a MA it is advantageous to use the internal optimizer of the software for the local search instead of external derivative free optimization methods. This way the derivative information that is available inside the process simulation software can be exploited. In this work, the AVEVA™ process simulation (APS) is used.

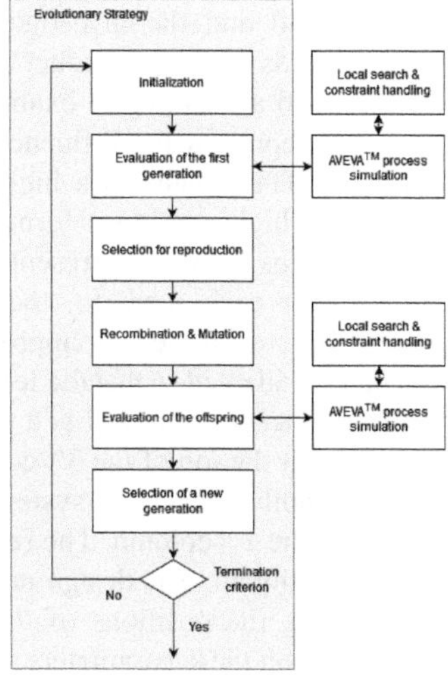

Figure 1: Representation of the algorithm.

2.1. Evolutionary Strategy

The ES searches for the optimum values of the design parameters of the process which are fixed for all scenarios. The ES applied is a $(\mu + \lambda)$-strategy in which the mutation strength is evolved together with the individuals, see Schwefel (1995). μ represents the number of individuals in the parent population, λ represents the number of individuals created during the reproduction step, and the plus denotes that the individuals from the parent generation are considered in the selection of the new generation as well. For this study, a value of $\mu = 10$ and $\lambda = 40$ is selected. The top three individuals from the previous generation are included in the selection process for the new generation. Two individuals from the parent generation are randomly selected for recombination. To utilize an ES in the design of chemical processes, a problem-specific representation must be created, along with problem-specific operators for recombination, mutation, repair, and function evaluation. These parameters are discussed in detail in the next section. The ES is implemented inside the python package *leap_ec*, a library for evolutionary algorithms in python.

2.2. Local Search

APS uses an equation oriented simulation approach (EO). The entire process model is solved as one big block of equations, instead of one single block per equipment as in the sequential modular simulation approach. While in general, the design and operating parameters need to be specified in the process simulation, the EO approach allows to exchange the original equality constraints with other equality constraints. While exchanging constraints, the entire system of equations remains correctly specified and therefore solvable. This means that instead of specifying operating parameters for example specifications on product concentrations can be chosen. This way a certain number of operating parameters can be calculated directly and these do not need to be included in the local search and will adapt to the realization of the uncertainty. The remaining operating parameters are computed by applying the internal optimization tool of the software which is based on a sequential quadratic programming approach. The second-stage optimization is performed separately for each scenario, and all operational parameters are adapted to the realizations of the uncertainty.

3. Case Study and Implementation

In this contribution, a downstream sequence for the separation of the oil that is provided by the catalytic pyrolysis of PUR is optimized. The assumed nominal composition of the pyrolysis oil and the investigated scenarios are shown in Table 1. Only aniline is considered as valuable product. The scenarios are derived from the base case in a way that leads to a meaningful examination of the influence of uncertainties. The first two scenarios represent the influence of a higher and a lower formation of aniline during pyrolysis. This results in a higher or lower formation of toluidine. Scenarios 3 and 4 represent a higher or lower formation of the high boilers in the system (TPG and MDA) and scenarios 5 and 6 represent a higher or lower formation of the low boilers in the system. For each scenario, the amount of material of the respective component is increased or decreased by approx. 10 wt% compared to the base case. The remaining streams are adapted so that the feed flowrate is the same for all scenarios. The downstream sequence that is optimized is a sequence of three distillation columns, where aniline is recovered at the top of the 3rd column at the desired product concentration of 99.5 wt%. The high boilers leave the system at the bottom of the 1st column and the low boilers at the top of the 2nd column. The remaining mid boilers will leave the system at the bottom of the 3rd column. The design parameters which are optimized are the number of stages per column, the positions of the feed stages and the diameters of the columns. The constraints on these parameters are shown in Table 2 and are handled by the ES.

The genome of an individual consists of the number of stages, the positions of the feed stages and the diameters per column, as well as the endogenous parameters of the ES. The numbers of stages and the positions of the feed streams are integer variables and the diameters of the columns can be changed in 10 cm increments. For recombination, a crossover is implemented so that blocks corresponding to one column are selected from one of the parents. Before the evaluation of the individuals and after recombination and mutation, a repair function is applied to the genomes ensuring that for each column the position of the feed stage is below the number of stages of that column.

During the evaluation step, the design parameters of the columns are set inside the APS. In a first step the simulation is initialized to solve the problem robustly for the new set of parameters. In the so called “configuration mode”, a reduced set of equations is used to model the columns. Afterwards the full set of equations is applied while the liquid and the vapor phase are not in contact yet. Finally, the full set of equations is used with the liquid and the vapor phase being in contact. Simultaneously, specifications on the temperatures of the reboilers and the condensers are set, which was found to be robust. The temperature of the reboiler in the first column is set to be below the degradation temperature of the desired product aniline and the temperatures of the condensers of columns one and two are set to 45 °C which will result in a partial condensation of the vapor stream from the columns. The larger part of the vapor streams is condensed and fed back to the column as defined by the reflux ratio for the liquid stream. Since all 3 columns are operated at pressures below 1 bar, structured packings are chosen as the internals of the columns and the flooding factors (F-factors) of the columns are specified to operate at an efficient point, which is chosen according to the packing specifications. In the last column, total condensation is applied and the concentration of the top stream is specified to reach an aniline concentration of 99.5 wt%. This way the boilup rate of the 2nd column is the last degree of freedom along the sequence. It is set in a way that a maximum stream of light boilers are transferred from the 2nd to the 3rd column, assuring that the desired aniline concentration can be reached. After the simulation has been solved in this manner for the base scenario, the local search is done by applying the internal optimization tool. The variables that are optimized are the boilup rate of the 2nd column, the reflux rate of the 3rd column and the F-factors of all three columns. Upper and lower bounds on the F-factors ensure proper dynamics inside the columns and a lower bound is imposed on the aniline concentration in the product stream of 99.5 wt%. The objective function is the annual profit as shown below. It consists of the variable operating and investment costs related to the three columns. C_i denotes the value or cost of stream *i*. *Aniline* is the product stream, *Waste* is the stream of the high boilers of column 1 and the low boilers of column 3, *Utilities* are the steam and the cooling water that are consumed during operation and *depreciation Invest* is the total investment cost calculated by the Lang-factor method and depreciated over 10 years.

$$obj = C_1 \cdot Aniline - C_2 \cdot Waste - C_3 \cdot Aniline - C_4 \cdot Utilities - depreciation\ Invest \quad (2)$$

The optimization is performed for each scenario separately, and the mean value over the 7 scenarios is the fitness value for each individual in the ES.

Table 1: Composition of the feed stream in wt % for the scenarios.

Component	Base	Sc. 1	Sc. 2	Sc. 3	Sc. 4	Sc. 5	Sc. 6
Acetone [wt %]	2.0	2.0	1.9	1.9	2.0	2.2	1.7
Water [wt %]	1.0	1.0	1.0	1.0	1.0	1.1	0.9
Styrene [wt %]	3.0	3.0	2.9	2.9	3.0	3.3	2.6
Indole [wt %]	7.9	8.0	7.8	7.8	7.9	8.8	6.9
Propanol [wt %]	6.9	7.0	6.8	6.8	6.9	7.7	6.1
O.Toluidine [wt %]	4.9	3.5	6.3	6.3	5.0	4.8	5.1
P-Toluidin [wt %]	14.8	12.0	17.5	17.5	14.9	14.4	15.3
Aniline [wt %]	29.6	33.1	26.3	26.3	29.7	28.7	30.6
Tripropylene Glycol [wt %]	24.7	25.1	24.3	24.3	25.3	24.0	25.5
4,4'-Methylen-dianiline [wt %]	4.9	5.0	4.9	4.9	4.2	4.8	5.1

Table 2: Boundaries on the design parameters in the ES.

	Column 1	Column 2	Column 3
Number of stages	5 - 40	5 – 40	10 – 60
Position feed stage	3 – 38	3 – 38	5 – 58
Diameter [m]	0.5 - 3	0.5 – 3	0.5 - 3

4. Results

Four runs of the MA were performed and the results of the best individual per run and generation are shown in Figure 2. All four runs performed similarly and outperformed the overdesigned flowsheet, showing the robustness of the approach. The parameters and the profit for the best found design and for the robust solution are shown in Table 3.

For the best 3 individuals of each run only the scenarios 1 and 6 results in positive values of the profit. All best designs of the 4 runs would give a positive profit if the heavies from column 1 did not need to be disposed. The mean run time for the evaluation of one individual is 17.8 s, whereas the evaluation of a successful individual took up to 3 min. The largest fraction of the computation time is

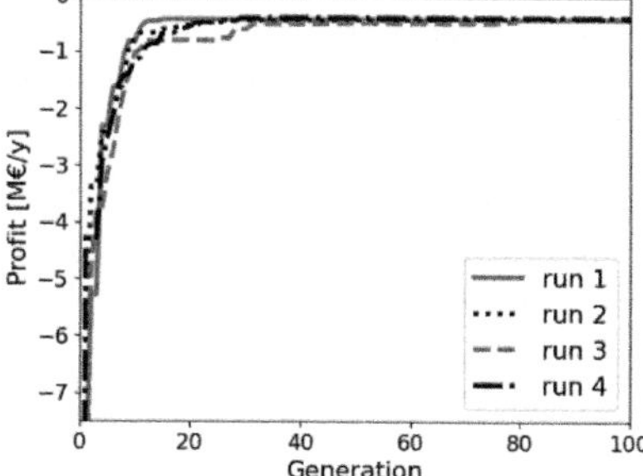

Figure 2: Results of the ES, showing the best individual per run and generation.

spent during the application of the internal optimization algorithm of APS which is called for every scenario. The algorithm was run on an AMD Ryzen 9 385X 16-core processor with 8 instances of APS running in parallel.

Table 3: Design parameters number of stages, position of the feed stream and diameter [m] of each column for the best and for the overdesigned flowsheet.

Design	Column 1	Column 2	Column 3	Profit [M€/y]
Best	35, 9, 1	14, 4, 0.7	36, 21, 9	-0.39
Robust	40, 20, 1	25, 15, 0.7	60, 30, 1	-3.12

5. Conclusion

In this paper, we formulated the design problem of the distillation sequence for the purification of pyrolysis oil obtained from hard PUR foams as a two-stage optimization problem and introduced an evolutionary strategy that is combined with a process simulation software with an internal continuous optimizer. Our solution performed significantly better than the robust design approach in all four test runs. The analysis of the scenarios shows the advantage of increasing the content of aniline and decreasing the amount of light boilers in the pyrolysis oil, while also identifying the further use of heavy boilers as a significant factor for further improvements. This information is especially valuable in the conceptual design phase, where modifications of the overall process design can be implemented. Recycling high boilers through pyrolysis or adjusting the catalysts to achieve higher aniline levels and minimize the amount of light boilers will improve the economics of the overall process. The ease of model building by using a process simulation software comes at the cost of longer computation times for the optimization.

Acknowledgements:

The project leading to this publication has received funding from the European Union's Horizon 2020 research and innovation programme under grant agreement No. 101036854 (project CIRCULAR FOAM)

References

A. M. Geoffrion, 1972, Generalized Benders Decomposition, Jounrnal of Optimization Theory and Applications Vol. 10 No. 4, 237-260

I. E. Grossmann, R. W. H. Sargent, 1978, Optimum Design of Chemical Plants with Uncertain Parameters, AIChE Vol. 24 No.6, 1021-1028

I. E. Grossmann, J. A. Caballero, H. Yeomans, 1999, Mathematical Progamming Approaches to the Synthesis of Chemical Process Synthesis, Korean Journal of Chemical Engineering Vol. 16 No. 4, 407-426

T. Janus, M. Cegla, S. Barkmann, S. Engell, 2019, Optimization of a hydroformulation process in a themomorphic solvent system using a cemmercial steady-state process simulato and a memetic algorithm, Computer Aided Chemical Engineering 46, 469-474

H. P. Schwefel, 1995, Evolution and optimum seeking, Sixth generation computer technology series, Wiley, New York

J. Steimel, S. Engell, 2015, Conceptual design and optimization of chemical processes under uncertainty by two-stage programming, Computers and Chemical Engineering 81, 200-217

M. Urselmann, S. Barkmann, G. Sand, S. Engell, 2011, Optimization-based design of reactive distillation columns using memetic algorithm, Computers and Chemical Engineering 35, 787-805

Flavio Manenti, Gintaras V. Reklaitis (Eds.), Proceedings of the 34th European Symposium on Computer Aided Process Engineering / 15th International Symposium on Process Systems Engineering (ESCAPE34/PSE24), June 2-6, 2024, Florence, Italy
 http://dx.doi.org/10.1016/B978-0-443-28824-1.50247-7

Dynamic analysis of reductant feed method on NH_3 synthesis from exhaust NO gas using NO-CO-H_2O-H_2 reaction

Huichan HWANG[a], Hideyuki MATSUMOTO[a,b*], Teruoki TAGO[a], Yuichi MANAKA[a,b], Tetsuya NANBA[b]

[a]Department of Chemical Science and Engineering, Tokyo Institute of Technology, Tokyo 152-8550, JAPAN

[b] Renewable Energy Research Center, AIST, Kooriyama 963-0215, JAPAN

*Corresponding Author's E-mail: matsumoto.h.ae@m.titech.ac.jp

Abstract

In recent years, a novel nitrogen cycling process known as NOx to Ammonia (NTA) has gained attention as a means to convert NOx from exhaust gases into ammonia (NH_3) for resource utilization. When adsorber of NO is installed upstream of the NTA reactor and the concentration of NO flowing out changes with time, the time variation for feed concentration of the reductant should be controlled in order to maximize the NH_3 yield. In the present study, we experimentally analyze influence of feeding reductant to behavior of NH_3 production in the NO-CO-H_2O-H_2 reaction using Pt/TiO_2 catalyst. Next, two different models for reaction rate equation are derived by changing the set of elementary reactions and mass balance equation for coverage of reaction intermediates on surface of catalyst. The two different models based on the Langmuir-Hinshelwood mechanism were derived on the assumption that formates were formed on the catalyst in the elementary reaction step. When the influence of existence of H* on formate dissociation was considered, the derived model has showed higher accuracy for estimation of the yields of NH_3 and N_2. Also, we have developed dynamic simulation system by combining the plug flow reactor model including the derived reaction rate equation with a one-dimensional simulation model for NO adsorption/desorption.

Keywords: nitrogen cycle, kinetic analysis, modelling and simulation, dynamic simulation

1. Introduction

The emission of reactive nitrogen oxides from combustor has become a significant cause of environmental pollution and climate change. In recent years, a novel nitrogen cycling process known as NOx to Ammonia (NTA) has gained attention as a means to convert NOx from exhaust gases into ammonia (NH_3) for resource utilization. The synthesis and evaluation of various NTA process systems have been investigated. In previous study (T. Nanba et al., 2008), production of NH_3 using NO-H_2 reaction has been reported. Then, K. Kobayashi et al. (2019) have developed NO-CO-H_2O reaction process using Pt/TiO_2 to convert NO into NH_3. When feeding CO produced by reforming of methane, it is necessary to consider the effective use of the generated hydrogen. Therefore, we propose to apply NO-CO-H_2O-H_2 reaction process in which feed ratio of H_2 to CO (H_2/CO) is controlled through a combination of different reforming processes of methane. If the concentration of NO feeding from the outlet of adsorber to the NTA reactor changes over time, the time variation for feed concentration of the reductant should be optimized in order to maximize the NH_3 yield.

An aim of this study is to analyze influence of unsteady operation of feeding reductant to behavior of the overall process system for NH_3 synthesis in the NO-CO-H_2O-H_2 reaction by dynamic process simulation. To develop the NTA reactor model for the simulation analysis, reaction data were experimentally collected by the pack bed reactor with Pt/TiO_2 catalyst. Subsequently, two different models for reaction rate equation was derived by changing the set of elementary reactions and mass balance equation for coverage of reaction intermediates on surface of catalyst. Then we will discussed on applicability of the developed NTA reactor models.

2. Data acquisition for NO-CO-H_2O-H_2 reaction

Figure 1 shows a schematic diagram for the experimental setup for acquisition of kinetic data. To derive rate equations for NO-CO-H_2O-H_2 reaction based on the Langmuir-Hinshelwood (L-H) mechanism, not only reactor temperature but also H_2/CO in the feed reductant gas were changed by using packed bed reactor with 0.25 g of 1 wt% Pt/TiO_2 (rutile-type). The temperature was changed in the range from 175 ℃ to 325 ℃. The ratio of H_2/CO was varied from 1 to 3 by considering application of combination of the methane steam reforming and the methane dry reforming.

Figure 2 (a) and (b) showed relationships between temperature and reaction efficiency for the case when H_2/CO was 2. The composition of feed gas was NO: 0.6 %, CO: 0.5 % H_2O: 0.9 %, H_2: 1 %. As the temperature increased, it was shown that the conversion of NO and CO increased and reached nearly 100 % at temperature over 275 °C. Moreover, there was a noticeable steep increase in the yield of NH_3 with increase in temperature. However, over 275 °C, change in the yield of NH_3 exhibits very small, whereas the yield of N_2 shows an increasing behaviour. The formation of a tiny amount of N_2O was also observed under condition of low temperature.

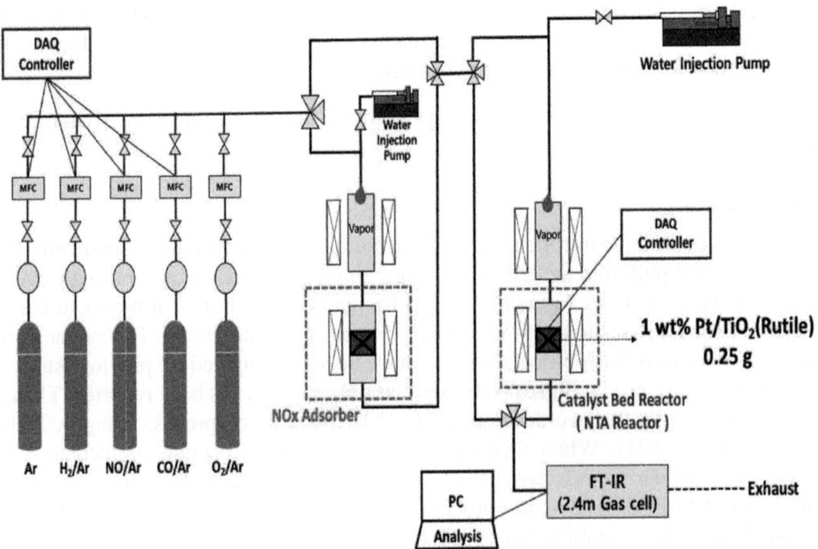

Figure 1 Experimental setup for acquisition of kinetic data

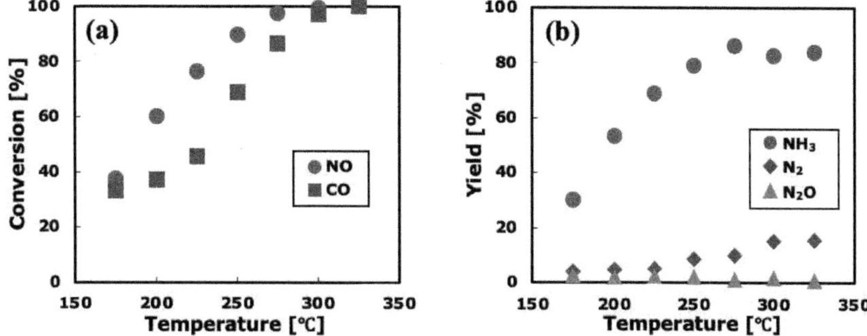

Figure 2 Relationships between temperature and reaction efficiency for the case when H_2/CO was 2; (a) Conversions of NO and CO, (b) Yields of NH_3, N_2, N_2O

For the case when the H_2/CO was 3, the conversion of NO and CO increased with increase in temperature and reached nearly 100 % at temperature over 275 °C, which was similar to the case when the H_2/CO was 2. It was showed that the yield of NH_3 increased with increase in temperature, while the yield slightly decreased over 300 °C. The cause of the decreasing trend in yield will be discussed in the next section using a reaction rate model. Hence, it has been demonstrated that behaviour of NH_3 formation could be controlled by the reaction temperature and the composition ratio of the reductant feed.

3. Derivation of reaction rate equations for NTA reactor model

In order to derive reaction rate equations based on the L-H mechanism, we investigated combination of multiple elementary reactions for the NO-CO-H_2O-H_2 reaction, as shown in Table 1. For NO-CO-H_2O reaction using Pt/TiO_2 catalyst, K. Kobayashi et al (2019) has reported formation of formate, which acted as the most abundant surface intermediates (MASI), could progress formation of ammonia. Thus, in order to develop the reaction rate equation model for NO-CO-H_2O-H_2 reaction, it was also considered that several chemical reactions on surface of the Pt/TiO_2 catalyst involved the adsorption of NO and CO, as well as intermediate reactions such as formate formation.

Reactions A*i* ~ C*i* in Table 1 represent the adsorption of NO and CO, dissociative adsorption of H_2O and H_2, and intermediate reactions including nitrogen hydride groups NH_x* related to NH_3 formation. D*i* represents the elementary reaction step for formation of N_2 as side reactions. It has been reported that the energy barrier to breaking N-O on the surface of Pt catalyst is high (Y. Bai and M. Mavrikakis 2017). Since direct dissociation of NO tends to proceed, it is necessary to consider reaction intermediates derived from NO* in the elementary reaction steps. Therefore, the reaction " NO* + N* → N_2O" can be considered, but as shown in Fig. 2(b), the concentration of N_2O produced is extremely small, so we did not include the formation of N_2O in the elementary reaction step in the present study. And formation of NH_3 (Eq. (11)) and N_2 (Eq. (12)) has assumed as the rate-determining step (RDS), respectively.

In the present paper, two models (model A and model B) were derived by setting the different assumption for coverage of reaction intermediates on surface of catalyst. In derivation of the model A, we assumed a mass balance equation written in Eq. 13, for coverage of chemical species on the the catalyst active sites.

$$\theta_{CO*} + \theta_{NO*} + \theta_{H*} + \theta_{OH*} + \theta_{COOH*} + \theta_{NHx*} + \theta_{*} = 1 \qquad (13)$$

Table 1 Elementary reactions and reaction rate equations

	Reaction	Rate expression	Eq
A1	NO(g) + * ↔ NO*	$\theta_{NO*} = k_{A,1}\theta_{*}P_{NO}$	(1)
A2	H_2O(g) + * ↔ H_2O*	$\theta_{H2O*} = k_{A,2}\theta_{*}P_{H2O}$	(2)
A3	H_2(g) + 2* ↔ 2H*	$\theta_{H*,1} = \theta_{*}\sqrt{k_{A,3}P_{H2}}$	(3)
A4	H_2O* + * ↔ H* + OH*	$\theta_{H*,2} = k_{A,4}\frac{\theta_{H2O*}\theta_{*}}{\theta_{OH*}}$	(4)
A5	CO(g) + * ↔ CO*	$\theta_{CO*} = k_{A,5}P_{CO}\theta_{*}$	(5)
B1	CO* + OH* ↔ COOH* + *	$\theta_{COOH*} = k_{B,1}\frac{\theta_{CO*}\theta_{OH*}}{\theta_{*}}$	(6)
B2	COOH* → H* + CO_2(g)	$\theta_{H*} = k_{B,2}\theta_{COOH*}$	(7)
C1	NO* + H* ↔ NOH* + *	$\theta_{NOH*} = k_{C,1}\frac{\theta_{NO*}\theta_{H*}}{\theta_{*}}$	(8)
C2	NOH* + H* ↔ NH* + OH*	$\theta_{NH*} = k_{C,2}\frac{\theta_{NOH*}\theta_{H*}}{\theta_{OH*}}$	(9)
C3	NH* + H* ↔ NH_2* + *	$\theta_{NH2*} = k_{C,3}\frac{\theta_{NH*}\theta_{H*}}{\theta_{*}}$	(10)
C4	NH_2* + H* → NH_3(g) + 2*	$r_{NH3} = k_{C,4}\theta_{NH2*}\theta_{H*}$	(11)
D1	NH* + NO* → N_2(g) + OH* + *	$r_{N2} = k_{D,1}\theta_{NH*}\theta_{NO*}$	(12)

Then, in model B, adsorption and reaction of H* and OH* that were not involved in reaction step B_i were also considered, and two reaction rate equations (Eqs. (15) and (16)) were introduced in addition to Eq. (14) including $\theta_{OH*,2}$ and $\theta_{NHx*,2}$. By introducing such an assumption, we observed a slight improvement in predictive performance compared to the model A.

$$\theta_{CO*} + \theta_{NO*} + \theta_{H*} + \theta_{OH*} + \theta_{OH*,2} + \theta_{COOH*} + \theta_{NHx*} + \theta_{NHx*,2} + \theta_{*} = 1 \qquad (14)$$

$$\theta_{OH*,2} = k_{OH*,2}{P_{H2O}}^{1}{P_{H2}}^{-1.5}\theta_{*} \qquad (15)$$

$$\theta_{NHx*,2} = k_{NHx*,2}\,P_{NO}\,{P_{H2O}}^{-1}{P_{H}}^{\alpha}\,\theta_{*} \qquad (16)$$

Furthermore, we supposed that dynamics of dissociation of formate on the catalyst influenced the rate of formation of NH_3, since formation of formate was largely related to NH_3 production that K. Kobayashi et al. (2019) have described. Thus, for rate expression of dissociation of formates (step B2 in Table 1), the influence of existence of H* on formate dissociation was considered in derivation of model B. In this study, the rate expression in step B2 was replaced with the rate equation for the equilibrium reaction.

Reaction rate expressions for formation of NH_3 and N_2 given by Eqs. (17) ~ (19) were drived for model B. Since influence of partial pressure of CO, H_2O on NH_3 synthesis step considered in model B, parameter β was introduced in the term related to NH* adsoprtion in Eq. (19). Also, regarding model A, some terms in the denominator of Eqs. (17) and (18) were different from model B. Furthermore, exponent of the denominator was set as $x = 4$ in model B, while $x = 2$ in model A.

$$r_{NH3,model\,B} = \frac{(k_{NH3f,1} P_{NO} P_{CO}{}^{2.5} P_{H2O}{}^{1.5} + k_{NH3f,2}\, P_{NO}\, P_{H2}{}^{2.5})}{f(P_j)^x} \tag{17}$$

$$r_{N2,model\,B} = \frac{(k_{N2f,1}\, P_{NO}{}^2\, P_{CO}{}^y + k_{N2f,2}\, P_{NO}{}^2\, P_{H2}{}^z)}{f(P_j)^2} \tag{18}$$

$$f(P_j) = 1 + k_{NO*} P_{NO} + k_{CO*}\, P_{CO} + \frac{k_{H*} P_{H2O}{}^{0.5} P_{CO}{}^{0.5}}{P_{CO2}{}^{0.5}} + \frac{k_{OH*} P_{H2O}{}^{0.5} P_{CO2}{}^{0.5}}{P_{CO}{}^{0.5}} + k_{OH*,2} P_{H2O} P_{H2}{}^{-1.5} \tag{19}$$

$$+ k_{COOH*} P_{H2O}{}^{0.5} P_{CO2}{}^{0.5} P_{CO}{}^{0.5} + \frac{k_{NH*}\, P_{NO}\, P_{H2O}{}^{\beta-0.5} P_{CO}{}^{\beta+0.5}}{P_{CO2}{}^{0.5}} + \frac{k_{NHx*,2}\, P_{NO}\, P_{H2}{}^{2.5}}{P_{H2O}}$$

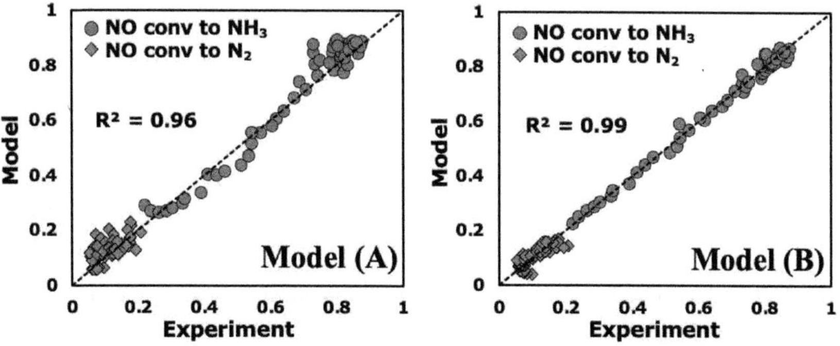

Figure 3 Results of parameter estimation for model A and model B

Figure 3 illustrates the differences between the model in terms of yield. Through parameter fitting using the above mentioned process data in Figure 2 (b) , the model B showed higher accuracy ($R^2 = 0.99$) for estimation of the yields of NH_3 and N_2 than the model A. In particular, application of Model B improved the predictive performance of ammonia yield in the temperature range of 275°C or higher. In this study, we employed a model where the reaction orders for the partial pressures of CO and H_2 were denoted as y and z on numerator following in Eq. (18) to investigate the influence of the H_2/CO supply ratio on the side reaction. As a result, the partial pressure of CO and H_2 that was assigned a reaction order represented $y = -0.68$ and $z = -0.94$ in model B as parameter estimation results. On the other hand, the derived reaction orders y and z were almost 0 in model A, which does not show any other effect of CO and H_2 feed.

4. Conclusion

We experimentally analyzed influence of feeding reductant to behavior of NH_3 production in the NO-CO-H_2O-H_2 reaction using Pt/TiO_2 catalyst. Next, two different models (model A, model B) for reaction rate equation are derived by changing the set of elementary reactions and mass balance equation for coverage of reaction intermediates on surface of catalyst. When the influence of existence of H* on formate dissociation was considered in deriving model B, the model B has showed higher accuracy for estimation of the yields of NH_3 and N_2 than model A. Also we have developed dynamic simulation system by combining the plug flow reactor model including the derived reaction rate equation with a one-dimensional simulation model for NO adsorption/desorption. Figure 4 shows an example of the results of the outlet gas concentration that were acquired by using the dynamic simulation system. In future work, methods for optimization of unsteady operation of flow rate and composition of reductants (CO, H_2, H_2O) for maximizing NH_3 yield and CO consumption will be investigated by the developed dynamic simulation system.

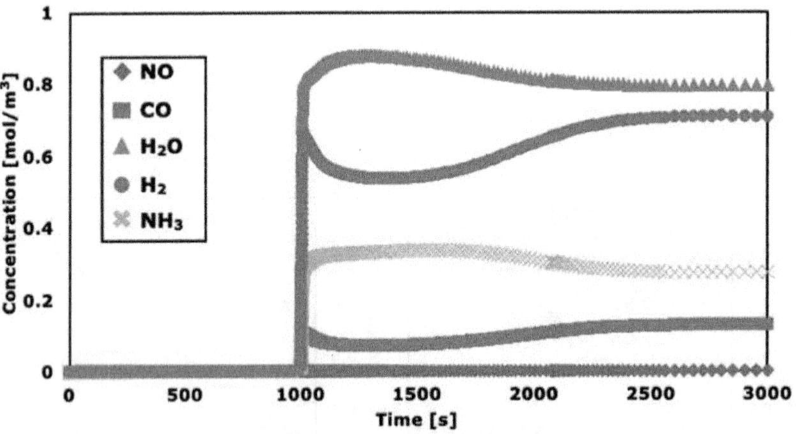

Figure 4 The result of outlet concentration using dynamic simulation for a case when H_2/CO ratio was 2 and the reactor temperature was 300°C

References

T. Nanba et al., 2008, Formation of Ammonia during the NO–H_2 Reaction over Pt/ZrO_2, J. Phys. Chem. C, 112, 46, 18157–18163.

K. Kobayashi et al., 2019, Effect of the TiO_2 crystal structure on the activity of TiO_2-supported platinum catalysts for ammonia synthesis via the NO–CO–H_2O reaction, Catal. Sci. Technol., vol. 9, no. 11, pp. 2898–2905.

Y. Bai and M. Mavrikakis 2017, Mechanistic Study of Nitric Oxide Reduction by Hydrogen on Pt(100) (I): A DFT Analysis of the Reaction Network, J. Phys. Chem. B, 122, 2, 432–443.

Flavio Manenti, Gintaras V. Reklaitis (Eds.), Proceedings of the 34th European Symposium on Computer Aided Process Engineering / 15th International Symposium on Process Systems Engineering (ESCAPE34/PSE24), June 2-6, 2024, Florence, Italy
 http://dx.doi.org/10.1016/B978-0-443-28824-1.50248-9

Computer-Aided Design of Intensified Separation Sequences for a Complex Mixture of Renewable Hydrocarbons

Isaac Oliva-González [a], Araceli Guadalupe Romero-Izquierdo [b,*], Claudia Gutiérrez-Antonio [b], Fernando Israel Gómez-Castro [c], Salvador Hernández [a]

[a] *Departamento de Ingeniería Química, División de Ciencias Naturales y Exactas, Campus Guanajuato, Universidad de Guanajuato, Noria Alta S/N, Guanajuato, Gto. 36050, México.*

[b] *Facultad de Ingeniería, Universidad Autónoma de Querétaro, Campus Amazcala, Carretera a Chichimequillas s/n km. 1, Amazcala, El Marqués, Qro., 76010, México.*

araceli.romero@uaq.mx

Abstract

In this work, four intensified distillation schemes are presented for the separation of Sustainable Aviation Fuel (SAF) and other biofuels. The intensified schemes include a Petlyuk sequence (PTK) and a double-wall sequence for the separation of three pseudo-components (DDWC-3), as well as a dividing wall sequence (DWC-4) and a double dividing wall column (DDWC-4) for the separation of four pseudo-components. It is important to note that the number of components in the hydrocarbon mixture to be separated is 49, obtained from two ASTM-certified production processes for the production of SAF. These complex designs have been evaluated from its energy requirements, realizing a deep sensitivity analysis in Aspen Plus V.11.0. According to results, 4.85 %, 4.83 %, 7.39 % and 4.08 % of energy savings are obtained from PTK, DWC-3, DWC-4, and DDWC-4, respectively, regarding to direct conventional sequence. The intensified schemes, when compared to the conventional one, demonstrate energy savings in each scenario. However, the DWC-4 scheme stands out by eliminating the need for two reboilers and two condensers, resulting in greater energy savings than other intensified sequences. These proposals are good alternatives for enhance the energetic performance of renewable processes for biofuels production.

Keywords: Complex renewable hydrocarbons mixture, process intensification, simulation, sustainable aviation fuel.

1. Introduction

Since 2020, due to the pandemic caused by virus SARS-CoV2, the aviation sector has aimed to reduce its environmental impact and achieved sustainable economic recovery (IEA, 2022); including 50 % reduction in CO2 emissions by 2050, necessitating fuels with a lower carbon footprint. In this context, the development of Sustainable Aviation Fuel (SAF) has been actively promoted as a resilient and promising medium to long-term strategy. In this sense, various efforts have focused on reducing the production cost of SAF, primarily linked to the high energy demand in product separation processes.

Gutiérrez-Antonio et al. (2015) pioneered an intensified hydroprocessing method for SAF separation through thermally coupled sequences involving 20 renewable hydrocarbons. This approach yielded a 21 % reduction in energy consumption for the thermally coupled direct sequence compared to the original process developed by UOP Honeywell (McCall et al., 2009). In 2018, a SAF production process using microalgae biomass was proposed, employing a directly thermally coupled sequence for renewable fuel purification. This method achieved a 34 % reduction in CO2 emissions compared to the conventional direct sequence (Gutiérrez-Antonio et al., 2018). Subsequently, Moreno-Gómez et al. (2021) presented modeling, simulation, and intensification of chicken fat hydroprocessing to produce SAF using 30 renewable hydrocarbons for separation. Results indicated that intensified schemes constituted the most favorable scenario concerning environmental and economic indicators. In the same year, energy intensification and integration were performed in the separation zone for the ATJ-SPK process, resulting in up to a 34.75% reduction in energy requirements (Romero-Izquierdo et al., 2021). Following this, Carrasco-Suárez et al. (2022) applied process intensification in the separation zone of a biorefinery scheme for SAF production derived from used cooking oil as raw material, this led to a 3.07% reduction in CO2 emissions and a 66.95% energy savings in the intensified scheme compared to the conventional one. It is evident that intensification proposals for SAF production have yielded energy savings. However, the mixing of renewable hydrocarbons before separation is limited to a specific number of compounds. Therefore, it's essential to consider blends that more accurately represent the real complexity of the issue. This work proposes the intensification of the SAF separation zone using the effluent from two processes: hydroprocessing (HP) and the alcohol to jet (ATJ). This effluent comprises a complex mixture of 49 components (Romero-Izquierdo, 2020), divided into four pseudo-components: light gases, naphtha, sustainable aviation fuel, and green diesel. The proposed separation schemes include four intensified sequences with multiple dividing walls for SAF production.

2. Modelling and simulation

According with Romero-Izquierdo (2020), the renewable hydrocarbon mixture to be separated is divided by four pseudo-components: light gases (A), naphtha (B), sustainable aviation fuel (C), and green diesel (D), as shown in Table 1, with their respective distributions and mass flows. The methodology towards intensification begins with the design of the Direct Conventional Sequence (DCS), followed by two thermally coupled distillation sequences: the Petlyuk sequence (PTK) and the three pseudo-component double-wall dividing sequence (DDWC-3). Next, for four pseudo-components: one dividing wall (DWC-4) and double-wall dividing sequence (DDWC-4) were designed, employing BK10 as the thermodynamic model in all cases. For each sequence, rigorous modeling was conducted, accompanied by sensitivity analysis to reduce the energy requirements of reboilers and condensers, achieving 99 % recovery for all key pseudo-components and carried out an average of 300 iterations per sequence. It's important to highlight that reboiler duty minimization was primarily accomplished through interconnection flows for PTK, DDWC-3 and DDWC-4. For the DWC-4 sequence was considered the feed stage as an additional variable apart from the interconnection flows. Also, in order to ensure the comparison of energy requirements, the reflux ratio was established as the main variable that maintained the product compositions in each sequence. Finally, it is worth to mention that the (A) product requires a partial-vapor condenser for the light gases separation, thus, for all designs, this component is obtained as the lighter cut, restricting the indirect distillation designs (Romero-Izquierdo, 2020).

Table 1. Renewable hydrocarbons mixture to separate.

Pseudo-compounds	Compound	Formula	Mass Flow (kg/h)	Pseudo-compounds	Compound	Formula	Mass Flow (kg/h)
Light gases (A)	Methane	CH_4	800.6508		N-Decane	$C_{10}H_{22}$	32232.1754
	Ethane	C_2H_6	13677.7170		N-Undecane	$C_{11}H_{24}$	14911.0443
	Propane	C_3H_8	2759.4941		2-Methylundecane	$C_{12}H_{26}$	10621.5727
	1-Butene	C_4H_8	483.0010		1-Decene	$C_{10}H_{20}$	64.5164
	N-Butane	C_4H_{10}	49719.4538		1-Dodecene	$C_{12}H_{24}$	64.5164
Naphtha (B)	2-Methylbutane	C_5H_{12}	0.1598		N-Dodecane	$C_{12}H_{26}$	25452.3104
	1-Pentene	C_5H_{10}	2.2834		Cycloundecane	$C_{11}H_{22}$	12.9029
	N-Pentane	C_5H_{12}	42308.8520		1-Undecene	$C_{11}H_{22}$	2.2834
	2-Methylpentane	C_6H_{14}	0.0013		1-Tetradecene	$C_{14}H_{24}$	64.5163
	N-Hexane	C_6H_{14}	40390.0284		N-Tridecane	$C_{13}H_{28}$	5739.7902
	1-Hexene	C_6H_{12}	357.1645		2,2,4,4,6,8,8-Heptamethylnonane	$C_{16}H_{34}$	16864.8346
	2-Methylhexane	C_7H_{16}	1457.1671		N-Tetradecane	$C_{14}H_{30}$	42065.2966
	1-Heptene	C_7H_{14}	2.2834		N-Pentadecane	$C_{15}H_{32}$	22157.0094
	N-Heptane	C_7H_{16}	10764.8198		1-Hexadecene	$C_{16}H_{32}$	64.5165
SAF (C)	2-Methylheptane	C_8H_{18}	18984.7220		1-Pentadecene	$C_{15}H_{30}$	2.2834
	1-Octene	C_8H_{16}	273.1774		N-Hexadecane	$C_{16}H_{34}$	11075.5625
	N-Octane	C_8H_{18}	57652.1169	Green diesel (D)	N-Heptadecane	$C_{17}H_{36}$	4623.5472
	Ethylbenzene	C_8H_{10}	6.1259		1-Octadecene	$C_{18}H_{36}$	64.5164
	3-Methyloctane	C_9H_{20}	9551.4866		N-Octadecane	$C_{18}H_{38}$	32503.4317
	1-Nonene	C_9H_{18}	2.2834		N-Nonadecane	$C_{19}H_{40}$	4456.0915
	N-Nonane	C_9H_{20}	2725.1832		N-Eicosane	$C_{20}H_{42}$	6536.7617
	Isopropylbenzene	C_9H_{12}	29.1798		N-Heneicosane	$C_{21}H_{44}$	29985.1641
	1-Heptadecene	$C_{17}H_{34}$	2.2834		1-Nonadecene	$C_{19}H_{38}$	2.2834
	N-Propylbenzene	C_9H_{12}	3.6869		1-Eicosene	$C_{20}H_{40}$	64.5164
	3-Methylnonane	$C_{10}H_{22}$	5265.9133				

The design procedure for each sequence is described below. Starting with the Direct Conventional Sequence (DCS) illustrated in Figure 1, each distillation column in the train is designed using shortcut methods (DSTWU module), and then is rigorously simulated using the RadFrac module. From the rigorous modelling of DCS, two thermally coupled sequences are obtained following the methodology of Rong and Errico (2012).

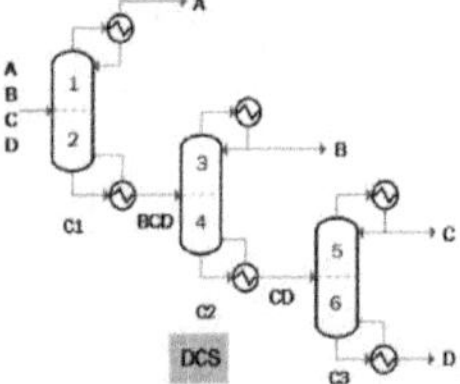

Column	**C1**		**C2**		**C3**	
Section	1	2	3	4	5	6
Number of stages	14	10	20	18	44	43
Feed stage	14		20		44	

Figure 1. Direct Conventional Sequence (DCS).

The design for the Petlyuk column (PTK) is shown in Figure 2, considering the recommendations from Caballero, (2009) and Petlyuk (1965). Initially, a conventional sequence is generated following the methodology presented by Rong and Errico (2012), using the minimum energy requirements for each sequence as the criteria selection. Then, two thermal couplings were performed to form the pre-fractionator, which, through interconnection flows and the movement of sections, generates the main column. The variables considered for the sensitivity analysis are the interconnection flows L1 and V2, in order to reduce the thermal load of the reboilers of C1 and C3.

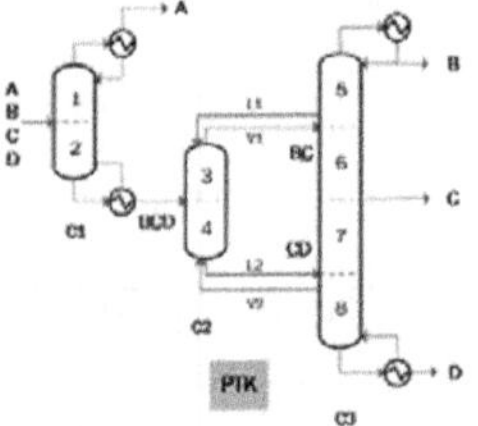

Column	C1		C2		C3			
Section	1	2	3	4	5	6	7	8
Number of stages	14	10	26	22	20	19	30	30
Feed stage	14		26		20		69	

Figure 2. Petlyuk sequence (PTK).

Next, the three pseudo-component double-wall sequence (DDWC-3) was developed for separation. This sequence is designed based on the design parameters of the thermally coupled sequences, involving modifications in the number of stages and interconnection flows, along with the addition of the post-fractionator (C3). The variables included for sensitivity analysis were the interconnection flows: L1, V2, L3, and V4. The DDWC-3 is depicted in Figure 3.

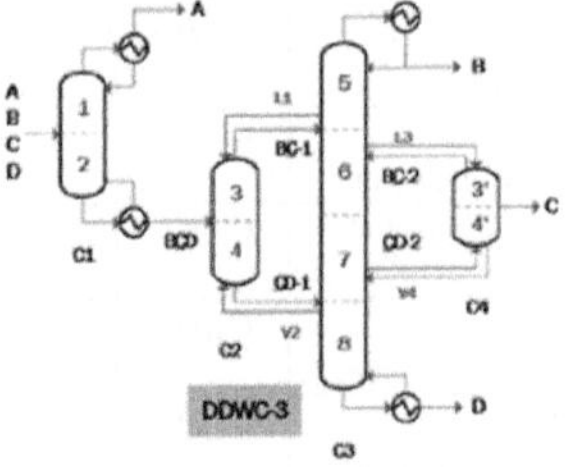

Column	C1		C2		C3				C4	
Section	1	2	3	4	5	6	7	8	3'	4'
Number of stages	14	10	26	22	20	19	35	30	10	30
Feed stage	14		26		20	39	74	94	1	40

Figure 3. Three pseudo-component double-wall sequence (DDWC-3).

The design of the four pseudo-component dividing wall sequence (DWC-4) is shown in Figure 4, derived from thermally coupled distillation sequences, with alterations in the feed stage and the number of stages in both post-fractionators generated through interconnection flows (L1, V2, L3, and V4) and analyzed to reduce the heat duty of C1.

The DDWC-4 scheme presented in Figure 5 has been designed based on the chosen parameters obtained from the Petlyuk and quaternary dividing wall sequences (DWC-4).

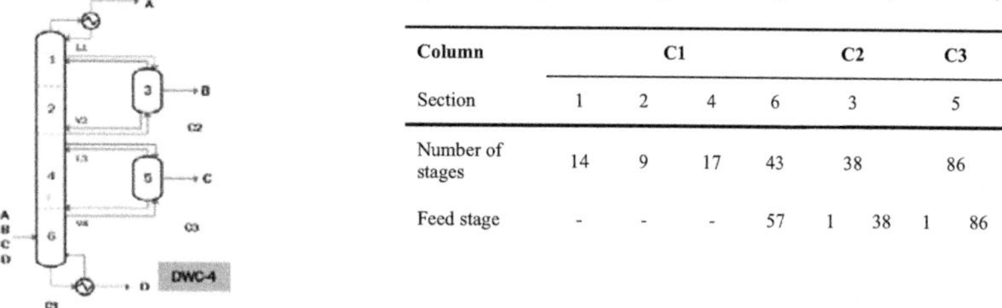

Column	C1				C2	C3
Section	1	2	4	6	3	5
Number of stages	14	9	17	43	38	86
Feed stage	-	-	-	57	1 38	1 86

Figure 4. Four pseudo-component dividing wall sequence (DWC-4)

A preliminary design is obtained by adopting the number of stages from the columns, interconnection flow feed stage, and reflux ratio of the base sequences. Subsequent modifications involve adjustments in the feed stage of all interconnection streams and the removal of unnecessary stages from each column. Sensitivity analysis is then conducted to reduce the reboiler duty using interconnection flows (L1, V2, L3, V4, L5, and V6).

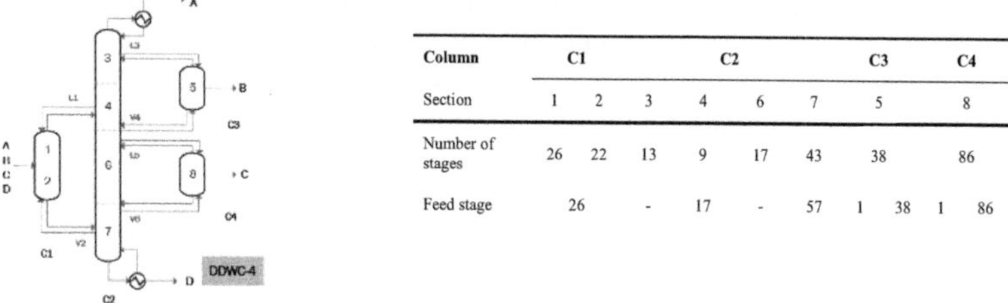

Column	C1		C2				C3	C4
Section	1	2	3	4	6	7	5	8
Number of stages	26	22	13	9	17	43	38	86
Feed stage	26		-	17	-	57	1 38	1 86

Figure 5. Four pseudo-component double-wall sequence (DDWC-4).

3. Results

Table 2 illustrates the comparison of number of stages, the stage feed, the interconnexion flows and the energy savings obtained regarding to the conventional scheme, for each designed sequence. In the case of DCS the number of stages is 149, this count is lower than the intensified sequences due to additional stages required for separation in those sequences. In most intensified sequences, the feed stage remains constant, except for DWC-4. In DWC-4, the mixture is fed from the stripping section instead of following the norm in other sequences. Moreover, the installation of posfractionators alongside multiple divided wall columns adjacent to corresponding principal column stages is crucial for ensuring efficient operation and maintaining proper flow within the system. In assessing energy savings achieved, each intensified sequence displays varying levels of energy savings in comparison with the conventional sequence. Based on the obtained savings, the DDWC-3 sequence yields the lowest savings of 3.14 % for the condenser and 4.83 % for the reboiler. In contrast, DWC-4 sequence demonstrates the most significant savings, reaching up to 11.06 % and 7.39 % for the condenser and reboiler, respectively. Meanwhile, the DDWC-4 sequence achieves savings of 6.94 % and 4.09 % for the condenser and reboiler, respectively. It is worth to note that the intensified schemes, when compared to the conventional one, demonstrate energy savings in each scenario. Notably, DWC-4 distinguishes itself by eliminating the need for two reboilers and condensers, resulting in the highest energy savings compared to other intensified sequences; its thermodynamic advantages are evident, exhibiting minimal thermodynamic losses in the flow mixture. Finally, it is mentioned that the control and optimization of these sequences are necessary to verify their operability and enhance their efficiency. Undoubtedly, this critical aspect of control and optimization will be the focus of future work, seeking to validate the feasibility and performance enhancements of these sequences in real-world operational environments.

Table 2. Comparison of main results of conventional and intensified sequences.

Parameters	Sequences				
	DCS	PTK	DDWC-3	DWC-4	DDWC-4
Number of stages	149	171	216	207	255
Condenser duty (MW)	- 71,77	- 64.64	- 69.52	- 63.83	- 66.79
Energy savings (%)	-	9.94 %	3.14 %	11.06 %	6.94 %
Reboiler duty (MW)	102.01	97.05	97.01	94.46	97.83
Energy savings (%)	-	4.85 %	4.83 %	7.39 %	4.08 %

4. Conclusion

In this work has been presented four intensified proposals for separating SAF from a complex mixture of 49 renewable hydrocarbons. The intensified schemes, when compared with the conventional scheme, demonstrate the technical feasibility and energy savings in each case. Among these, the double-wall sequence (DWC-4) sequence stands out by avoiding the use of two reboilers and two condensers, resulting in greater energy savings compared to the other intensified sequences. DWC-4 could be utilized as a promising sequence for separating SAF due to the energy savings of 11.06 % and 7.39 % in condenser and reboiler, respectively, resulting in the highest energy savings compared to other intensified sequences. The successful implementation of these intensified sequences relies on robust control mechanisms and optimized configurations to ensure operability and maximize efficiency. Further exploration and refinement in the control and optimization of these sequences are essential steps toward realizing their potential in practical applications.

References

J. A. Caballero. (2009). Thermally Coupled Distillation. Computer Aided Chemical Engineering, 27(C), 59–64.

M. T. Carrasco-Suárez, A. G. Romero-Izquierdo, C. Gutiérrez-Antonio, F. I. Gómez-Castro, & S. Hernández. (2022). Production of renewable aviation fuel by waste cooking oil processing in a biorefinery scheme: Intensification of the purification zone. Chemical Engineering and Processing - Process Intensification, 181, 109103.

C. Gutiérrez-Antonio, A. G. Romero-Izquierdo, F. I. Gómez-Castro, & S. Hernández. (2018). Modeling, simulation and intensification of hydroprocessing of micro-algae oil to produce renewable aviation fuel. Clean Technologies and Environmental Policy, 20(7), 1589–1598.

C. Gutiérrez-Antonio, F. I. Gómez-Castro, S. Hernández, & A. Briones-Ramírez. (2015). Intensification of a hydrotreating process to produce biojet fuel using thermally coupled distillation. Chemical Engineering and Processing: Process Intensification, 88, 29–36.

IEA. (2022, july). Aviation, IEA, Paris. Elsevier Ltd.

M. J. McCall, J. A. Kocal, A. Bhattacharyya, T. N. Kalnes, & T. A. Brandvold. (2009). Production of aviation fuel from renewable feedstocks.

A. L. Moreno-Gómez, C. Gutiérrez-Antonio, F. I. Gómez-Castro, & S. Hernández. (2021). Modelling, simulation and intensification of the hydroprocessing of chicken fat to produce renewable aviation fuel. Chemical Engineering and Processing - Process Intensification, 159, 108250.

F. Petlyuk. (1965). Thermodynamically Optimal Method for Separating Multicomponent Mixtures.

A. G. Romero-Izquierdo. (2020). Diseño, modelado y simulación de un esquema de biorefinería para el aprovechamiento integral de mezclas de materias primas renovables [Tesis de Doctorado]. Universidad de Guanajuato.

A. G. Romero-Izquierdo, F. I. Gómez-Castro, C. Gutiérrez-Antonio, S. Hernández, & M. Errico. (2021). Intensification of the alcohol-to-jet process to produce renewable aviation fuel. Chemical Engineering and Processing-Process Intensification, 160, 108270.

B. G. Rong, & M. Errico. (2012). Synthesis of intensified simple column configurations for multicomponent distillations. Chemical Engineering and Processing: Process Intensification, 62, 1–17.

Flavio Manenti, Gintaras V. Reklaitis (Eds.), Proceedings of the 34th European Symposium on Computer Aided Process Engineering / 15th International Symposium on Process Systems Engineering (ESCAPE34/PSE24), June 2-6, 2024, Florence, Italy
 http://dx.doi.org/10.1016/B978-0-443-28824-1.50249-0

Integration of Plant Scheduling Feasibility with Supply Chain Network Under Disruptions Using Machine Learning Surrogates

Daniel Ovalle[a], Javal Vyas[a], Carl D. Laird[a], Ignacio E. Grossmann[a,1]

[a] *Dept. of Chemical Engineering, Carnegie Mellon University, Pittsburgh, PA 15217*

grossmann@cmu.edu

Abstract

Integrating supply chain under disruptions with plant scheduling is challenging due to differing time scales. Our proposed approach utilizes a reactive supply chain model with linear model decision tree surrogates, capturing feasibility within scheduling constraints. The surrogate employs an aggregated variable space and an efficient sampling methodology, as demonstrated in a case study. Results highlight the integrated model's ability to ensure entirely feasible operations without compromising overall profitability within tractable solution time.

Keywords: Supply chain under disruptions, Feasibility, Machine learning surrogates.

1. Background

In an increasingly interconnected global landscape, the resilience of supply chains and manufacturing networks against disruptions is important across various industries. Disruptions in the supply chain can trigger a cascade effect, impacting the entire system in both upstream and downstream directions. Predicting these effects is challenging due to the intertwined material flows and the amplification of disruptions beyond neighbouring nodes (Snyder et al., 2016). Reactive models, such as the one introduced by Ovalle et al. (2023), address this by generating optimal schedules for large-scale supply chain problems with arbitrary network topologies. However, this model does not consider the lower-level dynamics of in-site plant scheduling. Therefore, solutions for this model may be infeasible with respect to plant scheduling constraints. Integrating decision-making levels across the supply chain enhances synergy and coordination, yielding superior solutions compared to isolated approaches (Grossmann, 2005). Thus, it is essential to integrate tactical reactive decisions at a global level with in-site plant scheduling, considering production constraints.

In integration of the planning and scheduling, the difference in timescales also presents a challenge, as the plants operate at a finer time scale (e.g., an hourly time discretization) whereas the higher-level supply chain decisions are made on a daily or weekly basis. A simple solution to this is to take all decisions at the timescale of the plant operation (e.g., on an hourly basis) (Grossmann, 2005), but this might render the problem intractable for longer time horizons and larger network topologies. The literature addresses this problem by either solving the full-space monolithic model (e.g., by decomposition), using relaxed or aggregated models for scheduling, or using surrogate models to capture scheduling feasibility. Previous research using surrogates has focused on the use of SVM with linear and Radial basis function kernels for integration of scheduling in planning-level problem (Badejo and Ierapetritou, 2022) and demonstrated the use of decision trees and artificial neural networks for feasibility analysis of the scheduling problem (Dias and Ierapetritou, 2019). In this work, we employ a linear model decision tree as a surrogate model to define the feasible region of the scheduling constraints for the plant. Our approach, akin to research by the previously mentioned authors, tackles the integration of plant operations with supply chain operations. We consider disruptions and arbitrary network topologies, particularly in the context of order management, as outlined in Ovalle et al. (2023).

2. Problem Statement

Consider a supply chain and manufacturing network characterized by an arbitrary topology, meaning no assumptions are made about the structure or connections within the network. In this scenario, a disruption has occurred. We have information about the operation time horizon, the time required to traverse each connection in the network, and the capacities of both warehouses and shipments. Additionally, we have data on the selling price of the product, as well as the costs associated with purchasing materials, production, shipping, and inventory holding. Furthermore, detailed information about plant production, including batch sizes, resource utilization, and production coefficients, is available.

The objective is to determine the optimal response to the disruption. This involves creating reactive schedules for shipping, purchasing, and production throughout the entire time horizon. Additionally, it entails establishing inventory levels for each node in the system. Moreover, the obtained schedules must allow for late delivery and order cancellation while still accounting for customer satisfaction. Although the solution is given for the higher-level supply chain, the obtained operation must be feasible with regards to the detailed scheduling for every plant at every time period.

The main goal is to achieve an integrated response that optimizes the overall profit of the operation. As the time horizon concludes, the solution should provide a sense of recovery from the disruption. This recovery is defined by bringing the final inventory levels as close as possible to their pre-disruption values. The reactive operation is expected to balance the existing trade-off between stressing the system and avoiding adverse effects on the company's goodwill, which can be impacted by delayed deliveries or order cancellations. In addressing this problem, we assume that pricing remains unaffected by the specific node of transaction, transportation cost is solely contingent on the shipped quantity, and transportation capacity is sufficient to obviate the need for vehicle routing.

3. Proposed Methodology

This section provides a concise explanation of the model for the reactive operation of a supply chain under disruptions from Ovalle et al. (2023). The optimal responses derived from this model, however, lack awareness of plant-level production constraints, potentially resulting in higher-level schedules that are not always feasible. To address this, we use binary classification LMDTs surrogates to capture the feasibility space of the scheduling constraints for the plant. Hence, we investigate the efficient integration of these surrogates into the model, proposing an aggregated feature representation that significantly reduces the size of the surrogate and the computational time required for dataset generation. Additionally, a brief overview of the Resource Task Network (RTN) framework is presented, accompanied by a sample generation scheme designed to effectively capture the specified boundaries of the feasibility space.

3.1 Base Model for Reactive Supply Chain Under Disruptions

A similar model to the one proposed in Ovalle et al. (2023) that yields the optimal reaction in a disrupted network composed of suppliers (S), warehouses (W), plants (P), and customers (C) over a discretized time horizon (T) is used. The mixed-integer linear programming (MILP) formulation is given as:

$$\begin{aligned} max\ \Sigma_{t\in \mathrm{T}} \Big[& \Sigma_{c\in \mathrm{C}}\Sigma_{m\in \mathrm{M_c}}\left(\lambda^{D}_{mct}D_{mct} - \lambda^{U}_{mct}U_{mct} - \lambda^{\delta}_{mct}y_{mct}\right) - \Sigma_{a\in \mathrm{A}}\Sigma_{m\in \mathrm{M_a}}\lambda^{F}_{mat}F^{Out}_{mat} \\ & - \Sigma_{s\in \mathrm{S}}\Sigma_{m\in \mathrm{M_s}}\lambda^{B}_{mat}B_{mst} - \Sigma_{p\in \mathrm{P}}\Sigma_{r\in \mathrm{R_p}}\lambda^{P}_{prt}P_{prt} \\ & - \Sigma_{m\in \mathrm{P\cup W}}\Sigma_{m\in \mathrm{M_n}}\lambda^{I}_{mnt}I_{mnt}\Big] - \Sigma_{m\in \mathrm{P\cup W}}\Sigma_{m\in \mathrm{M_n}}\lambda^{dev}_{mn}\left|I^{0}_{mn} - I_{mn|T|}\right| \end{aligned} \tag{1a}$$

$s.t.$

$$F^{In}_{mat} = F^{Out}_{ma\{t+\tau_{mat}\}} \qquad \forall a \in A, m \in M_a, t \in T: t + \tau_{mat} \leq |T| \tag{1b}$$

$$D_{mct} = \Sigma_{a\in \mathrm{A^{In}_c}}F^{Out}_{mat} \qquad \forall c \in C, m \in M_c, t \in T \tag{1c}$$

$$B_{mst} = \Sigma_{a\in \mathrm{A^{Out}_s}}F^{In}_{mat} \qquad \forall c \in C, m \in M_s, t \in T \tag{1d}$$

$$U_{mct} = U_{mc\{t-1\}} - D_{mct} + \delta_{mct}(1 - y_{mct}) \qquad \forall c \in C, m \in M_c, t \in T \tag{1e}$$

$$I_{mwt} = I_{mw\{t-1\}} + \Sigma_{a\in \mathrm{A^{In}_W}}F^{Out}_{mat} - \Sigma_{a\in \mathrm{A^{Out}_W}}F^{In}_{mat} \qquad \forall w \in W, m \in M_w, t \in T \tag{1f}$$

$$I_{mpt} = I_{mp\{t-1\}} + \Sigma_{a\in \mathrm{A^{In}_p}}F^{Out}_{mat} - \Sigma_{a\in \mathrm{A^{Out}_p}}F^{In}_{mat} + \Sigma_{r\in R_p}\phi_{rm}P_{prt} \qquad \forall p \in P, m \in M_p, t \in T \tag{1g}$$

$$D, B, U, F^{In}, F^{Out}, P, I \geq 0 \qquad y \in \{0,1\} \qquad \text{(1f)}$$

The objective function of the model, shown in Eq. (1a), represents profit maximization accounting for the sales (λ^D) as well as the costs of shipping (λ^F), buying material (λ^B), producing (λ^P) and holding inventory (λ^I). Moreover, this objective is penalized by a late deliveries (λ^U), order cancellations (λ^δ) and deviations from the nominal inventory level at the end of the operation (λ^{dev}). Equation (1b) models the time associated with traversing an arc, where F^{in} is the flow that enters the arc and F^{Out} stands for the same flow that leaves the arc after a time displacement τ. Equations (1c) and (1d) model the acquisitions (B) and deliveries (D) respectively. Order management is handled in Equation (1e) where an order δ is only accumulated as unmet demand (U) if it is not delivered nor cancelled ($y = 0$). Equations (1f) and (1g) account for the inventory (I) balances that take place in warehouses and plants respectively. Here the main difference is that the plant balance accounts for a material transformation term calculated as the mass stoichiometric coefficient (ϕ) and the production (P). Throughout the formulation, the sets A^{in}_n and A^{out}_n stand for the set of arcs that enter or leave (respectively) a given node $n \in N$. Finally, all variables are continuous, non-negative and bounded by their respective capacities except order cancellation y, which has a binary nature ($y \in \{0,1\}$). For further explanation and demonstration of disruption capturing flexibility and time-scalability, we refer the readers to (Ovalle et al., 2023).

3.2 Integrating the Base Model with Binary Classification Linear-Model Decision Tree Surrogates of the Schedule Feasibility

In constructing our surrogate model to effectively capture the plant feasibility, we employ linear model decision trees (LMDTs), a conventional decision tree variant featuring linear functions at nodes instead of constants (Ammari et al, 2023). Specifically, we utilize binary classification LMTDs to capture the feasibility of the plant scheduling based on the higher-level flow and inventory information at a given time period. The output of the binary classification LMDT is a continuous number and zero serves as the classification threshold, meaning positive outputs are classified as feasible, while negative outputs are interpreted as infeasible scheduling scenarios.

The delineation of the feature space for the LMDT surrogate needs to accurately capture the supply chain information of a plant across time periods. A naïve approach could inform the surrogate about all the terms involved in the plant material balance as shown in Eq (1g). This is considering previous and current inventories, productions, alongside with incoming and outgoing material flows for each individual material, resulting in the incorporation of five input variables per material species into the model as:

$$DT_{pt}(I_{mpt}, I_{mp\{t-1\}}, \Sigma_{r\in R_p}\phi_{rm}P_{prt}, \Sigma_{a\in A_p^{In}}F_{mat}^{Out}, \Sigma_{a\in A_w^{Out}}F_{mat}^{In}\ \forall m \in M_p) \geq \epsilon\ \ \forall p \in P, t \in T \tag{2a}$$

where ϵ is a small positive number that is used to tune the classification threshold. However, considering the substantial number of materials, particularly when accounting for intermediate species, the aforementioned approach runs the risk of generating an impractical number of variables. This concern arises from the well-established understanding that a suitable training dataset typically expands exponentially with the increasing number of features. To tackle this challenge, the surrogate's input space is reduced to two compound variables that capture the required input spaces as shown below by aggregating higher-level information from the material balance as:

$$V_{mpt} = I_{mp\{t-1\}} + \Sigma_{a\in A_p^{In}}F_{mat}^{Out} \qquad \forall p \in P, m \in M_p, t \in T \tag{2b}$$

$$Z_{mpt} = \max\{0, \Sigma_{r\in R_p|\phi_{rm}>0}\,\phi_{rm}P_{prt} - \Sigma_{a\in A_w^{Out}}F_{mat}^{In}\} \qquad \forall p \in P, m \in M_p, t \in T \tag{2c}$$

It is worth mentioning that these are not the only ways to aggregate the terms to accurately represent a similar concept given that the mass balance depicted in Eq. (1g) is still in place. The resulting surrogate model is defined as:

$$DT_{pt}(V_{mpt}\ , Z_{mpt}\ \forall m \in M_p) \geq \epsilon\ \ \forall p \in P, t \in T \tag{2d}$$

Constraint (2d) can be embedded into the optimization model described by Eqs. (1) together with Eq. (2b) and Eq. (2c) to obtain a reactive supply chain model that includes a surrogate for feasibility in the plant-level scheduling.

3.3 Efficient Data Generation Scheme Using Resource Task Networks

We use the Resource Task Network (RTN) framework to solve scheduling problems and obtain data for the feasibility surrogate. Here, tasks represent operations (e.g., material transformation) and resources represent all the entities involved in the process steps (e.g., raw materials, intermediates, products, and equipment where tasks take place) (Pantelides, 1994). The flexibility of RTN modeling enables it to be used in different problems in a compact manner gaining wide popularity for industrial applications (Perez et al., 2022).

In constructing the feature dataset, initially various scenarios of material availability and production demand were sampled. However, a straightforward Monte Carlo sampling technique within the bounds of V and Z proved insufficient in capturing instances enforced by the plant's optimal reaction on the higher-level. To address this limitation, we observed that the higher-level flows in the system are governed by Eq. (1g), ensuring a consistent adherence to a simple mass balance for internal supply and demand within the plant. Consequently, we narrowed the sampling space by imposing this condition on all samples. Additionally, recognizing that production costs outweigh inventory holding costs, plants often fulfill internal demand using existing inventory rather than production. Consequently, the demanded production frequently equals zero. To better represent this scenario, with probability $\alpha = 0.3$ we enforced $Z = 0$ for all materials, enhancing the dataset's ability to capture this particular region effectively.

After constructing the feature dataset, we proceeded to solve an RTN scheduling model for each instance, recording feasibility as a binary label indicating whether under those internal demand and supplies the rigorous schedule was viable or not. The open-source package `rtn_scheduling` was used to efficiently generate RTN models directly from data files on a reliable manner (Vyas et al., 2023).

4. Case Study and Results

To evaluate the proposed methodology, we employ a 24-node arbitrary supply chain topology (Figure 1) with two plants. The first plant addresses both internal and external demand for a total of four materials, while the second plant manages six materials. We evaluate the reactive schedule in response to an arc disruption limiting direct shipments between the plants. The task is to determine the optimal response over the next four months with daily time discretization.

Pyomo was utilized to construct the reactive supply chain model, while the training of the binary classification LMDT surrogate was performed using the linear-tree open-source package. Efficient integration into an equation-oriented approach was achieved through OMLT (Ceccon et al., 2022). The resultant MILP problem was solved using Gurobi v9.5.1 as the solver, executed on a Linux machine equipped with 8 Intel Xeon Gold 6234 CPUs running at 3.30 GHz, boasting 8 total hardware threads, and 1 TB of RAM operating within the Ubuntu environment.

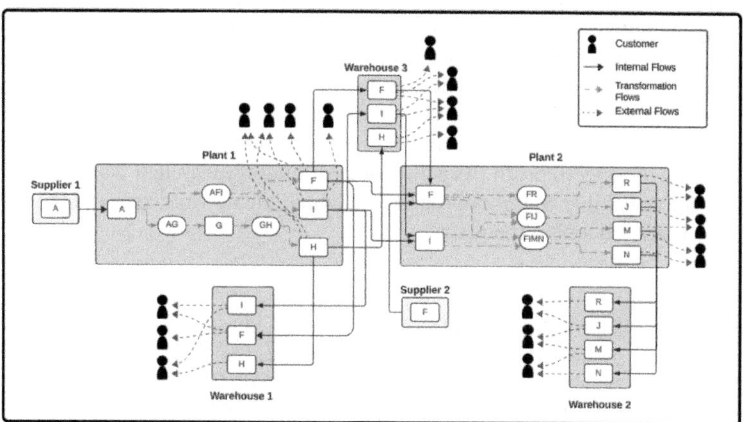

Figure 1: Case study supply chain and manufacturing network topology

We solve the reactive supply chain model outlined in Section 3.1, denoted as the Original Model, and further solve the identical model after the integration of LMDT feasibility surrogates for each plant and time period. This extended model is referred to as the Integrated Model and the results of these computational experiments are presented in Table 1.

Table 1: Result comparison before and after surrogate integration

	Objective [$]	Solution Time [s]	No. of Periods with Infeasible Schedule	No. Variables / No. Constraints
Original Model	9,338,083	0.16	5	25,590 / 17,115
Integrated Model	9,335,894	8.13	0	31,430 / 32,615

Table 1 reveals that over the course of 120 days of reactive operation, the Original Model prompted the plants to operate under infeasible conditions on five distinct occasions. In contrast, the model incorporating embedded surrogates exhibited 100% feasibility throughout the operational horizon. Notably, the feasibility was validated by solving the rigorous RTN model for each period and plant based on the solution from the models Hence, it can be observed that the proposed extension ensures the robustness and reliability of the schedule feasibility within the existent reactive supply chain optimization framework.

The revised operation, incorporating plant feasibility considerations, results in only a marginal 0.02% reduction in operational profit, demonstrating that operational viability can be ensured without significant sacrifice to overall profitability. It is noteworthy that the inclusion of surrogates increases the solution time by an order of magnitude, given an approximate increment of 22.8% in variables and 90.6% in constraints with respect to the original model. However, the full monolithic model, which rigorously integrates RTN scheduling with responsive supply chain operations on an hourly basis, presents an impractical scale with 682,482 variables and 544,275 constraints, representing an order of magnitude increase compared to the original and integrated models, making it intractable to solve. Therefore, despite the increased computational time, the proposed model with integrated surrogates remains a viable solution for an integrative reactive supply chain with plant-level scheduling.

5. Conclusions

This study enhances an existing reactive model designed for supply chain and manufacturing networks with arbitrary topologies, capable of handling disruptions. We integrated linear model decision tree surrogates to define the feasibility space associated with plant scheduling constraints. The efficacy of this integration has been demonstrated, showcasing a notable enhancement to the existing reactive model. The result yielded a feasible operation throughout all time periods in both plants, without significantly compromising the overall profit. As a direction for future research, it would be interesting to explore the scalability of this approach concerning the network size and the number of materials considered within the plants.

References

Ammari B. L., Johnson E. S., Stinchfield G., Kim T., Bynum M., Hart W. E., Pulsipher J. and Laird C. D., "Linear Model Decision Trees as Surrogates in Optimization of Engineering Applications." Computers & Chemical Engineering, vol. 178, Oct. 2023, p. 108347.

Badejo O. and Ierapetritou M., "Integrating Tactical Planning, Operational Planning and Scheduling Using Data-Driven Feasibility Analysis." Computers & Chemical Engineering, vol. 161, May 2022, p. 107759. ScienceDirect, https://doi.org/10.1016/j.compchemeng.2022.107759.

Ceccon F., Jalving J., Haddad J., Thebelt A., Tsay C., Laird C. D. and Misener R., "OMLT: Optimization machine learning toolkit," Journal of Machine Learning Research, vol. 23, no. 349, pp. 1-8, 2022 https://doi.org/10.48550/arXiv.2202.02414

Dias L. S. and Ierapetritou M. G., "Data-Driven Feasibility Analysis for the Integration of Planning and Scheduling Problems." Optimization and Engineering, vol. 20, no. 4, Dec. 2019, pp. 1029–66, https://doi.org/10.1007/s11081-019-09459-w

Grossmann I., "Enterprise-wide Optimization: A New Frontier in Process Systems Engineering." AIChE Journal, vol. 51, no. 7, July 2005, pp. 1846–57. DOI.org, ttps://doi.org/10.1002/aic.10617

Ovalle D., Ye Y., Harshbarger K., Bury S., Wassick J. M., Laird C. D. and Grossmann I. E., "Operation optimization of supply chain networks under disruptions in Proceedings of FOCAPO/CPC, 2023

Pantelides C. C., "Unified frameworks for optimal process planning and scheduling," in Proceedings of FOCAPO2 ,1994, pp.253-274

Perez H. D., Amaran S., Iyer S. S., Wassick J. M. and Grossmann I. E., "Applications of the RTN Scheduling Model in the Chemical Industry." Simulation and Optimization in Process Engineering, 2022, pp.365-400, http://dx.doi.org/10.1016/B978-0-323-85043-8.00006-4

Snyder L. V., Atan Z., Peng P., Rong Y., Schmitt A. J. and Sinsoysal B., "OR/MS models for supply chain disruptions: A review," IIE Transactions, vol. 48, no. 2, pp. 89–109, 2016

Vyas J., Ovalle D. and Laird C., "rtn_scheduling." [Online]. Available: https://github.com/JavalVyas2000/rtn_scheduling

Flavio Manenti, Gintaras V. Reklaitis (Eds.), Proceedings of the 34th European Symposium on Computer Aided Process Engineering / 15th International Symposium on Process Systems Engineering (ESCAPE34/PSE24), June 2-6, 2024, Florence, Italy
 http://dx.doi.org/10.1016/B978-0-443-28824-1.50250-7

Sustainability assessment of direct air capture and utilization processes at early-stage

Wonsuk Chung[a], Hyunyoung Kim[a], Ung Lee[a]

[a]*Korea Institute of Science and Technology, Hwarang-ro 14-gil 5, Seongbuk-gu, Seoul, 02792, South Korea*

ulee@kist.re.kr

Abstract

Direct air capture and utilization (DACU) which captures CO_2 from the atmosphere and convert it into chemicals can be a route to ultimate carbon neutrality as it can mitigate atmospheric CO_2 level directly. It is challenging to achieve reasonable CO_2 avoidance cost and studies have been conducted to develop new DACU technologies, yet all the technologies remain at early-stage. The purpose of this work is to discuss the development and assessment of early-stage technologies such as DACU, considering expansion of the lab-scale technologies into the process levels and how pertinent assumptions should be considered by each technology. Temperature-vacuum swing adsorption (TVSA) process combined with electrochemical CO_2 utilization into ethylene is an illustrating example. We hope to inspire worldwide researchers in both process system engineering field and technology development field who develop and design early-stage technologies and processes.

Keywords: direct carbon capture and utilization, early-stage evaluation, uncertainty assessment

1. Introduction

Mitigation of atmospheric CO_2 level is an urgent task to slower global climate change within 1.5°C (IPCC, 2021). It is regarded that the ultimate solution is direct air capture and utilization (DACU) which captures CO_2 from air directly and convert it to chemicals. Advantage of DACU then carbon sequestration is potential profitability through sales of the product; however, the major obstacle is high energy consumption of the process. Though many technologies for DACU have been proposed, including chemical absorption, temperature vacuum swing adsorption (TVSA), and membrane separation, great efforts should be required to reduce their immense capture energy (Sabatino et al, 2021). In carbon utilization field, relatively mature technologies such as CO_2 hydrogenation to methanol (Ushikoshi et al., 2000) is developed, and new technologies have been studied to synthesize high-valued chemicals (e. g. ethylene) (Liu et al., 2022).

One of the most important tasks is evaluation and identification of promising DACU technologies in terms of economics and carbon mitigation. Evaluation of such early-stage technologies is different from that of fully mature technologies due to the uncertain performances. Most of the technology-relevant factors in junction with the process evaluation results (CO_2 capture/conversion rate, energy consumption, and capital expenditure) carries uncertainties due to the technology immaturity, and adoption of renewable energy also puts uncertainties originated from site and weather dependency (Chung et al, 2022; Sendi et al, 2022). All the available data for the technologies are knowledge-based and lab-scale experimental results. Hence, uncertainty assessment with pertinent assumptions is the key for evaluation of DACU technologies (Roh et al, 2020).

In this work, an early-stage evaluation of DACU process which captures CO_2 by TVSA and synthesize ethylene by electrochemical CO_2 reduction (ECO_2R) is suggested. The case study evaluates both economics and carbon mitigation potential. All the endogenous and exogenous uncertainties are quantified for uncertainty assessment, and how the process performance can be improved is further discussed. We expect that this work can be a guideline for early-stage evaluation of immature technologies.

2. System description

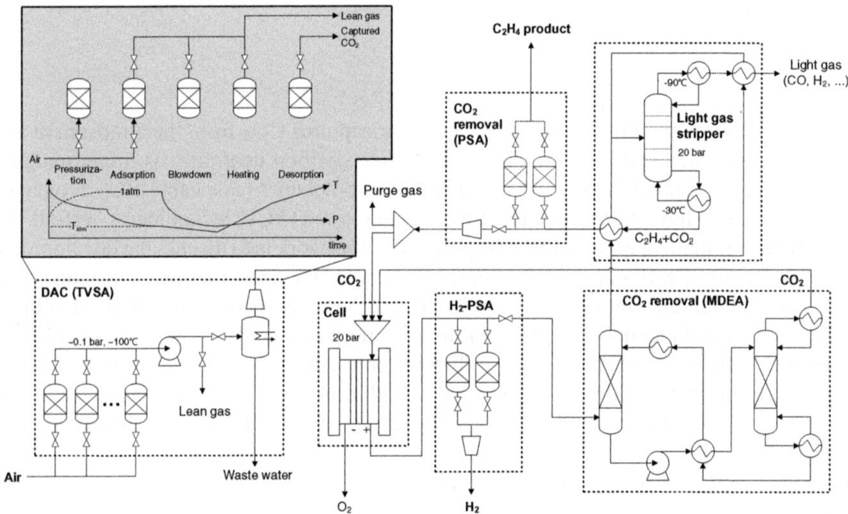

Figure 1. Process flow diagram of DACU process.

2.1. Temperature vacuum swing adsorption (TVSA) process

Overall process flow diagram of the DACU process is in Figure 1. CO_2 is captured by amine-functionalized polymer in TVSA fashion. Mechanism of CO_2 capture is chemisorption as carbamate formation onto amine functional group; hance, CO_2 uptake is affected by not only atmospheric CO_2 level and temperature but also moisture. This water-aided co-adsorption model of CO_2 (weighted average dual-site isotherm) is proposed by Young et al. (2021). N_2 is rarely adsorbed by the adsorbent.

The TVSA process consists of five steps: (1) the empty column below atmospheric pressure is filled by air in pressurization step, (2) air flows in the bed until CO_2 and H_2O is fully adsorbed, (3) vacuum pump is operated to reach 0.1 bar to discard N_2 in the bed, (4) thermal energy is supplied to the bed in the heating step, and (5) CO_2 and H_2O is desorbed. The product gas is cooled down to eliminate H_2O and high purity (>99%) CO_2 can be obtained. The electric work for vacuum pump and the thermal heating to 100°C is the main energy requirements. The dynamic process is modeled as ordinary differential equation in MATLAB. It is assumed that thermal energy is supplied by adopting heat pump which uses electric work, as suggested by Deutz and Bardow (2021).

2.2. Electrochemical CO_2 reduction (ECO_2R) process for ethylene synthesis

In the electrolyzer, Faradaic efficiency (FE) is the key factor in terms of both productivity and energy consumption as Eq. (1).

Table 1. Uncertain parameters for DACU process.

	Min	Base case	Max
Electricity price (\$/GJ)	10.3	14.7[a]	19.1
TVSA			
Air temperature (°C)	0	15	30
Relative humidity	20%	50%	80%
Heat of CO_2 adsorption	80%	100%[b]	120%
Heat of H_2O adsorption	90%	100%[b]	110%
Adsorbent price (\$/kg)	0.5	1	2
Adsorption time (hr)	2	4[b]	8
Adsorbent lifetime (yr)	10	20	30
ECO_2R			
CO_2 conversion	20%	50%	80%
C_2H_4 Faradaic efficiency	20%	50%	80%
Cell voltage efficiency	40%	60%	80%
Current density (mA cm^{-2})	200	300	400
Cell price (\$ m^{-2})	1,000	2,000	3,000

a (IRENA, 2019), b (Young et al., 2021)

$$FE_i = \frac{z_i CD_i}{\sum_j z_j CD_j} \quad (1)$$

where i is half-reaction, z is number of electrons in the reaction, and CD is current density. As multiple CO_2 reduction reactions and hydrogen evolution reaction competes in cathode, H_2 and CO is commonly synthesized as byproduct in addition to C_2H_4. Faradaic efficiency of C_2H_4 can be 50% and 80% in future (Liu et al., 2022).

As CO_2 conversion in cathode is not reaching 100%, gas product is mixture of C_2H_4, CO_2, CO, and H_2. As C_2H_4 and CO_2 forms an azeotrope (Haselden et al., 1951), it is challenging to synthesize the downstream gas separation process. Herein, we introduced pressure swing adsorption (PSA) to capture H_2 and remove CO_2, methyldiethanolamine (MDEA) based carbon capture process to recover unreacted CO_2, and cryogenic stripper to discard light gases (mainly CO) (Figure 1). It is possible to separate C_2H_4 and H_2 with high purity (>99%); however, light gas contains impurities and it is sent to the combustion chamber to generate electricity. O_2 from anode is not regarded as product as CO_2 is mixed to O_2 due to crossover issue.

2.3. Early-stage evaluation

As the process is on early-stage, many of the parameters carry uncertainties. Hence, the base case is first generated for prior evaluation and sensitivity analysis on the parameters are conducted. The uncertain parameters can be categorized in to exogenous parameters (electricity price, air temperature, and relative humidity) and endogenous parameters (adsorbent property and cell performance). Minimum and maximum values of the parameters are set as Table 1.

Techno-economic assessment (TEA) and CO_2 life-cycle assessment (LCA) is conducted by changing the parameter values. Energy analysis is also the important for energy-intensive DACU process. Equivalent work (W_{eq}) is widely introduced to conduct exergy analysis: equivalent work of electric energy consumption is identical to the electric energy; for thermal energy consumption,

Table 2. Mass and energy balance of the base case DACU process. All the units are specific values for 1 ton of captured CO_2.

	TVSA	ECO_2R	Total
Total production rate (ton)			
C_2H_4	-	0.0920	
H_2	-	0.0147	
Total equivalent work (GJ_{eq})	3.74	13.57	17.31
Heating (GJ)	8.15	2.47	10.62
Heating (GJ_{eq})	2.65	0.80	3.45
Electric work for capture/utilization	1.08	12.60	13.68
Electric work for compression/separation	0.35	1.96	2.31
Electricity generation by waste-gas combustion	-	-1.72	-1.72

$$W_{eq} = \frac{1}{\eta}\left(1 - \frac{T_{atm}}{T_h}\right) \quad (1)$$

where T_{atm} and T_h are atmospheric and heated temperature, respectively; η is cycle efficiency (due to pump or compression loss).

3. Results and discussion

3.1. Base case

In the base case, assuming Faradaic efficiency of C_2H_4, CO, and H_2 are 50%, 20%, and 30%, 0.092 ton and 0.0147 ton of ethylene and hydrogen are produced from one ton of CO_2 captured, respectively (Table 2). The equivalent work of the TVSA process is 3.74 GJ_{eq}/ton CO_2, considering both thermal energy and work done by vacuum pump and compressor. It is thought that solid sorbent DAC process can achieve 3 GJ_{eq}/ton CO_2 (Sabatino et al., 2021; Young et al., 2021), indicating that this TVSA process is near its optimum. In ECO_2R process, a great amount of electricity is used to evolve CO_2 reduction reaction, and additional separation energies are consumed in the separation processes (electric work: H_2-PSA, CO_2-PSA, and light-gas stripper; heating: MDEA). In total, 17.31 GJ_{eq}/ton CO_2 is consumed.

Table 3. Evaluation results of the base case DACU process. All the units are specific values for 1 ton of captured CO_2.

	TVSA	ECO_2R	Total
Total installation cost ($)	563	856	1,419
Annualized installation cost ($ yr^{-1})	28.2	42.8	71.0
Annualized utility cost ($ yr^{-1})	55.0	199.5	254.5
Annualized maintenance cost ($ yr^{-1})	92.8	158.3	251.1
Overhead & general expenses ($ yr^{-1})	16.9	29.6	46.5
Total production cost ($ yr^{-1})	192.8	430.3	623.1
Direct CO_2 emission (t_{CO2})	-1	0.711	-0.289
Indirect CO_2 emission (t_{CO2eq})	0.011	0.041	0.052
Net CO_2 emission (t_{CO2eq})	-0.989	0.752	-0.237
Reference CO_2 emission (t_{CO2eq})	-	0.504	0.504
Avoided CO_2 (t_{CO2eq})			0.741

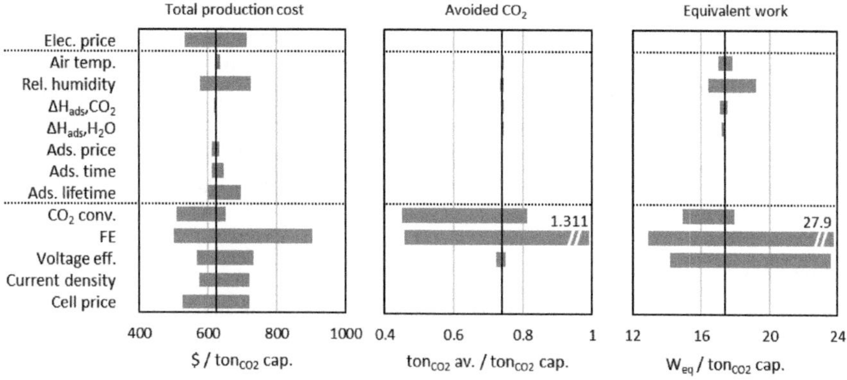

Figure 2. Sensitivity analysis results of the DACU process.

TEA and LCA results are summarized in Table 3. Notably, contribution of the capital expenditure to the total cost exceeds that of the utility cost for both TVSA and ECO_2R process. Though quite large amount of direct CO_2 emission exists as lean gas, the overall process is CO_2-reducing.

3.2. Sensitivity analysis

Sensitivity analysis is conducted for the uncertain parameters in Table 1, and the result is in Figure 2. In TVSA process, the most sensitive parameter is relative humidity. This is because the process captures ambient moisture in addition to CO_2, and the amount of both CO_2 and H_2O depends on the relative humidity.

In ECO_2R, CO_2 conversion and Faradaic efficiency are the most important factors especially for the avoided CO_2. If CO_2 conversion decreases, the CO_2 capture load in MDEA process increases greatly, resulting in decreasing CO_2 avoidance. As CO is assumed to be discarded after combustion, Faradaic efficiency of CO should be decreased. In the actual electrolyzer, current density, voltage efficiency, and Faradaic efficiencies of each reaction are linked together. Their relationships, known as Butler-Volmer equation, should be predicted by 2D-modelling considering charge transfer between cathode/anode and charge density in electrolyte, which can be complicated and time-consuming.

4. Conclusion and perspective

In this work, direct air capture and utilization (DACU) process which captures CO_2 by temperature-vacuum swing adsorption (TVSA) and utilizes it by electrochemical CO_2 reduction to ethylene is designed and evaluated. As both TVSA and ECO_2R remains on early-stage, pertinent assumptions based on literature survey are made for the base case values and the ranges on the uncertain parameters (e. g. heat of adsorption, Faradaic efficiency, CO_2 conversion). In order to separate ethylene from gas mixture, a separation process which adopts several mature separation technologies are synthesized. Techno-economic analysis and CO_2 life-cycle assessment indicate that this TVSA-ECO_2R process is sustainable in terms of CO_2 reduction. Sensitivity analysis results indicate that relative humidity can be a critical issue on the capture energy and the electrolyzer performance is the key to improve CO_2 reduction and economics.

The most important aspect in early-stage evaluation is quantification of uncertainties for the technology immaturities of which values should be plausible. This TVSA-ECO_2R process is an example of DACU process, and any other DACU process can be evaluated in this approach. As all DACU processes are on early-stage, it is also meaningful to evaluate multiple DACU pathways at once by superstructure approach, as similar to works done by Na et al. (2019) and Chung et al. (2020). We believe that this work can contribute to both evaluation of single DACU process and drawing an outlook of entire DACU.

References

W. Chung, H. Lim, J. Lee, A. Al-Hunaidy, H. Imran, A. Jamal, K. Roh, and J. Lee, Computer-aided identification and evaluation of technologies for sustainable carbon capture and utilization using a superstructure approach, *Journal of CO_2 Utilization* 61, 102032.

S. Deutz and A. Bardow, 2021, Life-cycle assessment of an industrial direct air capture process based on temperature–vacuum swing adsorption, *Nature Energy* 6, 203-213.

G. Haselden, D. Newitt, F. Shah, and S. Shah, Two-phase equilibrium in binary and ternary systems: V. Carbon dioxide-ethylene, VI. Carbon-dioxide-propylene, *Proceedings of the Royan Society A*, 209, 1096.

IPCC, 2021, Climate Change 2021: The Physical Science Basis.

IRENA, 2019, Renewable energy statistics.

W. Liu, P. Zhai, A. Li, K. Si, Y. Wei, X. Wang, G. Zhu, Q, Chen, X. Gu, R. Zhang, W. Zhou, and Y. Gong, Electrochemical CO_2 reduction to ethylene by ultrathin CuO nanoplate arrays, *Nature Communications* 13, 1877.

J. Na, B. Seo, J. Kim, C. Lee, H. Lee, Y. Hwang, B. Min, D. Lee, H. Oh, and U. Lee, 2019, General technoeconomic analysis for electrochemical coproduction coupling carbon dioxide reduction with organic oxidation, *Nature Communications* 10, 5193.

K. Roh, A. Bardow, D. Bongartz, J. Burre, W. Chung, S. Deutz, D. Han, M. Hesselmann, Y. Kohlhaas, A. Konig, J. Lee, R. Meys, S. Volker, M. Wessling, J. Lee, and A. Mitsos, 2020, Early-stage evaluation of emerging CO_2 utilization technologies at low technology readiness levels, *Green Chemistry* 22, 3842-3859.

F. Sabatino, A. Grimm, F. Gallucci, M. Annaland and G. Kramer, 2021, A comparative energy and cost assessment and optimization for direct air capture technologies, *Joule* 5, 2047-2076.

M. Sendi, M. Bui, N. McDowell, and P. Fennell, 2022, Geospatial analysis of regional climate impacts to accelerate cost-efficient direct air capture deployment, *One Earth* 5, 1153-1164.

K. Ushikoshi, K. Mori, T. Kubota, T. Watanabe, and M. Saito, 2000, Methanol synthesis from CO_2 and H_2 in a bench-scale test plant, *Applied Organometallic Chemistry* 14, 819-825.

J. Young, E. Garcia-Diez, S. Garcia, and M. van der Spek, 2021, The impact of binary water–CO_2 isotherm models on the optimal performance of sorbent-based direct air capture processes, *Energy and Environtal Science*, 14, 5377.

Flavio Manenti, Gintaras V. Reklaitis (Eds.), Proceedings of the 34th European Symposium on Computer Aided Process Engineering / 15th International Symposium on Process Systems Engineering (ESCAPE34/PSE24), June 2-6, 2024, Florence, Italy
 http://dx.doi.org/10.1016/B978-0-443-28824-1.50251-9

Optimization with Uncertainty for Pharmaceutical Process Design – Ibuprofen Synthesis as case study

Tuse Asrav, Merlin Alvarado-Morales, Gürkan Sin

Process and Systems Engineering Center (PROSYS), Department of Chemical and Biochemical Engineering, Technical University of Denmark (DTU), 2800, Kgs. Lyngby/Denmark

tusas@kt.dtu.dk

Abstract

By intensifying the manufacturing processes of active pharmaceutical ingredients, there is potential for enhanced productivity and efficiency. This approach may also contribute to a reduction in environmental impact and result in savings from both energy and cost. In this contribution, optimum operational conditions that maximize the concentration of 1-(4-isobutylphenyl)-ethanol (IBPE), which is an intermediate product for the synthesis of ibuprofen, are studied. The results from deterministic and stochastic optimization techniques are performed and discussed. Since the uncertainties are present in the process/kinetics models, we account for the uncertainties in assessing the robustness of the proposed solution. To this end, MOSKopt stochastic simulation-based optimization framework is used to deal with uncertain parameters in the constraints. The optimization under uncertainty yields different operational conditions with roughly 10 grams less of product in the batch. This optimization with uncertainty approach provides the engineer with the flexibility to generate and test robust design concepts as a trade-off between objective function (such as high yield) and confidence in the expected performance.

Keywords: Optimization under uncertainty, simulation-based optimization, Monte Carlo simulations, ibuprofen manufacturing

1. Introduction

Awareness surrounding the environmental impact of drug development is continuously growing, which leads manufacturers toward finding greener and more sustainable synthesis methods (Gernaey et al., 2012). In addition to environmental considerations, the increase in costs of creating new pharmaceutical ingredients is another challenge that the pharmaceutical industry is facing. Therefore, it is relevant to study if the existing synthesis methods are both cost-effective and environmentally friendly and can be carried out using methods and tools from the Process Systems Engineering (PSE) domain. Additionally, evaluating the operating conditions and identifying the influential variables or parameters could lead to improvements in achieving process objectives and implementing more advanced control strategies.

There are many studies about the synthesis of one of the widely used active pharmaceutical ingredients, namely ibuprofen. While some of these studies show that continuous manufacturing production is feasible (Jolliffe et al., 2016), however, a significant portion of the industry continues to depend on Hoechst batch production. For

some of the production steps, the reaction kinetics and the data could be found in the literature based on the experiments (Thakar et al., 2007). Montes et al. (2018), proposed a dynamic simulation model to study plantwide dynamics and operation including propagation of disturbances in the production of ibuprofen.
In this work, the aim is to study the feasibility of applying simulation-based optimization methods to explore the optimal operating conditions for the hydrogenation step of the ibuprofen synthesis while considering the uncertainties in the parameters. Given that parameters are derived through parameter estimation methods that may not yield precise outcomes, the uncertainties associated with the parameters should be considered to achieve greater robustness.

For the scope of the work, the optimization of the operating conditions is conducted through three different optimization approaches. As the initial approach, the optimization problem is formulated deterministically as a constrained nonlinear problem and solved using an interior-point algorithm implemented in Matlab by running fmincon solver in parallel from multiple start points. A simulation-based optimization with and without uncertainties is used for the other approaches. To this end, MOSKopt optimization framework is used, which employs a surrogate-based modeling approach to deal with uncertainties as described in Al et al. (2020).

2. Methodology

2.1. Simulation-based optimization: MOSKopt

MOSKopt, a stochastic simulation-based optimization framework, allows for solving constrained complex optimization problems. For efficient exploration of design space, surrogate models are employed which are created based on an initial set of design space using Latin hypercube sampling, and iteratively enhanced with additional samples based on infill criteria. The infill criterion is selected as multiple constrained feasibility enhanced expected improvement in this work since it separately considers the probability of feasibility for each stochastic constraint while simultaneously seeking enhancements in the objective value (Al et al., 2020). Stochastic Kriging model is used as a surrogate model because of the ability to handle intrinsic and extrinsic types of uncertainties of stochastic simulations by introducing an additional noise model (Ankenman et al., 2010).

2.1.1. Monte Carlo uncertainty simulations

Monte Carlo method is widely used to estimate the numerical outcomes of uncertain processes by employing random sampling strategies. Accordingly, Monte Carlo simulations can be integrated into the MOSKopt framework to account for uncertainties while searching for an optimal combination of design and operational decisions. The objective and constraints of the optimization problem can be calculated for each design sample considering the uncertainty scenarios provided by Monte Carlo simulations. To find the optimal design points in the design space, hedging strategies are used against uncertainties (Al et al., 2020). The selected hedging strategy for this work involves keeping the mean plus one standard deviation of constraint observations from Monte Carlo simulations below the constraint limit. This strategy of using mean plus sigma in the objective function is useful as it accounts for both average performance and the associated risk or variability into the decision-making process. Hence the resulting decision variables will be more robust against not only the most expected outcome but a wider range of outcomes (Wang and Ierapetritou, 2018).

3. Application to Ibuprofen Synthesis

3.1. Upstream Processes

In this work, ibuprofen is produced following the Hoescht synthesis pathway involving three main reaction steps: Friedel-Crafts acetylation, hydrogenation, and carbonylation (Elango et al., 1991). Since no data is available in the literature for the Friedel-Crafts acetylation, the initial reactant is assumed to be the product of the acetylation reaction, 4-isobutyl acetophenone (IBAP). Therefore, the synthesis begins with the reaction of IBAP to produce 1-(4-isobutylphenyl)-ethanol (IBPE) followed by a catalytic carbonylation of resulting IBPE to form ibuprofen along with byproducts. Given the significant influence of catalytic hydrogenation on the final products and its occurrence in the early stages, this work aims to determine the optimum process conditions for the hydrogenation step.

3.1.1. Hydrogenation

The reactions occurring during the hydrogenation step are shown in Figure 1.

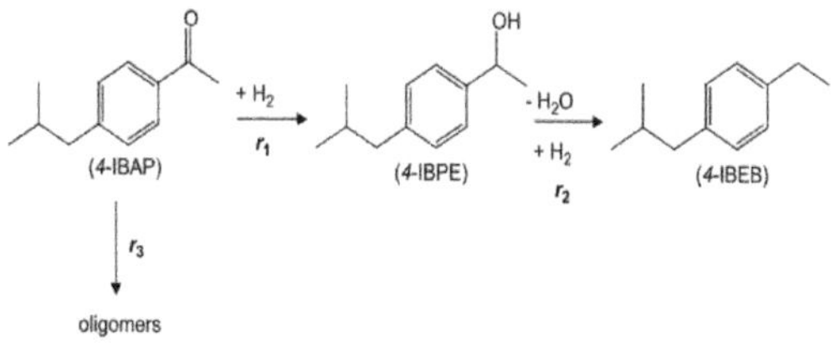

(4-IBAP) $\xrightarrow[r_1]{+H_2}$ (4-IBPE) $\xrightarrow[+H_2 \; r_2]{-H_2O}$ (4-IBEB)

(4-IBAP) $\xrightarrow{r_3}$ oligomers

Figure 1. Reactions during hydrogenation of IBAP over Pd/SiO_2 (Thakar et al., 2007).

Hydrogenation of IBAP to IBPE is the desired reaction while simultaneously occurring oligomerization because of the deactivation of the catalytic activity is the side reaction and hydrogenolysis of IBPE to IBEB is the undesired consecutive reaction.

The kinetic model ordinary differential equations in terms of concentrations for the hydrogenation of IBAP into 1-(4-isobutylphenyl)-ethanol (IBPE) over Pd/SiO_2 catalyst are taken from Thakar et al. (2007), assuming batch process occurring in a perfectly mixed batch reactor at isothermal conditions. The reaction rates are expressed as follows:

$$r_1 = \frac{C_{cat} a k_1 C_{IBAP} P_{H_2}}{(1 + K_{IBAP} C_{IBAP} + \sqrt{K_H P_{H_2}} + K_{H_2O} C_{H_2O})^2} \tag{1}$$

$$r_2 = \frac{C_{cat} a k_2 C_{IBPE} P_{H_2}}{\left(1 + K_{IBAP} C_{IBAP} + \sqrt{K_H P_{H_2}} + K_{H_2O} C_{H_2O}\right)^2} \tag{2}$$

$$r_3 = \frac{C_{cat} a k_3 C_{IBAP}^2}{\left(1 + K_{IBAP} C_{IBAP} + \sqrt{K_H P_{H_2}} + K_{H_2O} C_{H_2O}\right)^2} \tag{3}$$

Where a accounts for the loss of catalytic activity due to oligomerization.

The rate and equilibrium constants are reparametrized considering the dependence of temperature as follows:

$$k_{i(T)} = k_{i(T_0)} exp\left(-\frac{E_A}{R}\left(\frac{1}{T} - \frac{1}{T_0}\right)\right) \tag{4}$$

The parameters are taken based on the results of the parameter estimation of Thakar et al. (2007). Optimization without uncertainty is made by using the mean values of the parameters and optimization with uncertainty is made by using uncertainty space of the parameters considering their 95% confidence intervals. The uncertain parameters and their 95% confidence intervals when temperature is 373 K are given in Table 1.

Table 1. Estimated values of uncertain parameters and their 95% confidence intervals.

Rate constants	k_1 ($L/g_{cat}atm.s$)	1.14±0.25
	k_2 ($L/g_{cat}atm.s$)	0.095±0.02
	k_3 ($L^2/g_{cat}atm.s$)	0.024±0.004
Adsorption constants	K_{IBAP} (L/mol)	76.4±23.7
	K_{H2O} (L/mol)	529±106
Activation energies	Ea_1 (kJ/mol)	102±15
	Ea_2 (kJ/mol)	105±14
	Ea_3 (kJ/mol)	117±15

4. Results and Discussion

The optimization problem is defined to maximize IBPE concentration in the catalytic hydrogenation reaction, with IBPE yield calculated relative to initial IBAP concentration, by optimizing the temperature, hydrogen partial pressure, catalyst concentration, and residence time. Increasing the partial pressure of hydrogen can increase the yield of IBPE if the hydrogenation is more favorable than catalyst deactivation until the hydrogenolysis of IBPE to IBEB becomes favored. Beyond this point, increasing pressure may contribute to the undesired consecutive reaction. On the other hand, lower pressure may favor catalyst deactivation which allows a slower decrease of IBPE to form an undesired product which is also affected by the catalyst amount. Therefore, optimizing these decision variables is crucial for achieving the maximum yield of IBPE because of the tradeoffs inherent in the process.

Thakar et al. (2007) investigated the reaction kinetics of hydrogenation at various temperatures, hydrogen partial pressures, and catalyst concentrations, ranging from 333 to 373 K, 10 to 40 bar, and 0.26 to 0.78 g/L respectively. Consequently, in this work, the decision variable limits are selected based on these specified ranges. Additionally, the lower and upper bounds for the residence time are set at 10 and 60 minutes, respectively. The volume of the hydrogenation batch reactor is taken as 185 L and the initial concentration of IBPA is taken as 0.27 mol/L aiming to obtain approximately 7 kg per batch of IBPE.

Three different optimization procedures are applied in this work. The mean values of the parameters from the parameter estimations results are used for the deterministic solvers. On the other hand, using the mean and the standard deviation of the parameters, it is assumed that the uncertainties follow multivariate random normal distribution and employed for sampling for the stochastic solver. The maximum number of iterations for the optimization task is set to 150 for each MOSKopt algorithm. To account for the influence of the uncertainties on objective and constraints, 250 Monte Carlo simulations are performed for each iteration.

The optimal objective values along with the values of decision variables at the optimal for three different optimization approaches are given in Table 2.

Table 2. Optimization results.

	Decision variable	Lower bound	Upper bound	Optimal values	Best obj. (mol/L)
Interior-point algorithm	Temperature (K)	333	373	333	0.2192
	H_2 partial pressure (bar)	10	40	19.93	
	Catalyst amount (g)	48.1	144.3	58.95	
	Residence time (min)	10	60	32.06	
MOSKopt deterministic	Temperature (K)	333	373	333	0.2192
	H_2 partial pressure (bar)	10	40	14.36	
	Catalyst amount (g)	48.1	144.3	77.39	
	Residence time (min)	10	60	26.11	
MOSKopt with uncertainties	Temperature (K)	333	373	333	0.2189
	H_2 partial pressure (bar)	10	40	31.77	
	Catalyst amount (g)	48.1	144.3	88.59	
	Residence time (min)	10	60	17.5	

The ideal residence time is significantly influenced by catalyst concentration. If the catalyst concentration is low, it takes more time to reach the maximum yield and therefore more time to complete the production batch. On the other hand, for higher catalyst concentrations, the residence time becomes smaller causing a slight reduction in the yield of product. (Thakar et al., 2007). The tradeoff between the catalyst amount and residence time as explained above can be observed from the optimization results.

From Table 2, there are three competing design candidates. Multiple running of a local nonlinear programming solver with interior-point algorithm and MOSKopt using deterministic approach provided the same optimal objective value, albeit with different values for the decision variables. MOSKopt including uncertainties provided slightly lower objective value, approximately 10 g less desired product produced per batch volume of 185 L. Since the latter accounts for a range of likely outcomes, due to uncertainties inherent in the process, the provided solutions are considered more robust to the uncertainties considered.

Selectivity dynamics, illustrated in Figure 2 using optimal values of the temperature, hydrogen partial pressure and catalyst amount reveal an increase up to optimal residence time and decrease beyond this point, emphasizing the importance of optimizing residence time for desired selectivity. The influence of the uncertainties can also be observed from Figure 2.

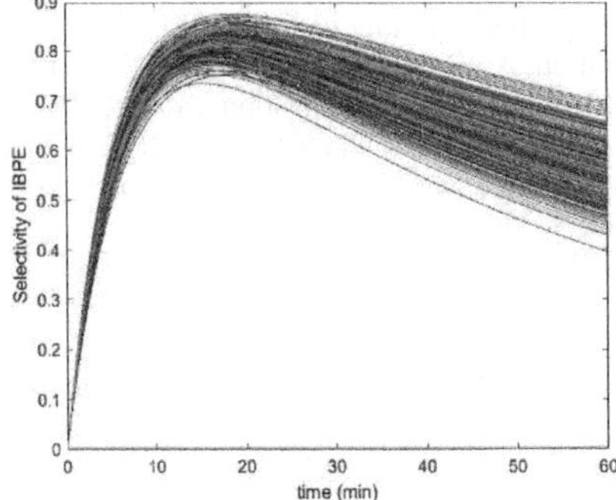

Figure 2. Selectivity of IBPE.

From a production capacity point of view, small residence time is preferred, however, it comes with the expense of increased production cost with a higher catalyst amount. A multi-objective optimization accounting for different priorities in the operation can be formulated to address this tradeoff. To this end, this study will be complemented with techno-economic metrics as well as sustainability to generate a holistic view of the process design.

5. Conclusions and Future Work

The study optimizes the hydrogenation step in ibuprofen synthesis, focusing on maximizing the yield of IBPE. Three optimization approaches: constrained nonlinear programming solver with the interior-point algorithm, and MOSKopt framework without and with the inclusion of uncertainties are employed. The uncertainties in the rate and adsorption constants and activation energies derived from experimental data are accounted for to assess the robustness of the optimization results. Considering their great influence on the reaction kinetics, incorporating uncertainties provides a more comprehensive understanding. It is observed that accounting for the uncertainties leads to variations in the optimal operating conditions causing a slight decrease in the objective value as expected since the variations of the performance are also accounted for in addition to the expected performance. Optimization with uncertainty favors faster batch completion but incurs higher production costs. To navigate the tradeoff, a multi-objective optimization approach can be developed encompassing perspectives from both techno-economic and sustainability considerations. The MOSKopt framework, coupled with Monte Carlo simulations for uncertainties, proved to be a valuable tool for addressing uncertainties and enhancing the robustness and reliability of the optimization of pharmaceutical processes. The pharmaceutical processes are sensitive to variations in conditions and parameters, therefore, the identification of optimal solutions that perform well across a range of likely outcomes enhances the adaptability to real-world variations. The findings can contribute to the ongoing efforts in pharmaceutical manufacturing to achieve greener, more sustainable, and cost-effective processes.

References

Al, R., Behera, C. R., Gernaey, K. V., Sin, G. (2020) Stochastic simulation-based superstructure optimization framework for process synthesis and design under uncertainty. *Comp. Chem. Eng., 143.*

Ankenman, B., Nelson, B. L., Staum, J. (2010) Stochastic Kriging for Simulation Metamodeling, *Oper. Res. 58 371-382.*

Elango, V., Murphy, M. A., Smith, B. L., Davenport, G. K., Mott, G. N., Zey, E.G., Zey, G. L. Method for producing Ibuprofen. *US Patent US 4981995A.*

Gernaey, K. V., Cervera-Padrell, A. E., Woodley, J. M. (2012) A perspective on PSE in pharmaceutical process development and innovation. *Comput. Chem. Eng. 42,15−29.*

Jolliffe, H. G.; Gerogiorgis, D. I. (2016) Plantwide design and economic evaluation of two ContinuousPharmaceutical Manufacturing (CPM) cases: Ibuprofen and Artemisinin. *Comput. Chem. Eng. 91, 269-188.*

Montes, F. C. C., Gernaey, K., Sin, G. (2018) Dynamic Plantwide Modeling, Uncertainty, and Sensitivity Analysis of a Pharmaceutical Upstream Synthesis: Ibuprofen Case Study. *Ind. Eng. Chem. Res., 57(30), 10026-10037.*

Thakar, N., Berger, R. J., Kapteijn, F., Moulijn, J. (2007) Modelling kinetics and deactivation for the selective hydrogenation ofan aromatic ketone over Pd/SiO2. *Chem. Eng. Sci. 62(18-20) 5322−5329.*

Wang, Z., Ierapetritou, M. (2018) Constrained optimization of black-box stochastic systems using a novel feasibility enhanced Kriging-based method. *Comput. Chem. Eng. 118, 210–223.*

Flavio Manenti, Gintaras V. Reklaitis (Eds.), Proceedings of the 34th European Symposium on Computer Aided Process Engineering / 15th International Symposium on Process Systems Engineering (ESCAPE34/PSE24), June 2-6, 2024, Florence, Italy
 http://dx.doi.org/10.1016/B978-0-443-28824-1.50252-0

Modelling\simulation and optimization of large-scale post-combustion CO_2 capture using a rotating packed bed absorber and packed bed stripper

Olajide Otitoju, Meihong Wang*

Department of Chemical and Biological Engineering, University of Sheffield, Sheffield, S1 3JD United Kingdom
Corresponding author: Meihong.Wang@sheffield.ac.uk

Abstract

Rotating packed bed (RPB) is capable of reducing the size, footprint, and cost of the post-combustion carbon capture (PCC) process when used as absorbers and strippers. RPB can be operated with higher monoethanolamine (MEA) concentration (>55 wt%). At these concentrations, there is potential for higher absorption performance and lower energy demand for solvent regeneration. However, previous studies have not investigated the optimal MEA concentration to operate the RPB absorber and PB stripper for large-scale PCC processes. This study investigates the optimal solvent concentration in MEA-based PCC using an RPB absorber and packed bed (PB) stripper for 250 MW combined cycle gas turbine (CCGT) power plants. The rate-based model of the RPB absorber was developed in Aspen Custom Modeller® (ACM) V11. The accuracy of the RPB absorber model was verified by validating it with experimental data. The RPB absorber model correctly predicted the experimental data and was then scaled up to deal with flue gas from a 250 MW CCGT power plant. The RPB Absorber model was exported to Aspen Plus® and integrated with PB stripper to develop the closed loop of the large-scale PCC process. This large-scale model was used for process analysis and optimization studies. Optimisation results showed that the lowest total energy consumption of 4.46 GJ/t_{CO2} was found at an optimal MEA concentration of 75 wt%. Going forward, we will perform an elaborate economic analysis based on the optimized process to determine the optimal MEA concentration that results in the lowest CO_2 capture cost.

Keywords: Post-combustion carbon capture, chemical absorption, rotating packed bed, Combined cycle gas turbine power plant, optimisation.

1. Introduction

Carbon dioxide is a greenhouse gas that is responsible for climate change. Fossil fuel-fired power plants are the largest CO_2 emitters. Hence CO_2 emissions reduction efforts must be targeted at these plants. The amine-based post-combustion capture (PCC) has a technology readiness level of 9 and has been deployed at a commercial scale to capture CO_2 from coal-fired plants at Boundary Dam in Canada and the Petra Nova project in the USA [1]. This makes the technology the most mature among the different carbon capture technologies. The amine-based PCC is mostly operated using packed bed (PB) columns as absorbers and strippers and 30 wt% MEA as a solvent. The bottlenecks of the process include the high energy demand and huge equipment sizes that result in high costs and a high plant footprint. These have prevented the rapid and extensive implementation of the process at a large scale. The rotating packed bed (RPB) technology can reduce the size and the costs of the PCC process when used to replace the PB absorber [2].

The RPB consists of an annular packed bed connected to two-side disks that are mounted on a rotating shaft and housed in a casing. The liquid generally flows radially outward from the inner periphery of the packing due to centrifugal acceleration while the gas enters into the casing and then flows radially inward from the outer periphery of the RPB due to the pressure gradient. The gas and the liquid phases are exposed to enormous centrifugal acceleration which is many times the gravitational acceleration in PBs. This enhances mass transfer in the bed and areas between the packing and the casing. This is the reason for the substantial reduction in packing volume in RPBs compared to PBs. RPB can also be operated with higher MEA concentration as it can break viscous high MEA concentration into tiny liquid films[3]. Higher MEA concentration could reduce solvent flow to the stripper and the regeneration energy demand. However, no study has demonstrated the optimal design and operation of the RPB absorber at different solvent concentrations. Therefore, this study aims to investigate the optimal solvent concentration in MEA-based PCC using an RPB absorber and PB stripper for a 250 MW CCGT power plant.

2. Model development for RPB absorber

2.1. Mass and energy balance equations

The rate-based model is used to describe the CO_2 absorption in RPB. The RPB is discretised radially into smaller packing segments. The mass and heat transfers, chemical reactions and hydrodynamics are considered in each discretised segment. All the equations used to describe the model were implemented and solved in the equation-oriented process simulator Aspen Custom Modeler® (ACM). The equation describing the mass balance in the gas and the liquid phases is given by Eqs. 1 and 2. The energy balance in the gas and liquid phases is described by Eqs. 3 and 4.

Mass balance

Gas phase

$$0 = \frac{1}{2\pi r Z}\frac{\partial(F_g y_i)}{\partial r} - a_{gl}N_i \tag{1}$$

Liquid Phase

$$0 = -\frac{1}{2\pi r Z}\frac{\partial(F_l x_i)}{\partial r} + a_{gl}N_i \tag{2}$$

Energy balance

Gas Phase

$$0 = \frac{1}{2\pi r Z}\frac{\partial(F_g C_{p,g} T_g)}{\partial r} - a_{gl}h_{gl}(T_l - T_g) \tag{3}$$

Liquid phase

$$0 = -\frac{1}{2\pi r Z}\frac{\partial(F_l C_{p,l} T_l)}{\partial r} + a_{gl}\left(h_{gl}(T_l - T_g) - \Delta H_{rxn} N_{CO2} - \Delta H_{vap,H2O} N_{H_2O}\right) \tag{4}$$

2.2. Mass transfer, heat transfer and hydrodynamic models

The gas and liquid mass transfer coefficients, gas-liquid interfacial area, liquid holdup, pressure drop and heat transfer coefficient in the RPB absorber model are estimated using correlations in Table 1.

Table 1 Correlations used for mass and heat transfers.

Correlations	Reference
Gas-phase mass transfer coefficient	Onda et al. [4]
Liquid-phase mass transfer coefficient	Tung and Mah [5]
Interfacial area	Billet and Schulte [6]
Liquid holdup	Burns et al. [7]
Pressure drop	Llerena-Chavez and Larachi [8]
Heat transfer coefficient	Chilton and Colburn [9]

3. Results and discussions

3.1. Model validation and scale-up

The RPB absorber model was validated with pilot scale data from Jassim et al. [10]. Case 1 with 4 experimental runs was chosen for model validation. The RPB has an inner diameter of 0.156 m, outer diameter of 0.398 m, and axial height of 0.025 m. It is packed with stainless steel small mesh packing. As shown in Figure 1, the RPB absorber model accurately predicted the CO_2 capture level compared to the experimental data in Jassim et al [10].

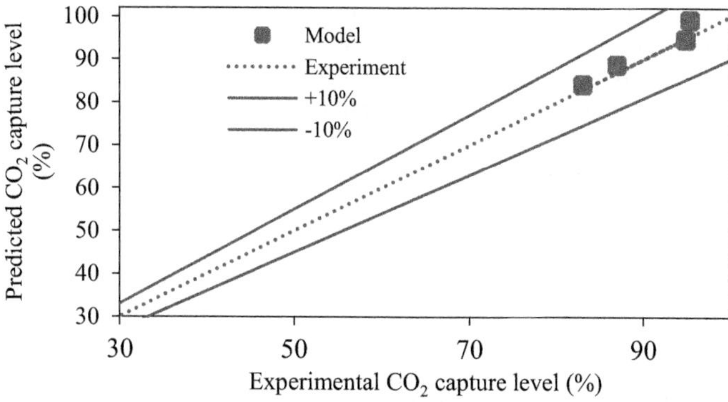

Figure 1: Model predictions vs. experimental data for capture level

Upon validation, the RPB absorber was scaled up using the procedure described by Otitoju et al. [2]. The scale-up involves determining the basic dimensions (inner packing radius, outer packing radius and axial height) of the RPB required to capture CO_2 from the flue gas of a 250 MW CCGT power plant.

3.2. Whole large-scale PCC process simulation

The large-scale RPB absorber model developed in ACM is packaged and exported as a custom model to Aspen Plus®. The RPB absorber model is integrated with the PB stripper model to develop the model of the whole process. For a detailed description of the stripper model, validation and scale-up, the reader is referred to Otitoju et al.[11].

Table 2: Summary of design specifications and operating conditions

Operating conditions	Absorber	Stripper
Type	RPB	PB
Inner diameter (ID) (m)	3	-
Outer diameter (OD) (m)	9.72	8.2
Height (m)	1.26	20
Packing type	Wire mesh	Flexipac 1Y
Pressure (atm)	1	1.6
Rotor speed (rpm)	200	-
MEA concentration (wt%)	30,55,65,75, 80	
Lean pump pressure (bar)	2	
Rich pump pressure (bar)	3	
Lean solvent temp (°C)	40	
Heat exch. temp approach (°C)	10	

3.3. Base process analysis

Process analysis of the large-scale PCC process investigates the influence of lean CO_2 loading on capture level for MEA concentrations of 30 wt% - 80 wt%. Results in Figure 2 indicate a gradual decrease in the capture level as lean loading increases from 0.18 to 0.3 mol_{CO2}/mol_{MEA} for all the MEA concentrations.

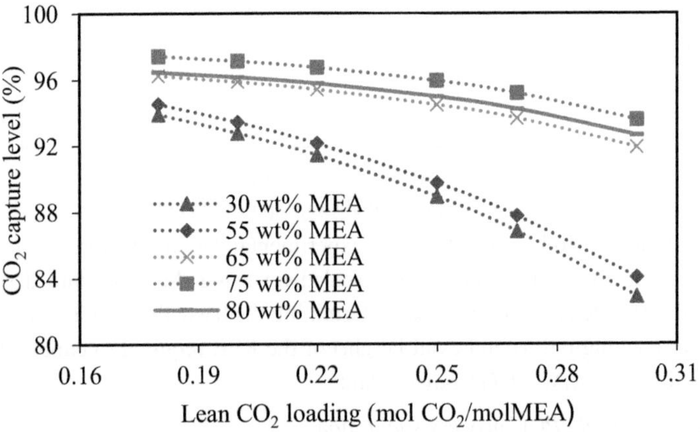

Figure 2: Influence of lean loading on CO_2 capture level

The energy consumed to rotate the RPB absorber at 200 rpm and 90% CO_2 capture level and the energy consumed for solvent regeneration energy (GJ/t_{CO2}) are shown in Figure 3.

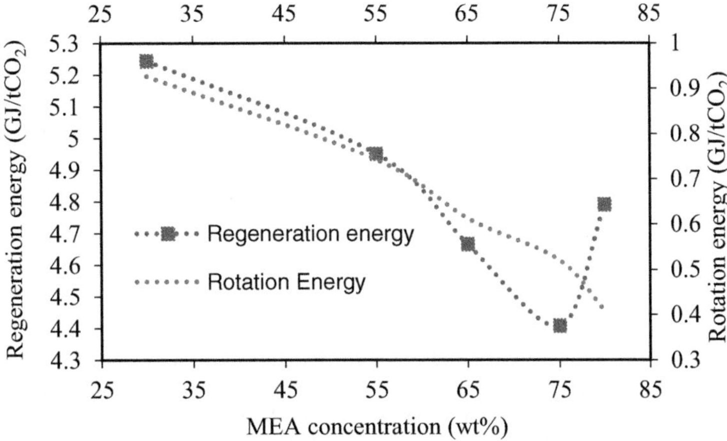

Figure 3: Energy consumption for absorber rotation and regeneration

3.4. Process optimisation

Process optimisation is performed to minimise the total energy consumption of the large-scale PCC process. Column internals, flue gas conditions and the operating conditions of pump and heat exchangers are kept constant for the optimisation. The details of the objective function and the constraints are shown below.

Objective: Minimise total energy consumption (E_{total}) which is the sum of regeneration energy (E_{reg}) and absorber rotational energy ($E_{rot, abs}$)

$$E_{total} = E_{reg} + E_{rot,abs} \tag{5}$$

Decision variables: lean solvent flow rate *(L)*, reboiler temperature (T_{reb}), condenser temperature (T_{cond}), and absorber rotor speed (ω_{abs}).

Constraints: Capture level ($CO_{2,cap}$) and CO_2 purity ($CO_{2,purity}$)

$$CO_{2,cap} = 90\% \tag{6}$$

$$CO_{2,purity} = 96 \tag{7}$$

The optimisation found a solution satisfying all the constraints and the results are shown in Table 3. The lowest total energy consumption of 4.46 GJ/t_{CO2} was found at an optimal MEA concentration of 75 wt%. At this MEA concentration, the rotational energy consumption of the RPB absorber is 0.47 GJ/ton_{CO2} while the regeneration energy consumption of the large-scale PCC process is 3.99 GJ/t_{CO2}.

Table 3: Optimisation results at 30, 55, 65, 75 and 80 wt% MEA concentrations

MEA conc. (wt%)	Objective value		
	$E_{rot,abs}$ (GJ/t_{CO2})	E_{reg} (GJ/t_{CO2})	E_{tot} (GJ/t_{CO2})
30	0.84	4.76	5.60
55	0.67	4.49	5.16
65	0.55	4.23	4.78
75	0.47	3.99	4.46
80	0.37	4.34	4.71

4. Conclusions and future work

A steady-state user-defined rate-based model of RPB absorber developed in ACM was validated at a pilot scale using experimental data and then scaled up to deal with flue gas from a 250 MW CCGT power plant. The large-scale RPB absorber model was exported from ACM to the Aspen Plus® environment. The RPB absorber was integrated with the PB stripper and other process equipment (pumps and heat exchangers) to develop the whole process for a large-scale PCC process. This large-scale model was used for process analysis and optimization studies. The lowest total energy consumption of 4.46 GJ/t_{CO2} was found at an optimal MEA concentration of 75 wt%. The regeneration energy contributed the largest share (3.99 GJ/t_{CO2}) to the total energy consumption. Future will include economic assessments to determine the optimal concentration that results in the lowest CO_2 capture cost.

References

[1] Bui M, Adjiman CS, Bardow A, Anthony EJ, Boston A, Brown S, et al. Carbon capture and storage (CCS): The way forward. Energy Environ Sci 2018;11:1062–176.

[2] Otitoju O, Oko E, Wang M. Modelling, scale-up and techno-economic assessment of rotating packed bed absorber for CO_2 capture from a 250 MW e combined cycle gas turbine power plant. Appl Energy 2023;335:120747.

[3] Oko E, Ramshaw C, Wang M. Study of intercooling for rotating packed bed absorbers in intensified solvent-based CO_2 capture process. Appl Energy 2018;223:302–16.

[4] Onda K, Takeuchi H, Okumoto Y. Mass transfer coefficients between gas and liquid phases in packed columns. J Chem Eng Japan 1968;1:56–62.

[5] Tung H-H, Mah RSH. Modeling liquid mass transfer in HIGEE separation process. Chem Eng Commun 1985;39:147–53.

[6] Billet R, Schultes M. Prediction of Mass Transfer Columns with Dumped and Arranged Packings. Chem Eng Res Des 1999;77:498–504.

[7] Burns JR, Jamil JN, Ramshaw C. Process intensification: operating characteristics of rotating packed beds — determination of liquid hold-up for a high-voidage structured packing. Chem Eng Sci 2000;55:2401–15.

[8] Llerena-Chavez H, Larachi F. Analysis of flow in rotating packed beds via CFD simulations—Dry pressure drop and gas flow maldistribution. Chem Eng Sci 2009;64:2113–26.

[9] Chilton TH, Colburn AP. Mass Transfer (Absorption) Coefficients: Prediction from Data on Heat Transfer and Fluid Friction. Ind Eng Chem 1934;26:1183–7.

[10] Jassim MS, Rochelle G, Eimer D, Ramshaw C. Carbon dioxide absorption and desorption in aqueous monoethanolamine solutions in a rotating packed bed. Ind Eng Chem Res 2007;46:2823–33.

[11] Otitoju O, Oko E, Wang M. A new method for scale-up of solvent-based post-combustion carbon capture process with packed columns. Int J Greenh Gas Control 2020;93:102900.

Flavio Manenti, Gintaras V. Reklaitis (Eds.), Proceedings of the 34th European Symposium on Computer Aided Process Engineering / 15th International Symposium on Process Systems Engineering (ESCAPE34/PSE24), June 2-6, 2024, Florence, Italy
 http://dx.doi.org/10.1016/B978-0-443-28824-1.50253-2

Sustainability-driven conceptual process design at the cooperative Cosun

Sara Conceição[a,c], Farzad Mousazadeh[a], John A. Posada[b], Juan Gutierrez[c], P.L.J. Swinkels[a], Andre de Haan[a,c,*]

[a] *Department of Chemical Engineering, Delft University of Technology, Van der Maasweg 9, 2629HZ, Delft, The Netherlands*
[b] *Department of Biotechnology, Delft University of Technology, Van der Maasweg 9, 2629HZ, Delft, The Netherlands*
[c] *Cosun Innovation Center, Kreekweg 1, 4671VA, Dinteloord, The Netherlands*
* *Corresponding Author: andre.de.haan@cosun.com*

Abstract

The aim of this study is to introduce and showcase the applicability of the 'Green-by-Design method', a tool created by the cooperative Cosun that integrates different indicators involving economic, environmental, inherent safety and health aspects for comparative analysis at an early design stage. Two case studies are presented to exemplify the evaluation principles and steps considered along the 'Green-by-Design method': ethylene glycol production and fava bean protein isolate extraction. The results indicate that the 'Green-by-Design method' provides a comprehensive comparison of different design concepts, by combining various indicators into a single score, enabling sustainability to be an integral aspect in the decision-making during an early design phase.

Keywords: green-by-design; sustainability assessment; early-stage conceptual design; single score sustainability index.

1. Introduction

Cosun is a leading agricultural cooperative producing high-quality plant-based products. As part of the company's strategy, Cosun has set ambitious goals to contribute to a sustainable world for current and future generations. In alignment with these objectives, Cosun is introducing an early-stage sustainability assessment tool named the 'Green-by-Design method'. This tool is designed to support decision-making in the early-stage conceptual design by facilitating both comparison of multiple design options and identification of process hotspots in relation to their sustainability potential. This methodology can be used in any process design innovation project when multiple design options need to be compared.

Various qualitative and quantitative methods fulfill similar purposes (Patel et al., 2015). Nevertheless, the literature review revealed a gap for approaches with easy and swift implementation in industry, tailored to support decision making in early stages of innovation projects.

2. Methodology description

The Green-by-Design method includes 13 indicators grouped into three main categories: Economic, Environment and Inherent Safety & Health. The rating is based on the summation of the score of these three groups, considering specific weight factors (see

Eq.(1)). The used weight of each category – *Economic* 40 % ($I^j_{Economic}$), *Environment* 30 % ($I^j_{Environment}$) and *Inherent Safety and Health* 30 % (I^j_{ISH}) - follows the idea that all three categories are similarly important to create green (sustainable) design concepts. The category *Economic* has a slightly higher weight because it is the primary requirement to implement a new design on industrial scale.

$$Final\ score = 0.40 \cdot I^j_{Economic} + 0.30 \cdot I^j_{Environment} + 0.30 \cdot I^j_{ISH} \tag{1}$$

Since each indicator has a specific unit of measure, the obtained values cannot be added directly. Therefore, the results are normalized by the maximum value (see Eq.(2)).

$$I^j_{i,norm.} = \frac{I^j_i}{\max(I_i)} \tag{2}$$

In Eq.(2), $I^j_{i,norm.}$ and I^j_i represent the normalized and non-normalized indicator i of the process option j, respectively and $\max(I_i)$ represents the highest value obtained for the indicator i among the results from the different process options.

The final score can vary between 0 and 1 and the higher the final score, the higher is the potential of the design concept under evaluation to be 'Green-by-Design'.

2.1. Economic category

The Economic category represents the economic viability of the process. It is composed of four indicators: *Economic Potential*, *Utility Costs*, *Process Complexity* and *Potential of Energy Recovery*.

Economic Potential (see Eq.(3)) has the highest weight since. As a general consensus from literature, it's the most important criterion to evaluate the potential of a process at an early stage. In addition, *Utility Costs* and *Process Complexity* have a higher chance to be the major cost contributions to capital expenditures and operational expenses while also being susceptible of changing when more details become available during process design.

Table 1: Green-by-Design indicators and weight factors of the Economic Category. a) In the 'Green-by-Design' method, a higher score represents a higher sustainability potential. As the variable represents a negative impacts/process parameters, the indicator is estimated as 1 divided by the variable; b) For endothermic/ exothermic reactions under 200 °C the given score is equal to zero (adapted from (Patel et al., 2015)). m: mass flow rate; P: commercial price; N: number of process steps.

Category: Economic (40%)					
Economic Potential (40 %)		**Utility Costs (20 %)** [a]			
$I^j_{EP} = \sum_{i=1}^{P} m_i^{Prod.} p_i^{Prod.} - \sum_{i=1}^{RM} m_i^{RM} p_i^{RM}$	(3)	$I^j_{UC} = \frac{1}{\sum_{i=1}^{u} m_i^u P_i^u}$			(4)
Process Complexity (20 %)		**Potential of Energy Recovery (20 %)** [b]			
		Heat of reaction (KJ/mol)		**Score**	
$I^j_{PC} = \frac{1}{(N_{up/downstream} + N_{reaction\ section})}$	(5)	>-100 kJ/mol	→	1	
		-100 – -300 kJ/mol	→	2	
		< -300 kJ/mol	→	3	

$$I^j_{Economic} = 0.4 \cdot I_{EP,\ norm.} + 0.2 \cdot I_{UC,\ norm.} + 0.2 \cdot I_{PC,norm.} + 0.2 \cdot I_{ER,norm.} \tag{6}$$

The fourth indicator, *Potential of Energy Recovery,* is used as a proxy to quantify the possibility to recover useful process energy which can be achieved when, exothermic reactions occur above 200°C (Patel et al., 2015). Hence, heat integration might reduce the amount of utilities required, and consequently the utility costs. Table 1 shows the equations and weighting factors used to calculate the Economic category.

2.2. Environmental category

The *Environmental* category intends to identify and compare different environmental impacts on Earth's natural systems: water resources, land and atmosphere. For this reason, one impact indicator per natural system is included in the tool – *Global Warming Potential*, *Wastewater* and *Land Use*. A fourth impact indicator, *Process Circularity*, is additionally accounted for in this category to evaluate the side-streams of each process option.

To categorize the side streams of each process, an inhouse framework is used – Cosun's pyramid for circular economy (Figure 1). 'Cosun's Pyramid for Circular Economy' was created drawing inspiration from the 'Waste Framework Directive' designed by the EU, also known as 'Waste Management Hierarchy' (European Commission, n.d.). It comprises a ranking system which identifies four different types of side-streams and an ideal scenario where side-streams are prevented. The side-streams are therefore scored between 1 to 4 according to their destinations. Table 2 summarizes the indicators included in the *Environment* category.

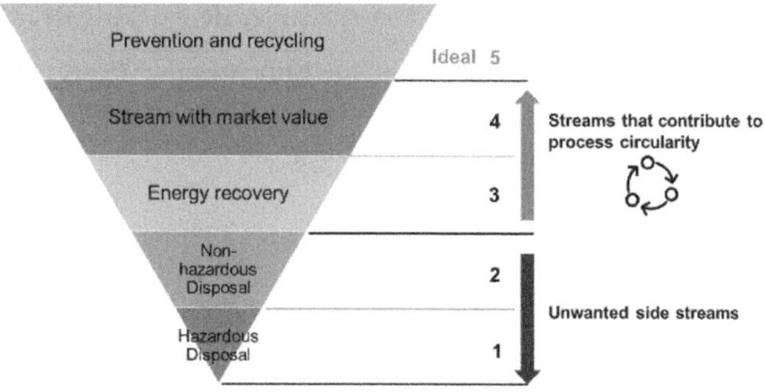

Figure 1: Cosun's Pyramid for Circular Economy. Adapted from (European Commission, n.d.)

Table 2: Green-by-design indicators and weight factors of the *Environmental* category. a) In the 'Green-by-Design' method, a higher score represents a higher sustainability potential. As the variable represents a negative impacts/process parameters, the indicator is estimated as 1 divided by the variable; b) Includes CO_2 footprint of the raw materials, process utilities and direct CO_2 emissions of the process; GHG: green-house gas emissions; a_i: score based on 'Cosun's Pyramid for Circular Economy'.

Category: Environmental Category (30%)			
Global warming potential (25%) a), b)		**Wastewater (25%) a)**	
$I_{GWP}^{j} = \dfrac{1}{GHG_{Cradle-to-gate}}$	(7)	$I_{water}^{j} = \dfrac{1}{m_{wastewater}}$	(8)
Land use (25%) a)		**Process Circularity (25%)**	
$I_{Land}^{j} = \dfrac{1}{Land\ use}$	(9)	$I_{P.Circularity}^{j} = \dfrac{1}{n}\sum_{i=1}^{n} a_i;\ 1 < a_i < 4$	(10)
$I_{Environment}^{j} = 0.25 \cdot I_{GWP,\ norm.} + 0.25 \cdot I_{water,\ norm.} + 0.25 \cdot I_{land,norm.} + 0.25 \cdot I_{P.Circ.,norm.}$			(11)

2.3. Inherent Safety and Health category

Inherent Safety and Health aims to compare the potential of health hazards to the employees and communities close to the production locations.

Index-based methods have been widely used since they are simple and user friendly and require information that is available at an early design stage. To select inherent safety and health indicators for the present tool, methods such as "Prototype of Inherent Safety"(Edwards & Lawrence, 1993), "Inherent Safety Index" (Heikkilä, 1999) and "Inherent Occupational Health Index" (Hassim & Hurme, 2010) were reviewed. The selection of indicators was based on three main requirements: the indicators are easily estimated with the input data available at an early design stage; double counting should be avoided; and the indicators should have a significant impact on safety and health hazards.

Inherent Safety and Health is divided into two subcategories: *Process Safety* (see Table 3), focusing on the evaluation of the process conditions and operation mode, and *Health Hazards* (refer to Table 4), which evaluates chemical properties of the components present in the process. Eq.(12) illustrates that indicators based on operational conditions carry a greater weight than operating mode, since critical operating conditions can pose a higher hazard compared to batch processes (Hassim & Hurme, 2010).

Table 3: Green-by-design indicators and weight factors of the *Inherent Safety and Health* category, *Process Safety* subcategory. Adapted from (Hassim & Hurme, 2010; Heikkilä, 1999).

Category: Inherent Safety & Health (40%) - Subcategory: Process Safety

Process Safety (50%)

$$I_{PS}^{j} = 0.2 \cdot I_{OP,\ norm.} + 0.4 \cdot I_{RS,\ norm.} + 0.4 \cdot I_{U/DS,\ norm.} \quad (12)$$

<u>*Overall Process (OP)*</u>

- Index-based indicator.

Operation mode		Score
Batch (100 %)	→	1
Semi-batch (50 % - 100 %)	→	2
Semi-batch (1 % - 50 %)	→	3
Continuous	→	4

<u>*Reaction Section (RS)*</u>

- Sum of index-based indicators (Heikkilä, 1999).
- Accounts for operating pressure/temperature of the reaction section and heat of reaction.

<u>*Up/Downstream Section (U/DS)*</u>

- Sum of index-based indicators (Heikkilä, 1999).
- Accounts for operating pressure/temperature of different units in upstream and downstream sections.
- The process step with most critical conditions is the one accounted for in the final score.

Pressure (bara)	Temperature (°C)	Heat of reaction (kJ/kg)		Score
>200	>600	≤ - 3000	→	1
50 – 200	300 – 600	> -3000	→	2
25 – 50	150 – 300	> -1200	→	3
5 – 25	70 – 150	< -600	→	4
0.5 – 5	0 – 70	≤ -200	→	5
0.2 – 0.5	< 0	-	→	4
0 – 0.2	-	-	→	3

Table 4: Green-by-Design indicators and weight factors of the *Inherent Safety and Health* category, *Health Hazards* subcategory. FP: flash point; BP: boiling point; LD_{50}: lethal dose. Adapted from (Erhirhie et al., 2018; Heikkilä, 1999)

Category: Inherent Safety & Health (40%) - Subcategory: Health Hazards

Health Hazards (50%)

$$I_{HH}^{j} = 0.5 \cdot I_{Toxicity,\ norm.} + 0.5 \cdot I_{Flammability,\ norm.} \quad (13)$$

Flammability

- Index-based indicator (dependent on the flash point values)(Heikkilä, 1999).
- The most flammable compound is the one accounted for in the final score.

Toxicity

- Index-based indicator (dependent on the LD_{50} values)(Erhirhie et al., 2018).
- The most toxic compound is the one accounted for in the final score.

Flammability	Toxicity		Score
Very flammable (FP< 0°C and BP ≤ 35 °C)	Extremely toxic (LD_{50} (mg/g) ≤ 5)	→	1
Easily flammable (FP < 21 °C)	Highly toxic (5 < LD_{50} < 50)	→	2
Flammable (FP ≤ 55 °C)	Moderately toxic (50 < LD_{50} < 500)	→	3
Combustible (FP > 55 °C)	Slightly toxic (500 < LD_{50} < 5000)	→	4
Nonflammable	Practically toxic (5000 < LD_{50} < 15000)	→	5
-	Non-toxic (15000 ≤ LD_{50})	→	6

$$I_{ISH}^{j} = 0.5 \cdot I_{PS,\ norm.} + 0.5 \cdot I_{HH,\ norm.} \quad (14)$$

3. Results and discussion

Applicability of the 'Green-by-Design method' is demonstrated in two case studies: ethylene glycol production and fava bean protein isolate extraction process. To generate the results depicted in Figure 2, data for each process option were collected, and the indicators outlined in the previous section were estimated using Microsoft Excel.

Three process options for ethylene glycol production are compared: the conventional process of ethylene (fossil-based) to glycols, sucrose hydrogenolysis and fermentation of thick juice to produce first ethylene and then glycols. The results obtained from the 'Green-by-Design method' are shown in Figure 2 a).

It can be concluded that the process with the highest economic potential is sucrose hydrogenation. The raw material is cheaper compared to the conventional process of producing ethylene glycol from ethylene and during the hydrogenation of sugars, other valuable products are obtained, such as glycerol and propylene glycol.

When comparing the three processes in terms of environmental impacts, the fossil-based process appears to have a better score than the other two processes. Despite the 'ethylene to glycols' process having a higher CO_2 footprint, the plant-based processes have larger wastewater streams and greater land use to produce the required raw materials. Regarding Inherent Safety and Health, the three processes have very similar scores.

In the second case study, two options are compared for the production of fava bean protein isolate production from fava flour: protein extraction using pH precipitation and ultrafiltration. Since there are no reaction sections in these processes, the ones related to the reaction section were left out of the evaluation for estimating the indicators with the 'Green-by-Design method'. This shows some flexibility on the application of the method.

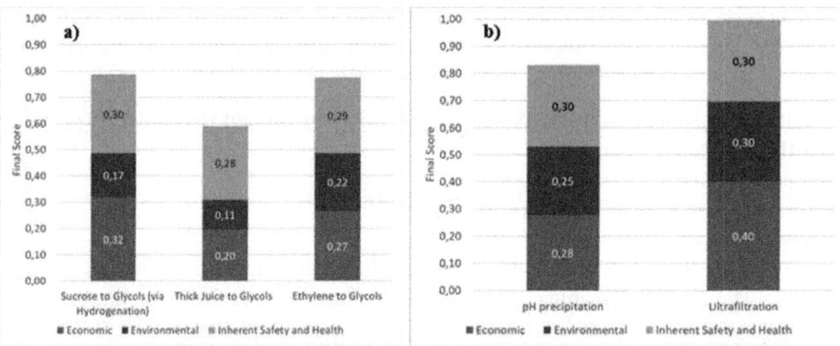

Figure 2: Comparative Results of the 'Green-by-Design method' of the two case studies: a) ethylene glycol production; b) fava bean protein isolate production. The final score can vary between 0 and 1 and the higher the final score, the higher is the sustainability potential of the design concept under evaluation.

As it can be seen in Figure 2 b), the process route using ultrafiltration has higher scores (meaning better performance) in two of the categories of the 'Green-by-Design method': Economic and Environmental. Ultrafiltration enhances the product functionalities, resulting in a higher selling price for the protein isolate. This makes ultrafiltration a more economically attractive choice. Regarding the environmental impacts, pH precipitation requires additional steps after the extraction step to neutralize the pH, and it produces larger wastewater streams. Therefore, the score for the Environmental category is considerably lower (meaning worse performance) compared to ultrafiltration.

4. Conclusions

The 'Green-by-Design method' developed at Cosun showed to be useful for comparing different design concepts and identifying hotspots in aspects related to three main sustainability related categories–Economic, Environmental and Inherent Safety & Health – to support decision making in an early design stage. In addition, the method is user friendly and flexible, by combining index-based indicators and indicators estimated by means of simple equations.

References

Edwards, D. W., & Lawrence, D. (1993). Assessing the Inherent Safety of Chemical Process Routes: Is There a Relation Between Plant Costs and Inherent Safety? *Trans IChemE*, *71*, 252–258.

Erhirhie, E. O., Ihekwereme, C. P., & Ilodigwe, E. E. (2018). Advances in acute toxicity testing: Strengths, weaknesses and regulatory acceptance. *Interdisciplinary Toxicology*, *11*(1), 5–12.

European Commission. (n.d.). Waste Framework Directive. https://environment.ec.europa.eu/topics/waste-and-recycling/waste-framework-directive

Hassim, M. H., & Hurme, M. (2010). Inherent occupational health assessment during process research and development stage. *Journal of Loss Prevention in the Process Industries*, *23*(1), 127–138. https://doi.org/10.1016/j.jlp.2009.06.009

Heikkilä, A.-Mari. (1999). *Inherent safety in process plant design. An index-based approach.* Technical Research Centre of Finland, VTT Publications 384.

Patel, A. D., Posada, J. A., Shen, L., & Patel, M. K. (2015). Early R&D Stage Sustainability Assessment: The 5-pillar method. In *Sustainability Assessment of Renewables-Based Products* (pp. 65–80). John Wiley & Sons, Ltd.

Flavio Manenti, Gintaras V. Reklaitis (Eds.), Proceedings of the 34th European Symposium on Computer Aided Process Engineering / 15th International Symposium on Process Systems Engineering (ESCAPE34/PSE24), June 2-6, 2024, Florence, Italy
 http://dx.doi.org/10.1016/B978-0-443-28824-1.50254-4

Towards pH Swing-based CO_2 Mineralization by Calcium Carbonate Precipitation: Modeling and Experimental Analysis

Chinmay Hegde[1,*]; Andreas Voigt[2]; Kai Sundmacher[1,2]

[1]*Institute of Process Engineering, Otto von Guericke University, Magdeburg, Germany*
[2]*Max Planck Institute for Dynamics of Complex Technical Systems, Magdeburg Germany*
* *corresponding author: chinmay.hegde@ovgu.de*

Abstract

In an effort to stop adverse climatic changes, greenhouse gas emissions must be reduced together with removing already-emitted CO_2 from the atmosphere. Mineral carbon sequestration is an effective way of storing carbon permanently. The most common alkaline earth metals, calcium, and magnesium, found in mineral compounds can be used as feedstocks. Our work illustrates the formulation of a model and the experimental validation for CO_2 capture as calcium carbonate ($CaCO_3$) precipitate using mine wastes. The model aims to facilitate the development of an adaptive controller that should enhance the productivity of precipitated carbonate particles while adhering to predefined particle size specifications. The precipitation is implemented via a liquid phase pH swing process. The factors influencing the efficiency of the process to precipitate $CaCO_3$ preferentially are investigated using dissolved Ca^{2+} ions solution in the presence of Mg^{2+} ions. Furthermore, the study of the influence of $CaCO_3$ seed particles on the particle size distribution and crystal growth kinetics indicated that kinetics significantly impact the precipitation, which could alter particle morphology. Though calcite seeds were used to induce crystal growth, morphology is dictated by primary nucleation. In the absence of impurities, both vaterite and calcite are precipitated, while the presence of Mg^{2+} ions delays the primary nucleation and leads to the preferred precipitation of smaller nucleates as aragonite. The pH of the solution is regulated in a semi-batch operating mode for the selective precipitation of desired carbonates. A novel model has been formulated to simulate this process.

Keywords: pH swing, calcium carbonate, nucleation, seed particles, crystal growth

1. Introduction

Ex situ mineral carbonation is regarded as a promising method for carbon dioxide capture and storage (CCS) because (i) the captured CO_2 can be permanently stored and (ii) industrial wastes, such as cement and lime kiln dust, steel and stainless-steel slags, and coal fly ash, can be recycled and turned into value-added carbonate materials by managing the polymorphs and properties of the mineral carbonate. Calcium and magnesium are the most abundant alkaline earth metals in nature as minerals and industrial wastes, and the mineral carbonates of $CaCO_3$ and $MgCO_3$ are particularly of interest. These can be produced in both direct and indirect processes. Owing to the high-purity products and higher conversion rates (Bobicki et al. 2012), indirect techniques are preferred. They can be accomplished via gas-solid mineral carbonation, the pH swing process, the molten salt process, acid extractions, and bioleaching. pH swing process is a liquid phase carbonation method involving four steps: (1) liquid-solid extraction of metal ions (Mg^{2+}, Ca^{2+}), (2) solid-liquid separation by filtration, (3) carbonation of the metal ions by use of CO_2, (4) separation of solid carbonate particles.

Precipitation of $CaCO_3$ is a significant process in the fields of geology, environmental science, and industrial applications. The ability to manufacture $CaCO_3$ with specific morphology, structure, and particle size is invaluable due to its wide application as filler in composite materials such as plastics, rubbers, paper, or paints. The precipitation of $CaCO_3$ is influenced by several factors, including the calcium concentration, the carbonate concentration, the pH value of the environment, and the presence of nucleation sites. The stoichiometric equation for calcium carbonation in the liquid phase is given as:

$$Ca^{2+}(aq) + CO_3^{2-}(aq) \rightleftharpoons CaCO_3(aq) \tag{1}$$

The Ca^{2+} ions also react with HCO_3^- to form $CaHCO_3^-$, but this reaction is not preferred kinetically, and thus $CaHCO_3^-$ concentrations are negligible (Koutsoukos & Kontoyannis 1984). The most important factor for $CaCO_3$ precipitation is the supersaturation S, which is the driving force for both nucleation and crystal growth:

$$S = \sqrt{\frac{a(Ca^{2+}) \cdot a(CO_3^{2-})}{k_{sp}}} \tag{2}$$

where k_{sp} is the solubility product of $CaCO_3$, and $a(Ca^{2+})$ and $a(CO_3^{2-})$ are the liquid phase activities of calcium ions and carbonate ions, respectively. The activity of the ions is dependent on temperature, pH and ionic strength. This investigation focuses on the controllability of the solubility based on the pH, the variation of which is provided in Figure 1(a). The change in the supersaturation influences the precipitation kinetics, which results in different crystal phases of $CaCO_3$, namely Calcite, Vaterite and Aragonite. The precipitation of $CaCO_3$ has been investigated in various studies. Liendo et al. (2022) observed, that when using Na_2CO_3 and $CaCl_2$ as starting chemicals, at high supersaturation the $CaCO_3$ crystallization was dominated by vaterite formation, which transformed to thermodynamically stable calcite over time. However, using $(NH_4)_2CO_3$ resulted in a stable vaterite formation without transformation to calcite. In another study conducted by Park et al. (2008), in the presence of Mg^{2+} ions, the metastable aragonite is preferred rather than vaterite along with calcite precipitation. Increasing the Mg^{2+} ion concentration resulted in aragonite dominance. While the presence of potassium ions resulted in the formation of calcite, which was shown in a study by Falini et al. (2009).

Controlling the precipitation kinetics not only influenced the crystal structure but also dictated the crystal sizes. Feng et al. (2007) found in their research that the average particle size in $CaCO_3$ precipitation is in the range of 1 - 3 μm. This was reduced by the decrease in the CO_2 bubble sizes. For the carbon capture, gaseous CO_2 is used to form carbonates which, when dissolved in an ionic solution, dissociates. Equations (3) - (6) summarise the reactions of CO_2 dissolution and dissociation. The concentration of the carbonates is pH dependent, as shown in Figure 1(b) (Bjerrum plot).

$$CO_2(g) \rightleftharpoons CO_2(aq) \qquad K_h \tag{3}$$

$$CO_2(aq) + H_2O(l) \rightleftharpoons H_2CO_3(aq) \qquad K_0 \tag{4}$$

$$H_2CO_3(aq) \rightleftharpoons HCO_3^-(aq) + H^+(aq) \qquad K_{a1} \tag{5}$$

$$HCO_3^-(aq) \rightleftharpoons CO_3^{2-}(aq) + H^+(aq) \qquad K_{a2} \tag{6}$$

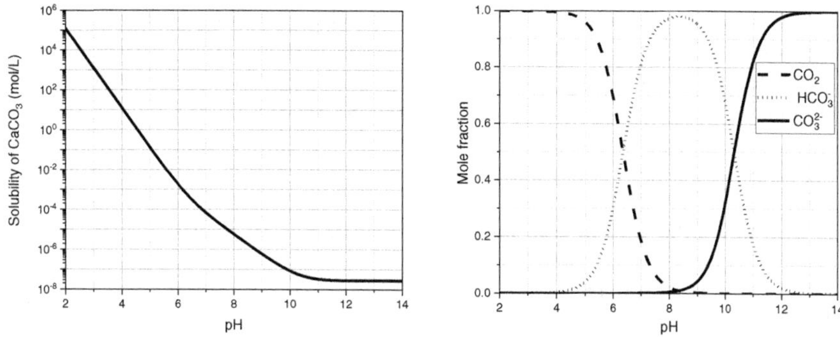

Figure 1: (L to R) (a) Solubility vs. pH plot for $CaCO_3$, (b) species' concentrations vs. pH (Bjerrum plot).

In this study, we focus on model development for the precipitation process of $CaCO_3$ in a semi-batch operation and experimental investigation of it. The ultimate goal is to develop a self-learning adaptive controller to produce calcium and magnesium carbonates selectively, starting from mine wastes. For controlling particle growth, we intend to add seed crystals in a well-dosed manner in such a way that nucleation in the solution, which is often difficult to control, should be largely suppressed.

2. Experimentation and Methods

2.1. Preparation of Calcium carbonate

The following reagents were used: HCl, $CaCl_2$, $MgCl_2$, CO_2(g), $Ca(OH)_2$ and $CaCO_3$ seed particles. A cylindrical vessel made of Pyrex glass with a 7.5 cm diameter and 500 ml volume was used as a reactor. Magnetic stirring was applied to homogenize the reaction mixture. The pH was monitored by the use of a Seven2Go meter (Mettler Toledo).

For the first set of experiments, different amounts of $CaCl_2$ were dissolved in HCl solution at pH 3. CO_2 was bubbled into this acidic solution through a gas flowmeter until saturation was reached. Since the carbonate precipitation takes place at higher pH values, saturated $Ca(OH)_2$ at pH 12.5 was added at a constant flow rate of 3 ml/min through a diaphragm pump. At pH 7, 60 mg of calcite seeds were added to the mixture. The reactor was stirred at 350 rpm. In the second set of experiments, along with $CaCl_2$, different amounts of $MgCl_2$ were dissolved in the HCl solution to study the impact of Mg on the $CaCO_3$ precipitation. The experiments were conducted at room temperature of 20 °C.

The precipitated particles formed were analyzed using X-ray diffraction (D2 Phaser, Bruker) and thermogravimetric analysis (TGA/DSC3, Mettler Toledo). The initial and final concentrations of the dissolved ions were evaluated using ion chromatography (Dionex Aquion, Thermo scientific). The particle size distributions were measured using laser diffraction (Mastersizer 30cc00, Malvern).

2.2. Methodology and Modeling

For a simple batch precipitation process, the population balance equation (PBE) reads:

$$\frac{\partial n(t,x)}{\partial t}+\frac{\partial(G(t,x)\cdot n(t,x))}{\partial x}=\dot{B}(t,x)-\dot{D}(t,x) \tag{7}$$

where n is the number density (#/m^3 of the solution), G is the growth rate, and $\dot{B}$ and $\dot{D}$ are the birth and death rates, respectively, due to nucleation, agglomeration and breakage.

For selective precipitation and high purity of the produced carbonates, it is desirable that the precipitation is dominated by the growth of the seeds added, rather than by nucleation. If this would be the case, assuming size-independent growth and an initial boundary condition for seeding, $n(t=0,x)=n_0(x)$, the PBE reads:

$$\frac{\partial n(x,t)}{\partial t}+G(t)\frac{\partial n(x,t)}{\partial x}=0 \tag{8}$$

The dynamics of the liquid phase concentration $c(t)$ is described by:

$$\frac{dc(t)}{dt}=-\rho^m k_v G(t) m_2(t) \tag{9}$$

where ρ^m is the molar density of the solid, k_v is the shape factor and m_2 is the second moment of the number density distribution, corresponding to the total surface area of the particle population. A similar approach was used to model the shape-specific crystal growth under controlled supersaturation by Eisenschmidt *et al.* (2015). For ideal batch operation of seeded selective precipitation of carbonates, the simulated dynamics of crystal growth and the simultaneous change of liquid phase concentration for a monodispersed solution are depicted in Figure 2, based on typical parameters taken from literature. The growth rates for the two types of crystals are different, the crystal with a larger rate grows more quickly than the other.

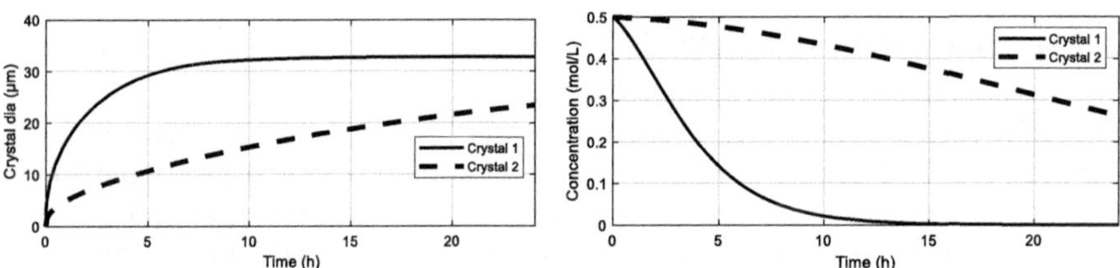

Figure 2: (L to R) (a) Crystal growth of two different carbonate species with different growth rates. (b) Simultaneous decay of the liquid concentration due to particle growth.

3. Results and Discussion

3.1. Particle size distribution

In order to extract the metallic ions from mine waste, the feedstocks were exposed to an acidic solution (HCl). This extraction process was investigated by researchers at the Karlsruhe Institute of Technology (KIT). The extracted solution was filtered and the ion-rich filtrate was supplied for carbonate precipitation in the authors' laboratory.

For the present study, however, pure substances at concentrations, similar to the concentrations obtained in the mine waste extraction solutions, were used. Carbonate precipitation was carried out by the pH swing method, i.e. by shifting the solution pH from 3 to 11 by addition of saturated $Ca(OH)_2$ solution at 3 ml/min. The resulting final particle size distribution of the precipitated carbonates was measured. To achieve a controlled precipitation of calcium carbonate, crystal growth was initiated by seeding of particles (secondary nucleation). For this purpose, 60 mg of Calcite seeds with a nominal size of 60-100 μm were added to the solution at pH 7, where the solubility of $CaCO_3$ was about 10^{-4} mol/L (see Figure 1(a)) such that the seeds did not dissolve.

The measured number density-based particle size distributions (PSD) are shown in Figure 3. The seed size of 60 -100 μm (Figure 3(a)) was chosen to be able to distinguish clearly between seed particles and possibly formed nuclei. When the pH was increased from 7 to 9, the precipitation of $CaCO_3$ proceeded via primary nucleation. This is evident from Figure 3(b), where nuclei were formed spontaneously, and consequently, the PSD shifted to the lower size class (towards the right). As the pH of the solution was further increased, the solution became turbid due to pronounced primary nucleation. The nuclei formed were in the range of 0.6 – 4 μm with a mean size of 0.9 μm, see Figure 3(c).

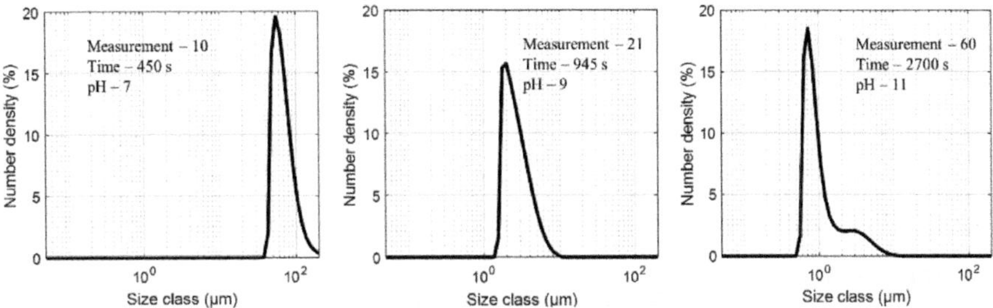

Figure 3: Particle size distribution (PSD) from the Mastersizer (a) Calcite seed crystals added. (b) Big number of small nuclei formed spontaneously. (c) PSD dominated by nuclei population.

As discussed in Section 2.2, the initial model assumes a batch precipitation process which is controlled by particle growth, starting from seeds. But the experimental results clearly indicate the need for a nucleation term to be incorporated in the PBE. In addition, we consider now a semi-batch reactor and then obtain the following model equations:

$$\frac{\partial n(x,t)}{\partial t} = -G(t)\frac{\partial n(x,t)}{\partial x} - J(t) f_{nuc}(t) \tag{10}$$

$$V(t)\frac{dc(t)}{dt} = -c(t)\,\dot{V}_{in} + r\,V(t) - \rho^m k_v\,G(t)\,m_2(t) - \rho^m\,v_{nuc}\,J(t) \tag{11}$$

where J is the rate of nucleation. A possible approach for calculating J, along with the method of its experimental measurement, is described in detail by Liendo et al. (2022). r stands for the rate of the chemical reaction, $\dot{V}_{in}$ is the feed rate of the base used for the pH swing, i.e. $Ca(OH)_2$. Eqs. (10) and (11) along with the initial boundary condition for seeding, $n(t = 0, x) = n_0(x)$ as mentioned before, can be used for the development of a suitable process controller.

3.2. Crystal morphology

As discussed in the previous section, precipitation was found to be dominated by primary nucleation, not by the growth of the seeds. One of the reasons for this observation could be the difference of the morphologies of the nuclei formed and the calcite seeds added. This difference is evident from the XRD analysis as well as the imaging of the precipitated particles. To investigate this further, two sets of precipitation measurements were performed: 1) with only $CaCl_2$ and 2) $MgCl_2$ along with $CaCl_2$. It was observed that for the first set, vaterite is precipitated predominantly, which over time, transforms to calcite. But, when the Mg^{2+} ions were introduced, metastable aragonite precipitates along with some amount of calcite. The XRD analysis for this material is shown in Figure 4. The size of the nuclei formed was, however, slightly smaller with than without Mg^{2+} ions. This could be due to the smaller size of the needle-like aragonite crystals compared to the orthorhombic vaterite crystals.

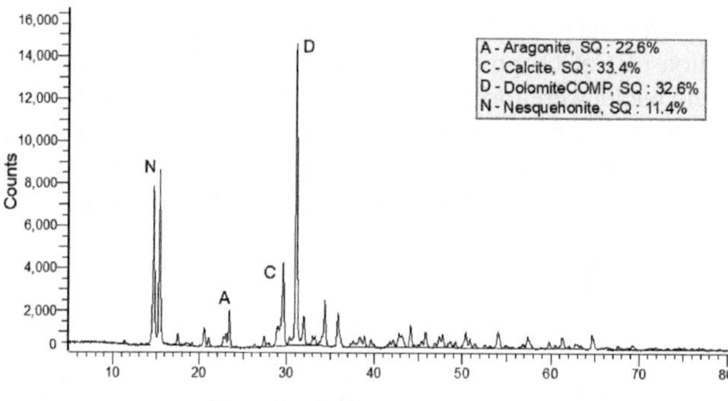

Figure 4: XRD analysis of calcium carbonate precipitates obtained in the presence of Mg^{2+} ions.

4. Conclusion

The experimental investigation of $CaCO_3$ precipitation showed that the precipitation is highly dependent on the kinetics of the reaction which is not only dependent on the Ca^{2+} and CO_3^{2-} ion concentrations but also affected by the presence of other ions. Depending on the reaction, nucleation, and growth kinetics, the morphology of the formed precipitate changes. The most important aspect is whether the precipitation of particles happens either via primary nucleation or via secondary nucleation (growth of seeds). In the absence of impurities, vaterite and calcite nuclei are formed, whereas by addition of Mg^{2+} ions aragonite is the preferred morphology. The nuclei formed were in the size class from 0.6 to 4.0 μm. At a pH level above 10, resulting in a correspondingly very high supersaturation S, the nuclei formed strongly dominate the particle size distribution. Therefore, the primary nucleation phenomenon needs to be incorporated in the model equations along with a suitable growth rate expression for calcium carbonate.

5. Acknowledgement

Funded by the Deutsche Forschungsgemeinschaft (DFG, German Research Foundation) - SPP 2364 "*Autonomous Processes in Particle Technology – Research and Testing of Concepts for Model-based Control of Particulate Processes*" - project no. 504852622.

6. References

Bobicki ER, Liu Q, Xu Z, Zeng H. 2012. Carbon capture and storage using alkaline industrial wastes. *Progress in Energy & Combustion Sci.* 38(2): 302-320.

Eisenschmidt H, Voigt A, Sundmacher K. 2015. Face-specific growth and dissolution kinetics of potassium dihydrogen phosphate crystals from batch crystallization experiments. *Cryst. Growth Des.* 15(1):219–227.

Falini G, Fermani S, Tosi G, Dinelli E. 2009. Calcium carbonate morphology and structure in the presence of seawater ions and humic acids. *Cryst. Growth Des.* 9(5):2065–2072.

Feng B, Yong AK, An H. 2007. Effect of various factors on the particle size of calcium carbonate formed in a precipitation process. *Materials Science and Engineering: A.* 445–446:170–79

Koutsoukos PG, Kontoyannis CG. 1984. Precipitation of Calcium Carbonate in aqueous solutions. *J. Chem. Soc. - Faraday Transactions I.* 80:1181-1192.

Liendo F, Arduino M, Deorsola FA, Bensaid S. 2022. Nucleation and growth kinetics of $CaCO_3$ crystals in the presence of foreign monovalent ions. *J. Cryst. Growth* 578:126406.

Park WK, Ko SJ, Lee SW, Cho KH, Ahn JW, Han C. 2008. Effects of magnesium chloride and organic additives on the synthesis of aragonite precipitated calcium carbonate. *J. Cryst. Growth* 310(10):2593–2601.

Flavio Manenti, Gintaras V. Reklaitis (Eds.), Proceedings of the 34th European Symposium on Computer Aided Process Engineering / 15th International Symposium on Process Systems Engineering (ESCAPE34/PSE24), June 2-6, 2024, Florence, Italy
 http://dx.doi.org/10.1016/B978-0-443-28824-1.50255-6

Analysis of the Catalytic Splitting of H_2S for H_2 Production

Anna Nova, Simone Caspani, Flavio Manenti*

Politecnico di Milano, CMIC Dept. "Giulio Natta", Piazza Leonardo da Vinci 32, Milan 20133, Italy

flavio.manenti@polimi.it

Abstract

The splitting of hydrogen sulphide to produce value-added products, namely hydrogen and elemental sulphur, represents a promising route for the treatment of H_2S, a hazardous waste gas, and for a circular production of hydrogen. The decomposition reaction has been studied in a plug flow reactor on the catalyst MoS_2 for temperatures ranging between 640 and 929 °C and with a H_2S partial pressure of 1.27 kPa. Equilibrium conversions have been reached for residence times below 3 s and the apparent activation energy of 71.894 kJ/mol has been calculated. The catalytic decomposition on MoS_2 results therefore to be an interesting pathway for the production of H_2 from H_2s.

Keywords: hydrogen sulphide, H_2S splitting, H_2 production, kinetics, molybdenum disulphide

1. Introduction

Hydrogen sulphide (H_2S) is a poisonous and dangerous compound, the presence of which affects many fossil and renewable resources. It is also produced in industrial processes that involve desulphurization. H_2S is usually processed through the Claus process, which partially oxidizes it into sulphur and water. An interesting alternative is represented by the splitting of H_2S (Chan et al., 2023), which leads to the production of hydrogen and sulphur. The reaction involved is the following:

$$H_2S \rightarrow H_2 + \frac{1}{2}S_2 \quad (1)$$

The production of hydrogen is particularly interesting for the energy sector and the chemical industry. In a previous study, the simulation of a plant producing H_2 through the thermal decomposition of H_2S has been developed, proving the commercial interest of the process (Nova et al., 2023b). A variety of H_2S decomposition methods have been studied, including thermal, catalytic, non-thermal plasma-based, electrolytic, and biological processes (Zheng et al., 2023). However, the upscale production of hydrogen from H_2S has not been realized. The most substantial quantities of hydrogen sulphide are produced by large-scale plants. For a possible industrial application, carrying out the reaction with high flow rates and therefore reduced residence times is of fundamental importance. For this reason, this study focused on the analysis of the catalytic H_2S splitting.

The chosen catalyst is MoS_2; one of the early investigated catalysts which still appears to be among the most active ones for the reaction of interest (Aljama et al., 2023). Understanding the reaction and its kinetics in presence of MoS_2 is fundamental to improve its energy efficiency and conversion. Few studies investigated the reaction and its kinetic aspects. A Hougen-Watson adsorption model was chosen to represent the reaction mechanism (Kaloidas and Papayannakos, 1991). The rate-determining step resulted to be the cleavage of the hydrogen-sulphur bonds of the H_2S adsorbed on the catalyst active sites. Burra et al. (2018) compared catalysts of their production with MoS_2 in H_2S partial pressures between 10 and 50 kPa. The particle size of their catalysts was ~400 μm. Below 1000 K, the yield of H_2 obtained from MoS_2 was higher than the one obtained with every other tested oxide catalyst. They also calculated activation energies and orders of reactions with respect to H_2S.

The present work aims at presenting a new set of experimental data, obtained by performing the reaction between 640 and 929 °C, and at a lower H_2S partial pressure (1.27 kPa), compared to previous studies. This allows kinetic evaluations, like the apparent activation energy of the reaction. Starting from the same data, it will be possible to develop a kinetic model and regress the kinetic parameters.

2. Experimental setup

The core of the setup built for the experimental campaigns (Figure 1) is the quartz reactor, designed as a Plug Flow Reactor (PFR) and placed inside a tubular oven. The feed is represented by a gaseous H_2S/N_2 mixture with a concentration of H_2S equal to 1.5 wt%. The flow rate can be tuned ranging between 1 and 100 L/h. At the exit of the reactor, the scrubbing of sulphur from the outlet reaction gas is performed by passing it through distilled water. A stilling chamber reduces the risk of potentially entrained water droplets. Suitable filters ensure the total removal of any solid and liquid particle from the stream. The gases are analyzed with an Agilent 490 Micro GC (Micro Gas Chromatograph). The catalyst
is constituted of 0.5 g of Molybdenum(IV) sulfide powder (particle size below 44 μm, 99% pure, Thermo Fisher), sandwiched between two layers of quartz wool and placed in the isothermal zone of the reactor.

The reliability of the experimental setup has first been tested by performing the H_2S splitting reaction in thermodynamic regime (Nova et al., 2023a). During the campaign investigating the catalytic splitting, temperatures from 640 to 929 °C have been considered and the total inlet gas flow rate has been varied to determine the conversion at different residence times. The reaction pressure has been kept at 1 bar.

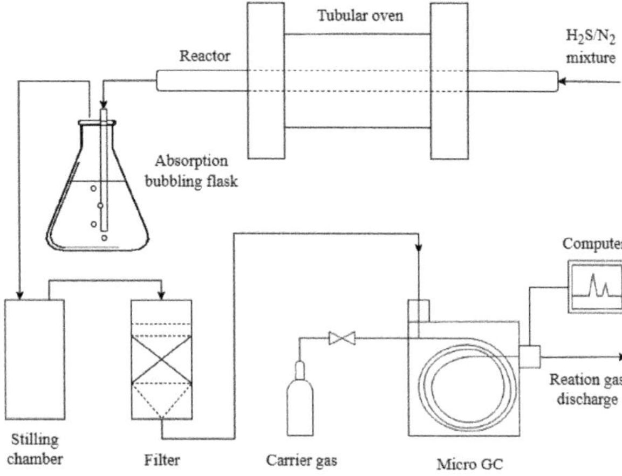

Figure 1 - Experimental setup.

3. Results and discussion

The reaction has been performed with a H_2S partial pressure of 1.27 kPa and at four different temperatures (640, 740, 831, and 929 °C). Five inlet flow rates have been considered (100, 80, 50, 30, and 10 L/h), corresponding to five different residence times inside the reactor. The experimentally obtained H_2 concentrations are reported in Table 1. The errors correspond to the standard deviation calculated from all the composition measurements.

Table 1 - Experimental H_2 concentrations obtained by performing the catalytic splitting of H_2S in the described conditions.

T [°C]	Inlet flow rate [L/h]	Residence time [s]	H_2 concentration [mol%]
640	100	0.8	0.029 ± 0.001
640	80	1.0	0.038 ± 0.001
640	50	1.6	0.055 ± 0.001
640	30	2.7	0.059 ± 0.001
640	10	8.0	0.089 ± 0.001
740	100	0.7	0.086 ± 0.001
740	80	0.9	0.099 ± 0.004
740	50	1.4	0.126 ± 0.053
740	30	2.4	0.152 ± 0.004
740	10	7.2	0.203 ± 0.004
831	100	0.7	0.195 ± 0.003
831	80	0.8	0.242 ± 0.012
831	50	1.3	0.270 ± 0.010
831	30	2.2	0.310 ± 0.006
831	10	6.7	0.333 ± 0.004
929	100	0.6	0.454 ± 0.001
929	80	0.8	0.483 ± 0.004
929	50	1.2	0.490 ± 0.005
929	30	2.0	0.498 ± 0.002
929	10	6.1	0.512 ± 0.005

Starting from the hydrogen concentrations, measured experimentally, the corresponding H_2S conversion has been calculated (see Figure 2).

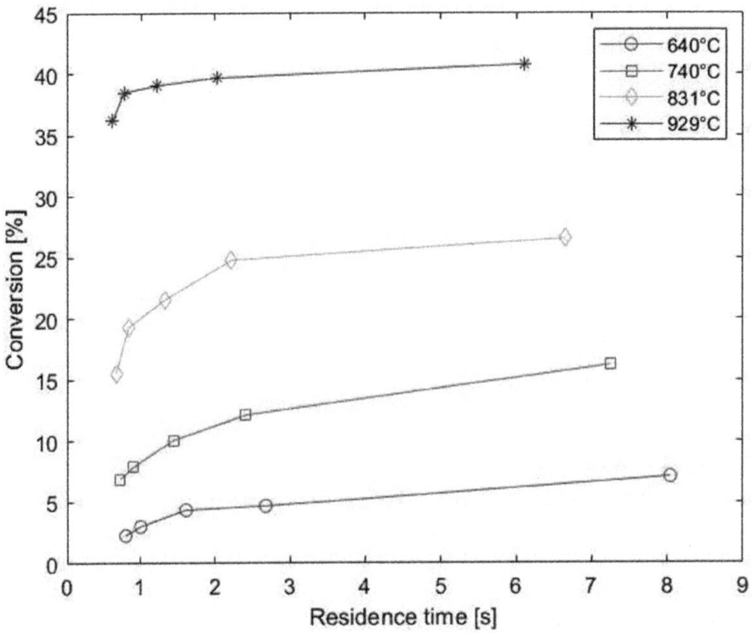

Figure 2 - H_2S conversion at different reaction temperatures and residence times.

The conversion increases with the residence time. In particular, values of conversions almost equal to those obtained at thermodynamic equilibrium start to be reached already at residence times comprised between 2 and 3 s. These residence times correspond to inlet gas flow rates of 30 L/h (see Table 1). These results can be compared with the conversions measured by performing the reaction with the same setup, working pressure, and inlet mixture, but in absence of a catalyst. In this case, the thermodynamic equilibrium is reached at residence times longer than 8 s (corresponding to a 2 L/h inlet flow rate). This shows that, in presence of the catalyst, the same value of conversion, the thermodynamic equilibrium value, is reached with shorter residence times. The experimental H_2 concentrations and corresponding conversions at equilibrium conditions are reported in Table 2.

Table 2 - H_2 concentrations and conversions at the thermodynamic equilibrium, measured by performing the reaction in absence of a catalyst and with a gas inlet flow rate of 2 L/h.

T [°C]	H_2 concentration [mol%]	Conversion [%]
640	0.063 ± 0.006	4.9 ± 0.6
740	0.173 ± 0.006	13.7 ± 0.6
831	0.34 ± 0.01	27 ± 1
929	0.533 ± 0.008	42.3 ± 0.8

To evaluate the reproducibility of the results, the deactivation trend of the catalyst, MoS_2, has been studied. A batch of fresh catalyst has been loaded into the reactor and a series of experiments have been carried out while monitoring the H_2 concentration as the catalyst working time progressed. In Figure 3 the results are presented for a reaction temperature of 740°C. As can be seen, no significant reduction of the catalyst efficiency can be observed. Therefore, in our operating conditions, in absence of impurities and within 10 h of activity, the MoS_2 powder is stable and does not show signs of deactivation or poisoning. This is in accordance with EDX analyses performed on MoS_2 after 2 h of activity, which highlighted no additional sulfur formation from the reaction (Burra et al., 2018)

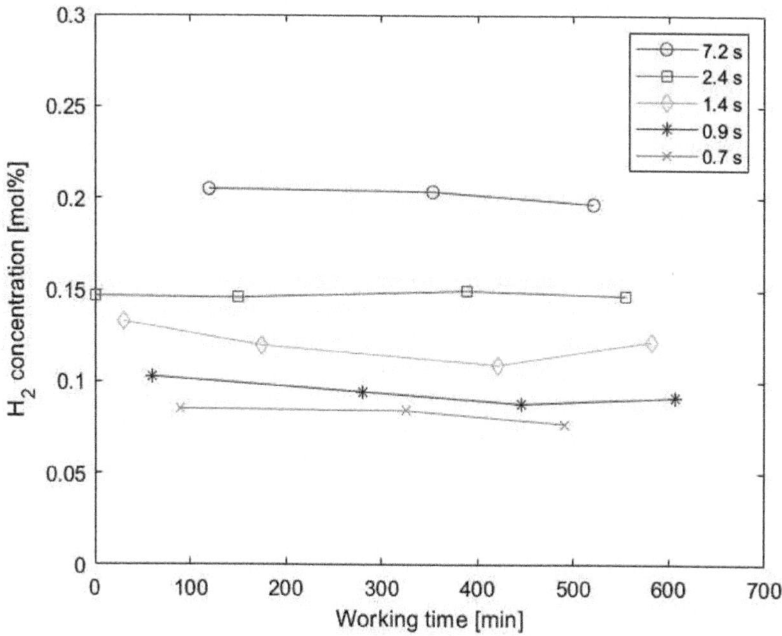

Figure 3 - H_2 concentration obtained by performing the splitting at 740°C, with different residence times, plotted against the time of activity of the catalyst.

For each inlet flow rate, the natural logarithm of the H_2S consumption rate has been plotted against the reciprocal of the reaction temperature . The slopes of the resulting lines represent the corresponding E/R values (where R denotes the universal gas constant and E the activation energy). In Figure 4 the Arrhenius plot for the 30 L/h case has been reported. The corresponding E is 67.470 kJ/mol. The activation energies obtained for each flow rate have been averaged to determine the apparent activation energy, equal to 71.894 kJ/mol. This value is in agreement with the literature data. For MoS_2, Burra et al. (2018) calculated an activation energy of around 50 kJ/mol. The difference is probably due to the lower H_2S inlet partial pressure employed in this study and to the smaller particle size of the catalyst. Also, the apparent activation energy is lower than that displayed by many catalysts, like metal oxides (γ-Al2O3, α-Fe2O3, V_2O_5) (Reshetenko et al., 2002) and sulphides (Meeyoo et al., 1996).

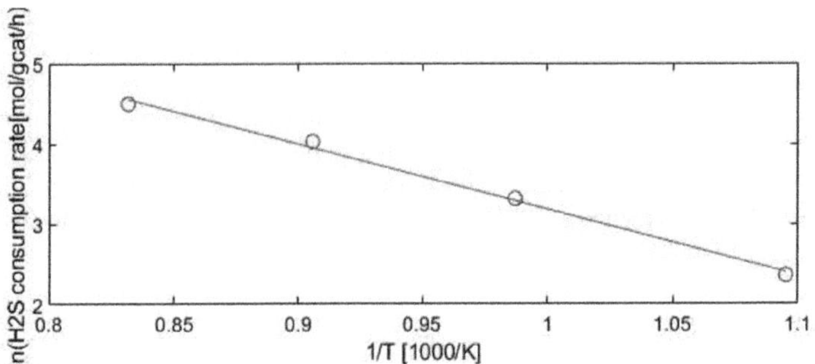

Figure 4 - Arrhenius plot, for the case of an inlet flow rate of 30 L/h.

4. Conclusions

The catalytic splitting of H_2S has been studied with an experimental campaign, in which the reaction has been performed at temperatures between 640 and 929 °C, with a partial pressure of H_2S of 1.27 kPa, and in the presence of MoS_2 as a catalyst. From the conversion values, it appears that thermodynamic equilibrium is reached with residence times lower than 3 s. The activity of the catalyst was monitored and up to 10 hours of activity no signs of reduction in the efficiency are shown. The apparent activation energy has been calculated and is equal to 71.894 kJ/mol. Starting from the set of data obtained, it will be possible to better understand the kinetics of the reaction, and eventually employ it in reactor and plant design. The splitting of H_2S could improve the performances of different plants and specifically of refineries, providing a source of hydrogen from a dangerous waste product.

References

H. Aljama, Z. Alaithan, A. Almofleh, 2023. Catalytic Conversion of H $_2$ S to H $_2$: Challenges and Catalyst Limitations. J. Phys. Chem. C 127, 9022–9029.

K.R.G. Burra, G. Bassioni, A.K. Gupta, 2018. Catalytic transformation of H2S for H2 production. International Journal of Hydrogen Energy 43, 22852–22860.

Y.H. Chan, A.C.M. Loy, K.W. Cheah, S.Y.W. Chai, L.H. Ngu, B.S. How, C. Li, S.S.M. Lock, M.K. Wong, C.L. Yiin, B.L.F. Chin, Z.P. Chan, S.S. Lam, 2023. Hydrogen sulfide (H2S) conversion to hydrogen (H2) and value-added chemicals: Progress, challenges and outlook. Chemical Engineering Journal 458, 141398.

V.E. Kaloidas, N.G. Papayannakos, 1991. Kinetic studies on the catalytic decomposition of hydrogen sulfide in a tubular reactor. Ind. Eng. Chem. Res. 30, 345–351.

V. Meeyoo, A.A. Adesina, G. Foulds, 1996. The kinetics of H2S decomposition over precipitated cobalt sulphide catalyst. Chemical Engineering Communications 144, 1–17.

A. Nova, F. Negri, F. Manenti, 2023a. Multi-scale Modelling and Experimental Investigation of Hydrogen Sulphide Thermal Decomposition. Computer Aided Chemical Engineering 52, 2411–2416.

A. Nova, K. Prifti, F. Negri, F. Manenti, 2023b. Multiscale techno-economic analysis of orange hydrogen synthesis. Energy 282.

T.V. Reshetenko, S.R. Khairulin, Z.R. Ismagilov, V.V. Kuznetsov, 2002. Study of the reaction of high-temperature H2S decomposition on metal oxides (γ-Al2O3, α-Fe2O3, V2O5). International Journal of Hydrogen Energy 27, 387–394.

X. Zheng, G. Lei, S. Wang, L. Shen, Y. Zhan, L. Jiang, 2023. Advances in Resources Recovery of H_2S: A Review of Desulfurization Processes and Catalysts. ACS Catal. 13, 11723–11752.

Flavio Manenti, Gintaras V. Reklaitis (Eds.), Proceedings of the 34th European Symposium on Computer Aided Process Engineering / 15th International Symposium on Process Systems Engineering (ESCAPE34/PSE24), June 2-6, 2024, Florence, Italy
 http://dx.doi.org/10.1016/B978-0-443-28824-1.50256-8

Spatially Distributed Power-to-Methanol Plants in Dissimilar Locations: Specific or Standardized Designs?

Tibor Svitnič [a,]* and Kai Sundmacher [a,b]

[a] *Max Planck Institute for Dynamics of Complex Technical Systems, Department for Process Systems Engineering, Sandtorstr. 1, 39106 Magdeburg, Germany*
[b] *Otto von Guericke University, Chair for Process Systems Engineering, Universitätsplatz 2, 39106 Magdeburg, Germany*
svitnic@mpi-magdeburg.mpg.de

Abstract

Fossil-based production of methanol is a strong contributor to the greenhouse gas emissions of the chemical industry. The Power-to-MeOH (PtM) process is an emerging alternative, which utilizes renewable resources making its rapid deployment desired in order to mitigate the negative consequences of climate change. This study explores the standardization of Power-to-Methanol (PtM) plants to reduce project timelines and engineering costs. The focus is on standardizing the production capacities of the deployed sub-processes of the production plants across locations with different renewable resource conditions. For this purpose, a multi-objective optimization approach is proposed, where PtM plants are designed for solar-dominant, wind-dominant, and mixed-solar/wind energy resource locations simultaneously, to evaluate the cost trade-off between standard and location-specific designs. Preliminary results, based on time-aggregated renewable resource profiles for one triplet of design locations, indicate that most processes can be standardized with relatively little cost increases due to the reduction of the degrees of freedom. Standardization of the PEM electrolyzer capacities accounts for the major proportion of the cost increases, suggesting it as the process, which should be designed for each location specifically. However, further investigation of additional locations with more detailed renewable resource profiles is needed for a more comprehensive understanding of the balance between design standardization and specificity.

Keywords: distributed production, modular design, standardization, Power-to-X.

1. Introduction

The transition to renewable sources of mass and energy is imperative to mitigate the environmental impact of conventional methanol production, which accounts for a tenth of the greenhouse gas emissions of the chemical sector (Tabibian and Sharifzadeh, 2023). First industrial scale Power-to-Methanol (PtM) production facilities, using captured carbon dioxide and hydrogen produced from water electrolysis are starting to emerge to address this need. Nonetheless, their combined installed capacities represent less than 0.2% of the total methanol production (Tabibian and Sharifzadeh, 2023). With the aim of speeding up the deployment of such facilities and identifying new competitive business cases, it is of interest to explore the concept of design standardization of geographically distributed production plants. This concept is closely tied to modular design principles already penetrating into the process engineering domain (Zhang et al. 2022), which could lead to overall reductions of engineering costs as well as shortening of project timelines (Baldea et al., 2017).

However, in particular, standardization of processes across locations with different renewable resource conditions (e.g. solar irradiation and wind speed profiles) is so far left unexplored. Such standardization could offer an opportunity to streamline the manufacturing and deployment procedures for engineering & construction companies with a global customer base. Yet, standardization inherently comes hand in hand with a reduction of degrees of freedom in the design problem, which could result in additional production costs if it would be too extensive and the specificity of the local renewable energy conditions would be excessively disregarded.

In order to find the right balance between specificity and standardization at an early stage of process synthesis, a multi-objective optimization method for the identification standardized process sections is proposed and applied to the PtM plant design case.

2. Method

Herein the design problems of the PtM plants are solved simultaneously for multiple locations having distinct renewable resource characteristics (in this study: Mejillones, Chile = solar-dominant, Cabo Negro, Chile = wind-dominant and Port Arthur, USA = mixed-solar/wind energy resources) with additional constraints imposing standardization.

The design problems incorporate the selection of installed capacities of the processes among the energy generation, chemical production, utility and storage subsystems together with the fluctuations of the energy resources and waste-heat utilization (Svitnič et al. 2023). The process network for the studied PtM process is shown in Figure 1.

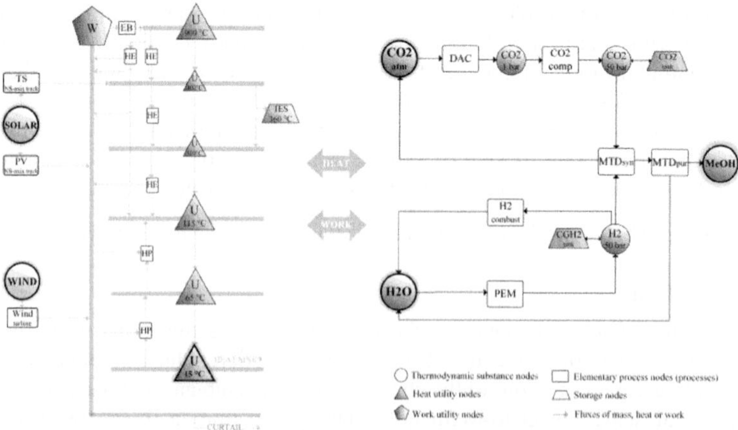

Figure 1 Power-to-Methanol process network showing the different processes considered for the design: DAC = direct air capture of CO_2, CO2comp = CO_2 compressor, CO2tank = CO_2 storage tank, MTDsyn = methanol synthesis process, MTDpur = methanol purification process, H2combust = hydrogen combustion chamber, CGH2 = compressed gaseous hydrogen storage, PEM = proton exchange membrane electrolyzer, EB = electric boiler, HE = heat engines (steam turbines), HP = heat pumps, TES = thermal energy storage (phase change material), TS = thermal solar energy generation (parabolic troughs, sun tracking with horizontal north-south axis), PV = photovoltaic panels (sun tracking with horizontal north-south axis).

Time-aggregation of the yearly renewable resource profiles of solar irradiation (Sengupta et al., 2018) and wind speed (Staffell and Pfenninger, 2016) for the year 2019 with a resolution of 1-hour was implemented based on a k-medoids clustering algorithm to reduce the computational complexity of the model (Kotzur et al., 2018). The underlying modeling approach with constraints and parameters of the optimization problem describing the functioning of the processes, storages and heat integration are described in detail in our previous work (Svitnič and Sundmacher, 2022). Here we report only relevant extensions exclusive to this study.

The objective of the resulting mixed-integer linear programming problem was to minimize the total levelized costs of methanol across all locations, shown in Eq. (1).

$$LCOMeOH_{total} = \sum_{l} LCOMeOH_{(l)} \qquad l,ll \in \{Meji,Cabo,Port\ Arthur\} \tag{1}$$

The second objective function, used as a measure of standardization, accounted for the total number of standard/common design pairs of processes and storages, which were selected to have equal installed capacities across the different locations. It was included into the optimization problem through the ϵ-constraint method (Eq. (2) and (3)).

$$N_{common} \geq \epsilon_{limit} \tag{2}$$

$$N_{common} = N_{common,p} + N_{common,s} \tag{3}$$

The numbers of common design pairs were calculated for a subset of processes and storages according to Eq. (4) and (5). The installed capacities for the energy-generation processes (photovoltaic panels, parabolic troughs, wind turbines) with their already standard modular structure were scaled for each location without imposing further standardization constraints to reach a methanol production of 40,000 t/y in each location.

$$N_{common,p} = \sum_{l:\, ord(l)>ord(ll)} \sum_{p_c} xp_{com,(p_c,l,ll)} \tag{4}$$

$$p_c \in \{PEM, MTD_{syn}, MTD_{pur}, DAC, CO2_{comp}, H2_{comb}, HE, HP, EB\}$$

$$N_{common,s} = \sum_{l:\, ord(l)>ord(ll)} \sum_{c_{stor}} xs_{com,(p_c,l,ll)} \qquad c_{stor} \in \{CGH2, CO2tank, TES\} \tag{5}$$

Binary variables (xp_{com} and xs_{com}) were used to identify the design pairs with identical installed process (λ_{nom}) or storage (S_{nom}) capacities selected across the different locations with the constraints shown in Eq. (6) and (7).

$$xp_{com,(p_c,l,ll)} = \begin{cases} 1, & \lambda_{nom,(p_c,l)} = \lambda_{nom,(p_c,ll)} \\ 0, & otherwise \end{cases} \qquad \forall l,ll:\ ord(l)>ord(ll) \tag{6}$$

$$xs_{com,(c_{stor},l,ll)} = \begin{cases} 1, & S_{nom,(c_{stor},l)} = S_{nom,(c_{stor},ll)} \\ 0, & otherwise \end{cases} \quad \forall l,ll:\ ord(l)>ord(ll) \tag{7}$$

The condition using the order function of the location index ($ord(l)$) imposed on Eq. (6) and (7) makes sure that all of the possible design pairs across the considered locations are accounted for exactly once and no redundant constraints/binary variables are introduced. This can be illustrated with the help of a location matrix (Eq. (8)) created by applying this condition for the studied three-location design case, which marks the design pairs across the different locations to be included in the optimization problem.

$$loc_{matrix} = \begin{matrix} & M & C & P \\ M & & & \\ C & & & \\ P & & & \end{matrix} \begin{pmatrix} 0 & 1 & 1 \\ 0 & 0 & 1 \\ 0 & 0 & 0 \end{pmatrix} \quad M{=}Mejillones,\ \ C{=}Cabo\ Negro,\ \ P{=}Port\ Arthur \tag{8}$$

3. Results

The main outcomes of this study are Pareto fronts, which highlight the increasing production costs due to reduced design flexibility for different extents of standardization across the various locations for a cost scenario with a reference year of 2018. An example Pareto front for an aggregated time-series using five typical days is shown in Figure 2. Here one can see the production-cost difference between a specific design for each location and a standard design for all locations (including the intermediate design solutions in-between).

The relatively big increase in costs towards the fully standardized design is due to the standardization of the PEM electrolyzer size (Figure 3), which adjusts the installed capacity according to the solar-dominant location, where the electrolyzer needs to be oversized to allow for storage of hydrogen during the night. This installed capacity is then imposed on the locations with stronger wind-energy conditions, where such electrolyzer overcapacity is not needed, leading to an increase of production costs.

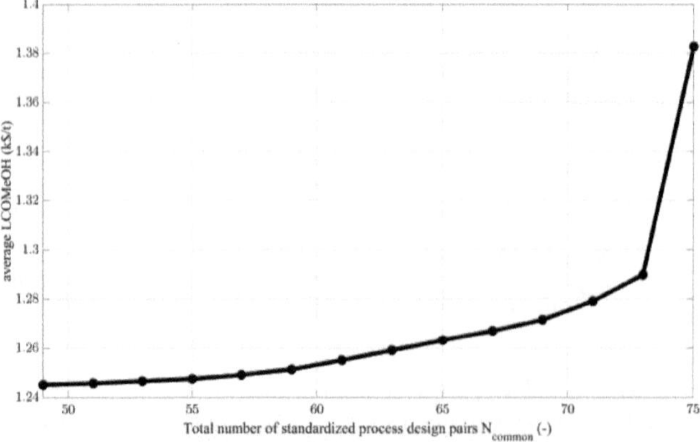

Figure 2 Pareto front of the average LCOMeOH in the three design locations and the total number of standardized processes design pairs (N_{common}) as the measure for the extent of standardization for renewable resource profiles aggregated with five typical days.

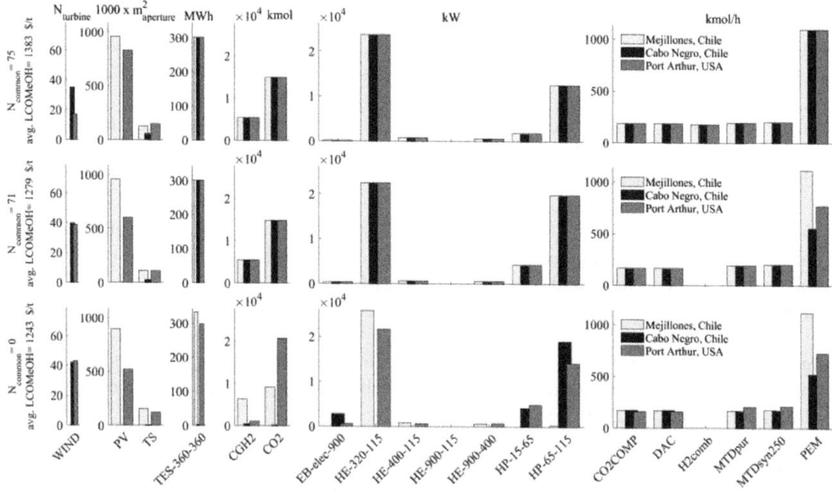

Figure 3 Selection of particular designs from the Pareto-front showing the installed process capacities of the identified designs with different levels of standardization; N_{common} equal to 0 (bottom) suggests that no standardization is imposed (i.e. fully specific designs), N_{common} equal to 75 (top), which is the maximum possible for our instance of the model, represents a fully standardized design deployed in all 3 locations, N_{common} equal to 71 (middle) is a possible intermediate solution with the only the PEM electrolyzer being designed specifically.

4. Conclusions

The preliminary results, with simplified renewable resource profiles, suggest that most of the processes can be standardized across the locations at a relatively little increase in costs (2.9%). Standardization of the installed capacities of the PEM electrolyzer is responsible for the majority of the cost-increases relative to the specific designs (8.4%, with the total increase of fully standard vs. specific designs being 11.3%), making it a prime candidate process to be designed specifically for each location with the rest of the plant being standardized. Nonetheless, further investigation is needed with more detailed renewable resource profiles for representative plant locations selected according to actual market potential. Additionally, the cost-reductions achievable by a more streamlined deployment of standardized plants, which could offset the identified cost-increases, need to be evaluated including a more detailed look at the intermediate solutions on the specific/standard design spectrum.

Acknowledgement

This work is part of the research initiative “SmartProSys: Intelligent Process Systems for the Sustainable Production of Chemicals” funded by the Ministry for Science, Energy, Climate Protection and the Environment of the State of Saxony-Anhalt.

References

M. Baldea, T.F. Edgar, B.L. Stanley and A.A. Kiss, 2017, Modular manufacturing processes: Status, challenges, and opportunities. AIChE J., 63, 4262-4272, https://doi.org/10.1002/aic.15872

L. Kotzur, P. Markewitz, M. Robinius and D. Stolten, 2018, Time series aggregation for energy system design: Modeling seasonal storage, Applied Energy, 326, 123-135, https://doi.org/10.1016/j.apenergy.2018.01.023.

S.S. Tabibian and M. Sharifzadeh, 2023, Statistical and analytical investigation of methanol applications, production technologies, value-chain and economy with a special focus on renewable methanol, Renewable and Sustainable Energy Reviews, 179, 113281, https://doi.org/10.1016/j.rser.2023.113281.

M. Sengupta, Y. Xie, A. Lopez, A. Habte, G. Maclaurin and J. Shelby, 2018, The National Solar Radiation Data Base (NSRDB), Renewable and Sustainable Energy Reviews, 89, 51-60, https://doi.org/10.1016/j.rser.2018.03.003.

I. Staffell and S. Pfenninger, 2016, Using bias-corrected reanalysis to simulate current and future wind power output, Energy, 114, 1224-1239, https://doi.org/10.1016/j.energy.2016.08.068.

T. Svitnič and K. Sundmacher, 2022, Renewable methanol production: Optimization-based design, scheduling and waste-heat utilization with the FluxMax approach, Applied Energy, 326, 120017, https://doi.org/10.1016/j.apenergy.2022.120017.

T. Svitnič, K. Beer, K. Sundmacher and M. Böcher, 2024, Optimal design of a sector-coupled renewable methanol production amid political goals and expected conflicts: Costs vs. land use, Sustainable Production and Consumption, 44, 123-150, https://doi.org/10.1016/j.spc.2023.12.003

C. Zhang, C. Jacobson, Q. Zhang, L. T. Biegler, J. C. Eslick, M. A. Zamarripa, D. Miller, G. Stinchfeld, J. D. Siirola, C. D. Laird, 2022, Optimization-based Design of Product Families with Common Components, Computer Aided Chemical Engineering, 49, 2022, 91-96, https://doi.org/10.1016/B978-0-323-85159-6.50015-4.

Flavio Manenti, Gintaras V. Reklaitis (Eds.), Proceedings of the 34th European Symposium on Computer Aided Process Engineering / 15th International Symposium on Process Systems Engineering (ESCAPE34/PSE24), June 2-6, 2024, Florence, Italy
 http://dx.doi.org/10.1016/B978-0-443-28824-1.50257-X

Flow regimes and reactivity assessment in arrow- and X-microreactors: a combined numerical and experimental approach

Sara Tomasi Masoni[a*], Alessandro Mariotti[a], Maria Vittoria Salvetti[a], Chiara Galletti[a], Elisabetta Brunazzi[a]

[a] *Dip. di Ingegneria Civile e Industriale, Università di Pisa, Largo Lucio Lazzarino 2, Pisa, Italy*

sara.tomasimasoni@phd.unipi.it

Abstract

In this study we use numerical simulations and experimental investigations to gain a comprehensive characterization of the flow dynamics inside microreactors. Two different simple geometries, namely the arrow- and the X-microreactors, are considered, both fed with reactive liquid streams. In both geometries, at low Reynolds number, Re, the streams stratify in the outlet channels due to the different densities of inlet solutions. At Re around 50, the X-microreactor exhibits a single central vortex in the mixing channels, leading to a highly mixed flow regime. By increasing the Reynolds number, the vortex elongates in the outlet channels and increases in size. Conversely, in the arrow-microreactor, three different flow regimes occur before transitioning to unsteady flow: the vortex, the engulfment, and the single-vortex regimes. Unlike the X-shaped geometry, the engulfment regime in the arrow geometry is characterized by the presence of two co-rotating vortices that extend in the outlet channel. The reaction yield is evaluated and compared in the two geometries, showing that higher performance is achieved when a single central vortex is present in the outlet channels.

Keywords: Microfluidics, microreactors, CFD simulations.

1. Introduction

Micromixers and microreactors consist of channels with a width ≤ 1mm. They ensure continuous operation and precise control over the reaction progress due to the large surface-to-volume ratio (Rossetti et al. 2016). This feature can be exploited to achieve very high reaction yields and selectivity, allowing the reduction of reagents and wastes.
As the efficient mixing is fundamental for ensuring high reaction yields, different designs have been proposed to enhance mixing because the typical flow regime is laminar. Among these, the T-micromixer is the most studied configuration. Despite its simple design, it exhibits different complex flow regimes as the Reynolds number increases (Mariotti et al. 2020).
In this work, we focus on two additional simple geometries, namely the X- and the arrow-microreactors, fed with reactive streams. The X- and the arrow-micromixer were characterized by feeding water (see Zhang et al. 2019 and Mariotti et al. 2019).
At low Reynolds numbers, in both geometries, the two inlet streams flow side by side in the mixing channel. By further increasing the Reynolds number, the vortex regime occurs in the arrow-micromixer, characterized by the presence of two U-shaped vortical structures in the mixing channel. Subsequently, at higher Reynolds numbers in the engulfment regime, only the two strongest legs persist in the outlet channel. With a further

increase in the Reynolds number in the arrow-micromixer, the two co-rotating vortices merge in the outlet channel, leading to a single-vortex regime.
Instead, the vortex regime does not occur in the X-micromixer, and the engulfment regime takes place at a lower Reynolds number compared to the arrow-geometry. In this case, the engulfment regime differs from that in the arrow-micromixer, in fact, it is characterized by a single vortical structure placed in the center of the outlet channels.
This work aims at characterizing the flow inside the X- and the arrow-microreactors, both fed with reactants, to ultimately investigate the impact on the reaction performance. More specifically, we analyze the reaction rate and the contact area between the two inlet reactive streams, to understand how flow regimes triggered by different geometries affect the reaction yield.

2. Geometries and reactive fluids

Figure (1) shows the geometries of the two microreactors. The arrow-microreactor has two identical inlet channels, each 40 mm long, with a square cross-section (W_i=H=1 mm), and an outlet channel, 60 mm long, with a rectangular cross-section (W_o= 2H= 2 mm). The angle between the x-axis and the inlet channels is 20°. The X-microreactor has four identical channels with a square cross-section (W_i=H=1 mm), each having a length of 60 mm. Such a X-microreactor is used in the impinging jet configuration, which means 2 inlets and 2 outlets.
The chemical reaction is the reduction of methylene blue (MB+), to the leucomethylene blue (LMB+), using ascorbic acid (AsA) with the hydrogen chloride (HCl) acting as the catalyst of the reaction. The dehydroascorbic acid (DA) is also a reaction product.

$$MB^+ + AsA \overset{HCl}{\longrightarrow} LMB^+ + DA \quad (1)$$

The progress of the reaction can be monitored by the decolorization of the fluid streams that progressively occurs as MB+ is consumed. The devices are made in transparent PMMA allowing us to experimentally follow the extent of the reaction.
The aqueous solution of methylene blue ([MB+] = $5.31 \cdot 10^{-5}$ mol/L) and hydrochloric acid ([HCl] = 2.19 mol/L) is fed to one inlet channel (indicated by the black arrow), while the aqueous solution of ascorbic acid ([AsA] = 1.7 mol/L) is fed into the other (indicated by the white arrow). The physical properties of the latter solution depend on the ascorbic acid content. The density is equal to ρ = 1.117 g/cm^3, and the dynamic viscosity is μ = 1.7 mPa·s for the above AsA concentration. The kinetic of the reaction follows a pseudo-first-order law in case of an excess of ascorbic acid (Mowry et al. 1999). At the concentrations of the present experiments the kinetic constant is equal to $k_{r,0}$ = 21.43 s^{-1}.

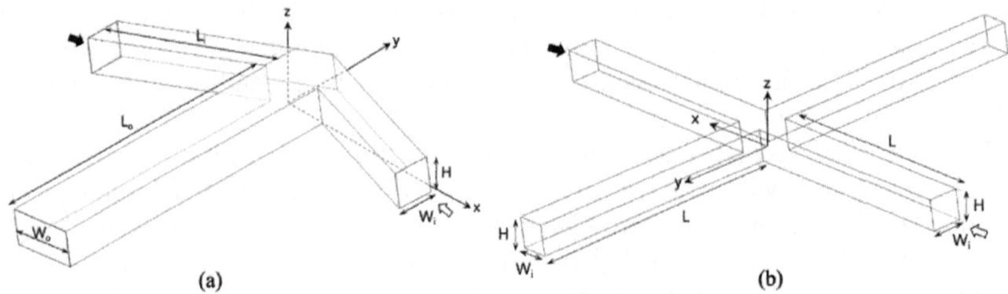

Figure 1: Geometries and reference system of the (a) arrow-microreactor and the (b) X-microreactor.

3. Numerical methodology

Steady Navier-Stokes equations and transport/reactions equations for all chemical species except water are solved with the finite volume code ANSYS Fluent v.20.

$$\nabla(\hat{\rho}\boldsymbol{u}) = 0 \tag{2}$$

$$\hat{\rho}\boldsymbol{u}\nabla\boldsymbol{u} = -\nabla p + \frac{1}{Re}\nabla\cdot[\hat{\mu}(\nabla u + \nabla u^T)] + Ri(\hat{\rho} - 1)\hat{g} \tag{3}$$

$$\hat{\rho}\mathrm{u}\cdot\nabla\phi_k = \frac{1}{Pe}\nabla\cdot\left(\hat{\rho}\widehat{\mathcal{D}}_k\nabla\phi_k\right) + \frac{d\dot{\omega}_k}{\rho U} \tag{4}$$

where lengths are normalized with the mixing channel hydraulic diameter d and velocities with the inlet bulk velocity U. In the above equations, $\boldsymbol{u}$ represents the non-dimensional velocity vector, p is the modified non-dimensional pressure, i.e. $p = (P - \rho_0\, g\, Z) / \rho_0\, U^2$, where P is the pressure, and g the gravity acceleration, while $\hat{g}$ is the non-dimensional gravity, i.e. $\hat{g} = \boldsymbol{g}/g$. $\hat{\rho} = \rho/\rho_0$ and $\hat{\mu} = \mu/\mu_0$ are non-dimensional density and viscosity, respectively, referred to pure water at 25°C, i.e., ρ_0 and μ_0. ϕ_k represents the mass fraction of the k-th chemical species while $\dot{\omega}_k$ is its rate of production or consumption due to chemical reactions, which, for instance is $\dot{\omega}_{MB+} = -\,k_r\,\rho\,\phi_{MB+}$ for the methylene blue. $\widehat{\mathcal{D}}_k = \widehat{\mathcal{D}}/\widehat{\mathcal{D}}_0$ is the non-dimensional diffusivity referred to the water self-diffusivity $\widehat{\mathcal{D}}_0$. The characteristic non-dimensional numbers are: the Reynolds number $Re = \rho_0\, U\, d\, /\, \mu_0$, the Richardson number, $Ri = gd\Delta\rho/\rho_0 U^2$, and the Peclet number $Pe = Ud/\mathcal{D}_0$, where $\Delta\rho$ is the density difference between the two inlet fluids. Since the fluid density and viscosity depend on the ascorbic acid content ϕ_{AsA}, their behaviour is implemented in the model.

Uniform velocity and concentration of the reactants are imposed at the entrance of the inlet channels, whereas no-slip velocity at the channel walls and pressure outlet conditions at ambient pressure are set at the outlet boundary.

A second-order upwind interpolation scheme is used for spatial discretization, and the SIMPLE algorithm is employed for the pressure and velocity coupling. Convergence is checked by monitoring normalized residuals for all equations (below 10^{-9}).

4. Results

An overview of the flow topology in the X- and arrow-microreactors is presented in Figs. (2) and (3) that show the contours of the reaction rate at different cross-sections in the outlet channel. The reaction rate highlights the contact region, which is a fingerprint of the flow regime, between the two inlet streams where the reaction takes place. A quantitative comparison of the reaction performance between X- and arrow-shaped microreactors is also carried out by estimating the reaction yield. The comparison is conducted in terms of the Reynolds number evaluated at the inlet channel, i.e., $Re_i = \rho\, Ud_i/\mu$, where d_i is the hydraulic diameter of the inlet channel. This approach enables a comparison of the two geometries with the same inlet flow rate. For the X-geometry Re = Re_i, as it has four identical channels. Instead, for the arrow-microreactors Re_i < Re due to the difference between the hydraulic diameter of the inlet channels and of the outlet channel.

Figure (2) summarizes the steady flow regimes in the arrow-microreactor. At low Reynolds numbers, the stratification effect leads to a tilting of the impinging plane between the two inlet streams, and the ascorbic acid solution occupies the bottom part of the channel due to its higher density. The lower the Re_i, the more upstream the stratification occurs (see Figs. (2a) and (2b)). The reaction takes place exclusively in the contact region between the inlet streams. For $Re_i>37.5$, the vortex regime occurs, which is characterized by two U-shaped counter-rotating vortical structures in the mixing channel. The stratification effect is still present but is visible further downstream in the outlet, leading to an asymmetry of the flow. Additionally, the reaction occurs at the interface between the two solutions.

The engulfment regime is observed in the range $75 < Re_i \leq 142.5$. In this regime, only the two strongest legs, which co-rotate, persist in the mixing channel. This results in a sudden enhancement of mixing between the reactive streams.

The intensity of the co-rotating vortical structures differs due to the distinct properties of the inlet streams, and this effect becomes more pronounced as the Reynolds number increases. Beyond $Re_i = 142.5$, in the single-vortex regime, only one vortical structure remains in the mixing channel. In the confluence region, four weaker vortical structures form due to the central vortex. The flow remains stable up to $Re_i = 232.5$.

In the engulfment and single-vortex regime, the reaction rate is low in the center of the vortex, instead is higher at the interface between the vortex and the bulk solution.

Figure (3) summarizes the steady flow regimes in the X-microreactor. At low Reynolds numbers, the stratified regime occurs in the device similarly to the arrow-geometry. The flow pattern at $Re_i = 40$ mirrors that of $Re_i = 10$. The impingement plane between the two streams tilts, and the ascorbic acid solution migrates toward the lower part of the channel. The contact regions between the two streams at $Y = 1, 2,$ and 3 exhibit slight corrugations. Similar to the arrow-geometry, in the stratified regime, the reaction occurs at the interface between the two solutions. For $Re_i > 50$, a single vortical structure emerges in the confluence region and extends into the outlet channels. In the X-microreactor, the intermediate vortex regime does not occur; thus, the engulfment regime is triggered at a very low Reynolds number compared to the arrow-microreactor.

By further increasing Reynolds, the central vortex strengthens and elongates in the outlet channels. In addition to the central vortex, two secondary counter-rotating vortices form, further enhancing the mixing of the streams (see Fig. (3d) and (3e)).

The highest reaction rate in the engulfment regime is obtained along the external border of the central vortex. Conversely, in the vortex core, the reaction rate is lower due to the stagnation of the reactants. The flow remains stable up to $Re_i = 375$.

The reaction yield is computed as:

$$\eta = 1 - 2\,\frac{C_{MB+,Y}}{C_{MB+,in}} \tag{5}$$

Where $C_{MB+,Y}$ and $C_{MB+,in}$ are the methylene blue concentrations evaluated at the Y cross-section and at the inlet channel, respectively.

Figure (4) presents a comparison of the reaction yield in the X- and arrow-microreactors, evaluated at the Y=-25 cross-section.

In the stratified regime, the reaction yield diminishes with increasing Reynolds for the two examined geometries. This behavior is attributed to the reduction in the residence time of fluid streams within the device. Specifically, as Re_i increases, the contact area between the streams remains unchanged, but the residence time decreases. Subsequently, η gradually increases in the vortex and engulfment regime in the arrow-geometry due to the increase in the contact area between the streams. In the X-microreactor, the yield starts to increase when the engulfment regime occurs, but after reaching a maximum at Re_i=80, the yield decreases. This is probably because, for Re_i>80, the contact area between the inlet streams does not significantly vary, but the residence time drastically diminishes. By further increasing Re_i, the single-vortex regime occurs in the arrow-geometry, leading to a sudden increase in the reaction yield. Conversely, in the X-microreactor, the yield continues to diminish.

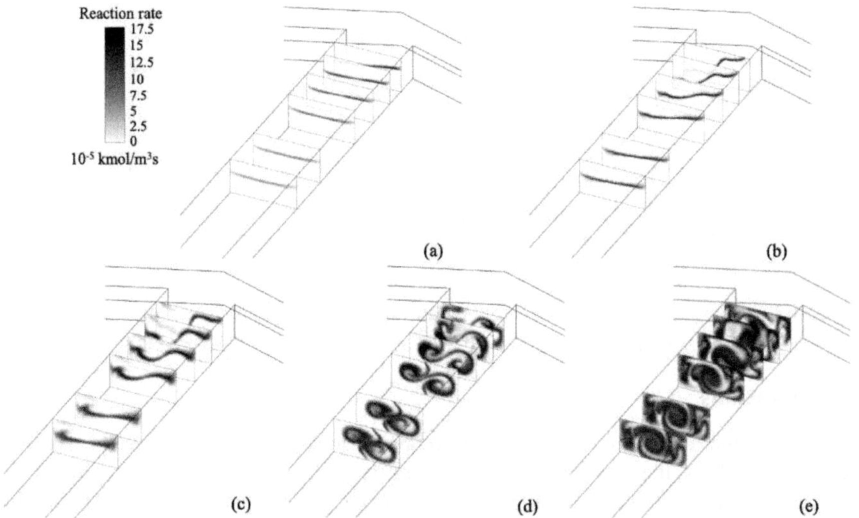

Figure 2: Contours of reaction rate in the arrow-microreactor at the Y = -1, -2, -3, -5, -8, -10 cross-sections along the outlet channel in numerical simulations at Re_i= (a) 7.5, (b) 37.5, (c) 60, (d) 112.5, and (e) 187.5.

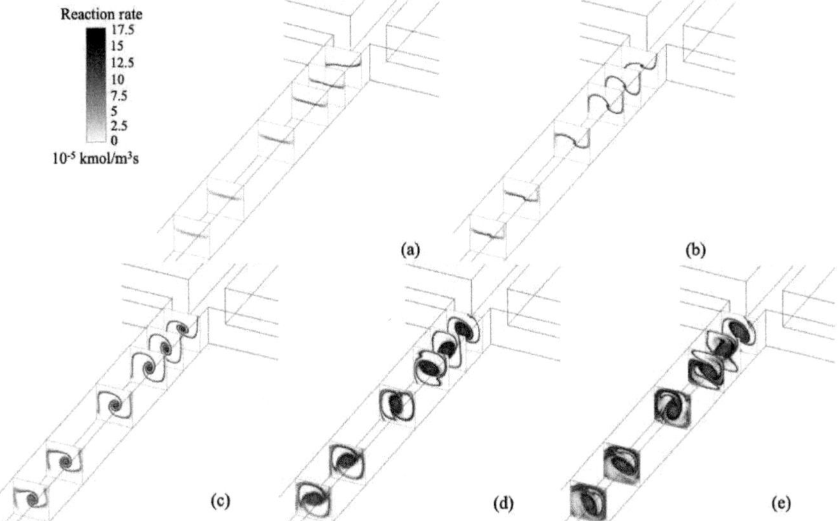

Figure 3: Contours of reaction rate in the X-microreactor at the Y = 1, 2, 3, 6, 8, 10 cross-sections along the outlet channel in numerical simulations at Re_i= (a) 10, (b) 40, (c) 50, (d) 100, and (e) 200.

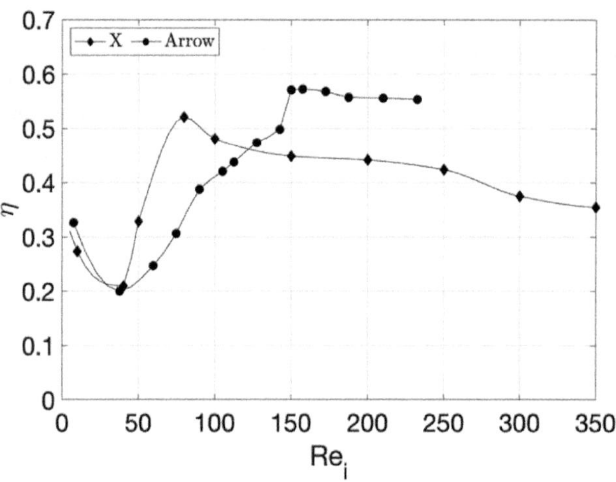

Figure 4: Reaction yield of the X- and arrow-microreactors at Y=-25 cross-section as a function of the Reynolds number evaluated at the inlet channel. Results are from numerical simulations.

5. Conclusions

The X- and the arrow-microreactors are compared in terms of reaction yield. At low Reynolds numbers, the two reactant streams stratify in the outlet channels, resulting in a low reaction yield that diminishes with increasing Re because of the reduction in residence time. At the vortex regime onset, the reaction yield increases in the arrow-microreactor, due to the expanded contact area between the inlet streams. By further increasing Reynolds, the engulfment regime promotes the progress of the reaction for both geometries. Indeed, the presence of vortical structures ensures effective mixing of the streams, leading to an increase in the yield. Above Re_i=80 in the X-microreactor, the contact area does not increase in size, but the residence time inside the device decreases, hence, the yield decreases.

The highest reaction yield in the steady regimes is achieved in the arrow-microreactor for Re_i>150, i.e., at the onset of the single-vortex regime. This regime provides the best compromise between the contact area of the inlet streams and the residence time inside the device.

References

A. Mariotti, C. Galletti, E. Brunazzi, M.V. Salvetti, Steady flow regimes and mixing performance in arrow-shaped micro-mixers, Physical Review Fluids, 4 (3) (2019) 1–20.

A. Mariotti, M. Antognoli, C. Galletti, R. Mauri, M.V. Salvetti, E. Brunazzi, The role of flow features and chemical kinetics on the reaction yield in a T-shaped micro-reactor, Chemical Engineering Journal, 396 (2020) 125223.

S. Mowry, P. Ogren, Kinetics of methylene blue reduction by ascorbic acid, Journal of Chemical Education, 76 (1999) 970-973.

I. Rossetti, M. Compagnoni, Chemical reaction engineering, process design and scale-up issues at the frontier of synthesis: Flow chemistry, Chemical Engineering Journal, 296 (2016) 56–70.

J.W. Zhang, W.F. Li, X.L. Xu, H.F. Liu, F.C. Wang, Experimental investigation of three-dimensional flow regimes in a cross-shaped reactor, Physics of Fluids, 31 (3) (2019) 034105.

Flavio Manenti, Gintaras V. Reklaitis (Eds.), Proceedings of the 34th European Symposium on Computer Aided Process Engineering / 15th International Symposium on Process Systems Engineering (ESCAPE34/PSE24), June 2-6, 2024, Florence, Italy
 http://dx.doi.org/10.1016/B978-0-443-28824-1.50258-1

Theoretical Control Properties Assessment for a Carbon-Hydrogen-Oxygen Symbiosis Network with Intensified Processes

Maricruz Júarez García[a], Juan Gabriel Segovia-Hernández[a*], José María Ponce Ortega[b], Gabriel Contreras-Zarazúa[c]

[a*]*Department of Chemical Engineering, Universidad de Guanajuato, Campus Guanajuato, Guanajuato, 36050, Mexico*

[b]*Chemical Engineering Department, Universidad Michoacana de San Nicolás de Hidalgo, Morelia, Michoacán 58060, Mexico*

[c]*CONACyT, CIATEC A.C. Center for Applied Innovation in Competitive Technologies, Omega 201, Col. Industrial Delta, León, Gto 37545, Mexico*

gsegovia@ugto.mx

Abstract

The introduction of intensified processes in the design of Carbon-Hydrogen-Oxygen Symbiosis Networks (CHOSYNs) leads to improve the general sustainability performance of the network; this mainly means lower costs and lower environmental impact. Due the complex nature of these networks, where several plants are interacting through integration lines and recycles, with the inclusion of intensified processes these networks result in even more complex systems where the control properties are well worth to investigate. In this context, this study aims to determine the theoretical control properties of a set of design solutions for a CHOSYN, including conventional processes and intensification performed in specific feasible zones of the network. The objective is to assess whether the intensification improves or worsens the controllability of the network, and in the latter case to identify a solution that balances the benefits of intensification with this possible drawback. The proposed case study is a CHOSYN configuration with two distillation sequences as areas for intensification. Twelve solutions or scenarios were generated for the network through combinations of conventional and different intensified options for these two sequences. The analysis of the control properties for the different scenarios was carried out using the condition number and the singular value decomposition (SVD). The results show that in some scenarios including intensified processes the control properties remain the same as in the conventional case, indicating that for these solutions the sustainability performance can be maintained without affecting the control of the network.

Keywords: process intensification, process integration, process control.

1. Introduction

The Carbon-Hydrogen-Oxygen symbiosis networks aims to enhance resource efficiency by integrating processing plants that handle mainly carbon, hydrogen and oxygen compounds (Noureldin & El-Halwagi, 2015). This inter-plant integration allows minimizing the overall requirements of raw materials and minimizing the waste generation, which leads to lower costs and sustainability of the process. However, improving individual processes within the network through other techniques such as process intensification enhances the overall efficiency of the network. Previously, it was reported that incorporating intensified processes in the design of the CHOSYNs, particularly distillation processes, improves the sustainability performance of the network (cost and environmental impact reduction) beyond what is allowed by integration due the intensive energy use and the inefficiency presented in these units (Júarez-Garcia et al. 2022).

However, another key aspect of the sustainability is the controllability of the process, and the inherent safety associated with it (Jiménez-González et al. 2012). The design of the CHOSYNs implies the allocation of multiple integration lines throughout the network and recycles from one plant to another, which implies that they are already complex systems with a high level of interaction between plants. Through the inclusion of intensified processes in the design, this complexity is likely to increase. This concern arises because intensified processes often result in more complex designs than their conventional counterparts such as distillation sequences. Therefore, it is worthwhile to analyze how the inclusion of these intensified processes in a complex processes such as CHOSYNs affects their control properties, whether it improves or worsens them, and in the case that control is negatively affected, analyze what level of intensification tradeoffs this effect with the benefits in the other sustainability indicators. This paper presents the analysis of the control properties of a case study, a previous CHOSYN design where the intensification is focused in two distillation columns. To assess the control properties it is proposed to use the condition number and the technique of Singular Value Decomposition (SVD), which has been used extensively in this context because it provides meaningful insights about controllability.

2. Proposed Approach

2.1. SVD technique

The Singular Value Decomposition method allows to measure in a qualitative way the control properties of a processing system. This technique is a matrix factorization method, and it decomposes a matrix (G) into three factors as shown in Eq. (1):

$$G = U\Sigma V^T \tag{1}$$

Where Σ contains all the non-zero singular values of G. The ratio of the maximum singular value (σ^*) to the minimum (σ_*) is the condition number of G:

$$\gamma = \frac{\sigma^*}{\sigma_*} \tag{2}$$

The condition number of a matrix is an indicator of how "well-conditioned" or sensitive is the matrix; it gives a measure of how much the output variables of the system change when the input variables experience a perturbation. In control context, the matrix G is the steady state gain matrix, which relates the control and manipulated variables of the system. Large condition numbers indicate that small disturbances in the system result in large changes in the control variables or that the system is more sensitive, conversely small condition numbers indicates a system less sensitive.

2.2. Case study

Juarez-Garcia et al. (2022) presented a CHOSYN configuration of nine processing plants with several shared streams: (P1) the auto thermal reforming of natural gas section of a gas to liquid process which shares residual streams containing H_2, CO_2 and CO with methanol production plants (P6 and P7). The ethylene plant and propane dehydrogenation process share waste streams containing CH_4 with the steam methane reforming process (P9) and H_2 streams with the methanol plants, which in turn feed the methanol to propylene process (P4) and acetic acid plant (P8). The acetic acid is sent to vinyl acetate monomer production plant (P5). In Figure 1, it is shown a schematic representation of this case study; the product streams (network outlets) are also displayed.

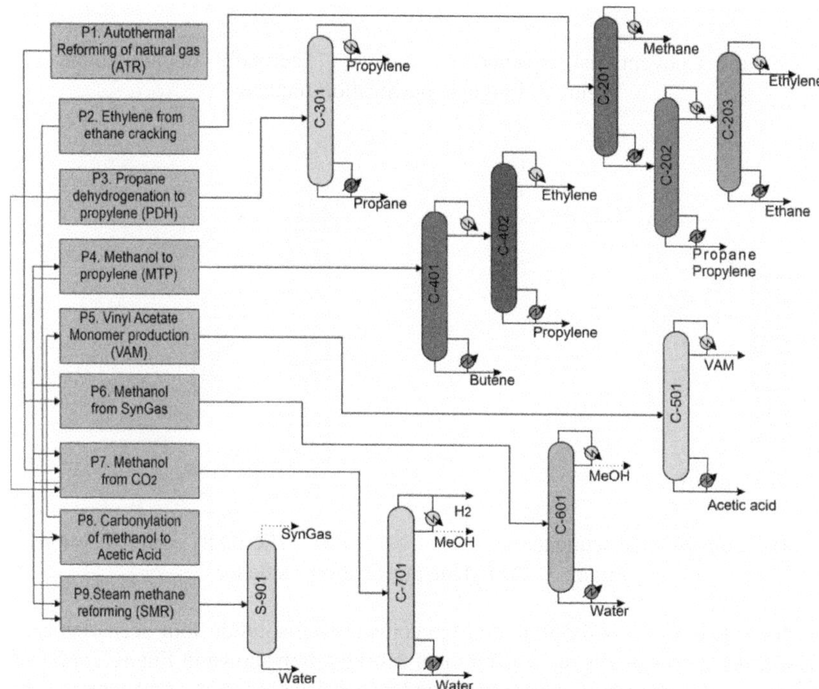

Figure 1. Schematic representation of the case study

The distillation sequences from ethylene process for ethylene purification and propylene purification from PDH plant were intensified. There were proposed thermally coupled sequences (see Figure 2 and 3), these processes compared to the conventional reported better economic performance, energy savings and CO_2 emissions reduction.

2.2.1. Intensified option for the case study

The sequence of the purification of ethylene is a three-column sequence, the intensified option is a retrofit design with two vapor/liquid couplings between columns; one replaces the reboiler of C-201 column, the other one replaces the condenser of C-202. The purification sequence of the propylene consists of two columns, this purifies a stream rich in propylene, and for this sequence, it is proposed a main column with a side stripper arrangement. For this sequence, unlike ethylene, a physical rearrangement of the sequence sections is implemented (Hernández & Jiménez, 1996).

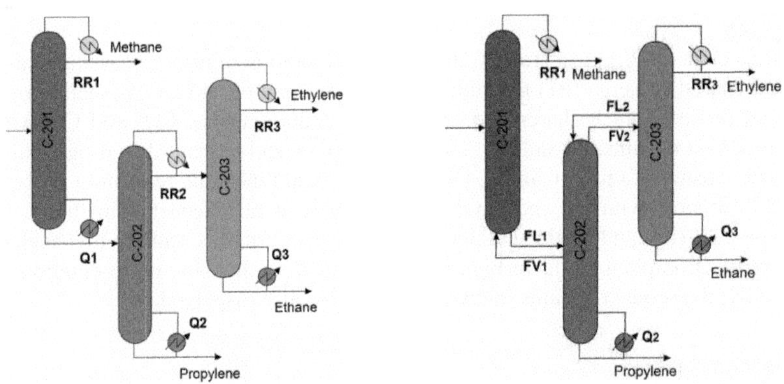

a) Conventional sequence b) Thermally coupled option

Figure 2. Ethylene purification sequence.

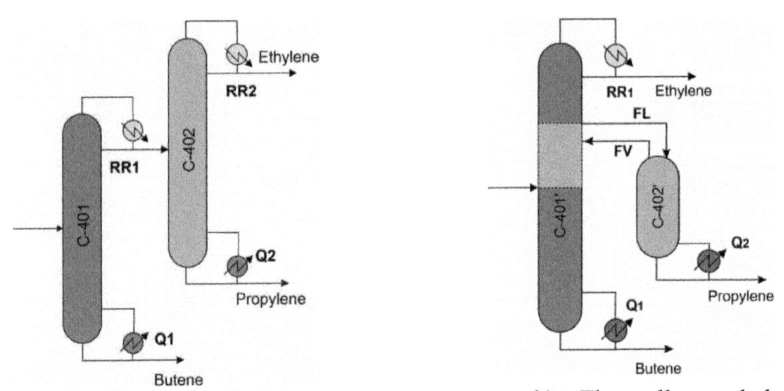

a) Conventional sequence b) Thermally coupled option

Figure 3. Propylene purification sequence.

From these two intensified option and the conventional solution four scenarios can be analysed, the scenario A is the conventional configuration shown in Figure 1, scenarios B and C are combinations of conventional and intensified processes, and Scenario D both intensified options replaced the conventional sequences.

Table 1. Proposed scenarios.

	Scenario A	Scenario B	Scenario C	Scenario D
Ethylene sequence P2	Conventional	Conventional	Intensified	Intensified
Propylene sequence P4	Conventional	Intensified	Conventional	Intensified

2.3. Methodology

The proposed methodology consists in two main tasks: setting the gain matrix and then determine the condition number through SVD technique.

To build the gain matrix, the first step is to define the control variables of interest for the analysis; in general, these variables should be the outlet streams of the network. However, being the objective to determine the influence of intensification over the network controllability and for the specific case study where the intensified zones coincide with network outlets, only control variables of these specific areas are used. This allows reducing the size of the matrix while guaranteeing the significance of the results. Table 2 summarizes the control variables (y_i), the molar purity of the distillate and bottoms of the two sequences, and the corresponding manipulated variable (u_i), the reflux ratio (RR) and reboiler duty (RD) of each column.

Table 2. Control variables-Manipulated variables pairing.

	u_i		y_i
u_1	RR_1 / C-201	y_1	$x_{methane}$ / Distillate C-201
u_2	RD_2 / C-202	y_2	$x_{propylene}$ / Bottoms C-202
u_3	RR_3 / C-203	y_3	$x_{ethylene}$ / Distillate C-203
u_4	RD_3 / C-203	y_4	x_{ethane} / Bottoms C-203
u_5	RD_1 / C-401	y_7	x_{butene} / Bottoms C-401
u_6	RR_2 / C-402	y_8	$x_{ethylene}$ / Distillate C-402
u_7	RD_2 / C-402	y_9	$x_{propylene}$ / Bottoms C-402

The next step consists is to generate a perturbation in each of the manipulated variables and measure the response in the control variables. For this, a perturbation of 0.5 % of the nominal value of the variable was used. The coefficients of the gain matrix are the difference between the molar purity of the component n after disturbance in the m manipulated variable ($x_n^{v_m}$) and the molar purity of the n component in the nominal state (x_n^{sp}) as it is shown in Eq. (3). These coefficients were determined using steady-state simulations in Aspen Plus.

$$\begin{bmatrix} G_{11} & \cdots & G_{1n} \\ \vdots & \ddots & \vdots \\ G_{m1} & \cdots & G_{mn} \end{bmatrix} = \begin{matrix} & y_1 & \cdots & y_n \\ u_1 & \frac{x_1^{v_1} - x^{sp}}{0.5} & \cdots & \frac{x_n^{v_1} - x^{sp}}{0.5p} \\ \vdots & \vdots & \ddots & \vdots \\ u_m & \frac{x_1^{v_m} - x^{sp}}{0.5} & \cdots & \frac{x_n^{v_m} - x^{sp}}{0.5p} \end{matrix} \tag{3}$$

3. Results and discussion.

Four 7x7 matrices were obtained, one for each scenario, the decomposition into singular values and the calculation of the condition number was computed in Matlab. The results are shown in Table 3.

Table 3. Condition number for each scenario.

	Scenario A	Scenario B	Scenario C	Scenario D
Condition number (γ)	376.6	376.6	893.1	893.1

As mentioned above, the condition number is an indicator of the control properties of a system; in this case, the conventional scenario A is the reference to compare the controllability of the scenarios B, C and D that include intensification. From the conventional scenario A to scenario B the condition number do not vary and it can be assumed that the control properties remain the same, therefore the topological difference between the conventional scenario and scenario B has no influence on the controllability of the network. For scenario C the number of conditions increases significantly, but is the same for scenario D, so the control properties for these two scenarios are the same. The scenario B and D use the intensified arrangement of the main column and the side stripper for the propylene purification sequence, consequently, using this intensified option does not alter the control of the network but maintains the benefits of energy savings, cost and emission reductions. On the other hand, the topological difference between scenarios A and B with scenarios C and D is the thermally coupled arrangement for ethylene purification, which in this case is the sequence that complicates the controllability of the system. In summary, the network configuration that includes the intensified sequence with a physical rearrangement (main column with side stripper) has as good control as its conventional equivalent, while the configuration with the retrofit sequence makes the network more sensitive to disturbances. To understand why this happens, see Figure 2, the coupling between C-201 and C-202 replaces the reboiler of C-201, as the whole design is fixed, then the steam flow generated in C-202 must supply both columns so a much higher steam flow than in the conventional sequence is expected. And a perturbation of Q2 would generate a backward perturbation affecting the composition of the C-201 distillate (something that does not happen with the conventional sequence), but in turn also affects the C-203 products forward. Something similar happens when looking at the coupling between C-203 and C-202, which replaces the C-202 condenser, and a variation in both, RR3 and Q3, affects both the purity of the C-203 products, as well as the purity of the C-202 and C-201 products. Then in the latter system, the variables have more interactions with each other, mathematically making the gain matrix more ill-conditioned.

4. Conclusions

This work presented a study of the control properties of intensified CHOSYNs complementing previous studies that allow advancing in the industrial implementation of CHOSYNs as schemes with responsible production aiming to reduce the environmental impact generated during the processing of carbon, hydrogen, and oxygen compounds. For the case study presented here, intensification was focused on the distillation units, the study findings demonstrate that the control properties of the intensified options are influenced by the specific structures and configurations of the thermodynamic equivalents. Therefore, with the results shown in this study, it is recommended for the case study to use the intensified option for propylene purification, for ethylene purification, other options should be explored.

References

C. Jiménez-González, D. J. C. Constable, and C. S. Ponder, 2012, Evaluating the 'Greenness' of chemical processes and products in the pharmaceutical industry—a green metrics primer, Chem. Soc. Rev., 41(4), 1485–1498.

M. Júarez-Garcia, G. Contreras-Zarazúa, J. G. Segovia-Hernandez, J. M. Ponce-Ortega. 2022, Improving Sustainable CHOSYN´s Targets through Process Intensification, European Symposium on Computer Aided Process Engineering, 51, 613–18.

M. M. B. Noureldin, M. M. El-Halwagi, 2015, Synthesis of C-H-O symbiosis networks. AIChE Journal, 61(4), 1242–1262.

S. Hernández, A. Jiménez, 1996, Design of optimal thermally-coupled distillation systems using a dynamic model. Chemical engineering research & design, 74(3), 357-362.

Flavio Manenti, Gintaras V. Reklaitis (Eds.), Proceedings of the 34th European Symposium on Computer Aided Process Engineering / 15th International Symposium on Process Systems Engineering (ESCAPE34/PSE24), June 2-6, 2024, Florence, Italy
 http://dx.doi.org/10.1016/B978-0-443-28824-1.50259-3

Nonlinear Model Predictive Control for Modified Claus Process

Jialin Liu,[a,*] Hao-Che Chien,[b] David Shan-Hill Wong,[b] Chun-Cheng Chang[c]

[a]*Research Center for Smart Sustainable Circular Economy, Tunghai University, Taiwan*
[b]*Department of Chemical Engineering, National Tsing Hua University, Taiwan*
[c]*Green Energy and System Integration Research and Development Department, China Steel Corporation, Taiwan*
jialin@thu.edu.tw

Abstract

The Claus process is the most significant gas desulfurizing process in industry, recovering elemental sulfur from gaseous hydrogen sulfide. However, the reactor temperature suffers a nonlinear process gain to the sulfur recovery because the Claus reaction is exothermic and reversible. In field operations, a traditional feedback controller for the outlet of SO_2 is left in open loop, because the disturbances cannot be compensated by the linear controller. In this study, a nonlinear controller is designed by the differential evolution algorithm with a surrogate model that is constructed by the sequence-to-sequence network. The results show that the process nonlinearity can be conquered and the emitted SO_2 concentration can be controlled by the reactor temperature.

Keywords: Nonlinear process control, modified Claus process, surrogate model.

1. Introduction

In the iron and steel industry, raw materials for steel production are coal and iron ore. The iron ore is sintered and taken to the blast furnace where it is mixed with coke, lime and blown air to produce pig iron. On the other hand, the coal is carbonized to produce coke at temperatures higher than 1000 °C in coke oven units. Coke oven gas (COG) is a by-product of the coke-making process, where volatile coal matter is generated as COG, leaving carbon intensive coke behind. The raw COG is carried out to washing stages where the regenerated water from the H_2S stripper is introduced at the top of the absorber to remove hydrogen sulfide from the COG. The captured H_2S is cracked and converted into H_2O and elemental sulfur through the Claus process. The cleaned COG, which is mainly composed of hydrogen and methane, is presently used for heating purposes in coke batteries or furnaces. The original Claus process produces elemental sulfur by oxidation of hydrogen sulfide with air at elevated temperatures using a metal oxide catalyst: $H_2S + 1/2\ O_2 \rightarrow 1/8\ S_8 + H_2O$. However, the associated temperature rise could not be controlled when significant amounts of H_2S are present. The drawback is overcome by dividing the reaction into thermal and catalytic steps, which is usually referred to as the modified Claus process. In the process, almost one third of H_2S is oxidized into SO_2 in the thermal reactor (furnace); thereafter, the serial catalytic reactors convert the left part of H_2S with SO_2 into elemental sulfur and H_2O (Clark, 2000).

2. Process description

Claus process consists of a thermal reaction furnace, a waste heat boiler (WHB), and a series of catalytic reactors and sulfur condensers, as shown in Figure 1. Due to the upstream load variations, a flow ratio controller is installed to maintain the primary air (F2) to the sour gas (F1) ratio. In the furnace, temperatures are usually in the order of 1000–1400 °C. A controller maintains the top temperature of burner (T8) through altering the set point of the fuel flow rate (F5) where an air-to-fuel ratio is regulated by adjusting the set point of the combustion air flow rate (F4). The oxidizing reaction, $H_2S + 3/2\ O_2 \rightarrow SO_2 + H_2O$, is exothermic and without any thermodynamic restriction. At the high temperature, some of the sulfur dioxide produced here reacts with hydrogen sulfide inside the furnace according to reaction: $2\ H_2S + SO_2 \leftrightarrow 3/2\ S_2 + 2\ H_2O$ to produce elemental sulfur. The hot outlet gas passes to the WHB at the end of combustion chamber and cools down to 300 °C by converting high pressure steam to the medium pressure.

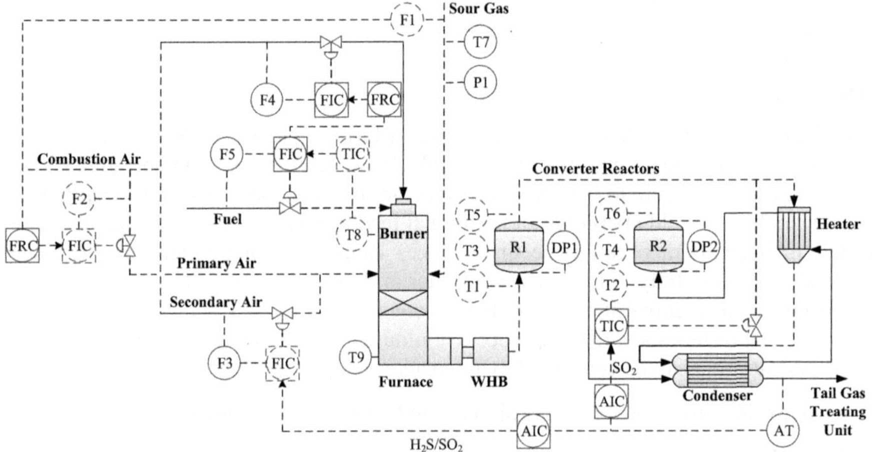

Figure 1. Flow diagram of modified Claus process.

The remaining H_2S, from the furnace, is reacted with the SO_2 at lower temperatures (about 200–300 °C) over an Al_2O_3 catalyst to make more sulfur: $2\ H_2S + SO_2 \leftrightarrow 1/2\ S_6 + 2\ H_2O$. In the catalytic stage mostly S_6 is produced, which is an exothermic reaction whereas in the thermal stage S_2 is the major product and the reaction is endothermic (Clark, 2000). The catalytic stages are operated at successively lower temperatures to achieve increased conversion to elemental sulfur. In the Claus reaction, the furnace produces SO_2 used to react with H_2S in a ratio of 2 (H_2S/SO_2). Therefore, a proper amount of oxygen, typically in the form of air, must be introduced to maintain the stoichiometric number. A tail gas analyzer is installed after the final catalytic stage, as shown in Figure 1. The set point of the secondary air flow rate (F3) is determined by the output of the molar ratio controller (H_2S/SO_2) from the tail gas analyzer. A condenser is installed downstream each converter to condensate the elemental sulfur. Thereafter, a reheater heats the effluent gases before entering the next converter. As shown in Figure 1, the inlet temperature of the second converter (T2) is controlled by bypassing the outlet flow from the previous converter, whereas the inlet temperature of the first converter (T1) is not regulated. The SO_2 concentration in the tail gas determines the set point of T2 controller. However, the inlet temperatures of the gases have a positive process gain to the sulfur recovery when the reaction temperatures are far below that of the equilibrium states, i.e., the rising of inlet temperatures may result in the reduction of the SO_2 concentration in the tail gas. On the other hand, the process gain of inlet temperatures to the sulfur recovery becomes negative once the reaction temperatures are higher than that of the equilibrium states due to the exothermic reaction. Therefore, the practical operation of a Claus converter is an interplay between equilibrium limitations and reaction kinetics.

3. Process model

In the present work, Aspen Plus V14 was used to simulate the Claus process in Figure 1 where the ideal gas model was applied. The reactions and their kinetic parameters for the furnace and converters were retrieved from the work of Nabikandi and Fatemi (2015). The feed conditions of the sour gas, combustion air, and fuel were also adapted from the same paper. The furnace length and diameter were 6.5 and 3.4 (m), in which the burner and combustion chamber are included. The adiabatic plug flow reactor (PFR) was applied to simulate the furnace and a heat exchanger was used for the WHB. For each catalytic converter, the length and diameter respectively were 6.0 and 1.4 (m), in which the catalyst loading is 36,000 (kg) with the particle density of 1.3 (g/cm^3). The temperatures of the sulfur condensers were maintained at 120 °C and the inlet gas temperatures for the converters were set at 230 and 210 °C, respectively. Table 1 lists the reported industrial data and the simulation results where the relative errors for the outlet temperatures and total molar flows are below 10%. In addition, the simulation results of H_2S and SO_2 (mol/s) from the reactors are comparable with the reported industrial data.

Table 1. Simulation results and reported industrial data (Nabikandi and Fatemi, 2015)

	Furnace				Converter 1				Converter 2			
	Temp. (°C)	Total (mol/s)	H_2S (mol/s)	SO_2 (mol/s)	Temp. (°C)	Total (mol/s)	H_2S (mol/s)	SO_2 (mol/s)	Temp. (°C)	Total (mol/s)	H_2S (mol/s)	SO_2 (mol/s)
Industrial case data	1000	355.82	12.28	9.73	307	335.29	5.41	2.70	222	331.93	1.45	0.73
Simulation result	1048	354.65	13.45	7.51	298	309.28	6.44	1.09	214	301.80	5.51	0.62

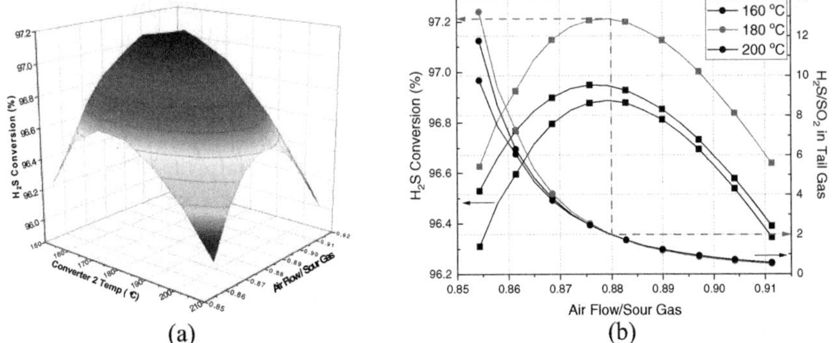

Figure 2. Results of sensitivity analysis on varying the air flow rate and T2, (a) the H_2S conversions, (b) correlation between the H_2S conversion and the H_2S/SO_2 in the tail gas.

As mentioned earlier, a proper amount of oxygen is needed in the furnace to produce SO_2 that maximizes the H_2S conversion to elemental sulfur in the Claus process. Figure 2 shows the results of sensitivity analysis on varying the molar flow ratio of the air to the sour gas and T2, whereas T1 is fixed at 230 °C. As shown in Figure 2(a), there exists an optimal temperature that maximizes the H_2S conversion for each molar flow ratio. Once the inlet temperature below that of the maximum conversion, the inlet temperature has a positive gain to the H_2S conversion; on the other hand, the process gain is negative. As shown in Figure 2(b), the H_2S conversions of maintaining T2 at 180 °C are higher than those of the counterparts operating at 160 and 200 °C. Figure 2(b) also shows that the maximum conversions can be found, once the H_2S/SO_2 in the tail gas are kept around 2. Therefore, maintaining the H_2S/SO_2 in the tail gas at 2 by adjusting the air flow rate, Figure 3 shows the SO_2 concentrations in the tail gas under varying T1 and T2. The concave surface shows that the SO_2 concentration (controlled variable, CV) suffers the nonlinear difficulty with the manipulated variable (MV) and disturbance variable (DV) where are T2 and T1, respectively.

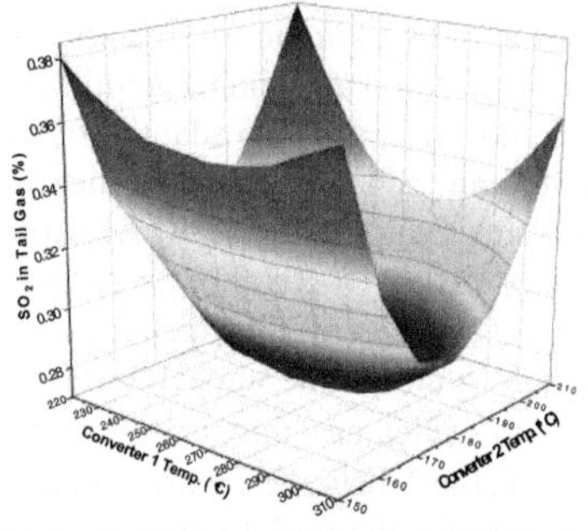

Figure 3. SO_2 concentrations in the tail gas on varying T2 and T1.

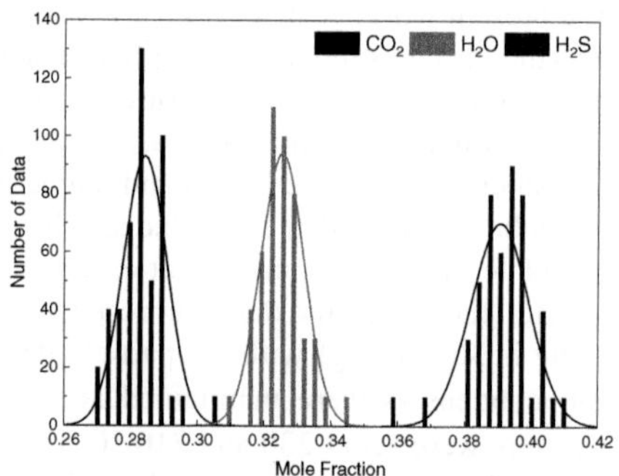

Figure 4. Sour gas composition variations for dynamic simulation.

4. Industrial example

4.1. Dynamic model

A pressure-driven dynamic model was developed by Aspen Plus Dynamics V14 based on the steady-state model described in the previous section. The configurations of control loops for the dynamic model are shown in Figure 1. In addition, the pressure controllers for the furnace, WHB, and both converters were implemented by regulating the corresponding outlet flows. The set point of T2 was determined by the tail gas analyzer controller (AIC) for maintaining the SO_2 concentration in the tail gas. However, the operators complained that the AIC is not functional; consequently, the AIC and T2 controllers were kept in open loop in the daily operations. The inlet compositions of the sour gas were not analyzed in the industrial process, only the data of pressure, temperature, and volume flow rate are collected. In the present work, the molar flows of H_2S and CO_2 were estimated from the previous scrubbing process and the balanced H_2O was estimated by the measured data of F1. Figure 4 shows the variations of the sour gas compositions for the dynamic simulation where a Gaussian distribution is applied with the standard deviation set as 2.5% of the average value for each component.

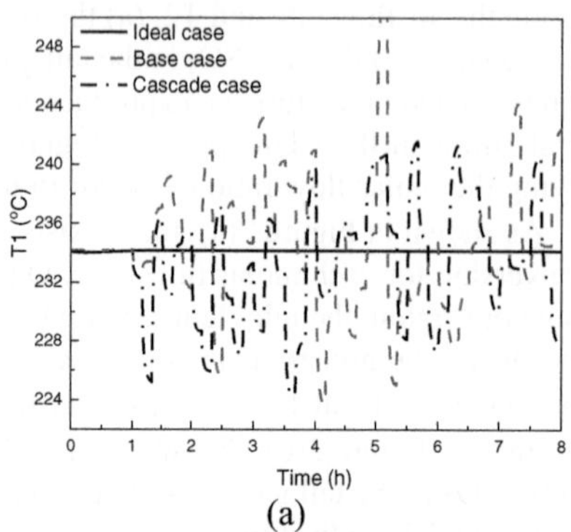

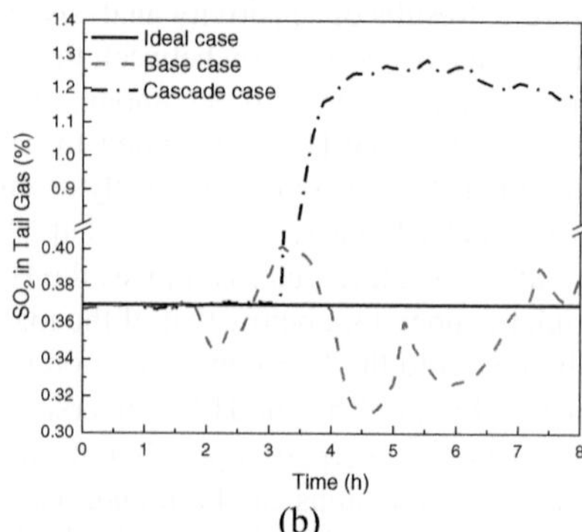

Figure 5. Dynamic simulation results, (a) the temperature variations of T1 and (b) SO_2 concentrations in the tail gas

In Figure 5, the ideal case simulated the inlet concentrations of sour gas by the means without variations in Figure 4. The base case simulated the field operations where T2 and the SO_2 concentration in the tail gas were not regulated, and the variations of the sour gas were introduced after one hour. In the cascade case, the set point of T2 was determined by the controller of the tail gas analyzer for maintaining the SO_2 concentration. Figure 5 shows the dynamic simulation results for the three cases where T1 were nearly unchanged for the ideal case in Figure 5(a). On the other hand, the temperature variations were between 224 and 248 °C for the other cases once the variations of inlet components were introduced. Figure 5(b) shows that the cascade controller for the SO_2 concentration in the tail gas was not practicable, because a linear controller cannot tackle the nonlinearity between CV (SO_2) and MV (T2), as shown in Figure 3.

4.2. Surrogate model

The SO_2 concentration in the tail gas, which is one of the CVs in the Claus process, exhibits a nonlinear characteristic for the MV (T2), because the Claus reaction is an exothermic and reversible reaction. In this study, a simplified nonlinear controller was designed based on a surrogate model that is constructed by the sequence-to-sequence (Seq2seq) network. The model contains the CV, MV, and DV, which are the SO_2 concentration, T2, and T1, respectively. The process dynamics could be extracted by the encoder of Seq2seq, where the gated recurrent unit (GRU) was applied and trained by the data of CV, MV, and DV from the cases of Aspen dynamic simulations. The input layer of the decoder connected to the hidden state output from the encoder and the data of MV, whereas the output layer is linked to the data of CV. The details of training the surrogate model by Seq2seq can be found in the previous work (Liu et al., 2023). The modeling window length for the encoder was determined by the open-loop tests of MV and DV regarding the CV. The window length for training the encoder was selected as six where ten-minute data were averaged as a training sample. The decoder was trained using the data immediately after training the encoder. The next three step data of MV and CV were connected to the input and output layers of the decoder, respectively. Meanwhile, the hidden state output from the encoder was also linked to the input layer of the decoder. Thereafter, the network parameters of encoder and decoder were simultaneously adjusted by minimizing the root mean squared error (RMSE) of the predicted CV through backpropagation. The R^2 of the training and test data were 0.92 and 0.88, respectively; meanwhile the mean absolute percentage error (MAPE) for the test data is around 5%. Therefore, the Seq2seq network is accurate to apply for the surrogate model of designing a model predictive controller (MPC).

The future MVs, which refer to the set points of T2, were evaluated by the differential evolution algorithm (DEA). The SO_2 concentrations were predicted by the Seq2seq network where the input layer of the decoder received the designed set points of T2. There were three options for each step of the MV, the current temperature ±0.5 °C and keeping unchanged. Since the next three steps of SO_2 were predicted in an evaluation, there were 27 possible combinations for the future set points of T2. The sums of the predicted SO_2 concentrations were minimized by selecting a proper combination for the future set points. Thereafter, only the first value of the best combination was implemented into Aspen Dynamics as the set point of T2 and integrated to the next time step. Figure 6 compares the simulation results of the base case, cascade case, and DEA where the input variations were introduced after one hour. As mentioned earlier, because T2 is not regulated in the daily operations (base case), the SO_2 concentrations in the tail gas suffer variations under process disturbances, as shown in Figure 6(a). In addition, the figure also shows that the cascade controller fails to regulate the SO_2 concentrations after the ninth hour, because the linear controller cannot tackle the nonlinearity between the CV and MV. As shown in Figure 6(b), the MV reaches its minimum setting after the ninth hour. On the other hand, the SO_2 concentrations of DEA results tend to a lower value in Figure 6(a). Figure 6(b) shows that T2 was guiding toward a lower value by the DEA, gradually.

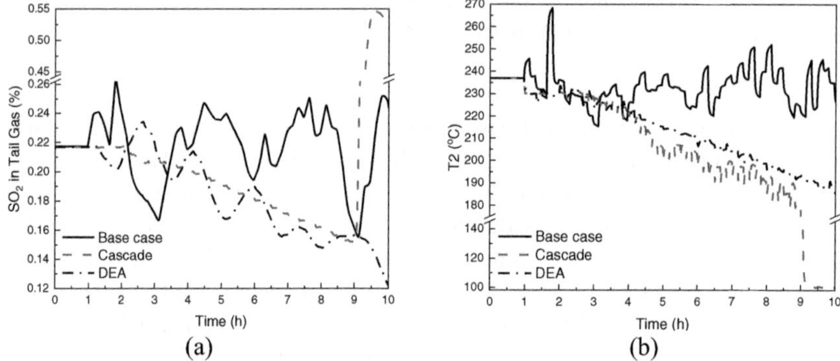

Figure 6. Results of base case and DEA, (a) SO_2 concentration in tail gas, (b) the inlet temperature of the second converter.

5. Conclusions

The Claus reaction exhibits the exothermic and reversible characteristics that leads a nonlinear process gain for the reactor temperature to the reaction conversion. The CV suffers the process disturbances that cannot be compensated by a traditional proportional–integral–derivative (PID) controller; therefore, the field operators chose to keep the SO_2 concentration controller in open-loop. In this study, the nonlinear difficulty between CV and MV was tackled by a simplified nonlinear surrogate model with the DEA. The plantwide controller for the industrial process is undergoing where the overall surrogate model is prepared to interact with the deep reinforcement learning based controller to maximize the sulfur recovery and minimize the SO_2 emission, simultaneously.

Acknowledgement

This work was supported by the National Science and Technology Council, Republic of China, under Grant NSTC 112-2221-E-007-105.

References

P. Clark, 2000, Sulfur and hydrogen sulfide recovery, Kirk-Othmer encyclopedia of chemical technology.

J. Liu, B. Tsai, D. Chen, 2023, Deep reinforcement learning based controller with dynamic feature extraction for an industrial Claus process. J. Taiwan Inst. Chem. Eng., 146, 104779.

N. Nabikandi, S. Fatemi, 2015, Kinetic modelling of a commercial sulfur recovery unit based on Claus straight through process: Comparison with equilibrium model, J. Ind. Eng. Chem., 30, 50-63.

Flavio Manenti, Gintaras V. Reklaitis (Eds.), Proceedings of the 34th European Symposium on Computer Aided Process Engineering / 15th International Symposium on Process Systems Engineering (ESCAPE34/PSE24), June 2-6, 2024, Florence, Italy
 http://dx.doi.org/10.1016/B978-0-443-28824-1.50260-X

Model-based Process Development and Operation of a Fluid Bed Granulation Unit to Manufacture Pharmaceutical Tablets

Salvador García Muñoz[a]*, Maitraye Sen[a], Shashwat Gupta[a], Ronald K. Ruff[a] and Pedro de Azevedo Delou[b].

[a] *Synthetic Molecule Design and Development, Eli Lilly and Company. USA.*

[b] *Siemens Industry Software Ltd. London UK.*

**sal.garcia@lilly.com*

Abstract

Fluid bed granulation is a complex yet versatile operation in the manufacturing of pharmaceutical oral solid dosages. A model was derived from the mass and energy balances on the unit while considering the available measurements. The model is built with considerations for pressure driven flow and the use of the temperature dependant drying equilibrium conditions as the driving force. The model was parametrized with available data across multiple operating conditions. Results from an estimability analysis were used to guide the parametrization of the model. The model was then utilized as the basis to build an Extended Kalman Filter (EKF) for the operation, the EKF approach is used to provide a real-time prediction (soft sensor) of the water content in the powder bed. The effectiveness of the EKF is demonstrated with batches operated at the commercial unit. These results clearly illustrate the benefits of an EKF approach over an on-line simulation specifically to provide estimates of unmeasured states.

Keywords: Fluid Bed Drying, Pharmaceuticals, soft sensor, extended Kalman filter, Process Modelling.

1. Introduction

Granulation is an important unit operation in the manufacturing of pharmaceutical oral dosage forms. The main objective of granulation is to increase the overall particle size and bulk density of a powder system. This drastically modifies its bulk behavior and allows the powder mixture to be further processed into an oral dosage (i.e. a tablet or a capsule). Wet granulation platforms span from those that use a relatively high shear processes in either a batch or a twin screw, to those that granulate using gentle shear phenomena imposed by a liquid spray and the fluidization of particles.

The fluid bed granulation unit (figure 1) utilizes the same chamber to create the granules by the addition of a binding liquid; and to dry them. The unit specifically studied consists of a cylindrical chamber where powder resides. In the bottom a perforated plate allows the drying air to come through and in the top a series of filters allow the air to escape the chamber while keeping the powder inside the unit. The binding liquid is atomized and sprayed with two-fluid nozzles located in the bottom of the chamber. The typical operation of the unit consists in the following steps: *a*) loading of the powders, *b*) spraying of a fixed and pre-determined amount of binder solution, *c*) drying of the granules until an acceptable level of moisture is reached, *d*) discharge the material from the unit.

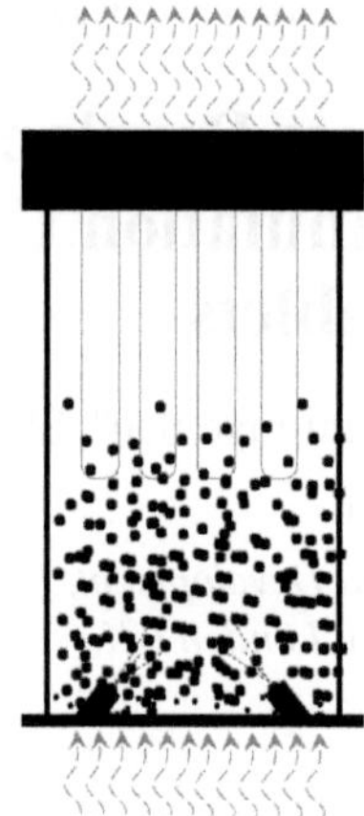

Figure 1. Schematic of a fluid bed granulation chamber

The unit is equipped with a series of sensors that provide real-time data as the machine is operating. These measurements include the temperature and humidity of the incoming and outgoing air, the temperature of the powder bed, the volumetric air flow, and the spray rate. Additionally, during the development of the process, samples of granules are taken throughout the process to be analyzed for water content using a Loss on Drying analyzer (LOD) (Figure 2). The available manipulated variables to operate this unit are a) The flowrate of the drying air during the spraying and the drying phase, b) temperature of the incoming air and d) spray rate. The incoming air is dehydrated by a chiller prior to entering the unit.

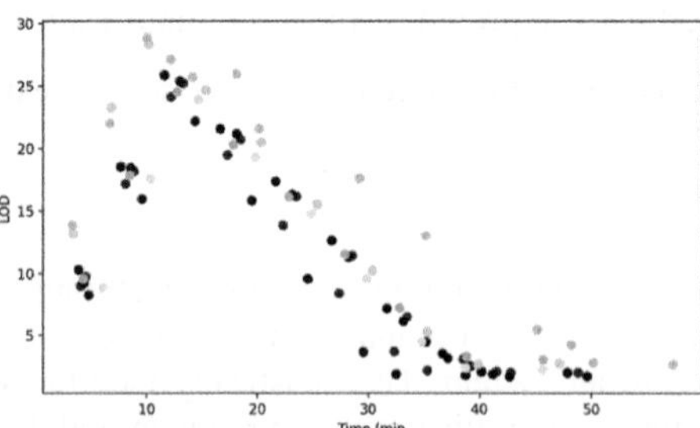

Figure 2. LOD Measurements taken throughout the fluid bed granulation process.

As any other process, this operation is subject to the effect of disturbances that can come through variations in raw materials, variations in the humidity of the incoming air or other environmental conditions affecting the agglomeration or the drying.

2. Modeling of the powder-water system

A mass and energy model for the fluid bed granulation process was proposed by (Ochsenbein, Billups et al. 2019). We implemented this model with some modifications to the driving forces for air flow and drying rate. From a physical properties standpoint, our implementation of this model requires the parametrization of the GAB equation with temperature dependent terms as proposed by (Quirijns, Van Boxtel et al. 2005) and the consideration that this equilibrium is also a function of the binder concentration that changes as spray is added. The energy balance is implemented with a small modification: due to the difficulty in measuring a representative temperature of the wall; the heat transfer between wall and powder bed was neglected. This energy transfer was included in a second version of the model after analyzing the real-time adjustments of the model parameters by the EKF.

The interface between the bed and the surrounding systems is the surface of each particle, as such, the total amount of surface area is a critical parameter that brings full coupling between the granule growth phenomena and the water intake/loss phenomena. We assume this available surface area does not change throughout the process. Albeit this is not true during granule growth; this assumption is easy to defend during the drying phase of the process since the granules are already formed and any changes in size distribution are due to potential attrition of fine particles in the filters and the unlikely breakage of granules. When the drying phenomena is at its strongest, it is reasonable to assume that the surface area per unit of mass is constant and pre-determined since this model does not account for granule growth.

3. Estimability and Parametrization

The full model construct includes nine parameters to be estimated from data (Tables 1 and 2). There were two data sets executed at opposite corners of the granulation phenomena. One set (Over granulation) was carried out at conditions that would promote granule growth and yield particles of large size; while the other set (Under granulation) was executed at conditions that grow smaller granules. Measurements for the final particle size were available for both scenarios.

Two parameter estimation (PE) exercises were initially carried out (Table 1), one per data set. Along with this initial PE, an estimability analysis (McLean and McAuley 2012) was also conducted to rank the model parameters from the most estimable one, to the least. At this point: two parameters were fixed to the average value obtained between the sets given their poor estimability from the data; two parameters were fixed to the average due to the small differences in the obtained values; and four parameters were re-estimated.

After the second round of PE, the estimated heat transfer coefficients between air and wall, and wall and the environment were fixed since these parameters should be agnostic to the granule properties. And after one last round of PE we are left with six parameters with common values for the over and under granulation sets, and three highly correlated parameters (Table 2). The correlated parameters are reflective of the high level of coupling between granulation and drying as the heat transfer between the bed and air, and the time constant for the evaporation rate are both correlated to the particle specific surface are (which the mechanistic part of the model cannot predict).

Table 1. First Round of Estimated Model Parameters and Estimability Results

Parameter	Optimal Estimate Over-granulation	Optimal Estimate Under-granulation	Estimability Ranking	What to do?
PARTICLES SPECIFIC SURFACE AREA	28.90	41.49	1	Fixed to measurement available
U BED AIR	1021.71	18758.15	2	**Re- Estimate**
SPRAYING EFFICIENCY TAU	40.00	42.96	3	Fix to avg due to small difference
K EVAP RATE TAU	15.00	41.62	4	**Re-Estimate**
U WALL ENV	2756.38	1594.07	5	**Re-Estimate**
ABS. HUMIDITY OUT CORRECTION FACTOR	1.34	1.33	6	Fix to avg due to small difference
U WALL AIR	2128.49	2492.03	7	**Re-Estimate**
OMEGA FACTOR	0.64	0.72	8	Fix to avg due to lack of estimability
K EVAP RATE K	0.79	0.51	9	Fix to avg due to lack of estimability
OBJ. FUNCTION	2.17525×10^7	1.08811×10^7		

Table 2. Final values of Parameters post-Estimability adjustments

Parameter	Common Parameters	New value for Over-gran	New Value for Under-gran
ABSOLUTE HUMIDITY OUT CORRECTION FACTOR	1.34		
K EVAP RATE K	0.65		
OMEGA FACTOR	0.68		
PARTICLES SPECIFIC SURFACE AREA		30.00	40.00
SPRAYING EFFICIENCY TAU	41.48		
K EVAP RATE TAU		19.19	25.96
U BED AIR		809.38	5000.00
U WALL AIR	2382.15		
U WALL ENV	1956.33		
OBJ FUNCTION		2.24151×10^{7}	1.26868×10^{7}

4. The Extended Kalman Filter

To streamline the operation of the unit, a soft sensor for the LOD is desired to avoid the need of sampling material. This was implemented using the commercial solution by Siemens Process Engineering using gPROMS Digital Applications. The Extended Kalman Filter (EKF) uses real-time data from all manipulated variables along with data from the bed temperature, outlet air temperature and the outlet air humidity to provide an updated estimate for the LOD. The EKF is also adjusting 6 parameters to keep the model contemporary with the last observed state of the process. The EKF was tuned to achieve optimal performance for the nominal operating conditions (center-conditions). This EKF implementation was then challenged by testing the behaviour of the EKF when the process was operated at opposite corners of the design space (slight under and slight over granulation). The estimated profiles for the unmeasured values of LOD are shown in figure 3, the end-point errors are between 0.46% and 1.32%. This uncertainty in the estimate is considered adequate for this application.

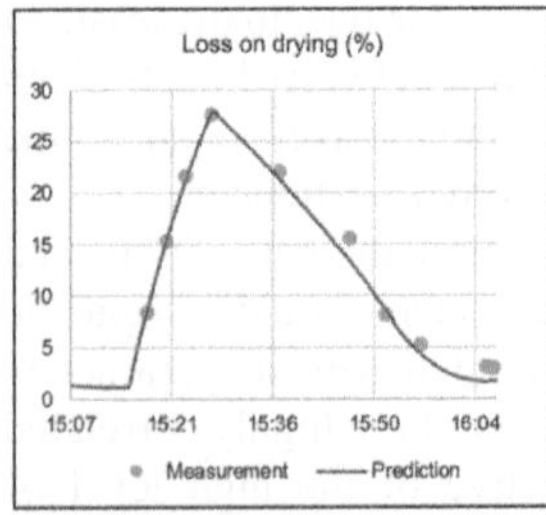

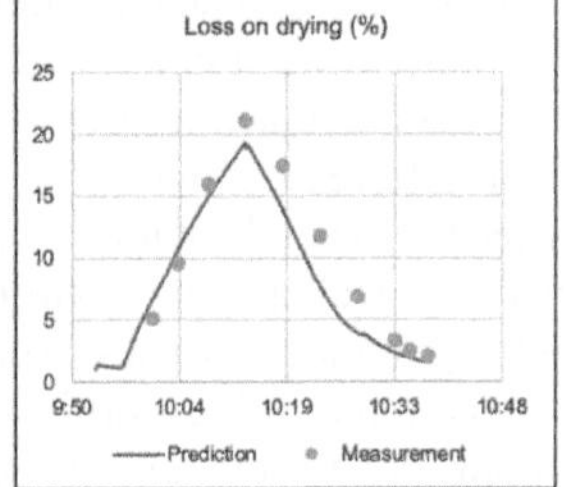

Figure 3. Estimated vs measured LOD for three test lots.

The model appears to also have exquisite tractability to predict the measured states, namely the temperature of the bed, and the temperature of the exhaust humidity (Figure 4). And despite small temporary deviations in one of the batches, the LOD estimate remains stable. The accuracy of the LOD prediction at the point that is needed is well withing the required uncertainty for the application.

All the model parametrization and initial testing of the EKF was conducted in a unit located in the pilot facilities in R&D. The process was later transferred to a commercial manufacture site, to a unit of the same brand and model (like for like). As an additional test of robustness, the EKF was applied to data acquired from the commercial site. These tech transfer lots are common practice to ensure the robustness of process conditions in ensuring product quality.

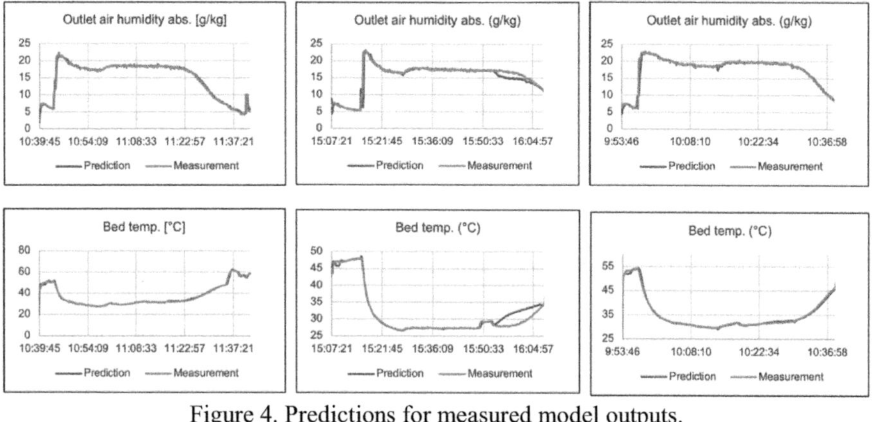

Figure 4. Predictions for measured model outputs.

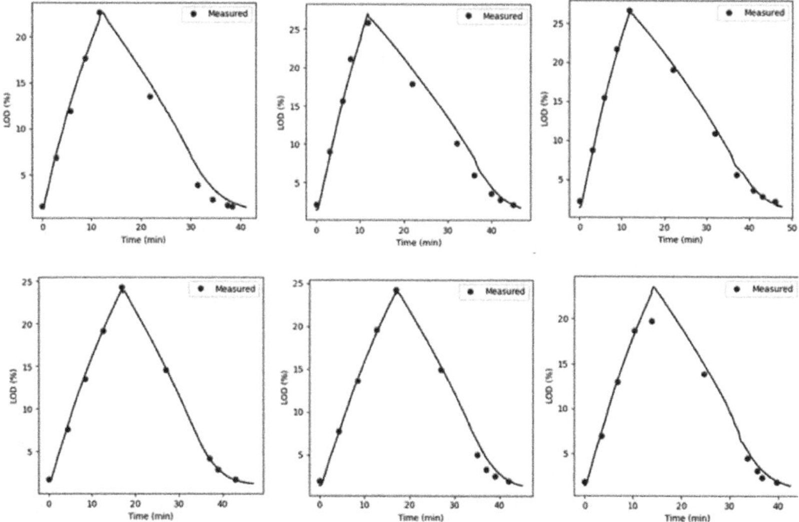

Figure 5. LOD estimated vs measured for 6 independent lots

And although the fluid bed granulation units are like-for-like, there were known differences in the utility lines that condition the air to the unit, aside from the environmental conditions from one geography to the other. No data from this commercial unit had been used in any way to parametrize the model or the EKF. The performance of the LOD estimates against the measured values of LOD in the commercial unit are shown in Figure 5. The implementation delivered remarkable results. The application of State estimation in pharmaceutical manufacture is in its early days, in pharma the use of a deterministic model in real-time is commonly interpreted as an on-line simulation exercise where real-time values of the manipulated variables are fed to a model to produce a result. Figure 6 illustrates the difference between on-line simulation (where the measured model outputs are neglected) with the results from a state estimation solution where the measured outputs are also considered hence bringing information about the effect of disturbances onto the system and thus providing superior estimates for the unmeasured states (the LOD in this case).

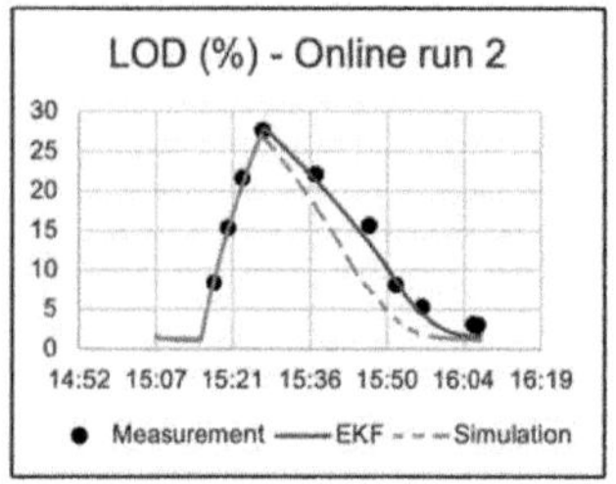

Figure 6. Comparison of results using on-line simulation vs state estimation

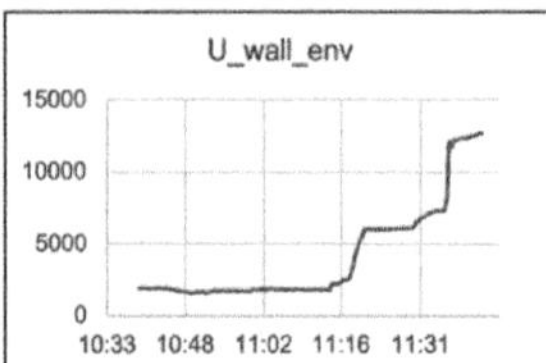

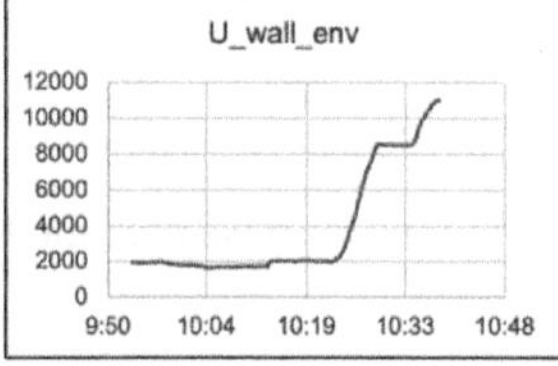

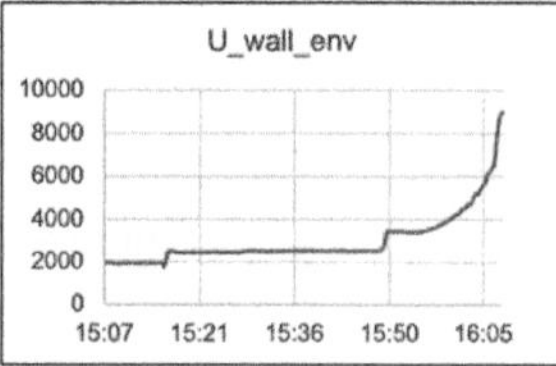

Figure 7. Main diagnostics from the EKF implementation

One notable behaviour from the EKF across all batches tested is the consistent increase of the heat transfer from the wall to the environment at the end of the batch (Fig 6). This diagnostic led us to review the energy flows and to add the transfer of energy from the wall to the powder. This heat transfer was initially neglected due to the inability to measure a representative temperature for the wall. The model was further refined with an additional term to the energy balance to account for the heat transfer between wall and powder bed. Upon re-parametrizing the model (and unsurprisingly) the $u_{wall \leftrightarrow bed}$ is the parameter with the least desirable statistical properties.

5. Concluding remarks

For industrial applications, the mathematics for a model needs to be established considering the available measurements and the potential estimability of the model parameters. The model built was adequate to be used as the basis for an extended Kalman filter to provide predictions of the LOD, the diagnostics from the proof of concept from the EKF were quite informative to refine the model. The EKF implementation provided accurate estimates for the unmeasured states (LOD) even when tested on data acquired in a different like to like unit. This illustrates the benefits from an optimization-based approach capable of updating the model with the most contemporary measurements, as opposed to a simple on-line simulation exercise.

References

K. A. McLean and K. B. McAuley, 2012, Mathematical modelling of chemical processes—obtaining the best model predictions and parameter estimates using identifiability and estimability procedures, The Canadian Journal of Chemical Engineering, 90,2, 351-366.

D. R. Ochsenbein, M. Billups, B. Hong, E. Schäfer, A. J. Marchut and O. K. Lyngberg, 2019, Industrial application of heat-and mass balance model for fluid-bed granulation for technology transfer and design space exploration, International journal of pharmaceutics: X, 1 100028.

E. J. Quirijns, A. J. Van Boxtel, W. K. van Loon and G. Van Straten, 2005, Sorption isotherms, GAB parameters and isosteric heat of sorption, Journal of the Science of Food and Agriculture, 85,11, 1805-1814.

Flavio Manenti, Gintaras V. Reklaitis (Eds.), Proceedings of the 34th European Symposium on Computer Aided Process Engineering / 15th International Symposium on Process Systems Engineering (ESCAPE34/PSE24), June 2-6, 2024, Florence, Italy
 http://dx.doi.org/10.1016/B978-0-443-28824-1.50261-1

Evaluating Performance of Hierarchical Scheduling Frameworks for Varying Matte Grades in Copper Smelting Process

Hussain Ahmed,[a*] Matti Vilkko[a]

[a]*Tampere University,Tampere, 33720, Finland*
hussain.ahmed@tuni.fi

Abstract

In the copper smelting process, a significant amount of copper is lost during copper production. The increasing demand for copper in various industries and the depletion of high-quality copper ores have accentuated the need to design innovative scheduling frameworks that minimize copper losses in the copper smelting process and ensure long-term benefits. One crucial factor influencing copper losses is the selection of matte grade. While previous studies have predominantly concentrated on enhancing throughput and batch time in the copper smelting process, they often overlooked the critical aspect of matte grade selection. This study conducts a sensitivity analysis of two hierarchical scheduling frameworks specifically designed for the copper smelting process. The objective is to compare their impact on copper losses and identify the framework that optimizes processes better through diverse matte-grade selections.

Keywords: copper smelting, process modelling, discrete-time optimization, coordination, hierarchical scheduling.

1. Introduction

The widespread demand for copper in various industries is increasing, but the availability of high-quality copper ores is declining, leading to lower-grade ores utilization. This shift raises production costs and reduces throughput, exacerbating the gap between demand and supply (Ahmed, et al., 2021; Schipper, et al., 2018). Copper smelters, a fundamental process for copper production, lead to copper loss, a challenge that becomes more evident with lower-grade ores utilization (Ahmed, et al., 2022). One possible solution to minimize copper losses is to design innovative scheduling solutions for the copper smelting process that can provide optimal operation and address long-term challenges.

The copper smelting process involves Flash Smelting Furnace (FSF), which produces matte with a predefined grade (Engell, 2008; Korpi, et al., 2019; Suominen, et al., 2016). This matte is loaded to the Peirce Smith Converters (PSCs) that remove the remaining unwanted elements from the matte by passing it through multiple blowing stages (Ahmed, et al., 2021). The final product of the PSC, known as white metal, is loaded into the Anode Furnace (AF) and then electrolysis for further processing.

For the copper smelting process, various scheduling solutions are presented. Suominen et al. (2016) introduced a centralized continuous-time Mixed Integer Linear Programming (MILP) framework that maximizes process throughput and respects operational constraints. Similarly, Harjunkoski et al. (2009) presented a MILP approach considering inter-dependencies among process units. In our previous work (Ahmed, et al., 2022), a discrete-time MILP hierarchical scheduling framework based on rigorous heuristics is proposed to optimize the operational point of the copper smelting process. In another work (Ahmed & Villko, 2023b), we introduced a price-based coordination approach for optimal scheduling of units. All the above studies overlook matte grade selection, thus curtailing their overall utility and effectiveness in smelting processes.

Motivated by finding the optimal matte grade that minimizes copper losses and increases the process throughput, this study provides the sensitivity analysis of two hierarchical scheduling frameworks with respect to the change in the matte grade. The objective is to compare both frameworks concerning copper losses and find the framework that provides better process operation with more matte grade selections.

2. Assumptions

This study considers a copper smelting process processing a specific concentrate type. The process involves an FSF that generates matte with a predetermined grade, transferred periodically to PSC units. The PSC units undergo slag-blowing and copper-blowing stages to produce blister copper batches. In this process, FSF inter-dependencies occur when matte levels exceed or fall below FSF storage capacity limits. In the PSC, logistic inter-dependencies arise due to timing issues in matte loading. Blow inter-dependencies among PSC units arise from gas pipeline handling capacities, highlighting critical aspects of the smelting operation.

3. Scheduling Frameworks

This study aims to optimize a copper smelting process involving one FSF, three PSC units, and one AF unit. The goal is to increase AF throughput by optimizing the FSF feed rate and minimizing copper losses during FSF and PSC operations, as shown in Eq. (1). Here, h represents the scheduling horizon, AF_{prod} stands for AF throughput, $feed_{FSF}^{h}$ is the FSF feed rate, Cu_{FSF} refers to copper losses during FSF operation, and Cu_{PSC} indicates copper losses during PSC operation.

$$\max_{feed_{FSF}, Cu_{FSF}, Cu_{PSC}} AF_{prod} = \sum_{h=1}^{H} feed_{FSF}^{h} - \sum_{h=1}^{H} (Cu_{FSF}^{h} + Cu_{PSC}^{h}) \tag{1}$$

This study considers two scheduling frameworks, each comprising an FSF model, a PSC model, and a coordinator to address process inter- dependencies. For further details, refer to (Ahmed, et al., 2022; Ahmed & Villko, 2023b).

3.1. FSF model

FSF matte production varies with feed rate and mate grade. The FSF aims to maximize concentrate utilization and minimize copper losses, as given in Eq. (2). The approach to address the FSF inter-dependencies depends on the framework type in use. Framework 1 ($pu_{FSF}^{h} = 0$) utilizes Eq. (3) to keep the matte in the FSF within storage capacity limits. Framework 2 uses Eq. (2) to resolve only the FSF upper storage capacity limit violations, while the lower storage capacity limit violations are addressed through the PSC model. Here, $lower_{FSF}^{h}$ and $upper_{FSF}^{h}$ are the FSF lower and upper storage limits, ut_{FSF}^{h} are the violating times, pu_{FSF}^{h} are the prices, and md_{PSC}^{h} is the FSF demand on the PSC units. At the end of each iteration, the FSF model sends back the mass trajectory $mass_{FSF}^{h}$ to the coordinator.

$$\max_{feed_{FSF}} f_{FSF} = \sum_{h=1}^{H} (feed_{FSF}^{h} - Cu_{FSF}^{h}) + \sum_{h \in ut_{FSF}^{h}}^{H} pu_{FSF}^{h} \times (md_{PSC}^{h} + upper_{FSF}^{h} - mass_{FSF}^{h}) \tag{2}$$

$$lower_{FSF}^{h} \leq mass_{FSF}^{h} \leq upper_{FSF}^{h} \tag{3}$$

3.2. PSC model

A PSC batch includes multiple matte loading (ml_i), slag blowing (sb_i), slag skimming (sk_i), and single copper-blowing (cb) operations. The order of PSC operations (z_i) is predefined and stored in the set Z, as given below.

$z_i \in Z = \{ml_i, sb_i, sr_i, cb\}$ $\quad$ i represents repeated operations $i \in \{1, 2, 3, \ldots, I\}$

The PSC batch has a shorter batch time than the scheduling horizon ($T \ll H$) and allows the execution of one PSC batch operation (b_{z_i}) at a time. Like the FSF, the PSC model resolves process inter-dependencies differently based on the employed framework. In Framework 1, it receives conflicting loading times ml_{PSC}^{t}, FSF lower storage capacity violating times ml_{FSF}^{t}, and blowing times scb_{PSC}^{t} and uses Eq. (4) to prevent the PSC unit from executing loading operations or blow operations at conflicting times. In Framework 2, the PSC model tackles loading and blow inter-dependencies between the PSC units similarly to Framework 1. However, it uses prices as a penalty in the objective function to address FSF lower storage capacity limit violations.

$$b_{z_i} = 0 \qquad \forall\, t = \{ml_{PSC}^{t}, ml_{FSF}^{t}, scb_{no}^{t}\} \tag{4}$$

$$\min_{Cu_{PSC}, mass_{ele}, idle} f_{PSC}^{n,b} = \sum_{t=1}^{T} (mass_{ele}^{t} + Cu_{PSC}^{t} + idle^{t}) + \sum_{t=1}^{lt_{FSF}} pl_{FSF}^{t} \times (mdo_{PSC}^{t} + md_{PSC}^{t} - lower_{FSF}^{t}) \tag{5}$$

The primary objective of the PSC model is to minimize unwanted elements in matte $mass_{ele}^{t}$, copper losses Cu_{PSC}^{t}, and unnecessary idle times $idle^{t}$, as given in Eq. (5). To address FSF lower storage capacity limit violations in Framework 2, this model incorporates prices pl_{FSF}^{t}, the earliest available time for the PSC batch to begin its loading operation without violating the FSF lower-capacity limit lt_{FSF}, FSF matte demanded by the conflicting batch md_{PSC}^{t}, and the FSF matte demanded by the batches on non-conflicting PSC units mdo_{PSC}^{t} in Eq. (5). At the end of each iteration, the PSC model returns the loading times, blowing times, and matte demand to the coordinator.

3.3. Coordinator

After each iteration, the coordinator collects the necessary information from the FSF and PSC models. Based on the framework employed, it uses two alternating approaches to address the process inter-dependencies. They are briefly discussed below.

3.3.1. Framework 1

Framework 1 employs rigorous heuristics to resolve FSF and PSC inter-dependencies. The coordinator arranges PSC batch loading times, blowing times, and FSF mass trajectory to determine ml_{PSC}^{t} , scb_{PSC}^{t} , and ml_{FSF}^{t} , and send them to the PSC model. FSF inter-dependencies are handled directly by the FSF model.

3.3.2. Framework 2

Framework 2 combines rigorous and flexible heuristics to manage inter-dependencies between FSF and PSC units. For PSC dependencies, it addresses PSC loading and blowing violations using the approach similar to Framework 1. For handling FSF inter-dependencies, the coordinator employs price-based heuristics, calculating optimal prices through a market-inspired scheme. These prices are calculated using proportional-integral (PI) controllers. These prices guide the allocation of matte to PSC units, allowing the resolution of FSF inter-dependencies at the unit level.

4. Simulations

This study analyzes a copper smelting setup that produces 15 PSC batches. The research explores the impact of matte grade (55% to 75%) on FSF performance, copper losses, PSC batch time, and computational demands. Both frameworks are simulated using literature-derived copper loss rates (Bellemans, et al., 2017; Tan, 2007). Matte grade varies incrementally by 0.1%. Results, including copper losses, FSF feed rate, batch time, and CPU time for both frameworks, are shown in Figures 1 to 5.

For low matte grades (below 61%), FSF matte production is high, and the PSC units require longer to process the matte, making them the bottleneck. Longer PSC blowing times lead to higher copper losses in the PSC, as shown in Figure 1. For high matte grades (above 71%), FSF processing time increases, consequently decreasing its production and making it the bottleneck. For the medium matte grade values (61% - 71%), both the FSF and PSC units are partially the source of the bottleneck.

In Framework 2, copper losses in the PSC are consistently higher across all matte grade values compared to Framework. It addresses FSF lower-storage limit violations by penalizing the PSC model objective function, but this approach leads to sub-optimal PSC blowing times, elevating copper losses. Furthermore, a higher price value penalized more the objective function, adding unnecessary idle times to the schedule, further inflating PSC batch times, as shown in Figure 2. In the FSF, copper losses for higher matte grade values in Framework 2 are lower than in Framework 1 due to reduced FSF feed rate.

PSC units are the bottleneck for low matte values; therefore, the frameworks keep the FSF feed rate lower to respect the FSF upper storage capacity limit. As the matte grade increases, the demand for the matte also increases, leading to an increase in the FSF feed rate. However, operating the FSF at higher matte grades yields an optimal FSF operation but also elevates copper losses within the FSF. As minimization of the copper loss and maximization of the feed rate are the prime objectives of the FSF in the copper smelting process, operating the copper smelting process at lower and higher matte grade values produces a sub-optimal solution.

Framework 2 does not offer a matte grade value conducive to achieving a solution with a high FSF feed rate and minimal FSF and PSC copper losses. In contrast, Framework 1 demonstrates optimal performance with matte grade values ranging from 67.3% to 71%. Within this range, total copper losses are minimal, the copper content in the AF input is high, and the FSF operates at maximum capacity, as illustrated in Figures 3 and 4.

Framework 1 calculates optimal PSC operation durations than Framework 2; thus, the computational demand of Framework 1 is higher than that of Framework 2, as shown in Figure 5. Therefore, from the perspective of framework complexity, Framework 2 provided solutions with lower computational demand. Since the copper industry is keenly interested in minimizing losses and maximizing input concentrate utilization, process personnel tend to favor Framework 1 despite these disparities.

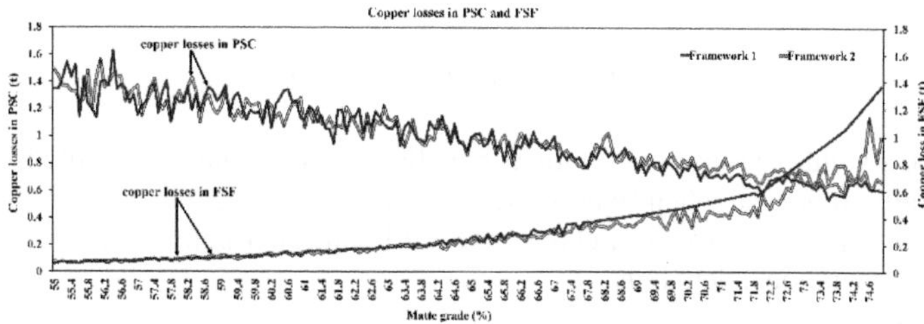

Figure 1: Copper losses in FSF and PSC units

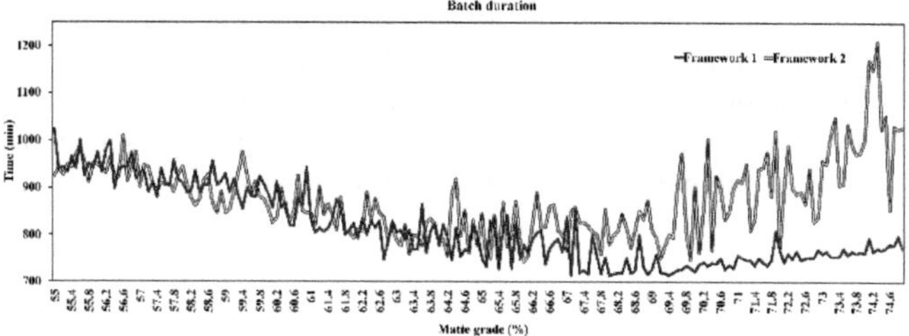

Figure 2: PSC batch time

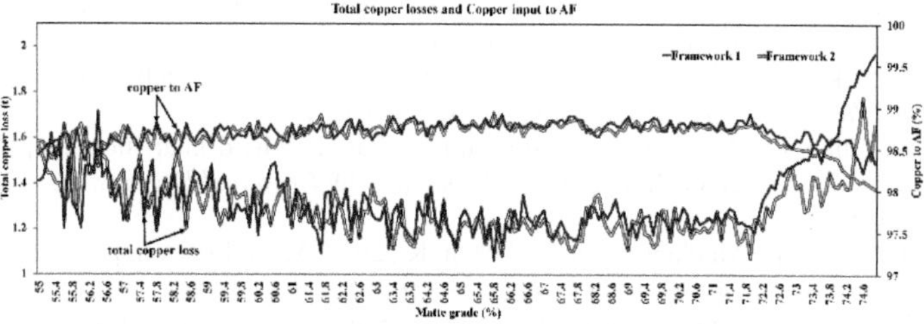

Figure 3: Total copper losses and copper to AF

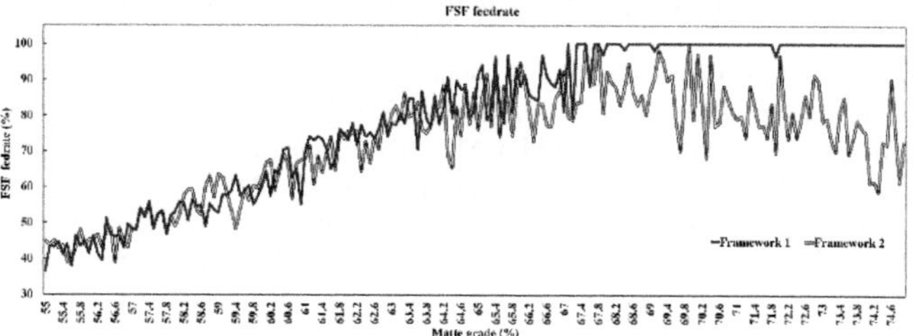

Figure 4: FSF feed rate

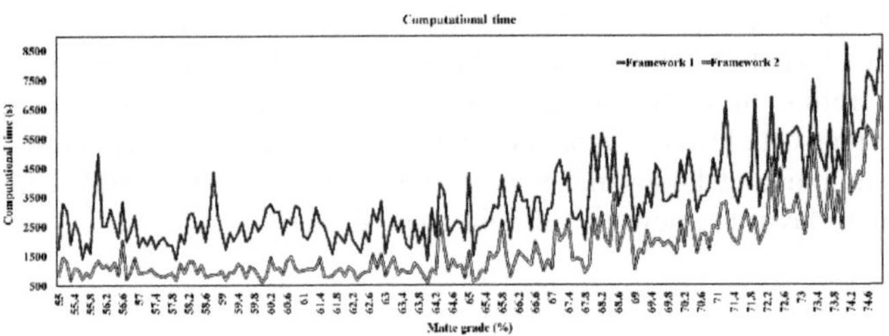

Figure 5: Computational demand

Framework 2 yields sub-optimal solutions but allows process units to handle FSF storage independently. It is ideal when rigorous scheduling is impractical in copper smelting. To enhance its quality, operators can choose lower PI controller gain values. However, this can raise computational demands.

5. Conclusion

This study examines how matte grade affects copper losses and smelting process throughput. Two scheduling frameworks with MILP-based FSF and PSC models are presented here. Simulation results favor Framework 1 due to optimal process operation for matte grade 67.3% to 71%. Future research will concentrate on sensitivity analysis and efficient price-updating mechanisms for enhanced solutions.

References

Ahmed, H., Ricardez-Sandoval, L. A. & Villko, M., 2022. Centralized and hierarchical scheduling frameworks for copper smelting process. *Computers & Chemical Engineering,* 164(0098-1354), p. 107864.

Ahmed, H., Ricardez-Sandoval, L. & Vilkko, M., 2021. Optimal Scheduling of the Peirce–Smith Converter in the Copper Smelting Process. *Processes,* 9(11).

Ahmed, H. & Vilkko, M., 2023a. Price-based coordination strategy for copper smelting process. *Computers & Chemical Engineering,* Volume 178, p. 108395.

Ahmed, H. & Villko, M., 2023b. Coordination strategy based on hard-heuristics and price-updating scheme for copper smelting process. *Computers \& Chemical Engineering,* 173(0098-1354), p. 108198.

Bellemans, I., De W., E., Moelans, N. & Verbeken, K., 2017. Metal losses in pyrometallurgical operations - A review. *Advances in Colloid and Interface Science,* Volume 255.

Engell, S., 2008. *Logistic Optimization of Chemical Production Processes.* s.l.:s.n.

Harjunkoski, I., Werner B., H. & Fahl, M., 2009. *Simultaneous scheduling and optimization of a copper plant.* s.l., Elsevier, pp. 1197 - 1202.

Korpi, M. et al., 2019. *Plant-wide optimization of a copper smelter : how to do it in practice?.* s.l., s.n.

Schipper, B. W. et al., 2018. Estimating global copper demand until 2100 with regression and stock dynamics. *Resources, Conservation and Recycling,* 132(0921-3449), pp. 28-36.

Suominen, O., Mörsky, V., Ritala, R. & Vilkko, M., 2016. *Framework for optimization and scheduling of a copper production plant.* s.l., Elsevier, pp. 1243-1248.

Tan, P., 2007. Applications of thermodynamic modeling in copper converting operations. *International Journal of Materials Research - INT J MATER RES,* Volume 98, pp. 995-1003.

Flavio Manenti, Gintaras V. Reklaitis (Eds.), Proceedings of the 34th European Symposium on Computer Aided Process Engineering / 15th International Symposium on Process Systems Engineering (ESCAPE34/PSE24), June 2-6, 2024, Florence, Italy
 http://dx.doi.org/10.1016/B978-0-443-28824-1.50262-3

Emission oriented scheduling optimization for sustainable processes

Alessandro Di Pretoro[a*], Ingy Tageldin[a,b], Ludovic Montastruc[a]

[a]*Laboratoire de Génie Chimique, Université de Toulouse, CNRS/INP, Toulouse, France*
[b]*Technische Universität München, Department of Chemistry, Lichtenbergstraße 4, Garching b. München 85748, Germany*

alessandro.dipretoro@ensiacet.fr

Abstract

As a consequence of the continuously increasing attention towards the environmental transition, a considerable mutation of the respective roles between energy and chemicals can be detected in the process industry. This aspect is of non-negligible importance when it comes to decide how to manage the plant sections from an operational perspective. The conventional design of a chemical production plant is based on a given productivity target to be achieved and the duty consumption is adapted consequently. However, this approach is not suitable whether the main focus of a chemical plant is to keep the emissions as low as possible. Whether the purpose of the plant is to use a chemical molecule as energy storage, the usual economic criteria for scheduling optimization could be replaced by new one allowing to take the maximum advantage from renewable energy availability. In this study, the possibility to operate a biomethanol production plant with a sustainable approach according to renewables availability trend is investigated from the design and sizing phase till the production scheduling one. The related emissions are assessed in terms of Global Warming Potential in order to verify the net emitted equivalent CO_2 and minimize it until negative emissions are achieved by this process. This methodology showed good results and proved not only that negative emissions chemical plants are possible but, more importantly, that the sustainability of a process is mainly a matter of methodology. Beyond this preliminary study, this approach is worth further investigation in order to extend the emission-based operation management to the entire production from raw materials supply to final product delivery.

Keywords: demand-side management, scheduling, methanol, renewables.

1. Introduction

The conventional procedure for chemical process scheduling has usually been based on optimization methods able to maximize the economic income for a given product demand to meet. This methodology relies on the principle of unconstrained availability of the energy source and prioritizes economics with respect to other aspects of the process system. However, in case sustainability results to be the major concern of the chemical industry, this approach does not ensure the lowest possible environmental impact. In fact, in order to be certain that the required demand is satisfied, at least one of the exploited energy sources should be largely available with no interruption in the supply. This is obviously not the case of renewable energy, whose nature is variable both in terms of peak power and overall quantity. The consequence of this inconsistency between fixed demand and renewables is the impossibility of ensuring at the same time the most sustainable and the most profitable and satisfactory production system.

However, since the current major concern of the industrial sector is to meet the emissions target fixed by the European Union for 2050 (UE, 2019), the study of the most sustainable process solutions has seen a considerably renewed interest in the engineering domain, even at the cost of a lower income. Based on the previous premises, it becomes evident that scheduling optimization is a fundamental step to achieve the best process operation with respect to renewable energy sources availability. For this reason, Demand-Side Management has become one of the most critical tools in the Process Systems Engineering domain to make the environmental transition a viable solution from both a qualitative and quantitative point of view (Shariatzadeh et al., 2015).
Therefore, in order to reverse the conventional design approach where productivity is targeted as first objective and, for a fixed production layout, emissions are minimized at a second stage, the ideal case of carbon-free utilities coupled with a negative emission chemical plant needs to be studied more in depth. Moreover, this operation layout could be also exploited as a potential storage of renewable energy into chemicals and it could be seen as the highest CO_2 removal potential scenario for the specific process.
Based on this premises, in this research work, a preliminary analysis of the renewable-based scheduling is carried out by using solar energy as CO_2 free source. However, since for safety reason some processes cannot be completely switched off when solar energy is not available, a second scenario exploiting biomass as backup duty is also evaluated and the comparison between the two scenario is performed. The negative emissions case study selected to test this methodology is the biogas-to-methanol process whose details are provided in the next section.

2. Case study

2.1. Biogas-to-methanol process

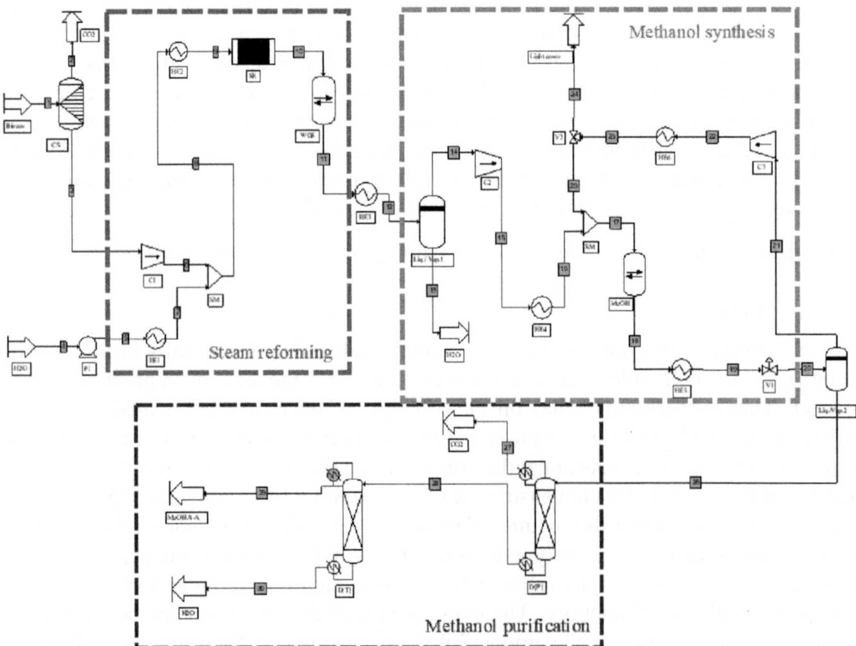

Figure 1 Biogas-to-methanol simulation flowsheet and sections

The selected case study for this research work is the biogas-to-methanol process. The reason behind this choice is based on the fact that it both allows to partially convert CO_2 into methanol (Fedeli et al., 2022) and serves as a power-to-chemical process able to store renewable energy by exploiting chemicals as energy vectors. A simplified flow scheme of the process simulation is presented in Figure 1. As it can be noticed, the plant includes three section as follows: (i) a preliminary steam reforming section where the biogas transformation into biosyngas is carried out; (ii) the reaction section and (iii) the purification section to obtain methanol at the grade AA purity (i.e. 0.9985 w/w). In this specific study, in order to assess the worst case conditions in terms of potential emissions, a layout without any process integration solution is considered. It is finally worth remarking that the case study choice is not restrictive since the proposed methodology can be applied to any process whose carbon balance on the process side is negative.

2.2. Renewables energy sources

As concerns the utility side, the selected renewable and backup energy sources are solar power and biomass respectively. Solar irradiation trend is the leading criteria for the plant operation scheduling. For this study, data retrieved from Global Solar Atlas concerning Toulouse (43.6047° N, 1.4442° E) were used to outline the average direct irradiation availability trend over the day for each month (cf Figure 2). As a reference for the nominal operating conditions, calculations will be carried out with the trend of August, but the procedure keeps being of general validity independently of the selected month. Details concerning the operation and the energy efficiency are better discussed in the next section. On the backup energy source side, as already mentioned, biomass is used for power and steam generation. The biomass properties in terms of specific net heating value and specific emissions (Phyllis) are provided in Table 1 along with those related natural gas, that is used as a reference value.

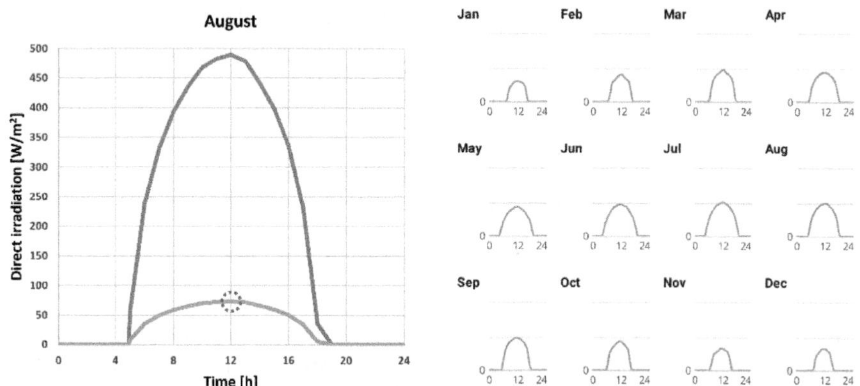

Figure 2 – Average hourly profiles for all months (left) and details for August (right)

Table 1 – Energy sources physical properties

Backup energy nature	Net Heating Value	Unit	Specific emissions	Unit
Photovoltaic	400	W/panel	/	kg_{CO2}/kg
Natural gas	51 600	kJ/kg	2.75	kg_{CO2}/kg
Biomass	13 000	kJ/kg	0,0055	kg_{CO2}/kg

In the ideal case, the process should be running only when solar power is available according to its intensity but, for safety and operational reasons (Mbatha et al., 2021), this is not always possible. However, the overall process could result in overall negative emissions even if part of the energy comes from non-renewable sources according to a proper scheduling. The methodology to evaluate the environmental indicator known as Global Warming Potential and the details concerning the emission-oriented optimal scheduling strategy are provided in the following section.

3. Methodology

3.1. Scheduling

With regards to the solar energy availability for scheduling, an overall panel efficiency equal to 15% is considered to assess the effective available solar power per panel unit surface (cf yellow trend in Figure 2 – left). On the process side, in case the reactor cannot be switched off due to the safety and operational constraints, biomass is burnt for steam generation in order to ensure the process functioning at the 10% of its design capacity (Mbatha et al., 2021). However, if the reactor is seized according to the peak energy availability, every time that the solar power falls below this minimum threshold, the biomass source needs to be used to provide the backup duty. As a consequence, the normalized daily energy consumption of the process can be calculated as:

$$E_{tot} = \frac{1}{W_{peak} \cdot 24} \cdot \int_{0}^{24} W(t) \cdot dt \qquad (1)$$

where W_{peak} is irradiation value corresponding to the process design operating conditions, W is the maximum between the available irradiation power and the 10% backup energy threshold and, finally, 24 is the conversion coefficient between day and hours.
However, since photovoltaics have zero specific emissions while backup energy sources correspond to a positive value, the backup energy fraction E^{backup} should be evaluated separately in order to assess the overall balance as better explained in the next section.

3.2. Emissions calculation

The calculation of the overall environmental impact is carried out by accounting for both process and utility side. To be more precise, the equivalent CO_2 balance is calculated as:

$$GWP_{tot} = \frac{E^{backup}}{\hat{E}^{biomass}} \cdot \widehat{CO}_{2,eq}^{biomass} + CO_2^{products} - CO_2^{feed} \qquad (2)$$

where the $CO_2^{products}$ term accounts for the carbon dioxide content in all process streams leaving the system while $\hat{E}^{biomass}$ and $\widehat{CO}_{2,eq}^{biomass}$ are respectively the biomass specific net heating value and emissions. As concerns the backup energy term $\hat{E}^{backup}$, it is different from zero only in case the 10% of the operating conditions should be maintained. As a final step, the value obtained by equation (2) is normalized with respect to the CO_2 fed to the process side in order to assess the percentage of net converted CO_2 of the process according to the equation:

$$\widehat{GWP} = \frac{GWP_{tot}}{CO_2^{feed}} \qquad (3)$$

where the specific $\widehat{GWP}$ value, whether negative can be considered as carbon dioxide removal potential. The detailed calculation result is presented in the following section.

4. Results

As a first result, the relative fraction of renewable and backup sources that are used as process duty can be assessed (cf Figure 3). In particular, the yellow curve represents the part of the total solar radiation (i.e. 15%) that is converted into energy by the photovoltaic panels while the green line corresponds to safety threshold, i.e. 10% of nominal operating conditions. In this case, the optimal scheduling trajectory follows the solar power availability curve with the exception of the part where the yellow trend falls below the minimum operating conditions threshold, in this case the backup energy source is used. In particular, three regions can be identified: (i) the yellow region where only photovoltaic power is used, (ii) a hybrid region where both solar irradiation and biomass are employed as energy sources and (iii) a green region where no solar power is available and only biomass is used to ensure the 10% of the operation capacity. From a graphical point of view, the total amount of energy is represented by the integral of the power over the operating time, i.e. the area below the operating curves. The relative weight of the three different utility sources is then quantified as 89% solar only, 1% hybrid and 10% biomass.

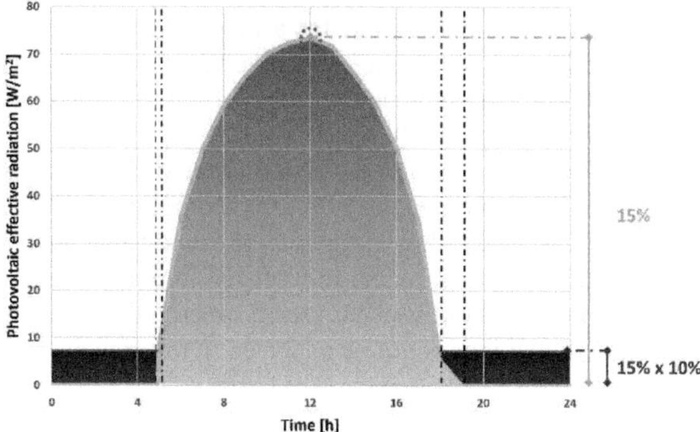

Figure 3 – Daily distribution of different energy sources (yellow-solar, green-biomass)

Given the relative weight of each region, the CO_2 removal potential for the different scenarios can be easily quantified according to the values provided in Table 2. If the process can be thoroughly scheduled according to the availability trend of solar irradiation, the 80% of the CO_2 in the feed is converted into methanol with no carbon dioxide production on the utility side. For this specific process, the -80% value also represents the minimum boundary that cannot be overcome without adjusting the operating conditions. For instance, even in case of an energy integrated configuration, the result would still be the same since the emissions related to the duty are equal to zero. On the other hand, the worst case scenario (i.e. 100% natural gas as energy source) would generate 4231% of the amount of CO2 fed to the methanol reactor.

Table 2 – Relative emissions vs. energy source

Backup energy nature	CO_2 removal [kg/kg in the feed]	Percentage of use
Photovoltaic	-80%	100%
Biomass	290%	10.5%
Natural gas	4231%	10.5%

When weighing this value with the renewable energy one according to the percentage of use, the overall process emissions would be 340% in case of natural gas used as backup energy source. Finally, when using biomass as backup utility, an intermediate value equal to -41% is obtained. This value comes from the combination of 290% biomass emissions and -80% of solar power weighed with respect to their percentage of use. As a final remark, although the obtained value in the latter case could considerably vary according to the selected biomass, it should always stay within the renewable and natural gas interval [-80, 340]%.

5. Conclusions

The main scope of the presented research work is to evaluate, in terms of sustainability, the effectiveness of an ideal emission-oriented operation scheduling where only renewable energy sources are employed for the production of methanol.

Based on the obtained results, some relevant conclusions can be drawn. First, the maximum carbon removal potential of negative emission processes, obtained by its conversion into chemicals, can be quantitatively assessed with respect to the capacity of the plant. To be more precise, it is achieved for a process scheduling that thoroughly follows the availability of the renewable energy source that is used. Second, whether the system could not be continuously switched on and off for safety or process control reasons, the integration of a backup energy source, such as biomass, can be accounted for by applying analogous calculation. Finally, the proposed procedure can be used to detect the most suitable locations that maximize the CO_2 removal potential for the given process according to the geographical availability of the selected renewable energy source.

Given the positive outcome of this approach, in terms of future perspectives, utilities of different nature as backup option could be compared on an environmental impact basis and systems with different behaviour could be analyzed in order to assess their response.

References

B. Bruns, A. Di Pretoro, M, Grünewald, J. Riese, 2021. Indirect demand response potential of large-scale chemical processes. Industrial & Engineering Chemistry Research, 61(1), 605-620.

The Commission to the European Parliament, the European Council, the Council, the European Economic and Social Committee and the Committee of the Regions, The European Green Deal; 2019. ⟨ https://eur-lex.europa.eu/homepage.html ⟩ (accessed 2023-11-19)

M. Fedeli, F., Manenti, 2022. Assessing process effectiveness with specific environmental and economic impact of heat, power & chemicals (HPC) option as future perspective in biogas. Cleaner Chemical Engineering 2, 100016.

Global Solar Atlas, accessed 02/11/2023 ⟨ https://globalsolaratlas.info/map ⟩

S. Mbatha, R.C. Everson, N.M. Musyoka, H.W. Langmi, A. Lanzini, W. Brilman, 2021. Power-to-methanol process: a review of electrolysis, methanol catalysts, kinetics, reactor designs and modelling, process integration, optimisation, and technoeconomics. Sustainable Energy & Fuels, 5(14), 3490–569.

Phyllis Database, ⟨ https://phyllis.nl/ ⟩, (accessed 2023-11-05).

F. Shariatzadeh, P. Mandal, A. K. Srivastava, 2015. Demand response for sustainable energy systems: A review, application and implementation strategy, Renewable and Sustainable Energy Reviews 45, 343-350.

Flavio Manenti, Gintaras V. Reklaitis (Eds.), Proceedings of the 34th European Symposium on Computer Aided Process Engineering / 15th International Symposium on Process Systems Engineering (ESCAPE34/PSE24), June 2-6, 2024, Florence, Italy
 http://dx.doi.org/10.1016/B978-0-443-28824-1.50263-5

Analyzing the effects of control Strategies for Determining Process Feasible Space

Margherita Geremia[a], Fabrizio Bezzo[a], Marianthi G. Ierapetritou[b,*]

[a]*CAPE-Lab – Computer-Aided Process Engineering Laboratory. Department of Industrial Engineering, University of Padova, via Marzolo 9, 35131 Padova (PD), Italy*
[b]*Department of Chemical and Biomolecular Engineering, University of Delaware, Newark, DE, USA*
Corresponding author e-mail: mgi@udel.edu

Abstract

The identification of process Design Space (DS) is key to support the development of pharmaceutical processes, where strict requirements on manufacturability and product quality must be satisfied. If the process can be controlled by a set of manipulated variables, the DS can be enlarged with respect to an open-loop scenario, where there are no controls in place. Since pharmaceutical models are typically complex and computationally expensive, surrogate-based feasibility analysis can be suitably exploited to determine whether the process satisfies all constraints by adjusting the process control inputs, and mitigate the effect of uncertainty. The approach is successfully implemented on a pharmaceutical case study; results demonstrate that different control actions can be effectively exploited to mitigate uncertainty and operate the process in a wider range of inputs. The framework can conveniently be exploited to support decisions on control strategies for real industrial applications.

Keywords: feasibility analysis, design space, pharmaceutical manufacturing, surrogate models, process control.

1. Introduction

Process Design Space (DS) is defined as the subset of combinations of input parameters that have been demonstrated to provide assurance of product quality and satisfy all the relevant operating and production constraints (ICH, 2009); its description is particularly relevant in highly regulated sectors such as the pharmaceutical industry, where assurance of manufacturability and quality of the product is key for process development and optimization (Destro and Barolo, 2022). Feasibility analysis can be exploited to determine the range of conditions within which the process can be safely operated, i.e., the subset of combinations of input factors that satisfy all the relevant operating, quality, and production constraints (Grossmann et al., 2014). If the process can be controlled by a set of manipulated variables, the DS may be enlarged with respect to an open-loop scenario, where there are no controls in place. Namely, feasibility analysis can be used to determine whether the process satisfies all process constraints by adjusting the process control inputs to operate in a larger range of input factors and reduce the effect of uncertainty.

The use of surrogate-based approaches for feasibility analysis has been demonstrated to effectively identify the boundaries of the process DS, particularly when the available model is computationally expensive or consists of various black-box constraints – which is typically the case of pharmaceutical manufacturing models (Wang and Ierapetritou, 2017). However, the influence of control variables has not been included.

In this study we adopt a surrogate-based feasibility approach with the objective of investigating the effect of manipulated variables in the characterization of the process DS and in mitigating sources of uncertainty. More specifically, we aim at analyzing and quantifying the benefits of a proper control action on the process DS for pharmaceutical manufacturing development.

2. Methodology

Feasibility analysis is mathematically formulated as the maximum of the process constraint violation (Grossmann et al., 2014):

$$\varphi(\boldsymbol{x}) = \min_{\boldsymbol{z}} \max_{j \in J} \{g_j(\boldsymbol{z}, \boldsymbol{x})\} \; s.t. \; \boldsymbol{x} \in \boldsymbol{X}, \tag{1}$$

where $\varphi(\boldsymbol{x})$ is the process feasibility function; $\boldsymbol{z}$ is the vector of control variables, and $\boldsymbol{x}$ is the vector of critical input variables (e.g., raw material properties and critical process parameters); g_j are the functions of the J process constraints in the form $g_j(\boldsymbol{z}, \boldsymbol{x}) \leq 0$ which must be satisfied during process operation. $\boldsymbol{X}$ defines the range in which critical inputs can vary: $\boldsymbol{X} = \{\boldsymbol{x} \mid \boldsymbol{x}^L \leq \boldsymbol{x} \leq \boldsymbol{x}^U\}$, with $\boldsymbol{x}^L$ and $\boldsymbol{x}^U$ representing lower and upper bounds, respectively. Solving problem (1) determines whether for given critical input variables $\boldsymbol{x}$, the control vector $\boldsymbol{z}$ can be adjusted to satisfy all the J problem constraints, g_j, and attain feasibility.

Since solution of Eq. (1) might be computational complex, we approximate the feasibility function using the surrogate-based approach proposed by Geremia et al. (2023), which is suitable to guide the selection of one best surrogate model for feasibility approximation and attain preset level of accuracy with the minimum requirement of additional training data. The procedure consists of three sequential steps (Figure 1), which are described in the following, and must be iteratively repeated until the surrogate approximates the real feasibility function with a given preset level of accuracy (stop criterion), or the total iterations exceeds the user-defined maximum number of iterations.

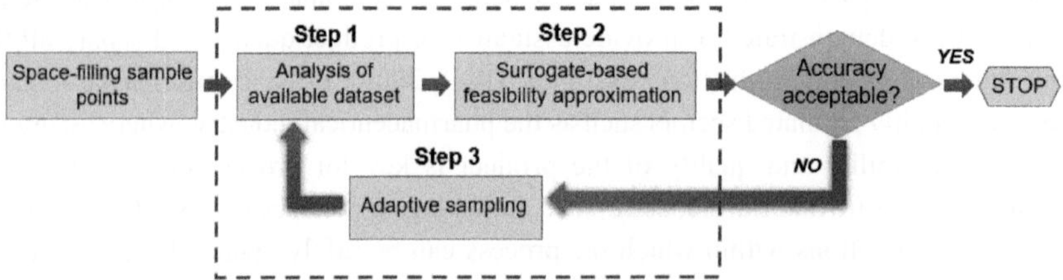

Figure 1. Schematic of the surrogate-based approach used in this study.

<u>Step 1. Analysis of the available dataset</u>

Before any candidate surrogate is trained, statistical metrics (Sun and Braatz, 2021) and topological data analysis (Smith and Zavala, 2021) are combined to assess problem characteristics and complexity. A statistical analysis is suitable to detect nonlinearity between predictors and response and correlations, while algebraic topology aims at number disjointed feasible regions – which correspond to 0-dimensional Betti numbers β_0 (Edelsbrunner and Harer, 2009). This is key to acquire information regarding the original feasibility function, and to consequently narrow down a number of surrogate models to be further trained.

Step 2. Surrogate-based feasibility approximation

After the training, quality of fitting and predictive capability of the different surrogates are compared, in such a way that it is possible to identify which of them best approximates the feasibility function. The Bayesian Information Criterion (BIC) is used to account for both model complexity and quality of fitting (Schwarz, 1978):

$$BIC(M_k) = -2logL(M_k) + klog(n), \tag{2}$$

where $L(M_k)$ is the likelihood corresponding to the model M_k, k is the number of model parameters, and n is the number of training points. The first term, $-2logL(M_k)$, acts as a measure of inaccuracy, with smaller values to be preferred, while $klog(n)$ is a penalty factor that increases with model complexity (higher k) and the number of training points (higher n). Therefore, the current best model is the one associated with the lowest value of BIC. Evaluation of accuracy is treated as a binary classification problem, relying on the metrics proposed by Wang and Ierapetritou (2017), namely the percentage of Correct Feasible region ($CF\%$), the percentage of Correct InFeasible region ($CIF\%$), and the percentage of Not Conservative feasible region ($NC\%$). If none of the trained surrogates guarantees the preset level of accuracy (stop criterion), new sampling points are needed.

Step 3. Adaptive sampling

To improve accuracy, new points are iteratively sampled and included within the initial dataset. To compute new samples, we use an adaptive strategy based on the minimization of the BIC of the current best surrogate. Under the assumption of independent errors, each new adaptive point is computed by solving the following minimization problem:

$$\min_{x} BIC = -2\left(-\frac{1}{2}log2\pi - \frac{1}{2}log\hat{s}^2 - \frac{\hat{y}^2}{2\hat{s}^2}\right) + klog(n), \tag{3}$$

where $\hat{s}$ is the standard error of the predictor, and $\hat{y}$ is the value of the feasibility function that is predicted by the current best surrogate. Note that the term $\left(-\frac{1}{2}log2\pi - \frac{1}{2}log\hat{s}^2 - \frac{\hat{y}^2}{2\hat{s}^2}\right)$ in Eq. (3) corresponds to $logL(M_k)$ in Eq. (2) (Bard, 1974).

2.1. Effect of uncertainty

Some critical input factors in vector $\boldsymbol{x}$ may be affected by uncertainty, e.g., material properties entering the process, affecting the characterization of the DS. We describe uncertain inputs using a uniform distribution around an expected value and analyze the level of uncertainty that propagates to the process DS by randomly selecting values of uncertain inputs from those distributions. We, then, quantify the reliability provided by the process DS through a probability figure of merit r (Peterson, 2008):

$$\{\boldsymbol{x} \mid \Pr(\varphi(\boldsymbol{x}) \leq 0) \geq \mathrm{r}\}\; s.t.\; \boldsymbol{x} \in \boldsymbol{X}, \mathrm{r} \in [0,1]. \tag{4}$$

r is the reliability factor representing the probability that process constraints are satisfied for a given set $\boldsymbol{x}$. If $\mathrm{r} = 0$, there is always at least one constraint that is being violated, namely no combination of inputs allows the process to be feasibly operated; if $\mathrm{r} = 1$, no constraint is being violated, namely the process is feasible for any combinations of inputs;

if 0 < r <1, some combinations of inputs satisfy all process contraints, while others don't. The closer r is to 1, the higher the probability that process constraints are satisfied.

3. Case Study

A pharmaceutical roller compaction process is used as case study. We rely on the model proposed by Hsu et al. (2010), which combines the Johanson's rolling theory (Johanson, 1965) with a dynamic material balance:

$$\frac{d}{dt}\left(\frac{h_0}{R}\right) = \frac{\omega\left[\rho_{in}cos(\theta_{in})\left(1+\frac{h_0}{R}-cos(\theta_{in})\right)\left(\frac{u_{in}}{\omega R}\right)-\rho_{exit}\left(\frac{h_0}{R}\right)\right]}{\int_0^{\theta_{in}}\rho(\theta)\,cos(\theta)\mathrm{d}\theta} \tag{5}$$

$$P_h = \frac{W}{A}\frac{\sigma_{exit}R}{(1+sin(\delta))}\int_0^{\alpha}\left[\frac{\frac{h_0}{R}}{\left(1+\frac{h_0}{R}-cos(\theta)\right)cos(\theta)}\right]^K cos(\theta)\mathrm{d}\theta\,, \tag{6}$$

$$\sigma_{exit} = C_1\rho_{exit}^K\,, \tag{7}$$

where R is the roll radius, W is the roll width, K and C_1 are compression parameters, A is the compact surface area, δ is the effective angle of friction, α is the nip angle, θ_{in} is the inlet angle, ρ_{in} is the inlet powder density, ω is the roll speed, P_h is the roll pressure, and u_{in} is the powder feed speed. The model is used to predict the critical quality attributes of the product, i.e., the ribbon density at outlet, ρ_{exit}, and the ribbon thickness, h_0, which must satisfy the requirements on product quality $\rho_{exit} \in$ [850–950] kg/m^3, and $h_0 \in [1.7 \times 10^{-3} - 1.9 \times 10^{-3}]$ m.

We account for the combined effect of the critical operating factors P_h and u_{in} on the identification of the process DS (i.e., $\boldsymbol{x} = [P_h, u_{in}]^{\mathrm{T}}$) and the benefits of a proper control action on ω (i.e., $\mathbf{z} = [\omega]$) while hedging against variability in raw material properties. We assume that ω can be manipulated in between $\pm$10% its nominal value in order to enlarge the process DS, and compare results with an open-loop scenario where the DS is only determined by the operating conditions $\boldsymbol{x}$. We account for the effect of variability in raw material properties assuming that ρ_{in} fluctuates as powder enters the process around its expected (nominal) value.

4. Results

We start with an initial dataset of 25 points, which are obtained using a Sobol's sampling strategy in order to uniformly map the input domain (Saltelli et al., 2010).

According to Step 1 of the presented procedure, statistical analysis of the available dataset indicates nonlinearity between predictors and response, and suggests the training of nonlinear candidate surrogates at Step 2. Algebraic topology does not detect the presence of disconnected components (β_0 =1), i.e., the process DS does not consist of disconnected feasible regions.

The inclusion of 186 new adaptive points to the initial dataset (Step 3) allows to accurately approximate the feasibility boundaries through a Gaussian Process ($\mathcal{GP}$) with exponential kernel ($CF\% \geq 98\%$, $CIF\% \geq 98\%$, $NC\% \leq 2\%$). The surrogate-based prediction of the feasible boundaries is shown in Figure 2a, and compared to both the original contour, and the one obtained for an open-loop scenario. It is evident that a proper control action can extensively enlarge the feasible DS, allowing the process to be safely operated in a wider range of u_{in}. For clarity purpose, values of control ω and effect on u_{in} defining the feasible DS for different levels of compaction pressure P_h are visualized in Figure 2b.

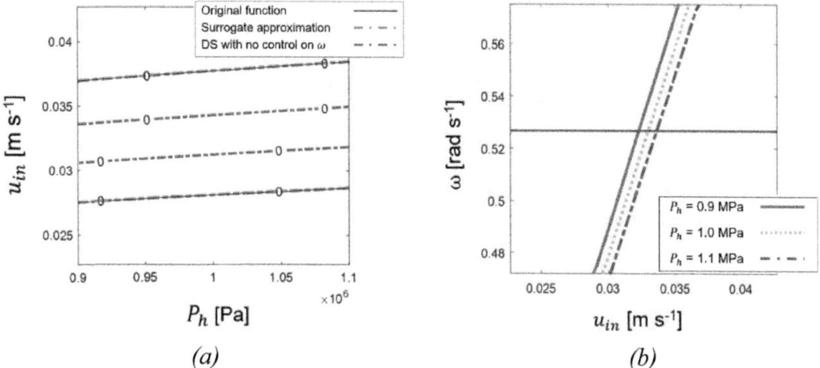

Figure 2. (a) Comparison between real contour plot of enlarged DS (continue black line) and surrogate-based approximation (dotted orange line) through a $\mathcal{GP}$ with exponential kernel after the inclusion of 186 adaptive samples. Blue dotted lines represent an open-loop scenario. (b) Values of control ω and effect on u_{in} for different levels P_h. Nominal value of ω (no control action) is shown as continuous red line.

4.1. Accounting for uncertainty in raw material

We assume that the inlet powder density, ρ_{in}, fluctuates as powder enters the process with a deviation of $\pm$ 25 kg/m^3 with respect to the nominal value of 300 kg/m^3. The stochastic DS is identified by evaluating the probability that all process constraints are satisfied for different values of ρ_{in}. 10^2 scenarios are simulated for any combination of operating conditions (P_h, u_{in}, and manipulated ω) by randomly selecting values of ρ_{in} in the predefined range of variability. 3600 evaluation points are used in order to heavenly map the input space (Kucherenko et al., 2015). Results are shown in Figure 3, from which it can be seen that a robust DS (i.e., r = 1) has shrink in width if compared to Figure 2a, where no uncertainty was considered. However, a proper control action on ω is suitable to operate in a larger range if compared to the case of an open-loop scenario.

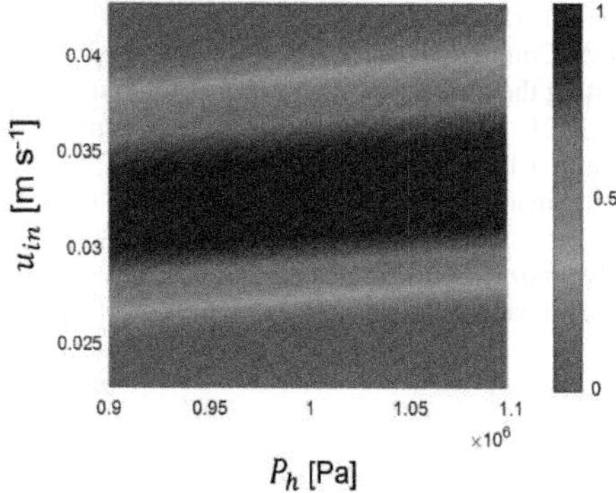

Figure 3. Stochastic DS considering a deviation of $\pm$ 25 kg/m^3 from the expected value of ρ_{in}.

5. Conclusions

In this study, we presented a surrogate-based approach, which combines different mathematical tools to: (*i*) identify the process DS relying on the available training dataset, and (*ii*) investigate the effect of manipulated variables in order to operate the process in a wider range of operating conditions. The presented workflow combines different mathematical tools which are proved to effectively identify the process DS while illustrating the effect of control variables, and can be suitably exploited to guide decisions on convenient control strategies for industrial processes.

Acknowledgments

M. G. acknowledges "Fondazione Cariparo" for her scholarship, and "Fondazione Ing. Aldo Gini" for financial support during her stay at University of Delaware.

References

Y. Bard, 1974. Nonlinear Parameter Estimation. Academic Press, New York, NY.

F. Destro, M. Barolo, 2022, A review on the modernization of pharmaceutical development and manufacturing – Trends and perspectives, and the role of mathemtical modeling. Int. J. Pharm., 620, 121715.

H. Edelsbrunner, J. Harer, 2009. Computational Topology: An Introduction. American Mathematical Society.

M. Geremia, F. Bezzo, M.G. Ierapetritou, 2023. A novel framework for the identification of complex feasible space. Comput. Chem. Eng., 79, 108427.

I.E. Grossmann, B.A. Calfa, P. Garcia-Herreros, 2014. Evolution of concepts and models for quantifying resiliency and flexibility of chemical processes. Comput. Chem. Eng., 70, 22–34.

S.H. Hsu, G.V. Rklaitis,V. Venkatasubramanian, 2010. Modeling and control of roller compaction for a pharmaceutical manufacturing. Part I: Process dynamics and control framework. J. Pharm. Innov., 5, 14–23.

ICH, 2009. ICH harmonised tripartite guideline, guidance for industry, pharmaceutical development Q8(R2). In: Proceedings of the International Conference on Harmonisation of Technical Requirements for Registration of Pharmaceuticals for Human Use. Silver Spring MD: ICH, 2009.

J.R. Johanson, 1965. A rolling theory for granular solids. J. Appl. Mech. B., 32, 842–848.

S. Kucherenko, D. Albrecht, A. Saltelli, 2015. Exploring multi-dimensional spaces: a Comparison of Latin Hypercube and Quasi Monte Carlo Sampling Techniques. ArXiv150502350 Stat.

J. Peterson, 2008. A Bayesian approach to the ICH Q8 definition of Design Space. J. Biopharm. Stat., 18, 959–975.

A. Saltelli, P. Annoni, I. Azzini, F. Campolongo, M. Ratto, S. Tarantola, 2010. Variance based sensitivity analysis of model output. Design and estimator for the total sensitivity index. Comput. Phys. Commun., 181, 259-270.

G. Schwarz, 1978. Estimating the dimension of a model. Ann. Stats., 6, 461–464.

A. Smith, V.M. Zavala, 2021. The Euler characteristic: A general topological descriptor for complex data. Comput. Chem. Eng., 154, 107463.

W. Sun, R.D. Braatz, 2021. Smart process analytics for predictive modeling. Comput. Chem. Eng., 144, 107134.

Z. Wang, M.S. Escotet-Espinoza, M. Ierapetritou, 2017. Process analysis and optimization of continuous pharmaceutical manufacturing using flowsheet models. Comput. Chem. Eng., 107, 77–91.

Flavio Manenti, Gintaras V. Reklaitis (Eds.), Proceedings of the 34th European Symposium on Computer Aided Process Engineering / 15th International Symposium on Process Systems Engineering (ESCAPE34/PSE24), June 2-6, 2024, Florence, Italy
 http://dx.doi.org/10.1016/B978-0-443-28824-1.50264-7

Data-Driven Chance-Constrained Optimization for Minimizing the Influence of Material Uncertainty on Product Quality

Qingbo Meng,[a] I. David L. Bogle,[a] Vassilis M. Charitopoulos[a]

[a]*Sargent Centre for Process Systems Engineering, Department of Chemical Engineering, University College London, UK*
v.charitopoulos@ucl.ac.uk

Abstract

Minimizing the impact of process uncertainties, caused by estimation and measurement errors, unplanned disturbances, or environmental changes, is one of the crucial practical challenges in the pharmaceutical industry. In this work we propose an approach using data-driven chance constraints to eliminate the influence caused by physical property uncertainty in the raw materials via model-based optimization. A flowsheet for the pharmaceutical tableting manufacturing process of the Diamond Pilot Plant (DiPP) at the University of Sheffield is used to test the methodology. Firstly, the Kernel Density Estimation (KDE) technique is applied to generate the inverse cumulative density function for the uncertain variable using historical raw material quality data obtained from the supplier. Different uncertainty risk levels are then considered when obtaining the optimal operating conditions to explore the trade-off between product quality and economic performance. Process operating limitations are addressed for different risk levels to guarantee the desired product quality. Results indicate that the proposed approach can effectively reduce the uncertainty in the product quality caused by raw material physical property changes.

Keywords: Data-driven chance-constrained; Kernel Density Estimation (KDE); Model-Based Optimization; Pharmaceutical Tableting Manufacturing Process.

1. Introduction and Background

The manufacturing industry is currently experiencing a profound revolution as it undergoes a paradigmatic shift towards smarter manufacturing, encompassing the industry 4.0 concepts. The smart manufacturing revolution has been divided into three phases (Bogle, 2017): factory and enterprise integration and plant-wide optimization, exploiting manufacturing intelligence, and creating disruptive business models.

Over the past few decades, significant progress has been made in the first phase and has resulted in plenty of benefits. The process systems engineering community (PSE) is now focusing on the integration of the first two phases to achieve more self-adaptive manufacturing to market changes or demands (Bogle, 2017). In the pharmaceutical industry uncertainty with changes in raw material supply is a key challenge in pharmaceutical formulated product manufactory (Litster and Bogle, 2019).

Uncertainty sources exist as a result of a diverse array of factors such as variation of raw material quality, changing customer or market demand, environmental conditions, or faults in measurement devices. In recent years, mathematical programming techniques have been proposed and enabled successful applications for solving the uncertainty issues

using techniques such as stochastic programming, robust optimization, and data-driven chance constrained optimization (Calfa et al, 2015).
Chance-constrained methods (CC) were first introduced by (Charnes and Cooper, 1959) and gained attention due to their ability to quantify profitability and reliability in a probabilistic formulation useable in optimization problems (Li et al, 2008). Applying chance constrained methods enables the model to be optimized with respect to an objective function while ensuring the solution satisfies the constraints with selected confidence level in the presence of uncertain parameters. The generic formulation of CC is described in Eq.1 (Calfa et al, 2015).

$$P\{g_j(x) \geq \delta_j\} \geq 1 - \alpha_j,\ j = 1, 2, \ldots, m \tag{1}$$

where P is the probability of an event, 1- $\boldsymbol{\alpha}$ stands for the confidence level, and $\boldsymbol{\alpha}$ the risk level within the range [0,1]. Eq.1 can be stated as "the probability of the random variable δ_j to achieve a value less than or equal to $g_j(x)$ must be at least $\mathbf{1} - \boldsymbol{\alpha}_j$". In the PSE community, CC is mostly applied for customer demand satisfaction, product quality specification, reliability level of chemical processes (Ning and You, 2019).
In this study, we apply data-driven chance constraint programming to reduce the uncertainty influence from raw materials on the product quality through optimization of the operation of a pharmaceutical formulation plant shown in Fig. 1. The intra-particle void fraction (IVF) of feeding material lactose is considered as the uncertain variable and granule moisture content (MC) exiting the fluid bed dryer is the controlled output which must be maintained at less than 8%. An assumption is made that the IVF information is obtainable from the material supplier and follows the normal distribution IVF ~ N (0.5, 0.05) (Fig. 2a). Based on the data, the Kernel Density Estimation technique is applied to generate the inverse cumulative distribution function for converting the probabilistic constraints into the equivalent deterministic algebraic constraints. Different confidence levels (or risk levels) are used to explain the trade-off between product quality and process reliability. The rest of this paper is organized as follows: in section 2, the proposed method is outlined, in section 3, we apply the data-driven CC on a segmented fluid bed dryer which is part of the DiPP, and present results and draw conclusion in section 4 and 5.

2. Problem Formulation

2.1. Raw Material Uncertainty – Intra-particle Void Fraction

Intra-particle void fraction (IVF) refers to the fraction of the total volume that is composed of void spaces or pores within the particle structure. A larger IVF value generally provides more void spaces which makes the moisture evaporating or escaping from the particles easier during the drying process and results in lower granule MC under the same operating condition. In the optimization problem, we obtain and implement the minimum corresponding IVF value via KDE as a boundary at different risk levels (Fig. 2b) to guarantee that the probability of 90% ($\boldsymbol{\alpha} = 0.1$), 95% ($\boldsymbol{\alpha} = 0.05$) or 99% ($\boldsymbol{\alpha} = 0.01$) random selected IVF values are larger than the corresponding IVF value.

2.2. Data-driven Chance Constraints

The data-driven chance constraint approach employed in this study was introduced by Calfa et al. (2015). It integrates observed data or historical information to approximate the level of uncertainty, rather than solely relying on a predetermined probability distribution. This allows more flexibility when the underlying probability distribution of the uncertainty is unknown or difficult to determine. It has been shown by (Jiang and Guan, 2013) that reformulation of classic CC and data-driven CC are equivalent. Therefore, according to Eq. 1, the reformulation of data-driven CC can be represented as follows (Calfa et al, 2015):

$$g_j(x) \geq F_{\delta_j}^{-1}(1-\alpha_j), j = 1, 2, \ldots, \mathrm{m} \quad (2)$$

Where $F_{\delta_j}^{-1}$ is the inverse cumulative density function that is estimated depending on the uncertain variable distribution/observed data information. Based on Eq.2, the uncertain variable value $g_j(x)$ can be calculated to satisfy the desired level of probability.

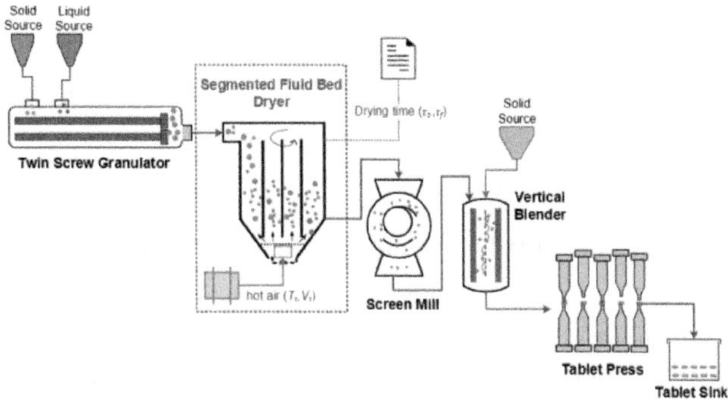

Figure 1. Flowsheet of continuous pharmaceutical tableting process (Jiang et al, 2022)

2.3. Kernel Density Estimation (KDE)

KDE is a probability density function (pdf) estimation technique. Compared to a traditional histogram, KDE has a number of advantages, for example (Weglarczyk, 2018):

- A smooth curve shows the details of the probability density function better,
- All data points are included to reveal comprehensive information and more convincing multimodality.

The KDE formulation is given by Bowman and Azzalini (1997):

$$\widehat{f}_h(x) = \frac{1}{nh}\sum_{i=1}^{n} K(\frac{x-x_i}{h}) \quad (3)$$

where $x_1, x_2, \ldots, x_n$ are random samples from distribution, n and h are the sample size and bandwidth, respectively, the normal kernel smoothing function is applied and represented using K. The formulation is given below:

$$K_i(x) = \frac{1}{\sqrt{2\pi}} e^{\frac{-(\frac{x-a_i}{h})^2}{2}} \quad (4)$$

where a_i is the a value at point i. In this study, the KDE technique is applied for finding the inverse cumulative distribution (quantile function) of the uncertain variable IVF to determine its corresponding values under different confidence levels (see Fig.2).

2.4. Dynamic Model Description

The dynamic model involved in this study includes a Twin-screw Granulator (TSG) and a segmented fluidized bed dryer (FBD), which are upstream process of the tableting manufacturing in a pharma plant (see Fig.1). gPROMS Formulated Products is the platform for the model implementation. Parameters have been validated using DiPP at the University of Sheffield. The solid and liquid binder source fed into TSG are lactose and water to mix and produce granules for FBD. In FBD, the granules are suspended in a hot air stream and moisture is evaporated to the desired target.

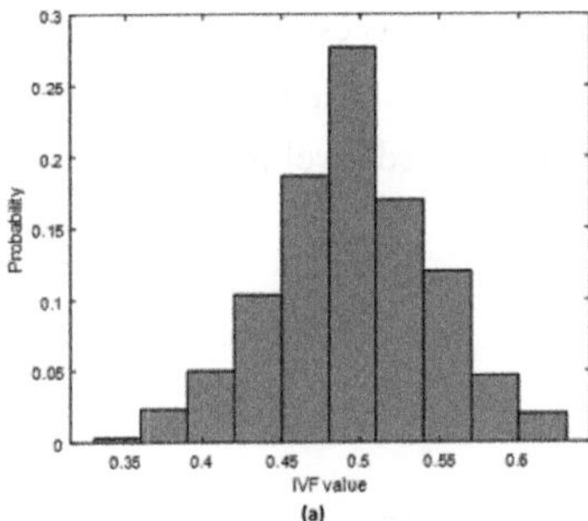

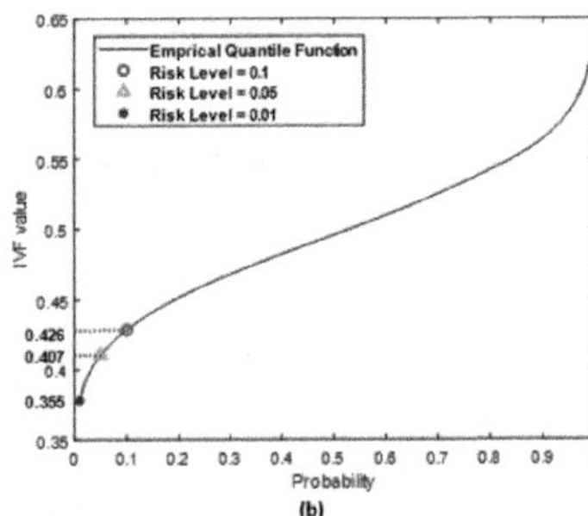

Figure 2. (a) Histogram of IVF, (b) Corresponding IVF values at different risk levels.

2.5. Optimization

The optimization strategy is required to ensure the best design options and optimal operating performance of the drying process. In this study the three decision variables are lactose (F_l) and water feed flowrate (F_w) to the TSG, and feed vapour temperature (T_v) to the FBD. The objective is to minimize the feed vapour flowrate (F_v) to the FBD. The uncertainty variable IVF has been converted from a probabilistic to a deterministic constraint via the KDE approach subject to different risk levels. To restrict the granule MC out from FBD less than 8% is the control objective. The optimization problem is expressed as follows:

$$\min_{F_w,F_l,T_v} \boldsymbol{F_v}$$

s.t. C1: $10\text{kg/h} \leq F_l \leq 20\text{kg/h}$

C2: $2\text{kg/h} \leq F_w \leq 6\text{kg/h}$

C3: $40°\text{C} \leq T_v \leq 80°\text{C}$

C4: $\text{MC} \leq 8\%$

C5: $800\mu\text{m} \leq \text{Pas} \leq 1000\mu\text{m}$

$$\text{C6:} \begin{cases} risk\ level\ (\boldsymbol{\alpha}) = 0.1,\ \boldsymbol{P} \geq 90\%, IVF \geq F_{\delta_j}^{-1}(0.1) = 0.426 \\ risk\ level\ (\boldsymbol{\alpha}) = 0.05,\ \boldsymbol{P} \geq 95\%, IVF \geq F_{\delta_j}^{-1}(0.05) = 0.407 \\ risk\ level\ (\boldsymbol{\alpha}) = 0.01,\ \boldsymbol{P} \geq 99\%, IVF \geq F_{\delta_j}^{-1}(0.01) = 0.354 \end{cases}$$

where the inequality constraints C1 to C3 indicate the operating range constraints of the three decision variables. MC and Pas in C4 and C5 are abbreviations for moisture content and average particle size, respectively. C6 describes the corresponding IVF values under different risk level ($\boldsymbol{\alpha}$)/confidence level ($\boldsymbol{P}$). $F_{\delta_j}^{-1}$ represents the quantile function (Eq.2).

3. Results and Discussions

3.1. Optimization Results

The overall drying process, comprising loading, drying, and discharging stages, has a total duration of 400 seconds, with 200 seconds allocated for loading and 50 seconds for discharging. The optimization process is divided into 4 time intervals. Decision variables are optimized (see Fig. 3) in each time interval within the constraints to minimize the vapour feed flowrate to the FBD to reach the desired MC level. The exact optimized vapour temperature values in bottom Fig.3 are 51.35°C (α=0.1), 52.52°C (α=0.05) and 53.1°C (α=0.01).

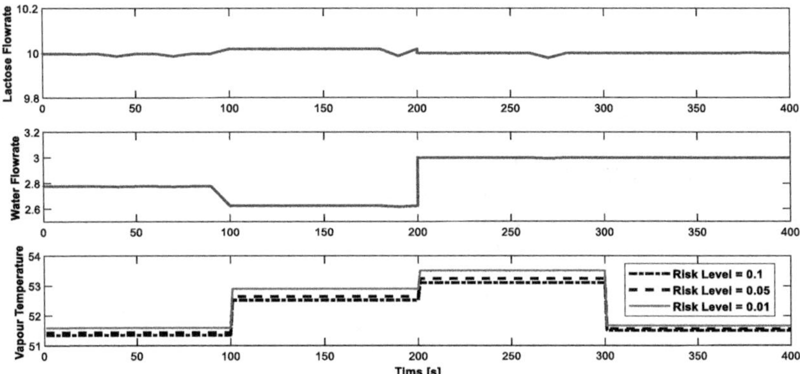

Figure 3. Optimized decision variables in each time interval

Fig.3 reveals that although a lower risk level represents a relatively smaller chance that the controlled granule MC exceeds the desired boundary (8%), it requires higher vapour temperature to achieve this objective which results in a higher energy consumption. This is a compromise between manufacturing reliability and cost-saving.

3.2. Validation Results

To validate the optimization performance, we randomly generated 18 different IVF values within the distribution range to run the drying process with optimized decision variables at each risk level. The aim is to observe how many IVF values lead to granules exceeding the desired MC level of 8% when discharged from the FBD. To avoid redundancy, a representative case where the IVF equals 0.551 is used to encompass other IVF values that result in output granule MC less than 8% (see Fig. 4).

It is noted (Fig. 4d, e, f) that when the risk level is reduced, the number of controlled MC higher than 8% is reduced. This observation highlights the inherent trade-off between the MC and temperature requirements across different risk levels.

4. Conclusions

A data-driven chance constrained approach is implemented in this study to minimize the impact of raw material uncertainty. Different risk levels were tested to explore the trade-off between the desired moisture content and energy consumption. Results demonstrate that the proposed approach can eliminate the uncertainty impact from raw material variation and guarantee the output MC at a desired value with various risk levels. Lower risk levels are associated with lower MC violation rate but necessitate a comparatively higher vapour temperature resulting in a trade-off between process reliability and energy consumption. This approach presents a structured framework to mitigate the impact of uncertainty through process optimization.

Acknowledgements: This work was funded by the EPSRC (EP/V034723/1) RiFTMaP

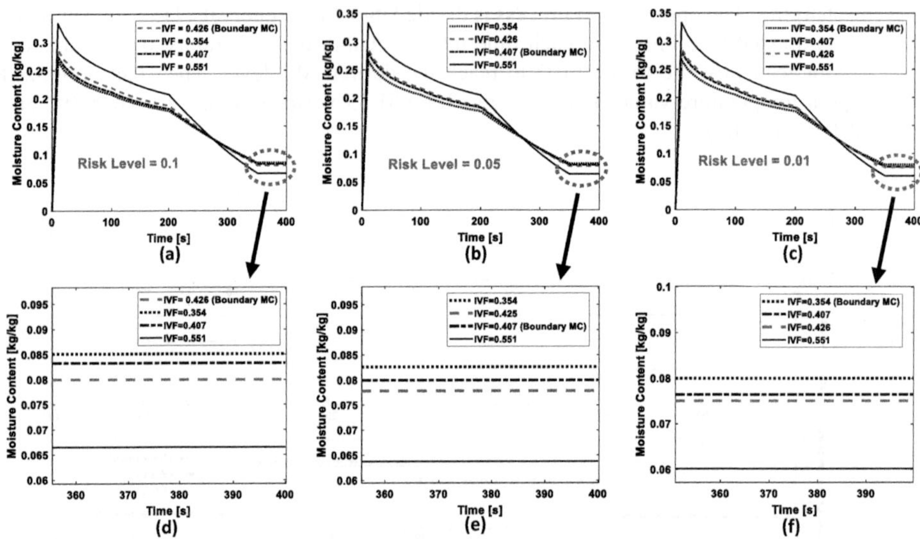

Figure 4. Validation results

Table 1 Moisture content violation rate at different risk level

Risk Level	Violations (MC ≥ 8%)	Rate
α=0.1	2/18	11.11%
α=0.05	1/18	5.56%
α=0.01	0/18	0

References:

A. Charnes, W.W. Cooper, 1959, Chance-constrained Programming, Management Science, 6 (1), 73-79.

A.W. Bowman, A. Azzalini, 1997, Applied Smoothing Techniques for Data Analysis, New York: Oxford University Press Inc.

B.A. Calfa, I.E. Grossmann, A. Agarwal, S.J. Bury, J.M. Wassick, 2015, Data-driven individual and joint chance-constrained optimization via kernel smoothing, Computers and Chemical Engineering, 78, 51-69.

C. Ning, F. You, 2019, Optimization under Uncertainty in the Era of Big Data and Deep Learning: When Machine Learning Meets Mathematical Programming, Comput. Chem. Eng., 125 (9), 434-448.

I.D.L. Bogle, 2017, A Perspective on Smart Process Manufacturing Research Challenges for Process Systems Engineers, Engineering, 3, 161-165.

J. Litster, I.D.L. Bogle, 2019, Smart Process Manufacturing for Formulated Products, Engineering, 5, 1003-1009.

P. Li, H. Arellano-Garcia, G. Wozny, 2008, Chance constrained programming approach to process optimization under uncertainty, Computers & Chemical Engineering, 32, 25-45.

S. Weglarczyk, 2018, Kernel density estimation and its application, ITM Web of Conferences 23, 00037.

S.L. Jiang, L.G. Papageorgiou, I.D.L. Bogle, V.M. Charitopoulos, 2022, Investigating the Trade-Off between Design and Operational Flexibility in Continuous Manufacturing of Pharmaceutical Tablets: A Cast Study of the Fluid Bed Dryer, Processes, 10, 454.

R. Jiang, Y. Guan, 2013, Data-driven chance constrained stochastic program, Optimization Online, http://www.optimization-online.org/DBFILE/2013/09/4044.pdf.

Flavio Manenti, Gintaras V. Reklaitis (Eds.), Proceedings of the 34th European Symposium on Computer Aided Process Engineering / 15th International Symposium on Process Systems Engineering (ESCAPE34/PSE24), June 2-6, 2024, Florence, Italy
 http://dx.doi.org/10.1016/B978-0-443-28824-1.50265-9

Model Predictive Control of bioreactors based on a reformulation of dynamic metabolic network models

Marius Fredriksen[a], Rafael David de Oliveira[a], Caroline Satye Nakama[a], Johannes Jäschke[a]

[a]*Department of Chemical Engineering, Norwegian University of Science and Technology, NTNU, NO-7491 Trondheim, Norway*
johannes.jaschke@ntnu.no

Abstract

The increasing popularity and utilization of dynamic Flux Balance Analysis (dFBA) models have allowed for the implementation of more advanced control structures, such as Model Predictive Control (MPC), for bioprocesses. The dFBA model is comprised of dynamic mass balance equations and an optimization that calculates the cell's metabolic fluxes. Thus, when MPC is applied, a bi-level optimization problem arises. Solving this bi-level optimization problem involves transforming the inner optimization into a set of algebraic equations using either the duality theory or the Karush–Kuhn–Tucker (KKT) optimality conditions. In this work, we assessed different reformulations of the dFBA model for continuous stirred tank (CSTR) bioreactors that would make the dFBA suitable for MPC applications. We conducted a case study of the *Escherichia coli* (*E. coli*) core metabolic network, where we applied MPC to the CSTR bioreactor. The controller was subjected to changes in setpoint and disturbances in the glucose feed concentration and the maximal glucose uptake for the cells. The MPC controller performed well, maintaining the biomass concentration close to the desired setpoint. Overall, the reformulation based on the penalized duality theory was more reliable than the penalized KKT reformulation.

Keywords: Bioprocess control, Dynamic Flux Balance Analysis, Model Predictive Control, Bi-level optimization

1. Introduction

Bioprocessing is an integral field of research as it is used in various food, chemical, and pharmaceutical industries (Doran, 2013). Bioprocessing refers to the use of cells and their components, like enzymes, to manufacture goods and destroy harmful waste. From its ancient origins in food production, bioprocessing has evolved to encompass the manufacturing of an extensive range of commercial products, from relatively cheap materials like industrial alcohol and organic solvents to more valuable products like antibiotics, vaccines, and therapeutic proteins (Doran, 2013).

The increasing competition, stricter regulations, and economic fluctuations in recent years have emphasized the importance of good process control and optimization, which is crucial for safe and efficient plant operations (Seborg et al., 2016). Current bioprocess control structures are recipe-based, with insufficient ability to handle uncertainties (Jabarivelisdeh et al., 2020). However, recent improvements in genome sequencing have given rise to models, such as the dynamic Flux Balance Analysis (dFBA) model, that allow us to apply more advanced control structures to bioprocesses due to their ability to

account for a broad range of cellular behavior and operation conditions (Nakama & Jäschke, 2022).
The dFBA model consists of dynamic mass balance equations and an optimization that calculates the cell's metabolic fluxes through the metabolic network. Thus, applying MPC results in a bi-level optimization problem, which is often very time-consuming to solve as we must analyze both the multiple upper-level optimization candidates as well as their corresponding lower-level candidates (Gupta et al., 2015).
The bi-level optimization problem can be avoided by reformulating the inner optimization with the KKT conditions, as shown by Ploch et al. (2020), which reformulated the dFBA into a differential-algebraic equation system. In order to embed the dFBA models into parameter optimization and optimal control problems, the system of equations can be discretized by applying orthogonal collocation with an adaptative mesh scheme (de Oliveira et al., 2023). The KKT reformulation of dFBA can also be used in model-based control, as shown by Nakama and Jäschke (2022).
However, these works have yet to explore the utilization of the duality theory reformulation, which is widely used in metabolic engineering (Zomorrodi & Maranas, 2013), for dFBA-based MPC. This work aims to apply MPC to a CSTR bioreactor based on the duality theory and KKT reformulations of the dFBA model of the *E. coli* core metabolic network and compare the solver time and reliability of the reformulations.

2. Methodology

The model developed in this work was based on the previous work of de Oliveira et al. (2023) and further extended using the duality theory approach and the CSTR mass balances. The purpose of this section is to provide a brief overview of the methodology used in that work. Readers are referred to the original publication for a more comprehensive description of the dFBA models.

2.1. Case study

We consider a CSTR with *E. coli*, strain K-12, sub-strain MG1655, operating under aerobic growth with glucose and acetate. The feed flow consists of glucose and water, and the feed flow rate is calculated from the dilution rate of the reactor. We assume that oxygen is always available in the system, and we only consider the core metabolic network of the *E. coli* cell, which contains 95 metabolic reactions and 72 metabolites. The *E. coli* core metabolism is chosen because it is relatively simple and well-established. The metabolic data are gathered from the BiGG Models database (King et al., 2016).

2.2. Flux Balance Analysis

The model is based on the Flux Balance Analysis (FBA) of the organism's metabolic network. The FBA is given as an optimization problem, and the objective is to maximize the cell's growth rate. To avoid multiple solutions, we use a variant of the FBA called the Parsimonious FBA (pFBA). The pFBA is expressed as presented by Ploch et al. (2020).

$$\begin{aligned} &\min_{\mathbf{v}} -\mathbf{c}^T\mathbf{v} + \mathbf{v}^T\boldsymbol{W}\mathbf{v} \\ &s.t.\ \ \mathbf{S}\mathbf{v} = 0 \\ &\qquad \mathbf{LB} - \mathbf{v} \leq 0 \\ &\qquad \mathbf{v} - \mathbf{UB} \leq 0 \end{aligned} \tag{1}$$

Here, **S** is the stoichiometric matrix for the metabolic reactions, **LB** and **UB** are vectors containing the lower and upper bounds for each reaction, **v** is a vector containing the metabolic fluxes, **c** is a vector containing weights that are multiplied with **v** to give the objective of the pFBA, and **W** is a diagonal matrix containing small weights, 10^{-6}.

The pFBA is reformulated into algebraic expressions using the duality theory and KKT optimality conditions. The main difference between the two methods is how they implement the strong duality theorem. The duality theory approach directly implements the strong duality theorem by stating that the primal solution equals the dual solution. In contrast, the KKT approach replaces this expression with the complementary slackness conditions (Zomorrodi & Maranas, 2013). However, the reformulations may be difficult for the interior point solver to handle, partly due to the non-smooth characteristics of the system (Nakama & Jäschke, 2022). Therefore, we use a penalization method to relax the strong duality theorem constraints by reverting the reformulations back into optimization problems and moving the strong duality theorem constraints to the objective functions (Oliveira et al., 2023). The duality theory reformulation is given below.

$$\min_{\mathbf{v},\lambda,\mu_L,\mu_U} \mathbf{c}^T\mathbf{v} - 2\mathbf{v}^T\mathbf{W}\mathbf{v} + \mu_L^T \boldsymbol{LB} - \mu_U^T\mathbf{UB}$$

$$\begin{aligned} \text{s.t. } & \mathbf{Sv} = 0 \\ & \mathbf{LB} - \mathbf{v} \le 0 \\ & \mathbf{v} - \mathbf{UB} \le 0 \\ & \mu_U, \mu_L \ge 0 \\ & -\mathbf{c} + 2\mathbf{Wv} + \mathbf{S}^T\lambda - \mu_L + \mu_U = 0 \end{aligned} \tag{2}$$

Here μ_U, μ_L, and λ are the Lagrangian multipliers. The KKT reformulation is given below.

$$\min_{\mathbf{v},\lambda,\mu_L,\mu_U} \mu_L^T(\mathbf{LB} - \mathbf{v}) + \mu_U^T(\mathbf{v} - \mathbf{UB})$$

$$\begin{aligned} \text{s.t. } & \mathbf{Sv} = 0 \\ & \mathbf{LB} - \mathbf{v} \le 0 \\ & \mathbf{v} - \mathbf{UB} \le 0 \\ & \mu_U, \mu_L \ge 0 \\ & -\mathbf{c} + 2\mathbf{Wv} + \mathbf{S}^T\lambda - \mu_L + \mu_U = 0 \end{aligned} \tag{3}$$

2.3. Dynamic FBA

The dFBA models assume that the intracellular reactions are much faster than the extracellular ones, therefore we consider the intracellular metabolites to be at quasi-steady state. The pFBA can thus be expanded to a dFBA by adding mass balances for the extracellular metabolites and kinetics for the uptake of the substrates. The dFBA is presented below.

$$\begin{aligned} & pFBA \\ s.t. \quad & \frac{d\mathbf{x}}{dt} = D(\mathbf{x}_{in} - \mathbf{x}) + x_{biomass}\mathbf{v} \\ & \mathbf{x} \ge 0 \\ & LB_i = v_{i,max}\frac{x_i}{K_{M,i} + x_i} \end{aligned} \tag{4}$$

Here D is the dilution rate, $\mathbf{x}$ is a vector containing the concentration of the extracellular metabolites, $v_{i,max}$ and $K_{M,i}$ are the maximal uptake and the Michaelis constant of the substrate i, respectively.

2.4. MPC implementation

Before we apply the MPC, we first discretize the set of ordinary differential equations (ODE). It was decided to use orthogonal collocation as this technique is found to be equivalent to an implicit Runge-Kutta method, considering accuracy and stability (de Oliveira et al. 2023). We used three Radau collocation points, over a finite number of elements. Finally, we implement the MPC by expanding the objective function of the dFBA reformulations and by adding constraints for the manipulated variable, the dilution rate. The implementation of the MPC based on the penalized duality theory reformulation of the dFBA is presented below.

$$\begin{aligned} \min_{\mathbf{v},\lambda,\mu_L,\mu_U,\mathbf{x},D} \sum \Big(& Q\left(X - X_{sp}\right)^2 + R(\Delta \mathrm{D})^2 \\ & + C\left(\mathbf{c}^T\mathbf{v} - 2\mathbf{v}^T\mathbf{W}\mathbf{v} + \mu_L^T \boldsymbol{LB} - \mu_U^T \mathbf{UB}\right)\Big) \\ \text{s.t. } & dFBA \\ & D_{min} \leq D \leq D_{max} \\ & \Delta D_{max} \geq |\Delta D| \end{aligned} \tag{5}$$

The MPC based on the KKT reformulation is presented below.

$$\begin{aligned} \min_{\mathbf{v},\lambda,\mu_L,\mu_U,\mathbf{x},D} \sum \Big(& Q\left(X - X_{sp}\right)^2 + R(\Delta \mathrm{D})^2 \\ & + C\left(\mu_L^T(\mathbf{LB} - \mathbf{v}) + \mu_U^T(\mathbf{v} - \mathbf{UB})\right)\Big) \\ \text{s.t. } & dFBA \\ & D_{min} \leq D \leq D_{max} \\ & \Delta D_{max} \geq |\Delta D| \end{aligned} \tag{6}$$

Here X is the biomass concentration, X_{sp} is the biomass concentration setpoint, ΔD is the change in the dilution rate, ΔD_{max} is the maximal allowed change in the dilution rate, D_{min} is the minimal value of the dilution rate, D_{max} is the maximal value of the dilution rate, and Q, R, and C are tuning parameters for the MPC. The tuning parameters are found by trial and error, and the same tuning parameters are used for both the duality theory and the KKT MPC reformulations.

2.5. Direct Approach for dFBA

We use the direct approach (DA) to develop a slightly different model of the system to use as a reference to our dFBA model reformulations and to act as the plant in our simulation with the MPC. In the DA model we apply an ODE solver that calls the pFBA model at each time step. The ODE solver calculates the metabolite concentrations and the lower bound of the substrates and provides them to our non-linear problem optimizer that solves the pFBA and returns the metabolic flux for each of the metabolites. We chose to use the DA as a reference because the DA solves the original pFBA problem and the adaptive step size utilized by the ODE solver makes the DA more accurate in areas with rapid change of the metabolite concentrations, given that the optimization problem returns feasible solutions at each time step. The ODE solver Quasi-constant time step Numerical Differentiation Function (QNDF) from the package DifferentialEquations (Rackauckas & Nie, 2017) is used, because the system is reasonably large, and the level of stiffness is unknown. The optimization problem is solved with the interior point optimizer IPOPT (Wächter & Biegler, 2016) with the MA97 linear solver from HSL (STFC, 2023).

3. Results and discussion

The MPC formulation based on the penalized duality theory (P. Dual) and the penalized KKT (P. KKT) are compared for a 35-hour simulation where the MPC was updated every hour and predicted 4 hours ahead of time. The simulation started at steady state and after 6 hours we increased the biomass setpoint with 50 % and reduced it back to the original value after 21 hours (Case 1). Figure 1 shows the biomass concentration and MPC solver time at each time step. We performed the same simulation for step changes in the glucose feed concentration (Case 2), and the maximal glucose uptake (Case 3), however we use a 50% decrease instead of increase in the glucose uptake parameter to avoid saturation.

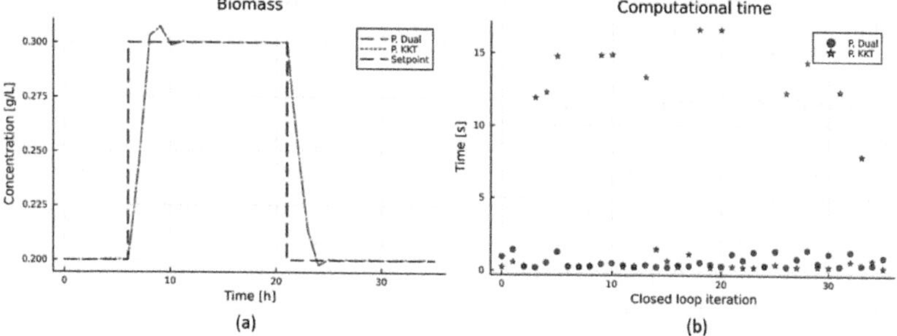

Figure 1: Biomass concentration (a) and computational time for each closed loop iteration (b) for simulation with 50 % increase in the biomass setpoint after 6 hours and a reduction back to the original value after 21 hours.

The average solver time, number of failed MPC optimizations, and the mean squared error (MSE) between the biomass concentration and the biomass concentration setpoint for the step changes in setpoint, maximal glucose uptake and glucose feed concentration are presented in Table 1.

Table 1: Average solver time, number of failed optimizations and mean squared error (MSE) for simulation with step changes in the biomass setpoint (Case 1), the glucose uptake (Case 2), and the glucose feed concentration (Case 3).

Method:	Average solver time: [s]	Maximum number of iterations exceeded:	Failed:	MSE:
Case 1:				
P. Dual	0.62	0 of 35	0 of 35	$7.48 \cdot 10^{-4}$
P. KKT	4.93	11 of 35	2 of 35	$7.48 \cdot 10^{-4}$
Case 2:				
P. Dual	0.74	0 of 35	0 of 35	$1.34 \cdot 10^{-4}$
P. KKT	4.64	10 of 35	0 of 35	$1.33 \cdot 10^{-4}$
Case 3:				
P. Dual	0.52	0 of 35	0 of 35	$1.31 \cdot 10^{-10}$
P. KKT	2.91	8 of 35	0 of 35	$2.39 \cdot 10^{-8}$

From the simulations it is apparent that the P. Dual reformulation is on average much, roughly 5 to 8 times, faster than the P. KKT reformulation. However, when we look at Figure 1, we notice that the computational times are quite similar for most of the closed-loop iterations, except for 12 outliers. This aligns with the fact that 11 closed-loop iterations reached the maximum number of iterations, and the large average solver time for the P. KKT reformulation is likely due to these closed-loop iterations.

It is also observed that the optimization of the P. KKT reformulation is less likely to converge than the P. Dual reformulation. The two restoration failed messages for the setpoint change are particularly concerning since it indicates that the solver was unable to find a feasible point for these two optimizations. The higher reliability of the P. Dual may be attributed to its more linear characteristics, as its objective function contains fewer non-linear terms than the P. KKT reformulation. However, it is also possible that the control parameter weighting used in the two reformulations could be a contributing factor. The MSE from the setpoint is relatively similar for the two approaches, which is likely due to most of the failed P. KKT optimizations being caused by the solver reaching the maximum number of iterations, thus failing to converge, but still getting very close to the true solution before the optimization is terminated.

4. Conclusion and future work

We have shown that MPC can be applied to CSTR bioreactors based on the P. Dual and the P. KKT reformulations of the dFBA. The MPC performed well and was able to keep the biomass concentration close to the desired setpoint and handle relatively large changes in the setpoint as well as disturbances in the glucose feed and in the maximal glucose uptake. Overall was the P. Dual reformulation found to be more reliable than the P. KKT reformulation when solved with the IPOPT solver. For future work the models need to be expanded to use a genome scale metabolic network of the *E. coli* and to be validated by experimental data.

5. Acknowledgements

This work was supported by the Research Council of Norway (RCN) through the FRIPRO Project SensPATH.

6. References

R. D. de Oliveira, G. A. C. Le Roux, and R. Mahadevan, 2023, Nonlinear programming reformulation of dynamic flux balance analysis models, Computers & Chemical Engineering 170, p. 108101.

P. M. Doran. 2013, Bioprocess Engineering Principles. 2nd ed, Academic Press.

A. Gupta, J. Mańdziuk, and Y. Ong, 2015, Evolutionary multitasking in bi-level optimization, Complex & Intelligent Systems 1, pp. 83–95.

B. Jabarivelisdeh et al., 2020, Adaptive predictive control of bioprocesses with constraint-based modeling and estimation, Computers Chemical Engineering 135, p. 106744.

Z. A. King et al., 2016, BiGG Models: A platform for integrating, standardizing and sharing genome-scale models, Nucleic acids research 44.D1, pp. D515–D522.

C. S. M. Nakama and J. Jäschke, 2022, Analysis of control models based on dFBA for fed-batch bioreactors solved by interior-point methods, IFAC-PapersOnLine 55.7, pp. 131–136.

T. Ploch et al., 2020, Simulation of differential-algebraic equation systems with optimization criteria embedded in Modelica, Computers Chemical Engineering140, p. 106920.

Science and Technology Facilities Council (STFC), 2023, A collection of Fortran codes for large scale scientific computation.

D. E. Seborg et al., 2016, Process Dynamics and Control. 4th ed., John Wiley & Sons.

C. Rackauckas and Q. Nie, 2017, Differentialequations.jl–a performant and feature-rich ecosystem for solving differential equations in julia, Journal of Open Research Software 5.1.

A. Wächter and L. T. Biegler, 2016, On the implementation of an interior-point filter line-search algorithm for large-scale nonlinear programming, Mathematical programming 106, pp. 25–57.

A. R. Zomorrodi and C. D. Maranas, 2013, Optimization methods in metabolic networks, John Wiley & Sons.

Flavio Manenti, Gintaras V. Reklaitis (Eds.), Proceedings of the 34th European Symposium on Computer Aided Process Engineering / 15th International Symposium on Process Systems Engineering (ESCAPE34/PSE24), June 2-6, 2024, Florence, Italy
 http://dx.doi.org/10.1016/B978-0-443-28824-1.50266-0

Characterization and Analysis of Multistage Stochastic Programming Problems with Type II Endogenous Uncertainty to Develop Universally Applicable Bounding Approaches

Yasuhiro Shoji*, Selen Cremaschi

Department of Chemical Engineering, Auburn University, Auburn, AL 36849, USA
yzs0108@auburn.edu, szc0113@auburn.edu

Abstract

Optimization challenges featuring endogenous uncertainties that unfold sequentially based on decisions are prevalent in the process industry. While multistage stochastic programming (MSSP) serves as a viable solution method, addressing real-world-scale problems poses computational challenges. This study examines and characterizes MSSP problems involving type II endogenous uncertainty, exploring the suitability of two heuristics: the absolute expected value solution (AEEV) and the generalized knapsack-problem-based decomposition algorithm (GKDA), developed by our research group. We applied the heuristics to eight MSSP problems, which revealed that both AEEV and GKDA may generate no feasible solutions when the MSSP problem lacks complete recourse. If the heuristics generate solutions, AEEV and GKDA provide 0 to 3 % and 0.5 to 45 % optimality gaps, respectively, with 0.003 to 0.3 % computational times compared to solving the MSSP problem.

Keywords: multistage stochastic program, endogenous uncertainty, heuristics

1. Introduction

Optimization challenges within the process industry frequently involve endogenous uncertainty (Goel & Grossmann, 2004; Tarhan & Grossmann, 2008; Solak et al., 2010). Goel & Grossmann (2006) classified endogenous uncertainty into two sub-classes: type I and type II, in which the probability distribution and realization time depend on the decisions, respectively. The constraints to enforce scenario indistinguishability before realization in type II endogenous uncertainty are referred to as non-anticipativity constraints (NACs). The exponential increase in the number of NACs with the growing number of scenarios leads to computational complexities when addressing real-world size problems (Apap & Grossmann, 2017). This challenge has prompted the development of various heuristic and decomposition solution approaches.

To tackle these issues, our research group has introduced two heuristics, AEEV (Zeng & Cremaschi, 2019) and GKDA (Zeng & Cremaschi, 2018), designed to generate feasible solutions for MSSP problems involving type II endogenous uncertainty. The heuristics decompose MSSP problems into deterministic sub-problems using expected values of uncertain parameters. They iterate constructing and solving sub-problems, judging scenario realizations, and determining recourse actions based on realized information until the end of the planning horizon. Universal applicability to any MSSP problem with type II endogenous uncertainty is among the anticipated properties of these heuristics besides the fast computational speed and providing tight bounds. However, the applicability of the heuristics depends on the characteristics of MSSP problems. We conducted an analysis of eight published problems using our heuristics. The paper compares the optimality gaps and computational times of successful instances where AEEV and GKDA provided a feasible solution. Then, it discusses the key properties limiting the applicability.

2. The framework of MSSP with type II endogenous uncertainty

MSSP problems involving type II endogenous uncertainty incorporate scenarios and a discretized time horizon. In these scenarios, here-and-now decisions progressively differentiate among potential outcomes over time. Wait-and-see decisions allow taking corrective action after the here-and-now decisions reveal the outcomes. The NACs ensure that the variables must take identical values when scenarios are indistinguishable. A general formulation of MSSP with endogenous uncertainties is shown in Equations (1) – (9). Note that the model is an extension of the formulation in Zeng & Cremaschi (2019).

$$\min \sum_{s} p_s \sum_{i,t} G_{i,t,s}\left(V_{i,t}, \theta_i^s, b_{i,t}^s, x_{i,t}^s, \gamma_{i,t}^s, y_{i,t}^s\right) \quad (1)$$

s.t.

$$g\left(\theta_i^s, b_{i,t}^s, x_{i,t}^s, \gamma_{i,t}^s, y_{i,t}^s\right) \leq 0 \quad \forall i \in I, t \in T, s \in S \quad (2)$$

$$h\left(\theta_i^s, b_{i,t}^s, x_{i,t}^s, \gamma_{i,t}^s, y_{i,t}^s\right) = 0 \quad \forall i \in I, t \in T, s \in S \quad (3)$$

$$b_{i,1}^s = b_{i,1}^{s'} \quad \forall i \in I, \forall s, s' \in S \quad (4)$$

$$x_{i,1}^s = x_{i,1}^{s'} \quad \forall i \in I, \forall s, s' \in S \quad (5)$$

$$\begin{bmatrix} Z_t^{s,s'} \\ b_{i,t}^s = b_{i,t}^{s'} \\ x_{i,t}^s = x_{i,t}^{s'} \end{bmatrix} \vee \left[\neg Z_t^{s,s'}\right] \quad \forall (i,s,s') \in S_E, \forall t \in T, t > 1 \quad (6)$$

$$\begin{bmatrix} Z_t^{s,s'} \\ \gamma_{i,t}^s = \gamma_{i,t}^{s'} \end{bmatrix} \vee \left[\neg Z_t^{s,s'}\right] \quad \forall (i,s,s') \in S_E, \forall t \in T \quad (7)$$

$$Z_t^{s,s'} \Leftrightarrow H\left(b_{i,1}^s, \dots, b_{i,t}^s, x_{i,1}^s, \dots, x_{i,t}^s\right) \forall (i,s,s') \in S_E, \forall t \in T \quad (8)$$

$$b_{i,t}^s, Z_t^{s,s'} \in \{0,1\}, x_{i,t}^s, \gamma_{i,t}^s, y_{i,t}^s \in \mathbb{R} \; \forall (i,s,s') \in S_E, \forall t \in T, \forall i \in I \quad (9)$$

The objective function (Eq. 1) comprises the contribution $G_{i,t,s}\left(V_{i,t}, \theta_i^s, b_{i,t}^s, x_{i,t}^s, \gamma_{i,t}^s, y_{i,t}^s\right)$ and the probability p_s of scenario s, where $V_{i,t}$ and θ_i^s denote predetermined deterministic and uncertain parameters, respectively. The model involves four variables, namely $b_{i,t}^s, x_{i,t}^s, \gamma_{i,t}^s$ and $y_{i,t}^s$, with uncertainty resource $i \in \mathcal{I} = \{1,2,\dots,I\}$, time horizon $t \in \mathcal{T} = \{1,2,\dots,T\}$, and scenario $s \in \mathcal{S} = \{1,2,\dots,S\}$. The two here-and-now decision variables, binary decision variables $b_{i,t}^s$ and continuous or integer decision variables $x_{i,t}^s$, are forced to take identical values by both the initial NACs (Eqs. 4 and 5) and the conditional NACs (Eq. 6) until scenario pairs s and s' become distinguishable. Conditional NACs constrain the wait-and-see decision variables $\gamma_{i,t}^s$ (Eq. 7). Equations 2 and 3 are scenario-specific inequality and equality constraints, such as demand and capacity constraints, and material balances. The conditional NACs (Eqs. 6 and 7) are enforced using binary variable $Z_{i,t}^{s,s'}$, determined based on here-and-now decisions via the expression $H(.)$ (Eq. 8), where $Z_{i,t}^{s,s'}$ takes a value of one if scenarios s and s' are indistinguishable and takes a value of zero otherwise.

3. Heuristics

3.1. Absolute Expected Value Solution Approach (AEEV)

A feasible solution was produced by AEEV (Zeng & Cremaschi, 2019) through the transformation of an MSSP problem into two distinct types of sub-problems: deterministic expected value sub-problems ($DEVSP$ s) and recourse deterministic expected value sub-problems ($DEVSP^{recourse}$ s). $DEVSP$ s and $DEVSP^{recourse}$ s are responsible for determining here-and-now decisions and the corresponding recourse actions. AEEV begins with the construction of a $DEVSP$ at $t = 1$. The endogenous uncertain parameters are replaced with their expected values of all outcomes for the $DEVSP$ at $t = 1$. AEEV solves the $DEVSP$ and stores the values of here-and-now decision variables of $t = 1$ while discarding the rest of the solution. Based on the recommended here-and-now decisions and realized outcomes, AEEV judges which scenarios can be differentiated. If realization occurs and the MSSP formulation has wait-and-see decision variables, $DEVSP^{recourse}$ s are generated and solved. AEEV only stores the values of wait-and-see decision variables of $t = 1$ and repeats constructing and solving $DEVSP$ s and $DEVSP^{recourse}$ s at each time. Equations 10 - 16 are general $DEVSP$ formulation.

$$\min \sum_{i,t} G_{i,t}^{est}\left(V_{i,t}, \underset{s}{E}[\theta_i^{s,n}], b_{i,t}, x_{i,t}, \gamma_{i,t}, y_{i,t}\right) \tag{10}$$

s.t.

$$g\left(\underset{s}{E}[\theta_i^{s,n}], b_{i,t}, x_{i,t}, \gamma_{i,t}, y_{i,t}\right) \le 0 \quad \forall i \in I, t \in T \tag{11}$$

$$h\left(\underset{s}{E}[\theta_i^{s,n}], b_{i,t}, x_{i,t}, \gamma_{i,t}, y_{i,t}\right) = 0 \quad \forall i \in I, t \in T \tag{12}$$

$$b_{i,t} = b_{i,t}^{fixed,n}|_{t<t^{AEEV}}, \qquad b_{i,t} \in \{0,1\}|_{t\ge t^{AEEV}} \quad \forall i \in I, t \in T \tag{13}$$

$$x_{i,t} = x_{i,t}^{fixed,n}|_{t<t^{AEEV}}, \qquad x_{i,t} \in \mathbb{R}|_{t\ge t^{AEEV}} \quad \forall i \in I, t \in T \tag{14}$$

$$\gamma_{i,t} = \gamma_{i,t}^{fixed,n}|_{t<t^{AEEV}}, \qquad \gamma_{i,t} \in \mathbb{R}|_{t\ge t^{AEEV}} \quad \forall i \in I, t \in T \tag{15}$$

$$y_{i,t} = y_{i,t}^{fixed,n}|_{t<t^{AEEV}}, \qquad y_{i,t} \in \mathbb{R}|_{t\ge t^{AEEV}} \quad \forall i \in I, t \in T \tag{16}$$

The objective function (Eq. 10) provides the optimum objective value of $DEVSP$ under the expected values of uncertain parameter $\underset{s}{E}[\theta_i^{s,n}]$ associated with sub-problem n. The expected values are updated in each sub-problem as scenarios are distinguished. Since AEEV decomposes scenarios, it removes NACs and indicator variable $Z_{i,t}^{s,s'}$ (Eqs. 4 to 8) and only has scenario-specific constraints (Eqs. 11 and 12). AEEV fixes all decisions made before t^{AEEV}, using fixed variables $b_{i,t}^{fixed,n}$, $x_{i,t}^{fixed,n}$, $\gamma_{i,t}^{fixed,n}$, and $y_{i,t}^{fixed,n}$ (Eqs. 13 to 16). General $DEVSP^{recourse}$ formulation is similar to the $DEVSP$ formulation. Equations (10) to (12), (15), and (16) are identical to those of the $DEVSP$ formulation, while Equations (13) and (14) are replaced with (17) and (18). The $DEVSP^{recourse}$ fixes here-and-now decisions ($b_{i,t}$, $x_{i,t}$) when $t \le t^{AEEV}$ because here-and-now decisions must be the same after realization at t^{AEEV}, while wait-and-see decisions can be different.

$$b_{i,t} = b_{i,t}^{fixed,n}|_{t\le t^{AEEV}}, \qquad b_{i,t} \in \{0,1\}|_{t> t^{AEEV}} \quad \forall i \in I, t \in T \tag{17}$$

$$x_{i,t} = x_{i,t}^{fixed,n}|_{t\le t^{AEEV}}, \qquad x_{i,t} \in \mathbb{R}|_{t> t^{AEEV}} \quad \forall i \in I, t \in T \tag{18}$$

3.2. Generalized Knapsack-Problem based Decomposition Algorithm (GKDA)

Zeng et al. (2018) transformed an MSSP problem into multiple sub-problems called knapsack sub-problems (KSPs) through the decomposition of the scenario and time indices, resulting in the generation of a feasible solution. GKDA converts the remaining indexes into the combination of them as an item set for KSPs and enumerates all admissible items into eligible item lists. GKDA assigns each item in the eligible item list with a computed item value, and both the eligible item list and the item values undergo updates with each KSP based on the prior KSP solutions. The solutions to KSPs determine both the here-and-now and wait-and-see decisions. At $t = 1$, GKDA generates the eligible item list and item values, then constructs and solves a KSP with the expected uncertain parameters over all scenarios. GKDA stores the values of here-and-now decision variables and judges distinguishable scenarios according to the realized outcomes. If realization occurs and the MSSP formulation has wait-and-see decision variables, GKDA generates and solves new KSPs with the expected uncertain parameters to find the recourse actions. After $t = 2$, GKDA persistently updates the item list and corresponding item values, construct KSPs, and figures them out until the end of the predetermined time. Equations 19 - 22 are the general KSP formulation.

$$\max -\sum_i G_i^{est}\left(V_i, \underset{s}{E}[\theta_i^{s,n}], b_i, x_i, \gamma_i, y_i\right) \tag{19}$$

s.t.

$$g\left(\underset{s}{E}[\theta_i^{s,n}], b_i, x_i, \gamma_i, y_i\right) \leq 0 \quad \forall i \in E \tag{20}$$

$$h\left(\underset{s}{E}[\theta_i^{s,n}], b_i, x_i, \gamma_i, y_i\right) = 0 \quad \forall i \in E \tag{21}$$

$$b_i \in \{0,1\}, x_i, \gamma_i, y_i \in \mathbb{R}, \forall i \in E \tag{22}$$

The objective function (Eq. 19) calculates the optimum objective value of KSPs under the expected uncertain parameter $\underset{s}{E}[\theta_i^{s,n}]$ associated with KSP n. The values of expected uncertain parameters are updated as scenarios are distinguished. As a result of GKDA's decomposition of scenarios and times in the MSSP formulation, the resulting expression retains solely scenario-specific constraints (Eq. 20 and 21) in the formulation with the set of items $i \in \mathcal{E} = \{1,2, \dots, E\}$. Except for sequencing constraints, these scenario-specific constraints work as KSP weight constraints. The sequencing constraints are removed from the formulation, and the eligible item lists substitute for them to abide by the rules the removed sequencing constraints define. Equations 23 and 24 are added to the formulation to fix here-and-now decisions to determine the wait-and-see decisions.

$$b_i = b_i^{fixed,n} \quad \forall i \in E \tag{23}$$

$$x_i = x_i^{fixed,n} \quad \forall i \in E \tag{24}$$

The main difference between AEEV and GKDA is that GKDA lacks time information while AEEV retains it. The item values help to find better feasible bounds by compensating for the information loss. Our group developed three approaches to estimate the item values of KSPs (Zeng et al., 2018). *The straightforward approach* transfers the objective function coefficients of the general MSSP formulation as the item values of KSPs. *The maximum potential gain approach (MPGA)* applies to maximization problems where the decision maker cannot earn revenue, gains, or returns until a specific stage or outcome in the planning horizon. *The capital recovery factor (CRF) approach* applies to problems that involve capital investment decisions. The approach annualizes the capital investment made only once in the planning horizon.

4. Case study results and discussion

We analyze eight published MSSP problems with type II endogenous uncertainty by applying our heuristics. Table 1 compares the optimality gaps and computational times of successful instances obtained by AEEV and GKDA. We chose Pyomo version 6.4.0

and CPLEX version 20.10 to formulate and solve all instances, employing 48 processors on a node from Auburn University Easley Cluster. The definition of the optimality gap is the relative error between the MSSP and our heuristic solutions.

Table 1. Optimality gaps and computational times of successful instances

Optimization problem (MILP) and authors	MSSP size		Optimality gap [%]		Computational time [s]		
	Variables	Constraints	AEEV	GKDA	MSSP	AEEV	GKDA
Oil/gas-field development (Goel & Grossmann, 2004)	167,752	978,805	0.7	10.2	8,308	243	41
Process network synthesis (Tarhan & Grossmann, 2008)	8,577	57,489	0.9	44.9	147,928	10	4
Open-pit mine production scheduling (Boland et al., 2008)	34,561	41,758,081	1.5	29.5	63,148	132	39
Clinical trial planning (Colvin & Maravelias, 2008)	1,359,873	4,677,633	0.7	2.2	68,387	37	3
R&D project portfolio (Solak et al., 2010)	14,273	138,625	2.7	0.5	17,444	27	5
Vehicle routing (Khaligh & MirHassani, 2016)	9,671	16,345	0.8	15.3	5,285	52	6

In most instances, AEEV provides tighter bounds than GKDA, while the computational time is shorter for GKDA than AEEV. The result implies that the optimality gap tends to be tight while the computational time tends to be long as the approaches retain more information in their formulation. In simpler terms, AEEV provides tighter bounds with longer computational time as it decomposes solely the scenario indexes and preserves the time information in the MSSP formulation, compared to GKDA which removes both scenario and time information by decomposing their indexes.

The analysis revealed two challenges for the general applicability of the heuristics. The first challenge is that AEEV and GKDA may fail to generate a feasible solution if the MSSP model does not have complete recourse, which ensures no outcome produces infeasible results. The example in Figure 1 is used to illustrate this challenge.

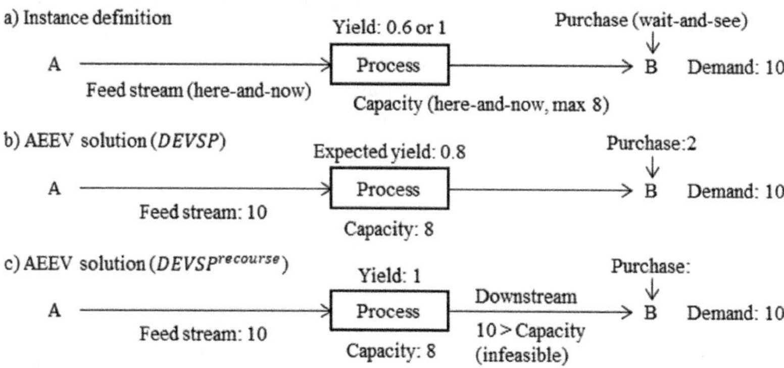

Figure 1. A process network illustrating the infeasibility of a sub-problem after realization.

The process in Figure 1 produces B from A with uncertain yield (0.6 or 1). The here-and-now decisions are the feed stream's flow rate and the installed process's capacity, and one wait-and-see decision is the amount of B purchased. Suppose the demand for B is 10, and the maximum capacity expansion is 8. AEEV first solves $DEVSP$ (Figure 1b) to determine here-and-now decisions with the expected yield (0.8). The installation of the process realizes actual yield, 0.6 or 1, and AEEV solves $DEVSP^{recourse}$ with fixed here-and-now decisions, i.e., 10 for the feed stream's flow rate and 8 for the capacity. Focusing on the outcome where the yield is 1 (Figure 1c), it is evident that the downstream flow rate is infeasible since the flow rate (10) exceeds the capacity. GKDA generates infeasible KSPs for the same reason. Thus, the updated uncertain parameter after realization does not always satisfy the constraints satisfied before realization without complete recourse. Table 2 complies with the studied MSSP problems, which reveals that most models do not have complete recourse. The second challenge arises from the lack of time information in GKDA. The item value estimation approaches to compensate for time information loss apply to most optimization problems (Table 2) except for the demand-side response planning problem. This problem has a time lag between decisions and implementations, which cannot be captured within the current GKDA.

Table 2. Complete recourse availability in MSSP and item value estimation approach in GKDA

Optimization problem and authors	Complete recourse	Item value estimation in GKDA
Size (Jonsbråten et al., 1998)	No	Straightforward
Oil/gas-field development (Goel & Grossmann, 2004)	No	CRF
Process network synthesis (Tarhan & Grossmann, 2008)	No	CRF
Open-pit mine production scheduling (Boland et al., 2008)	No	Straightforward
Clinical trial planning (Colvin & Maravelias, 2008)	Yes	MPGA
R&D project portfolio (Solak et al., 2010)	No	MPGA
Vehicle routing (Khaligh & MirHassani, 2016)	No	Straightforward
Demand-Side Response Planning (Giannelos et al., 2018)	No	None

5. Conclusions and future directions

We examined eight MSSP problems involving Type II endogenous uncertainty with AEEV and GKDA. For the cases with feasible solutions, AEEV provided tighter bounds than GKDA, while the computational time was shorter for GKDA. The analyses revealed two challenges for expanding the applicability of AEEV and GKDA. Future studies will focus on AEEV as it is more universally applicable and yields tighter bounds than GKDA. We will investigate two approaches. The first approach will add complete recourse to the MSSP problems, eliminating infeasibility without changing the optimum. The second approach will use weighted uncertain parameters instead of expected uncertain parameters, improving feasibility without changing the MSSP formulation.

References

Boland, N., Dumitrescu, I., & Froyland, G., 2008. A multistage stochastic programming approach to open pit mine production scheduling with uncertain geology. Optimization online, 1-33.

Colvin, M. & Maravelias, C. T., 2008. A stochastic programming approach for clinical trial planning in new drug development. Comput. & Chem. Eng., 32, 2626-2642.

Goel, V. & Grossmann, I. E., 2004. A stochastic programming approach to planning of offshore gas field developments under uncertainty in reserves. Comput. & Chem. Eng., 28(8), 1409-1429.

Goel, V. & Grossmann, I. E., 2006. A class of stochastic programs with decision dependent. uncertainty Math. Program., 108(2-3), 355-394.

Jonsbråten, T.W., Wets, R. J-B., & Woodruff, D.L., 1998. A class of stochastic programs with decision dependent random elements. Ann. Oper. Res., 82, 83-106.

Khaligh, F. H. & MirHassani, S. A., 2016. A mathematical model for vehicle routing problem under endogenous uncertainty. Int. J. Prod. Res., 54:2, 579-590.

Solak, S., Clarke, J. P. B., Johnson, E. L., & Barnes, E. R., 2010. Optimization of R&D project portfolios under endogenous uncertainty. EJOR, 207(1), 420-433.

Tarhan, B. & Grossmann, I. E., 2008. A multistage stochastic programming approach with strategies for uncertainty reduction in the synthesis of process networks with uncertain yields. Comput. & Chem. Eng., 32(4-5), 766-788.

Zeng, Z., Christian, B., & Cremaschi, S., 2018. A generalized knapsack-problem based decomposition heuristic for solving multistage stochastic programs with endogenous and/or exogenous uncertainties. Ind. Eng. Chem. Res., 57(28), 9185-9199.

Zeng, Z. & Cremaschi, S., 2019. A general primal bounding framework for large-scale multistage stochastic programs under endogenous uncertainties. Chem. Eng. Res. Des., 141, 464-480.

Flavio Manenti, Gintaras V. Reklaitis (Eds.), Proceedings of the 34th European Symposium on Computer Aided Process Engineering / 15th International Symposium on Process Systems Engineering (ESCAPE34/PSE24), June 2-6, 2024, Florence, Italy
 http://dx.doi.org/10.1016/B978-0-443-28824-1.50267-2

Fault detection and diagnosis on a gas-lifted oil well network control system

Rafael David de Oliveira[a], Edmary Altamiranda[b], Johannes Jäschke[a*]

[a] *Department of Chemical Engineering, Norwegian University of Science and Technology (NTNU), Trondheim, Norway.*

[b] *Technology Department, Aker BP ASA, Stavanger, Norway.*
johannes.jachke@ntnu.no

Abstract

This work proposes a control system for the gas-lifted oil well network that can be robust to minor faults and automatically detect persistent faults that may need maintenance interventions. An offset-free nonlinear model predictive control (NMPC) with a connected fault detection and isolation (FDI) system is evaluated. The FDI system works by systematically analysing the estimated disturbances and providing possible causes for the lack of performance of the controller. The methodology is evaluated through numerical simulations, and the results suggest that a simple disturbance model on the outputs can increase the robustness of the NMPC. Furthermore, faults on the pressure sensors, choke valves and reservoir can be isolated based on the estimated disturbances.

Keywords: Process control, Fault detection, Subsea operation, nonlinear model predictive control, gas-lift control.

1. Introduction

Gas-lift is an artificial lift method that consists of injecting gas into the wells to raise oil and consequently increase productivity. The amount of gas to be injected in each well will depend on the total amount of gas available, the gas-oil-ratio of each well, the upstream processing capabilities, process stabilization requirements and the equipment degradation conditions. The optimal gas injection rate can then be computed using metrics such as economics, when oil production is maximized or stability, when the bottom-hole pressure is kept constant. An automatic control system can be applied to reach these metrics in all these scenarios. Many methods have been proposed in the literature, and solutions go from simple feedback control structures (Krishnamoorthy et al., 2019) to model-based approaches using real-time optimization layers (Krishnamoorthy et al., 2016). Despite the range of proposed control solutions, the implementation in the industry is still challenging. Many solutions have been shown to work well in practice, but the main challenge is maintaining the control loop operation. Faults in Gas-lift systems can lead to decreased production efficiency and associated economic losses, fluctuations in well bore pressure, equipment wear and tear. Early fault detection and isolation for Gas-Lift systems can allow prompt response to support optimized production efficiency and maintenance planning, system stability, minimize downtime, extended equipment life span, cost savings to maximize overall system performance

Fault-tolerant control is a promising solution for these issues (Ojonugwa et al., 2023). However, they are heavily dependent on the pre-defined fault possibilities. A robust controller can be formulated to have a more general approach to dealing with the faults. Nevertheless, a robust controller solves a more complex optimization problem to guarantee robustness. An alternative is to use the offset-free NMPC that can handle disturbances by estimating them using a state estimator. This strategy is considerably easy to implement and has been shown to work for nonlinear models (Morari et al., 2012).

It is crucial that the control layer can handle disturbances and faults. However, quickly identifying the fault is also essential for possible maintenance corrective actions. Detecting faults in a closed-loop system is challenging, and it is a closed problem related to controller performance monitoring (CPM). Fault detection and isolation (FDI) are usually applied to identify faults quickly, and the methods can be based either on process data or models (Rolf, 2006). A monitoring system based on the prediction error sequence and connected with an off-set free linear MPC has already been explored (Pannocchia et al., 2014). Here, we extended that idea for a nonlinear case and directly monitored the estimated disturbance patterns. The main contribution of this work is to propose an offset-free NMPC for the gas-lift system based on a fault detection and isolation layer.

2. Case study: Gas-lifted oil well network

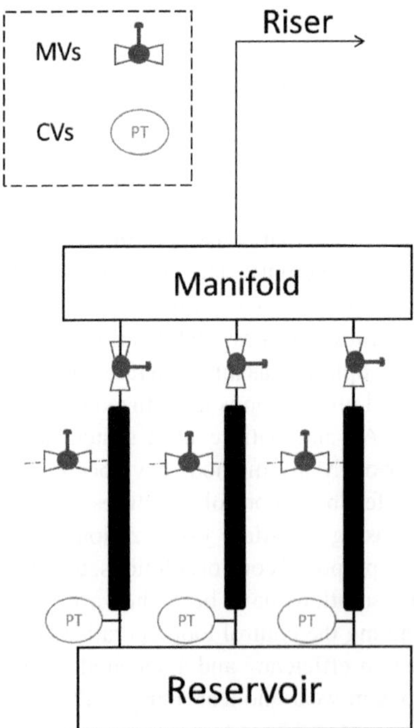

Figure 1 - Illustration of the oil and gas network with artificial gas-lift.

The case study used on this work is gas-lift well network system (Figure 1), and the model used is based on the work conducted by Krishnamoorthy et al., 2016. The mass balances for each well can be summarized as follows:

$$\dot{m}_{gt} = w_{lg} + w_{rg} - w_{pg} , \quad \dot{m}_{ot} = w_{ro} - w_{po} \tag{1}$$

Where the variable w_{lg} represents the mass flow rate of gas used for gas-lift, while w_{rg} and w_{ro} denote the mass flow rates of gas and oil extracted from the reservoir. Similarly, w_{pg} and w_{po} refer to the mass flow rates of the produced gas and oil. Additionally, m_{gt} and m_{ot} stand for the gas and oil mass holdup within the well. The gas-lift rate (w_{lg}), the flow through the choke valves on the top of the wells (w_{pv}) and the overall flow rate at the top facility (w_t) can be controlled by manipulating the opening and closing of valves. In this work, the opening of the valve at the top of the riser was kept constant while the others were used to control the bottom hole pressure (BHP). The valve equations are then used to characterize the flow rates.

$$w_t = Z_t C_{pc} \sqrt{\rho_w (p_{wh} - p_{out})} \tag{3}$$

$$w_{lg} = Z_{lg} C_{iv} \sqrt{\rho_a (p_a - p_{wi})} \tag{4}$$

$$w_{pv} = Z_{pv} C_{pv} \sqrt{\rho_w (p_{wh} - p_m)} \tag{5}$$

The variable Z_{lg}, Z_{lg} and Z_{pv} represents the opening of the gas lift injection valves, production choke valves and the top of the riser valve, respectively. Additionally, C_{pc}, C_{iv} and C_{pv} correspond to the valve coefficients. The pressures at different locations are denoted as p_{wh} for wellhead pressure, p_{out} for well outlet pressure, p_a for annulus pressure, p_m for manifold pressure and p_{wi} for injection point pressure. Furthermore, ρ_w, ρ_m and ρ_a stand for the densities of the fluids within the well tubes, manifold, and the annulus. By applying the ideal gas law, we can formulate the pressure within the annulus and the average density within the well tube can be expressed as follows:

$$\rho_w = \frac{m_{gt} + m_{ot} + \rho_O L_r A_r}{L_w A_w} , \quad \rho_a = \frac{M p_a}{T_a R} \tag{6}$$

where M represents the molar mass of the gas-lift gas, T_a is the temperature within the annulus, and R is the universal gas constant.

$$\rho_w = \frac{m_{gt} + m_{ot} + \rho_O L_r A_r}{L_w A_w} \tag{7}$$

where L_r, L_w and A_r, A_w are the lengths and cross-sectional area of the tubing above and below the gas injection point. The gas and oil flow from the reservoir is given by:

$$w_{ro} = PI \cdot (p_r - p_{bh}) , \quad w_{rg} = GOR \cdot w_{ro} \tag{8}$$

where PI is the productivity index, GOR is the gas-oil-ratio and p_r the reservoir pressure. The manipulated variables are the opening of the three gas-lift valves as well as the opening of the process valves (Figure 1). The controlled variables are the bottom-hole pressure (BHP) on the three wells. It is assumed that the set-point is given by upper control layers not included in the simulations. Keeping the BHP constant is important to stabilize the wells since many phenomena, such as slugging and casing heading, can lead to unstable wells that cause safety problems. It was assumed that the measurements available are the pressures at the annulus, wellhead, manifold, riser head, and the BHP. Besides that, the oil and gas production rate at the wellhead, riser head and the gas-lift rate are also measured. Random white noise was added to the measurements in all the simulations.

3. Offset-free Nonlinear MPC

A nonlinear MPC (NMPC) controller was chosen to control the gas-lift system. NMPC is a suitable controller for multi-variable systems since it automatically decides the value of all the manipulated variables without the need for pairing or the use of split-range controllers. Also, NMPC formulation as an optimization problem makes it easy to impose process constraints. NMPC needs all the states from the plant as input, and since they are not all measured quantities, a state estimator is needed. NMPC has inherent robustness since it is based on feedback entering the solution of the open-loop dynamic optimization problem through the initial condition states. However, it is known that an offset between the controlled variables setpoints and the measured variables can happen for larger disturbances and model mismatch. Single-loop controllers can deal with this offset by integrating the error. A similar effect can be achieved using NMPC by integrating the model error using a disturbance model (Morari et al., 2012). It was demonstrated that if the number of integrating disturbances equals the number of measurements, the original system is observable, and a stationary point can be achieved, then a zero offset is reached (Morari et al., 2012). The disturbances can enter the nonlinear model either in the inputs or the outputs. Also, the disturbance can enter in a linear or nonlinear way. Including the disturbances on the outputs can better handle different disturbances. However, depending on the type of disturbance, the controller can be sluggish. On the other hand, assuming that the disturbances are on the inputs can show better results, but how to properly set the influences of the disturbances on the states is still an open research question. Finally, the disturbance needs to be estimated using an augmented state vector, and then a state estimator is needed. This work applied an offset-free NMPC for the gas-lifted oil well network system, assuming that all the disturbances are on the output. An extended Kalman Filter (EKF) was implemented to estimate the states and the disturbances.

4. Fault detection on the control system

The methodology proposed in this paper is illustrated in Figure 2. The measurements are collected from the plant through sensors subjected to sensor faults ($\boldsymbol{f_s}$), e.g., sensor bias. The EKF uses the data to estimate the states and disturbances sent to the offset-free NMPC. The controller will compute the best control action but is subjected to faults ($\boldsymbol{f_c}$), e.g., tunning issues. The control action sent to the actuator can also have different faults ($\boldsymbol{f_a}$) depending on the type of actuator; in the case of valves, some faults can be characterized by changes in the flow coefficient ($\boldsymbol{C_v}$) (Ojonugwa et al., 2023). Finally, the control action will be implemented in the plant subjected to disturbances and faults ($\boldsymbol{f_p}$) that will cause a model mismatch between the controller and the plant. This methodology was evaluated on the gas-lift system network. All the simulations were performed in MATLAB using the Casadi package. The optimal control problem was solved using the orthogonal collocation method.

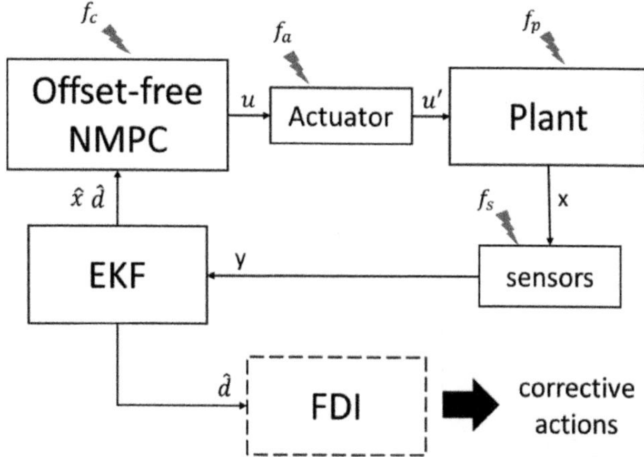

Figure 2 – Block diagram of the control structure and the FDI layer.

5. Results

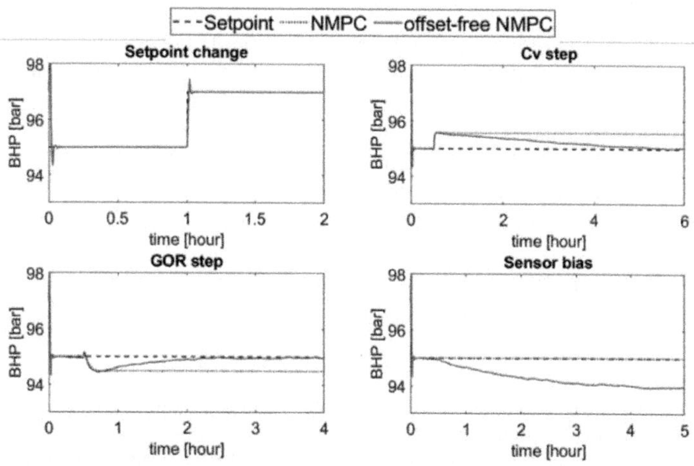

Figure 3 – Results of the simulations of the NMPC and offset-free NMPC on the gas-lift system network for a setpoint change and three faults in the system.

Four scenarios were simulated with a 10% change on the BHP setpoint, flow coefficient of the process valve, gas-oil-ratio (GOR) and a sensor bias on the BHP sensor. Figure 3 shows the true value of the BHP on one of the wells against time for the four scenarios. The performance of the offset-free NMPC is compared against the standard NMPC. As can be seen, no difference can be noted in the setpoint change. However, the offset-free NMPC could make the offset zero when the faults on the GOR occurred. Nevertheless, the controller was slower to achieve that. The only case in the standard NMPC performed better was when a sensor bias was added to the BHP sensor. The small bias on the sensor didn't affect the NMPC trajectory. However, the offset-free NMPC makes the measurement quantity biased towards offset-free, not the true value. That situation exemplifies that it is essential to identify the source of fault or disturbance. Figure 4 shows the estimated disturbance at the end of the time window for the four cases. The different patterns on the estimated output disturbances make it possible to conclude that the faults can be isolated. That information can be helpful in maintenance interventions.

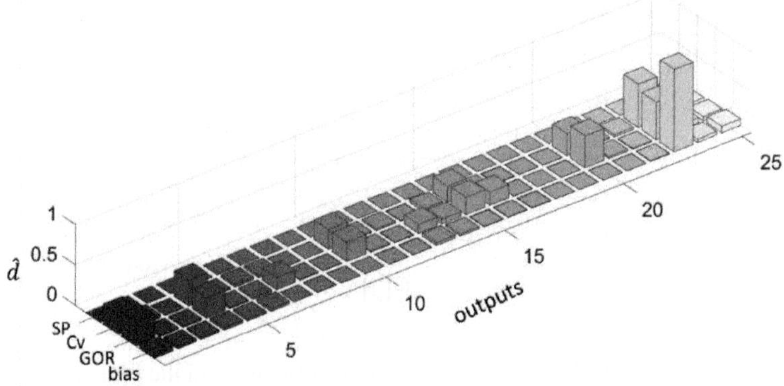

Figure 4 – Estimated disturbance in each output for the four cases scenarios.

6. Conclusions

This work presented an offset-free NMPC for a gas-lift oil well network system. An FDI layer was connected to the disturbance estimation to identify possible faults in the control system and the process. The results demonstrated the offset-free NMPC's efficiency in handling disturbances and the possibility of identifying faults based on those estimated disturbances. In future works, a dynamic change of the disturbance model based on the FDI can be explored. It is expected this monitoring system can aid the future implementation of gas-lift control and optimization strategies in the industry.

Acknowledgement: The authors acknowledge financial support from the Norwegian Research Council through the AutoPRO Project (RN: 309628).

References

A. Ojonugwa, D. Odloak, and F. K. Junior, 2023.,"Fault-Tolerant Control of Gas-Lifted Oil Well." IEEE Access 11: 24780–93.

G. Pannocchia, A. De Luca, and M. Bottai. 2014. "Prediction Error Based Performance Monitoring, Degradation Diagnosis and Remedies in Offset-Free MPC: Theory and Applications." Asian Journal of Control 16 (4): 995–1005.

I. Rolf, 2006. Fault-Diagnosis Systems: An Introduction from Fault Detection to Fault Tolerance. Springer Science & Business Media.

K. Dinesh, B. Foss, and S. Skogestad. 2016. "Real-Time Optimization under Uncertainty Applied to a Gas Lifted Well Network." Processes 4 (4): 52.

K. Dinesh, K. Fjalestad, and S. Skogestad. 2019. "Optimal Operation of Oil and Gas Production Using Simple Feedback Control Structures." Control Engineering Practice 91 (October): 104107.

M. Morari, and U. Maeder. 2012. "Nonlinear Offset-Free Model Predictive Control." Automatica 48 (9): 2059–67.

Flavio Manenti, Gintaras V. Reklaitis (Eds.), Proceedings of the 34th European Symposium on Computer Aided Process Engineering / 15th International Symposium on Process Systems Engineering (ESCAPE34/PSE24), June 2-6, 2024, Florence, Italy
 http://dx.doi.org/10.1016/B978-0-443-28824-1.50268-4

Multi-objective Optimization of Forced Periodic Operation of Methanol Synthesis in a Fixed-Bed Reactor

Johannes Leipold[a,*], Daliborka Nikolic[b], Andreas Seidel-Morgenstern[c], Achim Kienle[a,c]

[a]*Otto-von-Guericke-Universität, Universitätsplatz 2, D-39106 Magdeburg, Germany*
[b]*University of Belgrade, Institute of Chemistry, Technology and Metallurgy, Njegoseva 12, Belgrade*
[c]*Max-Planck-Institut für Dynamik komplexer technischer Systeme, Sandtorstrasse 1, D-39106 Magdeburg, Germany*
johannes.leipold@ovgu.de

Abstract

Methanol is usually produced in large amounts in fixed-bed reactors under steady-state conditions. Due to the nonlinearity of the process, the periodic stimulation of one or more inputs may improve the process behaviour compared to the traditional process realization. In this contribution, a rigorous optimization of a fixed-bed reactor is performed to investigate the potential of improvement by forced periodic operation of methanol synthesis. Axial temperature changes are included by solving simultaneously a dynamic energy balance. A multi-objective optimization with two objective functions is performed: (I) The flow rate of methanol at the reactor outlet and (II) the yield of methanol based on the amount of carbon in the feed. Following our previous work for an isothermal CSTR, simultaneous modulation of CO input concentration and overall feed rate with a phase shift - also to be optimized - is considered. This contribution considers different types of periodic input functions. The results show an improvement due to the forced periodic operation with harmonic forcing, triangle waves, and square waves. Square waves result in the best potential of improvement. Furthermore, it is shown that the optimal reactor temperature is lower in forced periodic operation compared to steady state operation, which leads to an additional advantage in terms of energy efficiency.

Keywords: Methanol synthesis, Fixed-bed reactor, Forced periodic operation, Multi-objective optimization, PDE-constrained optimization

1. Introduction

Methanol is an important raw material in chemical industry. It is produced in large amounts with $Cu/ZnO/Al_2O_3$-catalyst in fixed bed reactors. The following three reactions must be considered:

$$CO_2 + 3H_2 \rightleftarrows CH_3OH + H_2O, \quad \Delta H_R^0 = -50\ kJ\ mol^{-1}$$
$$CO + 2H_2 \rightleftarrows CH_3OH, \quad \Delta H_R^0 = -91\ kJ\ mol^{-1}$$
$$CO + H_2O \rightleftarrows CO_2 + H_2, \quad \Delta H_R^0 = -41\ kJmol^{-1}$$

The first and the second reactions describe the hydrogenation of CO and CO_2. The third equation is the water-gas-shift reaction. Optimization of methanol synthesis is a very active field of research. One opportunity to improve the behavior of such chemical processes is forced periodic operation (FPO). First investigations on this topic were made by Horn (1967). A detailed overview is given in Silveston (2013). The idea is to periodically modulate one or more inputs to achieve improvements compared to the steady-state operation. Based on the kinetic model published in Seidel et al. (2018), the FPO of methanol synthesis was recently investigated theoretically in a CSTR (Seidel et al.,2022) and in an isothermal fixed-bed reactor (Leipold et al., 2023). It was shown that significant improvements are possible. However, temperature effects were not considered. This contribution deals with the FPO of a non-isothermal fixed bed reactor, which is much more realistic than the isothermal case. A multi-objective optimization is performed to quantify the potential for improvement. Two objective functions are considered. The average molar flow rate of methanol and the yield of methanol based on the amount of carbon in the feed. The best possible steady-state solution is then compared to the best possible FPO. One difficulty in the implementation is the choice of modulated inputs. The NFR Method predicts for isothermal operation of a CSTR the best potential of improvement by modulation of the CO feed together with the overall flow rate with an optimized phase shift (Nikolic et al., 2022). This is, therefore, also used as a starting point for non-isothermal operation in this paper. Another essential degree of freedom is the type of periodic modulation. This contribution examines which input function promises the highest benefit. The FPO is modulated with harmonic functions, square waves, triangular waves, upward-sawtooth waves, and downward-sawtooth waves.

2. Modelling

2.1. Kinetics

The kinetic model from Seidel et al. (2018,2020) is used for the investigation in this contribution. It is based on the Langmuir Hinshelwood mechanism and also considers the catalyst dynamic. The model parameters are fitted to a set of 140 steady-state experiments and dynamic experiments (Seidel et al., 2021). Thus, this kinetic is very suitable for the FPO since it also represents the dynamic operation.

2.2. Reactor model

The methanol synthesis usually takes place in non-isothermal fixed-bed reactors. Under the assumption of constant pressure ideal plug flow and no heat conduction in solid phase the system equations are given in Table 1 (Leipold et al., 2023). The governing equations can be summarized by matrix-vector notation into the following general

Table 1: Governing equations

Component material balance:	$n^G\frac{\partial y_i}{\partial t}+\dot{n}\frac{V^G}{A_{int}}\frac{\partial y_i}{\partial z}+m_{cat}q_{sat}P\left(\sum_{k=1}^{N_k}\frac{\partial\Theta_i}{\partial p_k}\frac{\partial y_k}{\partial t}-y_i\sum_{i=1}^{N_k}\sum_{k=1}^{N_k}\frac{\partial\Theta_i}{\partial p_k}\frac{\partial y_k}{\partial t}\right)$ $=m_{\text{cat}}\left(\sum_{j=1}^{N_r}\nu_{i,j}r_j-y_i\sum_{i=1}^{N_k}\sum_{j=1}^{N_r}\nu_{i,j}r_j\right)$
Total material balance:	$\frac{\partial n^G}{\partial t}+\frac{V^G}{A_{int}}\frac{\partial\dot{n}}{\partial z}+m_{cat}q_{sat}\sum_{i=1}^{N_k}\sum_{k=1}^{N_k}\frac{\partial\Theta_i}{\partial p_k}\frac{dp_k}{dt}=m_{\text{cat}}\sum_{i=1}^{N_k}\sum_{j=1}^{N_r}\nu_{i,j}r_j$
Energy balance:	$\Big(\underbrace{n^G c_p^G}_{\text{gaseouse species}}+\underbrace{m_{cat}\,c_p^{kat}}_{\text{catalyst}}\Big)\frac{\partial T}{\partial t}+\underbrace{\frac{V^G}{A_{int}}\dot{n}c_p^G\frac{\partial T}{\partial z}}_{\text{convection}}+\underbrace{m_{\text{cat}}\sum_i\Delta H_{R,j}r_j}_{\text{heat of reaction}}$ $+\underbrace{\alpha_c A_w(T-T_c)}_{\text{heat of cooling}}+\underbrace{P_{bar}m_{cat}q_{sat}\Delta H_{ads}\sum_{i=1}^{N_k}\sum_{k=1}^{N_k}\frac{\partial\Theta_i}{\partial p_k}\frac{dy_k}{dt}}_{\text{heat of adsorption}}=0$

Table 2: Reactor properties and process parameter

Paremeter	Value	Unit
$\dot{n}_{in}$	1.326	mol/min
l	1.14	m
d_{int}	0.013	m
m_{cat}	168.5	g
ε_{bulk}	0.395	-
q_{sat}	0.98	mol/kg
ΔH_{ads}	10	kJ/mol
P	80	bar

system of partial differential equations (PDE).

$$\boldsymbol{M}(\boldsymbol{x},t,z)\frac{\partial \boldsymbol{x}}{\partial t} + \boldsymbol{W}(\boldsymbol{x},t,z)\frac{\partial \boldsymbol{x}}{\partial z} = \boldsymbol{f}(\boldsymbol{x},t,z) \tag{1}$$

with $\boldsymbol{x} = [y_{CH_4}, y_{CO_2}, y_{CO}, y_{H_2}, y_{H_2O}, y_{N_2}, \phi, \dot{n}, T]$. Heat capacities and heat of reaction are calculated with correlations in Reid et al. (1987). The heat transfer coefficient and all corresponding thermodynamical properties were taken from VDI e.V. (2013). For this investigation the lab scaled reactor from Nestler et al. (2021) is used. The process parameters are given in Table 2.

3. Methods

To validate the FPO a multi-objective optimization is performed. The objective functions are $\Phi_1 = \overline{n}_{CH_3OH}$, the average flow rate of methanol at the outlet and $\Phi_2 = \overline{n}_{CH_3OH,out}/(\overline{n}_{CO_2,in} + \overline{n}_{CO,in})$, the average yield of methanol based on the amount of carbon in the feed. To solve this problem, the ϵ-constraint method is used (Ehrgott, 2005). The second objective function is constrained by an ϵ, resulting in a single-optimization problem of the following form:

$$\max_{u} \quad \Phi_1(\boldsymbol{x}(t,z,\boldsymbol{u})) \tag{2}$$

$$s.t. \quad \boldsymbol{M}\frac{\partial \boldsymbol{x}}{\partial t} + \boldsymbol{W}\frac{\partial \boldsymbol{x}}{\partial z} = \boldsymbol{f} \tag{3}$$

$$\boldsymbol{x}(t,0,\boldsymbol{u}) = \boldsymbol{BC} \tag{4}$$

$$\boldsymbol{x}(0,z,\boldsymbol{u}) = \boldsymbol{IC} \tag{5}$$

$$\boldsymbol{h}(\boldsymbol{x},\boldsymbol{u}) = 0 \tag{6}$$

$$\boldsymbol{g}(\boldsymbol{x},\boldsymbol{u}) \leq 0 \tag{7}$$

$$\boldsymbol{lb} \leq \boldsymbol{u} \leq \boldsymbol{ub} \tag{8}$$

$$\epsilon - \Phi_2(\boldsymbol{x}(t,z,\boldsymbol{u})) \leq 0 \tag{9}$$

The problem must be solved for a range of ϵ's, where each ϵ represents one point on the Pareto front. The PDE in equation 6 is discretized with orthogonal collocation and converted to equality constraints (Hedengren et al., 2014). The boundary conditions define the states at the reactor inlet over the time and are given in equation 13.

$$\boldsymbol{x}(t,0,\boldsymbol{u}) = \begin{bmatrix} 0 \\ y_{CO,in}[1 + A_{CO}P(\omega t)] \\ y_{CO_2,in} \\ y_{H_2,in} \\ 0 \\ y_{N_2,in}[1 - A_{N_2}P(\omega t)] \\ \dot{n}_{in}[1 + A_f P(\omega t + \Delta\phi)] \\ T_{in} \end{bmatrix} \tag{10}$$

$$x(0,z,u) = x(0,\tau,u) \quad \text{with} \quad \tau = \frac{2\pi}{\omega} \tag{11}$$

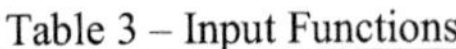
Table 3 – Input Functions

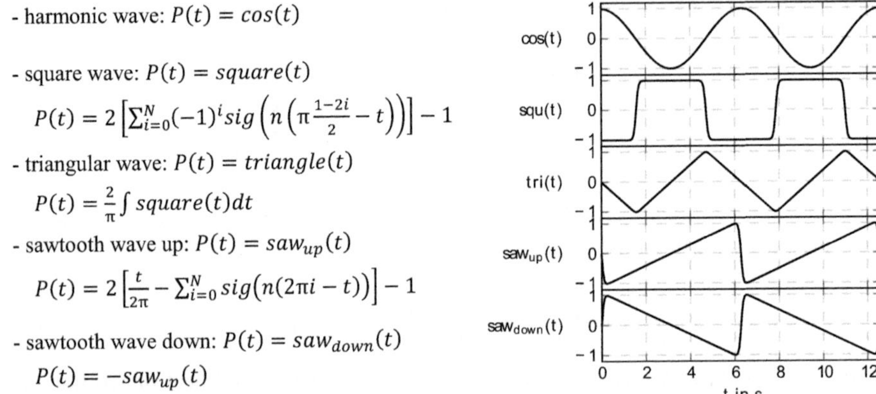

- harmonic wave: $P(t) = cos(t)$
- square wave: $P(t) = square(t)$
  $P(t) = 2\left[\sum_{i=0}^{N}(-1)^i sig\left(n\left(\pi\frac{1-2i}{2} - t\right)\right)\right] - 1$
- triangular wave: $P(t) = triangle(t)$
  $P(t) = \frac{2}{\pi}\int square(t)dt$
- sawtooth wave up: $P(t) = saw_{up}(t)$
  $P(t) = 2\left[\frac{t}{2\pi} - \sum_{i=0}^{N} sig(n(2\pi i - t))\right] - 1$
- sawtooth wave down: $P(t) = saw_{down}(t)$
  $P(t) = -saw_{up}(t)$

It is assumed that the temperature at the inlet T_{in} and the cooling temperature T_c are equal. The CO feed flow rate is periodically stimulated together with the overall feed flow rate with the same frequency but with phase shift. The N_2 feed is used to compensate the CO modulation, ensuring constant pressure in the reactor. P(t) is the periodic input function, which can be chosen between the five functions from Table 3. To avoid sharp fronts in the solution of the PDE's the input functions are approximated with a combination of sigmoid function ($\mathrm{sig}(t) = 1/(1 + \exp(t))$) and its integral. To ensure a periodic solution, the initial conditions are taken as in equation 14. Furthermore, the following equality and inequality constraints are considered:

$$\boldsymbol{h}(\boldsymbol{x}, \boldsymbol{u}) = \begin{bmatrix} \sum y_{i,in} - 1 \\ A_{CO}\, y_{CO,in} - A_{N_2} y_{N_2,in} \\ \bar{n}_{N_2}^{SS} - \bar{n}_{N_2}^{FOP} \end{bmatrix} \quad (12) \qquad \boldsymbol{g}(\boldsymbol{x}, \boldsymbol{u}) = \begin{bmatrix} 0.01 - y_{CO_2,in} - y_{CO,in} \\ -\dot{n}(t,z) \\ 453{,}15K - T_{in} \end{bmatrix} \quad (13)$$

The constraint h_1 and h_2 fulfill the summation condition of the mole fractions. To guarantee the same amount of nitrogen in the reactor in steady state operation and in FPO, the nitrogen condition is introduced with h_3 (Seidel et al., 2022). Due to the additional degree of freedom $y_{in,N2}$ can be also used as decision variable in the FPO. The inequality constraints g_1 and g_2 make sure that there is at least 1 percent carbon in the reactor and that the flow rate does not become negative. g_3 keeps the temperature always higher than 180°C since the gas mixture could start to condense below this temperature. With alle these adjustments, the vector of decision variables yields $\boldsymbol{u} = [y_{CO,in}, y_{CO_2,in}, y_{H_2,in}, y_{N_2,in}, A_f, A_{CO}, A_{N_2}, \tau, \Delta\phi, T_{in}]$. For optimizing the steady-state operation the amplitudes A_j are set to zero and 15% nitrogen is assumed in the inlet. The upper and lower bounds of the decision variables are as follows:

$$\begin{bmatrix} 0 \\ 0.35 \\ 18s \\ 0 \\ 453.15K \end{bmatrix} \leq \begin{bmatrix} y_{CO_2,in}, y_{CO,in}, y_{N_2,in}, A_f, A_{CO,in}, A_{N_2,in} \\ y_{H_2,in} \\ \tau \\ \Delta\phi \\ T_{in} \end{bmatrix} \leq \begin{bmatrix} 1 \\ 1 \\ 3600s \\ 2\pi \\ 800K \end{bmatrix} \quad (14)$$

The optimization problem is implemented in Julia and solved with the software package JuMP (Lubin et al., 2023) together with the solver Ipopt (Wächter and Biegler, 2004).

4. Results

Figure 1 shows the Pareto fronts for steady state operation compared to the Pareto fronts for FPO with different input functions. The FPO with harmonic, triangular, and square waves provides significant improvements compared to the steady state operation, where the amount of improvement increases from left to right. The two forms of sawtooth wave do not produce any improvement for most points. Only at very high yields, a minimal improvement of less than 1% is noticeable. The square waves deliver the highest benefits. Operating point 1 demonstrates this improvement. In steady state operation at a yield of 70%, a methanol flow rate of 333mmol/min/kg$_{cat}$ is achieved. At the same yield, the FPO with square waves can obtain a flow rate of 637mmol/min/kg$_{cat}$, which corresponds to an improvement of 91%. On the other hand, at a same outlet flow rate of 333mmol/min/kg$_{cat}$, the FPO with square waves can achieve a yield of 79%, which is an improvement of 13%. The right part of Figure 1 takes a closer look at the average inlet flow rates and the inlet temperature along the Pareto fronts. The optimal CO and CO_2 flow rates increase from left to right, while the optimal H_2 flow rate shows contrary behavior. It can be seen that the optimal average flow rates of H_2 in the FPO cases are lower than in the steady state, with square waves requiring the least amount of H_2. The optimal temperature starts in all cases at the lower bound and increases from left to right. The temperature with FPO is always lower than in steady state operation, with the lowest temperature also by using square waves.

5. Conclusions

This contribution investigates the impact of different input functions on the FPO in a non-isothermal fixed bed reactor for the methanol synthesis. The results show that the FPO with harmonic, triangular, and square waves show significant improvements compared to the steady state, especially for high yield. The FPO with sawtooth waves

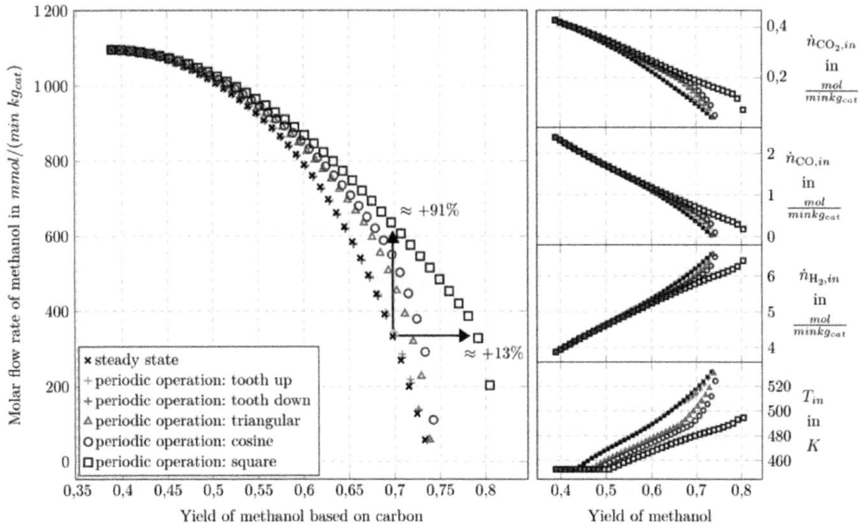

Figure 1. Pareto fronts and corresponding inlet characteristics for the steady state operation and the FPO with different input functions

only shows a negligibly small benefit for high yields and is not worth the effort that a dynamic process realization involves. The best potential of improvement is achieved with square wave modulation. This can be implemented by switching between two constant operating points and is, therefore also, the easiest to realize in practice. In fact, the energy costs and the costs due to wear and tear caused by dynamic operation are considerably higher than in stationary operation. However, a large part of the production costs is accounted for the H_2 supply. The FPO offers a further advantage here since less hydrogen is required in the feed. In addition, the optimal temperature in the FPO is lower than in the steady state, which is an advantage in terms of energy requirements. To identify these benefits more precisely, economic objective functions can be used in upcoming investigations. Further work will also focus on experimental validation of FPO.

Acknowledgments
Financial support by the German Research Foundation (DFG) is gratefully acknowledged through the priority program SPP 2080 under grant KI 417/6-2, NI 2222/1-2, SE 586/24-2.

References

M. Ehrgott, 2005, Multicriteria Optimization. Springer Berlin Heidelberg

J.D. Hedengren, R.A. Shishavan, K.M. Powell, T.F. Edgar, 2014, Nonlinear modeling, estimation and predictive control in apmonitor, Comput. Chem. Eng., 70, 133–148.

F. Horn, 1967, Periodic countercurrent processes. Ind. Eng. Chem. Process Des. Dev., 6, 30–35.

J. Leipold, C. Seidel, D. Nikolic, A. Seidel-Morgenstern, A. Kienle, 2023, Optimization of methanol synthesis under forced periodic operation in isothermal fixed-bed reactors. Comput. Chem. Eng., 175, 108285.

M. Lubin, O. Dowson, J. Dias Garcia, J. Huchette, B. Legat, J.P. Vielma, 2023, JuMP 1.0: Recent improvements to a modeling language for mathematical optimization. Math. Program. Comput., 15, 581-589.

F. Nestler, V.P. Müller, M. Ouda, M.J. Hadrich, A. Schaadt, S. Bajohr, T. Kolb, 2021, A novel approach for kinetic measurements in exothermic fixed bed reactors: Advancements in non-isothermal bed conditions demonstrated for methanol synthesis, React. Chem. Eng., 6, 1092–1107.

D. Nikolic, C. Seidel, M. Felischak, T. Miličić, A. Kienle, A. Seidel-Morgenstern, M. Petkovska, 2022, Forced periodic operations of a chemical reactor for methanol synthesis – The search for the best scenario based on Nonlinear Frequency Response Method. Part II Simultaneous modulation of two inputs, Chem. Eng. Sci., 248, 117133.

R.C. Reid, J.M. Prausnitz, B.E. Poling, 1987, The Properties of Gases and Liquids, Mcgraw-Hill Professional, 4th edition.

C. Seidel, A. Jörke, B. Vollbrecht, A. Seidel-Morgenstern, A. Kienle, 2018, Kinetic modeling of methanol synthesis from renewable resources, Chem. Eng. Sci., 175, 130–138.

C. Seidel, A. Jörke, B. Vollbrecht, A. Seidel-Morgenstern, A. Kienle, 2020, Corrigendum to "kinetic modeling of methanol synthesis from renewable resources" (chem. eng. sci. 175 (2018) 130–138)

C. Seidel, D. Nikolić, M. Felischak, M. Petkovska, A. Seidel-Morgenstern, A., Kienle, 2022, Forced Periodic Operation of Methanol Synthesis in an Isothermal Gradientless Reactor. Chem. Eng. Technol., 45, 2261-2272.

P. Silveston, R. Hudgins, 2013, Periodic Operation of Chemical Reactors. Butterworth-Heinemann,

VDI e. V., VDI-Wärmeatlas, 2013, Springer Berlin Heidelberg.

A. Wächter, L.T. Biegler, 2004, On the implementation of an interior-point filter line-search algorithm for large-scale nonlinear programming, Math. Program. 106, 25–57

Flavio Manenti, Gintaras V. Reklaitis (Eds.), Proceedings of the 34th European Symposium on Computer Aided Process Engineering / 15th International Symposium on Process Systems Engineering (ESCAPE34/PSE24), June 2-6, 2024, Florence, Italy
 http://dx.doi.org/10.1016/B978-0-443-28824-1.50269-6

Steady-State Optimality Analysis of MPC Controllers

Jozef Vargan,[a*] Jakub Puk,[b] Karol Ľubušký,[c] Miroslav Fikar,[a]

[a]*Slovak University of Technology in Bratislava, Bratislava 81237, Slovakia*
[b]*ATP spol. s.r.o., Bratislava 841 01, Slovakia*
[c]*Slovnaft, a.s., Bratislava 82412, Slovakia*
jozef.vargan@stuba.sk

Abstract

Due to their complexity, production units and equipment in petrochemical plants need to be controlled by advanced process controllers (APC). The optimality of APC control is closely connected with the setting of constraints, while their inappropriate setting leads to a loss of the generated profit. To inform the operator in time, we create a tool that analyses the effectiveness of constraints setting. We design a copy of the APC model as a static optimization problem with the implementation of soft constraints. Two methods are employed: local sensitivity analysis using Lagrange multipliers and non-local sensitivity analysis. An ordered list of recommendations is created for plant engineers, providing information on the effectiveness of constraint setting for a single point of operation or during a specific time interval.

Keywords: MPC Maintenance, FCC Unit, Optimal Steady-State, Constraints Analysis

1. Introduction

Model Predictive Control (MPC) represents an advanced process control strategy routinely applied in refineries nowadays (Lee, 2011; Schwenzer et al., 2021). This is due to increasing demand for profit increase, reduction of variability of products, or a reduced amount of off-specification products. In addition, it is possible to control multivariable units with dozens of input and output variables where manual control or a series of single-variable loops is either impractical or not realizable. All these favorable properties come with a price, which is the complexity of MPC controllers. Therefore, optimal operation is only guaranteed if all controller tuning knobs are set correctly and properly maintained (Arumugasamy and Ahmad, 2012).

MPC monitoring, assessment, diagnostics, and maintenance have a firm place in industrial packages that come along with the controller. Industrial view of performance monitoring and future trends can be found in Qin and Badgwell (2003); Forbes et al. (2015). There are several approaches to the sustainability of MPC performance. Some of these are outlined in Guerlain et al. (2002) where a decision system support is described and improvements in user interface are proposed for various hard-to-detect issues. Approaches to analyzing, interpreting, and visualizing the controller decisions are studied by Elnawawi et al. (2022). The patent of Peterson et al. (2011) uses pivoting of unconstrained and constrained variables to analyze allowable steady-state moves until some constraint is reached and to determine the sensitivity of the constraints on the profitability of the controller. Control performance improvements have been suggested and compared in Botelho et al. (2016); Godoy et al. (2017) using some global indicators. Continuous performance assessment concerning the MPC constraints, and their tuning was suggested in Agarwal et al. (2007).

Acknowledgments: This work is funded by the Slovak Research and Development Agency (project no. APVV-21-0019), by the Scientific Grant Agency of the Slovak Republic (grant no. 1/0691/21), and by the European Commission (grant no. 101079342, Fostering Opportunities Towards Slovak Excellence in Advanced Control for Smart Industries).

This work studies the effect of limit tightening by the operator's actions due to some operating conditions. As a case study, we will investigate a fluid catalytic cracking (FCC) production unit with many input/output signals where the effects of such changes cannot easily be evaluated. The result intended for the plant engineers is a priority list of constraints that should be returned to their factory values to guarantee plant profitability. Two methods are applied and compared: a precise but computationally less effective non-local sensitivity analysis and information provided by Lagrange multipliers that is only valid locally.

2. Design of APC Model

The examined device is a distillation column in a fluid catalytic cracking production unit. It consists of two parts – a fractionator (located at the head of the column) and six double-shaped floors (circular and disc). The coke trap ensures the purity of the products drained off at the bottom of the column. The heavy oil feed is fed to the first floor at the boiling temperature. The contact between the liquid and vapor phases results in the separation of the components of the reaction mixture, divided into several fractions – wet gases and naphtha at the top of the column, light (LCO) and heavy (HCO) circulation oils and products at the bottom of the main column (MCB). Wet gases are cooled and removed as a naphtha product or returned as heavy-side circulation naphtha (HCN). Ratio control is applied. LCOs are regulated via a withdrawal, with LCO maximized against HCO. HCO is similar to LCO, controlled via a withdrawal. MCB is subject to dual regulatory mechanisms, including control through flow rate and a ratio control that governs its withdrawal of MCB and subsequent recirculation.

This unit's Advanced process control is implemented using Honeywell's RMPCT Profit controller (Honeywell, 2012) to guarantee overall performance. The controller handles a total of 47 controlled (CV), manipulated (MV), and disturbance (DV) variables. These are constrained using hard (HC) and soft (SC) constraints. While the HCs must not be violated, placing SCs within HCs creates a buffer, making it difficult for variables to reach the HC. In addition, to improve the feasibility of the optimal solution, the high limits of HC are not defined for CVs (Vargan, 2023).

Following the limits' objectives, we distinguish between two types of constraints:

- Ideal constraint (IC) – the value of which is determined by the technical documentation for the APC control,
- Real constraint (RC) – temporarily set by the operators.

Real constraints are usually applied to mitigate the influence of some disturbance on the plant to stabilize some part of the process. Real constraints usually tighten the ideal constraints, but it can also happen that the operators relax some of the constraints. Once the disturbance terminates, the operator should return the control mode from RC to IC. Failing to do so, some RCs can "throttle" the controlled system, thus degrading the optimality of the operation. For a large process such as FCC, it is not always easy to detect suboptimal operation by visually inspecting all RMPCT parameters.

The original problem solved by RMPCT controller in each sampling time is specified by a quadratic cost function, equality constraints resulting from a dynamical process model and inequality constraints on all process variables defining the hard and soft constraints. The process model is characterized by a matrix of all transfer functions between inputs and outputs.

To simplify the analysis, we concentrate on static operation in our approach to systematic detection of control performance degradation due to constraints changes. This simplifies the dynamic optimization formulation of the original problem to quadratic programming. The soft constraints are implemented using slack variables and absolute value penalties in the cost function. Quadratic penalties were also tested but were more difficult to tune. The mathematical formulation of the problem is defined as follows:

$$\min_x J(x) = \sum_{i=1}^{s} b_{CV,i}\, CV_i + \sum_{i=1}^{s} a_{CV,i}^2 \left(CV_i - CV_{0,i}\right)^2 + \sum_{j=1}^{t} b_{MV,j}\, MV_j + \sum_{j=1}^{t} a_{MV,j}^2 \left(MV_j - MV_{0,j}\right)^2 + \sum_{i=1}^{s} Q_{CV,H,i}\, E_{CV,H,i} + \sum_{i=1}^{s} Q_{CV,L,i}\, E_{CV,L,i} + \sum_{j=1}^{t} Q_{MV,H,j}\, E_{MV,H,j} + \sum_{j=1}^{t} Q_{MV,L,j}\, E_{MV,L,j} \tag{1a}$$

$$s.t. \quad CV_i - CV_i^{SS} = \sum_{j=1}^{t} K_{i,j}\left(MV_j - MV_j^{SS}\right), \tag{1b}$$

$$CV_{L,i} + \Delta CV_{L,i} - \varepsilon_{CV,L,i} \le CV_i \le CV_{H,i} + \Delta CV_{H,i} - \varepsilon_{CV,H,i}, \tag{1c}$$

$$MV_{L,j} + \Delta MV_{L,j} - \varepsilon_{MV,L,j} \le MV_j \le MV_{H,j} + \Delta MV_{H,j} - \varepsilon_{MV,H,j}, \tag{1d}$$

$$0 \le \varepsilon_{CV,H,i}, \quad 0 \le \varepsilon_{CV,L,i}, \tag{1e}$$

$$0 \le \varepsilon_{MV,H,j} \le \Delta MV_{H,j}, \quad 0 \le \varepsilon_{MV,L,j} \le \Delta MV_{L,j}, \tag{1f}$$

$$-E_{CV,H,i} \le \varepsilon_{CV,H,i} \le E_{CV,H,i}, \quad -E_{CV,L,i} \le \varepsilon_{CV,L,i} \le E_{CV,L,i} \tag{1g}$$

$$-E_{MV,H,j} \le \varepsilon_{MV,H,j} \le E_{MV,H,j}, \quad -E_{MV,L,j} \le \varepsilon_{MV,L,j} \le E_{MV,L,j} \tag{1h}$$

where $x = \{CV, MV, \varepsilon, E\}$ are the optimized variables, i and j are indices of the i-th controlled (s in total) and j-th manipulated (t in total) variable. The original RMPCT quadratic cost function is contained in the first line of Eq. (1a), $CV_{0,i}$ and $MV_{0,j}$ are set-points, $b_{CV,i}$, $b_{MV,j}$ and $a_{CV,i}$, $a_{MV,j}$ are penalties of linear and quadratic terms. $Q_{CV,H,i}$, $Q_{CV,L,i}$, $Q_{MV,H,j}$ and $Q_{MV,L,j}$ are the penalty matrices of the auxiliary variables $E_{CV,H,i}$, $E_{CV,L,i}$, $E_{MV,H,j}$ and $E_{MV,L,j}$, which determine the absolute values of the slack variables $\varepsilon_{CV,H,i}$, $\varepsilon_{CV,L,i}$, $\varepsilon_{MV,H,j}$ and $\varepsilon_{MV,L,j}$. Eq. (1b) represents a steady-state model with CV_i^{SS} and MV_j^{SS} being the measured steady states, $K_{i,j}$ are coefficients of the the steady-state gain matrix. Eqs. (1c) and (1d) are inequality constraints on CVs and MVs, where $\Delta CV_{H,i}$, $\Delta CV_{L,i}$, $\Delta MV_{H,j}$ and $\Delta MV_{L,j}$ represent tightening the original constraints, $CV_{H,i}$, $CV_{L,i}$, $MV_{H,j}$ and $MV_{L,j}$. Slacks ε may violate the tightened constraints (if the solution for $\varepsilon = 0$ is not feasible), thus creating soft constraints – $\varepsilon_{MV,H,j}$ and $\varepsilon_{MV,L,j}$ are constrained by $MV_{H,j}$ and $MV_{L,j}$ in Eq. (1f). CV slack variables $\varepsilon_{CV,H,i}$ and $\varepsilon_{CV,L,i}$ can even violate limits $CV_{H,i}$ and $CV_{L,i}$ in Eq. (1e) – to maintain the feasibility of the solution. Eqs. (1g), (1h) are the constraints of the absolute penalty in a linear form.

A pair of slack variables belong to each CV and MV, a total of 78 constraints. Each slack variable is from the interval of auxiliary variables $[E_L, E_H]$, forming additional 116 constraints. Along with 58 soft CVs and MVs constraints, the optimization problem consists of 252 inequality constraints.

Variables $CV_{L,i}$, $CV_{H,i}$, $MV_{L,j}$, $MV_{H,j}$ can represent ideal or real constraints. Using either real or ideal constraints, the solution of Eq. (1) yields valuable insights into the optimal configuration of controlled and manipulated variables. Subsequent analysis of this data enables the identification and analysis of active constraints and the need to transform restrictive real constraints into ideal ones.

3. Constraint Sensitivity Analysis

Sensitivity analysis is a powerful tool that can be used to investigate the properties of the optimal solution in Eq. (1). Two approaches are applied in this contribution: local and non-local sensitivity analysis (Boyd and Vandenberghe, 2004; Bertsekas, 2009).

Local sensitivity analysis (LSA) utilizes optimal Lagrange multipliers, denoted as λ^* provided by the nominal solution of Eq. (1) with the real constraints: $J_{real}(x^*)$. Each Lagrange multiplier is related to the gradient of the optimal cost function with respect to the change of the respective constraint. It is the local sensitivity and thus exact only theoretically with infinitesimal constraint perturbations. However, it is obtained at no cost as supplementary information of the nominal solution.

Table 1: List of recommendations (Point 26).

Priority	Constraint Name	Constraint Type	Lagrange Multiplier	Verbal Recommendation
1	MV 2	HL	$2.4 \cdot 10^7$	Keep the constraint in place
2	CV 10	LL	$2.1 \cdot 10^7$	Keep the constraint in place
3	MV 4	LL	$8.1 \cdot 10^5$	Keep the constraint in place
4	CV 20	HL	9,999.0	Move the real constraint to the ideal
5	CV 8	HL	9,999.0	Move the real constraint to the ideal
6	CV 14	LL	1,380.4	Keep the constraint in place
7	CV 1	HL	100.0	Move the real constraint to the ideal

Conversely, non-local sensitivity analysis (NSA) approximates the gradient using both the nominal solution and the solution with the real constraint replaced by the corresponding ideal one:

$$\tilde{\lambda}_i^* = \frac{J_{real}(x^*) - J_{ideal,i}(x^*)}{RC_i - IC_i} \qquad (2)$$

This gives a precise characterization of the suboptimality related to the respective constraint. On the other hand, one additional optimization problem needs to be solved for each real constraint.

We study the optimal operation of the column for 48 hours and explain the procedure on the data denoted as Point 26 in Figure 1. From 58 defined constraints (high and low limits of 19 CV and 10 MV pairs), eight are saturated, and the corresponding multipliers are non-zero. Among these, the constraint CV 7 does not fall into the soft constraint region (violates the high soft limit), so it is not considered in further analysis. Therefore, seven constraints remain, and the values of their Lagrange multipliers are employed to formulate recommendations.

In both LSA and NSA approaches, a list of constraints can be produced that is sorted in descending order of Lagrange multipliers (Table 1). It contains the constraint name and its type (HL/LL – high/low limit), the value of the Lagrange multiplier, and a verbal recommendation to process engineers. Based on the characteristics of real and ideal constraints, the verbal recommendation can be as follows:

- Keep the constraint in place – the Lagrange multiplier is non-zero, but the real constraint is the same as the ideal constraint (additional recommendations).
- Move the real constraint to the ideal – the Lagrange multiplier is non-zero and the real constraint differs from the ideal constraint (real recommendations).

Both local and non-local sensitivity analyses are distinguished by positive and negative characteristics that can influence the final recommendations. To determine the applicability of the approaches in industrial conditions, we compare both using the edit distance method. It produces a numerical representation indicative of the accuracy in the arrangement of elements within the two lists (recommendations). The chosen method for determining the edit distance is the Levenshtein distance (Levenshtein, 1966). The data units under comparison consist of combinations of variable names (e.g., CV 20, CV 8) + constraint types (e.g., HL – high limit).

The results in Point 26 can be seen in Table 2, with the edit distance equal to 0. Moreover, the edit distance value is zero across the considered time interval. When comparing the values of Lagrange multipliers for NSA and LSA, all values practically coincide except for

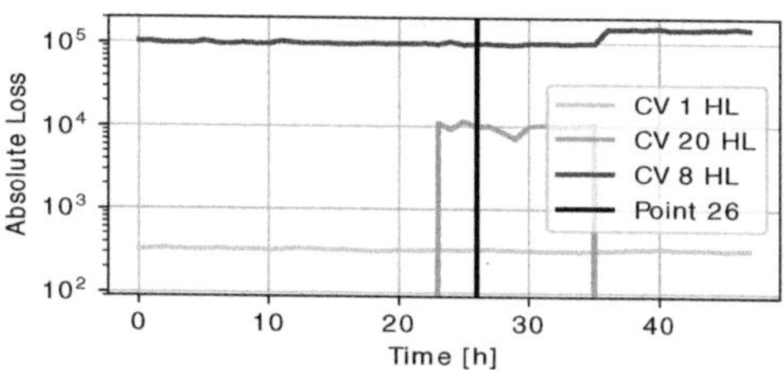

Figure 1: Long-term loss evolution.

the CV 1 high limit (6.8 % difference). The size of the change from the real to the ideal constraint, which ranges from 0.28 to 1.83 %, does not have a noticeable effect on the accuracy of the multipliers. If the differences were more significant, it can be expected that the structure of the optimal solution would change substantially, including a possible different order of the multipliers (and recommendations) for NSA and LSA. Therefore, it would be up to the control engineer to choose the more accurate NSA method for obtaining recommendations or to rely on the accuracy of the less computationally demanding LSA.

A similar analysis is conducted for the data from the studied time span. We provide graphical information on the detected long-term losses $J_{real}(x^*) - J_{ideal,i}(x^*)$. A process engineer can verify the course of the loss from an inefficiently set constraint, including (approximate) loss value and the time frame of its duration. Figure 1 shows the loss in a logarithmic scale. The data period is an hour.

We notice that the operator modified the constraint CV 20 HL for 12 hours of operation and then returned to its ideal position. On the other hand, the other two constraints should be investigated more closely.

When analysing the data, several solvers are examined in Python programming language – CPLEX, CVXOPT, Gurobi, MOSEK, OSQP, and Xpress. All these solvers are available within the convex optimization modelling framework CVXPY (Diamond and Boyd, 2016). We investigate the computation time of the optimization problem and the maximum Python memory allocation. The complete calculation time is considered – loading input data, solving the optimization problem, and communicating the recommendations to the process engineer. At one operating point (OOP) of the local sensitivity analysis, the average calculation time is 6 seconds (initial time information, ITI). The time for solving the optimization problem is significantly shorter. The values for individual solvers range from 0.013 (Gurobi) to 0.138 (CVXOPT) seconds. For a maximum memory allocation, the optimization solver needs from 12 to 144 Kbs (CVXOPT to CPLEX).

Priority	Constraint	Lagrange Multiplier NSA	LSA	Constraint Change	Constraint Real	Ideal	Edit Distance
1	MV 20 HL	9,999.0	9,999.0	1.0	368.0	369.0	
2	CV 8 HL	9,999.0	9,999.0	10.0	316.0	326.0	0
3	CV 1 HL	93.2	100.0	3.5	191.5	195.0	

Table 2: Edit distance comparison of Lagrange multipliers obtained by local (LSA) and non-local (NSA) sensitivity analysis

When analysing the entire time interval of data (2 days, 48 data points), one operating point takes about 7 seconds using the Gurobi solver. In the case of non-local sensitivity analysis, the overhead for additional optimization calculations is practically negligible as there are only three constraints on average to be investigated. Nevertheless, the local method provides two advantages: sufficient accuracy of recommendation calculations and shorter computation time

4. Conclusions

We treated the maintenance problem of advanced process controllers related to constraints on manipulated and controlled variables. The case study investigated the fluid catalytic cracking production unit controlled by the RMPCT Profit controller by Honeywell. The problem comprises 47 variables. We applied two sensitivity analysis methods: local using the optimal Lagrange multipliers and non-local based on actual values of ideal and real constraints settings. Edit distance metric was employed to compare both approaches. It was shown that local analysis can be used in industrial conditions as careful constraint tightening by the operators rarely significantly changes the structure of the optimal solution. On the other hand, non-local analysis was not significantly slower for the investigated case study plant.

We provide a list of ordered recommendations to process engineers and operators for actual operation or analysis on a longer time window. Open-source tools using Python programming language are proposed and the implemented procedure is used at the refinery. Further profiling of the script will be required to shorten the overall calculation time and to make it possible to analyse longer time intervals of operation.

References

N. Agarwal, B. Huang, E. C. Tamayo, 2007, Assessing model prediction control (MPC) performance. 1. probabilistic approach for constraint analysis, Industrial & Engineering Chemistry Research 46, 24, 8101–8111

S. K. Arumugasamy, Z. Ahmad, 2012, Model predictive control (MPC) and its current issues in chemical engineering, Chemical Engineering Communications 199, 4, 472–511

D. P. Bertsekas, 2009, Convex Optimization Theory, Athena Scientific

V. Botelho, J. O. Trierweiler, M. Farenzena, R. Duraiski, 2016, Perspectives and challenges in performance assessment of model predictive control, The Canadian Journal of Chemical Engineering 94, 7, 1225–1241

S. Boyd, L. Vandenberghe, 2004, Convex Optimization, Cambridge University Press

S. Diamond, S. Boyd, 2016, CVXPY: A Python-embedded modeling language for convex optimization, Journal of Machine Learning Research 17, 83, 1–5

S. Elnawawi, L. C. Siang, D. L. O'Connor, R. B. Gopaluni, 2022, Interactive visualization for diagnosis of industrial model predictive controllers with steady-state optimizers, Control Engineering Practice 121, 105056

M. G. Forbes, R. S. Patwardhan, H. Hamadah, R. B. Gopaluni, 2015, Model predictive control in industry: Challenges and opportunities, IFAC-PapersOnLine 48, 8, 531–538

J. Godoy, A. Ferramosca, A. González, 2017, Economic performance assessment and monitoring in LP-DMC type controller applications, Journal of Process Control 57, 26–37

S. Guerlain, G. A. Jamieson, P. Bullemer, R. Blair, 2002, The MPC elucidator: a case study in the design for human-automation interaction, IEEE Transactions on Systems, Man, and Cybernetics – Part A: Systems and Humans 32, 1, 25–40

Honeywell, 2012, Advanced Process Control – Profit Controller, Concepts Reference Guide, Honeywell International Inc.

J. H. Lee, 2011, Model predictive control: Review of the three decades of development, International Journal of Control, Automation and Systems 9, 3, 415–424

V. I. Levenshtein, 1966, Binary codes capable of correcting deletions, insertions, and reversals, Soviet Physics Doklady 10, 8, 707–710

T. J. Peterson, A. R. Punuru, K. F. Emigholz, R. K. Wang, D. Barrett-Payton, 2011, Model predictive controller solution analysis process, US Patent 7,949,417

S. J. Qin, T. A. Badgwell, 2003, A survey of industrial model predictive control technology, Control Engineering Practice 11, 7, 733–764

M. Schwenzer, M. Ay, T. Bergs, D. Abel, 2021, Review on model predictive control: an engineering perspective, The International Journal of Advanced Manufacturing Technology 117, 1327–1349

J. Vargan, 2023. Optimality analysis of MPC controller, Master thesis, UIAM FCFT STU in Bratislava, Radlinského 9, 812 37 Bratislava

Flavio Manenti, Gintaras V. Reklaitis (Eds.), Proceedings of the 34th European Symposium on Computer Aided Process Engineering / 15th International Symposium on Process Systems Engineering (ESCAPE34/PSE24), June 2-6, 2024, Florence, Italy
 http://dx.doi.org/10.1016/B978-0-443-28824-1.50270-2

Seasonal Setpoints Optimization of WWTP DO Control Based on Artificial Neural Networks Performance Indices Prediction

Norbert B. Mihály[a], Vasile M. Cristea[a*]

[a]Babeş-Bolyai University of Cluj-Napoca, 1 Mihail Kogalniceanu Street, 400028 Cluj-Napoca, Romania
mircea.cristea@ubbcluj.ro

Abstract

Adaptive and optimal setpoints for the aeration control system are necessary to maintain the high performance of wastewater treatment plant operation under generally variable seasonal weather conditions. By effectively achieving the optimization aims, models with shorter computation times and more dependable forecasts are highly valued components for real-time optimization activities. In order to forecast the wastewater treatment plant's Greenhouse Gas Emissions and Effluent Quality performance indicators, artificial neural network models were designed, trained, and evaluated. We took into consideration the nonlinear autoregressive network with exogenous inputs network type. The models of artificial neural networks were developed using data particular to each season. Using evolutionary algorithm optimizations and two distinct selection techniques based on the Pareto fronts of the two considered performance indicators, the optimal artificial neural network architecture and hyperparameters were identified for each of the four seasons. When tested, the trained network models showed high forecast accuracy for all seasons, with mean absolute percentage error values for the greenhouse gas emissions reaching 2.88% and the effluent quality index up to 4.25%. The optimization of aeration led to improvements in Effluent Equality, Greenhouse Gas Emissions, and Operational Cost performance throughout all seasons. The improvements ranged from 0.40% for Greenhouse Gas emissions to 13.31% for Effluent Quality Index.

Keywords: seasonal artificial neural network, genetic algorithm, aeration control, greenhouse gas emissions, wastewater treatment plant, performance indices.

1. Introduction

A rapidly expanding and growing important area of study for wastewater treatment plants (WWTPs) is greenhouse gas (GHG) emission reduction (Mannina et al., 2016). It was demonstrated to be advantageous to include these emissions in the evaluation of the environmental effects (Nguyen et al., 2020). Many models and tools for estimating greenhouse gas emissions have been created and used in various WWTP investigations, such as analyzing the effects of cutting-edge treatment techniques (e.g. thermal drying of sludge) on greenhouse gas emissions (Szypulska et al., 2021).
The nonlinear autoregressive network with exogenous input (NARX), a dynamic network that makes predictions based on historical data, is the best kind of network to handle sequential and complicated tasks. NARX has been shown to be an effective tool for predicting gaseous emissions in the influent chamber of WWTPs (Zounemat-Kermani et al., 2019). Simultaneously, few studies focused on the use of NARX models to dynamically analyze the performance of WWTP operation. Successful applications of

artificial neural network (ANN)-based GHG modeling include estimating GHG emissions in Europe (Antanasijević et al., 2014) and predicting the impacts of climate change on GHG emissions (Guo et al., 2021). Nevertheless, research has not yet been done on the modeling of a complete WWTP's GHG emissions using these models.
Optimizing controller settings can lead to the optimization of WWTP operations. The dissolved oxygen (DO) and nitrate (NO) controllers are common examples. Tejaswini et al. optimized the gain and integral time values of the controllers using simulated data, which resulted in a reduction in the effluent quality and total cost indices (Tejaswini et al., 2021). While looking at ways to optimize the operation of the WWTP through the use of aerated bioreactors, it is necessary to take GHG emissions into account.
The objective of the current study is to optimize the WWTP seasonal operation while accounting for the majority of intrinsic biological processes. To accomplish it, the dynamic ANN-based modeling of the complex Activated Sludge Model No. 2d (ASM2D) will be used. The novelty lies in the utilization of ANN models to assess the effluent quality index (EQI) and greenhouse gas emissions of the WWTP. These models are further employed in optimization with genetic algorithms (GAs) of the WWTP seasonal operation by finding the optimal setpoint of the DO control loop.

2. Methodology

2.1. Data Generation

The Benchmark Simulation Model no. 2 (BSM2) was used to generate the simulated data sets used in this work, with model characteristics being outlined in the corresponding technical report (Alex et al., 2018). The model used was an extended version of the BSM2, which is detailed in (Flores-Alsina et al., 2016; Solon et al., 2017). Besides C and N compounds, it further describes P, S, and Fe transformations. The ideal treatment is hard to forecast during times of changeable temperature since temperature affects a number of processes involved in wastewater treatment, such as the impact on the metabolic activity of microorganisms. Consequently, a one-year period of 364 days, beginning on day 45, was selected from the 609 days of BSM2 dynamic inputs. The 364 days of data were evenly divided into 4 sections, with each season being 91 days long.

2.2. GA-NARX models development

The 13 input features of the ANN consisted of influent and operational variables, while the two output features were the EQI and GHG emissions performance indices. To find the appropriate network hyperparameters that are: the training algorithm (TA), the tapped delay lines horizon (TD), the number of hidden layers, the number of neurons in each hidden layer, and the kind of transfer functions, the models were developed using a genetic algorithm. The three most commonly used backpropagation algorithms in the field of study were considered, i.e., Levenberg-Marquardt (LM), Quasi-Newton (BFGS), and scaled conjugate gradient (SCG) (Bahramian et al., 2023). The training process utilized 70% of the dataset, while two sets of 15% each were used for validation and testing. The number of sampling time delays for the input and output was searched from 2 to 20, and logistic sigmoid (log) and tangent sigmoid (tan) transfer functions (TF) were considered.
The most accurate GA-NARX networks were saved after all developed networks were assessed using three distinct assessment criteria to guarantee that the GA optimization produced the best-performing models. The mean squared error (MSE), mean absolute percentage error (MAPE), and coefficient of determination (R^2) were the assessment criteria used to choose the most accurate ANN models (Mihály et al., 2022).

2.3. Effluent quality index and GHG emissions estimation

2.3.1. Effluent quality index

The daily emitted mass of pollution, measured in kilograms of pollution units per day (kg PU/d), is described by the EQI. An extended version of the criterion was employed, as shown by Eq. (1) (Solon et al., 2017), in order to also account for pollution caused by P delivered to the receiving water bodies.

$$EQI = \frac{1}{1000 \cdot ts} \cdot \int_{t_i}^{t_{i+1}} \Big[PU_{TSS}(t) + PU_{COD}(t) + PU_{BOD_5}(t) + PU_{TKN}(t) + PU_{NO}(t) + PU_{P_{inorg}}(t) + PU_{P_{org}}(t)\Big] \cdot Q_e(t)dt \quad (1)$$

2.3.2. GHG emissions

The on-site emissions of CO_2 and N_2O by the aerobic biological processes, as well as the off-site, downstream N_2O emissions were taken into account as described in (Mihály et al., 2023), while the CO_2 and CH_4 emissions due to the anaerobic digestion were calculated as shown in Eq. (2) and (3).

$$P_{CO_2,CH_4} = 0.99 \cdot MP \cdot \frac{44}{16} \quad (2)$$

$$P_{CH_4} = 0.01 \cdot MP \cdot GWP_{CH_4} \quad (3)$$

It was assumed that of the generated methane (*MP*) 99% would burn in a gas engine and the remaining 1% would escape into the atmosphere. GWP_{CH_4} is the global warming potential relative to CO_2 for CH_4.

Utilizing a factor for the emission intensity of power generation, the GHG emissions (kg CO2 eq./d) resulting from the net energy consumption were calculated as shown in Eqs. (4) and (5). The difference between the daily energy demand (e_D) and energy recovery (e_R) was used to compute the WWTP's net energy consumption (kWh/d).

$$P_{CO_2,energy} = (e_D - e_R) \cdot EF_{energy} \quad (4)$$

$$e_D = AE + PE + ME + HE_{net} \quad (5)$$

$$e_R = 0.99 \cdot 6 \cdot MP \quad (6)$$

here, *EFenergy*, with a value of 0.275 kg CO_2 eq./kWh in 2021, represents the GHG emission intensity of electricity generation for the EU (EEA, 2022). Calculations of the *AE*, *PE*, *ME*, *HEnet*, and *MP* components were performed as described in (Gernaey, 2014).

The GHG emission due to sludge disposal was calculated as the CO_2 (kg CO_2/d) generated from the combustion of biogas in landfills:

$$P_{CO_2,landf} = \frac{110}{113} \cdot W_{S,landf} + \frac{40}{113} \cdot \frac{44}{16} \cdot W_{S,landf} \quad (7)$$

where, $W_{S,landf}$ is the amount of disposed sludge to landfills.

3. Results and discussion

Taking the concept of the most accurate model into consideration, two distinct selection scenarios were examined. If all three assessment criteria performed better than the best results that had been previously achieved in the selection process, the model was saved, and this was considered as Case 1 selection approach. While in Case 2 when any of the three measurements produced better outcomes than the prior top result of that metric in the selection process, the network was saved. Tables 1 and 2 contain these results.

The most effective networks for EQI modeling showed R^2 values ranging from 0.9930 to 0.9950. In contrast, the MAPE values were within the range of 3.53% and 4.25%. The ranges for these values, with regard to the GA-NARX modeling of GHG emissions, were

0.9867 to 0.9872 and 2.79% to 2.88% for R^2 and MAPE, respectively. The 8 GA-NARX models, whose predictions were highlighted in the tables, were found to have reliable accuracy to be further applied in the operation optimization of the WWTP operation.

Table 1. GA-NARX models for EQI and GHG emissions predictions in Case 1

Season	Out	TA	TD	Neurons Layer 1	Neurons Layer 2	Functions TF 1	Functions TF 2	Evaluation on testing data R^2	MSE·10^5	MAPE
Winter	**EQI**	**SCG**	**14**	**8**	**6**	**tan**	**tan**	**0.993**	**3.64**	**3.53**
	GHG	**BFG**	**12**	**14**	**9**	**tan**	**tan**	**0.987**	**2.67**	**2.83**
Spring	**EQI**	**LM**	**3**	**4**	**4**	**tan**	**tan**	**0.994**	**5.69**	**3.82**
	GHG	BFG	2	12	-	log	-	0.986	2.59	2.88
Summer	**EQI**	**LM**	**2**	**15**	**-**	**tan**	**-**	**0.993**	**5.32**	**4.25**
	GHG	BFG	9	14	9	log	log	0.987	2.69	2.85
Autumn	EQI	SCG	14	5	-	tan	-	0.995	5.06	3.98
	GHG	**LM**	**17**	**4**	**-**	**tan**	**-**	**0.987**	**2.51**	**2.87**

Table 2. GA-NARX models for EQI and GHG emissions predictions in Case 2

Season	Out	TA	TD	Neurons Layer 1	Neurons Layer 2	Functions TF 1	Functions TF 2	Evaluation on testing data R^2	MSE·10^5	MAPE
Winter	EQI	LM	14	14	-	tan	-	0.991	4.79	3.96
	GHG	SCG	5	15	10	tan	tan	0.984	3.14	2.96
Spring	EQI	SCG	16	12	-	tan	-	0.993	7.82	4.38
	GHG	**BFG**	**6**	**8**	**-**	**log**	**-**	**0.987**	**2.68**	**2.79**
Summer	EQI	LM	8	14	-	tan	-	0.993	5.07	4.32
	GHG	**LM**	**6**	**6**	**-**	**log**	**-**	**0.987**	**2.45**	**2.88**
Autumn	**EQI**	**BFG**	**14**	**8**	**-**	**tan**	**-**	**0.995**	**4.90**	**3.80**
	GHG	SCG	6	4	12	log	tan	0.985	2.90	2.92

The multi-objective method using GA yielded the best values of the DO control loop setpoint for each of the four seasons, utilizing the best GA-NARX models. From the non-dominated solutions represented by the Pareto front, the optimal DO values to be tested on the first-principle model were selected as: 1.373 mg O_2/L for winter, 1.911 mg O_2/L spring, 1.553 mg O_2/L summer, and 1.837 mg O_2/L for autumn. Each of the aforementioned values were applied as setpoints of the DO controller for the core 30-day period of each season.

The obtained EQI, GHG emissions, and overall cost index (OCI) were compared to the results obtained in the base case, which considers the setpoint for the DO control loop as 2.0 mg O_2/L. These results are presented in Table 3. The relative differences (Relative diff.) between the two cases were also calculated to better display the change that the optimized case brought relative to the base case. All seasonal data showed a simultaneous

drop in both EQI and OCI as a consequence of operation optimization, indicating the achievement of a more effective treatment procedure in terms of kg PU per OCI units.
Overall, the findings showed that in order to get better WWTP functioning, the various seasonal conditions needed varied settings. At the same time, reduction of GHG emissions was also achieved throughout the 4 seasons.
It is also crucial to highlight that the application of GA-NARX models significantly lowered the processing time to around 600 seconds and reduced the computational resources for the multi-objective optimization job. At the same time, a single 30-day simulation with the first-principle mathematical model required more than 630 seconds. It would take around 73 days of calculation if the optimization would use the first principle mathematical model for the objective function computation, if required to complete the same number of iterations as the ANN based optimization. This optimization task is performed by the developed GA-NARX models in 10 minutes.

Table 3. EQI, GHG, and OCI results obtained from the base and optimized cases

Case	Winter			Spring		
	EQI	GHG	OCI	EQI	GHG	OCI
	kg PU/d	kg CO_2 eq./d	-	kg PU/d	kg CO_2 eq./d	-
Base case	13158	11037	9256	12555	11116	9544
Optimized	12252	10979	9226	12355	11098	9518
Relative diff	-6.88	-0.53	-0.33	-1.60	-0.17	-0.26

Case	Summer			Autumn		
	EQI	GHG	OCI	EQI	GHG	OCI
	kg PU/d	kg CO_2 eq./d	-	kg PU/d	kg CO_2 eq./d	-
Base case	13034	11137	10384	12961	11146	10275
Optimized	11299	11039	10290	12375	11112	10249
Relative diff	-13.31	-0.87	-0.90	-4.52	-0.30	-0.25

4. Conclusions

In the current work, the seasonal WWTP performance indices were predicted using NARX type models with their associated hyperparameter values found through GA optimization. The resulting neural network models were highly accurate, with MAPE values less than 4.25%. The utilization of these models in the multi-objective optimization of seasonal setpoints for the DO control loop resulted in operation performance enhancements regarding the EQI, GHG emissions, as well as the OCI. Effluent pollution was reduced by up to 13.31%, while GHG emissions and OCI were decreased in all cases with less than 1%.
In summary, an adaptable and workable solution for enhanced and sustainable functioning of the WWT process in each seasonal situation was produced by the suggested modelling and optimization proposed methodologies. However, the unique optimal solutions identified for the various seasons imply that every season has its own

best parameters and operation conditions. As a result, the operation optimization should be examined seasonally when the yearly comprehensive WWTP optimization is considered.

References

J., Alex, L., Benedetti, J., Copp, K. V., Gernaey, U., Jeppsson, I., Nopens, M.-N.,Pons, J.-P., Steyer, P., Vanrolleghem, 2018. Benchmark Simulation Model no. 2 (BSM2). IWA 1, 99.

D.Z.,Antanasijević, M.D., Ristić, A.A., Perić-Grujić, V. V., Pocajt, 2014. Forecasting GHG emissions using an optimized artificial neural network model based on correlation and principal component analysis. International Journal of Greenhouse Gas Control 20, 244–253.

M., Bahramian, R.K., Dereli, W., Zhao, M., Giberti, E., Casey, 2023. Data to intelligence: The role of data-driven models in wastewater treatment. Expert Syst Appl.

EEA, 2022. Data visualization: Country level – Greenhouse gas emission intensity of electricity generation. https://www.eea.europa.eu/data-and-maps/daviz/co2-emission-intensity-12/#tab-chart_2 (accessed November 14, 2023).

X., Flores-Alsina, K., Solon, C., Kazadi Mbamba, S., Tait, K. V., Gernaey, U., Jeppsson, D.J., Batstone, 2016. Modelling phosphorus (P), sulfur (S) and iron (Fe) interactions for dynamic simulations of anaerobic digestion processes. Water Res 95, 370–382.

K.V., Gernaey, U., Jeppsson, P.A., Vanrolleghem, J.B., Copp, 2014. Benchmarking of Control Strategies for Wastewater Treatment Plants. IWA Publishing, London, UK. IWA Scientific and Technical Report No. 23.

L.N., Guo, C., She, D. Bin, Kong, S.L., Yan, Y.P., Xu, Khayatnezhad, M., Gholinia, F., 2021. Prediction of the effects of climate change on hydroelectric generation, electricity demand, and emissions of greenhouse gases under climatic scenarios and optimized ANN model. Energy Reports 7, 5431–5445.

G., Mannina, G., Ekama, D., Caniani, A., Cosenza, G., Esposito, R., Gori, M., Garrido-Baserba, D., Rosso, G., Olsson, 2016. Greenhouse gases from wastewater treatment - A review of modelling tools. Sci Total Environ 551-552, 254-270.

N.B., Mihály, A.V., Luca, M., Simon-Várhelyi, V.M., Cristea, 2023. Improvement of air flowrate distribution in the nitrification reactor of the waste water treatment plant by effluent quality, energy and greenhouse gas emissions optimization via artificial neural networks models. J Water Process Eng 54: 103935.

N.B., Mihály, M., Simon-Várhelyi, V.M., Cristea, 2022. Data-driven modelling based on artificial neural networks for predicting energy and effluent quality indices and wastewater treatment plant optimization. Opt Eng 23, 2235–2259.

T.K.L., Nguyen, H.H., Ngo, W.S., Guo, S.W., Chang, D.D., Nguyen, L.D., Nghiem, T. V., Nguyen, 2020. A critical review on life cycle assessment and plant-wide models towards emission control strategies for greenhouse gas from wastewater treatment plants. J Environ Manage 264: 110440.

K., Solon, X., Flores-Alsina, C., Kazadi Mbamba, D., Ikumi, E.I.P., Volcke, C., Vaneeckhaute, G., Ekama, P.A., Vanrolleghem, D.J., Batstone, K. V., Gernaey, U., Jeppsson, 2017. Plant-wide modelling of phosphorus transformations in wastewater treatment systems: Impacts of control and operational strategies. Water Res 113, 97–110.

D., Szypulska, Ł., Kokurewicz, B., Zięba, S., Miodoński, M., Muszyński-Huhajło, A., Jurga, K., Janiak, 2021. Impact of the thermal drying of sludge on the nitrogen mass balance of a WWTP, and GHG emissions with classical and novel treatment approach - A full-scale case study. J Environ Manage 294: 113049.

E.S.S., Tejaswini, S., Panjwani, U.B.B., Gara, S.R., Ambati, 2021. Multi-objective optimization based controller design for improved wastewater treatment plant operation. Environ Technol Innov 23, 1–12.

M., Zounemat-Kermani, D., Stephan, R., Hinkelmann, 2019. Multivariate NARX neural network in prediction gaseous emissions within the influent chamber of wastewater treatment plants. Atmos Pollut Res 10, 1812–1822.

Flavio Manenti, Gintaras V. Reklaitis (Eds.), Proceedings of the 34th European Symposium on Computer Aided Process Engineering / 15th International Symposium on Process Systems Engineering (ESCAPE34/PSE24), June 2-6, 2024, Florence, Italy
 http://dx.doi.org/10.1016/B978-0-443-28824-1.50271-4

Adversarially Robust Real-Time Optimization and Control with Adaptive Gaussian Process Learning

Akhil Ahmed[a], Antonio Del Rio Chanona[a], Mehmet Mercangöz[a*]

[a]*Imperial College London, London, SW7 2BX*

[*]*m.mercangoz@imperial.ac.uk*

Abstract

Real-Time Optimization (RTO) and control face two foundational challenges: effectively managing disturbances, noise, and implementation errors at the control layers, and addressing the pervasive issue of plant-model mismatch at the RTO layer. To tackle the first challenge, our recent work introduced the Adversarially Robust Real-Time Optimization and Control (ARRTOC) algorithm which utilises the RTO layer to identify set-points that are inherently robust to control layer perturbations and implementation errors. ARRTOC ensures the chosen set-points are tailored to the underlying controller designs. However, ARRTOC's strength hinges on an accurate steady-state model. To surmount this, in this work, we extend ARRTOC with Adaptive Gaussian Process Learning (AGPL) to make it more applicable in situations where accurate models are not available. AGPL employs Gaussian Process (GP) regression to learn the underlying steady-state model of the objective function and addresses plant-model mismatch through dynamic GP adaptation. The integration of AGPL and ARRTOC in this way tackles the two primary challenges in RTO and control: ARRTOC ensures robustness against control-layer implementation errors, while AGPL addresses plant-model mismatch.

Keywords: Adversarially Robust Optimization, Real-Time Optimization, Gaussian Processes, Process Control, Adversarial Machine Learning

1. Introduction

Real-Time Optimization (RTO) plays a crucial role in the process operation hierarchy by determining optimal set-points for the lower-level controllers. However, at the control layers, these set-points may be difficult to track because of challenges in implementation due to disturbances and noise. This could be handled by robustifying the controllers to these perturbations however this may add additional complexity to the already resource constrained control layer. Instead, to tackle this challenge, our recent work introduced the Adversarially Robust Real-Time Optimization and Control (ARRTOC) algorithm (Ahmed et al. 2023). Drawing inspiration from adversarial machine learning (Bertsimas et al. 2010), ARRTOC utilises the RTO layer to identify set-points that are inherently robust to implementation errors, such as disturbances, thus alleviating demands on the resource-limited controllers. ARRTOC handles the dual problem of optimality and operability seamlessly as part of an online RTO solution which is described in section 2.1. By design, the chosen set-point is insensitive to potential disturbances and noise. This concept is illustrated in Figure 1, where the performance of a controller around two possible set-points is compared: the global optimum (scenario 1 in blue) and the adversarially robust optimum (scenario 2 in red). We observe that operating at the adversarially robust optimum yields a 30% larger mean objective value compared to operating at the global optimum due to its inherent robustness.

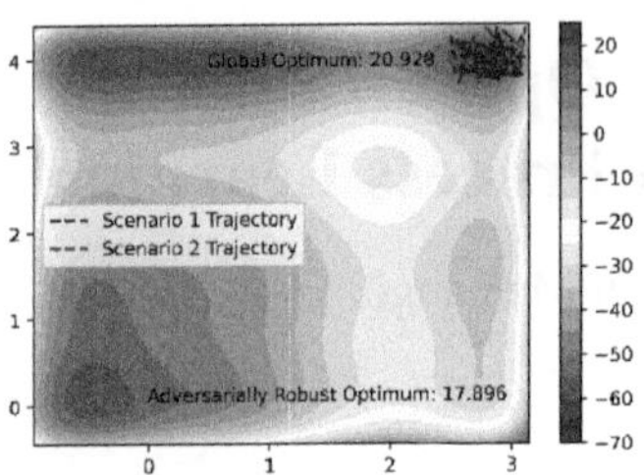

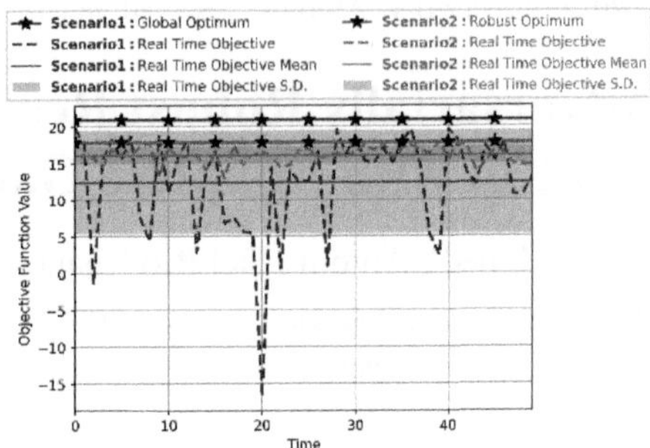

Figure 1: Scenario 1 shows fluctuating real-time objective value (dashed blue line) due to system disturbances, averaging 12.40—40% lower than the expected global optimum of 20.93 (solid blue line with black starred markers). In contrast, scenario 2 displays more stable real-time objective value (dashed red line), averaging 16.09, closer to the expected robust optimum of 17.90 (solid red line with black starred markers).

However, to operate successfully, ARRTOC relies on an accurate steady-state model of the system under consideration (Patrón et al. 2022). Indeed, this model dependency issue and the subsequent challenge of plant-model mismatch is common to all existing RTO formulations (Cortinovis et al. 2016). To address this, in this work, we extend ARRTOC with Adaptive Gaussian Process Learning (AGPL) (Ahmed et al. 2022). AGPL employs Gaussian Process (GP) regression to learn the underlying steady-state model of the objective function and overcomes plant-model mismatch through dynamic GP adaptation. Additionally, GPs, being a non-parametric modeling approach, possess a unique advantage – the ability to address structural mismatch in models, which is typically beyond the capabilities of current state-of-the-art approaches like model-parameter adaptation or modifier adaptation.

We illustrate the algorithm's capabilities through a case study of a multi-loop evaporator process. In this study, ARRTOC customises controller set-points for each loop based on anticipated disturbances, and AGPL minimizes plant-model disparities, ensuring an accurate solution is obtained. This extended framework showcases increased adaptability and robustness, effectively handling uncertainties at both RTO and control layers.

2. Background and Methodology

2.1. Adversarially Robust Real-Time Optimization and Control (ARRTOC)

In this section we provide a summary of the ARRTOC algorithm. For the interested reader, the full details can be found in Ahmed et al. (2023). The nominal RTO problem is to find a set point, $\boldsymbol{x} \in \mathbb{R}^{n_x}$ which optimizes some operating goal objective function, such as profit, $f: \mathbb{R}^{n_x} \rightarrow \mathbb{R}$, while satisfying operating constraints, $h_j: \mathbb{R}^{n_x} \rightarrow \mathbb{R}$:

$$\begin{aligned} &\min_{\boldsymbol{x}} f(\boldsymbol{x}) \\ &\text{s.t.}\, h_j(\boldsymbol{x}) \leq 0 \end{aligned} \tag{1}$$

For reasons outlined in section 1, we wish to use the RTO layer to identify set-points inherently robust to implementation errors. We denote implementation errors as $\Delta\boldsymbol{x} \in \mathbb{R}^{n_x}$ and we assume they reside within the n-ellipsoid uncertainty set defined as $\mathcal{U} = \left\{ \Delta\boldsymbol{x} \,\middle|\, \sum_i^{n_x} \frac{\Delta x_i^2}{\Gamma_i^2} \leq 1 \right\}$ where Γ_i represents the largest possible perturbation or implementation error we must safeguard against for the ith state. We seek an adversarially robust set-point i.e a set-point robust to the worst possible implementation error of our process:

$$\begin{aligned}&\min_{\boldsymbol{x}} \max_{\Delta \boldsymbol{x}} f(\boldsymbol{x}+\Delta \boldsymbol{x}) \\ &\text{s.t.} \max_{\Delta \boldsymbol{x}} h_j(\boldsymbol{x}+\Delta \boldsymbol{x}) \leq 0\end{aligned} \tag{2}$$

The problem formulation implies that a robust set-point should (i) minimize the worst-case cost as defined as $\max_{\Delta \boldsymbol{x}} f(\boldsymbol{x}+\Delta \boldsymbol{x})$ and (ii) simultaneously ensure no constraints are violated for any $\Delta \boldsymbol{x} \in \mathcal{U}$. Eq. (2) is solved via three mains steps: (i) Neighbourhood cost exploration, (ii) Neighbourhood constraint exploration and finally either (iiia) Robust local move if infeasible under perturbations or (iiib) Robust local move if feasible under perturbations. For brevity, a detailed explanation of these steps is not provided here, but Figure 2 offers an intuitive overview.

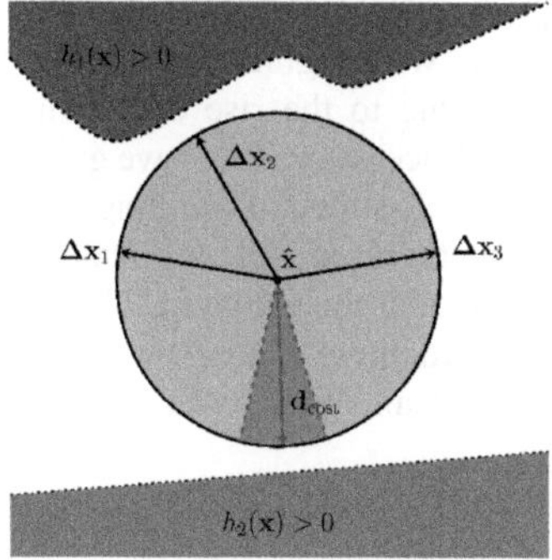

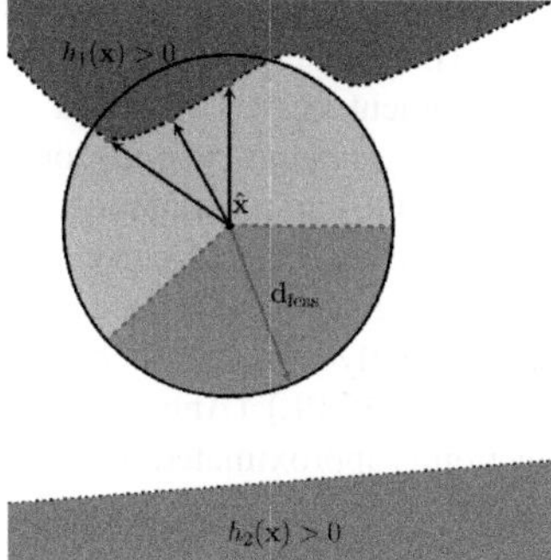

Figure 2: Left: No constraint violations in the neighborhood, algorithm aims to minimize worst-case cost. Right: Iterate infeasible due to intersecting infeasible region; algorithm seeks descent direction to restore feasibility.

Figure 2 depicts the two main scenarios during the algorithm's execution. The left subplot shows an iterate, where during step 2 of the algorithm, no constraint violating neighbours were found in the neighbourhood of the point (depicted as a grey circle based on the uncertainty set, $\mathcal{U}$) i.e. it is feasible under perturbations. In this scenario, cost considerations take precedence over constraints. The objective is to identify a robust local move that reduces the worst-case cost. This involves finding a direction, $\boldsymbol{d}_{cost}$, and step-size, ρ_{cost}, which moves away from the high-cost directions, depicted as black arrows. These high-cost directions were found during step 1 of the algorithm by solving the inner maximization problem, $\max_{\Delta \boldsymbol{x}} f(\boldsymbol{x}+\Delta \boldsymbol{x})$, via a multi-start gradient ascent algorithm. The direction and step-size were found by solving a Second Order Cone Program (SOCP). Alternatively, the right subplot shows an iterate, where during step 2 of the algorithm, constraint violating neighbours were found, rendering it infeasible under perturbations. In this scenario, constraints take precedence over cost, with the goal being to find a robust local move which guides the iterate back into the feasible region. Again, we must find a direction, $\boldsymbol{d}_{feas}$, and step-size, ρ_{feas}, which moves away from the constraint-violating neighbour directions, depicted as black arrows. These directions were found by solving the constraint maximization problem, $\max_{\Delta \boldsymbol{x}} h_j(\boldsymbol{x}+\Delta \boldsymbol{x})$. The algorithm iteratively follows the above steps until it reaches a robust local minimum, where (i) the point is surrounded by high-cost neighbours on all sides, meaning there is no direction to reduce the worst-case cost, and (ii) the neighbourhood of the point does not intersect with any of the constraint-violating regions.

2.2. Adaptive Gaussian Process Learning (AGPL)

As specified in the RTO problem formulation in Eq. (1), an accurate model of the objective function and constraints is essential for achieving an accurate solution and, consequently, effective set-points for the controllers. Without an up-to-date and accurate model, there is a risk that the system can be operated in a suboptimal manner due to plant-model mismatch. Over time, this mismatch can worsen as the system naturally degrades. This is a known challenge in the RTO literature and several adaptation strategies have been proposed to this end (Chachuat et al. 2009, Mendoza et al. 2015). Effective state-of-the-art approaches include: (i) Model-parameter adaptation whereby the model parameters are estimated and updated based on output measurements from the system. However, it assumes the model is structurally correct with only parametric mismatches, which is rarely the case in practice. (ii) Modifier adaptation where the objective function and constraints are modified before optimization to ensure the model and plant share the same optimality conditions. While not reliant on structural assumptions regarding the model, it is highly sensitive to noisy measurements, as gradients must be estimated from data. This makes the approach less robust when dealing with significant levels of measurement noise (Mendoza et al. 2015). Alternatively, due to the rise of machine learning, non-parametric approaches, particularly Gaussian Processes (GPs), have gained attention. GPs do not assume a fixed structural form and are well-suited to handling noisy measurements. They also excel in low data scenarios, making them valuable for modeling engineering systems. Indeed, their ability to address plant-model mismatch in RTO has been recently demonstrated in a process referred to as Adaptive Gaussian Process Learning (AGPL) (Ahmed et al. 2022, del Rio Chanona et al. 2021). The objective function is approximated with a GP:

$$\hat{J} = \hat{f}(\boldsymbol{x}) \tag{3}$$

where $\hat{J} \in \mathbb{R}$ is the objective function metric, $\hat{f}: \mathbb{R}^{n_x} \rightarrow \mathbb{R}$, represents the GP approximation of the objective function which depends on the set point, $\boldsymbol{x} \in \mathbb{R}^{n_x}$. As the system is operated and data is obtained from the system in the form of measurements, the GP regression problem can be re-solved with additional data to give an up-to-date model. We denote measurements from the system up to the kth sampling instant as $\boldsymbol{J}^k \in \mathbb{R}^k$ and $\boldsymbol{x}^k \in \mathbb{R}^{k \times n_x}$ of the objective value and state measurements respectively. Consequently, a data-driven approximation of the objective function, $\hat{f}$, can be obtained. This is achieved by fitting a GP on the input, $\boldsymbol{x}^k$, and output datasets, $\boldsymbol{J}^k$. The GP can be thought of as a multivariate Gaussian distribution over functions from which a function, g, can be sampled:

$$\begin{gathered} g(\boldsymbol{x}) \sim \mathcal{GP}(m(\cdot), k(\cdot,\cdot)) \\ \hat{f}(\boldsymbol{x}) = m(\cdot) \end{gathered} \tag{4}$$

where $m(\cdot)$ and $k(\cdot,\cdot)$, represent the mean function and covariance function of the GP trained with the input-output dataset (Rasmussen 2005).

3. Results and Discussion

The case study we employ in this paper is a multi-loop evaporator process (Ahmed et al. 2023). The system consists of a feed stream containing two components: a non-volatile solute dissolved in a volatile solvent. Heat is supplied via a steam line to evaporate the solvent. The evaporator has both vapour and liquid outlets. Our control strategy employs three PI controllers. The primary controlled variable is the solute composition in the liquid product stream, x_B, which is controlled via the steam temperature, T_s. We control the liquid level, h, by manipulating the liquid product stream flowrate, B, and the evaporator pressure, P, which is controlled by adjusting the vapour flow rate, D. The controller tuning was performed using a modified version of the sequential relay auto-tuning method combined with a derivative free optimizer (py-BOBYQA). The system model can be found in Ahmed et al. (2023). The RTO goal is to find the set-points for the states, which maximize the profit of the process subject to operational and safety constraints:

$$\begin{aligned}
\max_{x_B,h,P}\ & C_{product}Bx_B - C_{feed}F - C_{energy}T^{1.5} - C_{tank}h^2 \\
s.t.\ & \text{Steady state model equations} \\
& 400K \leq T_s \leq 450K, \qquad 2m \leq h \leq 8m \\
& 0.05MPa \leq P \leq 0.5MPa, \qquad x_B \leq 0.9
\end{aligned} \tag{6}$$

The objective function and constraints for the "true" system is depicted in the left subplot of Figure 3 while the mismatched model equivalent is shown in the right subplot. It is clear to see that there is a stark difference between the two plots due to the model mismatch.

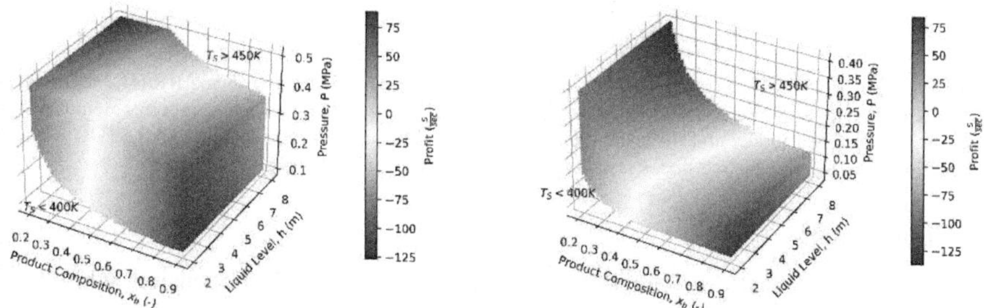

Figure 3: Objective function represented as a colour gradient from red to green indicating low and high profit respectively. Left: "True" system objective function and constraints. Right: Mismatched model objective function and constraints.

We consider 4 scenarios to demonstrate the importance of adopting both ARRTOC and GP adaptation. For all scenarios, we run simulations of 100 timesteps. We use either nominal RTO or the ARRTOC algorithm to solve Eq. (6) with the assumed model of the system depending on the scenario. The chosen set-points are then sent to the PI controllers and data is collected from the system. For the scenarios which employ GP adaptation, the data is used to correct the model every 10 timesteps as per section 2.2 and the RTO problem is re-solved. We perform 10 simulations for each scenario and report the mean profit delivered over the length of the simulation in Figure 4. Scenarios 1 and 2 serve as performance benchmarks, defining the best and worst-case situations. Scenario 1, the best-case, represents ARRTOC solved assuming perfect model knowledge. This is the best case as it accounts for the underlying controller robustness via ARRTOC and returns an accurate RTO solution as there is no model mismatch. This is depicted as a horizontal dashed green line in Figure 4. Scenario 2, the worst-case, represents nominal RTO solved with the incorrect model with no adaptation. This case neither accounts for the underlying controller design via ARRTOC nor does it address the plant-model mismatch. This is depicted as a horizontal dashed red line in Figure 4. Scenarios 3 and 4 demonstrate the significance of employing both ARRTOC and GP adaptation in tandem. Scenario 3 showcases ARRTOC with GP adaptation as a solid green line in Figure 4, while Scenario 4 illustrates nominal RTO with GP adaptation as a solid red line. Clearly, ARRTOC with adaptation outperforms nominal RTO with adaptation as it tends towards the best-case performance. This arises from the following distinction: while both approaches address the plant-model mismatch through GP adaptation, nominal RTO lacks an essential element, which is accounting for the underlying controller robustness. In the absence of such consideration, nominal RTO may lead to the selection of a set-point that is incompatible with the controllers, akin to the concept illustrated in Figure 1. On the contrary, ARRTOC ensures that the chosen set-points align with the underlying controller design, while GP adaptation diligently maintains model accuracy. This synergistic combination results in superior performance and more effective control in real-world applications.

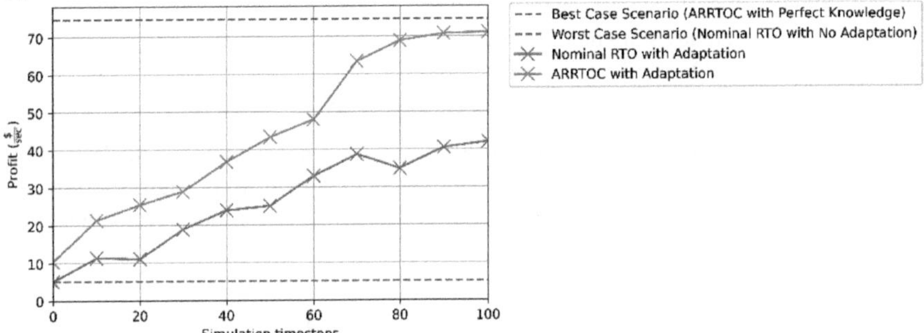

Figure 4: Scenario 1, best-case, depicted as a dashed green horizontal line represents ARRTOC with perfect model knowledge. Scenario 2, worst-case, depicted as a dashed red horizontal line represents nominal RTO with the mismatched model and no adaptation. Scenario 3, solid green line, showcases ARRTOC with GP adaptation. Scenario 4, solid red line, showcases nominal RTO with GP adaptation.

4. Conclusions

In conclusion, the ARRTOC algorithm, together with the AGPL extension, address the fundamental challenges of managing implementation errors and plant-model mismatch in a holistic manner. ARRTOC's ability to identify set-points robust to disturbances and noise, while AGPL's dynamic Gaussian Process adaptation overcomes plant-model disparities, collectively contribute to more adaptable and resilient process operations. The successful integration of these machine learning techniques with process systems engineering offers a promising pathway towards achieving enhanced operability and precision in real-time control strategies, ultimately facilitating more efficient and sustainable process operations.

References

A. Ahmed, E. A. del Rio-Chanona, M. Mercangöz, "ARRTOC: Adversarially Robust Real Time Optimization and Control", arXiv preprint, arXiv:2309.04386, 2023.

A. Ahmed, M. Zagorowska, E. A. del Rio-Chanona, M. Mercangöz, "Application of gaussian processes to online approximation of compressor maps for load-sharing in a compressor station," European Control Conference (ECC), 2022.

D. Bertsimas, O. Nohadani, and K. M. Teo, "Robust optimization for unconstrained simulation-based problems," Operations Research, vol. 58, 2010.

B. Chachuat, B. Srinivasan, D. Bonvin, "Adaptation strategies for real-time optimization," Computers & Chemical Engineering, vol. 33, 2009.

A. Cortinovis, M. Mercangöz, M. Zovadelli, D. Pareschi, A. De Marco S. Bittanti, "Online performance tracking and load sharing optimization for parallel operation of gas compressors," Computers & Chemical Engineering, vol. 88, 2016.

E. A. del Rio-Chanona, P. Petsagkourakis, B. Eric, J. E. A. Graciano, B. Chachuat, "Real-time optimization meets Bayesian optimization and derivative-free optimization: A tale of modifier adaptation," Computers & Chemical Engineering, vol. 147, 2021.

D. F. Mendoza, J. E. A. Graciano, F. S. Liporace G. Carrilo Le Roux, "Assessing the reliability of different real-time optimization methodologies," The Canadian Journal of Chemical Engineering , vol. 94, 2015.

G. D. Patrón and L. Ricardez-Sandoval, "An integrated real-time optimization, control, and estimation scheme for post-combustion co2 capture," Applied Energy, vol. 308, 2022.

C. E. Rasmussen and C. K. I. Williams, Gaussian Processes for Machine Learning, MIT Press, 2005.

Flavio Manenti, Gintaras V. Reklaitis (Eds.), Proceedings of the 34th European Symposium on Computer Aided Process Engineering / 15th International Symposium on Process Systems Engineering (ESCAPE34/PSE24), June 2-6, 2024, Florence, Italy
 http://dx.doi.org/10.1016/B978-0-443-28824-1.50272-6

Online Process Monitoring through Integration of Joint Recurrence Plot and Convolutional Neural Networks

Yiran Dong*, Jie Zhang, Chris O'Malley

School of Engineering, Merz Court, Newcastle University, Newcastle upon Tyne NE1 7RU, UK

y.dong15@newcastle.ac.uk

Abstract

This paper proposes a new method for online process fault diagnosis through integration of joint recurrence plot (JRP) and convolutional neural networks (CNN). JRP is used to extract features from the major principal component of the process operational data. The extracted features are used as the inputs to a CNN for fault diagnosis. To facility online fault diagnosis, a sliding window of the major principal components is used in generating JRP. The proposed method is demonstrated on a simulated continuous stirred tank reactor (CSTR). The results show that the proposed method can achieve diagnosis accuracy of 99.49% and 97.12% on the training and testing data sets respectively, higher than those of integrating recurrence plot and CNN.

Keywords: process control, fault diagnosis, principal component analysis, joint recurrence plot, convolution neural network.

1. Introduction

The enhancement of industrial processes such as efficiency, safety, profitability, stability through the utilization of industrial big data has drawn a lot of attention in the fourth industrial revolution. In this context, fault detection and diagnosis (FDD) play a crucial role. Through the continuous monitoring of the health conditions and offering diagnostic guidance of the operating procedures and machinery, FDD helps to maintain the manufacturing safety of the systems and preventing unwarranted production halts and safety incidents (Ye et al., 2023). Nowadays, many researchers are working on fault diagnosis based on the theory of 'recurrence'. For instance, Huang et al. (2023) used the combination of recurrence plot (RP) and Bayesian convolutional neural networks to classify the multi-class of electroencephalogram-based motor imagery and real execution. Ziaei-Halimejani et al. (2021) applied joint recurrence quantification analysis and clustering in chemical processes for fault detection and diagnosis with missing data. However, a typical chemical process usually contains a large number of measured process variables and it will be a huge workload if JRP for all these variables are produced.

This paper proposes a process monitoring method through the integration of principal component analysis (PCA), JRP and convolutional neural networks. To overcome the high dimensionality of industrial process data, data dimension reduction through PCA is carried out before generating JRP. The major principal components (PCs) representing the majority of data variation are used for JRP. CNN is then used to classify the extracted features in JRP into normal and various faulty conditions. Sliding windows are used for online process monitoring.

The paper is organized as follows. Section 2 presents the proposed online fault diagnosis method and the employed techniques. Section 3 presents the application results to a simulated continuous stirred tank reactor system. Conclusions are drawn in Section 4.

2. Methodologies

2.1. Joint Recurrence Plot

2.1.1. Recurrence Plot

RP was proposed by Eckmann et al. (1987) to determine the recurrence of a dynamic system and provide practical information when they do not reach the demand level. It is a binary plot generated from a recurrence matrix. Consider the following $x(i)$ constructed from the time series data u_i for a process variable,

$$x(i) = (u_i\,, u_{(i+\tau)}, \dots, u_{(i+(d-1)\tau)}) \tag{1}$$

where τ is the chosen suitable time delay and d is the embedding dimension. The recurrence matrix can be constructed through Eq(2):

$$R_{i,j} = \Theta(\varepsilon - \|x_i - x_j\|), \quad i,j = 1, \dots, N \tag{2}$$

where $\Theta(k)$ represents the Heaviside function, when $k \geq 0$, $\Theta(k) = 1$, when $k<0$, $\Theta(k) = 0$, ε is the selected threshold parameter, $\|\cdot\|$ is the Euclidean distance/norm, N is the number of measurement points in the data series $x(i)$. The RP will then be created through the corresponding recurrence matrix, when $R_{i,j} = 1$, a black dot will be displayed, when $R_{i,j} = 0$, a white dot will be displayed. Thus, the diagonal line in RP is constantly black and is called the line of identity (LOI) (Marwan et al., 2007) and an RP is symmetrical respecting to the LOI (Eckmann et al., 1987).

2.1.2. Joint Recurrence Plot

Joint recurrence plot (JRP) is an extension of recurrence plot and can examine two or more different time series in one plot. Eq(3) shows the formation of JRP matrix for two different time series x_i and y_i:

$$JR_{i,j}^{x,y} = \Theta(\varepsilon^x - \|x_i - x_j\|)\Theta(\varepsilon^y - \|y_i - y_j\|), \quad i,j = 1, \dots, N \tag{3}$$

In Eq(3), ε^x and ε^y represent the selected thresholds for the time series x and y respectively. In JRP, patterns symbolize concepts that are distinct with RP. Unlike RP, the diagonal line in JRP indicates that the similarity of the two time series with their dynamical behaviour happens. The black dots represent the coincidental similarity, and the large region of black dots represent ongoing dynamic similarity. Moreover, the large region of white dots denote divergence in dynamic behaviour, and the recurring patterns represent the dynamic similarity during the specific operational periods (Ziaei-Halimejani et al., 2021).

2.2. Convolutional Neural Network

Over the past a few decades, artificial neural network (ANN) has been extensively utilized for process fault detection and diagnosis (Kim, 2017). LeCun et al. (1989) first proposed CNN as a proficient deep neural network for learning and classifying images. CNN is an enhanced technology from ANN with additional capabilities and is an efficient tool for image recognition and classification. The visual cortex of the brain can be emulated for processing and recognition of images (Kim, 2017).

2.3. Process Monitoring through Integrating JRP and CNN

Figure 1 shows the flow chart of the proposed online fault diagnosis method. The collected data sets are reduced in dimension using PCA. Then, sliding windows are created for the retained PCs and JRPs are generated for all the sliding windows and used as the inputs for CNN. Finally, CNN is trained and tested to build the diagnosis model. It is worth noting that CNN training is done off-line, and the diagnosis is done online after CNN has been trained.

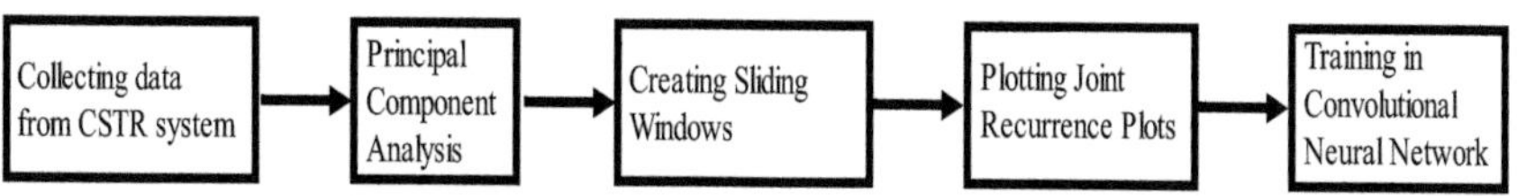

Figure 1. Flow chart of the proposed method

3. Application to a CSTR System

3.1. Experiment Data Collection

This simulated CSTR system shown in Figure 2 is used to generate data under normal and various faults scenarios. An irreversible exothermic reaction converting A to B occurs in the reaction vessel, with cooling provided by circulation of the reactor content through an external heat exchanger. Feedback control systems are employed to regulate the liquid level, temperature, and flow rate of the reactor (Zhang and Roberts, 1991).

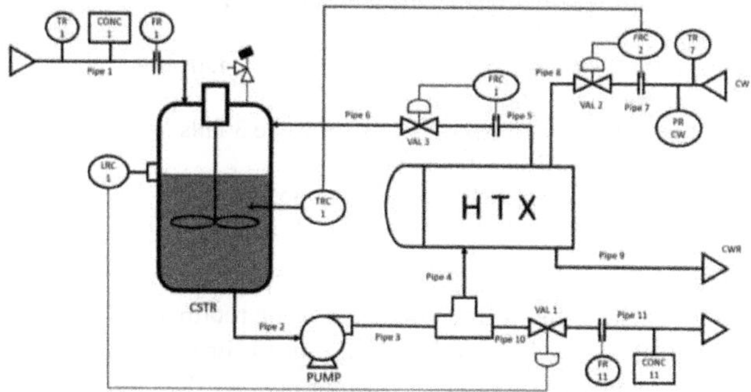

Figure 2. CSTR system (Wang and Zhang, 2021)

The data generated from the simulated CSTR system consist of one set of normal process operation data and 11 sets of different types of faulty process operation data. There are 13 variables including 10 measured process variables and 3 controller outputs. Measurement noises are added to the generated data. Table 1 gives the description of data sets with sample numbers.

3.2. Data Pre-processing

PCA is applied to the collected normal process operation data set for dimension reduction. All variables are scaled to zero mean and unit variance to mitigate the effects of varying data magnitudes. The mean and standard deviation from the normal process operation data set are also utilized for scaling the faulty data when extracting the PCs. Figure 3 shows that 8 PCs are able to represent 89.9% of data information. Hence, the data dimension of the collected data can be reduced from 13 to 8. A sliding window with 35 samples, determined through experiment, is created for each of the retained PCs as shown in Figure 4.

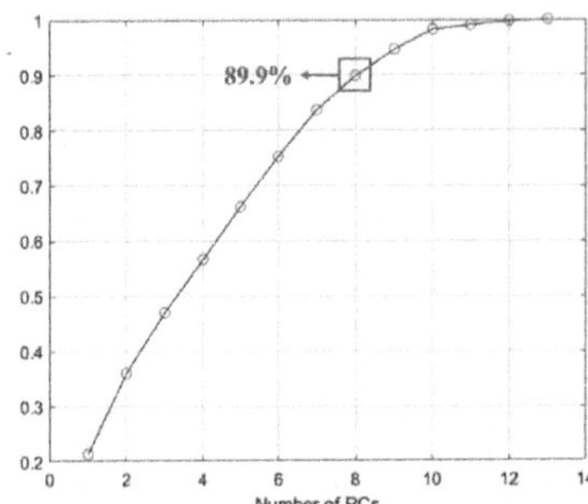

Figure 3. Cumulative data variations explained by PCs

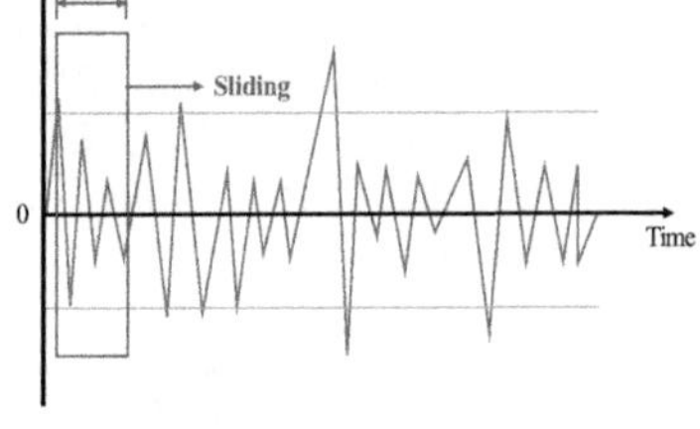

Figure 4. Sliding windows

Table 1. Simulated data sets

Data Types	Description	Samples
Normal	Process under normal operation (no fault)	148
Fault 1	Pipe 1 blockage	148
Fault 2	External feed-reactant flow rate too high	148
Fault 3	Pipe 2 or 3 is blocked or pump fails	148
Fault 4	Pipe 10 or 11 is blocked or control valve 1 fails low	148
Fault 5	External feed-reactant temperature abnormal	148
Fault 6	Control valve 2 fails high	148
Fault 7	Pipe 7, 8, or 9 is blocked or control valve 2 fails low	148
Fault 8	Control valve 1 fails high	148
Fault 9	Pipe 4, 5, or 6 is blocked or control valve 3 fails low	148
Fault 10	Control valve 3 fails too high	148
Fault 11	External feed-reactant concentration too low	148

3.3. Joint Recurrence Plot

A JRP is created for each of the sliding windows of the retained PCs. In the current study, the first two retained PCs (i.e. PC1 and PC2) are used for creating JRP. The parameters for generating joint recurrence matrix are important, so the first step is to define the parameters. With the intention of maintaining the unity of the two time series, they will share the value of embedding dimension d, time delay t, and the type of norm. The embedding dimension d is set to 3 and the time delay t is set to 1. In RP and JRP, three types of frequently used norms are $L\infty$-norm (maximum norm or supremum norm), L2-norm (Euclidean norm), and L1-norm (Sankararaman, 2022). All these three norms are evaluated, and the findings indicate that the $L\infty$-norm for each condition deliver the most optimal performance. The threshold parameter for PC1 time series has been set to 0.5 times of the standard deviation of PC1 of the normal process operation data, and the threshold parameter for PC2 time series has been set to 0.5 times of the standard deviation of PC2 of the normal process operation data.

Figure 5 shows the JRPs of the 100th sliding window (i.e., samples from 100 to 134 in both time series) with the situation of normal process operation and faulty process operation under faults 2, 5, and 8. It can be seen that these JRPs are quite different, hence, can be used for fault diagnosis.

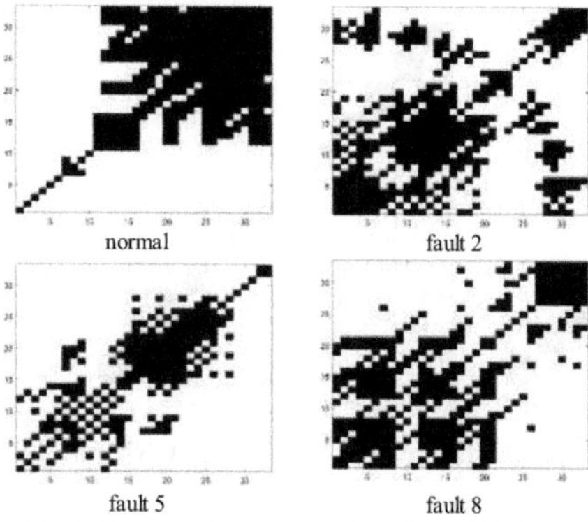

Figure 5. JRPs for the 100th sliding window (samples 100~134) for normal data and data under faults 2, 5, and 8

3.4. Convolutional Neural Network

Although the JRPs have shown distinct patterns for different process conditions, it is very challenging for a process control personnel to recognize and classify them manually. Here CNN is used to classify the generated JRPs. When building the CNN model, the obtained JRPs from historical process data are split randomly into training data set and testing data set with a ratio of 7:3. In the developed CNN, three convolutional layers have been established. The classification layer has 12 classes representing the normal condition and the 11 faults. The rectified linear unit (ReLU) is used as the activation function in this CNN model. Also, L2 regularization and a dropout layer are added to reduce the problem of overfitting.

Figures 6 and 7 show the CNN training and testing confusion charts of JRP for PC1 and 2, RP for PC1, and RP for PC2. Table 2 shows the comparison of their training and testing accuracy. It can be seen clearly that although the CNN training and testing accuracy for RP with PC1 and PC2 is high, the JRP with both PC1 and PC2 has higher accuracy. This is because JRP contains two times series so it can extract more information.

Table 2. Comparison of RPs and JRPs

RP/JRP	Training Accuracy	Testing Accuracy
JRP (PC1*PC2)	99.49%	97.12%
RP (PC1)	97.36%	92.41%
RP (PC2)	99.70%	94.50%

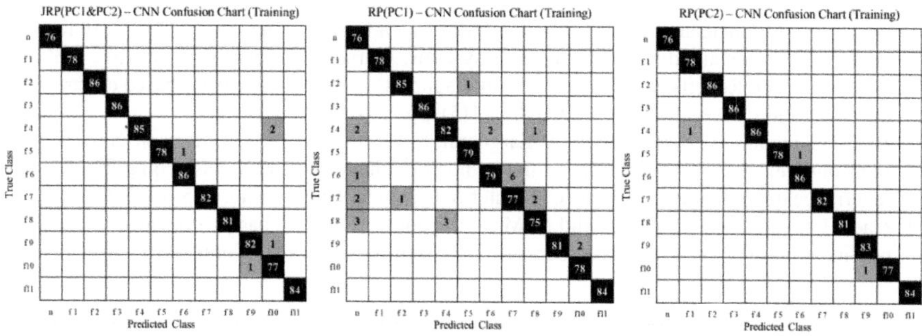

Figure 6. Confusion charts of JRP-CNN and RP-CNN models for training data

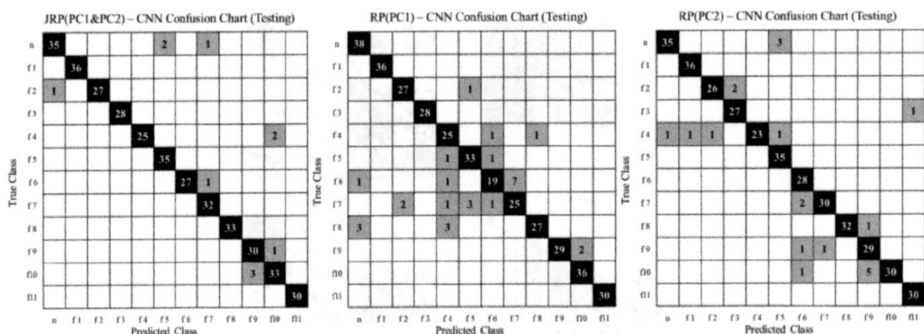

Figure 7. Confusion charts of JRP-CNN and RP-CNN models for testing data

4. Conclusion

The proposed online fault diagnosis method through the integration of JRP and CNN has been shown to be effective on a simulated CSTR system. The results show that the integration of JRP with CNN gives better performance than the integration of RP with CNN under the same condition. This is because JRP contains two time series with more information. In the future work, more time series for generating JRP and optimized data pre-processing methods will be explored.

References

J.-P. Eckmann, S.O. Kamphorst, and D. Ruelle, 1987, Recurrence plots of dynamical systems, Europhysics Letters, 4(9), pp. 973-977.

W. Huang, G. Yan, W. Chang, Y. Zhang, and Y. Yuan, 2023, EEG-based classification combining Bayesian convolutional neural networks with recurrence plot for motor movement/imagery, Pattern Recognition, 144, 109838.

P. Kim, 2017, MATLAB Deep Learning: With Machine Learning, Neural Networks and Artificial Intelligence, Apress, New York.

Y. LeCun, L.D. Jackel, B. Boseer, J.S. Denker, H.P. Graf, I. Guyon, D. Henderson, R.E. Howard, and W. Hubbard, 1989, Handwritten digit recognition: applications of neural network chips and automatic learning, IEEE Communications Magazine, 27(11), pp.41-46.

N. Marwan, M.C. Romano, M. Thiel, and J. Kurths, 2007, Recurrence plots for the analysis of complex systems, Physics Reports, 438, pp.237-329.

S. Sankararaman, 2022, Recurrence network and recurrence plot: A novel data analytic approach to molecular dynamics in thermal lensing, Journal of Molecular Liquids, 366(2022), 120353.

S. Wang and J. Zhang, 2021, An intelligent process fault diagnosis system based on neural networks and andrews plot, Process, 9(9), 1659.

L. Ye, H. Wu, Y. Chen, and Z. Fei, 2023, Interpret what a Convolutional Neural Network learns for fault detection and diagnosis in process systems, Journal of Process Control, 131, 103086.

J. Zhang and P. D. Roberts, 1991, Process fault diagnosis with diagnostic rules based on structural decomposition, Journal of Process Control, 1(5), pp.259-269.

H. Ziaei-Halimejani, N. Nazemzadeh, R. Zarghami, K.V. Gernaey, M.P. Andersson, S.S. Mansouri, and N. Mostoufi, 2021, Fault diagnosis of chemical process based on joint recurrence quantification analysis, Computer & Chemical Engineering, 155, 107549.

H. Ziaei-Halimejani, R. Zarghami, and N. Mostoufi, Joint recurrence based root cause analysis of nonlinear multivariate chemical processes, 2021, Journal of Process Control, 103, pp.19-33.

Flavio Manenti, Gintaras V. Reklaitis (Eds.), Proceedings of the 34th European Symposium on Computer Aided Process Engineering / 15th International Symposium on Process Systems Engineering (ESCAPE34/PSE24), June 2-6, 2024, Florence, Italy
 http://dx.doi.org/10.1016/B978-0-443-28824-1.50273-8

A Python implementation of a Steady-state Real Time Optimization (SRTO) and Realtime optimization with persistent adaptation (ROPA)

Carlos C. Sanza, Galo A.C. Le Rouxa
Department of Chemical Engineering, Polytechnic School, University of São Paulo
Av. Prof. Lineu Prestes, 580, Bloco 18, São Paulo, Brasil, galoroux@usp.br

Abstract

In recent years, the chemical/petrochemical industry has been under increasing pressure to optimize its processes. Economic, environmental, Industry 4.0, and circular economy considerations are some of the main drivers for this optimization. However, most companies rely on expensive software for process simulation and optimization algorithms. For leading chemical/petrochemical companies, this type of investment is not a problem. In some companies, an entire team is dedicated to this task. However, for medium-sized or small companies that are subject to the same constraints, such as environmental compliance or the most profitable operating point, the burden can be very high. Unfortunately, there are not many low-cost solutions available. In addition, in some cases, optimization should be performed in a small portion of the process, such as just a reactor or a distillation train. And, often, small companies tend to oversize the problem and the involved costs. **Keywords:** real-time optimization, python, real-time optimization persistente adptation

1. Introduction

SRTO requires the detection whether the system is at steady-state, it a complex task. One way to overcome the limitations of steady-state detection, is to use an alternative RTO method named Real-time Optimization with Persistent Adaptation (ROPA). Unlike standard RTO, which waits for a confirmed steady-state before updating model parameters, ROPA continually adjusts the model parameters using real-time online estimation methods, treating transient measurements as if they represent a steady-state condition. The goal is not to achieve continuous optimization per se, but to improve set-points over time until they align with the actual steady-state optimum, MATIAS, J. O. A , 2018

ROPA serves as an intermediary between static RTO and dynamic optimization approaches like Dynamic Real Time Optimization (DRTO) and Economic Model Predictive Control (EMPC), which are theoretically appealing but seldom implemented on a large scale due to the lack of comprehensive models for complex processes. By decoupling the estimation problem, ROPA allows for the use of well-established stationary economic optimization software and literature, while enabling asynchronous updates of the plant-wide model, tailored to sections with varying parameter update frequencies. This decoupled approach facilitates solving the steady-state optimization problem at any desired frequency, J. Matias, et al., 2022.

However, we aim at using simple and readably available Python libraries to check the possibilities of implementing such scheme in a smaller scale trying to bring optimization to small companies at a low cost. As far as we could find in the open literature, all Python libraries used in this paper have a permissive license, such as the Apache License 2.0, MIT License, BSD 3-Clause License. There were no changes or modifications on any library, the libraries were used "as it is".

2. Cases

We used two different problems, a simple binary column system and the well-known Williams-Otto reactor, which is part of the Willliams-Otto plant model, Williams, T. J., and Otto, R. E. 1960. The process for the Williams-Otto reactor system can be seen on Figure 1a. It is a CSTR with two pure inlet products A and B performing 3 simultaneous reactions, equations (1), (2) and (3).

$$r1: \; A + B \rightarrow C \quad (1)$$
$$r2: \; B + C \rightarrow P + E \quad (2)$$
$$r3: \; C + P \rightarrow G \quad (3)$$

It was assumed that the temperature T_r, of the CSTR could be changed instantly at any given time. Also, the flow rate of feed stream B can be controlled. On the other hand, the flow rate of A has only an indication and can have a step change at any time. Species E and P are measured at the reactor's outlet. There are no measurements for species A, B, C and G. The reactor system can be modeled by a set of 6 differential equations and one algebraic equation, as shown in Figure 1b. Table 1 shows the values of the constants for that system.

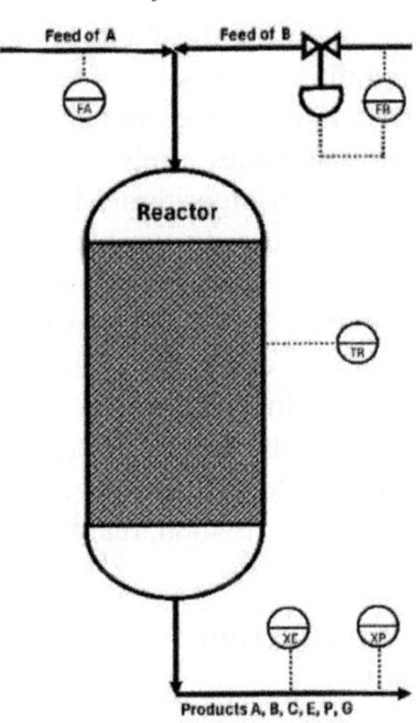

Figure 1a Williams-Otto reactor diagram

$$0 = F_R - F_A - F_B$$
$$\frac{\partial X_A}{\partial t} = f_{dyn,1}(\mathbf{X},\mathbf{u}) = \frac{(F_A - F_R X_A)}{M_t} - k_1 X_A X_B$$
$$\frac{\partial X_B}{\partial t} = f_{dyn,2}(\mathbf{X},\mathbf{u}) = \frac{(F_B - F_R X_B)}{M_t} - k_1 X_A X_B - k_2 X_B X_C$$
$$\frac{\partial X_C}{\partial t} = f_{dyn,3}(\mathbf{X},\mathbf{u}) = \frac{-F_R X_C}{M_t} + 2k_1 X_A X_B - 2k_2 X_B X_C - k_3 X_C X_P$$
$$\frac{\partial X_E}{\partial t} = f_{dyn,4}(\mathbf{X},\mathbf{u}) = \frac{-F_R X_E}{M_t} + 2k_2 X_B X_C$$
$$\frac{\partial X_P}{\partial t} = f_{dyn,5}(\mathbf{X},\mathbf{u}) = \frac{-F_R X_P}{M_t} + k_2 X_B X_C - 0.5k_3 X_C X_P$$
$$\frac{\partial X_G}{\partial t} = f_{dyn,6}(\mathbf{X},\mathbf{u}) = \frac{-F_R X_G}{M_t} + 1.5k_3 X_C X_P$$
$$k_i = A_i e^{-E_i/T_R}, \quad i = 1,\ldots,3$$

Figure 1b – Model of the Williams-Otto reactor

Table 1 – Reaction rate constants

	A_i	E_i
r1	1.6599 e6	6666.7
r2	7.2177e8	8333.3
r3	2.6745e12	11111

The binary distillation column follows what was described by S. Skogestad, 1997. The binary column system can be modeled by a set of differential equations. An extensive and comprehensive explanation may be found in S. Skogestad, 1997 and at his site. It is an excellent reference for this problem. Another reference may be found in W. L. Luyben, 1986, the author presents all material and energy balances required for a multicomponent distillation column.

A few considerations about the distillation column problem : a) It was assumed that the relative volatility of the two components remains constant throughout the column, b) no energy balance was performed, c) the vapor flow of the column was assumed constant. We must reinforce that the aim of this work was to verify if it was possible to simulate SRTO and ROPA with available python libraries, at this time the complexity of the model was not a concern. Clearly, for a more precise work, the model would have to be as complex as required, with a good physical properties package, energy balances, multicomponent, tray efficiencies, and so on.

The main purpose for the column problem was to assess the feasibility of using python to simulate a model and to verify cpu time with two different approaches (with and without jax library)

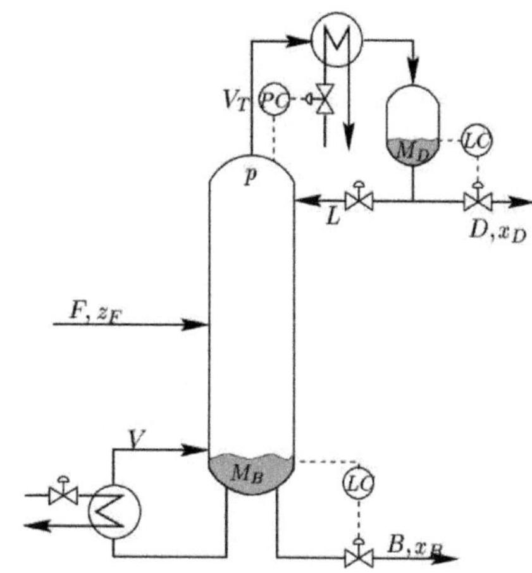

Figure 2: Binary Distillation Diagram

3-The optimization problem

Both ROPA and SRTO are well-known control/optimization schemes and have been extensively described in literature, such as in J.O.A. Matias (2018). Figure 3 provides a clear schematic representation of these schemes. In this work, we simplified the scheme by assuming a perfect controller and that the steady state could be attained quickly, with the total simulation spanning an 8-hour period. For the Williams-Otto reactor, we developed a function to evaluate the SRTO – MPA (Model Parameter Adaptation) for the unmeasured parameter, specifically the stream flow rate of component A.

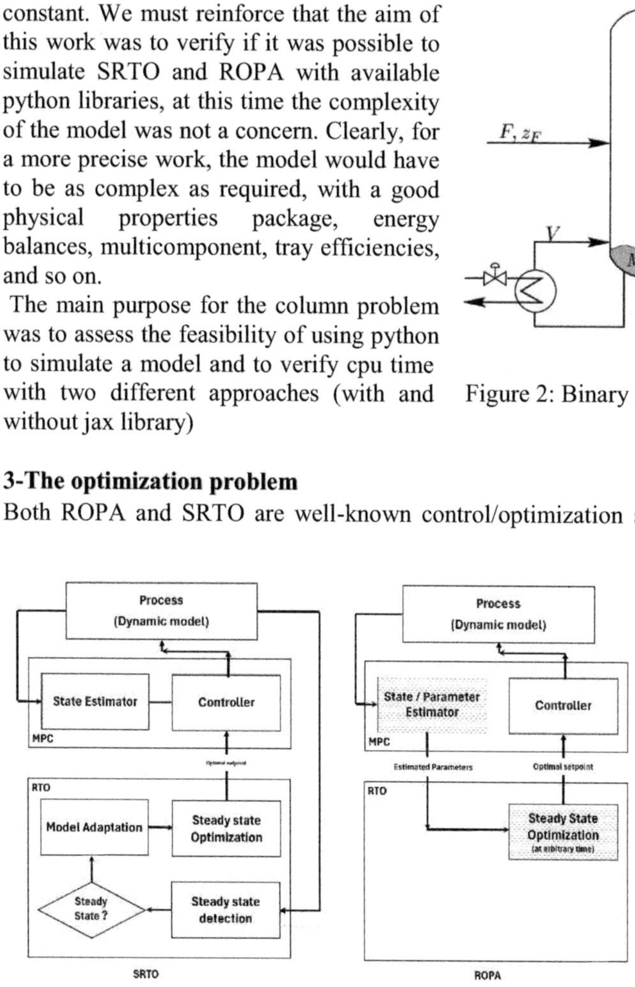

Figure 3: SRTO and ROPA Diagram

4-Implementation

In addition to code the model of the Williams-Otto reactor and the binary distillation column, we had to code for the ROPA case: a) an Extended Kalman Filter function, which is the state and parameter estimator for the ROPA measured variables prediction (xe and xp) and unmeasured variables evaluation(xa,xb,xc,xg and Fa; b) the profit optimization function and, for the SRTO case; c) evaluation of the unmeasured parameters, Fa (MPA). Basically we used the following Python libraries: jax.jacrev function that calculates the Jacobian of a system of equations by the reverse mode; jax.jit a function that compiles specific parts of the code increasing the cpu speed ; numpy a multipurpose library of the most important functions; scipy.integrate.solve_ivp a function to integrate initial value differential equations; matplotlib.pyplot a plotting dedicated library; scipy.optimize library for optimization of nonlinear problems; jax.experimental.ode (odeint) a function to integrate initial value differential equations. It would be very helpful if an easy installation and powerful orthogonal collocation library for python was readably available. There are some libraries for instance, SUNDIALS from Lawrence Livermore National Security and Southern Methodist University. However, its installation in a python environment is not straightforward. As python is a collaborative and open environment its almost certain that other libraries will follow.

To resolve the steady-state problem, we utilized our implementation (NRDA.py) of the Newton-Raphson algorithm, integrating JAX for automatic differentiation and JIT compilation. While Python code is typically interpreted, JAX's JIT feature compiles parts

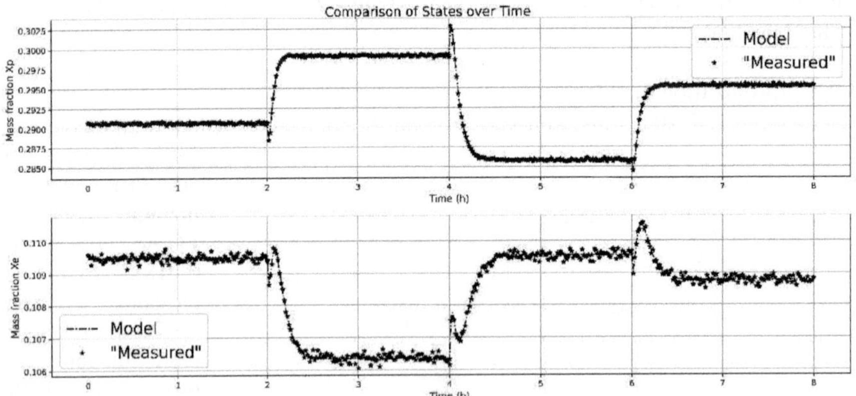

Figure 4: model output and output plus the gaussian noise

of the code, thereby substantially increasing execution speed and reducing computation time. Additionally, we developed Python code for an Extended Kalman Filter. The SRTO implementation includes a subroutine (model.py) containing the system of differential equations. This subroutine is used for steady-state calculations with the Newton-Raphson method (NRDA.py), setting the time-dependent derivative to zero, and for dynamic behavior using scipy.integrate.solve_ivp and jax.experimental.ode (odeint)

The process measurement was simulated using the process model (model.py) by adding Gaussian white noise (with zero mean) to the dynamic or steady-state simulation, as applicable. For example, Figure 4 for the Williams-Otto reactor displays both the model output and the output with added Gaussian noise. The plot illustrates the mass fractions of components E (xe) and P (xp), with Figure 4 depicting a step changes at 2.0 hours (to 2.3 kg/s), 4.0 hours (to 1.7 kg/s), and 6.0 hours (to 2.0 kg/s) over an 8-hour time horizon. In this plot, the solid line represents the model's prediction, while the dots indicate measured values. Figure 5 presents the model's behavior for the flow rate of component A alongside estimates from the implemented Model Parameter Estimation and the Extended Kalman Filter. The lag observed for MPA is minimal, though it would likely be longer in a real-world scenario. Notably, the estimates align closely with the model, even when the magnitude of the white noise increases. The reactor temperature and inlet flow rate of component B are setpoints for the controller, calculated by optimizing the objective function (equation 4), subject to constraints of the steady-state model and bounds for both variables.

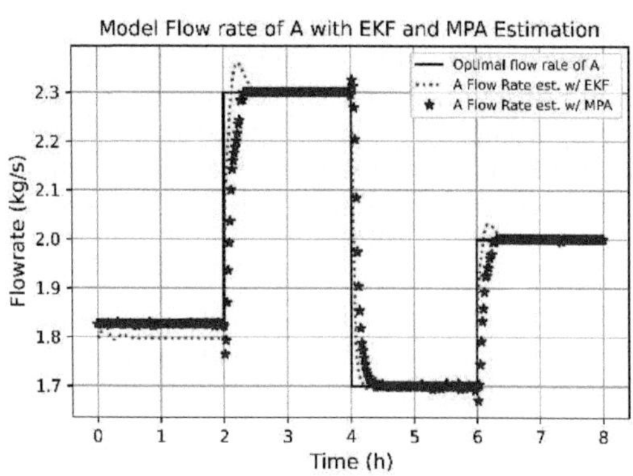

Figure 5: Flow rate estimated by EKF and MPA

$$Profit = 1143.38 \times xp \times Fr + 25.92 \times xe \times Fr - 72.63 \times Fa + 114.34 \times Fb \quad (4)$$

The objective function is subject to the system of equations constraints (shown in Figure 1b) and, it is required to satisfy the following bounds: Lower Bound temperature = 25°C, Lower Bound for B flow rate = 2 kg/s, Upper Bound temperature = 150°C, and Upper Bound for B flow rate = 8 kg/s.

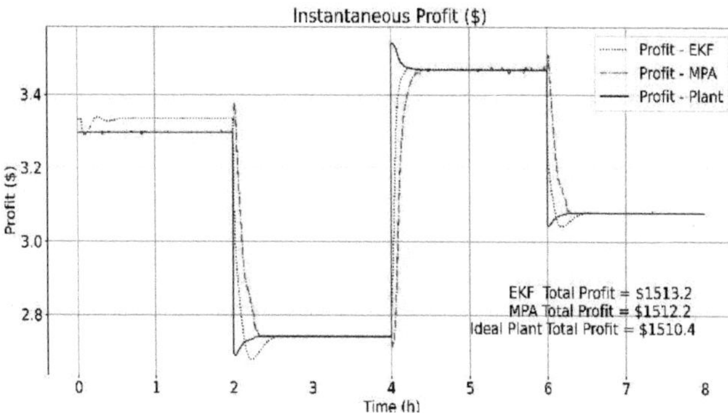

Figure 6: Instantaneous Profit.

The ROPA implementation scheme started with the same set of measured variables. The first step was to initialize the Extended Kalman Filter. For the Process noise covariance (Q) we use 0.5 for both variables (E and P). For the Measurement noise covariance (R) we used 0.001 for the Gaussian white noise. Figure 6 shows de final result, with MPA and the "traditional RTO" and with ROPA and the EKF filter.

5 – Conclusion

Simulating SRTO and ROPA processes using Python is indeed feasible. However, this approach presents several challenges that must be addressed. Utilizing JAX offers significant benefits, such as automatic differentiation and the capability for JIT compilation, resulting in faster execution. It is important to note, however, that JAX is specifically designed for 'pure' functions.

As a result, the use of certain Python libraries, like scipy.optimize and solve_ivp, is not recommended within a pure JAX environment. The jax.experimental.odeint function for integration, while available, is still in the experimental phase. Similarly, JAX's experimental optimization function lacks straightforward parameter passing, complicating its use. Python provides various packages for optimization and integrating systems of differential equations, yet some of the most powerful ones can be difficult to install. In terms of CPU time, functions utilizing JAX and JIT demonstrate exceptional performance, with improvements ranging from 5 to 15 times faster than non-compiled code. Implementing MPA or the Extended Kalman Filter did not pose significant issues, and the optimization of profit functions or parameter estimation for MPA proved to be effective.

Future work will involve integrating freeware software to simulate unit operation models and physical properties packages. This integration is crucial for obtaining suitable models if one intends to implement control systems effectively.

References

- Williams, T. J., and Otto, R. E. 1960. "A Generalized Chemical Processing Model for investigation of Computer Control." AIEE Trans 79: 458-68.
- S. Skogestad, 1997. Dynamics and control of distillation columns: A tutorial introduction. Chemical Engineering Research and Design 75 (6), 539-562.
- W. L. Luyben, 1986. Process Modeling, Simulation, and Control for Chemical Engineers", McGraw-Hill Book Company.
- Chun Y Chen, 1987. On-line Optimization Using a Two-Phase Approach: An Application Study. Ind. Eng. Chem. Res 26.
- Amrit R., Rawlings, J. Biegler, 2014. Optimizing Process Economics Online Using Model Predictive Control. Computers and Chemical Engineering 58
- MATIAS, J. O. A , 2018: Real-time Optimization with persistent parameter adaptation using online parameter estimation. PhD Thesis – Escola Politectica da USP
- CARNEIRO, A. A. B., 2018:Application of Real-time Optimization with Persistent Parameter Adaptation (ROPA) to Processes using Online Parameter Estimation.
- J. Matias, G. A. Le Roux, 2018. Real-time optimization with persistent parameter adaptation using online estimation parameters. Journal of Process Control 68, 195-204
- J. Matias, et al., 2022. Steady-state real-time optimization using transient measurements on anexperimental rig. Journal of Process Control 115, 181-196.
- J. Matias, et al., 2022. State and Parameter Estimation in Dynamic Real-time Optimization with Closed-loop Prediction. ESCAPE 2022 – Athens

Flavio Manenti, Gintaras V. Reklaitis (Eds.), Proceedings of the 34th European Symposium on Computer Aided Process Engineering / 15th International Symposium on Process Systems Engineering (ESCAPE34/PSE24), June 2-6, 2024, Florence, Italy
 http://dx.doi.org/10.1016/B978-0-443-28824-1.50274-X

Hierarchical Reinforcement Learning for Plantwide Control

Maximilian Bloor[a], Akhil Ahmed[a], Niki Kotecha[a], Calvin Tsay[a], Mehmet Mercangöz[a], Antonio del Rio-Chanona[a*]

[a]*Imperial College London, Exhibition Road, London, SW7 2AZ, United Kingdom*
**a.del-rio-chanona@imperial.ac.uk*

Abstract

In this paper, we introduce a novel hierarchical reinforcement learning algorithm for plant-wide control, combining a high-level artificial neural network with low-level PID controllers. We evaluate the algorithm's performance using a computational case study focused on setpoint tracking, noise control, and disturbance rejection. Comparative analysis with derivative-free optimization, multiloop relay tuning, and a nonlinear model predictive controller demonstrates that the hierarchical reinforcement learning algorithm consistently outperforms traditional PID tuning methods in terms of integral square error. However, the NMPC excels in scenarios where manipulating other system units enhances setpoint tracking beyond PID capabilities. We also assess the controllers' robustness through a parametric mismatch analysis, simulating reactor cooling jacket fouling and reactor catalyst degradation. This analysis highlights that the hierarchical reinforcement learning algorithm's lesser dependence from an accurate model gives it an advantage over NMPC when a plant-model mismatch exists.

1. Introduction

Industrial chemical processes are vital for the modern economy thus their efficient and safe operation is paramount. Plant-wide control, which considers multiple interconnected units, can enhance overall performance but presents challenges due to interactions and non-linearities (Rangaiah & Kariwala, 2012). Advanced control methods such as model predictive control can be effective but often face issues with model identification and uncertain plant conditions (Qin & Badgwell, 1997). In contrast, Proportional-Integral-Derivative (PID) controllers are widely used in the chemical industry for their simplicity, yet they require intricate tuning for system dynamics. Traditional methods such as the detuning method (Luyben, 1986) are developed to find a stable set of PID gains for a particular system's dynamics and may not find the optimal set with respect to setpoint tracking. To address this, we introduce a hierarchical reinforcement learning algorithm for plant-wide control, combining a high-level artificial neural network controller with lower-level PID controllers. This hierarchical approach reduces the policy space, enhancing the convergence rate compared to directly implementing a neural network controller (Hengst, 2010). Previous research has explored reinforcement learning for PID tuning, with applications in simulated and real-world systems (Dogru et al., 2022).

In this paper, our objective is to develop a hierarchical reinforcement learning algorithm for plant-wide control, aiming to enhance system performance and robustness. We assess the algorithm's effectiveness through a computational case study (Reactor-Separator-Recycle), comparing its performance to other PID tuning methods and nonlinear model predictive control. Robustness is evaluated through a parametric mismatch analysis simulating plant-model mismatch.

2. Background

2.1. PID Controllers

The discretized PID controller used in this paper can be written as Eq. (1):

$$u_t = \mathrm{K_p}\epsilon_t + \mathrm{K_i}\sum_{t=0}^{t}\epsilon_t + \mathrm{K_d}(\epsilon_t - \epsilon_{t-1}) \text{ with } \epsilon = \mathrm{SP}_t - x_t \tag{1}$$

Where u_t is the manipulated variable, $\mathrm{K_p}$ is the proportional constant, $\mathrm{K_i}$ is the integral constant, $\mathrm{K_d}$ is the derivative constant, and ϵ_t represents the error between the setpoint $\mathrm{SP_t}$ and the state x_t To assess the performance of the PID controller, the discretized integral square error (ISE) metric is used throughout this paper:

$$ISE = \sum_{t=t_0}^{t_f}(SP_t - x_t)^2 \tag{2}$$

2.2. Reinforcement Learning

Reinforcement learning involves an agent interacting with an environment to maximize cumulative rewards (Sutton & Barto, 2018). The goal is to learn an optimal policy, mapping states to actions in a Markov decision process (MDP). The state, denoted as x, and control action, u, exist in state space $\mathcal{X}$ and control action space $\mathcal{U}$, respectively. The agent receives a reward R_t when transitioning from x_t to x_{t+1}. $P(x_{t+1}| u_t, x_t)$ represents the probability of transitioning from x_t to x_{t+1} given the action u_t, which is approximated by a simulator.

Policy gradient algorithms such as REINFORCE (Williams, 1992) directly optimize the policy by computing gradients to maximize expected rewards. Value function-based methods, such as Q-learning (Watkins, 1989), estimate the value of each state-action pair to improve decision-making by updating value estimates towards better predictions. These policy and value functions are then represented by deep neural networks which gives rise to the name deep reinforcement learning.

Computing policy gradients or value functions can be computationally intensive as they require approximation. However, evolutionary strategies, like particle swarm optimization (PSO) (Eberhart & Kennedy, 1995), have shown computational efficiency without the need for gradients or value functions, albeit with a higher data requirement (Salimans et al., 2017). This paper utilizes PSO for policy optimization.

3. Methods

3.1. Problem Statement

The system dynamics can be approximated as a discrete stochastic nonlinear system:

$$x_{t+1} = f(x_t, u_t, d_t)\ \forall\, t \in [t_0, t_f] \tag{3}$$

Where $x_t \in \mathbb{R}^{n_x}$ are the states of the system, $u_t \in \mathbb{R}^{n_u}$ are the control actions, $d_t \in \mathbb{R}^{n_d}$ represents the disturbance to the system, and $f(\cdot)$ represents the nonlinear dynamics of the system. The hierarchical reinforcement learning method searches for an optimal policy to minimize the setpoint error with a control input penalty in a stochastic environment and under disturbances. The following Optimal Control Problem (OCP) represents this:

$$\min_{\pi_\theta} \sum_{t_0}^{t_f} R(x_t, u_t) = \sum_{t_0}^{t_f} |x_t - x_{sp,t}| + |u_t - u_{t-1}| + |u_t - u^L| \tag{4}$$

$$\text{s.t} \quad x_0 = x\,(0)$$
$$x_{t+1} = f(x_t, u_t, d_t)$$
$$\mathrm{u_t} = \pi_\theta(x_t)$$

Where x_{sp} is a vector of the state setpoints and u^L is a vector of the control's lower bounds. The first term of the reward function rewards the setpoint tracking of the policy and the two subsequent terms motivate smooth control inputs. The problem can now be represented in a closed-loop form as shown in Figure 1.

3.2. Hierarchical Reinforcement Learning

The agent in Figure 1 consists of two layers of policies arranged in a hierarchy. The top of the hierarchical structure is a policy formed by an Artificial Neural Network (ANN) that is parameterized θ_{ANN}. This takes the current state x_t, previous state x_{t-1} and the current setpoint $x_{sp,t}$. Then outputs the parameters $(K_{p,t}, K_{i,t}, K_{d,t})$ of the lower level of the hierarchy which is the PID policy. The PID policy takes these parameters along with the setpoint error and outputs the control action u_t. The structure of the hierarchical reinforcement learning algorithm is represented in Figure 1.

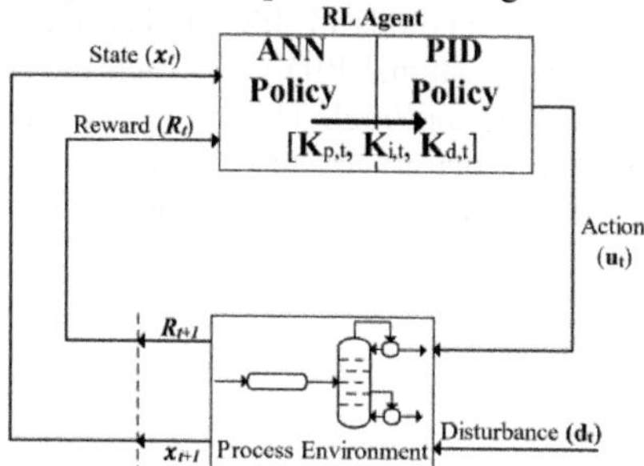

Figure 1. Closed-Loop Structure

3.3. Policy Optimization

To find the set of parameters θ_{ANN} which solves the OCP (4) a combination of a direct stochastic search and the evolutionary method PSO is used. The generic PSO algorithm is parameterized as follows: inertial weight ω which is set to 0.5, and the acceleration coefficients c_1 and c_2 which are set to 2.3 and 1.8, as suggested by Eberhart & Kennedy.

3.4. Training and Testing Methodology

The algorithm is trained on four different setpoint changes which vary in both magnitude and direction of the step and a disturbance to the feed temperature. The rewards from all setpoint changes and disturbance simulations are summed and used to evaluate a policy. After the reinforcement learning algorithm has been trained, it is tested on an unseen episode with two setpoint changes and the inclusion of a disturbance at the start of the simulation.

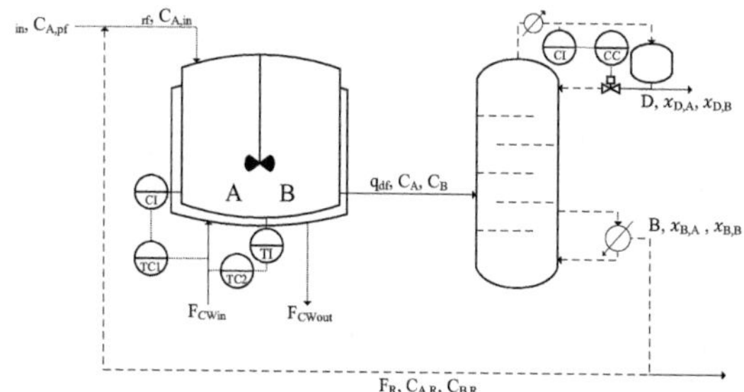

Figure 2. Case Study Process Flow Diagram

4. Computational Case Study

4.1. Simulation and Comparison

The algorithm is tested on a reactor-separator-recycle (RSR) case study (Figure 2). The hierarchical reinforcement learning policy is trained through 10 epochs using direct stochastic search and over 20 PSO iterations (Figure 3). The ANN control policy comprises an input layer, two fully connected layers, and an output layer. In the first layer, the reactor PID parameters use 20 neurons, and in the second, 5 neurons, while the distillation column employs 20 neurons in both layers. Sigmoid activation functions are applied between layers, with the ReLU activation function used for the output layer. Figure 4 presents simulation, control, and PID parameter trajectories, and Table 3 displays the corresponding ISEs. PID parameters obtained from relay multiloop tuning and DFO methods remain constant over time and are detailed in Table 2.

The multiloop relay and hierarchical reinforcement learning tuning methods follow a similar trajectory (Figure 4). The DFO method has significant oscillations when reaching the setpoint from the initial state, this is due to the high integral PID gain compared to the other PID tuning methods (Table 1). The hierarchical reinforcement learning algorithm reduces the proportional PID gain when the setpoint is increased to 0.98 mol/mol and decreased to 0.94 mol/mol. This reduces overshoot compared to the relay tuning method, resulting in a marginally lower ISE. The NMPC manipulates the jacket temperature as well as the reflux ratio to change the distillate composition.

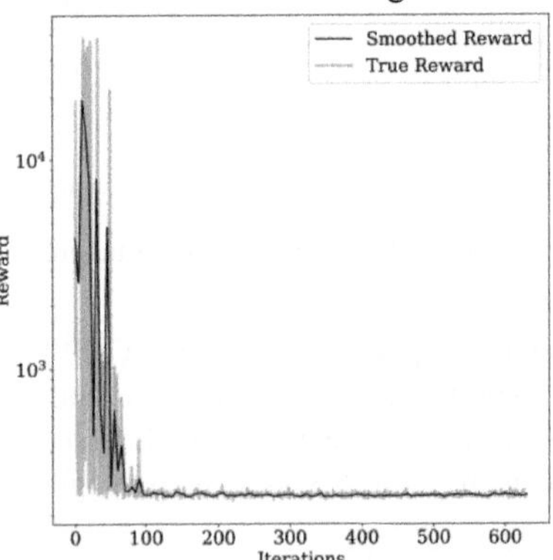

Figure 3. Learning Curve

Table 1. Static PID Gains

Control method	C_A-loop			T-loop			$x_{B,D}$-loop		
	K_p	K_i	K_d	K_p	K_i	K_d	K_p	K_i	K_d
Relay	17.16	5.13	5.97	0.23	0.06	0.08	261.50	32.95	222.90
DFO	5.73	5.75	9.27	0.32	0.38	0.21	175.10	556.80	458.40

Table 2. Control Method ISE

	HRL	DFO	NMPC	Relay
ISE ($x_{B,D}$) [mol/mol]	0.033	0.044	0.017	0.035

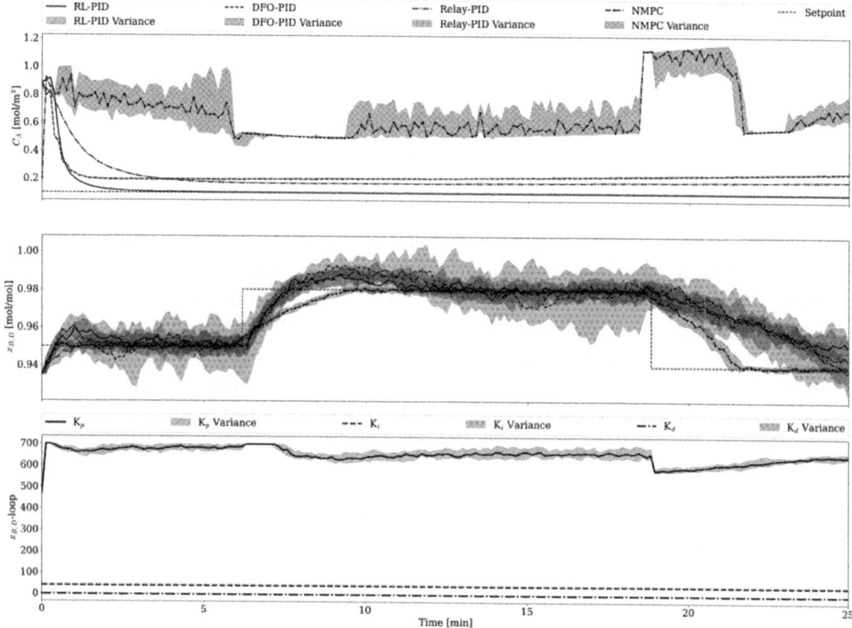

Figure 4. Reactor-Separator-Recycle Simulation

4.2. Parametric Mismatch

The catalyst activity varies within the range of 0.1-7.2 × 10^{10} s^{-1}, while the cooling jacket heat transfer coefficient spans from 0.1-7 × 10^5 W/K. Figure 5 illustrates the resulting ISE across these parameter variations. In the case of catalyst degradation PID-based control methods maintain a stable ISE across the parameter range until significant degradation occurs (Figure 5). In contrast, NMPC's ISE increases with catalyst degradation, indicating worsened setpoint tracking due to plant-model mismatch and the NMPC's reliance on jacket temperature for distillate composition control. During reactor jacket fouling all control methods, except DFO tuning, remain stable until significant fouling occurs. The DFO tuning method exhibits significant variance across parameters, primarily due to ineffective noise rejection caused by the large integral gain of the chosen PID gains (Figure 5).

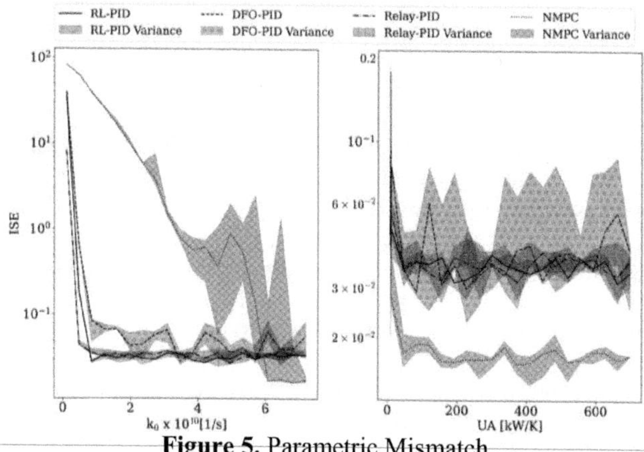

Figure 5. Parametric Mismatch

5. Conclusions and Future Work

This paper introduces a hierarchical reinforcement learning approach for PID controller tuning in plant-wide control. The method employs the PSO algorithm to optimize a hierarchical system comprising a high-level ANN and low-level PID controllers. In our computational case study, we compared the performance of the reinforcement learning algorithm with NMPC, DFO, and multiloop relay tuning. While the reinforcement learning algorithm outperformed traditional PID tuning methods, NMPC demonstrated superior performance by effectively manipulating multiple units to reach desired setpoints, resulting in significantly lower ISE across all case studies. We also conducted a parametric mismatch analysis, revealing that PID-based methods are more robust than NMPC when dealing with catalyst degradation due to NMPC's reliance on an accurate plant model. In future research, we aim to explore advanced strategies, such as allowing the high-level ANN policy to determine the PID controller setpoints or potentially replacing the PID policy with another reinforcement learning agent.

References

Dogru, O., Velswamy, K., Ibrahim, F., Wu, Y., Sundaramoorthy, A. S., Huang, B., Xu, S., Nixon, M., & Bell, N. (2022). Reinforcement learning approach to autonomous PID tuning. *Computers & Chemical Engineering*, *161*, 107760. https://doi.org/https://doi.org/10.1016/j.compchemeng.2022.107760

Eberhart, R., & Kennedy, J. (1995). A new optimizer using particle swarm theory. *MHS'95. Proceedings of the Sixth International Symposium on Micro Machine and Human Science*, 39–43. https://doi.org/10.1109/MHS.1995.494215

Hengst, B. (2010). Hierarchical Reinforcement Learning. In G. I. Sammut Claude and Webb (Ed.), *Encyclopedia of Machine Learning* (pp. 495–502). Springer US. https://doi.org/10.1007/978-0-387-30164-8_363

Luyben, W. L. (1986). Simple method for tuning SISO controllers in multivariable systems. *Industrial & Engineering Chemistry Process Design and Development*, *25*, 654–660. https://api.semanticscholar.org/CorpusID:97803930

Qin, S. J., & Badgwell, T. A. (1997). An overview of industrial model predictive control technology. *AIche Symposium Series*, *93*(316), 232–256.

Rangaiah, G. P., & Kariwala, V. (2012). *Plantwide control: Recent developments and applications*.

Salimans, T., Ho, J., Chen, X., & Sutskever, I. (2017). Evolution Strategies as a Scalable Alternative to Reinforcement Learning. *ArXiv*, *abs/1703.03864*. https://api.semanticscholar.org/CorpusID:11410889

Sutton, R. S., & Barto, A. G. (2018). *Reinforcement learning: An introduction*. MIT press.

Watkins, J. (1989). *Learning from Delayed Rewards*.

Williams, R. J. (1992). *Simple Statistical Gradient-Following Algorithms for Connectionist Reinforcement Learning* (Vol. 8).

Flavio Manenti, Gintaras V. Reklaitis (Eds.), Proceedings of the 34th European Symposium on Computer Aided Process Engineering / 15th International Symposium on Process Systems Engineering (ESCAPE34/PSE24), June 2-6, 2024, Florence, Italy
 http://dx.doi.org/10.1016/B978-0-443-28824-1.50275-1

Energy- and process real-time optimization through hybrid modeling – a case from Viking Malt A/S

Peter Jul-Rasmussen[a], Adem R.N. Aouichaoui[a], Maciej Korzepa[b], Kurt Engelbrecht[c], Katrine Kongsgaard[d], Jakob K. Huusom[a*]

[a]*Dept. of Chemical and Biochemical Engineering, Technical University of Denmark, Søltofts Plads 228A, 2800 Kgs. Lyngby, Denmark.*
[b]*BioLean ApS, Søndre Jernbanevej 32, 3400 Hillerød , Denmark*
[c]*Viegand Maagøe A/S, Nørre Søgade 35, 1370 København K, Denmark*
[d]*Viking Malt A/S, Spirevej 5, 4760 Vordingborg, Denmark*
jkh@kt.dtu.dk

Abstract

The production of barley malt is an energy-intensive process due to the need for cooling, drying, and heating. This work introduces model-based real-time energy- and process optimization for an industrial malting process. A hybrid model is introduced for the germination stage in the malting process by combining population- and mass balances with probabilistic ML, providing accurate predictions with no indication of overfitting when applied to historical process data. Based on the model predictions, optimal setpoint trajectory for the temperature of process air passing through the grain bed and the water/gibberellic acid addition are recommended for operators of the malting plant. Both the model and optimization algorithm are deployed to servers at the malting plant, and the recommendations are presented in a user-friendly dashboard at a dedicated monitor in the control room, enabling the decision-making in the process to be objective-driven rather than human-driven. No previous work has been found in the literature on applying hybrid model-based real-time optimization to the germination stage in an industrial-scale malting process.

Keywords: Malting process, Probabilistic hybrid modeling, Real-time energy optimization, Operator support tool.

1. Introduction

The quantity and quality of data acquired in the manufacturing industry has increased in recent years, but the full potential of the process data is often not realized due to the high cost, time-demanding development of applications, and high complexity of integrating the applications into production. The project "Machine Learning for Energy- and Process Optimization" (MLEEP) aims to implement machine learning (ML) algorithms directly in five Danish production facilities to investigate the potentials, opportunities, and barriers of using ML for energy- and process optimization (MLEEP, 2023). One such production facility is the Viking Malt A/S malting plant in Vordingborg (DK).
Malting is the process of turning grain, typically barley, through germination, into malt as a raw material for brewing. The malting process consists of three main stages: 1) steeping, 2) germination, and 3) kilning (MacLeod, 2004). In the steeping stage, the grains are hydrated using water, raising the moisture level of the grains from 10-15 wt.% to 42-47 wt.%. During germination, enzymes are synthesized and released, cell-wall breakdown

occurs in the endosperm, and acrospires and rootlets are grown typically at a moisture level of 45 wt.%. Finally, the growth of the grains is stopped in the kilning using a heat treatment, drying the grains to a moisture level of 4-5 wt.% for storage (MacLeod, 2004). The strict requirements for moisture levels, heating, cooling, and gas usage result in an energy-intensive process with the key utilities accounting for approximately 10 % of the total input costs (MacLeod, 2004). The high energy consumption of the malting process has been addressed in an optimization effort by Müller and Methner (2015) by increasing the steeping and germination temperature, thereby accelerating the whole process and reducing cost and energy consumption. However, applications of model-based real-time optimization of malting processes leveraging process data have not been found in the literature.

Over the previous 30 years, the field of hybrid modeling, combining first principles knowledge with ML, has been gaining increased interest (Sansana et al., 2021). Often hybrid models are constructed either as modular structures of interconnected ML algorithms representing different subsystems or as semi-parametric structures using first principles models and ML in tandem (Thon et al., 2021). Semi-parametric hybrid models allow the modeling of well-known phenomena using first principles, while unknown or uncertain phenomena can be modeled using ML (Sansana et al., 2021). Hybrid models have been shown to display robustness towards measurement noise and low measurement frequency to a point where the system dynamics are still seen in the data (Jul-Rasmussen et al., 2023). Semi-parametric hybrid models have been used for modeling particle processes by combining first principles population- and mass balances with ML (Nazemzadeh et al., 2021).

This work focuses on realizing optimal operation of the germination stage in a malting process through real-time energy optimization enabled by semi-parametric hybrid modeling. The introduction of real-time optimization for the germination stage enables decision-making in the process to be objective-driven rather than human-driven, eliminating human variance and biases in a process that is traditionally operated purely based on operator experience without the aid of simulation tools.

2. Germination Stage

Germination is typically performed over 3-5 days using a pneumatic system in vessels of different shapes, such as drums or rectangular Saladin boxes (Figure 1), and in varying sizes (MacLeod, 2004). The grains rest on perforated plates, allowing for temperature-controlled airflow from the bottom of the grain bed to provide cooling and oxygen supply while preventing overheating from grain respiration. The grain bed is turned regularly, keeping the grain bed loose, and allowing for proper airflow and distribution of water (MacLeod, 2004). Water and potentially gibberellic acid (GA) are added from the turner

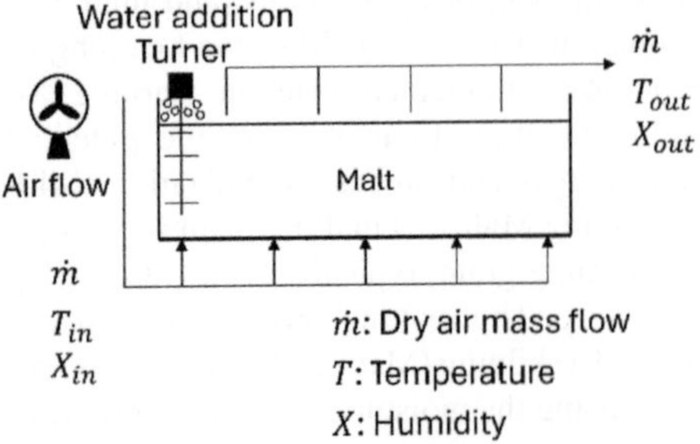

Figure 1: Schematic drawing of germination stage in malting process.

to maintain the water content at approximately 45 wt.% and to enhance growth. The main operating conditions affecting the germination are the germination time, the water content, the temperature in the grain bed, and processing aids, but also barley characteristics such as the barley variety and the crop year affect the growth rate (Müller and Methner, 2015).

3. Modeling of Germination Stage

The germination stage model consists of two key components: 1) a barley acrospire population balance predicting the length distribution of the acrospires, and 2) a water mass balance predicting the moisture in the grain bed.

3.1. Acrospire Population Balance

A population balance for the length distribution of the acrospires is introduced by discretizing the length domain into M bins. For each bin, the material balance is

$$N_{i,j+1} = N_{i,j} + N_{i-1,j} \cdot G_{i-1} - N_{i,j} \cdot G_i \qquad \text{for } i = 0 \dots M \tag{1}$$

where j is the index of the current time step, $N_{i,j}$ is the number of grains in bin i at time step j, and G_i is the growth rate of grains in bin i. The change in the length distribution of the acrospires is only due to growth i.e., $N_{i,j}$ is increased by the number of grains moved from bin $i-1$ to bin i and decreased by the number of grains moved from bin i to bin $i+1$. G_i is assumed to be represented by the expression $G_i = (1 - e^{-k_i \cdot \Delta t})$ where k_i is the growth constant for bin i and Δt is the time between two consecutive time steps. The resulting population balance model is

$$N_{i,j+1} = N_{i,j} + N_{i-1,j} \cdot (1 - e^{-k_{i-1} \cdot \Delta t}) - N_{i,j} \cdot (1 - e^{-k_i \cdot \Delta t}) \quad \text{for } i = 0 \dots M \tag{2}$$

The growth rates for the different bins are unknown and therefore inferred from process data. This is done using a probabilistic ML approach based on neural networks implemented by BioLean ApS using their proprietary ML framework. By using a probabilistic ML approach, the model not only accounts for the inherent noisiness of the data, but also for limited availability of data. When forecasting using the probabilistic ML model, a collection of process outcomes is sampled, allowing for the expectation to be calculated as the average and the uncertainty to be quantified. The setpoint for the temperature of the air leaving the grain bed, water content in the grain bed, barley variety, crop year, barley characteristics (protein, starch, water sensitivity, etc.), and addition of GA are used as inputs for the probabilistic ML model. The input data can be characterized in 3 different types: 1) the barley variety, crop year, and barley characteristics are fixed constants for a given batch, 2) the setpoint for the temperature of the air leaving the grain bed and the addition of GA can be directly manipulated, and 3) the water content is a state in the system which has to be predicted before the population balance can be used for forecasting.

3.2. Water Mass Balance

Changes in the water content in the grain bed are due to uptake of water in the humid air passing through the grain bed and addition of water from the turner. A mass balance for the water content can be introduced as

$$\frac{dm_{H_2O}}{dt} = \dot{m} \cdot (X_{in} - X_{out}) + \dot{m}_{H_2O,Turner} \tag{3}$$

where m_{H_2O} is the mass of water in the grain bed, $\dot{m}$ is the dry air mass flow passing through the grain bed, X_{in} and X_{out} is the humidity of the air entering and leaving the grain bed respectively, and $\dot{m}_{H_2O,Turner}$ is the water addition from the turner. However, Eq. (3) was found not to be feasible to use for the physical system, as no reliable measurements were available for $\dot{m}$, X_{in}, or X_{out} and as some of the water added to the grain bed would pass through the grain bed without increasing the water content. As an alternative to Eq. (3) the semi-parametric hybrid model is introduced based on the water mass fractions

$$x_{H_2O,j+1} = x_{H_2O,j} + \left(x_{H_2O,j} - x_{min}\right) \cdot \left(1 - e^{-k_{out} \cdot \Delta t}\right) + \left(x_{max} - x_{H_2O,j}\right) \cdot \left(1 - e^{-k_{in} \cdot \dot{m}_{H_2O,Turner} \cdot \Delta t}\right) \tag{4}$$

where $x_{H_2O,j}$ is the water mass fraction in the grain bed at time step j, k_{in} is the water uptake constant, k_{out} is the water usage constant, and the constants x_{min} and x_{max} are defined as

$$\lim_{t \to \infty} x_{H_2O} = \begin{cases} x_{min}, & \textit{No water addition} \\ x_{max}, & \textit{Constant water addition} \end{cases} \tag{5}$$

In Eq. (4), the first term is the water content at time step j, the second term represents the water usage, while the last term represents the water addition to the grain bed. The constants k_{in} and k_{out} are predicted using a probabilistic ML model with the setpoint for the temperature of the air leaving the grain bed, the water addition from the turner, the barley variety, and the crop year as input.

4. Case Study: Viking Malt A/S

The germination stage model, Eq. (2) and (4), is introduced using the malting process at the Viking Malt A/S malting plant in Vordingborg (DK) as a case study. The malting plant produces malts for the beer and distilling industries and has a production capacity of 120,000 t/y (Viking Malt, 2023). The malting process is operated manually and decision-making in the process is human-driven based on "best guesses" by the operators. The human-driven decision-making cannot reliably account for varying context (e.g. barley variety and crop year) and multiple operational subgoals and it is susceptible to the operator's biases (e.g. finding patterns in noise and risk-aversion), the operator's experience and heuristics, and the psychophysical state of the operator (e.g. illness, focus, and hurry). By introducing hybrid-model based real-time optimization, these issues are addressed by basing the decision-making on a well-defined objective and eliminating human variance and biases. The objective-driven decision-making is improved over time and adapts to momentary circumstances when new process data is available.

The semi-parametric hybrid model for the germination stage is trained using historical data from the malting plant from the previous 3.5 years (2020-2023). Measurements on the water content and the length of acrospires are taken once per day by sampling from the grain bed. Setpoints for the temperature of the air entering and leaving the grain bed, the water addition from the turner, the barley variety, the crop year, and the barley characteristics are recorded along with the measurement data from the malting plant. Using the historical data, a global (prior) model is trained. During operation, the prior model is updated for each new measurement, hereby training a batch specific (posterior) model. This approach allows for predictions to be made before the start of a batch purely using the prior model, while improved predictions are made as new measurements are available using the posterior model.

4.1. Real-time Optimization

A main contributor to the energy consumption in the malting process is the need for drying once germination is complete to achieve a water content that makes the malt stable for storage. Energy optimization can therefore be introduced by minimizing the water content at the end of the germination stage, while still achieving an acceptable length distribution of the acrospires. Depending on the type of product, optimal ranges for the distribution of the acrospire length, and optimal water content for the germination are defined along with penalty terms for deviating from the optimal values. The germination stage is optimized by finding the setpoint trajectory for the temperature of the air leaving the grain bed and the water/GA addition, which maximizes the utility function

$$U = 1 - \alpha \cdot p_d - \beta \cdot p_m \tag{6}$$

where p_d is the penalty on the acrospire distribution, p_m is the penalty on the moisture content, α is the penalty strength for the acrospire distribution, and β is the penalty strength for the moisture content. The utility function is optimized using four steps:

1) Setpoint trajectories are prepared based on historical data.
2) Setpoint trajectories are adjusted based on batch, product, and time-specific requirements.
3) The utility function is evaluated for predictions using each setpoint trajectory.
4) The setpoint trajectory with the highest utility is recommended to the operators.

Once new measurements are available, the optimization is re-run using the new posterior model, determining the optimal trajectory based on the available knowledge for the current batch. Both the germination model and the optimization algorithm are deployed to a server at the malting plant. The model predictions, sample measurements, setpoint on the air temperature, and the operator actions recommended by the optimization

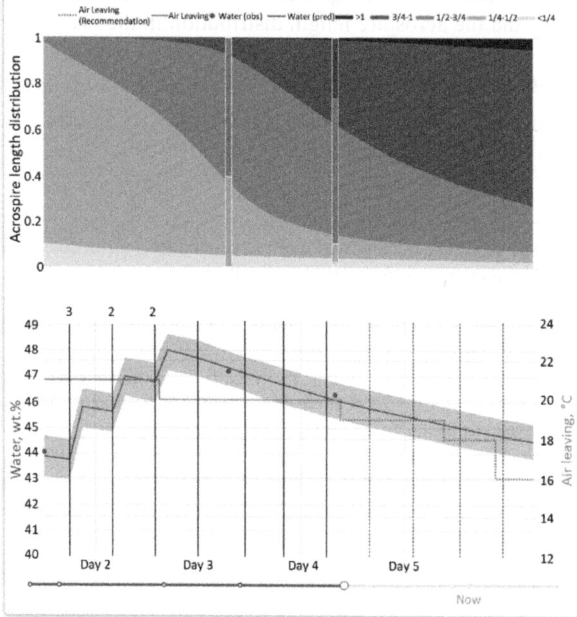

Figure 2: Dashboard with model predictions, sample measurements, setpoint on air temperature, and operator actions recommended by the optimization algorithm displayed in dedicated monitor.

algorithm are displayed in a dashboard (Figure 2) for the operators using a dedicated monitor.

4.2. Evaluation

From the prediction accuracy of the semi-parametric hybrid model (Table 1) it is apparent that the prior model performs well for both the train and test set in the historical data.

Table 1: Prior model mean absolute error (MAE) for the acrospire (length range 0.125-1.125) and water content based on the historical data.

Data Set	Acrospire (Average length)	Water Content (wt.%)
Train MAE	0.049	0.83%
Test MAE	0.052	0.88%

By minimizing the water content at the end of the germination stage, the energy consumption of the malting process can be reduced by up to 4 % due to the reduction in the heat demand for the kilning.

5. Conclusions

Data-based energy- and process optimization in production processes is enabled by the increased quantity and quality of process data in the manufacturing industry. This work introduces model-based, real-time optimization for an industrial malting process. A hybrid model is developed both for predicting the growth of acrospires and the water content in the grain bed, leveraging process knowledge and probabilistic ML. The model provides the expectation of the process outcome as well as quantification of uncertainty of the prediction. The predictions are used for real-time optimization, identifying the optimal setpoint trajectory for the temperature of the air leaving the grain bed and the water/GA addition. Future work will quantify the impact of the optimization on the energy consumption and the acrospire length distribution in the malting process.

Acknowledgments

This study was financially supported by the Danish agency of Energy. ELF221-496435: Machine Learning til Energi- og Proces-optimering (MLEEP).

References

C. Müller, F. J. Methner, 2015. An accelerated malting procedure - influences on malt quality and cost savings by reduced energy consumption and malting losses, J. Inst. Brew. , 121(2), 181-192.

C. Thon, B. Finke, A. Kwade, C. Schilde, 2021. Artificial Intelligence in Process Engineering, Adv. Itell. Syst., 3 (6), 2000261.

J. Sansana, M. N. Joswiak, I. Castillo, Z. Wang, R. Rendall, L. H. Chiang, M. S. Reis, 2021. Recent trends on hybrid modeling for Industry 4.0, Comput Chem Eng., 151, 107365.

L. MacLeod, 2004, Barley | Malting, In *Encyclopedia of Grain Science*, Elsevier-Academic Press, Oxford, 68-76.

MLEEP, Om projektet, mleep.dk, https://mleep.dk/om-projektet (Accessed at 23-11-2023)

N. Nazemzadeh, A. A. Malanca, R. F. Nielsen, K. V. Gernaey, M. P. Andersson, S. S. Mansouri, 2021. Integration of first-principle models and machine learning in a modeling framework: An application to flocculation, Chem. Eng. Sci. , 245, 116864.

P. Jul-Rasmussen, X. Liang, X. Zhang, J. K. Huusom, 2023. Developing robust hybrid-models, Comput. Aided Chem. Eng. , 52, 361-366.

Viking Malt, Our Malt houses, vikingmalt.com, https://vikingmalt.com/about-us/our-malt-houses/ (Accessed at 23-11-2023)

Flavio Manenti, Gintaras V. Reklaitis (Eds.), Proceedings of the 34th European Symposium on Computer Aided Process Engineering / 15th International Symposium on Process Systems Engineering (ESCAPE34/PSE24), June 2-6, 2024, Florence, Italy
 http://dx.doi.org/10.1016/B978-0-443-28824-1.50276-3

A MILP Model for the Minimization of Cycle Time in Periodic Production Scheduling using Flexible Operation Shifts

Georgios Georgiadis[a], Alexandros Koulouris[b,*]

[a]*Intelligen Europe, S. Kazantzidi 47, Thermi 57001, Greece*
[b]*International Hellenic University. P.O. Box 141, Sindos 57400, Greece*
akoul@ihu.gr

Abstract

Cycle time is critical for the efficiency of the many industries that choose to operate in a periodic scheduling mode since it largely affects the production throughput. This paper proposes a novel MILP model that addresses the cycle time minimization problem, while considering flexible unit allocation and timing of operations. Furthermore, a new process representation is proposed that successfully encompasses all details of the production reality and incorporates them to the optimization model. Thus, optimized schedules are generated without any loss in representation accuracy. The applicability and efficiency of the developed solution is demonstrated through an illustrative example.

Keywords: periodic production scheduling, cycle time minimization, MILP, flexible shifts

1. Introduction

Many industries find cyclic and, in particular, periodic scheduling favorable since it minimizes shop floor nervousness and results in easily applicable schedules. Moreover, it tends to generate more robust schedules compared to non-cyclic approaches. The main drawback of periodic scheduling is that it imposes timing restrictions that usually have a negative impact on the production makespan. This may be the reason behind the reduced efforts of the PSE research community to study this problem.

Periodic schedules follow a pattern defined by the process cycle time, which is the constant time interval between the initiation (or completion) of two successive batches. The cycle time is closely tied to throughput, hence minimizing the cycle time is critical for an effective plant operation, as well as for capacity-related studies. Most of the researchers that examined the cyclic scheduling problem assumed that the cycle time is a predefined parameter, while each task could only be processed in exactly one unit during the cyclic schedule (Rodrigues et al., 2014; Vieira et al., 2018). Wu and Maravelias (2019) addressed the latter by proposing an STN-based model that allows for the flexible assignment of tasks to units. Recently, Koulouris and Georgiadis (2023) were the first to address the cycle time minimization problem, while allowing for flexible task allocation. However, in this work the timing of each operation was assumed rigid, lacking any flexibility.

The optimal production scheduling problem is NP-hard, so it can easily become intractable. A way to moderate the complexity of large-scale scheduling problems is by deducing the model representation to an approximated rather than an actual depiction of the production reality, thus deteriorating the applicability of optimization-based solutions.

This is one of the main arguments against optimal production scheduling in real industrial scenarios, especially in a time where the implementation of digital twins in production is highly desired (Harjunkoski, 2016).

This paper's contribution is two-fold. First, a high-detail representation of the production process that can be implemented within a mixed-integer linear programming (MILP) model is proposed. Secondly, for the first time, a MILP model is proposed to tackle the cycle time minimization problem in periodic production scheduling, while taking into account flexible operation timing. The proposed model is general enough to be extended to include industry-specific constraints. A case study is used to demonstrate the application of the model; it has been modelled and scheduled within the scheduling software SchedulePro (Intelligen, Inc.), where the MILP models have also been implemented and solved using the SCIP open-source solver (Bestuzheva et al., 2021).

2. Problem Set-up

Let us assume a set of processing tasks I required for a single batch that is to be executed indefinitely. A cyclic schedule is conventionally defined as one that repeats every H time units, with H being the cycle time. Essentially, this means that if a processing task i of a batch starts at time $L_{i,b}$, then the same task of the subsequent batch will start at $L_{i,b}+H$. Now assume that a facility consists of a set of resources J. In the examined problem each task uses a pool of available resources for its execution. Different tasks may use the same resources; therefore, the resource pools may overlap (partially or fully) between tasks. In traditional cyclic scheduling each task can be processed in exactly one resource throughout the schedule. This assumption reduces production flexibility, and the utilization of the available facility resources thus may result in lower productivity. Therefore, the concept of "periodicity" is introduced in this paper. This parameter specific to every task i (π_i) denotes the periodicity with which the resource allocation decisions are repeated and is equal to the number of equipment that can process each task. For example, let's assume that a task i can be processed by a set of parallel units {J1, J2, J3}, thus having a periodicity of three. This denotes that if for the first three batches task i is allocated to J2, J3 and J1 respectively, then the schedule will follow the same allocation pattern for all remaining batches.

The proposed way of handling unit-task assignments guarantees that every task will be repeated with the same constant frequency and in a constant pattern dictated by parameter π_i. This is made clear in the simple example shown in Figure 1. In this example, four batches of two tasks I1 and I2 that share the same equipment pool (J1, J2, J3) are scheduled. Increasing the periodicity from 1 to 2 halves the cycle time and reduces the production makespan from 8 to 5 time units. Notice that knowing the cycle time and the resource allocation decisions of the first π_i batches (depicted with grey color in the figure) is enough information to schedule an infinite number of batches.

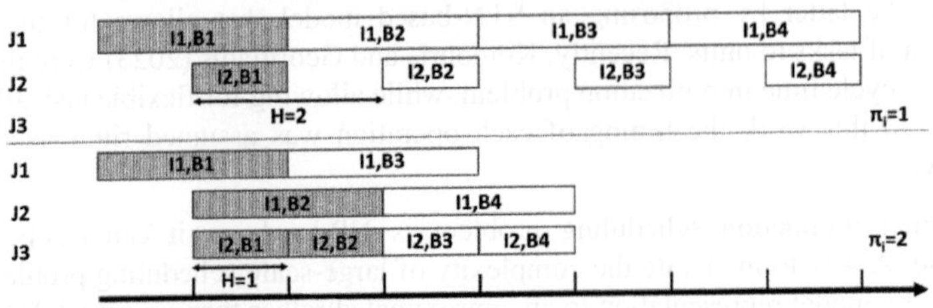

Figure 1. Impact of periodicity on cycle time

3. Mathematical Formulation

3.1. Detailed production process representation

To achieve a detailed representation of the production process, the concepts of procedures and operations are utilized. A production stage that utilizes a resource for its entire duration is called *procedure*. A procedure may consist of multiple distinct *operations* that may also require the use of additional resources. For example, a fermentation procedure may consist of operations such as: Loading of media and microorganisms, Heating, Fermenting, Transferring-out the broth and Cleaning-in-Place (CIP). The entire procedure will utilize a fermentation tank, but the CIP operation may, in addition, need the utilization of a CIP-skid for its execution.

The timing of all operations in a procedure and the entire production recipe is determined by strict dependency links. More specifically, the start or the end of an operation can be set to coincide with the start or the end of another operation plus a (positive or negative) fixed time shift. Additional links can be set also for the duration of operations if they are inter-dependent. Compared to traditional optimization-based approaches that represent the production process with outmost timing flexibility and then tighten up its execution with additional constraints, this is a more rigid representation, but also more realistic as far as chemical processing is concerned.

This rigid representation can be relaxed with the introduction of *flexible shifts* which represent positive or negative shifts in the execution of an operation if the production recipe allows them. For example, in the previously mentioned fermentation procedure, the CIP operation could potentially be delayed up to some time if the skid required for its execution is not available. In that case, a flexible operation shift up to a maximum value (the "dirty-hold" time) can be introduced for the start of the CIP operation with respect to the end of the Transfer-out operation in the fermentation procedure. Within this framework, intra-batch scheduling decisions can be optimized using the flexibilities introduced in the recipe either in the form of resource pools and/or flexible operation flexible shifts.

To mathematically represent the above structure, each operation is given a triplet of variables for its start, duration and end which we call "timing elements". A set N is introduced that includes all these timing elements for all operations. Flexible operation shifts are modelled as dummy operations that share the same triplet of timing elements. Because of the scheduling and duration links between all operations, all these timing elements are interdependent. If all these elements are sorted based on dependency links, a lower diagonal matrix $\sigma_{n,n'}$ can be composed which determines how a timing element can be calculated from the others of higher order in the dependency chain. The diagonal of the matrix represents fixed values (durations or shifts). In the case of dummy operations representing flexible shifts, the diagonal value of the duration element represents the upper bound in the flexible shift. For all tasks (procedures and operations) that need to be incorporated into the optimization problem, three additional mapping sets are introduced: $S_{i,n}^{MAP}$, $E_{i,n}^{MAP}$ and $D_{i,n}^{MAP}$ that correlate respectively the start, end and duration of task i to the above timing elements.

Figure 2 illustrates the use of these variable sets by considering the simple example of the fermentation procedure with only two operations (Fermentation and CIP) and a flexible shift on the CIP operation. For the total of 3 operations (two real and one dummy representing the flexible shift), nine timing elements are created (for the start, end and duration of each operation).

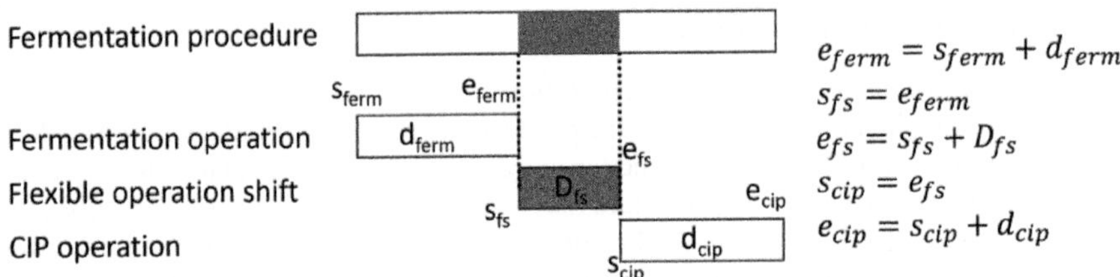

Figure 2. Detailed timing representation

3.2. MILP formulation

A MILP-based approach is developed here to address the cycle time minimization process. The proposed model is based on the general precedence modeling framework and the timing representation discussed above while assuming periodic execution of batches and allocation of resources. Given a number of batches B of processing tasks I to be processed in the available units J, the optimization model generates an optimal production schedule with minimum cycle time. It should be underlined that the set of processing tasks include all tasks (procedures and operations) that require the use of a resource. Two binary variable sets are employed to describe the allocation $Y_{i,b,j}$ and sequencing decisions $X_{i,b,i',b'}$. Moreover, continuous variables are introduced to model all time-related decisions like start ($L_{i,b}$) and completion ($C_{i,b}$) of tasks, value of timing elements ($V_{n,b}$) and duration of flexible operation shifts ($F_{n,b}$). The proposed model comprises of constraints (1)-(13) and the objective function (14).

$$\sum_{j \in IJ_{i,j}} Y_{i,b,j} = 1 \qquad \forall i \in I, b \in B : b \leq \pi_i \tag{1}$$

$$V_{n,b} = \sum_{n' \leq n} \sigma_{n,n'} \cdot V_{n',b} \qquad \forall n \notin Flex_n, b \in B : b \leq \pi_n \tag{2}$$

$$V_{n,b} = \sum_{n' < n} \sigma_{n,n'} \cdot V_{n',b} + F_{n,b} \qquad \forall n \in Flex_n, b \in B : b \leq \pi_n \tag{3}$$

$$L_{i,b} \leq V_{n,b} + (b-1) \cdot H \qquad \forall i \in I, b \in B, n \in S_{i,n} \tag{4}$$

$$C_{i,b,n} \geq V_{n,b} + (b-1) \cdot H \qquad \forall i \in I, b \in B, n \in E_{i.n} \tag{5}$$

$$L_{i,b} + H = L_{i,b+1} \qquad \forall i \in I, b \in B : b < |B| \tag{6}$$

$$L_{i',b'} \geq C_{i,b} - M \cdot (1 - X_{i,b,i',b'}) - M \cdot (2 - Y_{i,b,j} - Y_{i',b',j}) \\ \forall i \in I, i' \in I, b \in B, b' \in B, j \in (IJ_{i,j} \cap IJ_{i',j}) : i < i' \tag{7}$$

$$L_{i,b} \geq C_{i',b'} - M \cdot X_{i,b,i',b'} - M \cdot (2 - Y_{i,b,j} - Y_{i',b',j}) \\ \forall i \in I, i' \in I, b \in B, b' \in B, j \in (IJ_{i,j} \cap IJ_{i',j}) : i < i' \tag{8}$$

$$L_{i,b'} \geq C_{i,b} - M \cdot (2 - Y_{i,b,j} - Y_{i,b',j}) \\ \forall i \in I, b \in B, b' \in B, j \in IJ_{i,j} : b < b' \tag{9}$$

$$Y_{i,b+\pi_i,j} = Y_{i,b,j} \qquad \forall i \in I, b \in B, j \in J : b \leq (|B| - \pi_i) \tag{10}$$

$$V_{n,b+\pi_n} = V_{n,b} \qquad \forall n \in N, b \in B : b \leq (|B| - \pi_n) \tag{11}$$

$$F_{n,b+\pi_n} = F_{n,b} \qquad \forall n \in N, b \in B : b \leq (|B| - \pi_n) \tag{12}$$

$$L_{i,b+\pi_i} \geq C_{i,b} \qquad \forall i \in I, b \in B : b \leq (|B| - \pi_i) \tag{13}$$

$$\min H \tag{14}$$

Constraint set (1) states that each batch b of task i will be processed by exactly one unit j. Subset $IJ_{i,j}$ denotes the units that can process a task. Notice that since the allocation decisions are repeated in the cyclic schedule, only the batches dictated by the periodicity parameter are considered. In the two following constraints sets, the value of timing elements related to all operations ($n \notin Flex_n$) and flexible shifts ($n \in Flex_n$) are calculated based on their relative timings ($\sigma_{n.n'}$) and the variable duration of the flexible operation shifts. The periodicity of a timing element π_n is equal to the periodicity of the related task i. Constraints (4) ensure that the start time of a task will be less than the value of all relative start elements plus a time shift imposed by the cycle time H. Similarly, the completion times are calculated in the next constraint set (5). Notice that the inequalities are required since in the case of procedures a task may be comprised by numerous operations. Next, constraint set (6) imposes the cycle time constraints. Constraints (7) and (8) are complementary sequencing constraints that make use of a big-M parameter. Constraint set (9) guarantees that batch b' of task i will start after the completion of a batch $b<b'$ of the same task when both are processed in the same unit. Finally, constraint sets (10)-(13) are tightening constraints that take advantage of the schedule's cyclic nature to improve the model's computational efficiency.

Note that all variables introduced by the detailed timing representation are continuous, as a result the accuracy of the generated schedules is improved without significantly increasing the model's computational complexity. Furthermore, one of cyclic scheduling advantages is that only a small number of batches must be optimized. As a result, the model is expected to remain computationally efficient when dealing with large-scale industrial applications.

4. Illustrative example

An illustrative example is presented in this section to demonstrate the use of the proposed optimization model and the impact of flexible operation shifts on key production metrics. The production process consists of three procedures with 10 operations. The first and third procedures can be processed by a single equipment, T-101 and CEN-101 respectively, while the second can be processed by a pool of equipment (FR-101, FR-102 and FR-103). At the end of each procedure a cleaning operation takes place that necessitates the use of a CIP skid (CIP-1). The duration and start times in hours for all operations are {4, 0.33, 1.5, 0.33, 48, 6, 1.5, 6, 1.5, 4.5} and {0, 4, 4.33, 4, 4.33, 52.33, 58.33, 52.33, 58.33, 59.83} respectively. Flexible operation shifts with a maximum duration of 4 hours are introduced to the CIP operations. The proposed model has been applied to tackle the described problem and was able to generate optimal decisions instantaneously. The results are illustrated in Figure 3, where the Gantt charts of the optimal periodic schedule of 10 batches without (3a) and with (3b) flexible operations shifts are depicted. Introducing a flexible operation shift with duration of 1.83 h in the CIP operation of the third procedure has a significant impact on the production efficiency. In particular, the cycle time is reduced by 6.95 % (from 20 h to 18.61 h) and the production makespan by 4.4 % (from 244.3 h to 233.65 h). Notice also that applying the optimal timing flexibilities eliminates any unnecessary idle production times in the equipment pool of the second procedure.

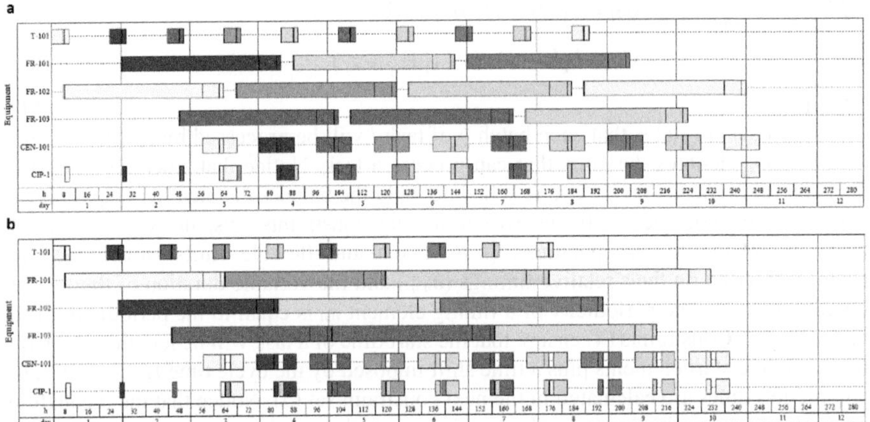

Figure 3. Gantt chart of 10 batches a) without and b) with flexible operation shifts

5. Conclusions

A MILP approach is presented in this paper for the calculation of the minimum cycle time in periodic batch process scheduling with resource sharing and flexible operation shifts. The applicability and efficiency of the developed model is shown through an illustrative example. Optimal periodic schedules can be promptly generated. The results clearly underline the beneficial effects of smartly chosen timing and resource selection flexibilities in key production metrics that can unlock the production's full potential and critically enhance its efficiency. The incorporation of industry-specific constraints in large-scale problems could potentially limit the efficient applicability of the proposed methodology. To address this issue, a meaningful future research direction would be the integration of the developed model within a decomposition scheme.

References

Bestuzheva, K., Besançon, M., Chen, W., Chmiela, A., Donkiewicz, T., van Doornmalen, J., Eifler, L., et.al. 2021. The SCIP Optimization Suite 8.0. arXiv preprint arXiv:2112.08872.

Harjunkoski, I. 2016. Deploying scheduling solutions in an industrial environment. Computers & Chemical Engineering, 91, 127-135. doi.org/10.1016/j.compchemeng.2016.03.029

Intelligen Inc. https://www.intelligen.com/products/schedulepro-overview/ (access November 2023)

Koulouris, A. and Georgiadis, G.P., 2023. On the minimization of cycle time in periodic production scheduling. Computer Aided Chemical Engineering, 52, 107-112. doi.org/10.1016/B978-0-443-15274-0.50018-4

Rodrigues, D., Castro, P.M., Matos, H.A., 2014. New Multiple Time Grid Continuous-Time Formulation for the Cyclic Scheduling of an Industrial Batch Plant, Computer Aided Chemical Engineering, 33, 1807-1812. doi.org/10.1016/B978-0-444-63455-9.50136-7.

Vieira, M., Paulo, H., Vilard, C., Pinto-Varela, T., Barbosa-Póvoa, A.P., 2018. Risk assessment for the design and scheduling optimization of periodic multipurpose batch plants under demand uncertainty. Computer Aided Chemical Engineering, 43, 991-996. doi.org/10.1016/B978-0-444-64235-6.50174-1.

Wu, Y. and Maravelias, C.T., 2019. A general model for periodic chemical production scheduling. Industrial & Engineering Chemistry Research, 59(6), pp.2505-2515. doi.org/10.1021/acs.iecr.9b04381

Flavio Manenti, Gintaras V. Reklaitis (Eds.), Proceedings of the 34th European Symposium on Computer Aided Process Engineering / 15th International Symposium on Process Systems Engineering (ESCAPE34/PSE24), June 2-6, 2024, Florence, Italy
 http://dx.doi.org/10.1016/B978-0-443-28824-1.50277-5

Nonlinear dynamic optimization for gas pipelines operation

Lavinia Ghilardi[a], Sakshi Naik[b], Emanuele Martelli[a,*], Francesco Casella[c], Lorenz T. Biegler[b,*]

[a]*Politecnico di Milano, Department of Energy, Milano, 20154, Italy*
[b]*Carnegie Mellon University, Pittsburgh, 15232, USA*
[c]*Politecnico di Milano, Dipartimento di Elettronica, Informazione e Bioingegneria, Milano, 20133, Italy*
[*] *lb01@andrew.cmu.edu, emanuele.martelli@polimi.it*

Abstract

Natural gas is one of the major energy resources employed in many sectors, and its transport is guaranteed by large-scale pipelines, which need to be properly managed in order to ensure an efficient operation. This paper proposes a Nonlinear Programming (NLP) algorithm to control the operation of gas networks and minimize the compressor energy consumption, as well as model the discretized dynamic gas transport equations in the pipelines, include detailed performance maps of compressors and their gas turbine drivers, and regulate control valves. This work proposes a nonlinear smoothing approach to model disjunctive operating configurations of the gas system, allowing to preserve the accuracy and exploit the computational speed of nonlinear algorithms. The algorithm is effectively applied to a test network featuring a complex branched topology, and the results are compared with a Mixed Integer Linear Programming (MILP) formulation, thus showing a significant reduction of the computational time, and an improvement in terms of accuracy of optimality of the solution.

Keywords: Gas networks, dynamic optimization, complementarity, nonlinear programming.

1. Introduction

Natural gas is currently one of the key energy resources, and its transport relies on infrastructures consisting of pipes, compressor stations, and valves. These systems are required to operate under time-varying conditions of gas demand and import, while complying with operating pressure limits. Given the complexity of the problem, optimization algorithms are needed to effectively support gas transmission operators in their decisions and suggest an efficient management strategy. From a modeling perspective, pipeline dynamics are governed by the gas transport equations, while the controllable part of the system can be described by nonlinear characteristic curves of the compressors and their drivers, along with valve regulation. The operation of the system is performed by adjusting the continuous load of the compressors, and defining configurations of machines and valves. Different techniques have been proposed to tackle this problem, either focusing on discrete decisions in a mixed-integer linear framework (Ghilardi et al., 2021), or on the formulation of nonlinear equations (Naik et al.,2023; Liu et al., 2020). Nevertheless, the solution of MILP models can be computationally expensive, while nonlinear approaches generally do not include disjunctive behaviors. Complementarity constraints offer an alternative path to bridge the gap between these two approaches, allowing to model disjunctive decisions in a nonlinear framework. In this framework, Schmidt et al. (2016) propose a Mathematical Programs with Equilibrium Constraints (MPEC) formulation with a penalty reformulation to address the validation of booked capacity in the gas market for a stationary model. However, being essentially a feasibility problem, this study does not accurately model the machines' performance. Meanwhile, Rose et al. (2016) address a continuous reformulation of the cost operational problem with higher level of detail, but they still limit the investigation to the stationary approach.

In this study, we address the dynamic operational problem of gas pipelines, aiming to minimize the energy consumption related to gas compression. The model includes the discretized gas transport equations, the combined operating maps of natural gas compressors and their drivers, and the regulation of control valves. The problem is reformulated with complementarity constraints, which can handle disjunctive decisions, while preserving the accuracy and leveraging the computational efficiency of nonlinear algorithms. The developed algorithm is applied to network instances featuring a branched topology and compared with the Mixed Integer Linear Programming by Ghilardi et al. (2022), thus demonstrating the effectiveness of the approach.

2. Optimization model

Gas pipeline operation is defined by the gas transport equations in pipes and nodes, along with control elements curves, namely compressor stations and control valves. In the following, the mathematical description of each of these components is provided.

2.1. Pipes and nodes

The transport of the gas in the pipes can be described by conservation equations for compressible fluids. Considering 1D isothermal gas flow in horizontal pipes with uniform composition, the mass and momentum equations depend on time t and axial coordinate z, according to gas speed u, density ρ, friction factor c_f, and pipe diameter D.

$$\frac{\partial \rho}{\partial t} + \frac{\partial (\rho u)}{\partial z} = 0 \tag{1}$$

$$\frac{\partial (\rho u)}{\partial t} + \frac{\partial (\rho u^2)}{\partial z} + \frac{\partial p}{\partial z} + \frac{c_f}{2D}\rho |u| u = 0 \tag{2}$$

In the framework of pipeline operations, the first two terms of momentum Eq. (2) can be neglected with minor approximations, due to low gas speed speed and time constant less than a few minutes (De Pascali et al., (2022)). In this way, the time derivative term appears only in the mass balance Eq. (1), and a steady solution can be imposed as its initial condition. Meanwhile, the flow reversal term, represented by the term $|u|u$ in Eq. (2), can be smoothed according to procedure in Section 3.

The resulting system of partial differential equations of Eq. (1) and (2) is discretized in space z with the finite volume staggered grid approach by Patankar (1981) applied on a step Δz, and in time domain t with backward Euler method on the interval Δt.

To fully describe the fluid volumetric behavior, the gas transport equations in the pipelines are integrated with nodal mass balances and pressure bounds, along with the nonideal equation of state for natural gas.

2.2. Control valves

Control valves (CV) decrease gas pressure to a setpoint $\tilde{p}_{max}$ to protect downstream lines by means of a degree of opening θ, assumed to vary between 0 (closed) and 1 (open). In this work, we adopt an ideal linearized valve model, correlating the pressure drop with the mass flow rate w_{cv} and θ by means of a tuning parameter $\widetilde{K}_{cv}$.

$$w_{cv} \leq \widetilde{K}_{cv} \cdot \theta \cdot (p_{in} - p_{out}) \tag{3}$$

Nevertheless, a switching condition is needed to guarantee that the valve is effectively fully closed ($\theta = 0$) when the outlet pressure p_{out} is higher than $\tilde{p}_{max}$. This problem is tackled with the smoothed complementarity formulation in Section 3.
Moreover, in real applications, control valves are generally equipped with a reverse-bypass valve, allowing gas to flow in the opposite direction ($w_{cv,by} \leq 0$) if the outlet pressure is higher than the inlet pressure. The consistency between the pressure drop and flow direction in this bypass is ensured by Eq. (4).

$$w_{cv,by} \cdot (p_{out} - p_{in}) \leq 0 \tag{4}$$

2.3. Compressor stations

Compressor stations (CS) consist of a set of centrifugal compressors in parallel, each driven by a gas turbine rotating on the same shaft. In this study, we assume the commitment of these units (on/off) to be established a priori. When all units are switched off, the gas can flow through the station through a bypass valve, facing a pressure drop $(p_{in} - p_{out})$, or the bypass can be completely closed, preventing gas from flowing into the station. This second mode of operation occurs when the outlet pressure p_{out} exceeds p_{in}, for example, during a compressor shutdown transient. This behavior is modelled by a linearized flow-pressure drop relationship similar to Eq. (3), where θ is replaced by a switching variable representing the discrete opening/closure of the valve (Section 3).
Once the general configuration of compressor stations is established, it is possible to analyze the performance maps of the single units in more detail. The compressor operation is characterized by the manufacturer's polynomials with coefficients ($c_1 - c_6$ and $a_1 - a_5$) relating the volumetric flow Q and the rotational speed N, with the adiabatic head H and efficiency η.

$$H = c_1 + c_2 \cdot Q + c_3 \cdot N + c_4 \cdot N \cdot Q + c_5 \cdot Q^2 + c_6 \cdot N^2 \tag{5}$$

$$\eta = a_1 + a_2 \cdot \left(\frac{Q}{N}\right) + a_3 \cdot \left(\frac{Q}{N}\right)^2 + a_4 \cdot N + a_5 \cdot N^2 \tag{6}$$

The mechanical power required by the compressor can be evaluated from the definition of adiabatic efficiency η, while a best-fit function of REFPROP data for natural gas relates the adiabatic head H, with inlet gas pressure p_{in} and outlet p_{out}. To complete the compressor model, we include the choking and surge limits, along with load sharing criteria between different units, thus enforcing parallel compressors to run at the same normalized distance between the choking and surge curves.
In this work, natural gas compressors are assumed to be driven by gas turbines. Therefore, shaft equilibrium constraints and performance maps of the drivers are introduced in the formulation. Gas turbine polynomials provided by manufacturers are usually defined with respect to power P_{ISO}, normalized to ISO conditions (15 °C, 101325 Pa) through correction coefficients f_{WT} and f_{WP}, which depend on ambient temperature and pressure.

$$P_{ISO} = \frac{P}{f_{WT} \cdot f_{WP}} \tag{7}$$

The ISO power must comply with the maximum load curve $P_{MAX,ISO}$, a second degree polynomial of the rotational speed, while the minimum load is represented by a fraction of this value (typically 50-70%), depending on the required pollutant emission targets. Once the normalization to standard ambient conditions is established, the heat rate of the gas turbine (equal to the ratio between fuel input and power output) can be evaluated from Eq. (8), depending on rotational speed N, power P_{ISO}, and a further correction factor f_{HT}.

$$HR = f_{HT} \cdot (b_1 + b_2 \cdot N + b_3 \cdot P_{ISO} + b_4 \cdot N \cdot P_{ISO} + b_5 \cdot N^2 + b_6 \cdot P_{ISO}{}^2) \tag{8}$$

2.4. Objective function

The objective of the problem is to minimize the energy consumption of the gas turbines driving the compressors, closely related to the goal of CO_2 emission reduction. An additional term is introduced to penalize the gap between initial and final pressures in each node, in order to avoid the gas depletion in the pipes and to stabilize the final state of the network.

3. Complementarity reformulation and smoothing

The formulation of the problem presented above is based on discrete operations (e.g. valves regulation and flow reversals), which would need binary variables and lead to a Mixed Integer NonLinear Program (MINLP) formulation. However, following the idea of Baumrucker et al. (2008), it is possible to a reformulate such discrete operation using only continuous variables by exploiting the KKT conditions of an auxiliary optimization problem (to be included within the constraints of the overall nonlinear optimization problem). In particular, for the case of the control valves, the auxiliary problem $\min_{\theta} \phi(\Delta p) \cdot \theta$, s. t. $0 \leq \theta \leq 1$ is related to the following KKT conditions:

$$\phi(\Delta p) - \lambda_0 + \lambda_1 = 0,\ 0 \leq \theta \perp \lambda_0 \geq 0,\ 0 \leq (1-\theta) \perp \lambda_1 \geq 0 \tag{9}$$

Where θ is the valve opening degree, λ_0 and λ_1 are the multipliers related to its bounds, and $\phi(\Delta p)$ is the difference between outlet pressure p_{out} and valve setpoint $\tilde{p}_{max}$. Therefore, we use Eq. (9) so that the switching variable θ approaches zero when valve outlet pressure p_{out} exceeds the required setpoint $\tilde{p}_{max}$, or otherwise approaches to 1. To address these complementarity constraints with NLP solution strategies, Eq. (9) must be reformulated to restore NLP regularity properties (Baumrucker et al. (2008)). Here, we apply a relaxation of Eq. (9) according to a smoothing parameter ϵ, which retrieves the solution of Eq. (9) by solving a sequence of problems with ϵ approaching zero. With this approach, the control valve complementarity condition is now regulated by the smoothed conditions in Eq. (10)

$$\lambda_0 + \theta - \sqrt{(\lambda_0 - \theta)^2 + \varepsilon},\ \lambda_1 + (1-\theta) + \sqrt{(\lambda_1 - (1-\theta))^2 + \varepsilon} \tag{10}$$

A similar approach is considered for the compressor stations, where the complementarity Eq. (9) and (10) model the opening/closure of the bypass valve on the basis of the pressure drop across the station $p_{out} - p_{in}$. With this description, the flow and pressure drop of the bypass can be related with a constraint similar to Eq. (3).

The last reformulation involves the flow reversal in pipelines represented by the term $u\,|u|$ in momentum Eq. (2), smoothed by Eq. (11).

$$u \cdot |u| = u \cdot \sqrt{u^2 + \varepsilon} \tag{11}$$

In this way, the nonlinear smoothed optimization model can be summarized as in (12).

$$\min \sum_{t} \sum_{c} P_{FUEL,c,t} + \mu \sum_{pipe} \sum_{vol} |p_{pipe,vol,t_0} - p_{pipe,vol,t_f}|$$

s.t. Discretized gas transport equations (1)-(2) and flow reversals (11)
Nodal mass balances and pressure bounds (12)
Control valves regulation (3)-(4)-(9)-(10)
Compressors and drivers constraints (5)-(6)-(7)-(8)
Compressor station bypass opening/closure (9)-(10)

4. Results

The developed algorithm is applied to a test network (Figure 1), featuring 32 nodes, 29 pipes, 2 control valves, and 4 compressor stations, which is representative of the main features of a high-pressure pipeline. The supply node boundary conditions are defined in Figure 1, while the daily total gas demand profile results from the combination of typical thermal users, industrial and power plant utilities. The pressure in demand nodes can vary between 50 and 75 bar, except for the subnetwork downstream of the 2 control valves, where the bounds are 45-55 bar. In the case study, 2 compressor units are assumed to be committed in station 1, 3 in station 2, 5 in station 3, while station 4 is completely shut down. The discretization scheme of gas transport Eq. (1) and Eq. (2) features a time discretization of 1 hour, and a space discretization of 100 km.

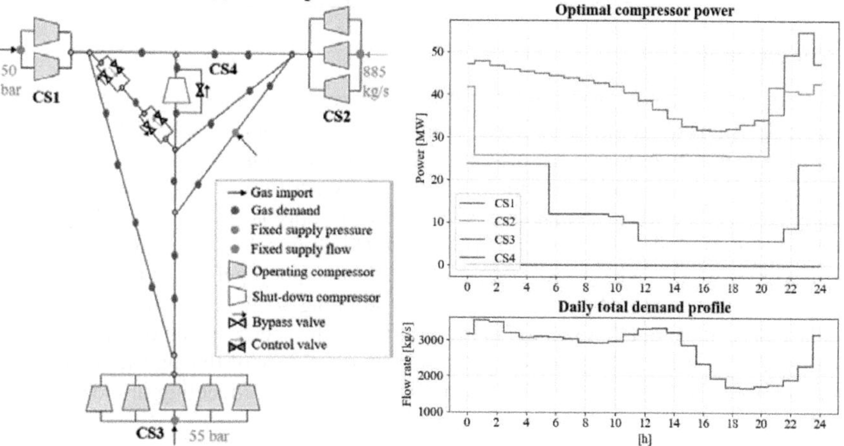

Figure 1. (Left) Gas network topology, (Upper Right) Optimal compressor power profiles, (Lower Right) Gas demand profile.

Under these assumptions, the corresponding MILP model developed by Ghilardi et al. (2022) features 418 binary variables, together with 5297 continuous variables and 10575 constraints. This MILP was solved in 750 CPU seconds to 2.5% MIP gap by Gurobi solver 10.0.3 on a laptop computer with Intel i7 CPU and 32 GB RAM.

Meanwhile, the proposed nonlinear smoothed model, with the same discretization grid of Eq. (1) and (2), exhibits 7460 variables, 7186 equality and 1140 inequality constraints. The NLP problem was solved with Ipopt version 3.13.2 directly, with a smoothing parameter 10^{-4}; in our experiments, this allows for a sufficiently accurate approximation function, and convergence to the solution without applying a sequence of instances. By initializing the problem to the steady state solution, convergence was achieved in 17.83 CPU seconds, and optimal compressor power profiles are shown in Figure 1.

Convergence to the same local solution was also exhibited with a simpler initialization technique (e.g. average pressure across the network, compressors at nominal operating conditions), which only slightly affected the computational time (25.83 CPU s), thus demonstrating the robustness of the NLP smoothed model. Regardless of the initialization technique, the NLP shows a significant gain in terms of computational time with respect to the MILP model. Another advantage of NLP solution strategies lies in their improved accuracy. To investigate this aspect, we simulate the NLP model with fixed compressor loads (NLP-FL) retrieved from the MILP solution. By comparing these case studies, it is possible to investigate the differences in terms of accuracy and optimality of the proposed NLP. The MILP solution overestimates the fuel consumption by 2.1% with respect to NLP-FL, due to the inexactness of the linearization of the compressor polynomials and gas transport equations. Moreover, the NLP solution suggests a slightly better result, showing a 2.1% fuel consumption reduction with respect to NLP-FL.

Table 1. Optimization results of the case study with different modelling approaches

Model	Runtime [CPU s]	Fuel consumption [MWh]
MILP	750	8209 (CS1: 984, CS2: 2614, CS3: 4611)
NLP-FL	12.83	8043 (CS1: 959, CS2: 2586, CS3: 4498)
NLP	17.83	7879 (CS1: 989, CS2: 2448, CS3: 4442)

5. Conclusions

This work presents a nonlinear formulation for the optimal operation of gas pipelines with discrete decisions to minimize compressor energy consumption. The model contains the dynamic gas transport equations, off-design maps of the compressors and their drivers, and control valves regulation. A smoothed complementarity formulation is proposed to bridge the gap between disjunctive and nonlinear approaches by modeling valve configurations and flow reversals. This NLP-based approach is applied to a network representative of the main characteristics of a high-pressure pipeline, and the results are compared with the Mixed Integer Linear Programming model, showing a significant decrease of computational time, and gains in terms of the accuracy and optimality of the solution. Future work will focus on evaluating the scalability of the algorithm on large-scale problems, and developing decomposition strategies for scheduling of the units.

References

B.T. Baumrucker et al. 2008, MPEC problem formulations and solution strategies with chemical engineering applications, Computers and Chemical Engineering, 32, 2903–2913

L.M.P. Ghilardi et al., 2022, A MILP approach for the operational optimization of gas networks, IFAC-PapersOnLine, 55, 321–326.

K. Liu et al., 2020, Dynamic optimization for gas blending in pipeline networks with gas interchangeability control, AIChE Journal, 66.

S. Naik et al., 2022, Multistage Economic NMPC for Gas Pipeline Networks with Uncertainty, Computer Aided Chemical Engineering, 52, 1847–1852.

S. V. Patankar, 1980. Numerical Heat Transfer and Fluid Flow, 1st ed. CRC Press .

M. De Pascali et al., 2022, Flexible object-oriented modeling for the control of large gas networks, IFAC-PapersOnLine, 55, 321–326.

D. Rose et al., 2016, Computational optimization of gas compressor stations: MINLP models versus continuous reformulations, Math Meth Oper Res, 83, 409–444

M. Schmidt et al., 2016, An MPEC-based heuristic, pp. 163-179, in *Evaluating Gas Network Capacities*, T. Koch et al. (eds.), Society for Industrial and Applied Mathematics

Flavio Manenti, Gintaras V. Reklaitis (Eds.), Proceedings of the 34th European Symposium on Computer Aided Process Engineering / 15th International Symposium on Process Systems Engineering (ESCAPE34/PSE24), June 2-6, 2024, Florence, Italy
 http://dx.doi.org/10.1016/B978-0-443-28824-1.50278-7

Learning to Recycle Benders Cuts for Mixed Integer Model Predictive Control

Ilias Mitrai,[a] Prodromos Daoutidis[a*]

[a] *Department of Chemical Engineering and Materials Science, University of Minnesota, Minneapolis, 55455 MN, USA*
daout001@umn.edu

Abstract

Mixed integer MPC problems arise frequently in cases where the operation of a system depends on continuous and discrete decisions, leading to mixed integer optimization problems. However, the online solution of such problems is computationally challenging. In this work, we develop a machine learning approach to determine which cuts should be used as a warm start (recycled) for Generalized Benders Decomposition for the solution of mixed integer MPC problems. Computational results on a case study regarding the operation of chemical processes show that the proposed approach leads to a significant reduction in solution time (up to 40% reduction).

Keywords: Model Predictive Control, Benders Decomposition, Mathematical Optimization, Machine Learning

1. Introduction

Model Predictive Control (MPC) is a widely used optimization-based control strategy for handling disturbances that affect the operation of process systems (Rawlings et al., (2017), Daoutidis et al., (2018)). The efficiency of an MPC strategy depends on the efficient online solution of an optimization problem. Despite significant advances in optimization theory and algorithms, the monolithic solution of mixed integer optimization (MIP) problems can be slow for online applications. Such problems arise in various applications such as unit commitment and online scheduling (Risbeck et al., (2020), McAllister and Rawlings (2022)). The standard approach to reduce the computational time is either to approximate the discrete problem with a continuous one (Masti et al., 2020) or use decomposition-based algorithms, such as Generalized Benders Decomposition (GBD) (Mitrai and Daoutidis (2022b)). Application of GBD to mixed integer MPC (MIP-MPC) decomposes the optimization problem into a master problem, which considers the integer (and potentially some continuous) variables, and a subproblem that considers the dynamic behavior of the system and whose solution depends on the values of the variables of the master problem (called complicating variables). These problems are solved repeatedly and coordinated via Benders cuts, which inform the master problem about the dynamic behavior of the system. Despite the reduction in solution time, the off-the-shelf implementation of GBD can be slow for online applications.

In recent work, we have shown that adding an initial set of cuts to the master problem (warm start) can reduce the solution time since the cuts contain information about the subproblem (Mitrai and Daoutidis, 2022b). However, determining which cuts to add is not apparent since the possible number of cuts can be very large. In this work, we propose a machine learning-based cut-recycling strategy for determining which cuts to recycle and ultimately accelerate GBD. Given a MIP-MPC problem, first, a set of high-quality integer feasible solutions is computed using a machine learning branch and check algorithm (Mitrai and Daoutidis, 2023b). The cuts associated with these integer feasible solutions are added (recycled) to the master problem, and GBD is implemented to obtain the solution of the MIP-MPC problem. We apply the proposed approach to a case study on the operation of an isothermal CSTR affected by changes in product demand and the inlet conditions. The results show that the proposed approach leads to a 40% reduction in solution time compared to the standard application of GBD.

2. Learning to recycle Benders cuts

2.1. Generalized Benders Decomposition

We assume that the following optimization problem must be solved

$$\min f_1(x,y) + f_2(y,z) \quad \text{s.t.} \quad g(x,y) \leq 0, h(z,y) \leq 0 \tag{1}$$

where $x \in R^{n_x}, y \in R^{n_y^c} \times Z^{n_y^d}, z \in R^{n_z}$ are the decision variables and g, h are the constraints related to the behaviour of the system, such as discretized differential equations. Based on the number of variables and constraints, the online solution of this problem can be computationally expensive. GBD is based on the observation that if variables x and y are fixed, then the resulting problem is continuous and is equal to

$$\mathcal{S}(y) \coloneqq \min_{\bar{y},z} f_2(\bar{y},z) \quad \text{s.t.}\, h(z,\bar{y}) \leq 0, \bar{y} = y \tag{2}$$

where $\mathcal{S}$ is the value function of the subproblem and we define as λ is the Lagrangean multipliers of the equality constraint $\bar{y} = y$. The original problem can be written as

$$\mathcal{M} \coloneqq \min_{x,y} f_1(x,y) + \mathcal{S}(y) \quad \text{s.t.}\, g(x,y) \leq 0 \tag{3}$$

The above problem cannot be solved directly since the value function $\mathcal{S}(y)$ is not known explicitly. In GBD, the value function is approximated via Benders cuts (Geoffrion, 1972)

$$\eta \geq \mathcal{S}(\bar{y}^l) - \lambda^l(y - \bar{y}^l) \tag{4}$$

where the index l denotes the number of cuts used (the set $\mathcal{L}$ contains all the cuts added). Given this approximation, the master problem can be written as

$$\min_{x,y,\eta} f_1(x,y) + \eta \quad \text{s.t.}\, g(x,y) \leq 0, \eta \geq \mathcal{S}(\bar{y}^l) - \lambda^l(y - \bar{y}^l) \forall l \in \mathcal{L}, \tag{5}$$

The algorithm alternates between the solution of the master problem, which provides a lower bound, and the subproblem, which provides an upper bound.

2.2. Learning to recycle Benders cuts

In GBD, the cuts are added iteratively as dictated by the solution of the master problem. Adding an initial set of cuts, which we will refer to as warm start cuts, can reduce the solution time since the master problem has a better approximation of the value function in the first iteration. However, determining which cuts to add is nontrivial since the possible number of cuts can be large, and the addition of warm start cuts increases the complexity of the master problem. Therefore, an oracle is needed to determine the cuts that provide the maximum amount of information while minimizing the increase in the complexity of the master problem. We use a recently proposed machine learning based GBD algorithm as an oracle to compute high quality integer feasible solutions (Mitrai and Daoutidis, 2023b) which determine the cuts that are recycled.

2.2.1. Machine Learning branch and check GBD

The standard application of GBD can be slow for online applications since the master problem and subproblem are solved repeatedly. Recently, a machine learning-based branch and check GBD algorithm has been proposed to obtain high-quality integer feasible solutions. In this approach, the master problem is solved using branch and bound, and once an integer feasible solution is found at a node ρ, approximate Benders cuts are added to all the open nodes in the tree and the branch and bound procedure continues until the bounds converge. The approximate cuts, $\eta \geq \tilde{S}(\bar{y}^{\rho}) - \tilde{\lambda}^{\rho}(y - \bar{y}^{\rho})$, are obtained using surrogate models to approximate the value function of the subproblem $\tilde{S}$ and the multipliers $\tilde{\lambda}$. The solution that is obtained is feasible, given that the subproblem is always feasible and the original problem is feasible since the cuts approximate the value function of the subproblem.

2.2.2. Cut Recycling strategy

The branch and check GBD algorithm provides a high-quality integer feasible solution and a set of integer feasible solutions that are explored during branch and check. We use these feasible solutions to determine the cuts that should be added (recycled) to the master problem in the first iteration. We define set $\mathcal{D} = \{y^i, \mathcal{S}(y^i), \lambda(y^i)\}_{i=1}^{N_c}$which contains all the cuts that can be potentially added. This set is obtained offline by solving the subproblem for different values of the complicating variables. We also define set $\mathcal{Y}_I = \{y^1, .., y^{N_{feas}}\}$ which contains the integer feasible solutions found during branch and check. For each integer feasible solution y^l, the value function $\mathcal{S}(y^i)$ and multipliers $\lambda(y^i)$ are obtained from the set $\mathcal{D}$ and the associated cut $\left(\eta \geq \mathcal{S}(y^l) - \lambda^l(y - y^l)\right)$ is added to the master problem. Once these warm start cuts are added, GBD is implemented.

3. Mixed Integer MPC formulation

We consider the application of the proposed approach to the optimal operation of chemical processes that can manufacture N_p products over a time horizon H discretized into N_s slots. It is assumed that the operation of the system is affected by disturbances in product demand and inlet conditions of the process, and a mixed integer MPC controller is used to determine the production sequence and dynamic behavior of the system. Under this setting, the system is either performing transitions between the products, is manufacturing a product, or is performing a transition from an intermediate state x_0 to the product manufactured in the first slot (see Mitrai and Daoutidis (2023a) for a detailed description of the problem).

3.1. Optimization model

We define as $\mathcal{I}_p = \{1, .., N_p\}$ the set of products and $\mathcal{I}_s = \{1, .., N_s\}$ the set of slots. We define binary variable W_{ik} which is equal to one if product i is manufactured in slot k and zero otherwise, variable Z_{ijk} which is equal to one if a transition occurs from product i to j in slot k, and variable $\hat{Z}_i$ which is equal to one if a transition occurs from an intermediate state to product i in the first slot. The logic constraints regarding the production sequence are

$$\sum_{i \in \mathcal{I}_p} W_{ik} = 1 \; \forall \, k \in \mathcal{I}_s$$

$$Z_{ijk} \geq W_{ik} + W_{j,k+1} - 1 \; \forall \, i \in \mathcal{I}_p, j \in \mathcal{I}_p, k \in \mathcal{I}_s \setminus \{N_s\} \tag{6}$$

$$\hat{Z}_i = W_{i1} \; \forall i \in \mathcal{I}_p$$

The starting and ending time of slot k are T_k^s, T_k^e ($T_1^s = 0, T_{N_s}^e = H - T_0, T_{k+1}^s = T_k^e$), the production time of product i in slot k is Θ_{ik} ($\Theta_{ik} \leq W_{ik}H$), the transition time in slot k is θ_k^t, and $\theta_{ijk}, \hat{\theta}_i$ are the transition time from product i to j in slot k and from x_0 to product i. The timing constraints are

$$T_k^e = T_k^s + \sum_{i \in \mathcal{I}_p} \Theta_{ik} + \theta_k^t \; \forall k \in \mathcal{I}_s$$

$$\theta_k^t = \sum_{i \in \mathcal{I}_p} \sum_{j \in \mathcal{I}_p} Z_{ijk} \theta_{ijk} \;\; \forall k \in \mathcal{I}_s \setminus \{1\} \tag{7}$$

$$\theta_1^t = \sum_{i \in \mathcal{I}_p} \sum_{j \in \mathcal{I}_p} Z_{ij1} \theta_{ij1} + \sum_{i \in \mathcal{I}_p} \hat{\theta}_i.$$

The production rate of product i is r_i, the inventory of product i in slot k is I_{ik} (the initial inventory is I_i^0), the amount of product i sold in slot k is S_{ik}, the demand is d_{ik} and is satisfied in the end of the time horizon $S_{iN_s} \geq d_i \; \forall i \in \mathcal{I}_p$. The inventory constraints are

$$I_{ik} = I_{ik-1} + r_i \Theta_{ik} - S_{ik} \; \forall i \in \mathcal{I}_p, k \in \mathcal{I}_s \tag{8}$$

where for $k = 1$, $I_{ik-1} = I_i^0$. The dynamic behaviour of the system is described by a set of differential equations $\dot{x}(t) = F(x, u)$ where x and u are the state and manipulated variables of the system. The differential equations F are discretized using N_c orthogonal collocation points and N_f finite elements ($\mathcal{I}_f = \{1, .., N_f\}, \mathcal{I}_c = \{1, .., N_C\}$). We consider simultaneously all the transitions between the products and define variables x_{ijfck}, u_{ijfck} as the value of the state and manipulated variables for a transition from product i to j in slot k and discretization point (c, f). Similarly, we define variables $\hat{x}_{ifc}, \hat{u}_{ifc}$ for a transition from the intermediate state x_0 to product i. The equations that describe the dynamic behaviour of the system have the following general form

$$G(x_{ijfck}, u_{ijfck}, \theta_{ijk}) \leq 0 \; \forall i \in \mathcal{I}_p, j \in \mathcal{I}_p, k \in \mathcal{I}_k, c \in \mathcal{I}_c, f \in \mathcal{I}_f \tag{9}$$

$$\hat{G}(\hat{x}_{ifc}, \hat{u}_{ifc}, \hat{\theta}_i, x_0) \leq 0 \; \forall i \in \mathcal{I}_p, c \in \mathcal{I}_c, f \in \mathcal{I}_f \tag{10}$$

The objective of the optimization problem has three terms. The first term is the profit minus the operating cost, the second term is the transition cost between the products, and the last term the transition cost from the intermediate state. The terms are equal to

$$\Phi_1 = \sum_{ik} (P_{ik} S_{ik} - C_{ik}^{op} q_{ik} - C^{inv} I_{ik}) - \sum_{ijk} C_{ij}^{tr} Z_{ijk}$$

$$\Phi_2 = \sum_{ijk} Z_{ijk} \sum_{fc} \left(\alpha_u N_{fe}^{-1} \, t_{ijfck} \Lambda_{cN_c} \left(u_{ijfck} - u_j^{ss} \right) \right) = \sum_{ijk} Z_{ijk} f_{ijk}^{dyn}$$

$$\Phi_3 = \sum_i \hat{Z}_i \sum_{fc} \left(\alpha_u N_{fe}^{-1} \hat{t}_{ifc} \Lambda_{cN_c} \left(\hat{u}_{ifc} - u_i^{ss} \right) \right) = \sum_i \hat{Z}_i \, \hat{f}_i^{dyn}$$

where P_{ik}, C_{ik} is the price and operating cost of product i in slot k, $C^{inv}$is the inventory cost, C_{ij}^{tr} is the fixed transition cost for product i to j, α_u is a weight coefficient, Λ is the collocation matrix, and $t_{ijfck}, \hat{t}_{ifc}$ is the time at discretization point (c, f) for a transition from product i to j in slot k and for the transition from x_0 to product i. The goal of the optimization problem is to maximize the profit $(\Phi_1 - \Phi_2 - \Phi_3)$ subject to constraints presented in Eq. 6-10.

3.2. Decomposition-based solution approach

The above problem is a large-scale Mixed Integer Nonlinear Programming problem which cannot be solved efficiently monolithically. However, if the scheduling related variables and transition times are fixed, the resulting optimization problem is to maximize $-\Phi_2 - \Phi_3$ subject to constraints 9,10. This problem can be decomposed into independent subproblems which consider the transitions between the products for given transition time θ_{ijk} and the transition from x_0 for a given $\hat{\theta}_i$. The subproblems are

$$\phi_{ijk}(\theta_{ijk}) = \min f_{ijk}^{dyn} \text{ s.t. } g_{ijk}^{dyn} \leq 0\ (Eq.9), \bar{\theta}_{ijk} = \theta_{ijk}$$

$$\hat{\phi}_i(\hat{\theta}_i) = \min \hat{f}_i^{dyn} \text{ s.t. } \hat{g}_i^{dyn} \leq 0\ (Eq.10), \bar{\hat{\theta}}_i = \hat{\theta}_i,$$

and the original problem can be written as

$$\max \Phi_1 - \textstyle\sum_{ijk} Z_{ijk}\phi_{ijk}(\theta_{ijk}) - \sum_i \hat{Z}_i\ \hat{\phi}_i(\hat{\theta}_i) \text{ subject to Eq. } 6-8.$$

Since the value functions $\phi_{ijk}, \hat{\phi}_i$ are not known explicitly they are approximated via Benders cuts as follows $\eta_{ijk} \geq \phi_{ijk}(\theta_{ijk}^l) - \lambda^l(\theta_{ijk} - \theta_{ijk}^l), \hat{\eta}_i \geq \hat{\phi}_i(\hat{\theta}_i^l) - \hat{\lambda}_i^k(\hat{\theta}_i - \hat{\theta}_i^l)$, where $\lambda_{ijk}, \hat{\lambda}_i$ are the Lagrangean Multipliers of the equality constraints $\bar{\theta}_{ijk} = \theta_{ijk}$ and $\bar{\hat{\theta}}_i = \hat{\theta}_i$ respectively. Given the above problem decomposition, the Benders cuts approximate the transition costs and we apply the proposed cut recycling strategy to determine which cuts to recycle as a warm start for accelerating GBD.

Table 1 Average solution time (in seconds) for the standard application of the multicut GBD, hybrid multicut GBD, and the proposed cut recycling approach.

Algorithm	Standard Implementation	Initialization strategy	
		OptSol	IntFeas
Multicut GBD	64	54 (16)	38 (40)
Hybrid multicut GBD	40	36 (10)	30 (25)

4. Case study and results

We will assume that the system is an isothermal CSTR where a third-order irreversible reaction occurs, and six products are manufactured by adjusting the inlet flow rate. The time horizon is 35 hours, and at a random time point in the first 15 hours of operation, the demand of the products and the inlet concentration of the reactor change simultaneously. We consider the effect of the proposed approach on accelerating two GBD algorithms (multicut and hybrid multicut GBD) from the literature (Mitrai and Daoutidis, 2022a) where no warm start cuts are added to the master problem. In the multicut algorithm, cuts are added only for given transitions, as dictated by the master problem, whereas in the hybrid multicut algorithm, the cuts for a given transition (ijk) are added for all transitions $(i,j,k')\ k' \in \mathcal{I}_s$. Furthermore, we compare the proposed approach with the case where only the optimal solution returned by the ML-based branch and check GBD algorithm is used to determine which cuts to recycle (OptSol). We generate 20 random feasible disturbances, and the solution time for the different approaches is presented in Table 1. From the results we observe that the proposed cut recycling approach leads to a significant reduction in solution time compared to standard and accelerated GBD. Specifically, the solution time of multicut GBD is 64 seconds and the solution time with the proposed approach is 38 seconds, a 40% reduction. Similar results are obtained for the accelerated GBD algorithm, where the solution time is reduced from 40 to 30 seconds (25 % reduction). Also, we observe that using all the cuts related to the integer feasible solutions leads to lower solution time, on average, compared to using the cuts from the optimal solution obtained from the ML-based Branch and Check GBD algorithm. This result shows that for the case of GBD, adding information related to high-quality integer feasible solutions is more beneficial than adding information related only to an approximation of the optimal solution, which is the common practice for monolithic solution methods (Bengio et al., 2021).

5. Conclusions

Mixed integer MPC applications arise in a wide range of applications, however, the efficient solution of the underlying optimization problem is computationally challenging. In this work we proposed a machine learning based cut recycling strategy to improve the computational performance of GBD. Application of the proposed approach to a case study on the operation of chemical processes, shows that the proposed approach leads to a significant reduction in solution time by exploiting information about multiple integer feasible solutions.

6. Acknowledgments

Financial support from NSF-CBET (award number 2313289) is gratefully acknowledged.

References

A. M. Geoffrion, 1972, Generalized benders decomposition. *Journal of Optimization Theory and Applications*, *10*, pp.237-260.

D. Masti, T. Pippia, A. Bemporad, and D. De Schutter, 2020, Learning approximate semi-explicit hybrid MPC with an application to microgrids. *IFAC-PapersOnLine*, *53*(2), pp.5207-5212.

I. Mitrai and P. Daoutidis, 2022a, A multicut generalized benders decomposition approach for the integration of process operations and dynamic optimization for continuous systems. *Computers & Chemical Engineering*, *164*, p.107859.

I. Mitrai and P. Daoutidis, 2022b, An adaptive multi-cut decomposition based algorithm for integrated closed loop scheduling and control. In *Computer Aided Chemical Engineering* (Vol. 49, pp. 475-480). Elsevier.

I. Mitrai, and P. Daoutidis, 2023a, Taking the human out of decomposition-based optimization via artificial intelligence: Part II. Learning to initialize. *arXiv preprint arXiv:2310.07082*.

I. Mitrai and P. Daoutidis, 2023b, Computationally efficient solution of mixed integer model predictive control problems via machine learning aided Benders Decomposition. *arXiv preprint arXiv:2309.16508*.

J.B. Rawlings, D.Q. Mayne, and M. Diehl, 2017, *Model predictive control: theory, computation, and design* (Vol. 2). Madison, WI: Nob Hill Publishing.

M.J. Risbeck, C.T. Maravelias, J.B. Rawlings, and R.D. Turney, 2020, Mixed-integer optimization methods for online scheduling in large-scale HVAC systems. *Optimization Letters*, *14*, pp.889-924.

P. Daoutidis, J.H. Lee, I. Harjunkoski, S. Skogestad, M. Baldea, and C. Georgakis, 2018, Integrating operations and control: A perspective and roadmap for future research. *Computers & Chemical Engineering*, *115*, pp.179-184.

R.D. McAllister, and J.B. Rawlings, 2022, Advances in mixed-integer model predictive control. In *2022 American Control Conference (ACC)* (pp. 364-369). IEEE.

Y. Bengio, A. Lodi, A. and A. Prouvost, 2021, Machine learning for combinatorial optimization: a methodological tour d'horizon. *European Journal of Operational Research*, *290*(2), pp.405-421.

Flavio Manenti, Gintaras V. Reklaitis (Eds.), Proceedings of the 34th European Symposium on Computer Aided Process Engineering / 15th International Symposium on Process Systems Engineering (ESCAPE34/PSE24), June 2-6, 2024, Florence, Italy
 http://dx.doi.org/10.1016/B978-0-443-28824-1.50279-9

Logical processing of sequential alarms for safer plant operation

Ryuto Tanaka[a] and Masaru Noda[a*]

[a]*Department of Chemical Engineering, Fukuoka University, Fukuoka 814-0180, Japan*

mnoda@fukuoka-u.ac.jp

Abstract

Logical alarm processing is a technique for processing signals from alarm sensors to generate more meaningful alarms for plant operators. This technique involves grouping and suppressing redundant alarms, and eclipsing of alarms on the same variable etc. While it can enhance the operational value of alarms, inappropriate deployment of logical alarm processing can result in safety hazards during plant operations. In this study, we propose a novel approach for logical alarm processing that focuses on suppressing sequential alarms. Sequential alarms refer to sets of alarms that occur in succession within a short period of time after the first waring alarm indicating an abnormality. These types of alarms reduce the ability of plant operators to cope with operation abnormalities as critical alarms are often lost in numerous other correlated ones. The proposed method comprises three parts: identifying sequential alarms in plant operation data through dot matrix analysis, detecting the occurrence of sequential alarms in real-time by matching patterns of alarms during plant operation, and suppressing unnecessary alarms in the detected sequential alarms. Application of the method to simulated operational data for a distillation column demonstrated that its capability to decrease the number of unnecessary alarms displayed to a plant operator.

Keywords: Logical Alarm Processing; Sequential Alarms; Dot Matrix Analysis, Plant Operation Data

1. Introduction

Advancements in distributed control systems (DCS) in the chemical industry have made it possible to inexpensively and easily install numerous alarms in DCS. While most alarms help operators to detect and identify abnormalities, some do not (Hollifield *et al.*, 2006). A poor alarm system might cause sequential alarms, which are a series of alarms that occur in succession within a short period of time after the first waring alarm indicating a plant abnormality. These sequential alarms reduce the operators' ability to cope with plant abnormalities because the critical alarms get buried under many unnecessary ones. To ensure safe plant operations, it is very important to suppress sequential alarms during plant operation.

Logical alarm processing is a technique for processing signals from alarm sensors to generate more meaningful alarms for plant operators, such as grouping alarms, suppression of redundant alarms, eclipsing of several alarms on the same variable, suppression of alarms according to plant operation mode (International Electrotechnical Commission, 2022). For instance, the suppressing relevant alarms during startup operation is appropriate as it may be difficult to avoid transiently exceeding the high limits that apply in steady operation. The utilization of logical alarm processing is highly advantageous, but it should be stressed that: the operator should be kept informed when logical processing is removing alarms from the display, any logical processing should be done in a manner which minimizes the possibility of error (Engineering Equipment & Material Users' Association, 2013).

In this study, we propose a new logical alarm processing method to suppress sequential alarms. In a sequential alarm, the alarms following the first few alarms do not provide useful information to the operator and thus should be suppressed. The proposed method consists of three parts, a database construction of sequential alarms using plant operation data, detection of the occurrence of sequential alarms during the plant operation, and the suppression of sequential alarms. The effectiveness of the proposed method is demonstrated through a case study.

2. Logical Alarm Processing of Sequential Alarms

2.1. Plant Operation Data

The plant operation data recorded in DCS generally includes the timing and tag information of the occurred alarms, as presented in Table 1. The notation A_k in Table 1 represents the alarm associated with the kth tag.

Table 1 Example plant operation data

Date – Time	Tag
2024/01/01 – 10:10:15	A_3
2024/01/01 – 10:12:36	A_1
2024/01/01 – 10:13:42	A_2
2024/01/01 – 10:14:58	A_3
2024/01/01 – 10:45:08	A_4
2024/01/01 – 10:51:21	A_1
2024/01/01 – 11:13:33	A_2
2024/01/01 – 11:31:21	A_1
2024/01/01 – 11:32:43	A_2
2024/01/01 – 11:33:18	A_3
2024/01/01 – 11:34:59	A_4
2024/01/01 – 11:45:30	A_2

Plant operation data is characterized by these tags and the order of alarm occurrence. Conversion of the plant-operation data in Table 1 by placing them in order by occurrence time gives alarm sequence S in Eq.(1):

$$S = A_3, A_1, A_2, A_3, A_4, A_1, A_2, A_1, A_2, A_3, A_4, A_2 \quad (1)$$

2.2. Identification of Sequential Alarms by Dot Matrix Analysis

Repeated alarm patterns in plant operation data can be classified as sequential alarms. Thus, the problem of identifying sequential alarms in plant operation data is formulated as the problem of searching for repeated subsequences S_i of alarms in alarm sequence S.

Previously, we proposed an identification method for sequential alarms buried in noisy plant operation data using dot matrix analysis (Wang *et al.*, 2017). The dot matrix analysis is originally a sequence alignment method for identifying similar regions in DNA or RNA, which may be a consequence of functional, structural, or evolutionary relationships between sequences (Mount, 2004)

In the dot matrix analysis of the alarm sequence S in Eq.(1), S is listed up the left side and across the bottom of the graph, as shown in Figure 1. The sequence comparison starts with the first alarm on the horizontal axis. The comparison moves across the graph in the first row, and a dot is placed in every column where the alarm is the same. Then, the second alarm in the sequence is compared to the entire sequence, and a dot is placed in the second row wherever a match occurs. This procedure is repeated until the graph is entirely filled with dots.

The diagonal lines in Figure 1 display the locations of the repeated regions in S. The longest diagonal line, running from the lower left to the upper right, does not represent a sequential alarm as it reflects the comparison of a sequence with itself. In contrast, two diagonal lines with four dots indicate the occurrence of repeated sequential alarms "A_1, A_2, A_3, A_4" twice during the plant operation. Dots that do not align on a diagonal row or align on a diagonal row with less than three dots represent random matches unrelated to the sequential alarms.

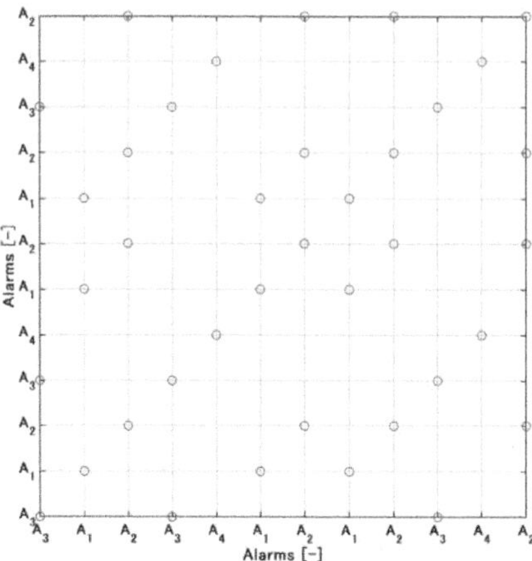

Figure 1 Example of single-sequence dot matrix analysis

The identified sequential alarms are used in constructing a database for suppressing sequential alarms during plant operation, as shown in Table 2. The time period of sequential alarms $\triangle t_1$ in Table 2 is period between the first and the last alarms in the sequential alarm S_1.

Table 2 Example of sequential alarms identified using dot matrix analysis

Sequential alarms	Alarm sequence	Time period of sequential alarms
S_1	A_1, A_2, A_3, A_4	$\triangle t_1$

2.3. Detection and Suppression of Sequential Alarms

Sequential alarm S_i identified through the dot matrix analysis is divided into a pattern matching part and a suppression part. The patter matching part with the first few alarms in S_i is used to detect the occurrence of sequential alarms during the plant operation, while the suppression part is the remaining alarms in S_i. Once the pattern matching part of S_i is found during plant operation, the method detects the occurrence of S_i and suppresses the alarms in the suppression part of S_i. A size of the matching part N_d should be the minimum number enough to distinguish all sequential alarms identified by the dot matrix analysis.

Table 3 shows an example of database for detecting the occurrence of S_1 in plant operation, where N_d is selected as two. When "A_1, A_2" is detected during plant operation, "A_3" and "A_4" are suppressed for the suppression time $\triangle t_1$.

Table 3 Example of database for detecting the occurrence of sequential alarms

Sequential alarms	Matching part	Suppression part	Suppression time of sequential alarms
S_1	A_1, A_2	A_3, A_4	$\triangle t_1$

3. Case Study

The proposed method was applied to simulation data obtained from a distillation column. There are four high alarms in the DCS: column top temperature, column bottom temperature, reflux flow rate, and steam flow rate, which are denoted by A_1-A_4 as shown in Table 4. The alarms A_1-A_4 are activated when corresponding process variables exceed their high alarm thresholds, respectively.

Table 4 Installed alarms in distillation column

Alarms	Description
A_1	High alarm of column top temperature
A_2	High alarm of column bottom temperature
A_3	High alarm of reflux flow rate
A_4	High alarm of steam flow rate

During the process simulation of 480 minutes, we intentionally induced four types of malfunctions. The plant operation data recorded a total of 143 alarm occurrences, which are illustrated in Figure 2.

The dot matrix analysis was applied to the plant operation data in Figure 2. Eight sequential alarms S_1–S_8 in Table 5 were identified. One of the longest sequential alarms S_1 occurred twice in 480 minutes, which includes ten alarms with a 6.6-minute time span between the first and the last alarms A_2. Any alarms following the first alarm A_2 in S_1 do not provide useful information to the operator, therefore they should be suppressed through logical alarm processing. The total number of alarms in the eight sequential alarms was 116, which accounts for 81% of the number of alarms that occurred in 480 minutes. This indicates that it is possible to reduce the number of alarms by 81% at most through the logical alarm processing.

$$
\begin{aligned}
S = \ & A_3, A_4, A_2, A_3, A_4, A_2, A_3, A_4, A_1, A_2, A_3, A_1,\\
& A_2, A_3, A_4, A_3, A_2, A_4, A_1, A_3, A_2, A_4, A_3, A_1,\\
& A_2, A_4, A_1, A_2, A_3, A_2, A_1, A_3, A_1, A_4, A_1, A_3,\\
& A_1, A_3, A_1, A_2, A_3, A_4, A_1, A_3, A_2, A_4, A_1, A_3,\\
& A_2, A_3, A_4, A_2, A_3, A_2, A_4, A_1, A_3, A_2, A_4, A_1,\\
& A_3, A_2, A_1, A_3, A_2, A_4, A_2, A_3, A_1, A_2, A_4, A_1,\\
& A_3, A_2, A_4, A_1, A_3, A_2, A_1, A_3, A_2, A_4, A_2, A_3,\\
& A_1, A_2, A_1, A_3, A_4, A_2, A_3, A_4, A_2, A_3, A_4, A_1,\\
& A_2, A_1, A_2, A_3, A_4, A_3, A_2, A_4, A_1, A_3, A_2, A_1,\\
& A_1, A_2, A_3, A_4, A_1, A_3, A_2, A_4, A_1, A_3, A_2, A_4,\\
& A_3, A_1, A_2, A_3, A_4, A_2, A_3, A_2, A_4, A_1, A_2, A_3,\\
& A_2, A_1, A_3, A_1, A_3, A_2, A_4, A_1, A_3, A_1, A_3
\end{aligned}
$$

Figure 2 Simulated plant operation data

Table 5 Identified sequential alarms by dot matrix analysis

S_i	Alarm sequence	Freq.	Time length of sequential alarms [min]
S_1	A_2, A_3, A_4, A_1, A_2, A_3, A_4, A_1, A_3, A_2	2	6.6
S_2	A_3, A_4, A_2, A_3, A_4, A_2, A_3, A_4, A_1, A_2	2	10.2
S_3	A_1, A_2, A_3, A_4, A_3, A_2, A_4, A_1, A_3, A_2	2	8.3
S_4	A_4, A_1, A_2, A_3, A_2, A_1, A_3, A_1	2	7.4
S_5	A_4, A_1, A_3, A_2, A_4, A_1, A_3, A_2	2	4.7
S_6	A_3, A_4, A_2, A_3	2	3.8
S_7	A_2, A_3, A_1, A_2	2	3.5
S_8	A_1, A_3, A_2, A_4	2	2.7

The database for supressing sequential alarms was constructed based on a list of identified sequential alarms using the dot matrix analysis in Table 5, as detailed in Table 6. The size of pattern matching part N_d was selected as three, which is the minimum required number of alarms to identify the sequential alarms except for S_6. It is impossible to distinguish S_2 and S_6 when N_d is three as the sequence of the first three alarms of S_6 are same as that of S_2. Nevertheless, N_d cannot be more than four, because the number of alarms in S_6-S_8 is four. For instance, when the alarm sequence "A_2, A_3, A_4" is detected during the plant operation, alarms A_1, A_2, A_3, and A_4 are suppressed for 6.6 min through the logical alarm processing.

Table 6 Database for suppression of sequential alarms

S_i	Matching part	Suppression part	Suppression time [min]
S_1	A_2, A_3, A_4	A_1, A_2, A_3, A_4	6.6
S_2	A_3, A_4, A_2	A_1, A_2, A_3, A_4	10.2
S_3	A_1, A_2, A_3	A_1, A_2, A_3, A_4	8.3
S_4	A_4, A_1, A_2	A_1, A_2, A_3	7.4
S_5	A_4, A_1, A_3	A_1, A_2, A_3, A_4	4.7
S_7	A_2, A_3, A_1	A_2	3.5
S_8	A_1, A_3, A_2	A_4	2.7

The proposed logical alarm processing method was applied to the plant operation data in Figure 2. Figure 3 reveals the alarms displayed to the operator with the dotted box denoting suppressed alarms that were not notified by the proposed method. This suggests that 55% reduction in alarms is feasible without sacrificing the first three alarms, which provide useful information to the operator.

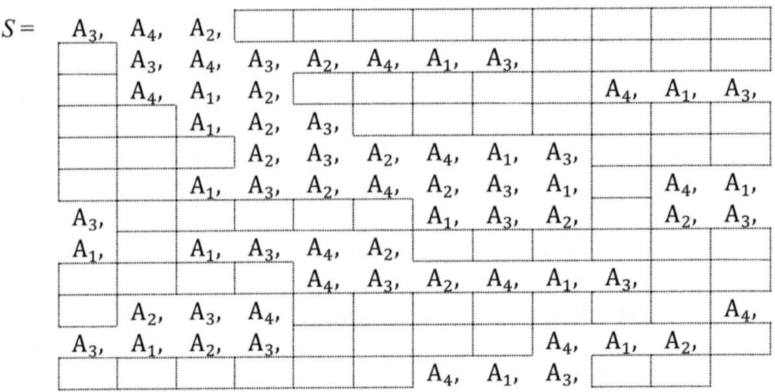

Figure 3 Suppression of Sequential Alarms by logical alarm processing

Conclusions

We developed a new logical alarm processing method to prevent sequential alarms. Our method includes three parts: constructing a database construction of sequential alarms by analysing plant operation data using the dot matrix analysis, detecting of the occurrence of sequential alarms during the plant operation by pattern matching, and suppressing sequential alarms. Application of the proposed method to simulated plant operation data of a distillation column showed that the proposed method can effectively suppress sequential alarms while ensuring that critical alarms are displayed to the operator.

Acknowledgement

This work was supported by JSPS KAKENHI Grant Numbers JP20K05213 and JP23K04491.

References

B. R. Hollifield and E. Habibi, 2006, The Alarm Management Handbook A Comprehensive Guide, PAS, Houston

International Electrotechnical Commission (IEC), 2022, IEC 62682 Management of Alarm Systems for the Process Industries 2nd edition, IEC, Geneva

Engineering Equipment & Material Users' Association (EEMUA), 2013, Alarm Systems – a Guide to Design, Management and Procurement, EEMUA Publication No.191 3rd Edition, EEMUA, London

Z. Wang and M. Noda, 2017, Identification of Repeated Sequential Alarms in Noisy Plant Operation Data Using Dot Matrix Method with Sliding Window, *Journal of Chemical Engineering of Japan,* 50(6), 445-449

D. W. Mount, 2004, Bioinformatics Sequence and Genome Analysis Second Edition, Cold Spring Harbor Laboratory Press, New York

Flavio Manenti, Gintaras V. Reklaitis (Eds.), Proceedings of the 34th European Symposium on Computer Aided Process Engineering / 15th International Symposium on Process Systems Engineering (ESCAPE34/PSE24), June 2-6, 2024, Florence, Italy
 http://dx.doi.org/10.1016/B978-0-443-28824-1.50280-5

Design of a Predictive Functional Controller Based on Combination of Data-Driven Tuning and Prediction Methods

Yoichiro Ashida,[a*] Masanobu Obika[b]

[a]*National Institute of Technology, Matsue College, 14-4 Nishiikuma cho, Matsue, 690-8518, Japan*

[b]*ADAPTEX Co., Ltd., 13-60, Kagamiyama 3, Higashi-Hiroshima, Hiroshima, Japan*
yashida@matsue-ct.ac.jp

Abstract

PID control has been used for a long time and still one of the most important controllers especially in process control. However, higher performance controllers are requested. Predictive functional controller (PFC) is a simple model predictive controller (MPC), and suitable for replacing PID controllers because it includes PI controller as a special case. This paper proposes a Fictitious Reference Iterative Tuning (FRIT) based two-stage data-driven design of the PFC. Firstly, most of the control parameters are tuned by FRIT. However, a robustness related parameter is not suitable for adjustment with FRIT because FRIT aims to make exact model matching. To tune this parameter, a FRIT based prediction is employed as the second stage. Designer determines the parameter by looking at the predicted waveforms. The effectiveness of the proposed method is verified by a numerical example. The proposed scheme could be applied to various processes.

Keywords: predictive functional control, data-driven design, data-driven prediction, fictitious reference iterative tuning.

1. Introduction

In process control, well-known PID controllers have been still widely used. Especially for complex controlled system, PID controllers are often employed because of their ease of tuning and high stability. However, control performance has become important to keep competitive power in last some decades. Although Model Predictive Controller (MPC) is famous high-performance controller, it is not easy to replace the PID controllers due to the difficulty of controller parameters tuning. In contrast, simpler MPC, Predictive Functional Controller (PFC) has been proposed by Richalet et al. (2009). Because PFC contains a PI controller as a special case, it is suitable for replacing the PID controller. However, though PFC is simpler than MPC, tuning control parameters of PFC is still a problem.

Among many controls parameter tuning methods, data-driven tuning methods are actively researched. Typical methods are iterative feed-back tuning (IFT) which uses repeated experiment proposed by Hjalmarsson et al. (1998), fictitious reference iterative tuning (FRIT) which uses only off-line optimizations proposed by Soma et al. (2004). The methods can tune controller without any system parameters. Effectiveness of the schemes are verified for experiments. For example, Nakamoto (2003) and Kano et al., (2011) apply

IFT and extended-FRIT methods to processes respectively. Thus, this paper utilizes FRIT to tune PFC.

Most control parameters are determined by FRIT, but the coincidence point h is a robustness-tuning parameter, which is impossible to adjust because FRIT aims to exact model matching. In this paper, FRIT based data-driven prediction method proposed by Takahashi et al. (2019) is employed to tune h. The method predicts input and output signals without any actual controls and system models. By using the proposed tuning scheme, operators can determine h which gives an acceptable control result.

This paper proposes a FRIT based tuning scheme of PFC. In the proposed scheme, internal model of PFC is determined by FRIT, and a control parameter named coincidence point is tuned by FRIT based prediction method. Effectiveness of the proposing design scheme is checked by a numerical example. The application is not limited to any particular target, but is considered applicable to various processes.

2. Proposed control scheme

2.1. Predictive Functional Control (PFC)

In this paper, considering the control of process systems, a high order system without any resonance points is considered as a controlled system, and reference signal is assumed to be stepwise one. In PFC, an internal model is expressed as a superposition of first-order systems shown as

$$\hat{y}(t) = \sum_{i=1}^{fu} y_{ui}(t), \tag{1}$$

$$y_{ui}(t) = G_i(z^{-1})u(t), \tag{2}$$

$$G_i(z^{-1}) = \frac{b_i z^{-1}}{1 + a_i z^{-1}}, \tag{3}$$

where $\hat{y}(t)$ and $u(t)$ are model output and input, and z^{-1} is a delay operator as $z^{-1}u(t) = u(t-1)$. This model cannot represent a control target with resonance points. Please refer to the literature by Richalet et al. (2009) for such a target. The following model represents only a rational function part excluding the time-delay, and the compensation of the time-delay will be explained later. Eq. (2) can be rewritten as

$$y_{ui}(t) = -a_i y_{ui}(t-1) + b_i u(t-1). \tag{4}$$

Based on this, the predicted value $y_{ui}(t)$ of time $t+h$ at time t is calculated as

$$y_{ui}(t+h|t) = (-a_i)^h y_{ui}(t) + b_i[1, \dots, (-a_i)^{h-1}][u(t+h-1), \dots, u(t)]^T. \tag{5}$$

Assume that future input is constant because reference signal is also constant, Eq. (5) is

$$y_{ui}(t+h|t) = (-a_i)^h y_{ui}(t) + b_i \frac{1-(-a_i)^h}{1-(-a_i)} u(t). \tag{6}$$

When the reference signal is a lamp signal, the future input must assume to be a lamp to obtain trackability. Eq. (6) leads the model output $\hat{y}(t+h|t)$ as

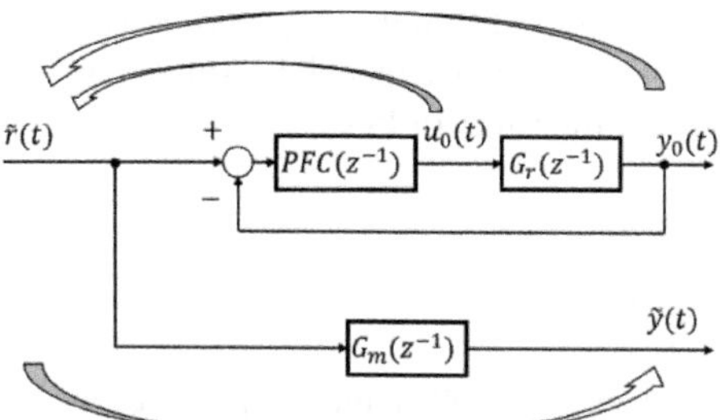

Figure 1: Conceptual diagram of FRIT

$$\hat{y}(t+h|t) = \sum_{i=1}^{f_u}(-a_i)^h y_{ui}(t) + \sum_{i=1}^{f_u} b_i \frac{1-(-a_i)^h}{1-(-a_i)} u(t), \tag{7}$$

and amount of change $\delta\hat{y}(t+h|t) = \hat{y}(t+h|t) - \hat{y}(t)$ is

$$\delta\hat{y}(t+h|t) = \sum_{i=1}^{f_u}\{(-a_i)^h - 1\}y_{ui}(t) + \sum_{i=1}^{f_u} b_i \frac{1-(-a_i)^h}{1-(-a_i)} u(t). \tag{8}$$

Next, variation of a reference trajectory of a first order model $\delta y_m(t+h|t)$ is defined as

$$\delta y_m(t+h|t) := \left\{1 - \exp\left(\frac{T_m}{3}\right)^h\right\} e(t), \tag{9}$$

where $e(t) := r(t) - y(t)$. T_m denotes 95% settling time and $r(t), y(t)$ are a reference signal end an output signal, respectively. When $\delta\hat{y}(t+h|t)$ becomes the same as $\delta y_m(t+h|t)$, the following equation holds:

$$\sum_{i=1}^{f_u}\{(-a_i)^h - 1\}y_{ui}(t) + \sum_{i=1}^{f_u} b_i \frac{1-(-a_i)^h}{1-(-a_i)} u(t) = \left\{1 - \exp\left(\frac{T_m}{3}\right)^h\right\} e(t). \tag{10}$$

Because h is a point of matching the model output and the reference trajectory, it is called "coincidence point". As a result, $u(t)$ is calculated by

$$u(t) = \frac{\left\{1 - \exp\left(-\frac{3}{T_m}\right)^h\right\} e(t) + \sum_{i=1}^{f_u}\{1 - (-a_i)^h\}y_{ui}(t)}{\sum_{i=1}^{f_u} b_i \frac{1-(-a_i)^h}{1-(-a_i)}}. \tag{11}$$

In order to treat time-delay, $e(t)$ of Eq. (11) is replaced by

$$e'(t) = e(t) - \{\hat{y}(t) - \hat{y}(t-k)\}, \tag{12}$$

where k is a number of steps of the time-delay.

2.2. Fictitious Reference Iterative Tuning (FRIT)

Soma et al. (2004) has proposed data-driven controller tuning named fictitious reference iterative tuning (FRIT) to tune feed-back controllers. FRIT tunes controller parameters based on one set of operating input-output data without system models. This paper applies FRIT to PFC. Conceptual diagram of proposing FRIT is shown in Figure 1.

$PFC(z^{-1})$ is a transfer function of PFC, and $u_0(t)$ and $y_0(t)$ are the initial data. Additionally, $G_m(z^{-1})$ denotes a reference model determined by the following equation to be the same as the reference trajectory of PFC.

$$G_m(z^{-1}) = \frac{1 - \exp\left(-\frac{3}{T_m}\right)}{1 - \exp\left(-\frac{3}{T_m}\right) z^{-1}} z^{-(k+1)}. \tag{13}$$

If any kind of $PFC(z^{-1})$ is determined, $\tilde{r}(t)$ and $\tilde{y}(t)$ can be calculated as

$$\tilde{r}(t) = PFC(z^{-1})^{-1} u(t) + y(t), \tag{14}$$

$$\tilde{y}(t) = G_m(z^{-1}) \tilde{r}(t). \tag{15}$$

By minimize the following J with the parameters included in $PFC(z^{-1})$ as optimization variables, the feedback loop constructed with $PFC(z^{-1})$ and $G_r(z^{-1})$ becomes the same as a reference model $G_m(z^{-1})$:

$$J = \sum_{j=1}^{N} \{G_m(z^{-1}) \tilde{r}(t) - y_0(t)\}^2 , \tag{16}$$

where N denotes the length of the initial data. As can be seen from the above, FRIT aims to make the closed-loop characteristic the same as reference model's one. In the parameters of PFC, the coincidence point h is a robustness related parameter. When h = 1, the control result exactly matches the reference trajectory, and when h is large, the result is sluggish but robust. Thus, FRIT is not suitable to tune h. Therefore, h is set as 1 while FRIT, and this paper employs the data-driven prediction method to tune that.

2.3. FRIT based Data-Driven Prediction

As mentioned before, FRIT aims model matching to reference model, and how to design the model has been a problem. To deal with this problem, a FRIT based data-driven prediction method has been proposed by Takahashi et al. (2019). By using the prediction method, various types of evaluation criterions can be set.

In the data-driven prediction method, minimizing J of Eq. (16) is similar as FRIT, but optimization variables are not $PFC(z^{-1})$ but $G_m(z^{-1})$. When initial data and $PFC(z^{-1})$ are determined, $\tilde{r}(t)$ is also fixed. As a result, closed-loop transfer function can be obtained in the form of $G_m(z^{-1})$ by minimizing J. In the proposed scheme, various predicted signals are obtained by calculating $G_m(z^{-1})$ corresponding to various h, and a designer determine h based on these signals.

3. Numerical example

This example utilized the following transfer function as a controlled system:

$$G_r(s) = \frac{10}{(100s+1)(80s+1)(20s+1)(0.9s+1)} \mathrm{e}^{-10s}, \tag{17}$$

and by discretizing it by sampling time $t_s = 1$, $G_r(z^{-1})$ was

$$G_r(z^{-1}) = \frac{2.32 \times 10^{-6}(1+8.03z^{-1})(1+0.79z^{-1})(1+0.077z^{-1})z^{-11}}{(1-0.991z^{-1})(1-0.988z^{-1})(1-0.329z^{-1})(1-0.951z^{-1})}. \tag{18}$$

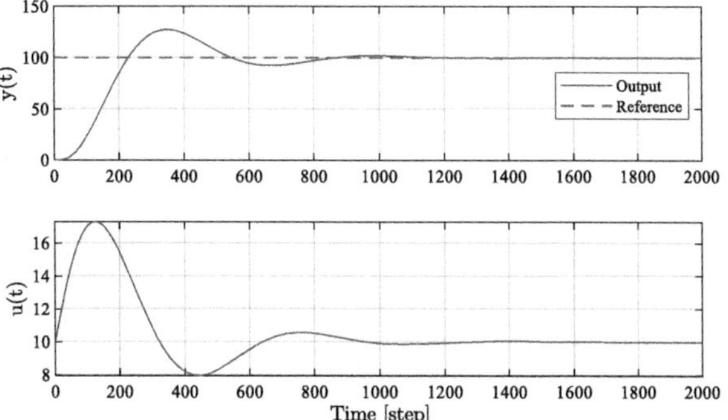

Figure 2: Initial data obtained by a PID controller.

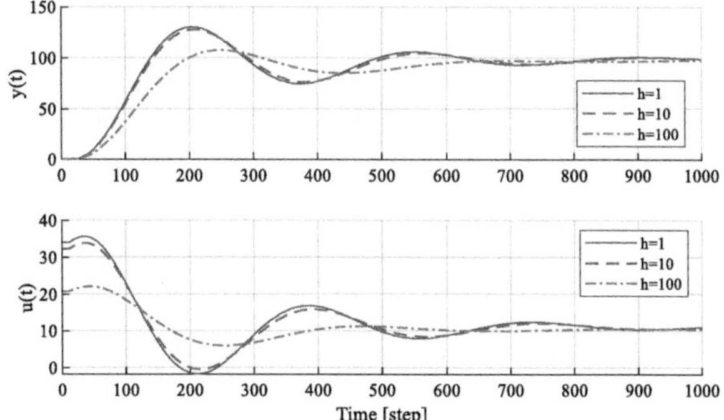

Figure 3: Prediction results using the data-driven prediction.

Eq. (18) shows that $G_r(z^{-1})$ has an unstable zero. Firstly, initial operating data was obtained using a PI controller with proportional gain 0.1 and integral gain 0.001, and Figure 2 shows the data. Based on this data, FRIT calculated PFC with $h = 1$ as:

$$u(t) = 0.3393e(t) + 0.0755\hat{y}(t), \tag{19}$$

where the order of the internal model was set as $f_u = 1$, and 95% settling time $T_m = 200$. The controlled system was high-order, and the controller was first order, so it was impossible to match the closed-loop to the reference model. For this reason, the data-driven prediction method was used to check a response using Eq. (19) and tune h. Figure 3 shows prediction results as $h = 1$, $h = 10$, and $h = 100$. The result of $h = 100$ has smallest overshoot and settling time while rise time was slowest. Although the value of h will depend on the control objective, this simulation selected $h = 100$. Without the prediction, h is selected by trial and error, and may take much time and cost.

Figure 4 shows control results of $h = 1$ and $h = 100$, and the prediction result of $h = 100$. Clearly, the control result (broken line) and predicted result (solid line) were similar, and likely the same especially with respect to output $y(t)$. Comparing figures using $h = 1$ and $h = 10$ are omitted for reasons of space but mean absolute error between actual and predicted input and output are shown in Table 1. In all cases, especially prediction error of output is very small. It means that the prediction is good, and the proposed method is useful. Control result itself is not so good in this simulation because the order

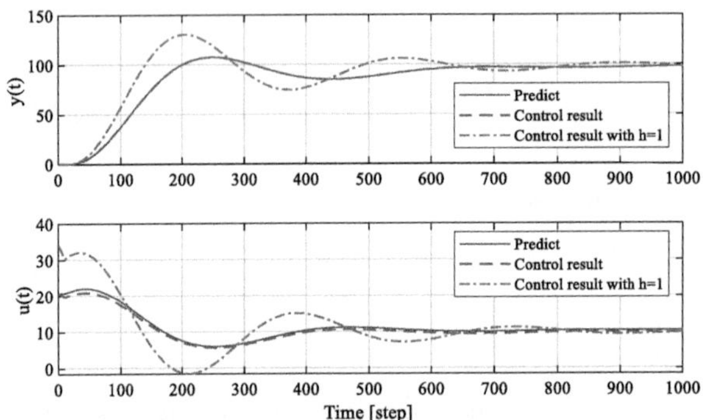

Figure 4: Control and prediction results using h=100 and h=1.

Table 1: Mean absolute error between actual and predicted input and output.

h	1	10	100
Output	1.72×10^{-7}	1.36×10^{-7}	5.26×10^{-8}
Input	1.14	1.05	0.54

of internal model of PFC is only first order. In the proposed method, it is considered to change the order and execute FRIT again.

4. Conclusions

This paper has proposed the control scheme using PFC, the data-driven design, and the data-driven prediction method. In the proposed scheme, most of the controller parameters of PFC, expected to replace a PID controller, are determined by using FRIT, a data-driven tuning. In addition, only coincidence point h, the robustness-related parameter is tuned by the FRIT based prediction method. By using the proposed method, more stable control can be realized than the conventional tuning only using FRIT which are forced to set h as 1. A numerical example has verified the effectiveness of the proposed scheme in this paper. To apply the proposed scheme for actual examples and more complex numerical examples, and proposing the unified way of controller parameters determination based on the prediction method are future works. We plan to apply the method for an aluminium block temperature control system by a heater.

References

J. Richalet, and D. O'Donovan, 2009, Predictive Functional Control Principles and Industrial Applications, Springer

H. Hjalmarsson, M. Gevers, S. Gunnarsson, and O. Lequin, 1998, Iterative Feedback Tuning: Theory and Applications, IEEE Control Systems Magazine, 18, 8, 26-41

S. Soma, O. Kaneko, and T. Fujii, 2004, A New Method of Controller Parameter Tuning based on Input-Output Data – Fictitious Reference Iterative Tuning (FRIT) –, IFAC Proceedings Volumes, 37, 12, 789–794

M. Nakamoto, 2003, An Application of Iterative Feedback Tuning for a Process Control, Trans. of the Society of Instrument and Control Engineers, 39, 10, 924-932

M. Kano, K. Tasaka, M. Ogawa, A. Takinami, S. Takahashi, and S. Yoshii, 2011, Extended Fictitious Reference Iterative Tuning and Its Application to Chemical Processes, Proc. of 2011 International Symposium on Advanced Control of Industrial Processes

E. Takahashi, and O. Kaneko, 2019, A New Approach to Prediction of Responses in Closed Loop Systems Based on the Direct Usage of One-shot Experimental Data, Transactions of the Society of Instrument and Control Engineers, 55, 4, 324-330 (in Japanese)

Flavio Manenti, Gintaras V. Reklaitis (Eds.), Proceedings of the 34th European Symposium on Computer Aided Process Engineering / 15th International Symposium on Process Systems Engineering (ESCAPE34/PSE24), June 2-6, 2024, Florence, Italy
 http://dx.doi.org/10.1016/B978-0-443-28824-1.50281-7

Optimal Control of Industrial Solvent-Based CO_2 Capture Plants

Fredrik Gjertsen,[a,*] Adriaen Verheyleweghen,[a] Svein Olav Hauger,[a] Vemund Tjessem,[a] Thor Mejdell,[b] Hanne M. Kvamsdal [b]

[a] *Cybernetica AS, Leirfossv. 27, N-7038 Trondheim, Norway*

[b] *SINTEF Industry, P.O. Box 4760 Torgarden, N-7465 Trondheim, Norway*

[*] *Corresponding author: fredrik.gjertsen@cybernetica.no*

Abstract

Solutions for advanced control of CO_2 capture processes have been developed and tested on pilot scale, with full-height absorber and desorber columns, representative of operation on an industrial scale. This paper presents new results from live demonstrations of non-linear model predictive control (NMPC) in pilot scale, using the HiPerCap solvent HS3 on the SINTEF Tiller CO_2LAB pilot, including ongoing work in the AURORA project, to build on the established results in this field, hereunder published case studies and pilot demonstrations.

The results indicate that industrial deployment of NMPC for solvent-based CO_2 capture processes is imminent, and that it will constitute a valuable tool to automate the operation. The demonstrated outcome for the end-users is energy-optimal operation handling all operating conditions, with less operator interventions. Furthermore, the approach has possible extensions to combat advanced operational challenges.

Keywords: Absorption, nonlinear model predictive control, optimal control, OPEX reduction, flexible operation

1. Introduction

For solvent-based post-combustion carbon capture (PCC) plants, the published literature contains several investigations into the use of advanced process control for optimal operation, albeit mainly for simulated case-studies. Panahi & Skogestad (2011) assessed a PCC process with self-optimizing control, using existing conventional PI(D) controllers for economically efficient operation, where selecting controlled variables that are suitable across a wide range of operating conditions proved challenging. Hereunder, choosing temperature(s) to control for the desorber, and the target values thereof, is a non-trivial task (Mejdell et al., 2017). In a follow-up study, Panahi & Skogestad (2012) compared several control structures with linear MPC. In terms of performance the investigations qualified MPC as a suitable approach for such a capture process, although the MPC was costly to establish compared to effective use of the base-layer controllers. Inspired by these indications, particularly the observed linearity between reboiler heat flux and optimal solvent rate, Arce et al. (2012) studied MPC for a simulated PCC facility, where the reboiler was the focal point of the study. Interestingly, the study found promising potential for cost savings by exploiting time-varying price regimes for energy and CO_2, like the ideas investigated by Kvamsdal et al. (2018). Furthermore, Wu et al. (2020) made a comprehensive review of flexible operation of PCC plants via advanced process control, hereunder considering the use of (N)MPC. They point out an observed gap, where the simple data-driven models are insufficiently accurate, while the rigorous first-principles models are too complex to be calculated efficiently and robustly. The goal of the work presented here is to address the gap in these findings regarding the suitability of (N)MPC for optimization and control of PCC processes. The demonstrated results address the reported challenges with computational efficiency and robustness, to establish NMPC with first-principles models as a viable solution for industrial use in real time.

Recently, NMPC demonstration projects have revealed the possibility of explicit and simultaneous control of capture rates and energy costs (Hauger et al., 2019). CO_2 capture rates were controlled either instantaneously or to average values (e.g., daily), while energy usage was minimized. Applicability was demonstrated for a wide range of flue gas conditions and targeted CO_2 capture rates. The NMPC showed promising results when tested in operation, using the CESAR1 solvent (Mejdell et al., 2022). Kvamsdal et al. (2018) argue that an NMPC will perform similarly or better than an attentive, experienced plant operator, as demonstrated at the Technology Centre Mongstad (TCM) pilot facility. Additionally, Mejdell et al. (2022) reported that the NMPC can maintain acceptable lean loading during periods where the energy input is heavily restricted. This functionality is particularly useful for when optimal use of excess heat as reboiler duty, with varying availability, in accordance with the conclusions of Arce et al. (2012), where the lean solvent loading was declared a key variable of interest for cost optimization. This concept is readdressed in the work presented here.

Chikukwa et al. (2012) reviewed the available literature on dynamic modeling of absorption-based CO_2 capture processes, including identification of knowledge gaps. They highlighted the need for understanding the transient behavior of capture plants when operating conditions change and the role of dynamic models thereof, particularly for power plants as target upstream processes. While they acknowledged the advances in dynamic modeling, they also identified the notable lack of model validation with dynamic data and the observation that most models are based on steady-state data. Nevertheless, headway has been made since, e.g., with the mentioned NMPC demonstration projects.

In the currently ongoing Horizon Europe (HEU) project AURORA, the NMPC models used in previous demonstrations are being further developed and improved to meet industrial requirements, hereunder simplifications for model efficiency and robustness. Pilot-scale demonstrations will be made for both Tiller and TCM pilot facilities using the CESAR1 solvent. Results from preliminary pilot-scale NMPC tests for various operating scenarios are presented in Section 4 and indicate that NMPC is not only viable but can enable improved flexibility and energy efficiency of the operation.

2. Model

While the exact model developed for the PCC process is too detailed to be presented in full in this paper, some fundamental modeling principles that were found to be critical for success are discussed. The NMPC models are mechanistic, dynamic models developed from first principles, including energy balances and mass balances for all process units, such as the absorber, desorber, reboiler, and heat exchangers. Crucially, as highlighted by Chikukwa et al. (2012) and Wu et al. (2020), the model equations must be implemented in a computationally efficient way to get appropriate real-time performance. To achieve this, the models have inherent simplifications to arrive at a level of balanced complexity where both the computational efficiency and the accuracy of the model are adequate.

A module-based strategy has been chosen for implementation of the models, with a tripartite division as shown in Figure 1. The model consists of a generic part, a solvent-specific part, and a plant-specific part. This promotes reusability and versatility of the common, general principles of the capture processes, which eases the deployment of NMPC for a known solvent in a new capture plant, e.g., or the introduction of a new solvent in the NMPC for known plants.

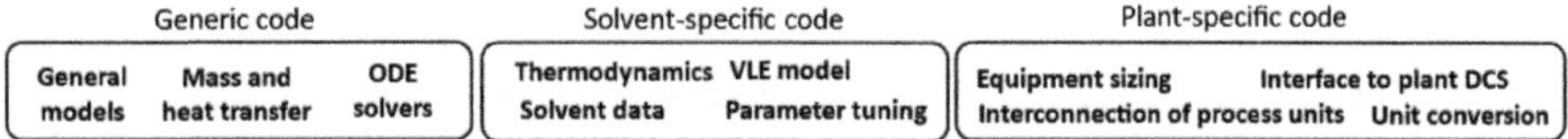

Figure 1: Tripartite, modular approach to process modeling for deployment with NMPC.

3. Advanced Process Control System

For the present work, the Cybernetica CENIT software suite was used. The central building blocks of the CENIT NMPC are shown in Figure 2. The core is the mechanistic process model, as mentioned in Sec. 2, which is formulated in C/C++ for numerical efficiency and compliance with the other components of the framework.

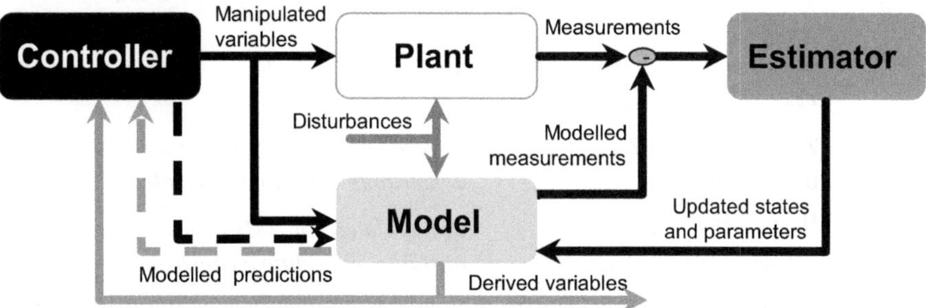

Figure 2: Block diagram illustrating the central components of the NMPC application(s), including the interconnection between them.

3.1. Nonlinear Kalman Filter

A crucial difference between in-silico studies of PCC processes and industrial implementations is the need for accurate online state and parameter estimation schemes. Without them, any model-based controller may be vulnerable to plant-model mismatch, e.g., caused by changes in amine concentrations due to degradation, loss of solvent through emissions, water balance issues, and other unforeseen process changes. The online estimation scheme is necessary to align the mechanistic process model with the measured plant behavior, to enable accurate predictions for near-future operation.

The Kalman filter estimator is a two-step process where *a priori* estimates are obtained based on the previous estimate in time by model prediction, after which the *a posteriori* estimates are found by correcting the model predictions with the measurements. The model predictions for states, parameters and measurements are shown in Eqs. (1)-(3), including process noise ($\bar{\boldsymbol{v}}_{k-1}$) and measurement noise ($\bar{\boldsymbol{w}}_k$). The following measurement correction is shown in Eq. (4).

Model prediction:

$$\bar{\boldsymbol{x}}_k = \boldsymbol{f}(\hat{\boldsymbol{x}}_{k-1}, \hat{\boldsymbol{\theta}}_{k-1}, \boldsymbol{u}_{k-1}, \bar{\boldsymbol{v}}_{k-1}) \quad \text{a priori state estimates} \tag{1}$$

$$\bar{\boldsymbol{\theta}}_k = \hat{\boldsymbol{\theta}}_{k-1} + \bar{\boldsymbol{v}}_{k-1} \quad \text{a priori parameter estimates} \tag{2}$$

$$\bar{\boldsymbol{y}}_k = \boldsymbol{g}(\bar{\boldsymbol{x}}_k, \hat{\boldsymbol{\theta}}_k, \boldsymbol{u}_{k-1}) + \bar{\boldsymbol{w}}_k \quad \text{a priori measurement estimates} \tag{3}$$

Measurement correction:

$$\begin{bmatrix} \hat{\boldsymbol{x}}_k \\ \hat{\boldsymbol{\theta}}_k \end{bmatrix} = \begin{bmatrix} \bar{\boldsymbol{x}}_k \\ \bar{\boldsymbol{\theta}}_k \end{bmatrix} + \boldsymbol{K}(k)(\boldsymbol{y}_{M,k} - \bar{\boldsymbol{y}}_k) \quad \textit{a posteriori} \text{ state and param. est.} \tag{4}$$

3.2. NMPC

The functionality of the CENIT NMPC is described in more detail by Foss & Schei (2007). At its core, it is based on a sequential quadratic programming (SQP) algorithm inspired by the work of Biegler and coworkers (de Oliveira & Biegler, 1995). The general cost function to be minimized is shown in Eq. (5), subject to the conditions specified in Eqs. (6)-(8). This approach will find the optimal input moves for the specified control horizon while penalizing setpoint deviations ($\boldsymbol{Z} - \boldsymbol{Z}_{ref}$), input moves ($\boldsymbol{\Delta U}$) and constraint violations ($\boldsymbol{\varepsilon}$), each with their respective weights ($\boldsymbol{Q}$, $\boldsymbol{S}$, $\boldsymbol{r}_1$ and $\boldsymbol{r}_2$).

$$\min_{\Delta U} J = \frac{1}{2}(\boldsymbol{Z} - \boldsymbol{Z}_{ref})^T \boldsymbol{Q}(\boldsymbol{Z} - \boldsymbol{Z}_{ref}) + \frac{1}{2}(\boldsymbol{\Delta U}^T \boldsymbol{S} \boldsymbol{\Delta U}) + \boldsymbol{r}_1^T \boldsymbol{\varepsilon} + \frac{1}{2}\boldsymbol{\varepsilon}^T diag(\boldsymbol{r}_2)\boldsymbol{\varepsilon} \tag{5}$$

s.t

$$\begin{aligned} \mathbf{x}_{k+j} &= \mathbf{f}(\mathbf{x}_{k+j-1}, \mathbf{u}_{k+j-1}, \mathbf{v}_k) \\ \mathbf{z}_{k+j} &= \mathbf{h}(\mathbf{x}_{k+j}, \mathbf{u}_{k+j}) \end{aligned} \quad \textit{Model predictions} \tag{6}$$

$$\begin{aligned} \mathbf{Z}_{\min} - \boldsymbol{\varepsilon} < \mathbf{Z} < \mathbf{Z}_{\max} + \boldsymbol{\varepsilon} \\ \mathbf{0} \le \boldsymbol{\varepsilon} \le \boldsymbol{\varepsilon}_{\max} \end{aligned} \quad \textit{Controlled variables (CVs) soft constraints with slack variables} \tag{7}$$

$$\begin{aligned} \mathbf{U}_{\min} \le \mathbf{U} \le \mathbf{U}_{\max} \\ \Delta\mathbf{U}_{\min} \le \Delta\mathbf{U} \le \Delta\mathbf{U}_{\max} \end{aligned} \quad \textit{Manipulated var. (MV) constraints, absolute and relative constraints} \tag{8}$$

For the PCC process, the NMPC has two CVs of central importance. These are the CO_2 capture rate, which is controlled to a specified setpoint, and the specific reboiler duty, which is minimized. Furthermore, the lean loading is constrained in the optimization criterion to avoid build-up of dissolved CO_2 in the lean solvent over time. The available MVs are the reboiler duty and the flow rate of lean solvent into the absorber top, which are both controlled within their respective constraints. In the demonstrated application, the sample time is 30 seconds, with a prediction horizon of 5 hours, hence the strict requirements for computational efficiency.

4. Results

The test scenarios were designed to address the existing shortcomings and research gaps highlighted by Mejdell et al. (2022). Additional tests were performed but are omitted from this work for brevity. The omitted demonstrations include temporary reboiler stops (e.g., for power plant grid stabilization), capture rate setpoint changes and flue gas ramps (both with and without prior knowledge, for feedforward functionality).

4.1. Scenario I: Energy availability for reboiler is heavily restricted.

A live demonstration of the proposed NMPC during limited availability of energy is shown in Figure 3, Scenario I. As a result of the reduced energy availability, the CO_2 capture rate is reduced temporarily. Whereas a short-sighted controller, i.e., PID or a feed-forward controller, without knowledge of the dynamics and the constraint regions, would attempt to maintain a high capture rate, the NMPC backs down on the capture rate for the time being to prevent an unwanted increase in lean loading. It is observed that regaining the capture rate is relatively quick, given that lean loading is appropriately low compared to what it would take to regain the lean loading once it has escalated. The lean loading was directly constrained in the cost function to motivate this behavior.

4.2. Scenario II: Load following with large, rapid changes in inlet CO_2 flow rate.

During another live demonstration, a load following scenario was tested, as shown in Figure 3, Scenario II. In this case, the flue gas is changed rapidly and unpredictably to replicate the behavior of an upstream emitter with changing operating conditions, e.g., a power plant that is required to participate in grid power regulation, as pointed out by Wu et al. (2020), among others. In practice, this will incur changes in the flue gas inlet flow rate, the flue gas CO_2 concentration, or both. The purpose of the NMPC is to obey the specific capture rate setpoint, as prescribed by the plant operator while approaching the point of optimal operation in terms of energy usage. The results indicate that the control system is responsive to large disturbances, even when the capture plant is pushed towards the constraints, i.e., its design- and operational boundaries.

5. Conclusions

NMPC has been demonstrated on pilot scale for a CO_2 capture facility, using mechanistic process models in the Cybernetica CENIT control software. Two scenarios were studied to assess the viability of NMPC for industrial PCC: In the first scenario, reboiler duty was heavily restricted, temporarily. In response, the NMPC reduced the CO_2 capture rate

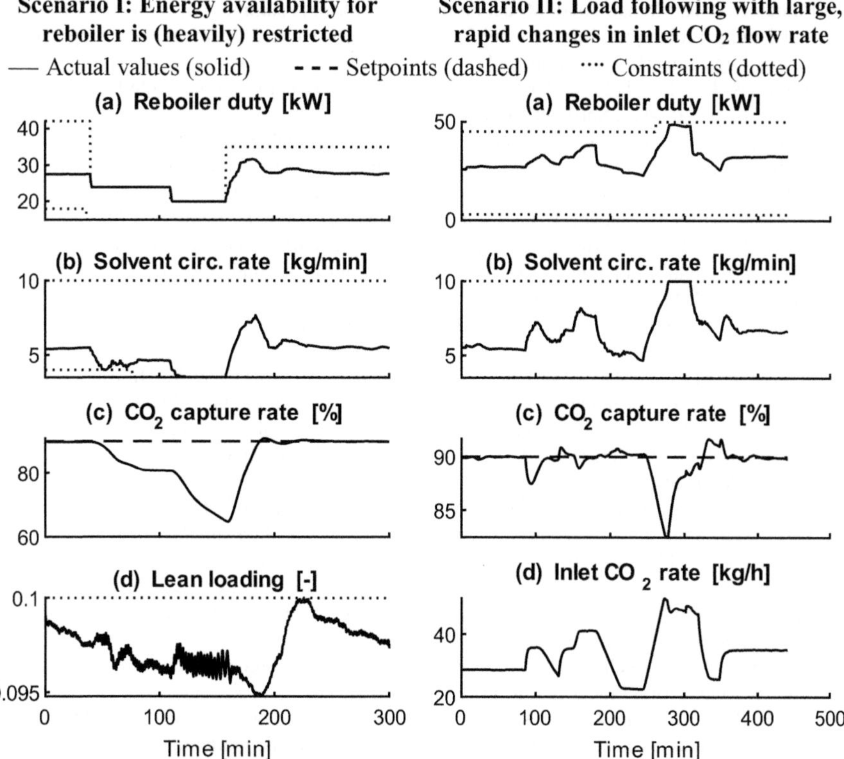

Figure 3: Results from live demonstration of optimal control using NMPC at the Tiller pilot plant, for two separate scenarios with challenging operating conditions.

temporarily to prevent an increase in lean loading. In the second scenario, the CO_2 concentration in the inlet stream varied rapidly and unpredictably. The CO_2 capture rate was kept on the setpoint, despite these large deviations. This demonstration is important evidence of the robustness of the NMPC. As demonstrated in these scenarios, NMPC solutions are suitable for industrial application, with versatility for various solvents and plant-specific variations. Concerns regarding robustness and computational efficiency have been calmed after extensive testing in live operation.

Acknowledgements

This work has received funding from the European Union's Horizon Europe and Horizon 2020 research and innovation programmes under grant agreements No. 101096521 and 884266, respectively.

References

A. Arce, N. Mac Dowell, N. Shah & L. F. Vega, 2012, Flexible operation of solvent regeneration systems for CO_2 capture processes using advanced control techniques: Towards operational cost minimisation, International Journal of Greenhouse Gas Control, Vol. 11, pp. 236-250

A. Chikukwa, N. Enaasen, H. M. Kvamsdal & M. Hillestad, 2012, Dynamic Modeling of Post-combustion CO_2 Capture Using Amines – A Review, Energy Procedia, Vol. 23, pp. 82-91

S. M. Elgsæter, P. Kittilsen & S. O. Hauger, 2012. Designing large-scale balanced-complexity models for online use. IFAC Proceedings Volumes, Vol. 45, Iss. 8, pp. 157–162

A. Emhemed & R. Mamat, 2020, Model Predictive Control: A summary of Industrial Challenges and Tuning Techniques, International Journal of Mechatronics, Electrical and Computer Technology, Vol. 10, Iss. 35, pp. 4441-4459

B. A. Foss & T. S. Schei, 2007, Putting Nonlinear Model Predictive Control into Use, LNCIS, Vol. 358, pp. 407-417, Springer Verlag

S. O. Hauger, N. E. Flø, H. M. Kvamsdal, F. Gjertsen, T. Mejdell & M. Hillestad, 2019, Demonstration of non-linear model predictive control of post-combustion CO_2 capture processes; Computers and Chemical Engineering 123, pp. 184-195

H. M. Kvamsdal, S. O. Hauger, F. Gjertsen, T. Mejdell, N. E. Flø, K. Johnsen & M. Hillestad, 2018, Demonstration of two-level nonlinear model predictive control of CO_2 capture plants, 14th International Conference on Greenhouse Gas Control Technologies, GHGT-14, 21st – 25th October 2018, Melbourne, Australia

T. Mejdell, G. Haugen, A. Rieder & H. M. Kvamsdal, 2017, Dynamic and control of an absorber - desorber plant at Heilbronn, Energy Procedia, Vol. 114, pp. 1231–1244

T. Mejdell, H. M. Kvamsdal, S. O. Hauger, F. Gjertsen, F. A. Tobiesen & M. Hillestad, 2022, Demonstration of non-linear model predictive control for optimal flexible operation of a CO_2 capture plant, International Journal of Greenhouse Gas Control, Vol. 117, 103645N. M. C. de Oliveria & L. T. Biegler, 1995, An extension of Newton-type algorithms for nonlinear process control, Automatica, Vol. 31, Iss. 2, pp. 281-286

M. Panahi & S. Skogestad, 2011, Economically efficient operation of CO_2 capturing process. Part I. Self-optimizing procedure for selecting the best controlled variables, Chemical Engineering and Processing: Process Intensification, Vol. 50, Iss. 3, pp. 247–253

M. Panahi & S. Skogestad, 2012, Economically efficient operation of CO_2 capturing process. Part II. Design of control layer, Chemical Engineering and Processing: Process Intensification, Vol. 52, pp. 112–124

S. J. Qin & T. A. Badgwell, 2003, A survey of industrial model predictive control technology, Control Engineering Practice, Vol. 11, Iss. 7, pp. 733-764

X. Wu, M. Wang, P. Liao, J. Shen & Y. Li, 2020, Solvent-based post-combustion CO2 capture for power plants: A critical review and perspective on dynamic modelling, system identification, process control and flexible operation, Applied Energy, Vol. 257, 113941

Flavio Manenti, Gintaras V. Reklaitis (Eds.), Proceedings of the 34th European Symposium on Computer Aided Process Engineering / 15th International Symposium on Process Systems Engineering (ESCAPE34/PSE24), June 2-6, 2024, Florence, Italy
 http://dx.doi.org/10.1016/B978-0-443-28824-1.50282-9

A novel hydrogen-based desalination system for a self-sustaining community

Du Wen[a*], François Maréchal[a]

[a]*Industrial Process and Energy Systems Engineering, Swiss Federal Institute of Technology in Lausanne (EPFL), Rue de l'Industrie 17, Sion 1951, Switzerland*
du.wen@epfl.ch

Abstract

This work proposes a novel hydrogen-based desalination system to replace fossil fuel-based plants. The system has a water-hydrogen nexus framework to achieve an efficient operation, providing electricity, potable water, and green hydrogen. Through optimal planning, less operation cost is found by considering the variation in supply and demand. Results show that the system has an average efficiency of 43.3%, higher than other renewable desalination systems. Meanwhile, the lower water production cost of 0.15$/t makes it competitive compared to membrane-based systems. The system well presents the merits of the water-hydrogen nexus.

Keywords: renewable energy, desalination, hydrogen, optimization.

1. Introduction

Thermal-based seawater desalination technologies, such as multi-effect distillation (MED), release the stress on the global water scarcity crisis. It has a long lifespan, great tolerance to feedwater salinity and quality, low prices, and strong scalability for various applications. However, it is energy-intensive, leading to considerable environmental problems and ecological risks (Lee et al., 2021). To compete with the membrane-based process, researchers are working on finding a way to integrate renewable energy into the thermal-based desalination system. The intermittent nature of renewable energy makes it unsuitable for continuous water supply. The promising solution to this erratic supply is energy storage technology, particularly chemical energy storage, such as power-to-gas. A certain chemical is produced using excess renewable energy and used in a supply shortage. Hydrogen is an up-and-coming candidate due to its zero-carbon fuel status and high energy density. Because of these qualities, it can be used to buffer the balance between supply and demand and facilitate the integration of renewable energy into desalination systems, particularly thermal-based systems where hydrogen can be used directly to produce thermal energy. Another heat source is the waste heat generated during the hydrogen production process.

Researchers have designed many systems to show the merits of this integration. Wang et al. (Wang et al., 2022) proposed a biomass-based system, comprising solid oxide electrolyzers, a biomass gasifier, a steam Rankine cycle, and MED units. Hydrogen is used to consume excess electricity, while the waste heat is used in MED units. The energy and exergy efficiencies of the system are 36.44% and 17.10%, respectively, with a freshwater production rate of 2.74 kg/s and a production cost of 16.6 USD/GJ. A hybrid energy system that integrates solid oxide fuel cells, a gas turbine, and proton exchange membrane (PEM) electrolyzers was studied by Musharavati and Khanmohammadi (Musharavati et al., 2022). Similarly, the waste heat is used in MED units. The system can produce 0.002 kg/s of hydrogen and 53.5 kg/s of desalinated water with an energy efficiency of 36.45%. Shahverdian et al. (Shahverdian et al., 2023) investigated the combination of solar, geothermal, PEM electrolyzers, MED, and Kalina cycle. The freshwater supply can reach 2.1 kg/s with an energy efficiency of 6.23%.

Those studies still have limitations, such as, they are not a net-zero system, hydrogen plays a single role of consuming excess electricity, and the nexus of energy, hydrogen, and water are not well displayed. According to those limitations, this work designs a novel hydrogen-based desalination system, which characterizes net-zero emission as it only uses renewable energy and hydrogen. Hydrogen is involved in the energy storage and MED processes. It is evaluated on different weather conditions throughout the year. The optimal system is determined by optimal planning. This work contributes to proposing a hydrogen-fueled system with relatively high energy efficiency and low cost.

2. Materials and methods

2.1. Scenario descriptions

The schematic of the hydrogen-based desalination system is shown in **Figure 1**. It provides electricity and freshwater to a community. This standalone net-zero system has two parts. In the power system, solar PV and wind turbine satisfy the electricity demand, while proton exchange membrane water electrolysis and fuel cells (hereafter, abbreviated as PEMEC and PEMFC, respectively) are used to deal with the mismatch between supply and demand. Excess electricity is stored in the form of hydrogen and released when needed. The second part is a MED system. Seawater undergoes an even distribution, dividing into four streams that are sprayed from the reactor's top. It experiences partial evaporation on the heat exchanger's surface and partial flashing upon entering the next stage from the bottom due to pressure changes. The resulting fluid, a mixture of evaporated and flashed seawater, combines with incoming seawater before being injected into the subsequent reactor. Meanwhile, the vapor produced progresses to the next-stage heat exchanger, where further condensation occurs. The necessary heat for the initial effect (E1) is supplied by a hydrogen-fueled boiler. Distilled water is directed into a flash box, separating flash vapor and condensed water.

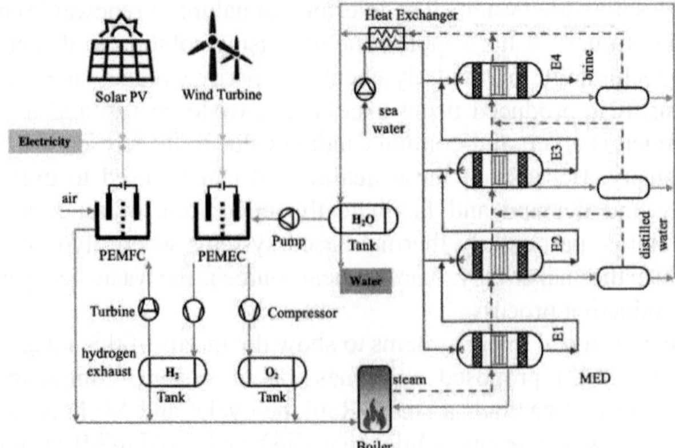

Figure 1. Schematic of the hydrogen-based desalination system.

2.2. Problem formulation

2.2.1. Objective function

The optimal planning of the system is described as a series of mixed-integer linear programming problems, of which the objective function is:

$$\text{Obj}=\max(REV_t - OPEX_t) \tag{1}$$

where REV_t is the revenue at time t, considering the revenue from selling electricity and hydrogen, USD; $OPEX_t$ is the operating expenditure at time t, USD.

$$CAPEX_{\mathrm{a}}=CAPEX_{\mathrm{r}}\left(\frac{A_a}{A_r}\right)^n \tag{2}$$

where $CAPEX_{\mathrm{a}}$ is the capital expenditure of component a in the system, USD; $CAPEX_{\mathrm{r}}$ is the capital expenditure of component a from the reference, USD; A is the equipment cost attribute, which is determined by the specific component; n is the cost exponent, -. The economic assumption is shown in **Table 1**.

Table 1 Economic assumptions (Wen et al., 2022, 2024).

Name	Value	Name	Value
System lifetime	25 y	CAPEX of PEM stack	385 USD/kW
CAPEX of solar PV	1,166 USD/kW	CAPEX of desalination [a]	195.8 USD/(t/h)
CAPEX of wind turbine	1,411 USD/kW	CAPEX of hydrogen storage	90.1 USD/kg

[a] The CAPEX of desalination is evaluated according to the reference (Turton et al., 2008).

2.2.2. Main constraints

The objective function is restricted by two main constraints, which are shown thereafter.
Energy balance constraint:

$$P_{\mathrm{demand}} + P_{\mathrm{curtailment}} = P_{\mathrm{solar\ PV}} + P_{\mathrm{wind\ turbine}} + P_{\mathrm{PEMFC}} - P_{\mathrm{PEMEC}} \tag{4}$$

where P_{demand} is the electricity demand from the community, kW; $P_{\mathrm{curtailment}}$ is the curtailment caused by the supply and demand mismatch, kW; $P_{\mathrm{solar\ PV}}$, and $P_{\mathrm{wind\ turbine}}$, P_{PEMFC} are the electricity generated by solar PV, wind turbine, and PEMFC, respectively, kW; P_{PEMEC} is the consumed electricity by PEMEC, kW.

Mass balance constraints consider the storage limitation of hydrogen and portable water:

$$m^t_{\mathrm{H_2,sto}}=m^{t\text{-}1}_{\mathrm{H_2,sto}}+m^t_{\mathrm{H_2,PEMEC}}+m^t_{\mathrm{H_2,exhaust}} - m^t_{\mathrm{H_2,MED}} - m^t_{\mathrm{H_2,PEMFC}} \tag{5}$$

$$m^t_{\mathrm{H_2O,sto}}=m^{t\text{-}1}_{\mathrm{H_2O,sto}}+m^t_{\mathrm{H_2O,MED}}+m^t_{\mathrm{H_2O,exhaust}}+m^t_{\mathrm{H_2O,PEMFC}} - m^t_{\mathrm{H_2O,PEMEC}} - m^t_{\mathrm{H_2O,supply}} \tag{6}$$

$$0 \le m^t_{\mathrm{H_2,sto}} \le M_{\mathrm{H_2},max},\ 0 \le m^t_{\mathrm{H_2O,sto}} \le M_{\mathrm{H_2O},max} \tag{7}$$

where $m^t_{\mathrm{H_2,sto}}$ and $m^{t\text{-}1}_{\mathrm{H_2,sto}}$ are the hydrogen storage capacity at time t and t-1, respectively, kg; $m^t_{\mathrm{H_2,PEMEC}}$ is the hydrogen production rate of PEMEC, kg/h; $m^t_{\mathrm{H_2,exhaust}}$ is the remaining hydrogen in the exhaust gas of PEMFC, kg/h; $m^t_{\mathrm{H_2,MED}}$ is the hydrogen consumption rate of MED, kg/h; $m^t_{\mathrm{H_2,PEMFC}}$ is the hydrogen consumption rate of PEMFC, kg/h; $m^t_{\mathrm{H_2O,MED}}$ is the water production rate of MED, kg/h; $m^t_{\mathrm{H_2O,exhaust}}$ is the water production rate from hydrogen combustion, kg/h; $m^t_{\mathrm{H_2O,PEMFC}}$ is the water production rate of PEMFC, kg/h; $m^t_{\mathrm{H_2O,PEMEC}}$ is the water consumption rate of PEMEC, kg/h.

System component constraints are constructed based on (Wen et al., 2022).

Solar PV:

$$P_{\mathrm{solar\ PV}} = \eta_{\mathrm{cell}} P_{\mathrm{rated}} \left[1 + \gamma \left(t_{\mathrm{a}} + I \left[\frac{t_{\mathrm{n}} - 20°\mathrm{C}}{800\mathrm{W{\cdot}m^{-2}}}\right] - 25°\mathrm{C}\right)\right] \tag{6}$$

where η_{cell} is energy efficiency of the solar cell, -; P_{rated} is the rated power, kW; γ is temperature coefficient, %/°C; t_{a} is ambient temperature, °C; I is solar irradiance, W/m^2; t_{n} is normal operating cell temperature, °C.

Wind turbine:

$$P_{\text{wind turbine}} = \frac{1}{2}\rho A_s v^3 C_p \eta_m \tag{7}$$

where ρ is air density, kg/m^3; A_s is the swept area of the rotor, m^2; v is the average wind speed at rotor height, m/s; C_p is the power coefficient, -; η_m is the mechanical efficiency. PEMEL and PEMFC share a similar approach (Wen et al., 2022):

$$P_{\text{PEMEC}} = J_{\text{PEMEC}} V_{\text{PEMEC}} A_{\text{PEMEC}} \tag{8}$$

$$m^t_{\text{H}_2,\text{PEMEC}} = \frac{J_{\text{PEMEC}}}{2\text{F}} M_{\text{H}_2} A_{\text{PEMEC}} \tag{9}$$

where J_{PEMEC} is current density, A/ m^2; V_{PEMEC} is the working voltage, V; A_{PEMEC} is the membrane area, m^2; F is Faraday constant; M_{H_2} is the mole mass of hydrogen, g/mol.
A hydrogen driven four-effect seawater desalination (MED) system is adapted from reference (Liponi et al., 2020) and modeled in Aspen Plus V11 (Aspen Tech, 2021). The system consists of a flash chamber, evaporator, demister, steam mixer, and condensation unit. The design parameters of the MED system are shown in **Table 2**.

Table 2 Design parameters of MED system.

Name	Value	Name	Value
Feed seawater	5000 kg/h	Top brine temperature in effect 1	66.3 °C
Distilled water	727.5 kg/h	Top brine temperature in effect 2	57.5 °C
Preheated seawater temperature	40 °C	Top brine temperature in effect 3	48.8 °C
Recovery ratio in this work	0.146	Top brine temperature in effect 4	40.1 °C

2.3. Key performance indicator

Energy efficiency considers the main inputs and outputs of the system:

$$\eta = \frac{P_{\text{solar PV}} + P_{\text{wind turbine}} + P_{\text{PEMFC}} + m^t_{\text{H}_2,\text{PEMEC}}\text{LHVH} + m^t_{\text{H}_2\text{O},\text{MED}} h_{\text{water}}}{P_{\text{solar}} + P_{\text{wind}} + m^t_{\text{H}_2,\text{PEMFC}}\text{LHVH} + m^t_{\text{H}_2,\text{MED}}\text{LHVH}} \tag{10}$$

where LHVH is the lower heating value of hydrogen, kJ/kg; h_{water} is the specific entropy of the potable water, kJ/kg; P_{solar} is the rated output of solar PV, kW; P_{wind} is the wind energy potential, kW.
Annual Levelized cost of water (LCOW) denotes the production cost of freshwater:

$$\text{LCOW} = \frac{\sum CAPEX \frac{i(1+i)^n}{(1+i)^n - 1} + \sum OPEX - \sum REV}{\sum m_{\text{H}_2\text{O},\text{MED}}} \tag{11}$$

where n is system lifetime, y; i is annual interest.

3. Results and discussions

The system is examined on the yearly supply and demand data, which are provided by the MERRA-2 database (Global Modelling and Assimilation Office (GMAO), 2015) and the Renewable Energy Institute of Japan.

3.1. Technical performance

Figure 2. shows the hourly and monthly average of system efficiency. The distribution curves characterize a flattened bowl shape as depicted on the left. It is around 30% during the day, while it is around 55% during the night. The common effect of all subsystems contributes to this characteristic, where solar dominates the lowest efficiency and PEM electrolyzers domine the highest efficiency because the solar system has a maximum efficiency of 15.3% (less than the valley point of 25%) and PEM electrolyzers have a maximum efficiency of 70% (over than the peak point of 55%). The monthly variation mainly depends on solar output. In January, when there is less solar energy potential, the monthly average system efficiency is the highest. On the contrary, In June, the increasing proportion of solar output decreases the system efficiency.

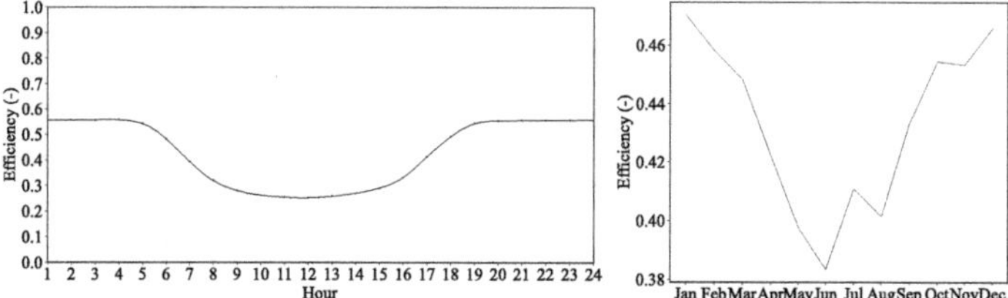

Figure 2. Hourly and monthly average of system efficiency.

The monthly share of net hydrogen production is shown in **Figure 3**. Because of the constant operation of the MED system, the variation is determined by PEMEC and PEMFC systems. The peaks occur in March, April, and October when there is a high utilization rate of the PEMEL system. Over 25 tones of hydrogen per month is accumulated at that time. The valley in August requires an extra 14.7 tones of hydrogen, which can be satisfied by the accumulation. The PEMFC system in August consumes almost double that in other months. The hydrogen consumption rate of the MED system ranges from 40 – 45 tones per month. The exhaust gas from the PEMFC system can be used to provide heat duty in the MED system for the sake of fuel saving.

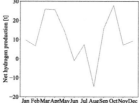

Figure 3. Monthly net hydrogen production.

3.2. Economic performance

The breakdown of CAPEX is shown in **Figure 4**. It is 51.3 MUSD in total, where wind turbine (WT) takes the majority of it, followed by solar PV, PEM electrolyzers, MED, and storage tank. Since the water, fuel, heating, and cooling are satisfied inside the system, only fixed OEPX is considered, which is 1.26 MUSD. The revenue from electricity and hydrogen makes the production cost of fresher water cheaper than expected, as shown in **Table 3**. Compared with other works, this system also has a high efficiency.

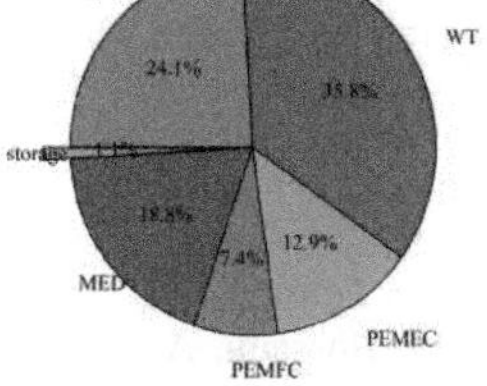

Figure 4. Breakdown of CAPEX.

3.3. Comparison with other systems

Table 3 Comparison of different desalination systems.

Configuration	Efficiency	Power supply	Hydrogen supply	Water supply	Cost	Ref.
This work	43.3%	8.2 MW	12.1 kg/h	9.7 t/h	0.15 $/t	-
ORC, SOEC, AEC, RO	37.9 %	6.3 MW	169.2 kg/h	5.9 t/h	1.86 $/t	(Lee et al., 2022)
Gasification, SRC, SOEC, MED	36.4 %	1.7 MW	12.3 kg/h	9.9 t/h	16.6 $/GJ	(Wang et al., 2022)
Gas turbine, PEMEC, SOFC, MED	36.5 %	54.8 MW	7.4 kg/h	192.6 t/h	-	(Musharavati et al., 2022)
Solar, KC, PEMEC, PEMFC, MED	6.2 %	81.4 MWh	1.3 kg/h	7.6 t/h	-	(Shahverdian et al., 2023)

4. Conclusions

In this study, a novel hydrogen-based desalination system is proposed for a self-sustaining community. It uses hydrogen as a substitute for fossil fuels and as an energy carrier. It is a net-zero system and flexible enough to satisfy the fluctuating electricity demand, while at the same time providing a constant water supply. After the evaluation on the hourly supply and demand data, the conclusions are summarized as follows: the system has a higher energy efficiency of 43.3% and a lower production cost of 0.15$/t, compared to previous works. The system well presents the merits of the water-hydrogen nexus.

References

K. Lee, W. Jepson, 2021, Environmental impact of desalination: A systematic review of Life Cycle Assessment, Desalination, 509, 115066.

R. Turton, R.C. Bailie, W.B. Whiting, J.A. Shaeiwitz, 2008, Analysis, synthesis, and design of chemical processes, 3ed, Pearson Education.

Du Wen, Muhammad Aziz, 2022, Techno-economic analyses of power-to-ammonia-to-power and biomass-to-ammonia-to-power pathways for carbon neutrality scenario, Applied Energy, Volume 319, 119272.

Du Wen, Muhammad Aziz, 2024, Perspective of staged hydrogen economy in Japan: A case study based on the data-driven method, Renewable and Sustainable Energy Reviews, Volume 189, Part A, 113907.

A. Liponi, C. Wieland, A. Baccioli, 2020, Multi-effect distillation plants for small-scale seawater desalination: thermodynamic and economic improvement, Energy Conversion and Management, Volume 205, 112337.

Aspen Tech, Aspen Plus Simulation Software, 2021.

Global Modelling and Assimilation Office (GMAO), 2015, MERRA-2 tavg1_2d_rad_Nx: 2d,1-Hourly,Time-Averaged,Single-Level,Assimilation,Radiation Diagnostics V5.12.4, Greenbelt, MD, USA, Goddard Earth Sciences Data and Information Services Center (GES DISC).

J.M. Lee, S.H. Lee, J.H. Baik, K. Park, 2022, Techno-economic analysis of hydrogen production electrically coupled to a hybrid desalination process, Desalination, Volume 539, 115949.

S. Wang, H. Lin, A.M. Abed, A. Sharma, H. Fooladi, 2022, Exergoeconomic assessment of a biomass-based hydrogen, electricity and freshwater production cycle combined with an electrolyzer, steam turbine and a thermal desalination process, International Journal of Hydrogen Energy, Volume 47, 33699-33718.

F. Musharavati, S. Khanmohammadi, 2022, Design and exergy based optimization of a clean energy system with fuel Cell/MED and hydrogen storage option, International Journal of Hydrogen Energy, Volume 47, 26715-26727.

M.H. Shahverdian, S. Sedayevatan, M. Hosseini, A. Sohani, R. Javadijam, H. Sayyaadi, 2023, Multi-objective technoeconomic optimization of an off-grid solar-ground-source driven cycle with hydrogen storage for power and fresh water production, International Journal of Hydrogen Energy, Volume 48, 19772-19791.

Flavio Manenti, Gintaras V. Reklaitis (Eds.), Proceedings of the 34th European Symposium on Computer Aided Process Engineering / 15th International Symposium on Process Systems Engineering (ESCAPE34/PSE24), June 2-6, 2024, Florence, Italy
 http://dx.doi.org/10.1016/B978-0-443-28824-1.50283-0

Machine Learning-Based Soft Sensor for a Sugar Factory's Batch Crystallizer

Mohammad Reza Boskabadi, Abhishek Sivaram, Gürkan Sin, Seyed Soheil Mansouri*

Department of Chemical and Biochemical Engineering, Søltofts Plads, Building 228A, Technical University of Denmark, 2800 Kgs. Lyngby, Denmark
**seso@kt.dtu.dk*

Abstract

In the contemporary industrial landscape, the utilization of real-time data for the surveillance and enhancement of operational processes stands as an imperative, contributing significantly to the refinement of operational efficiency and product quality across a multitude of sectors. This work presents the development of a machine-learning soft sensor utilizing Multivariate Linear Regression (MLR), Generalized Regression Neural Network (GRNN), Decision Tree, and Support Vector Regression (SVR) based on real historical data from a sugar factory. The soft sensor is designed to estimate the Brix index in the vacuum batch crystallizer. Various models have demonstrated robust performance in predicting Brix sensor values. The framework involves three key steps: data pre-processing, model construction employing selected algorithms, and the evaluation of well-performing models. While non-linear techniques, specifically Generalized Regression Neural Network (GRNN) and Decision Trees, exhibited superior performance in line with evaluation criteria, linear methods, such as Multivariate Linear Regression (MLR), closely matched the effectiveness of these advanced approaches.
Keywords: Data-driven Modelling, Soft Sensor, Plant-Wide Operation, Crystallization

1. Introduction and process description

Sugar production from sugar beets is a complex and intricate process that involves several crucial stages. At the heart of this process is a sugar factory equipped with various specialized units. In Figure 1, we present an overview of the key stages in sugar beet processing. The journey begins with the arrival of trucks at the weight bridge, where the beets undergo initial assessments. Subsequently, the beets proceed through a series of stages including sampling, unloading, beet washing, slicing, and extraction tower. The extracted juice undergoes purification in the juice purification unit before moving through stages such as evaporation, crystallization, centrifuging, and drying. The final product is then stored in silos before being dispatched from the service center. Each stage plays a pivotal role in the overall sugar production process, contributing to the high-quality sugar that results from this intricate industrial sequence. A comprehensive understanding of each stage is essential for optimizing production efficiency and ensuring the consistent quality of the final product.

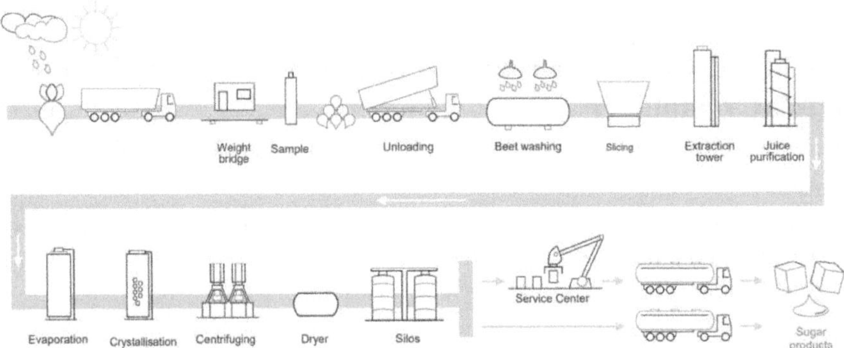

Figure 1- Sugar factory schematic from sugar beet to final product including sampling, washing, extraction, juice purification, evaporation, crystallization, centrifugation, silos and service center. (Credit NurdZucker)

Between the above-mentioned processes, crystallization stands out as one of the most pivotal unit operations in sugar production, exerting a profound influence on the final product specifications, energy consumption, and the overall carbon footprint of the factory. The sugar beet crystallization process is a multifaceted operation, characterized not only by the transformation of syrup into massecuite but also by its inherently nonlinear and non-stationary nature (Meng, et al., 2019). The complex interactions between nucleation, growth, and aggregation mechanisms of crystals unfold during this process. Despite its paramount significance, the sugar beet crystallization process lacks a reliable mechanistic model that comprehensively describes the intricate relationship between crystallization dynamics and operating conditions. Consequently, the control strategies employed in sugar beet crystallization often hinge on online measurements of key process parameters. It is noteworthy that any deviation from the normal operation of the sugar crystallization process can have cascading effects on the plant. Anomalies might prompt the centrifuge to reintroduce small crystals to different batch boilers, necessitating additional energy input and consequently elevating CO2 production. In essence, the balance of sugar crystallization underscores the critical need for a nuanced understanding and effective control measures to optimize efficiency and minimize environmental impact.

In sugar production, the crucial crystallization stage involves interconnected processes. This study employs two strategies to enhance this operation: leveraging insights from mother liquor crystal size distribution through process optimization and first-principle modelling, and integrating data from various sensors to design a robust soft sensor for superior process control. Soft sensors serve as a reliable backup in case of sensor failures, crucial for uninterrupted operation and adaptability to changes. Their significance is particularly evident in complex processes like sugar crystallization, where continuous control is vital for optimal performance and resource efficiency. However, the lack of soft sensors for batch and continuous processes remains a major challenge in implementing various control strategies (Paengjuntuek et al., 2008). This work delves into the intricacies of the developed soft sensor for the Brix index in sugar crystallization batch unit operations, where the Brix index is a key parameter for the control system, representing the mass of total dissolved solids per 100 mass units of solution.

2. Data-driven modeling

In the development of soft sensors tailored to operational parameters, the dataset underwent a meticulous reduction and categorization process, with distinct batches assigned to elucidate the operational nuances inherent in the data. Table 1 delineates the input and output variables within the final dataset. Employing a versatile approach, the soft sensor design employed various regression techniques, including Linear Regression, Neural Network, Support Vector Machine, and Decision Tree models. To assess the efficacy of these models, the Mean Absolute Percentage Error (MAPE), Mean Squared Error (MSE), Determination Coefficient (R^2), and Mean Absolute Error (MAE) served as key performance metrics. The formulae for each index are detailed in Table 2. The ensuing section delves into an exploration of the machine-learning algorithms implemented for soft sensor design.

Table 1- Input and output variables for the data-driven model in the sugar-crystallization unit

No.	Description	Range	Unit
X_1	Temperature	[50,90]	°C
X_2	Vacuum Pressure	[0.15,0.35]	bar
X_3	Steam Pressure	[0.4,1.5]	bar
X_4	Level	[0,400]	Cm
Y_1	Brix Index	[70,100]	Bx

Table 2- Model performance evaluation index and their identification

Index	Formula
MAPE	$MAPE = \frac{\sum_{i=1}^{m} \frac{\lvert y_i - f_i \rvert}{y_i}}{m} \times 100\%$
MSE	$MSE = \frac{1}{n} \sum_{i=1}^{m} (y_i - f_i)^2$
R^2	$R^2 = \frac{\sum_{i=1}^{m} (y_i - f_i)^2}{\sum_{i=}^{m} (y_i - \bar{y}_i)^2}$
MAE	$MAE = \frac{\sum_{i=1}^{m} \lvert y_i - f_i \rvert}{m}$

2.1. Multivariate Linear Regression (MLR)

Multivariate Linear Regression (MLR) (Höskuldsson, 1996) stands out as an extensively utilized regression technique in the realm of soft sensor design(Wang et al., 2009). This method intricately establishes a linear polynomial relationship between the predictor variable X and the response variable y. The vector X encompasses diverse types of data, including monitoring data, electrochemical data, and univariate operational process data such as temperature, vacuum pressure, steam pressure, viscosity, density, flow rate, and more, denoted as b_k ($k = 1, \ldots, m$). Here, $b = [b_1, b_2, \ldots, b_m]$ represents the regression coefficients, while ε denotes the residual.

$$y = b_1 x_1 + b_2 x_2 + \cdots + b_m x_m + \varepsilon \qquad (1)$$

2.2. Generalized Regression Neural Network (GRNN)

The utilization of neural networks is a prevalent approach in the development of soft sensors (Kadlec et al., 2009). Specht (Specht, 1991)originally proposed this method for non-linear function approximation. In the general regression algorithm, the relationship between input and output is articulated through a probability density function derived from observed data, as represented by Eq. (2). The Euclidean distance between two input vectors, denoted as D^2, is defined by Eq. (3). A typical GRNN comprises four layers: an input layer, a pattern layer, a summation layer, and the output layer. The input layer contains neurons equal to the number of input variables, while the pattern layer features neurons corresponding to the number of training cases.

$$\hat{y} = \frac{\sum_{i=1}^{m} y_i \times \exp(\frac{-D_i^2}{2\sigma^2})}{\sum_{i=1}^{n} \exp(\frac{-D_i^2}{2\sigma^2})} \tag{2}$$

$$D_i^2 = (x - x_i)^T (x - x_i) \tag{3}$$

2.3. Support Vector Regression(SVR)

Owing to its strong foundation in statistical learning theory, Support Vector Machines (SVM) have garnered growing interest among soft sensor developers (Meng, et al., 2019). The overarching SVR algorithm was initially introduced by (Drucker et al., 1996) The initial phase of the SVR algorithm involves creating a linear function in a high-dimensional space using a kernel function, as depicted by Eq. (4). Here, φ() denotes a kernel function that maps the m-dimensional data to a higher-dimensional space. The objective is to optimize the parameters ω and b, as outlined in Eq. (5).

$$\hat{y} = \omega^T \varphi(\text{x}) + \text{b} \tag{4}$$

$$|y - \omega^T \varphi(\text{x}) - \text{b}| < \epsilon \tag{5}$$

2.4. Decision Tree Regression(DTR)

A decision tree is a hierarchical structure that categorizes instances by recursively splitting them based on input variables. During training, an algorithm optimizes the tree's fitness by minimizing errors between predicted and actual values(Loh, 2011). This study applies a regression model to the target variable using each independent variable. The dataset undergoes multiple splits, and at each split, the algorithm selects the variable resulting in the lowest error for further division. This iterative process is repeated to construct the decision tree

3. Result and discussion

To create a strong soft sensor for sugar crystallization, operational data from a real sugar factory was thoroughly analyzed. The factory used batch-based crystallization designs and a sophisticated process control system monitoring key parameters at one-minute intervals. Initial data analysis involved separating batches based on operational parameters. Time-series data were labeled, and a correlation matrix was used to identify relationships among

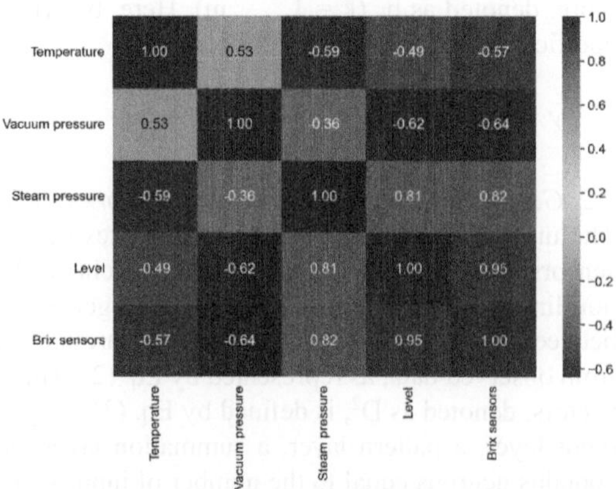

Figure 2- Correlation matrix between operational parameterspositive value means direct correlation and negative value shows reverse correlation.

various sensors, particularly for predicting Brix sensors (depicted in Figure 2). Recognizing the importance of Brix sensors in determining crystallization completion time, regression models were then employed to predict Brix sensor behavior based on data from other sensors—a crucial step toward developing a data-driven soft sensor for real-time process optimization.

In the initial phase, a correlation matrix was used to explore relationships among various parameters in a vacuum batch crystallizer, revealing a significant correlation of 0.95 between the level and Brix sensors. Recognizing the crucial role of Brix sensors in indicating batch cessation, a strategic decision was made to develop a Brix soft sensor based on the level parameter. Various regression models (MLR, GRNN, SVR, DTR) were employed and rigorously assessed, using 40% of the dataset for training and 60% for testing. The dataset comprised 6772 data points and 60 batches.

Table 3- Model performance evaluation index and their identification

Index/ Method	MLR	GRNN	SVR	DTR
MAPE(%)	1.00	0.47	0.88	0.44
MSE	1.98	0.67	2.17	0.77
R^2	0.91	0.97	0.90	0.97
MAE	0.79	0.38	0.68	0.35

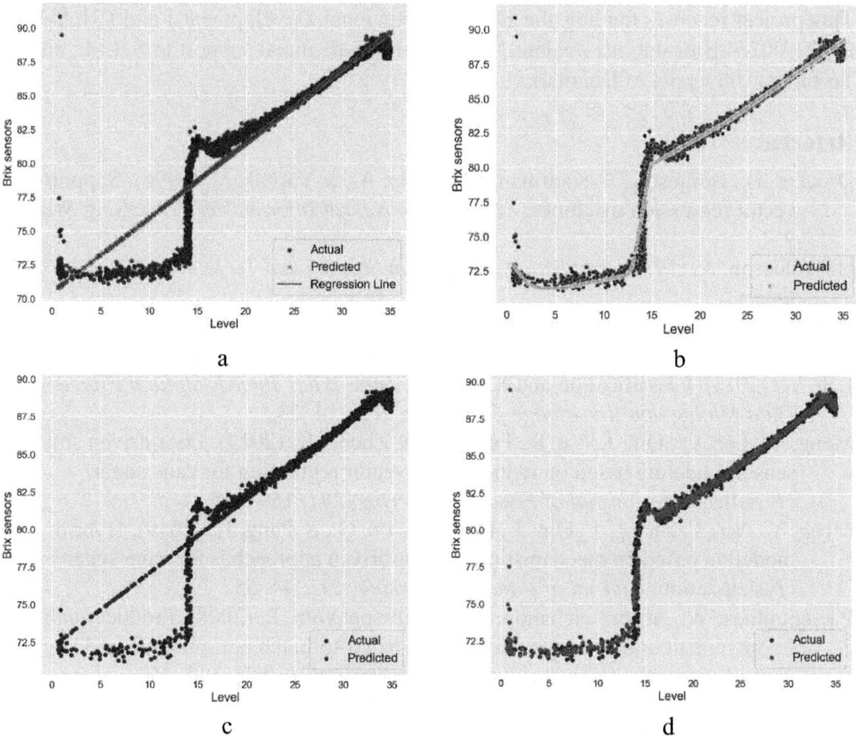

Figure 3- Actual and predicted Brix index from. a) MLR b) GRNN c) SVR d) DTR

As depicted in Table 3, various models demonstrated their capability to predict Brix sensors based on the input from the level sensor in the crystallizer. In scenarios where the Brix sensor data is unavailable for a particular batch in the crystallizer, the utilization of a soft sensor becomes essential for Brix prediction. Figure 3 shows the result of different regression models for brix index prediction.

4. Conclusions

In this research, a data-driven method for creating a customized soft sensor that predicts the Brix index in real-time during the crystallization stage in a sugar factory has been introduced. The model was trained using operational data from an industrial sugar factory, and various machine-learning methods were applied. Non-linear methods like GRNN and DTR showed superior performance, although linear methods like MLR performed similarly well, except for predicting low massecuite levels in the crystallization tank, which has minimal impact on the overall evaluation due to the crystallizer level typically being above 20 Decimeters during most operations. The models generated by these machine learning approaches were thoroughly tested with different datasets, consistently demonstrating robust performance. This comprehensive assessment highlights the effectiveness of both non-linear and linear methods in constructing accurate soft sensor models for real-time Brix index prediction in the sugar crystallization process.

5. Acknowledgement

This project receives funding the European Regional Development Fund (REACT-EU RF-21-0025 "Biosolutions Zealand") for providing financial support to S.S.M.; and The Technical University of Denmark.

References

Drucker, H., Burges, C. J., Kaufman, L., Smola, A., & Vapnik, V. (1996). Support vector regression machines. *Advances in Neural Information Processing Systems*, *9*.

Höskuldsson, A. (1996). *Prediction Methods in Science and Technology.: Vol 1. Basic theory*.

Kadlec, P., Gabrys, B., & Strandt, S. (2009). Data-driven soft sensors in the process industry. *Computers & Chemical Engineering*, *33*(4), 795–814.

Loh, W. (2011). Classification and regression trees. *Wiley Interdisciplinary Reviews: Data Mining and Knowledge Discovery*, *1*(1), 14–23.

Meng, Y., Lan, Q., Qin, J., Yu, S., Pang, H., & Zheng, K. (2019). Data-driven soft sensor modeling based on twin support vector regression for cane sugar crystallization. *Journal of Food Engineering*, *241*, 159–165.

Meng, Y., Yu, S., Zhang, J., Qin, J., Dong, Z., Lu, G., & Pang, H. (2019). Hybrid modeling based on mechanistic and data-driven approaches for cane sugar crystallization. *Journal of Food Engineering*, *257*, 44–55.

Paengjuntuek, W., Arpornwichanop, A., & Kittisupakorn, P. (2008). Product quality improvement of batch crystallizers by a batch-to-batch optimization and nonlinear control approach. *Chemical Engineering Journal*, *139*(2), 344–350.

Specht, D. F. (1991). A general regression neural network. *IEEE Transactions on Neural Networks*, *2*(6), 568–576.

Wang, D., Liu, J., & Srinivasan, R. (2009). Data-driven soft sensor approach for quality prediction in a refining process. *IEEE Transactions on Industrial Informatics*, *6*(1), 11–17

Flavio Manenti, Gintaras V. Reklaitis (Eds.), Proceedings of the 34th European Symposium on Computer Aided Process Engineering / 15th International Symposium on Process Systems Engineering (ESCAPE34/PSE24), June 2-6, 2024, Florence, Italy
 http://dx.doi.org/10.1016/B978-0-443-28824-1.50284-2

Handling nonlinearities and uncertainties of fed-batch cultivations with difference of convex functions tube MPC

Niels Krausch,[a] Martin Doff-Sotta,[b] Mark Canon,[b*] Peter Neubauer,[a] Mariano Nicolas Cruz-Bournazou,[a]

[a]*Technische Universität Berlin, Institute of Biotechnology, Bioprocess engineering, Berlin, ACK24, Ackerstr. 76, 13355 Berlin, Germany*

[b]*University of Oxford, Department of Engineering Science, Parks Road, Oxford, UK*

mark.cannon@eng.ox.ac.uk

Abstract

Bioprocesses are often characterized by nonlinear and uncertain dynamics. This poses particular challenges in the context of model predictive control (MPC). Several approaches have been proposed to solve this problem, such as robust or stochastic MPC, but they can be computationally expensive when the system is nonlinear. Recent advances in optimal control theory have shown that concepts from convex optimization, tube-based MPC, and difference of convex functions (DC) enable stable and robust online process control. The approach is based on systematic DC decompositions of the dynamics and successive linearizations around feasible trajectories. By convexity, the linearization errors can be bounded tightly and treated as bounded disturbances in a robust tube-based MPC framework. However, finding the DC composition can be a difficult task. To overcome this problem, we used a neural network with special convex structure to learn the dynamics in DC form and express the uncertainty sets using simplices to maximize the product formation rate of a cultivation with uncertain substrate concentration in the feed. The results show that this is a promising approach for computationally tractable data-driven robust MPC of bioprocesses.

Keywords: Robust tube MPC, Data-driven control, Convex optimization, Bioprocesses

1. Introduction

1.1. Rapid bioprocess development

The accelerating demand for cost-effective production of biologic drugs and sustainable biomaterials intensifies the need for rapid bioprocess development. This is particularly true in the early project stages, characterized by limited process information and a broad spectrum of potential optimal conditions. Advanced control approaches like MPC coupled with online parameter estimation of the model have proven to be successful even when incomplete process information is available (Krausch et al., 2022), but have been restricted to relatively stable process conditions. For example, Kager et al., (2020) were able to increase total product formation in a fungal process, but their approach is limited to the nominal case. Mowbray et al. (2022) used Neural Networks (NN) to deal with uncertainties but required heavy offline training.

1.2. Tube-based MPC with difference of convex functions

A popular approach in advanced control to deal with uncertain dynamic systems is tube-based MPC (TMPC). TMPC has been mainly applied to linear systems because nonlinear robust MPC requires online solution of nonconvex optimization problems, which can be computationally expensive. A common strategy for applying TMPC to nonlinear systems is to treat the nonlinearity as bounded disturbances of the system and perform successive linear approximations around predicted trajectories. These approaches, nevertheless, rely on conservative estimates of the linearization error and can lead to poor performance (Yu et al., 2013).

Recent studies have shown that tighter bounds on the linearization error can be achieved if the problem can be expressed as a difference of convex functions (Doff-Sotta & Cannon 2022). This is based on the observation that the necessarily convex linearization error is maximum at the boundary of the set on which it is evaluated. Tight bounds can thus be derived and treated as disturbances in a robust TMPC framework. Moreover, the difference of convex functions (DC) structure of the dynamics is attractive as it results in a sequence of convex programs that can be solved with predictable computational effort. Even though any twice continuously differentiable function can be expressed in DC form, finding such functions can be a difficult task. To solve this problem, we have harnessed an NN by restricting the kernel weights to non-negative values and used a convex activation function (ReLU, $\sigma(x) = \max(0, x)$) leading to a so-called input-convex NN (ICNN) (Amos et al., 2017). Two ICNNs can thus be stacked and their output subtracted to learn the dynamics of the function in DC form (Sankaranarayanan & Rengaswamy, 2022). Moreover, in the context of TMPC, the parameterization of the tube plays an important role in the computational complexity of the optimization problem. Doff-Sotta & Cannon (2022) propose state tube cross sections parameterized by elementwise bounds, yielding 2^{n_x+1} (with n_x the number of states) inequality constraints and causing a significant computational burden for large number of states. In this regard, using simplex tubes is a computationally efficient alternative with only $n_x + 1$ inequality constraints. Hence, this contribution describes a TMPC algorithm leveraging a NN for learning the dynamics in DC form, implementing a simplex tube and optimizing product formation in a case study of a fed-batch bioreactor for the production of penicillin.

2. Modelling and DC approximation with neural networks

Let us consider a perfectly mixed isothermal fed-batch bioreactor, a popular case study example from Srinivasan et al. (2003). The model states are the cell concentration X [g L^{-1}], product concentration P [g L^{-1}], substrate concentration S [g L^{-1}] and volume V [L]. The input is the feed flow rate F [L h^{-1}] of S. The inlet substrate concentration $S_i \in [180, 220]$ [g L^{-1}] is an uncertain parameter. The dynamics of the system are given by

$$\begin{aligned} \dot{X} &= \mu(S)X - FX/V \\ \dot{S} &= -\frac{\mu(S)X}{Y_{X/S}} - \frac{vX}{Y_{P/S}} + \frac{F}{V}(S_i - S) \\ \dot{P} &= vX - FP/V \\ \dot{V} &= F \end{aligned} \tag{1}$$

where $\mu(S) = \mu_{max} \frac{S}{S+K_S+S^2/K_i}$ and μ_{max} denotes the maximal growth rate (0.02 h^{-1}), K_S the affinity constant of the cells towards the substrate (0.05 g L^{-1}), K_i an inhibition constant which inhibits growth at high substrate concentrations (5 g L^{-1}), v the production rate (0.004 L h⁻¹), $Y_{X/S}$ the yield coefficient of biomass per substrate (0.5 g_X g_S^{-1}) and $Y_{P/X}$ the yield coefficient of product per substrate (1.2 g_P g_S^{-1}). The initial conditions are $X(0) = 1$ g L^{-1}, $S(0) = 0.5$ g L^{-1}, $P(0) = 0$ g L^{-1} and $V(0) = 120$ L.

An NN framework was used to approximate the nonconvex dynamics as a difference of convex functions by subtracting the outputs of two ICNN subnetworks. An ICNN with L layers is characterized by a parameter set $\theta = \{\Theta_{1:L-1}, \Phi_{0:L-1}, b_{0:L-1}\}$ and input-output map given by $z_L = f(y;\theta)$, defined $\forall l \in \{0, \dots, L-1\}$ by

$$z_{l+1} = \sigma(\Theta_l z_l + \Phi_l x + b_l) \tag{2}$$

where y is the input, z_l is the layer activation, Θ_l are positively constrained kernel weights ($\{\Theta_l\}_{ij} \geq 0, \forall i,j\ \forall l \in \{1, \dots, L-1\}$), Φ_l are input passthrough weights, b_l are bias and $\sigma(\cdot)$ is a convex activation function (ReLU). Each layer of an ICNN thus consists in the composition of a convex function with a nondecreasing convex function, which implies that $z_{l+1} = f(y;\theta)$ is convex with respect to y. Choosing $z_{l+1} = \dot{x}$ and $y = (x,u)$, where $x = (X,S,P,V)$ and $u = F$ are the state and input of (1), two ICNN whose outputs are subtracted can be trained simultaneously to learn the nonconvex dynamics in (1) as a difference of (elementwise) convex functions f_1, f_2:

$$\dot{x} = f_1(x,u) - f_2(x,u) \tag{3}$$

The two ICNNs each consist of a single input layer, two hidden layers with 64 nodes each and an output layer. This setup showed the best performance during hyperparameter tuning with different numbers of layers (1, 2 or 3) and nodes (32, 64 or 128). The network was implemented in Keras and trained over 10 epochs with the RMSProp optimizer on 100,000 random samples of (1), which were divided into 80% training and 20% validation sets. Convexity of the models was evaluated by checking the numerical Hessian matrix of the functions for positive semidefiniteness, i.e. $\nabla^2 f_i(x,u;\theta) \succcurlyeq 0, \forall x \in \mathbb{R}^{n_x}, \forall i = \{1,2\}$. Figure 1 depicts a 3D projection of the DC decomposition for fixed values of the states and input. As illustrated, the NN was able to obtain a good fit (MAE: 0.016) for the predictions of the ODEs (blue dots and blue surface), and the DC form of the decomposition is apparent (orange and green surfaces).

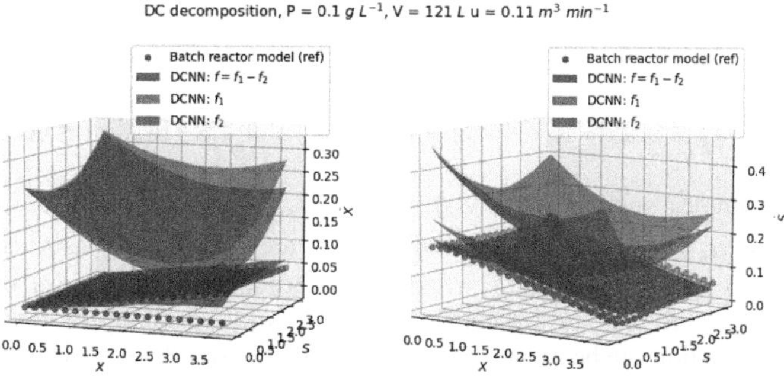

Figure 1: DC decomposition. Depicted are the results from the actual model (blue dots), the results from the DC decomposition $f = f_1 - f_2$ (blue plane) and the respective DC part convex functions f_1 (orange) and f_2 (green) at a given product concentration, volume and feed rate for two states. Left: Biomass $\dot{X}$. Right: Substrate $\dot{S}$. Each in dependence of different concentrations of X and S.

3. DC-TMPC framework with simplices

Doff-Sotta & Cannon (2022) proposed a robust TMPC algorithm based on successive linearisation for DC systems. The so-called DC-TMPC algorithm capitalises on the idea that the successive linearisation steps yield necessarily convex linearisation error functions that can be bounded tightly and treated as disturbances by a robust MPC scheme. We extend that approach to nonconvex systems learned in DC form and consider a state tube parameterized by simplices to reduce computational burden. The system in DC form in (3) is discretized and successively linearized around previously computed predicted trajectories $\overset{\circ}{x}_k$, $\overset{\circ}{u}_k$ with state and input perturbations $s_k = x_k - \overset{\circ}{x}_k$ and $v_k = u_k - \overset{\circ}{u}_k$. As per the TMPC paradigm, v_k is parameterized by a two degree of freedom control law $v_k = K_k s_k + c_k$ where K_k is a feedback gain and c_k is a feedforward control sequence computed at every time step. The sequence of sets $\mathcal{S}_k \ni s_k, \forall k$, defines the cross sections of an uncertainty tube in which the system trajectories lie under all realisations of the uncertainty and whose dynamics are given by

$$s_{k+1} = (\Phi_{1,k} - \Phi_{2,k})s_k + (B_{1,k} - B_{2,k})c_k + g_1(s_k, c_k \overset{\circ}{x}_k, \overset{\circ}{u}_k) - g_2(s_k, c_k \overset{\circ}{x}_k, \overset{\circ}{u}_k) \quad (4)$$

where for $i = 1, 2$, $g_i = f_i(\overset{\circ}{x}_k + s_k, \overset{\circ}{u}_k + K_k s_k + c_k) - f_i(\overset{\circ}{x}_k, \overset{\circ}{u}_k) - \Phi_{i,k} s_k - B_{i,k} c_k$ are the (necessarily convex) linearization errors of f_i, $A_{i,k} = \frac{\partial f_i}{\partial x}(\overset{\circ}{x}_k, \overset{\circ}{u}_k)$, $B_{i,k} = \frac{\partial f_i}{\partial u}(\overset{\circ}{x}_k, \overset{\circ}{u}_k)$ and $\Phi_{i,k} = A_{i,k} + B_{i,k} K_k$. The linearization errors become smaller as the number of iterations of the workflow increases. As this is an iterative solution of a convex program, the runtime is not greatly affected. While the approach in Doff-Sotta & Cannon (2022) was to parameterize the tube with elementwise bounds, resulting in an exponential increase of the inequality constraints, we consider here parameterizations of $\mathcal{S}_k$ in terms of simplices

$$Q s_k \leq \alpha_k, \qquad Q = \begin{bmatrix} -I \\ 1^T \end{bmatrix} \quad (5)$$

where $I \in \mathbb{R}^{n_x \times n_x}$ is the identity matrix, $1 \in \mathbb{R}^{n_x \times 1}$ is a vector of ones. The vector $\alpha_k \in \mathbb{R}^{(n_x+1)\times 1}$ is an optimization variable. Consequently, the state perturbation dynamics can now be expressed as $n_x + 1$ inequalities as follows, combining (4) and (5)

$$\begin{aligned} &\max_{s \in \mathcal{V}(\mathcal{S}_k)} \left(-\Phi_{1,k} s - B_{1,k} c_k + f_2(\overset{\circ}{x}_k + s, \overset{\circ}{u}_k + K_k s + c_k) - f_2(\overset{\circ}{x}_k, \overset{\circ}{u}_k)\right) \leq [\alpha_{k+1}]_{1:n_x} \\ &\max_{s \in \mathcal{V}(\mathcal{S}_k)} 1^T \left(f_1(\overset{\circ}{x}_k + s, \overset{\circ}{u}_k + K_k s + c_k) - f_1(\overset{\circ}{x}_k, \overset{\circ}{u}_k) - \Phi_{2,k} s - B_{2,k} c_k\right) \leq [\alpha_{k+1}]_{n_x+1} \end{aligned} \quad (6)$$

where the simplex vertices are $\mathcal{V}(\mathcal{S}_k) = \{-[\alpha_k]_{1:n_x}, -[\alpha_k]_{1:n_x} + e_1\sigma_k, \dots, -[\alpha_k]_{1:n_x} + e_n\sigma_k\}$, $\sigma_k = [\alpha_k]_{n_x+1} + 1^T[\alpha_k]_{1:n_x}$, and $e_1, \dots, e_n$ are the standard basis vectors of $\mathbb{R}^{n_x}$. To obtain (6), we exploited the convexity of g_i to obtain a tight lower bound on α_k. Moreover, we note that (6) are convex inequalities by convexity of f_i and that each maximum operation can be reduced to a discrete search over the vertices $\mathcal{V}(\mathcal{S}_k)$ since the maximum of a convex function on a polytope occurs at one of the vertices. We design a TMPC controller to optimize the feedforward sequence c_k and tube sets $\mathcal{S}_k$ subject to (6) and $x_k \in \mathcal{X} \subset \mathbb{R}^{n_x}$, $u_k \in \mathcal{U} \subset \mathbb{R}^{n_u}, \forall k$. At each iteration we solve

$$\begin{aligned} &\min_{c,\alpha} \textstyle\sum_{k=0}^{N-1} \max_{s \in \mathcal{V}(\mathcal{S}_k)} \|x_k^0 + s - x_r\|_Q^2 + \max_{s \in \mathcal{V}(\mathcal{S}_k)} \|u_k^0 + K_k s + c_k - u_r\|_R^2 \\ &\text{s.t. } \forall k \in \{0, \dots, N-1\}, \forall s \in \mathcal{V}(\mathcal{S}_k): \end{aligned} \quad (7)$$

$$\max_{s\in\mathcal{V}(\mathcal{S}_k)} \left(-\Phi_{1,k}s - B_{1,k}c_k + f_2(\mathring{x}_k + s, \mathring{u}_k + K_k s + c_k) - f_2(\mathring{x}_k, \mathring{u}_k)\right) \le [\alpha_{k+1}]_{1:n_x}$$
$$\max_{s\in\mathcal{V}(\mathcal{S}_k)} 1^T\left(f_1(\mathring{x}_k + s, \mathring{u}_k + K_k s + c_k) - f_1(\mathring{x}_k, \mathring{u}_k) - \Phi_{2,k}s - B_{2,k}c_k\right) \le [\alpha_{k+1}]_{n_x+1}$$

$$\mathring{x}_k + s \in \mathcal{X},\ u_k^0 + K_k s + c_k \in \mathcal{U},\ \alpha_0 = 0$$

with a shrinking horizon N. The solution from (7) is used to update the state and input guess trajectories (x°, u°) at next iteration with

$$\begin{aligned} s_0 &\leftarrow 0 \\ \mathring{u}_k &\leftarrow \mathring{u}_k + c_k + K_k s_k \\ s_{k+1} &\leftarrow f(\mathring{x}_k, \mathring{u}_k) - \mathring{x}_{k+1} \\ \mathring{x}_{k+1} &\leftarrow f(\mathring{x}_k, \mathring{u}_k) \end{aligned} \tag{8}$$

We run (7) and (8) repeatedly until $\sum_{k=0}^{N-1}\|c_k\|^2 < \epsilon_{tol}$ or a maximum number of iterations is reached. The control input is then implemented at time n by $u[n] = \mathring{u}_0$. At time $n+1$, we set $\mathring{x}_0 = x[n+1]$ and the guess trajectory is updated by

$$\begin{aligned} \mathring{u}_k &\leftarrow \mathring{u}_{k+1} \\ \mathring{x}_{k+1} &\leftarrow f(\mathring{x}_k, \mathring{u}_k) \\ u_{N-1} &\leftarrow K(\mathring{x}_{N-1} - x^r) + u^r \\ \mathring{x}_N &\leftarrow f(\mathring{x}_{N-1}, \mathring{u}_{N-1}) \end{aligned} \tag{9}$$

4. Results and discussion

The proposed control algorithm was simulated on the batch reactor problem over a shrinking horizon of 20 h with a step size of 1 h using CVXPY and solver MOSEK. As shown in Figure 2, the controller was able to maximize the product concentration with parametric uncertainty of the substrate concentration in the feed, demonstrating the applicability of this approach to complex nonlinear systems with Monod-type nonlinear substrate affinity and substrate inhibition, making the search for an optimal feed rate non-trivial. The presented DC-TMPC algorithm outperforms nominal MPC approaches in terms of final product concentration for this case study (Lucia & Engell, 2013) as depicted in Figure 2, by considering the uneven substrate concentration in the feed by augmenting the NN with the uncertain parameter, considering that the worst case scenario occurs at the vertices of the parameter set. Further tuning is however necessary, to find an optimal trade-off between substrate concentration in the reactor to avoid overfeeding (Pimentel et al., 2015).

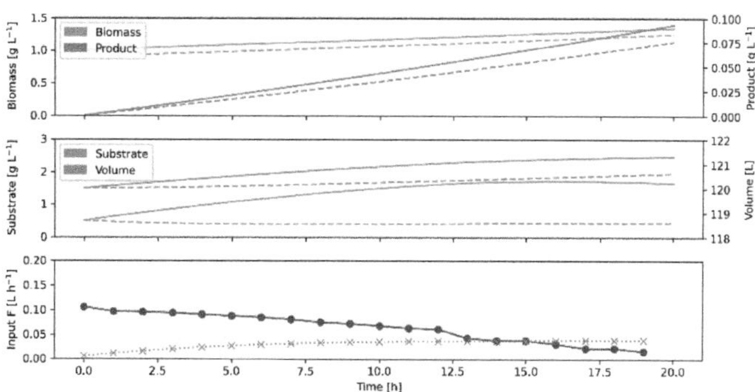

Figure 2: Results from the DC-TMPC optimization. Results from the nominal case (Lucia &Engell, 2013) are depicted as dashed lines for comparison.

5. Conclusion

In this study, we show that successive linearization robust tube MPC can be an adequate tool to optimize a bioprocess under parametric uncertainty. Our approach was to decompose the nonconvex dynamics as a difference of convex functions (DC) using a neural network with convex structure and treat the necessarily convex linearization errors as bounded disturbances. Crucially, by convexity, these bounds are tight and the resulting controller is less conservative than classical TMPC based on successive linearization. This approach is relatively new and has so far only been applied to problems that already exist in DC form. Moreover, by using tubes parameterized with simplex sets, the computational effort could be significantly reduced, making it attractive for real-time optimization. Future work will incorporate more complex models and test it in a real-world bioprocess with online optimization of production in a fast-growing *E. coli* strain.

Acknowledgments
We gratefully acknowledge the financial support of the German Federal Ministry of Education and Research (BMBF) (project no. 01DD20002A – KIWI Biolab) and the EPSRC (UKRI) Doctoral Prize scheme (grant reference number EP/W524311/1).

References

Amos, B., Xu, L., & Kolter, J. Z. (2017). Input Convex Neural Networks. In D. Precup & Y. W. Teh (Eds.), *Proceedings of Machine Learning Research, Proceedings of the 34th International Conference on Machine Learning* (pp. 146–155). PMLR. https://proceedings.mlr.press/v70/amos17b.html

Doff-Sotta, M., & Cannon, M. (2022). Difference of convex functions in robust tube nonlinear MPC. In *2022 IEEE 61st Conference on Decision and Control (CDC)* (pp. 3044–3050). IEEE. https://doi.org/10.1109/CDC51059.2022.9993390

Kager, J., Tuveri, A., Ulonska, S., Kroll, P., & Herwig, C. (2020). Experimental verification and comparison of model predictive, PID and model inversion control in a Penicillium chrysogenum fed-batch process. *Process Biochemistry*, *90*, 1–11. https://doi.org/10.1016/j.procbio.2019.11.023

Krausch, N., Kim, J. W., Barz, T., Lucia, S., Groß, S., Huber, M. C., Schiller, S. M., Neubauer, P., & Cruz Bournazou, M. N. (2022). High-throughput screening of optimal process conditions using model predictive control. *Biotechnology and Bioengineering*, *119*(12), 3584–3595. https://doi.org/10.1002/bit.28236

Lucia, S., & Engell, S. (2013). Robust nonlinear model predictive control of a batch bioreactor using multi-stage stochastic programming. In *2013 European Control Conference (ECC)* (pp. 4124–4129). IEEE. https://doi.org/10.23919/ECC.2013.6669521

Mowbray, M. R., Petsagkourakis, P., Del Rio Chanona, E. A., & Zhang, D. (2022). Safe chance constrained reinforcement learning for batch process control. *Computers & Chemical Engineering*, *157*, 107630. https://doi.org/10.1016/j.compchemeng.2021.107630

Pimentel, G. A., Benavides, M., Dewasme, L., Coutinho, D., & Wouwer, A. V. (2015). An Observer-based Robust Control Strategy for Overflow Metabolism Cultures in Fed-Batch Bioreactors. *IFAC-PapersOnLine*, *48*(8), 1081–1086. https://doi.org/10.1016/j.ifacol.2015.09.112

Sankaranarayanan, P., & Rengaswamy, R. (2022). CDiNN – Convex difference neural networks. *Neurocomputing*, *495*, 153–168. https://doi.org/10.1016/j.neucom.2022.01.024

Srinivasan, B., Bonvin, D., Visser, E., & Palanki, S. (2003). Dynamic optimization of batch processes. *Computers & Chemical Engineering*, *27*(1), 27–44. https://doi.org/10.1016/S0098-1354(02)00117-5

Yu, S., Maier, C., Chen, H., & Allgöwer, F. (2013). Tube MPC scheme based on robust control invariant set with application to Lipschitz nonlinear systems. *Systems & Control Letters*, *62*(2), 194–200. https://doi.org/10.1016/j.sysconle.2012.11.004

Flavio Manenti, Gintaras V. Reklaitis (Eds.), Proceedings of the 34th European Symposium on Computer Aided Process Engineering / 15th International Symposium on Process Systems Engineering (ESCAPE34/PSE24), June 2-6, 2024, Florence, Italy
 http://dx.doi.org/10.1016/B978-0-443-28824-1.50285-4

Optimal feed scheduling and co-digestion for anaerobic digestion sites with dynamic demands

Meshkat Dolat[a], Rohit Murali[a], Ruosi Zhang[a], Mohammadamin Zarei[a], Duo Zhang[c], Dongda Zhang[d], Jhuma Sadhukhan[b,c], Michael Short[a,b *]

[a] *School of Chemistry and Chemical Engineering, University of Surrey, Guildford, GU2 7XH, U.K.*

[b] *Institute for Sustainability, University of Surrey, Guildford, GU2 7XH, U.K.*

[c] *Centre for Environment and Sustainability, University of Surrey, Guildford, GU2 7XH, U.K.*

[d] *School of Chemical Engineering and Analytical Science, University of Manchester, Manchester, M1 3AL, U.K.*

**m.short@surrey.ac.uk*

Abstract

Sustainable feed supply to anaerobic digestion (AD) plants is a significant challenge, particularly considering uncertainties in the energy demand market. This study proposes a new approach to feed scheduling and optimisation to address this challenge. A practical framework is proposed to determine the optimal co-digestion strategy for efficiently managing time-varying demands. Additionally, the research explores the impact of storage capacity and demonstrates the adaptability of the proposed model in contributing to emission reduction policies. Two case studies illustrate the model's flexibility and the impact of storage on increased productivity. The storage increase, results in a 23% reduction in gas grid reliance for the case study. Also, incorporating global warming potential in the objective function results in negligible changes to production metrics.

Keywords: *Feed Scheduling, Optimisation, Anaerobic Digestion, Co-digestion*

1. Introduction

During the last decade, there has been a rise in interest in anaerobic digestion (AD) as a renewable technology for energy recovery from biogas generation to overcome the intermittency challenges of other renewable sources. In line with the UK Biomass Strategy, AD can use sustainable biomass and contribute to the UK's net-zero target, while providing benefits like food waste recycling and reducing natural gas imports (GOV.UK, 2023). However, when considering the availability of feedstock for scheduling and demand-oriented models based on AD plant capacities, research on the technology for large-scale operations has been limited. This study aims to optimise AD processes by integrating demand profiles, feedstock scheduling, co-digestion, and global warming potential (GWP) minimisation in an optimisation framework. Since there is currently no tool available to operators, this kind of integration is crucial for optimising AD. The approach helps operators make strategic decisions about feedstock selection, scheduling, and striking a balance between biogas potential and reducing emissions. Current modelling approaches, such as modifications to Batstone et al.'s (2002) Anaerobic Digestion Model Number 1 (ADM1), which takes co-digestion and demand-oriented models into consideration, present challenges for real-time optimisation due to its non-linearity and data availability.

Demand-oriented models, which solely consider demand profiles and storage capacities, assume continuous feedstock availability, simplifying the AD process. This simplicity lowers the precision with which models can estimate whether demand can be met. Feedstock supply and scheduling needs to be considered simultaneously to generate reliable estimates. Liu et al., (2021) employed a hybrid model with simplified system boundaries and a one-day modelling timeframe to optimise co-digestion in a demand-oriented biogas supply chain. More accurate simulations of co-digestion and biogas output are provided by a recent digital twin of AD proposed by Moretta et al. (2022), however feedstock acquisition, timing, and co-digestion is not considered. According to Lv et al. (2014), feeding schedule changes increased the unpredictability of biogas output and hence impacts operators' decision-making. Supply chain logistics, the growth of energy crops, and possible feedstock storage degradation are some of the factors that affect feedstock selection and whether it can meet demand. Current modeling approaches predominantly cover short time periods of a few months. However, AD processes at a large scale necessitate an annual timeframe that provides a more accurate representation of biogas demand throughout the year, to help decision-making early on for future predictions. Hence, it is important to devise a methodology that considers all these factors to help operators with key decision-making by optimising the best outcome in meeting demand while considering emission reduction.

2. Methodology

To formulate the optimal feeding plan for an AD reactor, several considerations must be addressed. This involves optimising the acquisition of feeds through an optimal blending pattern to exploit synergies, minimising feeding rates while maximising biomethane yield. Simultaneously, the feeding rate needs regulation to align closely with the fluctuating and uncertain market demand or price profile. Additionally, environmental concerns, specifically GWP factors, should be factored into the decision-making process.

The model comprises two distinct optimisation stages implemented in Pyomo, a Python-based package for optimisation. The initial stage computes the optimal blending pattern using a simplified approach proposed by Moretta et al. (2022). The goal is to optimise the feeding ratio of components (x_j) that results in the highest ultimate biomethane yield in the co-digestion process (i.e., the objective is to maximise B_{CoD}).

$$B_{CoD} = \sum_{j=1}^{3} x_j B_j + \left[\sum_{j,k \in feed\ pairs} x_j x_k + \prod_{j=1}^{3} x_j \right] B_{mix} \quad (1)$$

$$B_{mix} = \beta_0 + \beta_1 \sum_{j=1}^{3} x_j \left(\frac{C}{N}\right)_j + \beta_2 BD_{mix} + \beta_3 \left(\sum_{j=1}^{3} x_j \left(\frac{C}{N}\right)_j\right)^2 + \beta_4 BD^2{}_{mix} \quad (2)$$

$$BD_{mix} = \sum_{j=1}^{3} x_j \frac{B_j}{TB_j} \quad (3)$$

$$TB_j = \frac{\left(\frac{n}{2} + \frac{a}{8} - \frac{b}{4} - \frac{3c}{8} - \frac{d}{4}\right)_j 22415}{(12n + a + 16b + 14c + 32d)_j} \quad (4)$$

The model is limited to three substrates j, in our illustrative example, and the B_{CoD} is calculated based on feed data parameters such as the experimental biomethane yield for each substrate (B_j) and their mixture (B_{mix}), carbon to nitrogen ratio (*C/N*) and the theoretical biomethane yield (TB_j) of each of the substrates. The parameters such as a, b, c, d and n in Eq. (3) are the number of atoms in each mole of substrate based on the chemical formula of $C_nH_aO_bN_cS_d$. The regression parameters ($\boldsymbol{\beta_0}, \boldsymbol{\beta_1}, \boldsymbol{\beta_2}, \boldsymbol{\beta_3}, \boldsymbol{\beta_4}$) used in Eq. (2) are 21.7, 1.26, 445.7, -0.02 and -7.82 respectively according to Moretta et al. (2022).

It is important to highlight that the co-digestion correlations mentioned above do not consider complex phenomena such as the inoculum effect. The first stage's output is contingent upon the number of feed substrates *j*, resulting in collections of either two- or three-component sets *I*. These sets subsequently serve as potential feedstocks for the second optimisation step.

The second optimisation step utilises the output from the first and the demand profile (biogas demand as a function of time/day) as inputs. It then generates the optimal feeding schedule that aligns plant production with the demand profile.

$$Objective: \quad min \sum_{d \epsilon Days} (P_d - D_d)^2 + \gamma_{grd} S^-{}_d + \gamma_{stg} S^+{}_d + \gamma_{gwp} \mathrm{GWP}_t \tag{5}$$

$$S^+{}_d = P_d + S^+{}_{d-1} + S^-{}_d - D_d \tag{6}$$

$$P_d = \sum\nolimits_{i \epsilon I} \left(\frac{B_i}{t_{duration_i}} \right) w_i \, y_{p_{i,d}} \quad \forall\, d \in Days, \forall \, \mathrm{i} \in \mathrm{I} \tag{7}$$

$$t_{start_i} - M(1 - y_{p_{i,d}}) \leq d \leq t_{finish_i} + M(1 - y_{p_{i,d}}) \quad \forall\, d \in Days, \forall \, \mathrm{i} \in \mathrm{I} \tag{8}$$

$$\sum\nolimits_{d \,\in\, Days} S^+{}_d \leq S_{max} \tag{9}$$

In this model the gas production (P_d), demand (D_d), storage (or surplus of gas $S^+{}_d$) and deficit (or gas production shortage supplied from the grid, $S^-{}_d$) are indexed on a "daily" basis. The feed set *I* consists of mix-feeds *i,* which includes 2 or 3-components of j (depending on the first optimisation step output). The penalty factor for daily supply of gas from the grid (deficit of gas compared to the daily demand), unnecessary storage and GWP are specified as γ_{grd}, γ_{stg} and γ_{gwp} respectively. The time required to process the whole feed blend *i* ($t_{duration_i}$) is calculated according to the substrates' weights and plant feeding capacity. The binary variable $y_{p_{i,d}}$ determines the selection of a feed mixture *i* to be fed into the digester for $t_{duration_i}$ days. The plant maximum cumulative storage capacity of surplus production is indicated as S_{max}.

The total global warming potential GWP_t is the sum of cultivation, transportation, plant's external energy consumption and leakage GWPs:

$$\mathrm{GWP}_t = GWP_C + GWP_T + GWP_E + GWP_L + GWP_{CHP} \tag{10}$$

Which can be expressed using the detailed formula as:

$$\mathrm{GWP}_t = (1.1 \sum\nolimits_{\mathrm{j} \in \mathrm{I}} w_j \, Ts_j \, \alpha_{C_j} \, \widehat{y_j}) + (\sum\nolimits_{j \,\epsilon J} w_j \, \alpha_{T_j} \, L_j + \sum\nolimits_{j \,\in \mathrm{I}} w'_j \, \alpha'_{T_j} \, L'_j) + (\alpha_E \, E_{elect} + \alpha_H \, E_{heat}) + (18.09 \, B_j \, \alpha_L \, f_{CH_4}) + (\alpha_{\acute{E}} \, E_{elect} + \alpha_{\acute{H}} \, E_{heat}) \tag{11}$$

Eq. (11) details the individual GWPs defined in Eq. (10). The AD system carbon footprint is calculated by creating formulas using some existing processes provided by various datasets, literatures, and government reports. The methodology of the framework incorporates environmental burdens associated with the principal products and processes analysed in this study. The GWP factors α_C, α_T, $\alpha_{E/H}$, α_L and $\alpha_{\acute{E}/\acute{H}}$ represent cultivation, transportation, imported electricity/heat, leakage, and CHP produced electricity and heat. These parameters are obtained from other LCA studies such as the work of Slorach et al., (2019). Substrates' weight and total solids are defined as w_j and Ts_j respectively. $\widehat{y_j}$ is the user-defined binary parameter indicating the cultivation of specific substrate *j*. L_j is the distance of j from its origin (L'_j) relates to the digestate disposal distance. In the leakage term, f_{CH_4} is the fraction of methane in the biogas.

3. Case study

A consumption profile representing 3000 households is generated based on random distribution, using the annual average natural gas consumption of a medium-sized household in the UK as the demand profile. Consumption values are reported on a weekly basis for computational efficiency. Three substrates, namely "Maize," "Straw," and "Sheep manure," are chosen as example feed candidates, with specified characteristics from the work of Moretta et al. (2022). The plant feeding rate is constrained to a maximum 100 tonnes per day and the storage capacity is assumed to be 5000 m^3.

To investigate the impact of storage capacity and GWP factors, two distinct case studies were conducted. In the first case study, GWP effects were excluded, and optimisation was performed for storage capacities of 5000 m^3 and 10,000 m^3. In the second case, GWP was considered for a fixed storage capacity of 5000 m^3, with the simplifying assumption of neglecting GWP effects related to leakage and heat-electricity supply. The penalty factors for grid supply and storage are considered as 10^8 and for GWP it is set to 10^3. This is to ensure that gas supply has low reliance on the national grid while minimising unnecessary storage providing GWP with a sufficient impact on the objective function. The feeding system was assumed to be able to mix two component types (resulting in three 2-substrate feeding scenarios). Decision-making was limited to selecting among these three feeding scenarios to address three major intervals of the year: low, medium, and high consumption periods. The model is formulated as a Mixed-Integer Nonlinear Programming (MINLP) problem in Pyomo and is solved using BARON with the statistics provided in Table 1.

Table 1: Model statistics

No. of Continuous variables	No. of Binary & Integer variables	No. of Constraints	Solution time
173	179	506	53 s

4. Results and discussions

As per the initial optimisation step, Table 2 presents the optimal blending pattern for the three available substrates along with their predicted biomethane yields. This optimal blending is subsequently employed by the second optimisation step as the set of available feeding scenarios for scheduling purposes.

Table 2: The result of the first optimisation step which optimises co-digestion patterns

Feed No.	**Two-component Co-digestion**	**Composition %**	**Methane yield (m^3/t$_{feed}$)**
1	Comp. 1: Sheep manure Comp. 2: Straw	Comp. 1: 33% Comp. 2: 67%	163
2	Comp. 1: Sheep manure Comp. 2: Maize	Comp. 1: 67% Comp. 2: 33%	189
3	Comp. 1: Straw Comp. 2: Maize	Comp. 1: 57% Comp. 2: 43%	219

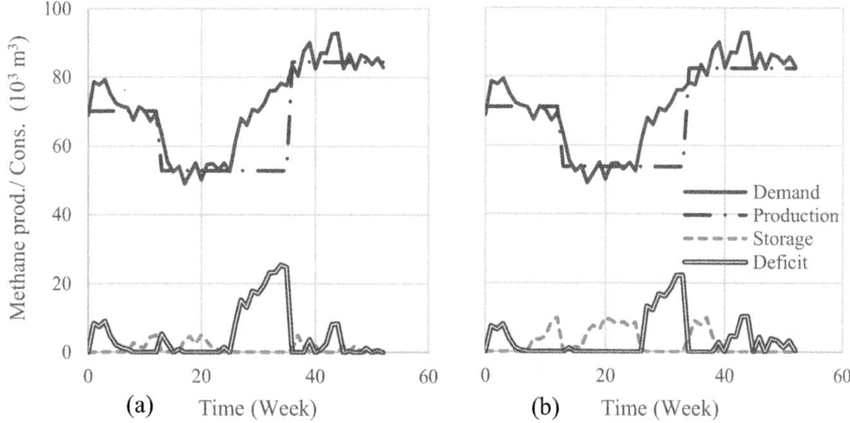

Figure 1: The presentation of optimisation results for matching the average production rate with the gas demand of a prototype district with 3000 households by an AD plant with (a) 5000 m^3 and (b) 10,000 m^3 storage capacity. GWP is not considered.

The first case study results are plotted in Figure 1, where the effect of increasing the storage on the reduction of gas deficit and the increase in production are presented. As seen in Table 3, doubling the storage capacity from its base case value has led to an approximately 58,000 m^3 increase in production, thereby reducing grid supply by 23% and with a modest 3% saving on feedstock procurement. Furthermore, considering the implementation of the GWP in the optimisation results, Table 3 clearly indicates the

Table 3: The result of the second optimisation function, demand-oriented supply, with and without considering GWP

	Case study	Total gas product (m^3)	Total gas deficit (m^3)	Total feed weight (tonnes)	Total GWP (t CO_2)
1	5000 m^3 storage	3,567,115	259,520	18,470	2,761
	10,000 m^3 storage	3,625,202	200,695	17,913	
2	5000 m^3 storage, No GWP	3,567,115	259,520	18,470	2,761
	5000 m^3 storage, with GWP	3,567,115	259,520	18,590	2,127

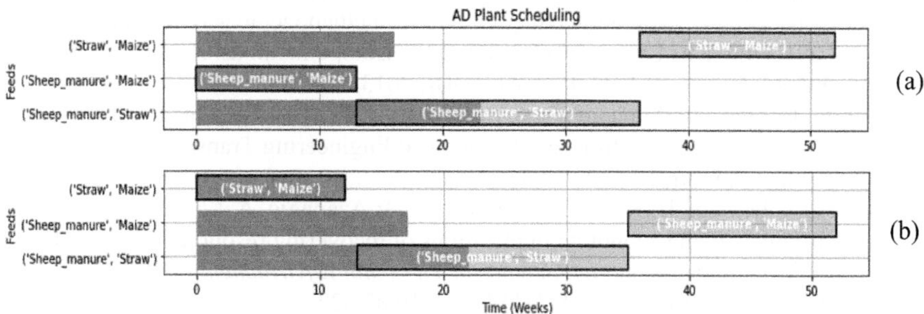

Figure 2: (a). AD plant feed scheduling for the base case scenario (b) Feed scheduling for the scenario considering GWP.

model's adaptability in incorporating GWP without a significant impact on feed consumption. Figure 2 illustrates how the optimiser has adjusted the feeding schedule in response to the inclusion of the GWP factor.

A comparison between Figure 2(a) with (b) reveals a shift in the choice of candidate feeds between ("Straw", "Maize") and ("Sheep manure", "Maize") for the initial production period, which is the shortest duration. Given that the GWP related to cultivation outweighs that of transportation, it is evident that the Straw and Maize should be allocated to the shortest period of operation (i.e., the smallest number of feedstocks).

5. Conclusions

The proposed methodology introduces an intuitive and streamlined approach for optimal scheduling of diverse feedstocks in response to dynamic demand profiles. The model underscores the pivotal role of storage capacity in augmenting the flexibility of AD plants, navigating the challenges of fluctuating gas demand, and enhancing production rates within the confines of plant infrastructure. The case study illustrates 23% reduction in grid supply reliance by doubling the initial 5000 m^3 storage capacity. Furthermore, by delineating the optimal blending pattern for substrates, the model adeptly addresses concerns associated with GWP with negligible changes to the production rate, presenting potential advantages to the plant in anticipation of the growing prevalence of carbon credit and trading mechanisms.

6. Acknowledgments

We would like to acknowledge that this work was supported by the Engineering and Physical Sciences Research Council (EPSRC) [grant number EP/Y005600/1].

7. References

Batstone, D., Keller, J., Angelidaki, I., Kalyuzhnyi, S., Pavlostathis, S., Rozzi, A., Sanders, W., Siegrist, H., & Vavilin, V. (2002). Anaerobic digestion model No 1 (ADM1). *Water Science and Technology : A Journal of the International Association on Water Pollution Research*, *45*, 65–73.

GOV.UK (2023). *Biomass Strategy 2023 - GOV.UK*. Retrieved November 29, 2023, from https://www.gov.uk/government/publications/biomass-strategy

Liu Y, Huang T, Peng D, Huang J, Maurer C, Kranert M. Optimizing the co-digestion supply chain of sewage sludge and food waste by the demand oriented biogas supplying mechanism. Waste Management & Research. 2021;39(2):302-313. doi:10.1177/0734242X20953491

Lv, Z., Leite, A. F., Harms, H., Richnow, H. H., Liebetrau, J., & Nikolausz, M. (2014). Influences of the substrate feeding regime on methanogenic activity in biogas reactors approached by molecular and stable isotope methods. *Anaerobe*, *29*, 91–99. https://doi.org/10.1016/J.ANAEROBE.2013.11.005

Moretta, F., Goracci, A., Manenti, F., & Bozzano, G. (2022). Anaerobic Co-digestion Feedstock Blending Optimization. Chemical Engineering Transactions, 96, 295-300. https://doi.org/10.3303/CET2296050

Slorach, P. C., Jeswani, H. K., Cuéllar-Franca, R., & Azapagic, A. (2019a). Environmental and economic implications of recovering resources from food waste in a circular economy. *Science of The Total Environment*, *693*, 133516. https://doi.org/10.1016/J.SCITOTENV.2019.07.322

Flavio Manenti, Gintaras V. Reklaitis (Eds.), Proceedings of the 34th European Symposium on Computer Aided Process Engineering / 15th International Symposium on Process Systems Engineering (ESCAPE34/PSE24), June 2-6, 2024, Florence, Italy
 http://dx.doi.org/10.1016/B978-0-443-28824-1.50286-6

Digital Twins for Process Monitoring and Anomaly Detection

Anziel Malandri,[a] Mehmet Mercangöz[b]*

[a]*Fluor Corporation, 140 Pinehurst Road, Farnborough GU14 7BF, United Kingdom*
[b]*Imperial College London, Imperial College Rd, London SW7 2AZ, United Kingdom*
m.mercangoz@imperial.ac.uk

Abstract

As industrial processes become more intricate over time, data-driven process monitoring has emerged as an effective approach for detecting faults within these complex systems. However, the requirement for large volumes of historical data poses a challenge when implementing data-driven process monitoring in greenfield plants lacking such data. This paper introduces a novel solution by proposing the utilisation of digital twins for the implementation of data-driven process monitoring, specifically based on principal component analysis (PCA). By employing simulations used during the design stage, synthetic training data can be generated to emulate the behaviour and correlations observed in the real process. The synthetic data can be used to train a PCA model, eliminating the need for an extensive data set to achieve reliable results. Consequently, this approach expedites the implementation of data-driven process monitoring. The effectiveness of this method is shown through case studies involving a reactive absorption process. The results show that some amount of actual process data is still required for recalibration, but the proposed approach can be built with 75% fewer samples compared to a method based purely on process data to operate with equivalent or better performance.

Keywords: PCA, Digital Twins, Fault Detection, Transfer Learning

1. Introduction

Industrial processes become progressively more complex as they expand. This growing complexity makes it increasingly impractical to depend solely on human operators to identify and manage faults and emergencies. Neglecting to spot faulty conditions promptly can result in substantial safety, environmental, and financial problems. Consequently, there is a need for the creation of automated process monitoring techniques to aid operators in addressing faulty conditions (Harrou et al., 2021). To accomplish this goal, many data-driven process monitoring and fault detection methods were formulated (Jiang et al., 2019). Nevertheless, the demand for a substantial amount of historical data presents a significant hurdle for data-driven models for greenfield chemical plants, where data may be scarce or utterly absent if the plant has not yet been commissioned. To address this issue, the present paper proposes leveraging digital twins based on design-stage models to generate synthetic data. Said data is used to train a data-driven process monitoring method based on principal component analysis (PCA).

The contribution of this paper is the investigation of digital twins to expedite the implementation of data-driven process monitoring methods when plant data is scarce or not available – and the demonstration of this approach on an experimental facility. The remaining sections of the paper are organised in the following manner: The background is presented in section 2. Section 3 describes the methodology of this implementation. Section 4 will illustrate and discuss the results of implementing the proposed method. Finally, section 5 provides conclusions and prospects for future work.

2. Background

This section overviews principal component analysis, the monitoring statistics to be used alongside PCA, and the Sobol sequence.

2.1. Principal Component Analysis (PCA)

PCA is a dimensionality reduction method that can discover underlying features and correlations within a multivariate dataset. It projects the dataset into a lower dimensional subspace using singular value decomposition (SVD) (Abdi and Williams, 2010). Before SVD is applied, the input dataset $\mathrm{X} = [\mathrm{x}_1^{\mathrm{T}}, \ldots., \mathrm{x}_n^{\mathrm{T}}] \in R^{n \times m}$, is first standardised using its mean and variance. From here on, X refers to the standardised data. After which, a covariance matrix S is calculated to obtain the loading matrix W and Λ using Eq. (2).

$$S = \frac{1}{n-1} X^T X = W \Lambda W^T \tag{2}$$

where $\Lambda = diag(\lambda_1^2, \ldots \lambda_m^2)$ is a contains the eigenvalues of the covariance matrix. The eigenvalues are equivalent to the variance of each principal component. Typically, only the first k principal components ($k < m$) are used to construct the PCA model.

2.2. Monitoring Statistics

This subsection will describe the monitoring statistics T^2, SPE, and One Class Support Vector Machines (OCSVMs). PCA also provides a means to isolate the detected faults, but this will be outside the scope of the presented work.

2.2.1. Hotelling T^2

The T^2 statistic calculates the variations solely within the PC values at each time point. Specifically, the T^2 value is determined by summing the squares of the retained PC scores and dividing this sum by the corresponding eigenvalue derived from non-faulty data as seen in Eq. (3) (Hotelling, 1933).

$$T^2 = x^T \widehat{W} \widehat{\Lambda}^{-1} \widehat{W}^T x = \sum_{i=1}^{k} \frac{t_i^2}{\lambda_i} \tag{3}$$

Where $\widehat{W}$ and $\widehat{\Lambda}$ are the retained loading matrix and eigenvalues of the PCA model.

2.2.2. SPE

The SPE, or Q metric, is used to detect faults within the reconstruction space, SPE is calculated by Eq. (5) (Joe Qin, 2003).

$$SPE = [X - \hat{X}]^T [X - \hat{X}] \tag{5}$$

Where $\hat{X}$ is the reconstructed value of the input X.

2.2.3. OCSVM

OCSVM is a method that classifies data into groups based on a kernel function. (Wang et al., 2006). In broad terms, the OCSVM procedure typically employs a kernel function to map input data points into a higher-dimensional feature space. The differentiation between normal and anomalous data becomes more distinct and manageable in this elevated feature space.

2.3. Sobol Sequence

The Sobol sequence is a type of quasi-random, low-discrepancy sequence frequently employed in Monte Carlo simulations for conducting sensitivity analyses. The objective of Monte Carlo simulations itself is to comprehensively explore the entire input space using a reasonably sized sample (Burhenne et al., 2011).

3. Methodology

3.1. Experiments on the Reactive Absorption Process

The real data is generated via experiments using an experimental reactive absorption process for CO_2. The normal samples are compiled from many runs with variations within a specific operating protocol. Faulty conditions are generated by (1) substantially increasing the CO_2 flow rate and decreasing the air flow rate, (2) External cooling of the feed gas inlet of the absorber column, (3) Induced failures of the column outlet pump, causing flooding to occur within the column. Additionally, occasional sensor failures cause faults to occur within the normal operation protocol as well.

3.2. Absorption Rig Model

The process is modelled using Aspen Plus V11. The input variables used are based on the controllable values of the process. The specifications of the absorption column are based on the equipment's design data to replicate the design stage's fidelity. The heat exchangers are modelled by specifying a constant heat flow to replicate the effect of instantaneous fluctuations in flow rate. The schematic of the model is illustrated in Figure 1.

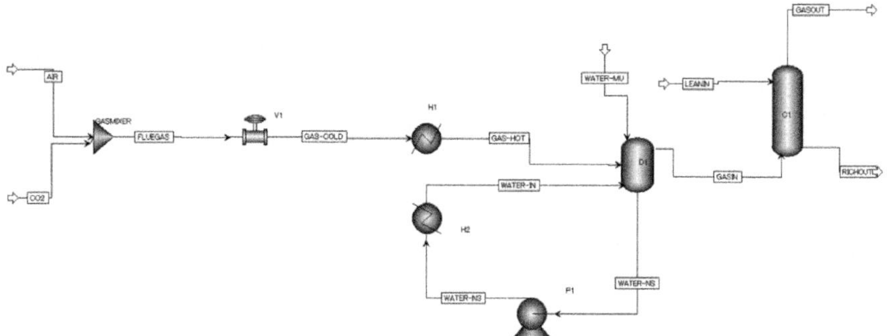

Figure 1. Aspen Plus model schematic

3.3. Synthetic Data Generation

Based on the available measurements, eight variables are chosen as listed in Table 1. Measurements 1-5 are input variables, whereas 6-8 are the output variables within the Aspen Plus model. As such, five variables must be varied for the synthetic data generation. Using the Sobol sequence, 2048 data points are generated with the lower and upper bounds specified according to a 95% confidence interval of the actual measurements.

Table 1. Chosen measurements.

No.	Stream/Unit	Variable	Description
1	WATER-IN	Temperature	Process water temperature
2	CO2	Flow rate	CO2 flow rate
3	AIR	Flow rate	Air flow rate
4	GAS-COLD	Pressure	Feed gas pressure
5	LEANIN	pH	Lean solvent pH
6	RICHOUT	pH	Rich solvent pH
7	C1	Level	Column liquid level
8	GAS-HOT	Temperature	Feed gas temperature

3.4. Synthetic Data Generation

The training procedure begins by standardising the data using its mean and variance. The PCA model is then computed using the SVD method to obtain each principal component's loading matrix and eigenvalues. The eigenvalues are then normalised and sorted in descending order to obtain the explained variance ratio of each principal component. Typically, the number of principal components retained corresponds with a cumulative explained variance ratio of 95%. However, for this study only the first two principal components with a lower cumulative explained variance are selected for ease of analysis. Afterwards, the training data is used to obtain the feature and reconstruction space values used to calculate the T^2 and SPE thresholds and train the OCSVM.

3.5. Recalibration

To address the mismatch in the centring of the operating points of the data and the simulation, the PCA needs to be recalibrated using incremental amounts of the actual data set over time. While previous studies recalibrate by updating the digital twin (Kubosawa et al., 2022). This study opts to recalibrate by directly updating the PCA model.

The PCA is recalibrated by first recalculating the mean and variance of the data, for standardisation. The PCA is then retrained and thresholds for T^2 and SPE are recalculated. Another method is to retrain the OCSVM without updating the mean and variance.

To measure the impact of recalibration, the false alarm rate (FAR) metric is used as described in Eq. (7). The entire real data on normal conditions are fed through the PCA, classifying the data as faulty or otherwise.

$$FAR = \frac{\text{number of false positives}}{\text{number of data points}} \tag{7}$$

4. Results and Discussion

4.1. Synthetic PCA Performance

The model is tested using real data sets on normal and anomalous conditions to analyse the synthetic PCA's performance. The results are illustrated in Figure 2. The T^2 performance is rather poor, where some data points in the anomalous region have lower T^2 values than the normal region. On the other hand, The SPE metric distinguishes faulty conditions rather well. This issue may arise from the inherent errors of the Aspen model's calculations and the lack of statistical information from the real data set. The latter appears more significant since the data is standardised using mean and variance. Therefore, having different means will shift the PC score's centre. And because the T^2 metric measures deviations in PC values away from 0, the T^2 evaluation will be inaccurate. Another issue arising from a lack of statistical information is that there is no reliable way of determining the monitoring statistic's thresholds, as the 99.5% confidence intervals are a property of the real data set.

As the lack of statistical information is inherent at the design stage, a method is required to recalibrate the data set and determine thresholds.

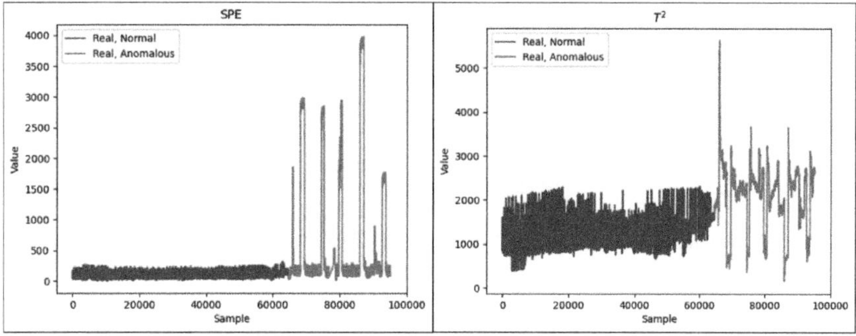

Figure 2. Synthetic PCA SPE (left) and T^2 (right) values.

4.2. Synthetic-PCA Recalibration

Recalibration is conducted over increments of 1000 data points of the actual data set on normal conditions. As a comparison, a PCA trained over the actual data set is also constructed. The FAR values of this incremental recalibration are illustrated in Figure 3. The results show that the FAR values for the T^2 and SPE recalibration drop the fastest, requiring only 15000 data points to achieve a 0.5% FAR. At the same time, the OCSVM achieves 0.5% FAR by using all the actual data and the true PCA using around 20000 data points. The discrepancy between the T^2 and SPE with OCSVM may arise because the threshold calculation for T^2 and SPE uses the F and normal distributions, respectively. In contrast, OCSVM approximates a kernel map, thus creating a tighter confidence interval than T^2 and SPE. Regarding the discrepancy between the synthetic and non-synthetic PCA, it may arise due to random errors within the actual data set skewing the PCA fit. Whereas the synthetic data set provides a clear correlation with a much smaller error. To further illustrate the recalibration's performance, a synthetic PCA recalibrated with 15000 data points are tested and shown in Figure 4. This model can have low FAR while still detecting the faults within the anomalous data set. Therefore, using synthetic PCA with T^2 and SPE appears to be optimal. Not shown in the paper is an alternative approach where the input process data were fed to the Aspen model and the Aspen model outputs were compared with actual output process data to generate an error metric analogous to an SPE value. This approach did not perform very well as it cannot account for large deviations, which are compatible with model predictions.

5. Conclusions

This study introduced a concept for leveraging synthetic training data for a PCA-based process monitoring approach. Synthetic training data allows data-driven process monitoring methods to be trained on minimal real data. The proposed method was validated by testing the PCA on real data, both normal and faulty. Upon recalibration, the synthetic-trained PCA could perform on-par or better compared to a PCA using real data with 75% less training samples. This method can be extended by using higher fidelity design information such as detailed heat exchangers and valve models. More complex models such as adversarial auto-encoders can also be used to generate SPE values to account for the nonlinearity in the process. It is well-known that closed-loop controllers influence the distribution of process data. Replicating the control architecture in the simulations to generate closed-loop data and analysing the impact of synthetic closed-loop data on the performance of the proposed approach is a direction for future work.

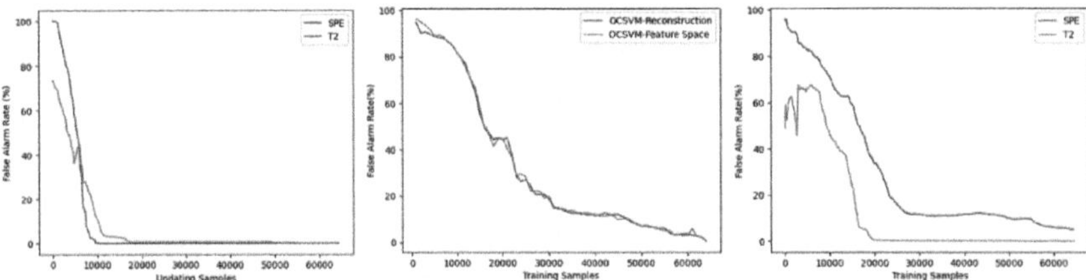

Figure 3. FAR values for recalibrating T^2 and SPE (left), OCSVM (centre), and non-artificial (right) PCA.

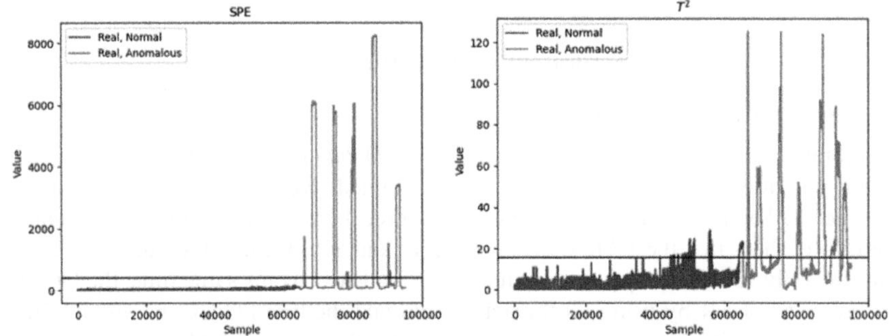

Figure 4. SPE (left) and T^2 (right) values for Synthetic PCA updated with 15000 samples.

References

Abdi, H., Williams, L.J., 2010. Principal component analysis. WIREs Comp Stat 2: 433--459.

Burhenne, S., Jacob, D., Henze, G.P., others, 2011. Sampling based on Sobol'sequences for Monte Carlo techniques applied to building simulations, in: Proc. Int. Conf. Build. Simulat. pp. 1816–1823.

Harrou, F., Sun, Y., Hering, A.S., Madakyaru, M., Dairi, A., 2021. Statistical Process Monitoring Using Advanced Data-Driven and Deep Learning Approaches, Statistical Process Monitoring Using Advanced Data-Driven and Deep Learning Approaches. Elsevier.

Hotelling, H., 1933. Analysis of a complex of statistical variables into principal components. J. Educ. Psychol. 24, 417.

Jiang, Q., Yan, X., Huang, B., 2019. Review and Perspectives of Data-Driven Distributed Monitoring for Industrial Plant-Wide Processes. Ind. Eng. Chem. Res. 58, 12899–12912.

Joe Qin, S., 2003. Statistical process monitoring: basics and beyond. J. Chemom. A J. Chemom. Soc. 17, 480–502.

Kubosawa, S., Onishi, T. and Tsuruoka, Y., 2022. Sim-to-real transfer in reinforcement learning-based, non-steady-state control for chemical plants. SICE Journal of Control, Measurement, and System Integration, 15, 10-23.

Wang, D., Yeung, D.S., Tsang, E.C.C., 2006. Structured one-class classification. IEEE Trans. Syst. Man, Cybern. Part B 36, 1283–1295.

Flavio Manenti, Gintaras V. Reklaitis (Eds.), Proceedings of the 34th European Symposium on Computer Aided Process Engineering / 15th International Symposium on Process Systems Engineering (ESCAPE34/PSE24), June 2-6, 2024, Florence, Italy
 http://dx.doi.org/10.1016/B978-0-443-28824-1.50287-8

An implementable zone-based NMPC with Echo State Networks applied to an ESP-lifted oil well for maximum oil production

Odilon S.L. de Abreu[a], Marcos Pellegrini Ribeiro[b], Bernardo Pereira Foresti[b], Leizer Schnitman[a], Márcio A.F. Martins[a]

[a]*Programa de Pós-Graduação em Mecatrônica, Escola Politécnica, Universidade Federal da Bahia, Rua Prof. Aristides Novis, 2, Federação, 40210-630, Salvador, Bahia, Brasil*
[b]*CENPES, Petrobras R\&D Center, Av. Horácio Macedo 950, Cid. Universitária, Ilha do Fundão, Rio de Janeiro, RJ, Brasil*
**Corresponding author: marciomartins@ufba.br*

Abstract

This study proposes an implementable approach involving nonlinear model predictive control (NMPC) with economic objectives for optimizing the production of an electrical submersible pump (ESP)-operated artificial lift system in the oil industry. The controller considers a zone control scheme to systematically accommodate the time-varying operational constraints commonly encountered in ESP systems (downthrust and upthrust). The constraints are effectively managed by incorporating these features into the control approach, thus yielding a nonlinear programming solution feasible for real-time implementation. Aiming to improve the computational challenges of the proposed NMPC law, an Echo State Network (ESN)-based data-driven model is integrated into the closed-loop feedback system for predicting controlled variables of the oil production system equipped with ESP installations. The ESN-based NMPC approach is implemented using open-source software, namely Python/CasAdi. The results obtained from the simulated scenarios indicate economic gains when the controller drives the ESP plant in the region of maximum flow rate, meeting the operational limits of the process. Furthermore, the controller's low computational time suggests the feasibility of embedding the algorithm in industrial hardware (PLC), making it more attractive for field operations.

Keywords: Nonlinear model predictive control, Echo state network, Electrical submersible pump, Artificial lift method, Oil production

1. Introduction

Advanced control of oil wells operated by electrical submersible pumps (ESP) has recently received significant attention. This interest is due to maximizing production, minimizing operating costs, and increasing equipment safety. In this context, the use of model predictive control (MPC) along with its extensions has emerged as a potential technique for the optimal operation of oil production processes equipped with ESP installations (Pavlov et al., 2014; Fontes et al. 2020; Santana et al., 2022).

In many systems operated by ESP, especially in offshore environments, building phenomenological models for MPC presents a considerable challenge. In this regard, data-driven modeling efforts have emerged as a promising alternative. Recent scientific research has focused on developing data-oriented, model-based MPC for ESP systems. Jordanou et al., (2022) introduce two distinct NMPC formulations based on Echo State Networks (ESN) for ESP control in simulated environments showing promising results. Similarly, Grønningsæter (2023) used an ESN-based model to compensate for process disturbances and to improve NMPC performance in an ESP system. However, it is essential to highlight some limitations of these controllers. The operational constraints of the pump, often referred to as the operating envelope, were not directly incorporated into the formulation of the control law, implying that the control system did not explicitly address specific pump limitations, such as downthrust and upthrust. Another critical point is that the controllers did not focus on maximizing production goals in ESP systems, considering that extracting significant volumes of oil from wells is a feature of ESP systems, which is an advantage compared to other methods.

To overcome the mentioned limitations, Matos et al., (2022) propose the implementation of a controller based on a data-oriented linear fuzzy model. This approach considers the pump's operational constraints (downthrust and upthrust) in formulating the control law. Furthermore, economic objectives are incorporated into the controller. The results were evaluated through a simulation scheme, specifically in scenarios with disturbances. However, it is essential to note that the controller utilizes a linear model set with parameter variations. This aspect presents challenges in implementing the control law in the real world, which is subject to changes based on the conditions of the oil field, as well as in the reservoir and fluid properties, which are dynamic. Additionally, the model does not provide predictions of other variables important to the system. For example, the average flow rate in the production column is used to represent the operating envelope of the pump indirectly.

Therefore, this paper attempts to fill the following gaps: *i*) the implementation of a zone nonlinear model predictive control that explicitly considers pump constraints (downthrust and upthrust) and seeks economic objectives, and *ii*) the integration of ESN-based NMPC, which considers process variables in the model, as well as the average production rate flow in the ESP system. This includes analyzing the controller's computational time for possible implementation in industrial hardware.

The remainder of this paper is structured as follows: Section 2 details the ESP dynamic model and explains the theoretical foundations of the control law and ESN. Section 3 presents the simulated results, and Section 4 concludes the paper, providing overarching insights and potential avenues for future work.

2. The proposed zone NMPC with echo state networks scheme for economic performance in ESP system

2.1. Model of ESP-lifted oil well

The mathematical model that describes the behavior of an oil field with ESP installations is presented by Costa et al., (2021). The equations are written as follows:

$$\frac{dL_a}{dt} = \frac{1}{A_{\text{ann}}}(q_r - q_m), \tag{1}$$

$$\frac{dp_{wh}}{dt} = \frac{\beta_2}{V_2}(q_m - q_c), \tag{2}$$

$$\frac{dq_m}{dt} = \frac{\bar{A}}{\bar{\rho}\bar{l}}(p_{bh} - p_{wh} + \Delta p_p - \Delta p_h - \Delta p_f), \tag{3}$$

where L_a is the annulus level; q_r, q_m and q_c represent the reservoir flow rate, the flow rate in the production column, and the flow rate in the choke, respectively. P_{wh} means the wellhead pressure, while P_{bh} stands out to the bottom hole pressure. Δp_p is the pressure increment provided by the pump that is defined by H (head), given by the manufacturer. Finally, Δp_h and Δp_f represent the variation in hydrostatic pressure, and the pressure drop through friction. More details about the model parameters ($A_{ann}, \beta_2, V_2, \bar{A}, \bar{\rho}, \bar{l}$), and the constitutive equations that make up the model defined in (1)-(3) can be found in Costa et al., (2021).

2.2. The proposed zone NMPC+ESN with economic performance

The NMPC law, integrated with an ESN, explicitly accommodates the ESP operational envelope constraints (upthrust and downthrust) via a zone control scheme that seeks to solve the following optimization problem:

$$\underbrace{\min}_{\Delta u_k, y_{sp,k}} \; J_k = \sum_{j=1}^{H_p} \|\hat{\mathbf{y}}(k+j|k) - \mathbf{y}_{sp,k} + \mathbf{e}(k|k)\|_{Q_y}^2 + \sum_{j=0}^{H_c-1} \|\Delta \boldsymbol{u}(k+j|k)\|_R^2 + \sum_{j=0}^{H_c} \|\boldsymbol{u}(k+j|k) - \boldsymbol{u}_{des,k}\|_{Q_u}^2$$

subject to:

$$\hat{\mathbf{y}}(k+j|k) = \mathbf{g}(\hat{\mathbf{x}}(k+j|k), \boldsymbol{u}(k+j-1|k)) \quad j = 1, \dots, Hp \tag{5}$$

$$-\Delta \boldsymbol{u}_{max} \leq \Delta \boldsymbol{u}(k+j|k) \leq \Delta \boldsymbol{u}_{max} \quad j = 0, \dots, H_c - 1 \tag{6}$$

$$\boldsymbol{u}_{min} \leq \boldsymbol{u}(k-1) + \sum_{i=0}^{j} \Delta \boldsymbol{u}(k+i|k) \leq \boldsymbol{u}_{max} \quad j = 0, \dots, H_c - 1 \tag{7}$$

$$\mathbf{y}_{min} \leq \mathbf{y}_{sp,k} \leq \mathbf{y}_{max} \quad j = 1, \dots, H_p \tag{8}$$

where $\hat{\mathbf{y}}(k+j|k)$ is the vector of the controlled output prediction, i.e., $\hat{L}_a$ and $\hat{H}$, and $\hat{\mathbf{x}}(k+j|k)$ is the vector of the proposed ESN outputs that have been trained, namely $\boldsymbol{w} = [\hat{L}_a, \hat{H}, \hat{q}_m]^\top$, at time step $k+j$ based on the plant information at time step k. $\mathbf{e}(k|k)$ is used as an output disturbance-type integral action in the optimization problem, and $\Delta \mathbf{u}(k+j|k)$ is the vector of the control actions $[f, Z_c]^\top$, making up the entire control sequence computed by optimizer $\Delta \mathbf{u}_k = [\Delta \mathbf{u} \ (k|k)^\top \cdots \ \Delta \mathbf{u} \ (k+1|k)^\top \cdots \Delta \mathbf{u} \ (k+H_c-1|k)^\top]^\top$; $\boldsymbol{Q}_y$ and $\boldsymbol{R}$ are the adjustment parameters for the controlled variables and the control efforts; H_p and H_c define the prediction and control horizons that make up the remaining controller tuning parameters; $\boldsymbol{u}_{des,k}$represents the vector of economic targets on the manipulated variables, whereas $\boldsymbol{Q}_u$ is its associated weighting matrix.

Assumption 1: The controlled variables will have their $\mathbf{y}_{sp,k} = [L_a; H]^\top$ as a decision variable vector in the resulting control optimization problem, being able to assume any value within the output range in Eq. 7. In particular, H is defined as a controlled variable by zone tracking rather than setpoint, whose downthrust and upthrust envelope-type time-varying operational limits are calculated ($H_{min,k} \leq H_{sp,k} \leq H_{max,k}$) from rotational frequency f. This control zone scheme yields a softening NMPC law, providing a solution with a lower computational load and thus meeting the real-time implementation requirements. Furthermore, the nonlinear program (NLP) is solved through the package IPOPT (Interior Point Optimizer) in the open-source software Python/CasADi to find the optimal solution at every time step.

Assumption 2: The controller employs an ESN-based predictive model, initially introduced by Jaeger (2001). This model is defined in discrete state equation as follows:

$$\mathbf{z}(k+1) = [1-\lambda]\, \mathbf{z}(k) + \lambda \boldsymbol{h}[\boldsymbol{W}_x \mathbf{z}(k) + \boldsymbol{W}_{in}\, \boldsymbol{u}(k) + \boldsymbol{b}], \tag{8}$$

$$\boldsymbol{w}(k+1) = \boldsymbol{W}_{out}\, \mathbf{z}(k+1). \tag{9}$$

In this formulation, the state associated with the hidden layer (reservoir) is represented by $\boldsymbol{W}_x$, $\boldsymbol{z}(k)$ represents the network's internal states, whereas $\boldsymbol{u}(k)$ and $\boldsymbol{w}(k)$ are the ESP input and output; λ acts as the leak rate parameter; the weights $\boldsymbol{W}_{in}$, $\boldsymbol{b}$, and $\boldsymbol{W}_{out}$ are associated with the inputs, bias, and outputs, respectively. The activation function in this context is denoted by $\boldsymbol{h}$ (hyperbolic tangent). Additional details can be referred to Jordanou et al., (2022) for a more in-depth discussion. It is important to emphasize that the output vector is made up by $[L_a;\ H; q_m]^\top$, in which data corresponding to q_m is obtained from a nonlinear state estimator coupled with the phenomenological model.
A visual representation of the integrated zone NMPC and ESN approach within the ESP system is illustrated in a block diagram, as shown in Fig. 1.

3. Results and discussion

This section presents the simulated results of NMPC+ESN applied to an oil well equipped with ESP. For this study, we created scenarios that simulate realistic conditions in ESP. These scenarios cover: *i*) well startup in manual mode; *ii*) controller activation and disturbance compensation; and *iii*) economic benefits, such as maximum flow rate, while maintaining compliance with operational constraints (upthrust or downthrust). To meet these objectives, control actions were designed with a bounded variation, i.e., $\Delta\boldsymbol{u}_{max} = [1\ Hz;\ 0.5\ \%]^\top$, along with the control signal constraints are $\boldsymbol{u}_{min} = [40\ Hz;\ 10\ \%]^\top$ and $\boldsymbol{u}_{max} = [60\ Hz;\ 40\ \%]^\top$.
Additional NMPC parameters ensuring feasibility include: a sampling time of $\Delta t = 30\ seconds$; diagonal matrices for output and control penalties $\boldsymbol{Q_y} = diag([100\ m^{-2};\ 10\ m^{-2}])$, $\boldsymbol{R} = diag([5\ Hz^{-2};\ 10\ \%^{-2}])$ and $\boldsymbol{Q_u} = diag([0;\ 100\ \%^{-2}])$. Note that $\boldsymbol{Q_u}$ weights just choke valve opening (maximum production goal). Finally, the ESN was trained and validated using datasets generated by the open-loop model, as described in Eqs. (1)-(3). Due to the complexities involved in measuring the flow rate in the production column q_m, an Extended Kalman Filter (EKF) was used to capture the dynamics of this variable. The hyper-parameters obtained in the network test were: reservoir size = 20; λ = 0.10; and bias_scale = 5.

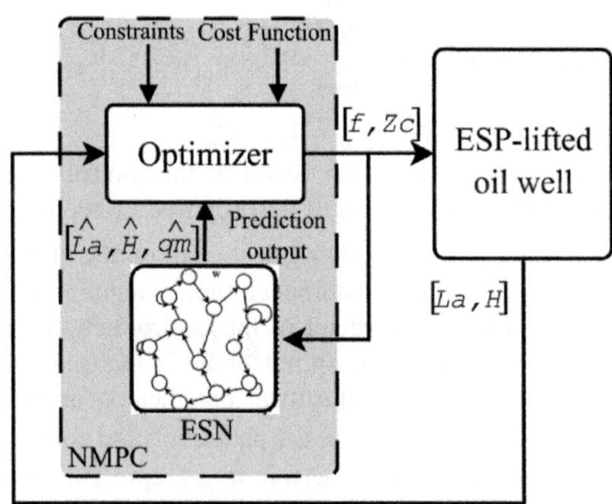

Figure 1: Implementation diagram of the zone NMPC scheme using an ESN model to control an ESP-lifted oil well.

Fig. 2 shows the simulated results of the closed-loop system. The ESP is started up with a frequency of 20 Hz and a choke valve position of 0 %. The operator increases the frequency to 40 Hz and adjusts the choke valve to 20 %. After 2.0 h, the pressure (head) and the flow rate in the well are within the operational envelope (see Fig. 2 (f)). Then, the operator activates the controller ("Control ON") to regulate the annulus level (L_a), which affects the intake pressure of the pump. The controller starts at $\boldsymbol{y}_k(0) = [11\ m;\ 71\ m]^\top$and $\boldsymbol{u}_k(0) = [40\ Hz;\ 20\ \%]^\top$. The controlled variables are outside the ideal zone. The controller identifies the prediction error and redirects (L_a) to an optimal point, indicated by $*$. After 2.5 h, a disturbance was introduced into the plant to simulate a change in the reservoir pressure. The controller effectively compensated for this disturbance by adjusting L_a to within the predefined operating zone. This adjustment was made within the limits of upthrust and downthrust, involving modifications in the manipulated variables (MV), as shown in Fig. 2 (a-b | d-e). Such actions are aligned with **Assumption 1** since ESP operates safely within time-varying limits that guarantee the viability of the control law (optimal solution).

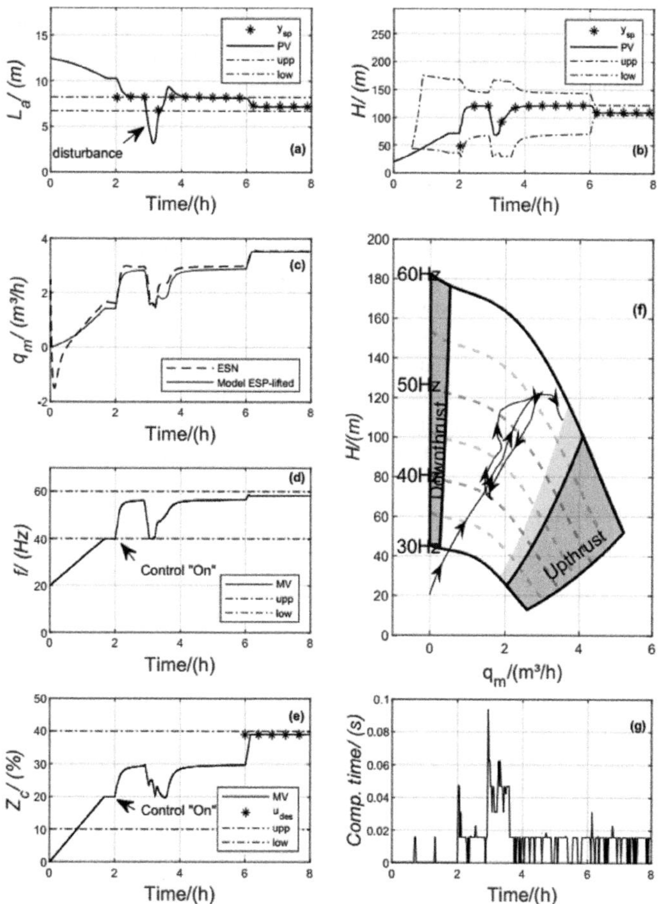

Figure 2: Simulated results of the closed-loop ESP system.

Due to the need to increase production after reaching a steady state in 5.0 h, the operator activated the economic target. The target for the manipulated variable (Z_c) was defined in 39 %. Subsequently, the controller adjusted the choke valve to drive the plant to its maximum production flow rate in 6.0 h. This was achieved while respecting the operational constraints of the pump and the limitations of the final control elements (see Fig. 2 (e)).

Fig. 2 (f) illustrates the operational envelope of the ESP throughout the simulation. The ESN-based model was trained offline using the average flow rate data from the production column, acquired through the proposed EKF. The results, represented in Fig. 2 (c), demonstrate dynamics very similar to those of the actual model used for simulation. Combined with PV (*H*), it made it possible to trace the operational trajectory of the plant. Notably, ESP maintained operational limits (upthrust or downthrust) in varied scenarios. In Fig. 2 (g), the average computational time of NMPC+ESN is shown. When the controller is active, the solution time at each time step is approximately 0.01 s. During perturbation scenarios, this time can extend up to 0.07 s without compromising the required sampling time of the controller. In this sense, this result proves to be promising for implementing industrial hardware (PLC), commonly used in oil wells equipped with ESP.

4. Conclusions

This paper presents an implementable ESN-oriented NMPC method that employs a zone scheme to manage an ESP-lifted oil well. The proposed controller is designed to meet control objectives while seeking economic benefits. The controller effectively maintained the plant within defined operational limits and economic production targets upon activation. Furthermore, the computational requirements for this approach are feasible for implementation on industrial hardware such as PLCs. As a future work, we will implement the proposed algorithm on a fully instrumented pilot plant installed at the Artificial Lift Laboratory (LEA) of the Federal University of Bahia (UFBA), representing dynamics close to the reality of an oil well equipped with ESP.

Acknowledgements

The authors thank CNPq (under grant 408339/2021-7), CAPES (financial code 001), and Petrobras for their financial support.

References

Costa, E A et al. 2021. "A Bayesian Approach to the Dynamic Modeling of ESP-Lifted Oil Well Systems: An Experimental Validation on an ESP Prototype." *Journal of Petroleum Science and Engineering* 205(October 2020): 108880. https://doi.org/10.1016/j.petrol.2021.108880.

Fontes, R.M., Costa, E.A., Abreu, O.S.L., Martins, M.A.F., Schnitman, L., 2020. On application of a zone IHMPC to an ESP-lifted oil well system. In: XXI *Congresso Brasileiro de Automática*. http://dx.doi.org/10.48011/asba.v2i1.1700

Grønningsæter, Ola Solli. 2023. "Echo State Network Based Inverse Models for Feedforward Assisted Optimal Control of Electrical Submersible Pumps (Master's thesis). *Norwegian University of Science*.

Jaeger, Herbert. 2001. "The 'Echo State' Approach to Analysing and Training Recurrent Neural Networks." *GMD Report*.

Jordanou, Jean P. et al. 2022. "Nonlinear Model Predictive Control of Electrical Submersible Pumps Based on Echo State Networks." *Advanced Engineering Informatics* 52(March): 101553. https://doi.org/10.1016/j.aei.2022.101553.

Krishnamoorthy, Dinesh et al. 2016. "Modelling and Robustness Analysis of Model Predictive Control for Electrical Submersible Pump Lifted Heavy Oil Wells." *IFAC-PapersOnLine* 49(7): 544–49. http://dx.doi.org/10.1016/j.ifacol.2016.07.399.

Matos, Victor S., Bruno A. Santana, Thiago P. Chagas, and Márcio A.F. Martins. 2022. "Embedded Predictive Controller Based on Fuzzy Linear Parameter-Varying Model: A Hardware-in-the-Loop Application to an ESP-Lifted Oil Well System." *Digital Chemical Engineering*: 100054. (August 31, 2022).

Pavlov, Alexey et al. 2014. "Modelling and Model Predictive Control of Oil Wells with Electric Submersible Pumps." *2014 IEEE Conference on Control Applications, CCA 2014* (3905): 586–92.

Santana, Bruno A., Raony M. Fontes, and Márcio A.F. Martins. 2022. "An Implementable Zone NMPC Applied to an ESP-Lifted Oil Well System: Handling the Lack of Measurements with Nonlinear State Estimator Coupling." *Journal of Petroleum Science and Engineering* 216(May): 110816. https://doi.org/10.1016/j.petrol.2022.110816.

Flavio Manenti, Gintaras V. Reklaitis (Eds.), Proceedings of the 34th European Symposium on Computer Aided Process Engineering / 15th International Symposium on Process Systems Engineering (ESCAPE34/PSE24), June 2-6, 2024, Florence, Italy
 http://dx.doi.org/10.1016/B978-0-443-28824-1.50288-X

Ribbon Splitting in Roller Compaction and Monitoring of a Dry Granulation Process

David Sixon,[a] Josie Kirsch,[a] Adam Georgopoulos,[a] Rexonni Lagare,[a] Marcial Gonzalez,[b,c] Zoltan Nagy,[a] Gintaras Reklaitis[a]*

[a]*Davidson School of Chemical Engineering, Purdue University, West Lafayette, IN 47907, USA*
[b]*School of Mechanical Engineering, Purdue University, West Lafayette, IN 47907, USA*
[c]*Ray W. Herrick Laboratories, Purdue University, West Lafayette, IN 47907, USA*
**Corresponding Author: reklaiti@purdue.edu*

Abstract

While ribbon splitting is an observable and measurable occurrence, the design of production-scale roller compactors obscures the operator's view of ribbon splitting and may have contributed to the lack of literature on the phenomenon. However, as the principles of continuous manufacturing are applied to processes that use roller compaction (such as continuous dry granulation), ribbon splitting may be able to serve as a novel way to monitor the system. This study demonstrates how roller compactor parameters are connected to ribbon splitting and how this relationship can be used to potentially detect issues upstream. First, using pure excipient powder, the behavior of ribbon splitting was mapped out as a function of roller compactor variables: roll gap and hydraulic pressure. As the roller compactor's hydraulic pressure and roll gap decreases, the ribbon splitting behavior goes from splitting to not-splitting. With a general idea of ribbon splitting conditions laid out, the composition of the powder fed into the roller compactor was varied to show that changes in composition can lead to changes in ribbon splitting. A shift in the behavior of ribbon splitting (from not-splitting to splitting) demonstrated the potential that ribbon splitting has to offer as a signal suitable for monitoring roller compaction in a continuous process, giving a roller compactor operator a real time tool to identify possible deviations from normal behavior upstream. However, changing the feed composition did not always cause a change in the ribbon splitting behavior, suggesting that there is a complex relationship between parameters of the roller compactor, the composition, and ribbon splitting. Ongoing work is focused on generating a larger set of data points of split and not-split conditions under a wider range of values of operating variables with the goal of developing a machine learning for predicting ribbon splitting.

Keywords: Ribbon Splitting, Roller Compactor, Dry Granulation, Continuous Manufacturing

1. Introduction

As the implementation of continuous manufacturing occurs across many industries, new methods and measures need to be developed to monitor the unit operations without disturbing the continuous flow of materials. The pharmaceutical industry has several processes that are being converted from batch to continuous operation: one of these is dry granulation-based tablet manufacture. In this process, a powder blend of active pharmaceutical ingredient (API) and excipient is converted into a solid tablet without the introduction of solvents or moisture. The process consists of feeding the powder components continuously, blending them together, increasing particle size using a roller compactor, and forming the tablets in a tablet press. The roller compactor serves multiple functions: to mitigate the tendency of powders in the blend to segregate, to produce granules of increased particle size, to improve the flow of the resulting granular material, and to reduce the fraction of fine particles which must be processed in the tablet press (Sun et al, 2016). In the roller compactor, the powder blend is first compressed into a thin ribbon, and then the ribbon is milled into granules of a desired size.

The roller compactor is thus an essential part of the dry granulation process. Several studies have attempted to model the roller compactor with the goal of controlling and optimizing the process, most recently Y.-S. Huang et al (2023). These studies have also employed various sensors to monitor critical roller compactor variables and the properties of the ribbon/granules produced. However, most of the properties are measured off-line, making the measurements difficult to use for monitoring and controlling continuous operation.

Ribbon splitting offers a real-time solution to this at-line/off-line measurement problem. Ribbon splitting occurs when ribbon leaves the rollers of the roller compactor as two ribbons instead of the expected one, as shown in Figure 1. This phenomenon is rather easy to observe, since the ribbons leaving the roller compactor can be classified as split or not-split if the observer's view of the roller compactor's rollers is not obstructed.

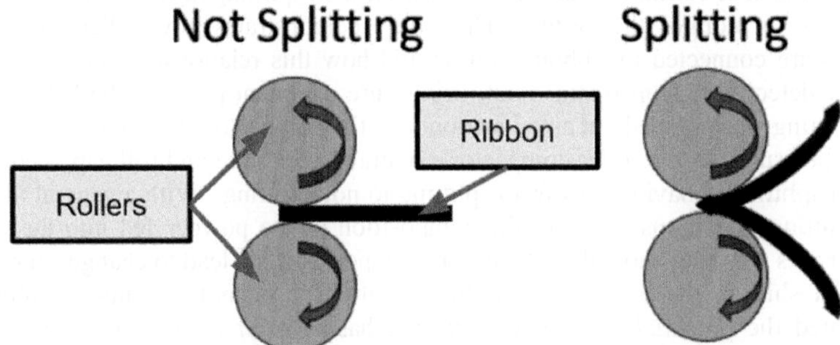

Figure 1. The not-split ribbon case is shown on the left, while the split ribbon case is shown on the right.

Several attempts have been made to model/explain ribbon splitting, including Mahmah et al (2019). As more data is collected on ribbon splitting behavior at different sets of conditions, predictions of splitting or not-splitting can be made. These predictions can be further enhanced and automated with a machine learning model, which could characterize an inputted set of conditions as split or not-split. Furthermore, with a camera sensor and some redesigning of the roller compactors, the ribbon splitting behavior could be monitored and compared to a machine learning model's prediction automatically. Then, if the ribbon splitting behavior deviates from the predictions, the roller compactor would alert the operator, who could diagnose possible issues upstream or with the roller compactor and possibly initiate corrective action. With the end goal of building a machine learning model for ribbon splitting, this study aims to explore how roller compactor parameters and the composition of the powder mixture fed into the roller compactor impact ribbon splitting, and how ribbon splitting could be used as a monitoring strategy in a continuous dry granulation process.

2. Methodology

2.1.1 Mapping of Roller Compactor Parameters

For purposes of the first part of this study, the roller compactor receives a powder flow originating from a feeder located on the top floor of the pilot plant and proceeding through a blender at a constant flow rate, as shown on the left-hand side of Figure 2. A feed screw pushes powder from the roller compactor hopper to between the rollers which compact the powder into a ribbon which may or may not undergo splitting. The key roller compactor parameters are shown in the right-hand side of Figure 2.

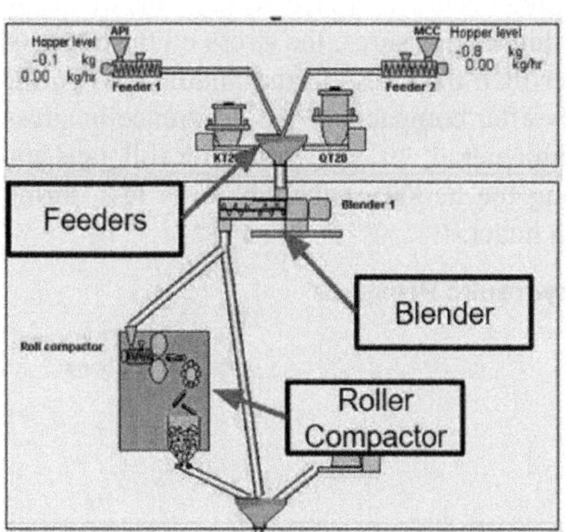

Figure 2. Pilot Plant and Roller Compactor Setup

For the following experiments, the controlled variables and their ranges are as follows: Roll Gap (1.6-2.8 mm), Roll Speed (4 RPM), Hydraulic Pressure (30-90 bar), and Feed-Screw Speed (20-50 RPM). Roll gap and hydraulic pressure are the two main variables of focus. It is important to note that all experiments mapping the roller compactor parameters were conducted using pure Microcrystalline Cellulose (MCC) 102 to simplify both the procedure and results. The incorporation of the effects of variation in composition on ribbon splitting is part of the second phase of the study. The roller compactor, feeder, and hopper were cleaned between runs as any stray powder can risk contamination of the ribbon and lead to inaccurate results. Runs were conducted for five minutes, to ensure steady-state was reached, and the steady-state process data was collected. This process data would be crucial to building a machine learning model for ribbon splitting in future works. Most sets of conditions were replicated.

2.1.2 Change of Composition Experiments

The second feeder in the pilot plant was added into the experimental design to vary the composition of the powder blend produced in the blender. The same procedure was followed, but this time, a focus was put on roller compactor conditions that resulted in not-split ribbons. After observing that the ribbon was not-splitting, and that the roller compactor was in steady-state, the second feeder was manually activated (introducing another material), and further observations were made to see if the ribbon splitting behavior changed. The first feeder (supplying MCC) flow rate was set at 9.00 kg/h, while the second feeder (supplying the API) flow rate was set at 1.00 kg/h. In these experiments, the API was Acetaminophen.

3. Results and Discussion

3.1.1 Mapping of Roller Compactor Parameters

Once all the process data for each run at a set of Roller Compactor parameters was collected, the relationships between splitting parameters and ribbon splitting could be illustrated. Figure 3 demonstrates one of these relationships. In ongoing work, a machine learning model is being developed to capture these relationships.

As shown in Figure 3, there are clear regions where ribbon splitting occurs. At higher pressures and larger roll gaps, the ribbon splitting occurs, and vice versa. This trend can be explained as follows: at larger roll gaps or higher pressures, the stress on the edges of the ribbon during compaction is much greater than the stress in the middle. When the ribbon is allowed to recover elasticity directly after compaction, the difference in stress is too much and the ribbon splits in two (Mahmah et al, 2019). At smaller roll gaps and lower pressures, the difference in stress along the height of the ribbon is less during compaction, allowing for the ribbon to remain intact.

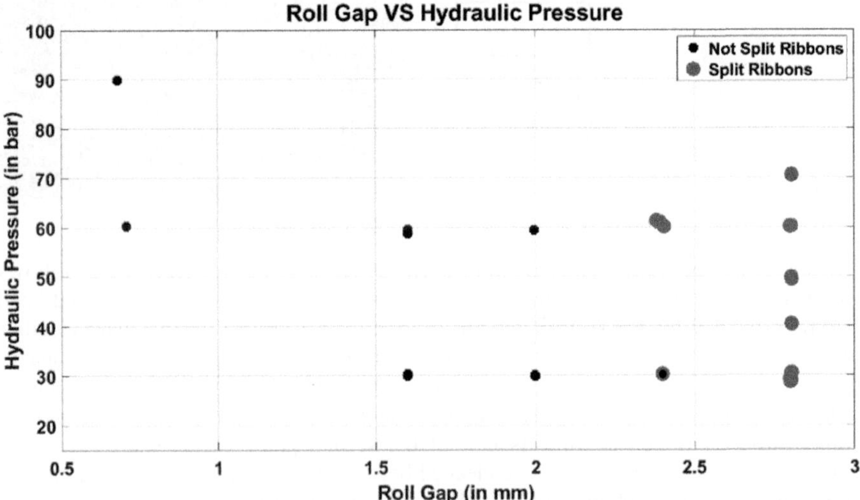

Figure 3. Average Roll Gap at Steady State vs Average Hydraulic Pressure at Steady State, with each point denoted as Split or Not-Split Ribbon. The red points signify split ribbons, while the black points show not-split ribbons.

3.2.1 Change of Composition Experiments

With a map of roll gap and hydraulic pressure defined in Figure 3, the ribbon splitting phenomena can be explored as a possible monitoring tooling for the continuous dry granulation process. The map gives a prediction of ribbon splitting behavior for 100% excipient composition. The composition was changed under two different roller compactor sets of variables. The first set of roller compactor parameters was closer to the boundary between splitting and not-splitting regions, while the second condition was farther away from this boundary. The goal was to see how much composition impacts ribbon splitting, since the conditions closer to the possible ribbon splitting boundary should be more sensitive to changes in feed composition when compared to conditions farther from the boundary.

3.2.2. Changing Composition Impacts Ribbon Splitting Behavior Example

Figure 4 (A) shows the timeline of a trial in which the Roller Compactor is set at 60 bar and a roll gap of 2.0 mm. As predicted by the ribbon splitting map in Figure 3, the ribbon does not split initially. However, at t = 90 seconds, the API feeder is turned on, continuously adding the second component (API) to the feed. At t = 265 seconds, the ribbon splitting behaviour changes from not-splitting to splitting.

The delay between contaminant being added to the system and ribbon splitting behaviour changing is due to the residence time of the contaminant in the blender and Roller Compactor Hopper. The ribbon splitting behaviour could not change until the contaminated mixture reached the Roller Compactor, and there was change in the composition of the material being compressed.

3.2.3. Changing Composition Does Not Impact Ribbon Splitting Behavior Example

While there was a change in ribbon splitting behaviour in the previous example, this is not always the case. Figure 4 (B) shows the timeline of a run in which the Roller Compactor is set at 60 bar and a roll gap of 1.6 mm. As predicted by the ribbon splitting map in Figure 3, this ribbon does not split initially. When looking at Figure 3 and the previous example, one might expect this experiment to have a switch in ribbon splitting behaviour once the second component is added. However, that is not the case.

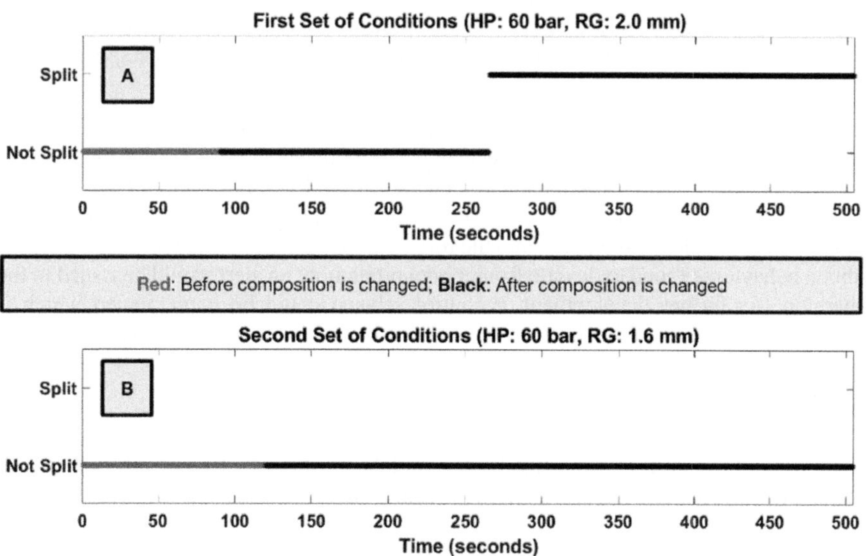

Figure 4. (A) First Set of Roller Compactor Conditions: Hydraulic Pressure: 60 bar; Roll Gap: 2.0 mm. Ribbon splitting occurs at 265 seconds. (B) Second Set of Roller Compactor Conditions: Hydraulic Pressure: 60 bar; Roll Gap: 1.6 mm. In both cases, API Feeder turned on at 90 seconds.

Despite a change in composition, the ribbon splitting behavior did not change. This demonstrates that while ribbon splitting is a function of composition, the operating variables of the roller compactor are also important. This supports the idea that there exists a more complex boundary in the ribbon splitting map, separating the not-split and split ribbon conditions. The closer a condition is to that boundary; the more sensitive ribbon splitting is to changes in composition.

3.3.1 Monitoring Roller Compactor Operating Errors

While generating Figure 3 to find regions of splitting and not-splitting amongst the roller compactor parameters, the roller compactor would malfunction from time to time. Table 1 shows one of these cases, where the relative standard deviations for the second run are much higher than the first, and ribbon splitting behavior changes. Instead of having to check the process data for unusual variations around the set point, the ribbon splitting could be monitored. If the ribbon splitting had unexpected behaviour, that could notify the operator that something is wrong and stop the process for inspection.

Table 1. Ribbon Splitting Experiments where the Roller Compactor Malfunctioned

Roll Gap Set Point	Average Roll Gap	Roll Gap Relative St Dev	Hydraulic Pressure Set Point	Average Hydraulic Pressure	Hydraulic Pressure Relative St Dev	Expected Splitting Behavior	Splitting Behavior
2.0	1.996	0.0116	60	59.425	0.0018	Not-Split	Not-Split
2.0	1.992	0.1885	60	59.716	0.0109	Not-Split	Split

4. Conclusions

Ribbon Splitting can be controlled, in part, by hydraulic pressure and roll gap. At higher pressures and larger roll gaps, the ribbon is more likely to split when it leaves the rollers. Composition can also impact ribbon splitting. In ongoing work, additional data is being generated to fill out the ribbon splitting map to better define the split and not-split regions.

Using the additional data points generated at different compositions, a machine learning model will be implemented to more precisely quantify the boundary between the split and not-split regions. Using this model, for the given feed composition and set of roller compactor conditions, prediction of the behavior of ribbon splitting will be enabled. A camera sensor could be integrated into the roller compactor to monitor the ribbon state. If ribbon behavior is found to deviate from model prediction, an alert would be issued to the operator. As further development, a control schema could be implemented which if splitting occurred would adjust compactor variables to achieve a feasible no-split condition.

Acknowledgements

This work was supported by the NSF under grant #2140452. The authors would like to thank Abigail Delaney, Dr. Yan-Shu Huang, and the Purdue CP3 lab, as well as Prof. Jim Lister and Dr. Chalak Omar from Sheffield University.

References

Y-. S. Huang, D. Sixon, P. Bailey, R. Lagare, M. Gonzalez, Z. Nagy, G. Reklaitis, 2023, A Machine Learning-assisted Hybrid Model to Predict Ribbon Solid Fraction, Granule Size Distribution and Throughput in a Dry Granulation Process, Computer Aided Chemical Engineering, 52, 813-818.

O. Mahmah, M. J. Adams, C. Omar, B. Gururajan, A. Salman, 2019, Roller compaction: Ribbon splitting and sticking, International Journal of Pharmaceutics, 559, 156-172.

C. Sun, P. Kleinebudde, 2016, Mini review: Mechanisms to the loss of tabletability by dry granulation, European Journal of Pharmaceutics and Biopharmaceutics, 106, 9-14.

Flavio Manenti, Gintaras V. Reklaitis (Eds.), Proceedings of the 34th European Symposium on Computer Aided Process Engineering / 15th International Symposium on Process Systems Engineering (ESCAPE34/PSE24), June 2-6, 2024, Florence, Italy
 http://dx.doi.org/10.1016/B978-0-443-28824-1.50289-1

A Deep Reinforcement Learning PI Tuning Strategy for Closed-loop Operation of a Recirculating Aquaculture System

Hao Wang,[a] Luis A. Ricardez-Sandoval[a,*]

[a]*Department of Chemical Engineering, University of Waterloo, Waterloo, ON N2L 3G1, Canada*

**Corresponding author. E-mail address: laricard@uwaterloo.ca*

Abstract

Adequate water quality is key for fish production in recirculating aquaculture systems (RAS). In this study, we formulate the control of RAS water quality parameters using a deep Reinforcement Learning (RL) based multi-loop proportional-integral (PI) tuning strategy. The key novelty is the design of an adaptive RL agent to respond to the nonlinear and highly interactive behaviour of the multiple-input, multiple-output RAS in real-time while handling constraints for water quality parameters and sensor malfunctions. We tested our tuning strategy in a scenario where multiple sensors can malfunction simultaneously. The proposed RL agent significantly outperformed conventional PI controllers in oxygen concentration setpoint tracking while reducing critical and supersaturation dissolved oxygen level violations. The setpoint tracking performances of total ammonia and nitrate concentrations were slightly sacrificed, but this did not compromise fish health as these concentrations remained well below toxic levels. The RL-based PI tuning strategy exhibits acceptable control performance for water quality parameters and sheds light on future applications of RL-based closed-loop RAS operation.

Keywords: Recirculating aquaculture systems, Reinforcement Learning, PI controllers

1. Introduction

Recirculating aquaculture systems (RAS) are attractive options for fish production due to their substantial benefits, including decreased water usage, environmentally friendly, and improved productivity (Kamali et al., 2022). Adequate control of RAS in terms of water quality is crucial for fish growth (Kamali et al., 2023). While conventional proportional-integral-derivative (PID) controllers with fixed tuning parameters remain the most widely adopted and popular controllers in the industry, they may not perform well for multiple-input, multiple-output (MIMO) RAS given the nonlinear and highly interactive behaviour of these systems. For instance, conventional PID controllers cannot account for process constraints and real-time response to major changes during operation, such as sensor malfunction. Hence, studies involving adaptive PID controllers that maintain RAS operation on target have emerged. Zhou et al. (2021 & 2022) proposed a differential evolution algorithm-optimized radial basis function neural network PID controller and a fuzzy rule-optimized single-neuron adaptive PID controller for dissolved oxygen (DO) control in RAS, respectively. Those studies only considered a single-input, single-output RAS and did not include water quality constraints. In recent years, studies of Reinforcement Learning (RL) in adaptive PID control have become popular. For instance, Carlucho et al. (2020) proposed a deep RL-based adaptive MIMO PID tuning approach using an inverted deep deterministic policy gradient (IDDPG) algorithm to control mobile robots. Yu et al. (2022) constructed a model-free self-adaptive SAC-PID control approach for mobile robots using the soft actor-critic algorithm.

This study formulates a deep RL-based proportional-integral (PI) tuning approach for controlling water quality parameters under constraints, i.e., oxygen and total ammonia (TAN), in MIMO RAS subjected to water quality sensor malfunctions, which are aspects that have not been addressed in the literature; hence, the novelty of the proposed framework. The proposed control scheme is an adaption of the IDDPG algorithm proposed by Carlucho et al. (2020) with a tailored RL agent design. To the authors' knowledge, the present study is the first that considers RL for closed-loop RAS operation.

2. Problem Statement

In this study, the dynamic mechanistic model proposed by Kamali et al. (2022) is adopted to predict the transient behaviour of RAS. The model consists of a fish-rearing tank, a mechanical filter, and two moving bed biofilm reactors (BRs) to treat the water leaving RAS. The model mainly involves mass balances of waste components and oxygen. There are 14 waste components (i) in the RAS model, including nitrate nitrogen and TAN. The fish-rearing tank is modelled as a well-mixed reactor. The mass balance of waste components' concentrations (Z_i) in the fish tank is as follows:

$$V_{FT}dZ_i/dt = Q_{FT}\left(Z_{i,in} - Z_i\right) + W_i + L_i \tag{1}$$

where Z_i refers to either the concentration of the soluble (S_i) or particulate (X_i) waste component and $Z_{i,in}$ is the corresponding inlet concentration; V_{FT} and Q_{FT} are the volume and flow rate to the fish tank, respectively. W_i and L_i are the waste production rate and feed loss of waste component i, respectively, i.e. TAN and nitrate,

$$\eta dW_i/dt = (1 - \psi_{loss})\zeta_i F(t) - W_i; \;\; L_i = \psi_{loss}\delta_i F(t) \tag{2}$$

where ζ_i and δ_i are the fractions of component i in waste and feed, respectively. η, ψ_{loss}, and $F(t)$ are the feed residence time, feed loss fraction, and feeding rate, respectively. It is assumed that fish growth is slow and negligible compared to changes in the waste components and oxygen concentrations. Also, the removal rate of the mechanical filter downstream of the fish-rearing tank is assumed constant and operated at steady-state.

In this study, BRs are modelled using a zero-dimensional biofilm model. Thus, the biochemical conversions in the bulk and biofilm for suspended particulate (X_i^S), dissolved (S_i), and biofilm particulate (X_i^B) waste components are described as follows:

$$V_{BR}dY_i/dt = Q_{BR}\left(Y_{i,in} - Y_i\right) + r_i \tag{3}$$

where V_{BR} and Q_{BR} are the volume and flow rate to BRs, respectively; Y_i represents X_i^S, S_i, or X_i^B; $Y_{i,in}$ is the inlet concentration; r_i is the rate of change of component i.

The oxygen concentration mass balance is the same for the fish-rearing tank (FT) and BRs. Thus, for $q \in \{FT, BR1, BR2\}$, the expression is as follows:

$$V_q dS_O^q/dt = Q_q\left(S_{O,in}^q - S_O^q\right) + r_{O_2}^q + m_{O_2}^q \tag{4}$$

where S_O^q, $S_{O,in}^q$, r_{O_2}, and $m_{O_2}^q$ are the oxygen's bulk concentration, inlet concentration, consumption rate, and addition rate, respectively; V_q is the volume and Q_q is the flow rate. The complete list of waste components (i) and additional modelling details can be found in Kamali et al. (2022).

The controlled variables and manipulated variables available to maintain a suitable environment for fish rearing are $\boldsymbol{y} = [S_O^{FT}, S_{NH}^{FT}, S_{NO_3}^{FT}]$ and $\boldsymbol{u} = [m_{O_2}^{FT}, m_{O_2}^{BR1}, Q_m]$, respectively. S_O^{FT}, S_{NH}^{FT}, and $S_{NO_3}^{FT}$ are the oxygen, TAN, and nitrate concentrations in the fish tank, respectively; Q_m denotes the make-up water flow rate to the fish tank. Through a Relative Gain Array analysis (not shown for brevity), three control loop pairings were identified for this process, i.e., $S_O^{FT} - m_{O_2}^{FT}$, $S_{NH}^{FT} - m_{O_2}^{BR1}$, and $S_{NO_3}^{FT} - Q_m$. The control objective is to use the three control loops to change values in $\boldsymbol{u}$ to maintain $\boldsymbol{y}$ close to a setpoint $\boldsymbol{y_{sp}} \in R^3$. Since $\boldsymbol{y}$ consists of water quality parameters, it is desired to keep $\boldsymbol{y}$ within known fish species-dependent ranges for optimal fish growth, i.e., $\boldsymbol{y_{min}} = [DO_c$, 0, 0] and $\boldsymbol{y_{max}} = [DO_s, UL_{NH}, UL_{NO_3}]$. DO_c, DO_s, UL_{NH}, and UL_{NO_3} are the critical DO, supersaturation DO, TAN toxic, and nitrate toxic levels, respectively. The multiloop PI control scheme is constructed as follows. For each control loop k, a sensor and a PI controller with proportional gain (K_c^k) and integral time constant (τ_I^k) are considered. The tuning parameters are denoted as $\boldsymbol{a} = (\boldsymbol{a^1}, \boldsymbol{a^2}, \boldsymbol{a^3})$; $\boldsymbol{a^k} = (K_c^k, \tau_I^k)$ for $k = 1, 2, 3$.
According to a report from the Government of Newfoundland & Labrador (2014), water quality sensors are prone to calibration and biofouling drifts. This condition has not been widely explored for MIMO RAS. In this work, we consider a potential sensor malfunction in the three water quality sensors measuring $\boldsymbol{y}$ with measurements $\boldsymbol{y_m}$. It is assumed that the deployment period for all sensors is P days. During this period, each sensor may start to malfunction on Days D_1, D_2, or D_3 with respective probabilities p_1^k, p_2^k, and p_3^k. That is, a sensor k would start to malfunction on Day D_1 and persist until the end of the P-day period if $g_1^k < p_1^k$, where g_1^k is a random number sampled from a uniform distribution, i.e., $g_1^k \sim U(0, 1)$. This procedure is repeated if the sensor is operating normally on Days D_2 or D_3. At the end of the P-day period, all sensors are re-calibrated and ready for the next P-day deployment period. The realization of the sensor malfunction is in the form of a zero-mean Gaussian noise (e^k) with a standard deviation of x^k% sensor measurement added to the actual sensor measurement (y_m^k).
The objective of the problem constructed in this study is to design multi-loop PI controllers for the RAS plant model presented above under sensor malfunctions and water quality parameter constraints by tuning the PI controller parameters $\boldsymbol{a}$. Typically, $\boldsymbol{a}$ is tuned offline using conventional PI tuning methods such as Internal Model Control (IMC). However, such tuning approaches usually lead to poor control performance due to a lack of real-time response to the nonlinear and highly interactive behaviour of MIMO RAS in the presence of sensor malfunctions and water quality parameter constraints. To tackle this problem, this work presents an adaptive RL-based PI tuning approach which is described in the next section.

3. Mathematical Framework

Our mathematical framework was adapted from the IDDPG algorithm proposed by Carlucho et al. (2020), as it allows a wide continuous action space range ($[-\infty, \infty]$) and constraints output actions within bounds and prevents saturation by inverting the critic's gradients. IDDPG contains the basic elements for an RL agent, i.e., state $\boldsymbol{s}$, action $\boldsymbol{a}$, and reward r. Also, since IDDPG is a model-free, off-policy, actor-critic algorithm, it also consists of an actor-network $\mu(\boldsymbol{s}|\theta^\mu)$ and a critic-network $Q(\boldsymbol{s}, \boldsymbol{a}|\theta^Q)$ with weights θ^μ and θ^Q, target networks $\mu'(\boldsymbol{s}|\theta^{\mu'})$ and $Q'(\boldsymbol{s}, \boldsymbol{a}|\theta^{Q'})$ with weights $\theta^{\mu'}$ and $\theta^{Q'}$ to soft update the learned networks, and a replay buffer $\boldsymbol{R}$ to store transitions $(\boldsymbol{s_j}, \boldsymbol{a_j}, r_j, \boldsymbol{s_{j+1}})$ to be used for RL agent training. Details of IDDPG can be found in Carlucho et al. (2020).

A key novelty in our framework involves designing our own action vector and reward function for the RL agent. Our framework also considers RAS sensor malfunctions in the RL agent training. For an episode with maximum simulation time t_{max} and sampling time Δt, the selection of $\boldsymbol{a_z}$ at a sampling time step z is expressed as follows:

$$\boldsymbol{a_z} = clip\left[\left(\mu(\boldsymbol{s_z}|\theta^{\mu}) + \beta\boldsymbol{\epsilon_{a_z}} \times (\boldsymbol{a_{max}} - \boldsymbol{a_{min}})/2\right), \boldsymbol{a_{min}}, \boldsymbol{a_{max}}\right] \quad (5)$$

where $\boldsymbol{a_{max}}$ and $\boldsymbol{a_{min}}$ are the upper and lower bounds of $\boldsymbol{a}$. Unlike Carlucho et al. (2020), we utilize noise $\boldsymbol{\epsilon_{a_z}}$ sampled from a Gaussian noise process $\mathcal{N}(\varphi, \boldsymbol{I} \cdot \sigma)$ with mean φ, standard deviation σ, and an identity matrix $\boldsymbol{I}$ to encourage exploration. Also, we apply a logistic action noise scaling factor $\beta = 1/(1 + e^{b(episode\ \# - c)})$ with constants b and c for the scheduled reduction of action noise with increases in the number of episodes to improve the robustness of the learning process in our framework. Through executing $\boldsymbol{a_z}$, sensor measurements $\boldsymbol{y_{m_z}}$ are recorded. For any sensor that malfunctions, a sensor noise e_z^k is added to $y_{m_z}^k$ such that $y_{m_z}^k = y_{m_z}^k + e_z^k$. The sensor malfunction is then introduced into the RL agent training by constructing the next state $\boldsymbol{s_{z+1}}$ with $\boldsymbol{a_z}$, $\boldsymbol{y_z} = \boldsymbol{y_{m_z}}$, and the error vector $\boldsymbol{\varepsilon_z} = \boldsymbol{y_{sp}} - \boldsymbol{y_z}$. The reward function makes use of the sum of squares error (SSE) for setpoint tracking while penalizing constraint violations in $\boldsymbol{y_{min}}$ and $\boldsymbol{y_{max}}$, i.e.,

$$r_z = \sum_{k=1}^{3} r_z{}^k \quad where\ \ r_z{}^k = \begin{cases} -\left(y_{sp}^k - y_z^k\right)^2 & if\ \ y_{min}^k \leq y_z^k \leq y_{max}^k \\ -50 & otherwise \end{cases} \quad (6)$$

The episodic return is thus calculated as ER=$\sum_{z=1}^{z=t_{max}/\Delta t} r_z$. Note that subscript z and superscript k above refer to the sampling time step and controller/sensor, respectively.

4. Results and Discussions

4.1. Case study

The RL strategy presented in the previous section was tested on a case study of the MIMO RAS plant model presented in Kamali et al. (2023). The details of the RAS described in Section 2 are as follows. The volumes of the fish-rearing tank (V_{FT}) and two BRs (V_{BR1}, V_{BR2}) are 5.5 m^3, 0.4 m^3, and 0.4 m^3, respectively; a 40 μm drum filter is used as the mechanical filter. The RAS is used to raise rainbow trout at 19 °C with a constant body weight of 0.045 kg. The feed schedule is 6 hours per day with a 3 kg/day feed rate. $\boldsymbol{y_{sp}}$ = [0.008, 0.00062, 0.0209] kg/m^3, $\boldsymbol{y_{min}}$ = [0.007, 0, 0] kg/m^3, and $\boldsymbol{y_{max}}$ = [0.013, 0.013, 0.075] kg/m^3. The rest of the model parameters and nominal conditions can be found in Kamali et al. (2023). Moreover, for sensor malfunctions, a common deployment period of $P = 30$ days is considered; D_1, D_2, and D_3 are set to Days 1, 11, and 21. For all k, p_1^k = 10 %, p_2^k = 30 %, and p_3^k = 50 %, respectively; also, x^k % = 10 %. For comparison, the three PI controllers were also tuned using IMC followed by a manual adjustment for better control performance. The resulting PI tuning parameters are $\boldsymbol{a}^*$ = [[14.5, 0.3], [-8945.437, 0.15], [-500, 0.8]]. $\boldsymbol{a_{max}}$ and $\boldsymbol{a_{min}}$ in Eq. (5) are defined as $\boldsymbol{a_{max}}$ = [[25, 5], [-1000, 5], [-80, 5]] and $\boldsymbol{a_{min}}$ = [[0.1, 0.02], [-9000, 0.02], [-800, 0.02]].

4.2. RL agent settings, training, and validation

In terms of RL agent settings, the parameter values used in this study for the Gaussian noise and the logistic schedular in action exploration: φ, σ, b, and c were set to 0, 0.01, 0.02, and 250, respectively. For the RL agent training, Δt was set to 0.1 days to accommodate the timescale differences and daily fluctuations in RAS. To train the agent with diverse sensor malfunction instances, t_{max} was set to 90 days to allow three 30-day deployment periods (P) within an episode. The agent underwent 1,500 training episodes on a PC with Intel® Core™ i7-9700K CPU @ 3.60 GHz and 64 GB of RAM using TensorFlow 1 in Python. The RAS model was simulated using an interior-point solver.

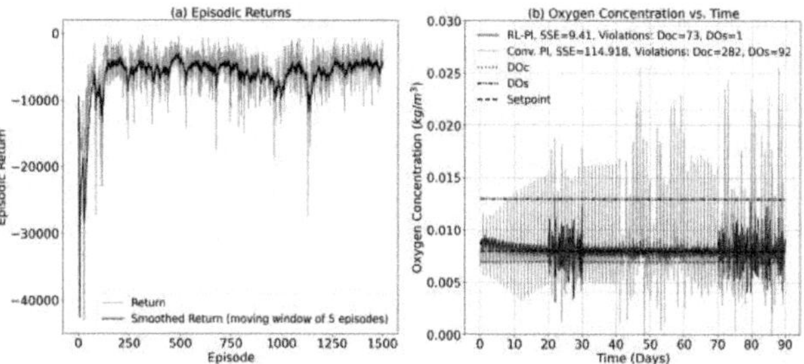

Figure 1. (a) Episodic returns and smoothed returns of the RL agent; (b) Oxygen concentration setpoint tracking performances of both control methods under one sensor malfunction instance.

As shown in Figure 1a, although some fluctuations were observed at the beginning of the learning curve, the agent's training converged after around 250 episodes. The setpoint tracking performances of the agent were validated using 200 testing runs with different sensor malfunction instances. A comparison was made with $\boldsymbol{a}^*$ in terms of the means and standard deviations of SSEs and constraint violation counts for DO_c, DO_s, UL_{NH}, and UL_{NO_3}. For better visualization, SSEs were magnified by a factor of 10^4. As depicted in Table 1, the agent significantly outperforms $\boldsymbol{a}^*$ in S_O^{FT} setpoint tracking and reducing violations in DO_c and DO_s. Compared to $\boldsymbol{a}^*$, the agent reduced the means of SSE of S_O^{FT} and DO_s violation count by 2 orders of magnitude and the mean of DO_c violation count by 1 order of magnitude. Nevertheless, these good performances came at the expense of slightly sacrificing S_{NH}^{FT} and $S_{NO_3}^{FT}$ setpoint tracking performances. That is, the agent produced actions that resulted in the means of SSEs of S_{NH}^{FT} and $S_{NO_3}^{FT}$ that are 0.80 % and 14.36 % higher than those obtained for $\boldsymbol{a}^*$, respectively. However, fish health was not compromised as S_{NH}^{FT} and $S_{NO_3}^{FT}$ remained below toxic levels, i.e., no violations in UL_{NH} and UL_{NO_3} were observed. Regarding standard deviations, compared to $\boldsymbol{a}^*$, the agent reduced the variability in most SSEs and violation counts, except for the SSE of $S_{NO_3}^{FT}$ and DO_c violation count. This indicates that for the agent, the different combinations of sensors that may malfunction during operation can create variability in $S_{NO_3}^{FT}$ setpoint tracking performance and DO_c violation count, and may lead to cases of large SSE of $S_{NO_3}^{FT}$ and high DO_c violation count.

The oxygen concentration setpoint tracking performances for both the RL agent and conventional PI controllers under one sensor malfunction instance from the 200 testing runs are illustrated in Figure 1b. For this instance, the oxygen, TAN, and nitrate concentration sensors malfunction on Days 21~30 and 71~90, Days 41~60 and 71~90, and Days 21~30 and 61~90, respectively. As shown in Figure 1b, for the RL agent, DO_c and DO_s constraint violations only occur when there are oxygen concentration sensor malfunctions (Days 21~30 and 71~90), which is reflected by the large variability observed in this parameter. For the rest of the simulation time, the RL agent is able to track the setpoint and avoid constraint violations, even in the presence of other sensor malfunctions. Conversely, conventional PI controllers continuously violate DO_c and DO_s limits with large variability due to sensor malfunctions.

Table 1. Comparison of setpoint tracking performances in the form of mean and standard deviation (mean $\pm$ deviation) of SSEs and constraint violation counts.

Controlled Variables ($\boldsymbol{y}$)	SSE: RL-PI $\times 10^4$	SSE: PI $\times 10^4$
Oxygen Concentration (S_O^{FT})	9.475 ± 3.858	103.824 ± 14.570
TAN Concentration (S_{NH}^{FT})	0.9783 ± 0.0037	0.9705 ± 0.0044
Nitrate Concentration ($S_{NO_3}^{FT}$)	20.432 ± 10.029	17.866 ± 8.990
Constraints	Violation Count: RL-PI	Violation Count: PI
DO Critical (DO_c)	86.15 ± 43.40	299.49 ± 21.62
DO Supersaturation (DO_s)	0.47 ± 0.67	87.24 ± 6.13
Toxic Levels UL_{NH} & UL_{NO_3}	0 ± 0	0 ± 0

5. Conclusions

This study presents a mathematical framework of a deep RL-base tuning strategy to solve the multi-loop PI tuning problem for the control of RAS water quality parameters (i.e., oxygen, TAN, and nitrate concentrations) with fish species-dependent constraints and subject to multiple water quality sensor malfunctions. The key novelties of this work are the application of deep RL to closed-loop RAS operation, improvements to the IDDPG algorithm by RL agent design, and incorporation of water quality sensor malfunction into RL agent training. We applied the proposed strategy to the closed-loop operation of RAS, where multiple sensors could malfunction simultaneously. The results showed that the proposed RL strategy exhibits acceptable control performances for water quality parameters and significantly reduced critical and supersaturation DO level violations. Thus, this RL strategy has the potential to be implemented online for closed-loop RAS operations to maintain water quality to their setpoints while reducing potential risks to fish health. Future work includes improving the proposed strategy by incorporating fish growth dynamics into RAS and optimizing for fish growth and water quality control.

References

I. Carlucho, M. De Paula, & G. G. Acosta, 2020, An adaptive deep reinforcement learning approach for MIMO PID control of mobile robots, ISA transactions, 102, 280-294.

S. Kamali, V. C. A. Ward, & L. Ricardez-Sandoval, 2022, Dynamic modeling of recirculating aquaculture systems: Effect of management strategies and water quality parameters on fish performance, Aquacultural Engineering, 99, 102294.

S. Kamali, V. C. A. Ward, & L. Ricardez-Sandoval, 2023, Closed-loop operation of a simulated recirculating aquaculture system with an integrated application of nonlinear model predictive control and moving horizon estimation, Computers and Electronics in Agriculture, 209, 107820.

Water Resources Management Division, Department of Environment and Conservation, Government of Newfoundland & Labrador, 2014, Protocols manual for RTWQ monitoring in NL – calibration and maintenance guide for industry partners, https://www.gov.nl.ca/ecc/files/waterres-rti-rtwq-nl-rtwq-manual-calibration.pdf

X. Yu, Y. Fan, S. Xu, & L. Ou, 2022, A self-adaptive SAC-PID control approach based on reinforcement learning for mobile robots, International journal of robust and nonlinear control, 32(18), 9625-9643.

X. Zhou, D. Li, L. Zhang, & Q. Duan, 2021, Application of an adaptive PID controller enhanced by a differential evolution algorithm for precise control of dissolved oxygen in recirculating aquaculture systems, Biosystems Engineering, 208, 186-198.

X. Zhou, J. Wang, L. Huang, D. Li, & Q. Duan, 2022, Modelling and controlling dissolved oxygen in recirculating aquaculture systems based on mechanism analysis and an adaptive PID controller, Computers and Electronics in Agriculture, 192, 106583.

Flavio Manenti, Gintaras V. Reklaitis (Eds.), Proceedings of the 34th European Symposium on Computer Aided Process Engineering / 15th International Symposium on Process Systems Engineering (ESCAPE34/PSE24), June 2-6, 2024, Florence, Italy
 http://dx.doi.org/10.1016/B978-0-443-28824-1.50290-8

A Prediction Error Adaptive Kalman filter for on-line spectral measurement correction and concentration estimation

Daniel Sbarbaro[a*], Tor Arne Johansen[b], Jorge Yañez[c]

[a]*Departement of Electrical Engineering, Universidad de Concepción, Concepción, Chile*

[b]*Department of Engineering Cybernetics, Norwegian University of Science and Technology, Trondheim, Norway*

[c]*Department of Analytical and Inorganic Chemistry, Faculty of Chemical Sciences, Universidad de Concepcion, Concepcin, Chile*

dsbarbar@udec.cl

Abstract

Spectral measurements offer real-time insights into the composition and concentration of species in process samples. However, they are sensitive to external factors such as temperature, pressure, and particle size distribution, all of which have a significant impact on the precision of spectroscopic measurements. In this study, we introduce an integrated discrete-time nonlinear model considering the dynamic aspects of the process, alongside a physics-based sensor model. Additionally, we propose an innovative application of two alternative Prediction Error Adaptive Kalman Filters to estimate both concentrations and sensor model parameters. The simulation of a simple ternary mixing process enables a comparison of the key characteristics of the proposed adaptive Kalman filters with a standard Extended Kalman Filter. The simulation results show that both Prediction Error Kalman filters can estimate concentrations and sensor parameters with minimal error, even in the presence of temperature variations and measurement noise. However, the proposed filters offer advantages in terms of ease of tuning and convergence.

1. Introduction

Spectroscopic instrumentation plays an important role in the context of Process Analytical Technologies (PAT) since it provides vital information for monitoring and controlling industrial processes. It is widely used in various process industries and is capable of fast measurements with no sample preparation, making it ideal for on-line applications. The sensing principles are based on the interaction between light and matter, acquired by opto-electronic components. To estimate relevant information from spectroscopic measurements, it is necessary to model their dependencies. Data-driven models, based on a linear assumption, have been successfully applied to estimate concentrations of constituents in a mixture from spectral information. However, these models do not always properly represent nonlinear interactions, resulting in limited extrapolation capabilities. Kriesten et al. (2008) proposed the Indirect Hard Modeling (IHM) approach, a physics-based spectral method that incorporates the physicochemical information of the elements. Under this approach, pure components are parametrized as peak models, accounting for nonlinear effects such as peak shifts and deformations.

As spectroscopic signals can be influenced by the characteristics of the transmission media between the analyzed sample or changes in their properties, it is necessary to correct these effects for accurate concentration estimation. Several data-driven approaches can be employed to compensate for temperature in Near-Infrared spectra (Hageman et al., 2005). The main limitations of these approaches are their requirement for a set of informative data for calibration, which is performed offline. In this contribution, we propose extending the Indirect Hard Modeling (IHM) approach to achieve a compact and interpretable parametric representation of the temperature's effect on the mixture spectra.

Thus, the sensor model combined with the process model results in a nonlinear state-space representation. It is noteworthy that standard Kalman filters have been utilized in analytical chemistry for solving various problems, such as multicomponent curve resolution and concentration estimation, among others (Rutan, 1987). However, in this case, since the model's structure is nonlinear, standard Kalman filters cannot be applied. Extended Kalman Filters can be applied, but their convergence cannot be guaranteed. In a previous work (Sbarbaro et al., 2023), a nonlinear transformation was proposed to address the nonlinearity problem and use a standard Kalman filter. This approach leads to an over-parametrized model. The main drawback of this approach lies in the increased dimension of the problem, and tuning can be challenging as parameters can no longer be associated with the noise covariances.

In this study, we explore two alternative approaches based on prediction error methods, making use of a minimal set of variables. The first approach, referred to as the Dual EKF (Jakoby, 1987), involves the utilization of two EKFs and the total derivative of the prediction error. This enables the separate estimation of concentration and sensor parameters, effectively reducing computational time. The second approach introduces a Recursive Prediction Error EKF, utilizing a single EKF for concentration estimation, with parameter estimation achieved through the minimization of a predictive error metric (Riva et al., 2015). The paper organization is as follows: Section 2 describe the model, Section 3 presents the problem and the proposed Kalman filters, Section 4 illustrates and compares their performance with respect a standard EKF. Finally, in section 5, some conclusion and future works are outlined.

Acknowledgement: This work was supported by Fondecyt project 1221225.

2. Model description

This work considers the process of mixing several constituents in a main stream by using static mixer in a main stream, as depicted in figure 1.

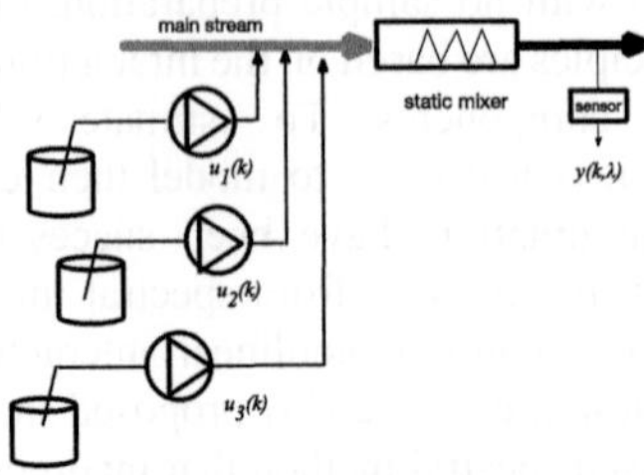

Figure 1. Mixing process

2.1. Process model

The process dynamic describing the concentration of each constituent in the main steam at the output of the static mixer can be represented by a discrete-time state space model

$$\boldsymbol{x}(k+1) = \boldsymbol{A}\boldsymbol{x}(k) + \boldsymbol{B}\boldsymbol{u}(k) + \boldsymbol{\omega}(k) \tag{1}$$

$$\boldsymbol{w}(k) = \boldsymbol{C}\boldsymbol{x}(k) \tag{2}$$

where the vector $\boldsymbol{w} \in \mathbb{R}^m$ represents the concentration of each constituent, $\boldsymbol{x} \in \mathbb{R}^n$ the state of the model representing the dynamic of the concentrations, $\boldsymbol{u} \in \mathbb{R}^m$ the pump's speed and $\boldsymbol{\omega} \in \mathbb{R}^n$ an input disturbance. The matrices $\boldsymbol{A} \in \mathbb{R}^{n\times n}$, $\boldsymbol{B} \in \mathbb{R}^{n\times m}$, and $\boldsymbol{C} \in \mathbb{R}^{m\times n}$ define the dynamic characteristic of the model.

2.2. Sensor model

In a mixture of m components, and based on the Lambert-Beer law, the mixture absorbance spectrum consists in a weighted sum of the constituent absorbance spectra. Since the sensor has a limited spectral resolution, it delivers a vector of values $\boldsymbol{y}$ corresponding to the light intensity $y(k,\lambda)$ measured at L equally spaced wavelength values of λ, therefore the spectral output can be modeled as follows:

$$\boldsymbol{y}(k) = \boldsymbol{d} + \sum_{i=1}^{m} w_i(k)\, \boldsymbol{\phi}_i(v(k)) + \boldsymbol{\xi}(k) \tag{3}$$

where $\boldsymbol{y}(k) \in \mathbb{R}^L$, $\boldsymbol{d} \in \mathbb{R}^L$, $\boldsymbol{\xi}(k) \in \mathbb{R}^L$, and $\boldsymbol{\phi}_i(v(k)) \in \mathbb{R}^L$. These vector represent samples values of the baseline offset $d(\lambda)$, the absorbance of each constituent $\phi_i(\lambda, v(k))$; which it also depends of some external variable $v(k)$, and the sensor noise modeled by the random variable $\boldsymbol{\xi}(k)$. According to the IHM approach, the absorbance of each constituent can be expressed in terms of peak shaped functions as follows:

$$\phi_i(\lambda, v(k)) = \sum_{j=1}^{N_i} \alpha_{ij}(v(k))\, \psi_{ij}(\lambda) \tag{4}$$

where N_i is the number of peak functions required to model constituent i, $\psi_{ij}(\lambda)$ are peak functions. The effect of the exogenous variable, $v(k)$, over the constituent spectra is modeled as changes in the linear factors. These changes can be parametrized in terms of known functions and a set calibration parameters

$$\alpha_{ij}(v(k)) = \sum_{q=1}^{N_{\alpha_{ij}}} \beta_{ijq}\varphi_{ijq}(v(k)) \tag{5}$$

where $\varphi_{ijp}(v(k))$ are known functions, for instance polynomials. Collecting all the calibration parameters in a single vector $\boldsymbol{\theta} = [\beta_{111}\ \beta_{112}\ \cdots\ \beta_{mN_mN_{\alpha_{mN_m}}}]^T \in \mathbb{R}^{N_p}$ with $N_p = \sum_{i=1}^{m}\sum_{j=1}^{N_i} N_{\alpha_{ij}}$ the sensor equation can be written in vector notation

$$\boldsymbol{y}(k) = \boldsymbol{d} + \sum_{q=1}^{N_p} \theta_q\, \boldsymbol{\Psi}_q(v(k))\boldsymbol{w}(k) + \boldsymbol{\xi}(k) \tag{6}$$

where the matrix $\boldsymbol{\Psi}_q(v(k)) \in \mathbb{R}^{L\times m}$ has the cross products between $\varphi_{ijp}(v(k))$ and $\psi_{ij}(\lambda)$.

3. The estimation problem and adaptive Kalman filters

The model describing both the process dynamics and the sensor is

$$\boldsymbol{x}(k+1) = \boldsymbol{A}\boldsymbol{x}(k) + \boldsymbol{B}\boldsymbol{u}(k) + \boldsymbol{\omega}(k) \tag{7}$$

$$\boldsymbol{w}(k) = \boldsymbol{C}\boldsymbol{x}(k) \tag{8}$$

$$\boldsymbol{y}(k) = \sum_{i=1}^{N_p} \theta_i \boldsymbol{\Psi}_i(v(k))\, \boldsymbol{w}(k) + \boldsymbol{\xi}(k) \tag{9}$$

To estimate the unknown calibration parameters, they are modelled as

$$\boldsymbol{\theta}(k+1) = \boldsymbol{\theta}(k) + \boldsymbol{\omega}_{\boldsymbol{\theta}}(k) \tag{10}$$

where the zero-mean random variable $\boldsymbol{\omega}_{\boldsymbol{\theta}} \in \mathbb{R}^{N_p}$ models the parameter temporal uncertainty. The estimation problem can be stated as follows: given the system equations; i.e. Eq. (7), Eq. (8), Eq. (9) and Eq. (10), and the measurements $\boldsymbol{y}(k), v(k), \boldsymbol{u}(k)$ estimates the concentrations $\boldsymbol{w}(k)$ and calibration parameters θ_i.

3.1. Dual Extended Kalman filter

The dual Extended Kalman filter considers two independent Kalman filters. One for the state and one for parameters as defined by the following equations:

State update:

$\hat{\boldsymbol{x}}^-(k) = \boldsymbol{A}\hat{\boldsymbol{x}}(k-1) + \boldsymbol{B}\boldsymbol{u}(k-1)$
$\boldsymbol{P}_{\boldsymbol{x}}^-(k) = \boldsymbol{A}\boldsymbol{P}_{\boldsymbol{x}}(k-1)\boldsymbol{A}^T + \boldsymbol{Q}_{\boldsymbol{x}}$
$\boldsymbol{E}_x(k) = \boldsymbol{C}_x(k)\boldsymbol{P}_{\boldsymbol{x}}^-(k)\boldsymbol{C}_x^T(k) + \boldsymbol{R}$
$\boldsymbol{K}_x(k) = \boldsymbol{P}_{\boldsymbol{x}}^-(k)\boldsymbol{C}_x^T(k)\boldsymbol{E}_x(k)^{-1}$
$\hat{\boldsymbol{x}}(k) = \hat{\boldsymbol{x}}^-(k) + \boldsymbol{K}_x(k)\boldsymbol{e}(k)$
$\boldsymbol{P}_x(k) = (\boldsymbol{I}_n - \boldsymbol{K}_x(k)\boldsymbol{C}_x(k))\boldsymbol{P}_{\boldsymbol{x}}^-(k)$

Parameter update:

$\hat{\boldsymbol{\theta}}^-(k) = \hat{\boldsymbol{\theta}}(k-1)$
$\boldsymbol{P}_{\boldsymbol{\theta}}^-(k) = \boldsymbol{P}_{\boldsymbol{\theta}}(k-1) + \boldsymbol{Q}_{\boldsymbol{\theta}}$
$\boldsymbol{E}_{\boldsymbol{\theta}}(k) = \boldsymbol{H}_{\boldsymbol{\theta}}(k)\boldsymbol{P}_{\boldsymbol{\theta}}^-(k)\boldsymbol{H}_{\boldsymbol{\theta}}^T(k) + \boldsymbol{R}$
$\boldsymbol{K}_{\boldsymbol{\theta}}(k) = \boldsymbol{P}_{\boldsymbol{\theta}}^-(k)\boldsymbol{H}_{\boldsymbol{\theta}}^T(k)\boldsymbol{E}_{\boldsymbol{\theta}}(k)^{-1}$
$\hat{\boldsymbol{\theta}}(k) = \hat{\boldsymbol{\theta}}^-(k) + \boldsymbol{K}_{\boldsymbol{\theta}}(k)\boldsymbol{e}(k)$
$\boldsymbol{P}_{\boldsymbol{\theta}}(k) = (\boldsymbol{I}_{N_p} - \boldsymbol{K}_{\boldsymbol{\theta}}(k)\boldsymbol{H}_{\boldsymbol{\theta}}(k))\boldsymbol{P}_{\boldsymbol{\theta}}^-(k)$

where the error $\boldsymbol{e}(k)$ and the time varying matrices $\boldsymbol{C}_x(k)$ and $\boldsymbol{C}_{\boldsymbol{\theta}}(k)$ are calculated as:

$$\boldsymbol{e}(k) = \boldsymbol{y}(k) - \textstyle\sum_{i=1}^{N_p} \hat{\theta}_i \boldsymbol{\Psi}_i(v(k))\hat{\boldsymbol{w}}(k), \tag{11}$$

$$\boldsymbol{C}_x(k) = \textstyle\sum_{i=1}^{N_p} \hat{\theta}_i \boldsymbol{\Psi}_i(v(k)), \qquad \boldsymbol{C}_{\boldsymbol{\theta}}(k) = \left[\boldsymbol{\Psi}_1(v(k))\hat{\boldsymbol{w}}(k) \cdots \boldsymbol{\Psi}_{N_p}(v(k))\hat{\boldsymbol{w}}(k)\right] \tag{12}$$

The total differential of the output is calculated as follows

$$\boldsymbol{H}_{\boldsymbol{\theta}}(k) = \left.\frac{\partial \hat{\boldsymbol{y}}}{\partial \boldsymbol{\theta}}\right|_{\hat{\boldsymbol{x}}^-(k),\hat{\boldsymbol{\theta}}^-(k)} = \boldsymbol{C}_{\boldsymbol{\theta}}(k) + \boldsymbol{C}_x(k)\frac{\partial \hat{\boldsymbol{x}}^-(k)}{\partial \boldsymbol{\theta}} \tag{13}$$

where $\frac{\partial \hat{\boldsymbol{x}}^-(k)}{\partial \boldsymbol{\theta}} = A\frac{\partial \hat{\boldsymbol{x}}(k-1)}{\partial \boldsymbol{\theta}}$ and assuming that $\boldsymbol{K}_x(k-1)$ weakly depends on $\boldsymbol{\theta}$ as suggested by Plett (2004),

$$\frac{\partial \hat{\boldsymbol{x}}(k-1)}{\partial \boldsymbol{\theta}} = \frac{\partial \hat{\boldsymbol{x}}^-(k-1)}{\partial \boldsymbol{\theta}} - \boldsymbol{K}_x(k-1)\boldsymbol{C}_{\boldsymbol{\theta}}(k-1). \tag{14}$$

The initialization step considers $\hat{\boldsymbol{\theta}}(0) = 0$, $\boldsymbol{P}_{\boldsymbol{\theta}}(0) = \gamma_1 \boldsymbol{I}$, $\boldsymbol{P}_x(0) = \gamma_2 \boldsymbol{I}$ where γ_1, γ_2 are positive real constants, and $\boldsymbol{Q}_{\boldsymbol{\theta}}$, $\boldsymbol{Q}_x$, $\boldsymbol{R}$ represent the noise covariance matrices for the parameters, the states and the measurement respectively.

3.2. Prediction Error Adaptive Kalman filter

The PE Adaptive EKF estimates parameters by minimizing a cost function of the prediction error. To this end the sensitivities of the predictions with respect to the parameter must be calculated. The state and the parameters updates are defined by the following equations:

State update

$\hat{\boldsymbol{x}}^-(k) = \boldsymbol{A}\hat{\boldsymbol{x}}(k-1) + \boldsymbol{B}\boldsymbol{u}(k-1)$
$\boldsymbol{P}_{\boldsymbol{x}}^-(k) = \boldsymbol{A}\boldsymbol{P}_x(k-1)\boldsymbol{A}^T + \boldsymbol{Q}_x$
$\boldsymbol{E}_x(k) = \boldsymbol{C}_x(k)\boldsymbol{P}_{\boldsymbol{x}}^-(k)\boldsymbol{C}_x^T(k)$
$\boldsymbol{K}_x(k) = \boldsymbol{P}_{\boldsymbol{x}}^-(k)\boldsymbol{C}_x^T(k)\boldsymbol{E}_x(k)^{-1}$
$\hat{\boldsymbol{x}}(k) = \hat{\boldsymbol{x}}^-(k) + \boldsymbol{K}_x(k)\boldsymbol{e}(k)$
$\boldsymbol{P}_x(k) = (\boldsymbol{I}_n - \boldsymbol{K}_x(k)\boldsymbol{C}_x(k))\boldsymbol{P}_{\boldsymbol{x}}^-(k)$

Parameter update

$\hat{\boldsymbol{\theta}}(k) = \hat{\boldsymbol{\theta}}(k-1) + \boldsymbol{L}(k)\boldsymbol{e}(k)$
$\boldsymbol{V}(k) = \lambda \boldsymbol{V}(k-1) + (1-\lambda)(\,\boldsymbol{e}(k)\boldsymbol{e}(k)^T)$
$\boldsymbol{L}(k) = \boldsymbol{O}(k-1)\boldsymbol{S}_{\hat{\boldsymbol{y}}}(k)^T\left(\lambda \boldsymbol{V}(k) + \boldsymbol{S}_{\hat{\boldsymbol{y}}}(k)\boldsymbol{O}(k-1)\boldsymbol{S}_{\hat{\boldsymbol{y}}}(k)^T\right)^{-1}$
$\boldsymbol{O}(k) = \left(\boldsymbol{I}_{N_p} - \boldsymbol{L}(k)\boldsymbol{S}_{\hat{\boldsymbol{y}}}(k)\right)\boldsymbol{O}(k-1)\left(\boldsymbol{I}_{N_p} - \boldsymbol{L}(k)\boldsymbol{S}_{\hat{\boldsymbol{y}}}(k)\right) + \boldsymbol{L}(k)\boldsymbol{V}(k)\boldsymbol{L}(k)^T$

The error, $\boldsymbol{e}(k)$, is calculated as Eq. (11). The initialization step requires the following initial conditions $\hat{\boldsymbol{\theta}}(0) = \boldsymbol{0}$, $\boldsymbol{V}(0) = \boldsymbol{0}$ and $\boldsymbol{P}_x(0) = \gamma_1 \boldsymbol{I}$ where γ_1 is a positive real constant and $\boldsymbol{Q}_x$, $\boldsymbol{R}$ matrices representing the noise covariance matrices for the states and the measurement respectively. The parameter λ represents a forgetting factor and it is a positive real number. The output sensitivity $\boldsymbol{S}_{\hat{\boldsymbol{y}}}(k)$ can be written as

$$\boldsymbol{S}_{\hat{\boldsymbol{y}}}(k) = \boldsymbol{C}_x(k)\boldsymbol{S}_{\hat{\boldsymbol{x}}}(k)^- + \boldsymbol{C}_{\boldsymbol{\theta}}(k) \tag{15}$$

where the sensitivity of the predicted state $\hat{\boldsymbol{x}}^-(k)$ and matrix $\boldsymbol{P}_{\boldsymbol{x}}^-(k)$ are respectively

$$\boldsymbol{S}_{\hat{\boldsymbol{x}}}(k)^- = \boldsymbol{A}\boldsymbol{S}_{\hat{\boldsymbol{x}}}(k-1), \qquad \boldsymbol{S}_{\boldsymbol{P}}(k)^- = \boldsymbol{A}\boldsymbol{S}_{\boldsymbol{P}}(k-1)(\boldsymbol{I}_{N_p} \otimes \boldsymbol{P}_x(k-1)\boldsymbol{A}^T), \tag{16}$$

where $\otimes$ is the Kronecker product, and the Kalman gain sensitivity

$$\boldsymbol{S}_{\boldsymbol{K}}(k) = \boldsymbol{S}_{\boldsymbol{P}}(k)^-\left(\boldsymbol{I}_{N_p} \otimes \boldsymbol{C}_x(k)^T\boldsymbol{E}_x(k)^{-1}\right) + \boldsymbol{P}_{\boldsymbol{x}}^-(k)\boldsymbol{S}_{\boldsymbol{C}}(k)^T\left(\boldsymbol{I}_{N_p} \otimes \boldsymbol{E}_x(k)^{-1}\right) + \boldsymbol{P}_{\boldsymbol{x}}^-(k)\boldsymbol{C}_x^T(k)\frac{\partial \boldsymbol{E}(k)^{-1}}{\partial \boldsymbol{\theta}} \tag{17}$$

$$\frac{\partial \boldsymbol{E}(k)^{-1}}{\partial \boldsymbol{\theta}} = -\boldsymbol{E}(k)^{-1}\frac{\partial \boldsymbol{E}(k)}{\partial \boldsymbol{\theta}}\left(\boldsymbol{I}_{N_p} \otimes \boldsymbol{E}(k)^{-1}\right) \tag{18}$$

$$\frac{\partial \boldsymbol{E}(k)}{\partial \boldsymbol{\theta}} = \boldsymbol{S}_{\boldsymbol{C}}(k)^T\left(\boldsymbol{I}_{N_p} \otimes \boldsymbol{P}_x(k)\boldsymbol{C}_x(k)^T\right) + \boldsymbol{C}_x(k)\boldsymbol{S}_{\boldsymbol{P}}(k)^-\left(\boldsymbol{I}_{N_p} \otimes \boldsymbol{C}_x(k)^T\right) + \boldsymbol{C}_x(k)\boldsymbol{P}_{\boldsymbol{x}}^-(k)\boldsymbol{S}_{\boldsymbol{C}}(k)^T \tag{19}$$

and finally, for the update step

$$\boldsymbol{S}_{\hat{\boldsymbol{x}}}(k) = \boldsymbol{S}_{\hat{\boldsymbol{x}}}(k)^- + \boldsymbol{K}(k)\boldsymbol{S}_{\hat{\boldsymbol{y}}}(k) + \boldsymbol{S}_{\boldsymbol{K}}(k)\left(\boldsymbol{I}_{N_p} \otimes \boldsymbol{e}(k)\right) \tag{20}$$

$$\boldsymbol{S}_{\boldsymbol{P}}(k) = \left(\boldsymbol{I}_{N_p} - \boldsymbol{K}(k)\boldsymbol{C}_x(k)^T\right)\boldsymbol{S}_{\boldsymbol{P}}(k)^- - \boldsymbol{S}_{\boldsymbol{k}}(k)\left(\boldsymbol{I}_{N_p} \otimes \boldsymbol{C}(k)\boldsymbol{P}_{\boldsymbol{x}}^-(k)\right) - \boldsymbol{K}(k)\boldsymbol{S}_{\boldsymbol{c}}(k)\left(\boldsymbol{I}_{N_p} \otimes \boldsymbol{P}_{\boldsymbol{x}}^-(k)\right) \tag{21}$$

4. Simulation results

The mixing of three components having temperature dependant absorbance illustrates the performance of the adaptive Kalman filters. A spectrometer measures the spectra at the output of the mixing stage, as depicted in Figure 1.

4.1. Absorbance modelling

The model of the absorbance of each constituent considers a linear combination of two Gaussian peaks, where some of them are affected by the measured temperature, $v(k)$, as described by the following equations:
$\boldsymbol{\phi}_1(v(k)) = \theta_1\boldsymbol{\psi}_{11} + \theta_2 v(k)\boldsymbol{\psi}_{12}$ $\boldsymbol{\phi}_2(v(k)) = \theta_1 v(k)\boldsymbol{\psi}_{21} + \theta_2\boldsymbol{\psi}_{22}$ $\boldsymbol{\phi}_3(v(k)) = \theta_1\boldsymbol{\psi}_{31} + \theta_2 v(k)\boldsymbol{\psi}_{32}$
thus, vectors $\boldsymbol{\Psi}_q$ in the model Eq. (6) are $\boldsymbol{\Psi}_1 = [\boldsymbol{\psi}_{11}\ \mathbf{0}\ \mathbf{0}]$, $\boldsymbol{\Psi}_2 = [v(k)\boldsymbol{\psi}_{12}\ \mathbf{0}\ \mathbf{0}]$, $\boldsymbol{\Psi}_3 = [\mathbf{0}\ v(k)\boldsymbol{\psi}_{21}\ \mathbf{0}]$, $\boldsymbol{\Psi}_4 = [\mathbf{0}\ \boldsymbol{\psi}_{22}\ \mathbf{0}]$, $\boldsymbol{\Psi}_5 = [\mathbf{0}\ \mathbf{0}\ \boldsymbol{\psi}_{31}]$, and $\boldsymbol{\Psi}_6 = [\mathbf{0}\ \mathbf{0}\ v(k)\boldsymbol{\psi}_{32}]$. The nominal values of the parameters are $\boldsymbol{\theta} = [\,2.2\ \ 0.09\ \ 0.08\ \ 1\ \ 1.3\ \ 0.06\,]$. The dynamic of the static mixer is characterized by a linear dynamic system. The sampling period is one second. Step changes in the flow-rates of each components and periodic variation in the temperature, as shown in Figure 2, are considered.

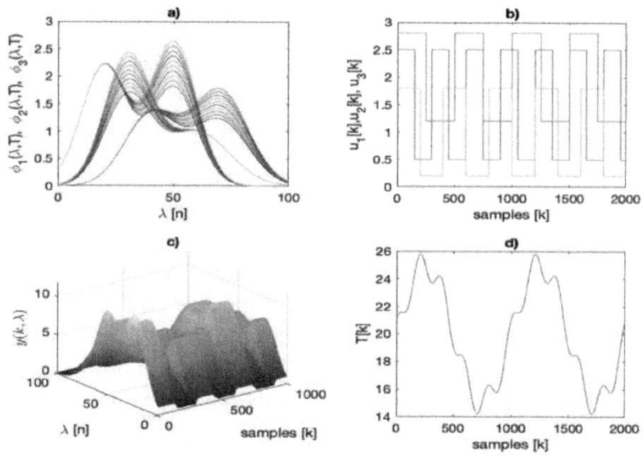

Figure 2 a) absorbance b) flowrates c) sensor output d) temperature

4.2. Parameter and state estimation results

The initial parameters of all Kalman filters are $\boldsymbol{Q}_x = 10^{-2}\boldsymbol{I}$, $\boldsymbol{R} = 0.1\boldsymbol{I}$, $\boldsymbol{P}_x = 10^{-2}\boldsymbol{I}$, and $\boldsymbol{\lambda}$=0.98. The observer initial conditions for states and parameters are set to zero. The evolution of the variables for all the algorithms is depicted in Figure 3. EKF and DEKF exhibit similar behaviour, converging faster in the estimation of concentrations but much slower in the parameters compared to PEAKF. The smallest Average Execution Time (AET) is achieved by EKF followed by DEKF. However, their parameter estimation accuracy is not as good as that obtained by PEAKF, as shown in Table 1.

Table 1: Summary results

Algorithm	$I(\boldsymbol{x})$	$I(\boldsymbol{\theta})$	Estimated parameters $\boldsymbol{\theta}$	AET (ms)
EKF	2.9518	0.3594	2.2082 0.0918 0.0816 0.9934 1.2434 0.0627	0.4774
DEKF	5.7662	0.3598	2.2164 0.0924 0.0818 0.9962 1.2438 0.0623	0.7549
PEAKF	4.1621	0.1078	2.2040 0.0902 0.0799 0.9905 1.3105 0.0613	6.3156

$$I(\boldsymbol{x}) = \frac{1}{1000}\sum_{i=0}^{1000} \|\boldsymbol{x}(k) - \hat{\boldsymbol{x}}(k)\|$$

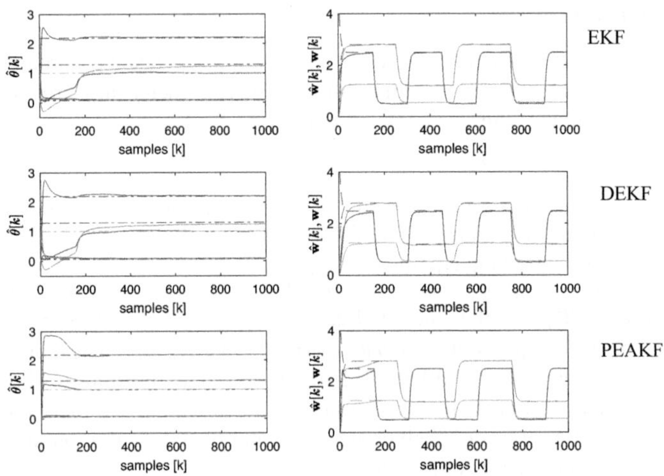

Figure 3 Evolution of parameters and concentrations

5. Conclusions

The application of Prediction Error Adaptive Kalman filters to estimate both concentrations and sensor model parameters using a discrete-time nonlinear model is investigated. Simulations of a simple ternary mixing process reveal that the proposed adaptive Kalman filters have relative merits compared to the standard EKF. In the simulated system, PEAKF demonstrates the fastest convergence and improved accuracy in terms of sensor parameters, albeit at the expense of increased calculations. DEKF results are comparable to those obtained by the EKF. Thus, the proposed adaptive EKFs offer advantages in terms of ease of tuning and convergence. Future work will involve a more in-depth analysis of DEKF without simplifying assumptions, a comparative analysis with Unscented Kalman Filters, and the robust and efficient implementation of the algorithms.

References

S.C. Rutan, 1987,S. C. Kalman Filtering Approaches for Solving Problems in Analytical Chemistry. J. Chemom. 1, 7–18.

Z. Chen Z, J. Morris, 2009, Process analytical technology and compensating for nonlinear effects in process spectroscopic data for improved process monitoring and control. Biotechnol J., 4(5), 610-9.

J. Hageman, J. Westerhuis, and A. Smilde, 2005, Temperature robust multivariate calibration: An overview of methods for dealing with temperature influences on near infrared spectra, J. Near Infrared Spectrosc., 13(2), 53–62.

W. Jakoby, M. Pandit, 1987, A prediction-error-method for recursive identification of nonlinear systems, Automatica, 23(4), 491-496.

M. H. Riva, D. Beckmann, M. Dagen and T. Ortmaier, 2015, Online parameter and process covariance estimation using adaptive EKF and SRCuKF approaches, IEEE Conference on Control Applications (CCA), Sydney, Australia, 1203-1210, doi: 10.1109/CCA.2015.7320776.

D. Sbarbaro, T. A. Johansen and J. Yañez, 2023, Adaptive Kalman Filter for On-Line Spectroscopic Sensor Corrections, 9th International Conference on Control, Decision and Information Technologies, Rome, Italy, 2109-2114, doi: 10.1109/CoDIT58514.2023.10284429.

G. L. Plett, 2004, Extended Kalman filtering for battery management systems of LiPB-based HEV battery packs: Part 3. State and parameter estimation, Journal of Power Sources, 134(2), 277-292.

Flavio Manenti, Gintaras V. Reklaitis (Eds.), Proceedings of the 34th European Symposium on Computer Aided Process Engineering / 15th International Symposium on Process Systems Engineering (ESCAPE34/PSE24), June 2-6, 2024, Florence, Italy
 http://dx.doi.org/10.1016/B978-0-443-28824-1.50291-X

Novel Panoramic Indicators for Process Operation Stability Assessment through Clustering and Frequency Analysis

Tetsuya Wada, Yoshiyuki Yamashita
Department of Applied Physics and Chemical Engineering
Tokyo University of Agriculture and Technology
2-24-16 Naka-cho Koganei, Tokyo 184-8588, Japan
Tetsuya.wada@chem-vision.com

Abstract

The paper highlights the significance of ensuring stable operation and profitability in a process plant. It introduces new panoramic and frequency analysis-based indicators for evaluating process stability. The study also addresses the challenge of quantitatively assessing operational instability from clustering analysis results. By quantifying instability, priorities for operational stabilization can be set within engineering constraints. The paper further examines how fluctuations in individual variables affect overall process stability by applying wavelet transform to isolate and analyze high-frequency band noise. This approach, validated in several chemical process plants, provides a quantitative tool for assessing operational instability across various process plants.

Keywords: Operational Stability, Fault Detection, Machine Learning, Clustering, Wavelet Transformation

1. Introduction

Unstable operation can lead to significant fluctuations in operating variables, making it impossible to control product quality near target values. Anomaly detection has been studied in three areas: knowledge-based, model-based, and data-driven studies. Data-driven anomaly detection has been extensively studied and does not require theoretical formulas or experts. Most past research has focused on understanding sudden anomalies, but there are cases where anomalies occur all the time and are the norm. These are called continuous anomalies.

An abnormality in plant operation refers to a condition where the dynamics occurring in plant operation exhibit unusual behavior [1][2]. In general, fault detection in plant operation means detecting abnormalities that occur suddenly in a continuous operating state. These sudden abnormalities can be caused by sticking at control valves, sudden mechanical abnormalities at rotating machines, or sudden blockages in distillation or reaction columns. When detecting this sudden change in behavior, the operating behavior before the sudden change is considered stable, not abnormal. However, abnormalities in operation are not limited to those that occur suddenly. Some equipment continues to operate with abnormalities in operating behavior without any sudden change. This may be caused by insufficient tuning of control system parameters, smaller cavitation and surging at rotating machines, entrainment such as jet-flooding and weeping in distillation columns, as well as distribution abnormalities in reaction columns.

In actual unit operation, more units operate with continuous anomalies than with sudden fluctuations. Therefore, when detecting anomalies related to the operation of a process plant, it is more important to detect anomalies in behavior that occur on a steady basis in operation than to detect anomalies with sudden changes. This regularly occurring operational abnormality is called unstable operation. However, while technology has been developed to detect suddenly occurring abnormalities, little focus has been placed on developing technology to analyze unstable operation. There are no clear criteria for quantitatively indicating stability/unstable operation. Process plant operators have a sensory perception of operational instability, but after a period of time, unstable conditions become ordinary.

In this study, we aimed to quantify the stability/instability of process operation using clustering analysis techniques from time series operation data of multiple variables. Additionally, we attempted to quantify the stability/instability of individual variables in the frequency domain using wavelet transform.

2. Clustering Analysis Applied to Observe Abnormalities

The Distributed Control System (DCS) has a limit to the information it can display, and operational stability/instability recognition is generally managed by alarm management with upper and lower thresholds, which are set with empirical consideration. Therefore, instability occurring within the upper and lower thresholds cannot be checked. An indicator that can quantitatively assess operational stability/instability and is independent from the upper and lower thresholds and from the experience or skills of the operator would be very useful for establishing safe and efficient operation through further improvement. In addition, if continuous instability is occurring due to damage of the hardware, etc., evaluation by means of indicators will contribute significantly to identifying the location of such instability.

Clustering analysis, classified as unsupervised learning, has been used to identify abnormal conditions due to sudden changes in operation from historical big data [3]. Attempts have also been made to develop offline monitoring models to identify it [4]. However, while it is used as an anomaly detection technique to find sudden anomalies, it has not been applied to check continuous operational stability/instability.
Clustering analysis is a technique that assigns cluster numbers to data from a group of variables related at different times so that the distance from the center of each cluster is minimized. Fluctuations that occur suddenly are easy to detect because the cluster numbers assigned change significantly. However, it has not been applied to instabilities that occur continuously because there is no significant change in the cluster number.
Our research on several real datasets has found that clustering analysis techniques are effective for the qualitative analysis of continuous instabilities. In stable operations, cluster numbers change infrequently at consecutive times, while in unstable operations, cluster numbers change frequently. Therefore, by graphing the clustering analysis results and judging them visually, a certain degree of stability/instability analysis is possible. However, it may be difficult to make qualitative judgments in the case of multiple datasets with different sampling periods. It is also impossible to quantitatively assess the results of the analysis.

An example of quantitative stability evaluation with clustering analysis is in the field of biometrics, where multiple predictions were made using the Bootstrap Resampling method and the available Gold Standard. The Jaccard Coefficient was used to carry out the evaluation [5]. However, this method requires the Gold Standard to evaluate stability and also evaluates by similarity using silhouette analysis [6]. In other words, it is an evaluation method that assumes stability if the number of data contained in a certain cluster is high and is not suitable for stability analysis of time-series data.
Therefore, we have developed a new evaluation method called Process Operation Stability Indicator (POSI) as an operational stability indicator that can be calculated from clustering analysis results. The advantages of this POSI for stability/instability assessment are:

(i) Stability/instability is expressed quantitatively from clustering analysis results,
(ii) It is independent from the number of variables in the data set and the sampling period,
(iii) Multiple sections can be assessed using the same criteria, and
(iv) It can be calculated continuously or at regular intervals to Trend management of stability/ instability is possible.

The k-means method is a method to find the cluster that minimize J in Equation (1).

$$J = \sum_{j=1}^{k} \sum_{x_i \in S_j} \left\| \boldsymbol{x}_i - \boldsymbol{c}_j \right\|^2 , \tag{1}$$

where $\boldsymbol{c}_j$ is the mean value in cluster S_j .

In addition, we developed our own Process Operation Stability Indicator (POSI), shown below, as an indicator for evaluating stability/instability.

$$POSI = 100 \times n(V)/N \tag{2}$$

$V = \{ i \mid cl(\boldsymbol{x}_i) = cl(\boldsymbol{x}_{i+1}), 1 \leq i \leq N-1 \}$, where $cl(\boldsymbol{x}_i) = j$,
if the observation $\boldsymbol{x}_i$ lies in cluster j, $n(V)$ is the number of elements in V.

To put it differently, this index is calculated by counting the number of times there is no change in adjacent cluster numbers and not counting when there is a change, based on the results of the cluster analysis calculation, for all time axes in the sampling window. The number of counts obtained from this process is then expressed as a percentage of the total number of time axes. If the value of POSI is large, the behavior of the process operation is relatively stable because the number of adjacent clusters rarely changes.

3. Clustering Examples

3.1. Stability/instability evaluation of a column with positive degrees of freedom

One of the key factors for stable operation of a distillation column is to have zero operational degrees of freedom. This degree of freedom (N_f) is the number of disturbances and constraints and products (N_v) minus the number of independent control systems (N_e), which must be $N_\mathrm{f} = N_\mathrm{v} - N_\mathrm{e} = 0$.

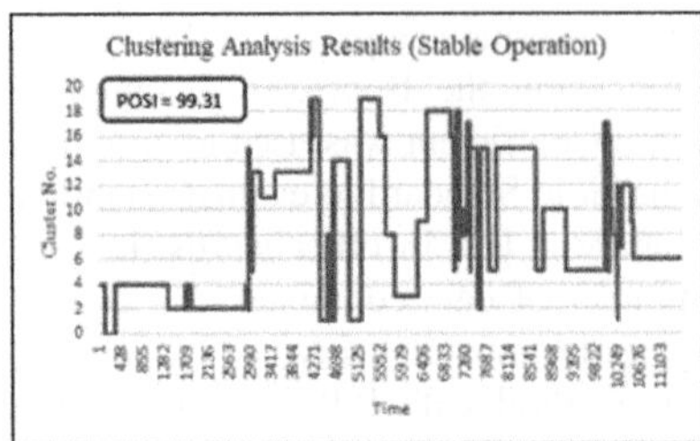

Fig. 1. Zero Degree of Freedom

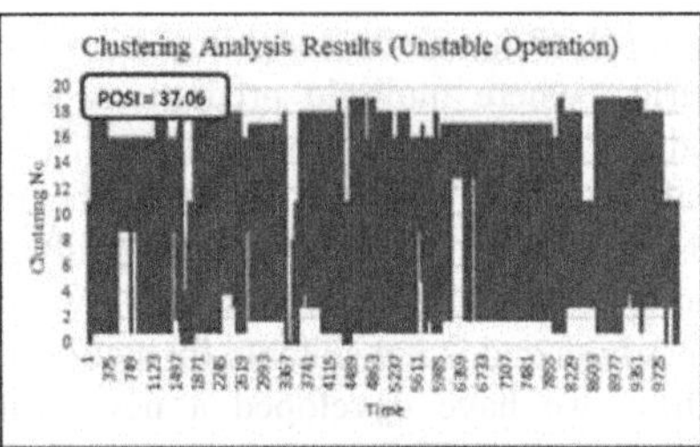

Fig. 2. One Degree of Freedom

For example, if the flow rate and temperature of the feedstock are the disturbances, the levels at the top receiver and bottom of the column are the constraints, and the outflow at the top of the column is the product, then $N_v = 5$. So, the distillation column needs five independent control systems. In general, the main controls will be control of the feed flow rate, control of the reboiler heat rate, and control of the top of the column pressure. Also, the top product flow and bottom withdraw are used to meet the constraints of the top receiver and bottom level of the column. The reflux flow rate is dependent on the feedstock flow rate and the reboiler flow rate and cannot be used to calculate the degrees of freedom.

Figures 1 and 2 show the results of the clustering analysis and POSI calculations for a distillation column operating under similar conditions. Figure 1 shows the results for a distillation column with top pressure control (zero degrees of freedom), and Fig. 2 shows the results for a distillation column without top pressure control (one degree of freedom). When the degree of freedom is zero, the operation of the distillation column is normally very stable, but when the degree of freedom is set to one or positive value, the operation of the distillation column becomes very unstable.

3.2. Stability/instability analysis of continuous BTX columns

Figure 3 shows three consecutive BTX distillation columns (Benzene, Xylene, and Xylene columns) that separate each component from a mixture of Benzene, Toluene, Xylene, and AC9+. The column top pressures are 0.002 MPaG, 0.005 MPaG, and 0.016 MPaG, respectively. The top pressure of each column is maintained by injecting hydrogen into the top section. The same amount of hydrogen is injected into each of the three columns. Figures 4, 5 and 6 display the results of the Clustering analysis and POSI calculations for these three distillation columns. From these POSI results, the operation of the Benzene column is stable, while the Toluene and Xylene columns are unstable.

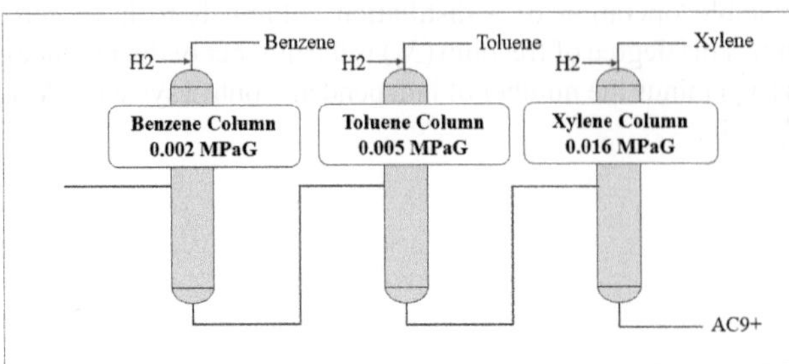

Fig.3. BTX Separation Columns

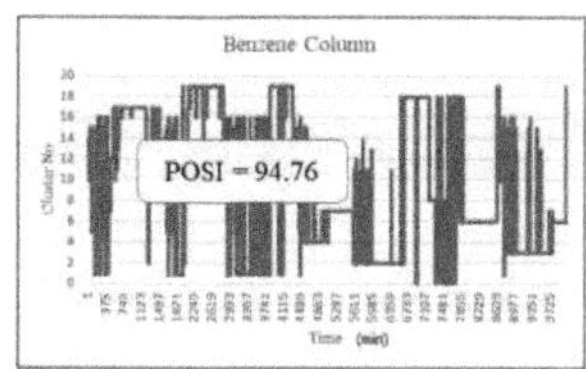

Fig.4. Benzene Column

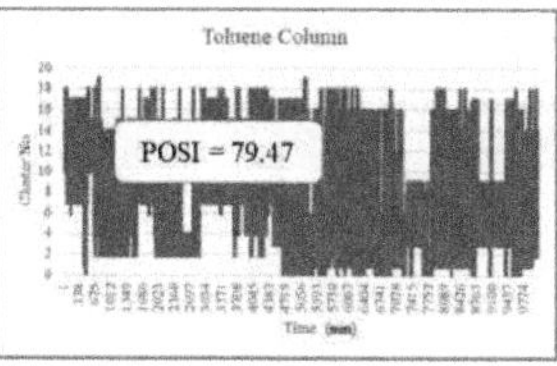

Fig.5. Toluene Column

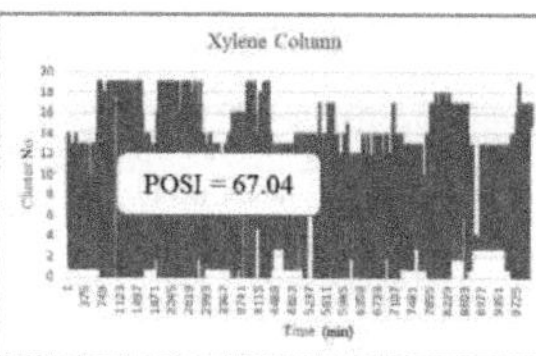

Fig.6. Xylene Column

4. Frequency Analysis with Wavelet Transformation

"Wavelet transformation" is often used to detect anomalies in individual variables [7][8]. In particular, it is still the subject of much research in the detection of anomalies in rotating equipment, including in combination with modern techniques such as machine learning. However, the main focus of most studies is to use wavelet transformation as a filter to find the frequency band containing fault features.

In process operation, it is not only rotating equipment that exhibits fluctuating features in specific frequency bands. Similar characteristics appear in unstable control systems and the variables affected by these control systems. When these characteristics appear in the high frequency band, they are often due to operation beyond the capacity of the equipment or inadequate adjustment of control parameters.

This indicator is calculated using the following formula. This indicator is also named Frequency Analysis Stability Indicator (FASI). The Daubechies wavelet was applied as the orthogonal wavelet in this study, but no significant differences were found in the calculation results using other orthogonal wavelets.

$$FASI = \left(\sum_{n=1} \boldsymbol{a_n x_n}^2 \right)^{1/2} \tag{3}$$

where $\boldsymbol{a_n}$is the weighted factor and $\boldsymbol{x_n}$ is the standard deviation in decomposed noise at **n**th decomposition.

5. Example

Table-1 shows the results of FASI calculations for a group of variables related to a certain distillation column: a high FASI value which means that there is a possibility of periodic fluctuations. If the variable is a control system and the FASI value is high, it is necessary to tune the parameters first. Also, if the FASI value of the Indicator is high, it is likely to be affected by the control system.
Thus, the periodic instability of the control system can be identified from the FASI calculation, so it is possible to identify which parameters of which variables should be tuned. In addition, as the instability can be quantified, it is easy to prioritise which variables should be considered first.

6. Conclusion

In process operation, abnormality detection is commonly used to manage the trend of operating data for each variable with alarms of upper and lower limit values. However, this method cannot detect operational abnormalities that can be detected with operational

Tabel 1 FASI Calculation Example

Name	Description	HFSI	Name	Description	HFSI
FC1	Flow	8.4492303	PC1	Pressure	4.8144224
FC2	Flow	8.6457316	PC2	Pressure	8.2333931
FC3	Flow	6.1887527	TC1	Temperature	4.6091582
FC4	Flow	7.7088494	TI2	Temperature	3.1618211
FC5	Flow	7.8404739	TI3	Temperature	2.5218181
FC6	Flow	8.1538899	TI4	Temperature	3.5909635
LC1	Level	4.6231317	TI5	Temperature	5.5075342
LC2	Level	8.1870617	TI6	Temperature	8.1458304
LC3	Level	7.5523294	TI7	Temperature	2.0977877

data of multiple variables or that occur in a specific frequency band. Furthermore, no technology has been developed to practically quantify operational stability, including abnormality detection by trend.

POSI, described in the previous section, can identify and quantify abnormalities that occur routinely in plant operation from a bird's-eye view of the operating data of several relevant variables. FASI can also identify and quantify cyclical anomalies in individual variables. By using these two indicators, it is possible to provide operators and engineers with quantitative information on operational stability/instability, which was not possible with the conventional alarm management of upper and lower limits. If the causes of operational instability are identified and countermeasures taken before alarms occur, it is possible to nip abnormalities in the bud before alarms occur, and achieving incident-free operation is not just a dream.

References

[1] D. M. Himmelblau, Fault detection and diagnosis in chemical and petrochemical processes, Elsevier Scientific Pub. Co., Amsterdam, 1978.

[2] V. Venkatasubramanian, R. Rengaswamy, K. Yin, S. N. Kavuri, "A review of process fault detection and diagnosis Part I: Quantitative model-based methods," *Computers and Chemical Engineering*, Vol 27, pp. 293-311, 2003.

[3] I. A. Udugama, C. L. Gargalo, Y. Yamashita, M. A. Taube, A. Palazoglu, B. R. Young, K. V. Gernaey, M. Kulahci, C. Bayer, "The Role of Big Data in Industrial (Bio)chemical Process Operations," *Industrial & Engineering Chemistry Research,* Vol. 59, no. 34, pp.15283-15297, 2020.

[4] M. C. Thomas, W. Zhu, J. A. Romagnoli, "Data mining and clustering in chemical process databases for monitoring and knowledge discovery," *Journal of Process Control*, Vol. 67, pp. 160-175, 2018.

[5] J. A. Bernabé-Díaz, M. Franco, J.-M. Vivo, M. Quesada-Martínezc, J. T. Fernández-Breis, "An automated process for supporting decisions in clustering-based data analysis," *Computer Methods and Programs in Biomedicine*, Vol. 219, 106765, 2022.

[6] P. J. Rousseuw, "Silhouettes: a graphical aid to the interpretation and validation of cluster analysis," *Journal of Computational and Applied Mathematics*, Vol. 20, pp. 53-65, 1987.

[7] R. Yan, R.X. Gao, X. Chen, "Wavelets for fault diagnosis of rotary machines: A review with applications," *Signal Processing*, Vol. 96, pp. 1–15, 2014

[8] T. Guo, T. Zhang, E. Lim, M. Lopez-Benitez, F. Ma, L. Yu, "A review of wavelet analysis and its applications: challenges and opportunities," *IEEE Access*, Vol.10, pp.58869-59803, 2022

Flavio Manenti, Gintaras V. Reklaitis (Eds.), Proceedings of the 34th European Symposium on Computer Aided Process Engineering / 15th International Symposium on Process Systems Engineering (ESCAPE34/PSE24), June 2-6, 2024, Florence, Italy
 http://dx.doi.org/10.1016/B978-0-443-28824-1.50292-1

Industrial EP(D)M Polymerization Reactor Simulation: Process Dynamics and Control

Franco Scaglia[a], Giovanni Regattieri[a], Gianni Marchetti[a,*]

[a]*Basic Chemicals and Plastics Research Centre, Versalis S.p.A., via G. Taliercio 14, 46100, Mantova, Italy*
gianni.marchetti@versalis.eni.com

Abstract

Ethylene-Propylene-(Diene) rubber, also referred to as EP(D)M, is one of the most globally used polymers and has many applications due to its durability and flexibility. Versalis produces EP(D)M rubber via suspension copolymerization, without solvent, initiated by metallorganic component (Ziegler-Natta catalysts).

Scaglia et al. (2023) recently introduced a first-principle model and implemented it in a steady-state Aspen Polymer® simulation; both model calibration and cross-validation were performed using Versalis plant data. In this work, the dynamic behaviour of the polymerization reactor is explored: the model is tested for unsteady plant conditions; open-loop responses to step-change in input variables are investigated, and possible control strategies to maintain rubber quality within specification ranges are postulated. Dynamic simulations can successfully be employed to improve process understanding, to troubleshoot upset conditions, to monitor plant performance, and to explore future process/product developments.

Keywords: modelling, simulation, dynamics, control, polymerization.

1. Introduction

EP(D)M elastomers are synthetic rubbers prepared by polymerization of ethylene, propylene, and optionally a non-conjugated diene. They are amorphous, random polymers with excellent resistance to ageing, weather, ozone and high temperatures due to their saturated backbone structure. Primary applications include automotive parts, single-ply roofing, appliance parts, modification of other polymers (thermoplastic olefins), wire and cable, hoses, and Viscosity Index Improvers (VII) for lubricating oils. Two forms of ethylene-propylene elastomers are currently produced: (i) Ethylene-Propylene Copolymers, which contain a saturated chain and necessitate vulcanization via free radical generators such as organic peroxides or a combination of sulphur and peroxides, and (ii) Ethylene-Propylene Terpolymers, which are essentially ethylene-propylene-diene terpolymers with a saturated chain and a diene in the side chain.

The first Versalis EP(D)M production plant with suspension technology (60 kt/y) was built at Versalis site in Ferrara (Italy) in 1974; in 1991 the plant was expanded with the construction of a new line, increasing the plant capacity up to 100 kt/y, and recently (2018) a further line with a capacity of 48 kt/y was started-up. Two more lines, with a total capacity of 96 kt/y, are on stream since 2017 in the Far East (Versalis, 2022).

In the following sections, EP(D)M polymerization and industrial plant are briefly described, along with the main features of the first-principle model proposed by Scaglia et al. (2023).

1.1. EP(D)M Polymerization

EP(D)M rubbers are created by polymerizing ethylene and propylene with a small quantity (3-12%w) of a nonconjugated diene; the most employed diene is ethylidene norbornene (ENB) (NexantEAC, 2022). Common systems used to produce EP(D)M are Ziegler-Natta and Metallocene catalyst (Baldwin and Ver Strate, 1972). Ziegler-Natta catalysts involve a transition metal salt and an organometallic compound, also known as a co-catalyst. The interaction between these species leads to the formation of the active site for reactions. Polymerizations studies are mainly focused on titanium catalyst, because precursors components are easily separated and identified; fewer vanadium-based systems are fully disclosed (Ver Strate, 1986). Vanadium-aluminum alkyl halide combinations produce complexes soluble in non-polar hydrocarbons; multiple vanadium-aluminum alkyl halide combinations can be drawn; the presence of multiple species affects the Molecular Weight Distribution (MWD) and the compositional distribution of the polymer.

There are several Ziegler-Natta combinations, each of which offers varying degrees of performance. The scientific and patent literature discloses methods of synthesizing catalysts with enhanced characteristics such as higher activity and improved control of molecular weight (Baldwin and Ver Strate, 1972; Ver Strate, 1986).

Versalis has recently introduced an improved, novel, vanadium-based Ziegler-Natta catalyst system; the new catalyst system was scaled-up to the industrial plant and employed in Versalis proprietary slurry process to obtain new EP(D)M grades (Perretta and Vallieri, 2013).

1.2. EP(D)M Industrial Plant

Ethylene, propylene and propane are fed to the polymerization reactor (see Figure 1) along with the catalyst system (pre-catalyst, co-catalyst and activator). ENB is employed in case of Terpolymer production. Hydrogen is fed as a Molecular Weight (MW) controller.

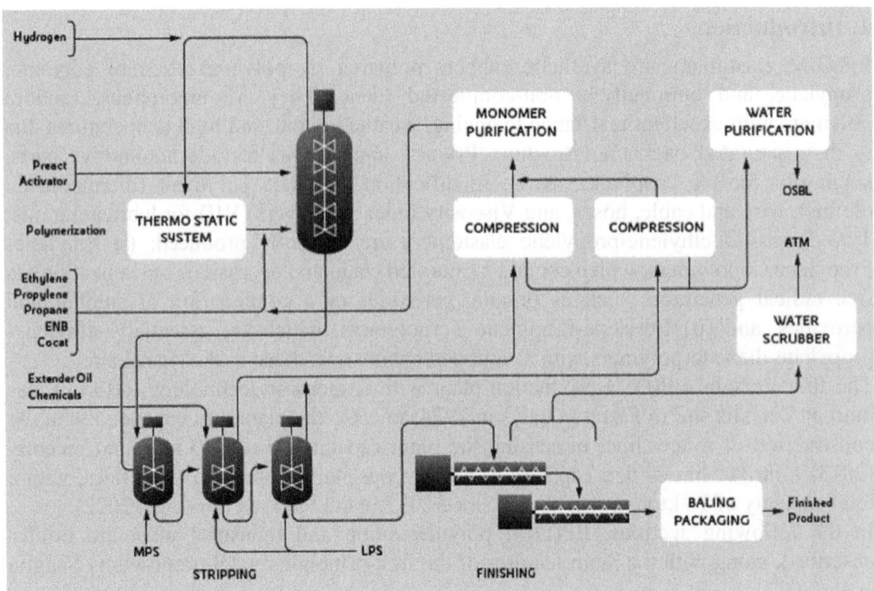

Figure 1: EP(D)M industrial plant process scheme (Versalis, 2022).

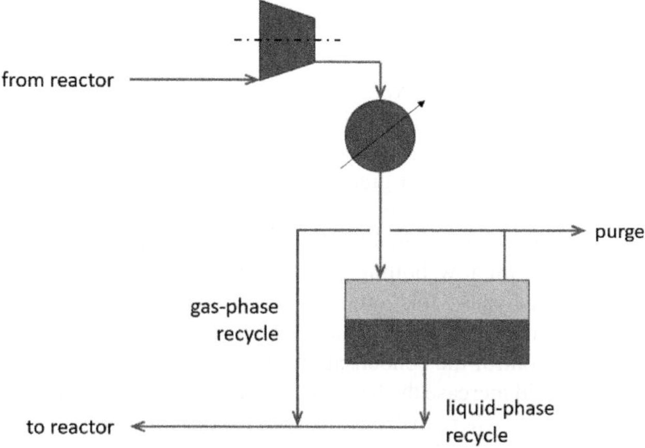

Figure 2: Thermostatic system scheme.

Since the reaction is exothermic and temperature and pressure are kept constant in the reactor, a direct thermostatic system (Figure 2) based on compression and recycle of reaction vapours is provided: vapours from reactor are compressed and partially condensed; liquid condensate is totally recycled back to the reactor, while non-condensable fraction is partially recycled and partially purged from the system.

Ethylene conversion in reactor discharge reaches about 99%, while propylene conversion is around 30% and depends on production rate and grade. Reaction behaviour is controlled by a proprietary Advanced Process Control (APC) system, based on gas chromatograph analysers on the reactor vapour phase for continuous control of the concentration of the monomers. The polymer slurry discharged from the reactor is transferred to the stripping section: steam is injected to remove the unreacted monomers, recycled water from finishing section is fed to the stripper to keep constant the watery slurry concentration. The crumb slurry is finally fed to the finishing section for drying, baling and packaging of the finished product. Further details can be found elsewhere (Versalis, 2022).

1.3. First-Principle Model

A novel first-principle model for an industrial EP(D)M production plant was developed by Scaglia et al. (2023) and implemented in a steady-state Aspen Polymer® simulation. The polymerization scheme used in the simulation includes the phases of (i) catalyst activation, (ii) polymer chain initialization, (iii) polymer chain propagation, and (iv) polymer chain termination. During the catalyst activation phase, pre-catalyst and co-catalyst interaction leads to the formation of multiple active sites. Once the active sites are formed, the polymerization chain may start with the initialization phase. After the first ethylene monomer reacts with the active site, polymer chain propagation may take place; restrictions on the chain propagation apply based on the last monomer in chain. Two mechanisms were considered for polymer chain termination: a thermal (spontaneous) chain termination and hydrogen chain termination. After termination, the reaction site is no longer active, but may be turned on again by the activator.

Further model details, along with model calibration and validation strategies, can be found in the referenced paper by Scaglia et al. (2023).

2. Steady State Analysis

The model introduced by Scaglia et al. (2023) was calibrated and cross-validated using steady state industrial plant data; errors were well below 10%, assessing an acceptable model accuracy. In this section, a steady state model analysis is presented, that goes beyond available industrial plant data and leads to noteworthy general considerations. Analysis was limited to one polymer grade, namely Grade A from Scaglia et al. (2023).
The thermostatic system depicted in Figure 2 is not peculiar to EP(D)M process; analogous schemes can be found in literature whenever heat removal is required for vapour-phase streams with low boiling point. Variations may include multiple-stage condensers and recycle/bypass for compressor control, along with knock-out drums, filters and other ancillaries. The purge stream from the condensate drum shown in Figure 2 may be included to control the condensate drum pressure. However, purging the non-condensable phase would increase the heavy fraction of the stream returning to the reactor and, for the EP(D)M case where hydrogen is used as a chain termination agent, purging may also affect both polymer composition and MWD. Finally, it goes without saying that any purged quantity represents a material (and hence economic) loss.
Nonetheless, there is at least another way to somehow affect the condensate drum pressure that does not involve purging. The gas-phase recycle stream may be regulated (manually or automatically) with a control valve: with a gas-phase recycle flowrate decrease the non-condensable fraction tends to accumulate inside the condensate drum, thus rising its pressure, and vice versa. Since this stream represents an internal recycle to the reactor, any change in the gas-phase recycle flowrate will not affect the steady state of the reactor itself but will affect the Vapour-Liquid Equilibrium (VLE) in the condensate drum and hence its steady state pressure. This phenomenon was explored in a steady state simulation sensitivity analysis, whose main results are reported in Figure 3: condensate drum pressure is plotted against gas-phase flowrate; due to confidentiality, both variables are normalized with reference to the central steady state operating condition.

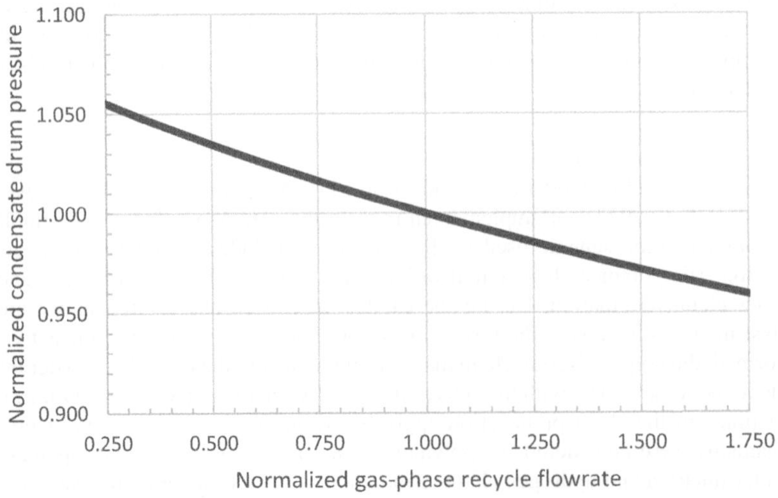

Figure 3 Steady state simulation sensitivity analysis: normalized condensate drum pressure against normalized gas-phase recycle flowrate.

3. Unsteady State Analysis

In Section §2 some general considerations about the steady state behaviour of the system were presented; in this Section, the analysis is extended to the unsteady state condition.

3.1. Open-Loop Response

First, some open-loop responses are investigated, namely a step-response to fresh hydrogen feed flowrate and a step-response to gas-phase recycle flowrate. As previously described, hydrogen is employed as a polymer MW regulator; thus, a step-change in fresh hydrogen feed flowrate is expected to affect the polymer MW, and hence Mooney viscosity. As mentioned in Section §2, gas-phase recycle flowrate affects condensate drum pressure without affecting steady state reactor performance; however, it may introduce a significant transient shift in the system performance, whose recovery may take a substantial time, leading to temporary off-spec production.

In Figure 4 the open-loop response to a step-change in fresh hydrogen feed flowrate is reported (step-change occurs at t = 0); both 50 % increase (solid line) and decrease (dashed line) are plotted. Due to confidentiality, values are normalized with reference to initial steady state condition. As can be inferred, the input step change generates a prolong, sluggish transient response that eventually leads to a new steady state condition i.e., the production of a polymer with significant modified properties.

In Figure 5 the open-loop response to a step-change in gas-phase recycle flowrate is reported (step-change occurs at t = 0); both 90 % increase (solid line) and decrease (dashed line) are plotted. Due to confidentiality, values are normalized with reference to initial steady state condition. As can be inferred, the step change generates a sharp, quick transient response that is eventually recovered to the initial steady state. Basically, the condensate drum acts as a hydrogen reservoir in a recycle loop, and the gas-phase recycle stream temporarily releases (or retains) that hydrogen to the reactor.

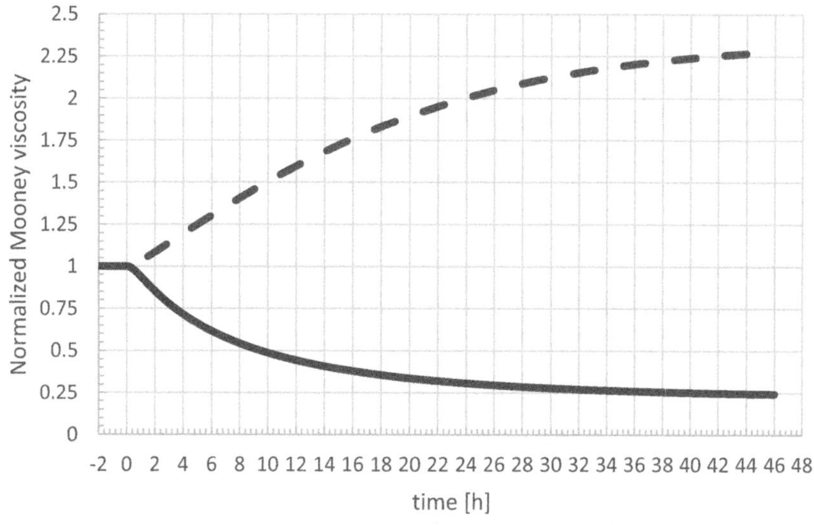

Figure 4 Transient Mooney viscosity response (normalized) to a step-change in fresh hydrogen flowrate: 50 % increase (solid) and 50 % decrease (dashed).

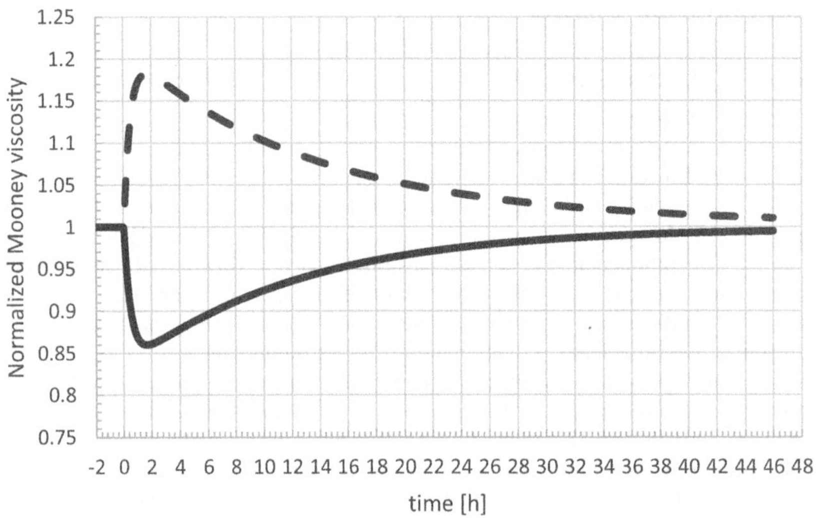

Figure 5 Transient polymer Mooney response (normalized) to a step-change in gas-phase recycle flowrate: 90 % increase (solid) and 90 % decrease (dashed).

3.2. Control

As described in Section §3.1, a change in the hydrogen feed induces a slow transient response that leads to a new steady state; on the other hand, a change in the gas-phase recycle induces a quick transient response, that eventually is recovered. This suggests that a model-based control strategy, that involves an optimal combination of both changes, may be developed to accomplish an effective advanced process control.

4. Conclusions

A first-principle model for an industrial EP(D)M plant was employed to extend steady state analysis beyond available plant data. Unsteady state analysis highlighted the transient behaviour to possible step-changes, suggesting the future investigation for a model-based control strategy. Generalization to analogous process systems may apply.

References

F. P. Baldwin, G. Ver Strate, 1972, Polyolefin Elastomers Based on Ethylene and Propylene, Rubber Chemistry and Technology, 45 (3), 709–881.

NexantECA, 2022, Market Analytics: Ethylene Propylene Diene Monomer (EPDM).

C. Perretta, A. Vallieri, 2013, Process for the preparation of a copolymer of ethylene, Patent EP2782940B1.

F. Scaglia, A. Mazzini, C. Perretta, G. Regattieri, G. Marchetti, 2023, Industrial EP(D)M Rubber Production Process: a First-Principle Data-Driven Modelling Approach, Chemical Engineering Transactions, 100, 163-168.

Versalis, 2022, <versalis.eni.com/assets/documents/versalis/it/documentazione/licensing/elastomeri/EP(D)M.pdf> accessed 11.10.2022.

G. Ver Strate, 1986, Ethylene Propylene Elastomers, Encyclopedia of Polymer Science and Engineering, 522-564.

Flavio Manenti, Gintaras V. Reklaitis (Eds.), Proceedings of the 34th European Symposium on Computer Aided Process Engineering / 15th International Symposium on Process Systems Engineering (ESCAPE34/PSE24), June 2-6, 2024, Florence, Italy
 http://dx.doi.org/10.1016/B978-0-443-28824-1.50293-3

Low Concentrated P- and K-based Fertilizers for Localized Agricultural Supply Chains

Brenno C. Menezes,[a,b*] Matheus Duarte,[b,c] Caiubi Kuhn,[d] Ana Gomes,[d] Mohammed Yaqot,[a] Kim Moloney[e]

[a]*Division of Engineering Management and Decision Sciences, College of Science and Engineering, Hamad Bin Khalifa University, Qatar Foundation, Doha, Qatar*
[b]*Induagro, Production Planning and Supply Chain, Mato Grosso, Cuiaba, Brazil*
[c]*Department of Civil Engineering, Federal University of Mato Grosso, Barra do Garca, Brazil*
[d]*Department of Mining Engineering, Federal University of Mato Grosso, Cuiaba, Brazil*
[e]*College of Public Policy, Hamad Bin Khalifa University, Qatar Foundation, Doha, Qatar*
bmenezes@hbku.edu.qa

Abstract

Fertilizer can be made of organic materials like animal or green manure. However, such materials are less than 1% of total fertilizers worldwide. Instead, fertilizers are usually compounds of inorganic components based on nitrogen (N), phosphorus (P) and potassium (K) elements, forming the so-called NPK-fertilizer. Natural gas is the resource for N-based fertilizer plants producing ammonia and urea. On the contrary, for P and K components, mined from concentrated mineral reservoirs, their production is restricted to local producers where high levels of P- and K-based concentrated reservoirs are abundant. Concentrated mineral reservoirs of P-based components are mostly found in China and Morocco. K-based ones are largely located in Canada and China. NPK-based fertilizers can be blended to create a finished agriculture production input to be sold within a global market supply chain of fertilizers. However, we suggest something different. Localized supply chains of low concentrated fertilizers of P- and K-bases can be an option for agricultural sites. The non-metallic mineral mining reservoirs of the so-called *agri-minerals* or *rock-for-crops* are worth exploring by localized final consumers in the agricultural supply chain. Brazil is the world's largest importer of fertilizers due to its thick and nutrient-depleted tropical soils. By mapping locations of natural resources and agricultural sites in the State of Mato Grosso (represents 30% of grains production in Brazil), we suggest a capacity expansion of processing plants connected to the natural resource sites of low concentrated agri-minerals and the distribution of the final processed product to the fertilizer end-use stage among local farmers.

Keywords: Supply chain, agriculture, fertilizers, agri-minerals, rocks-for-crops.

1. Introduction

The agriculture business operates in a frequent uncertainty given variations in the cost and supply of inputs (such as fertilizers in seasonal demand variations). Unexpected conditions, such as outbreaks and strikes, and disruptions in environmental conditions such as precipitation of rains, extreme weather events, among others, directly impact production performance. Fertilizers are a complex input for feed/food supply chains. This is because the natural resource reservoirs are based in a few countries worldwide. Fertilizer plays a vital role in ensuring plant growth and improved yields. Various factors influence the quantities, qualities, and properties for the use of fertilizer in the agriculture business. It includes the type of fertilizer, crop type, soil type, and nutrient requirements. Besides the carbon, hydrogen, and oxygen elements (captured by the plants from the atmosphere and water), numerous essential nutrients for plant growth and health are provided by fertilizers. The main components of fertilizer are nitrogen (N), phosphorus (P), and potassium (K). Secondary contributions include sulphur (S), magnesium (Mg), calcium (Ca), and several metals such as zinc (Zn) and iron (Fe). Mineral fertilizer plays an essential role in our food systems. It increases the volume of food that can be grown on a fixed amount of land. Approximately half the food we eat today has been produced thanks to mineral fertilizer (IFA, 2023). The maintenance of fertilizer production as essential to food security as it is for farmer livelihoods (Cordell et al, 2010).

International Fertilizer Association (IFA) indicated that in 2020, the global consumption of nitrogen, phosphorus, and potassium (NPK) fertilizers was approximately 184 million tonnes, 51 million tonnes, and 38 million tonnes, respectively. Furthermore, according to the Food and Agriculture Organization (FAO) of the United Nations, Asia is the largest consumer of fertilizers, accounting for about 60% of global consumption. China is the world's largest consumer and producer of fertilizers, accounting for approximately 30% of global consumption and 33% of global production.

To reduce the imports of fertilizers and to increase the sovereign resilience of nations toward its feed/food production, localized supply chains of low concentrated P- and K-based fertilizers can be connected from the natural resources that feed the *agri-minerals* or *rock-for-crops* needs on agricultural sites. While it is worth exploring localized final consumers in the agricultural supply chain for the low concentrated P- and K-based fertilizer (LCPKF), there is a trade-off between the production and logistics costs. Considering that 90% of the LCPKF is made of non-useful materials such as sand or rocks without P and K-components, the processing and transportation costs may not be sufficient to fully replace imports of P- and K-concentrated fertilizers.

2. Worldwide agriculture and fertilizer production

The IFA estimates that 85% of global soils are deficient in nitrogen, 73% of the soils are deficient in phosphorus, and 55% lack potassium. Growing food in soil with a good balance of nutrients is key to preventing malnourishment and diseases caused by calorie deficiency. Figure 1 represents how much mineral fertilizer is applied to different crops.

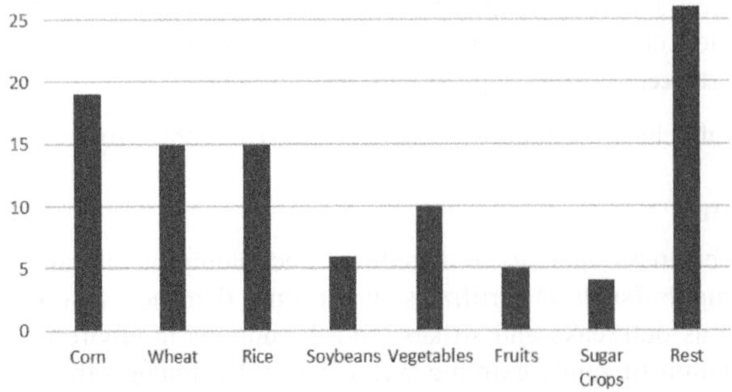

Figure 1. Utilization of fertilizers among crops/plants (IFA, 2023).

Understanding nutrient requirements of different crops is essential to plot the impact of nutrient-related policies and plan farming processes. It is also a prerequisite for other forms of market research and scientific assessment. Global balances of commodities for resilient supply chains for fertilizers in the feed/food lifecycle are necessary to understand if a country is to appropriately link resource availability, food security, and its fiscal bottom line. Global purchases of imported fertilizers cost a total US$151 billion in 2022 (Worldstopexports, 2023). The overall value of fertilizers imported in 2022 increased by an average 119.4% from all importing countries since 2018 when fertilizers purchases were valued at $68.8 billion. Year over year, international purchases of fertilizers accelerated via a 53.7% advance compared to $98.2 billion during 2021 (IFA, 2023). The biggest importers of fertilizers in 2022 were Brazil, India, USA, mainland China, and France. That cohort of major fertilizers buyers, as seen in Figure 2, provided over two-fifths (43.1%) of total international spending on fertilizers imported in 2022.

Globally, the ingredients to analyze agricultural businesses' risks and trade-offs, or any sort of input and output are:

- Output 1: Levels of imports and exports on fertilizers. Inputs include (1) natural gas or concentrated rocks-for-crop fertilizer reservoirs, (2) number and wealth of populations, and (3) arable land in both size and soil quality and landscape.
- Output 2: Agricultural production. Inputs include (1) arable land; (2) number and wealth of population (3) fertilizers' supply chains.
- Input-Output Processer: Fertilizer plants. Inputs: (1) global reservoirs of concentrated fertilizers (or natural gas for N-based fertilizer), (2) local reservoirs of P- and K-based fertilizers.

For localized fertilizer supply chains (SCs), the inputs and outputs of integrating fertilizers to agricultural output demands create the possibility of exploring low concentrated P- and K-based fertilizer SCs via locating processing sites near PK-reservoirs can assist agricultural production. By understanding the differences of production on the NPK-fertilizers (as seen in Figure 3) and the agriculture-fertilizer supply chain nexus at global and local scales, one can foresee research avenues that may diminish fertilizer import needs. One case is the road-mapping of the localized agriculture-fertilizer supply chain nexus in Brazil, in state of Mato Grosso, representing 30% of Brazil's agricultural production overall.

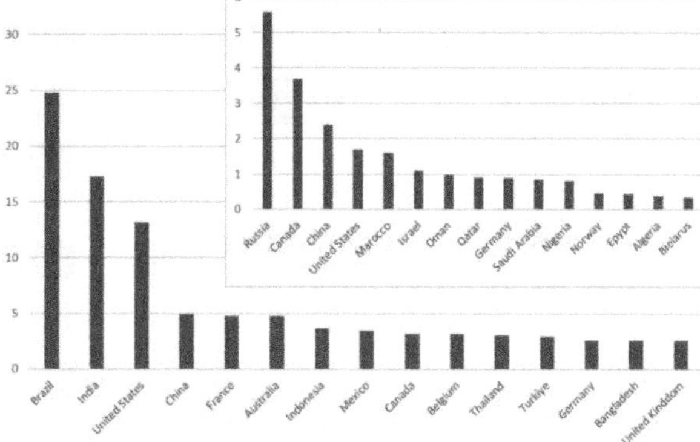

Figure 2. Fertilizer Imports by billions of USD (Worldtoexports, 2023).

3. NPK-based fertilizers

Among categories of imported fertilizers, almost three-quarters (73.6%) in 2022 were nitrogen-based products (IFA, 2023). Potassic fertilizers represent 23% of important compared to phosphatic fertilizers at 2.7%. Animal or vegetable fertilizers accounted for the remaining 0.8%. Although N-based are dependent on natural gas as a feed-process, the P- and K-based fertilizer components are mined from agri-rocks or rock-for-crops reservoirs (as seen in Figure 3). The fertilizer industry largely exports high concentrated P- and K-based fertilizer; however, there is the potential to explore locally produced low concentrated P- and K-based fertilizer (at 10% purity) if the logistics and transporting costs to nearby end-user farmers is financially feasible.

3.1. Nitrogen (N)

Nitrogen-based fertilizers are primarily manufactured through the Haber-Bosch process, a method developed over 100 years ago to create ammonia by heating and pressurizing nitrogen from the air over a hydrogen source (typically from natural gas or coal). The resultant ammonia is further processed to create nitrogen fertilizers in solid and liquid forms. Urea is the most produced and consumed nitrogen fertilizer globally while nitric acid-based fertilizers are also popular.

3.2. Phosphorous (P)

Phosphorus-based fertilizers are created from phosphate rock, which is a mined material. Phosphate rock is treated with sulfuric acid to separate the phosphorus. Phosphoric acid is created in this process, and can be further combined with ammonia and sulfur to create a variety of fertilizer products.

3.3. Potassium (K)

Potassium-based fertilizers originate from potash (potassium chloride), another mined material. Potassium chloride is processed into downstream products and granulated for ease of use and efficient uptake by plants.

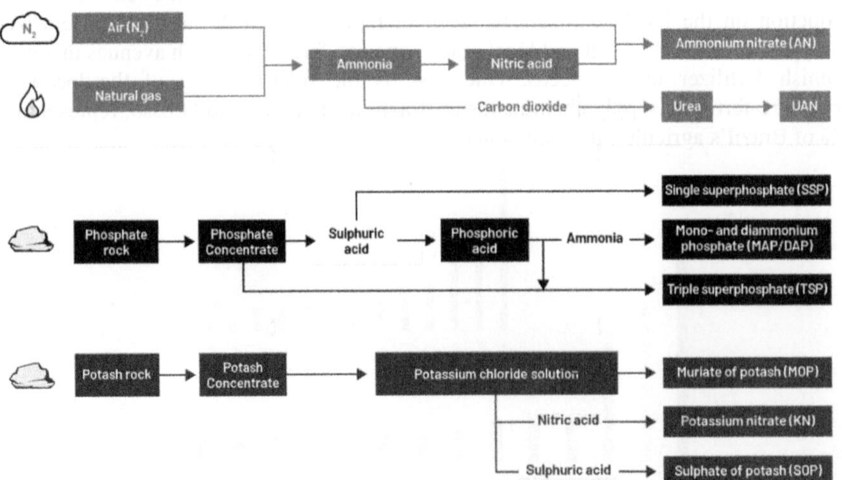

Figure 3. Schematics of the N-, P-, and K-based fertilizers.

4. Capacity expansion and distribution of low concentrated rocks-for-crops

Figure 4 shows the rain precipitation in Brazil for soybean and corn rotations and their seasons. Using the State of Mato Grosso as a case study and a typical farm in Brazil producing soybeans (1st production) and corn (2nd production) in 2019 (Langemeier, 2021), and considering the cost of imported fertilizers and the conditions of demands, climate, and other resources in the agriculture business, one can calculate the capacity installation needed for low concentrated P- and K-based fertilizers (LCPKF) and the range of their distribution in the State of Mato Grosso (as seen in Figure 4). There, huge reservoirs of low concentrated P- and K-based rocks for crops are recently under study to determine the purity and their impacts on the yields of soybeans and corn plantations.

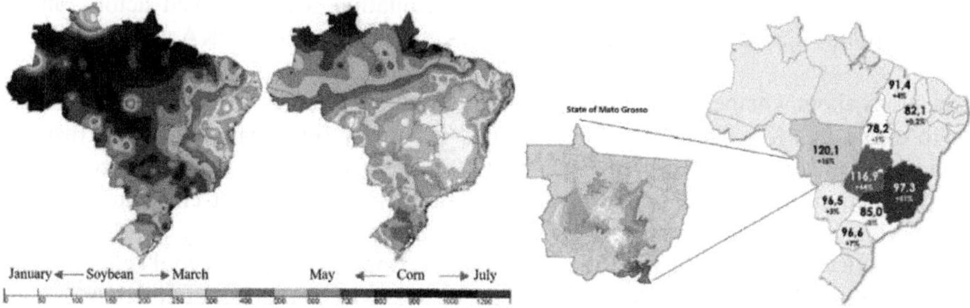

Figure 4. Rain precipitation for soybean and corn seasonal productions in Brazil.

Today the State of Mato Grosso, responsible for 30% of the agricultural production in Brazil presents one of the highest productivity on bushels per hectare (around 120) in the world. This near to Iowa and West Central Indiana (both in the United States) benchmarks. It is due to heavy Brazilian investments in both soil preparation but also via fertilizer imports. The creation of a LCPKF market will require regulation, public policy conversations, stakeholders meetings, and specialized consultancies to develop business plans for a new agricultural model based on localized P- and K-fertilizer solutions.

5. Public policies and international de-risk of feed and food supply chains

Robust, resilient, and adaptive public policies play a pivotal role in mitigating risks and ensuring stability within global feed and food supply chains. This is especially true for the global fertilizer market and the new potential for locally mined and produced LCPKA. This is a policy issue not just for local governments, local farmers, local miners, and local markets but also for national and international interaction. Food production is neither a local-only nor a global-only endeavor. It is a multilevel policy arena with a multiplicity of interested actors. Governments and international organizations can collaborate to craft comprehensive regulatory and policy frameworks for risk management, to anticipate and address disruptions in vital agricultural inputs like fertilizers, and to encourage local stakeholder discussions. To-date, there has been limited engagement of LCPKA from both the FAO and separately, the International Fund for Agricultural Development. It is also an under-researched policy arena for governments and related actors. This limited discussion carries forward to the agricultural nations, like Brazil, which important significant amounts of high concentrated fertilizer from abroad (25 billion USD/year).

Governments and interested actors may wish to employ any number of potential policy tools. *Regulatory tools* may include new laws, direct regulation, indirect regulation, voluntary regulation, incentive-based regulation, licenses, quotas, public consultations, and even the creation of associational actors. If appropriately utilized, regulatory tools can incentivize transparency, fair competition, and sustainability in the fertilizer market. *Financial tools* include encouraging public investments in research, innovation, and alternative technologies. It may also include public-private partnerships, cash-based direct transfers, grants, subsidies, tax incentives, and where appropriate, user fees. *Information tools* include instruments that disseminate information (moral suasion, government billboards, pamphlets, and product labelling), collect information (statistical and national planning agency involvement and increased data collection), and release information (polling, Freedom of Information Acts, stakeholder willingness to blow the whistle, and investigatory means). Each policy tool option (regulatory, financial, information) requires careful consideration, consultation with involved actors, and a flexible policy design whereby the policy mixes appropriate for LCPKA are created.

Questions about whether to exclusively import highly concentrated fertilizer from abroad or to create LCPKA via new local producers will rarely find a single answer. Instead, policy conversations are required. Such conversations should encourage fertilizer source diversification, local developments where agri-minerals or rock-for-crops are present, appropriate investment climates for such new developments while ensuring any resulting trade practices are equitable to farmers of all sizes. Appropriate policy tool selection and local-international collaboration are key contributors to LCPKA market creation.

6. Conclusions

Given the extensive exploration of fertilizer dynamics and global agriculture presented in this paper, it is evident that localized supply chains for low-concentrated P- and K-based fertilizers could offer strategic solutions amid uncertainties. The existing centralized production, coupled with a heavy reliance on imports, poses challenges to stability and sustainability in agricultural supply chains. Despite the potential production and transportation costs in establishing localized chains, leveraging non-traditional resources like low concentrated agri-minerals or rock-for-crops presents a promising alternative. However, such a shift will demand meticulous attention to regulatory framework development and the public policies that can foster collaboration, transparency, and equity-focused trading practices. Robust international cooperation and investments in research and innovation will be pivotal in fortifying global food security and mitigating vulnerabilities within agricultural supply chains while laying the groundwork for a resilient and sustainable future.

References

D. Cordell, J. Drangert, S. White, 2009, The story of phosphorus: Global food security and food for thought, Global Environmental Change, Volume 19, Issue 2, 292-305,

IFA, 2023, International Fertilizer Association, accessed on 20/11/2023 at: www.fertilizer.org.

M. Langemeier, 2012, International Benchmarks for Corn Production (2021) - Purdue Center for Commercial Agriculture: https://ag.purdue.edu/commercialag/home/resource/2021/06/international-benchmarks-for-corn-production-2021/

Top Fertilizers Imports by Country 2022, , accessed on 21/11/2023 https://www.worldstopexports.com/top-fertilizers-imports-by-country/?expand_article=1

Rally da Safra. Rally da Safra 2024 - Uma viagem pelo Brasil que produz Resultados da Safra 2022/2023. Accessed: http://rallydasafra.com

Flavio Manenti, Gintaras V. Reklaitis (Eds.), Proceedings of the 34th European Symposium on Computer Aided Process Engineering / 15th International Symposium on Process Systems Engineering (ESCAPE34/PSE24), June 2-6, 2024, Florence, Italy
 http://dx.doi.org/10.1016/B978-0-443-28824-1.50294-5

Experimental Implementation of an Economic Model Predictive Control for Froth Flotation

Paulina Quintanilla[a,*], Daniel Navia[b], Stephen Neethling[a], Pablo Brito-Parada[a]

[a] *Department of Earth Science and Engineering, Royal School of Mines, Imperial College London, London SW7 2BP, United Kingdom*

[b] *Departamento de Ingeniería Química y Ambiental, Universidad Técnica Federico Santa María, Campus San Joaquín, Santiago 8940897, Chile*

p.quintanilla@imperial.ac.uk

Abstract

We present the implementation of a novel economic model predictive control (E-MPC) strategy for froth flotation, the largest tonnage mineral separation process. A previously calibrated and validated dynamic model incorporating froth physics was used, which overcomes the limitations of previous simplified models reported in the literature. The E-MPC's optimal control problem was solved using full discretization with orthogonal collocation over finite elements, employing automatic differentiation via CasADi. This approach was applied in a 30-litre laboratory-scale flotation cell, significantly improving mineral recovery from 9% to 29% under feed flowrate disturbances while maintaining a minimum concentrate grade of 20%.

Keywords: Dynamic physics-based modelling, Economic model predictive control, Experimental validation, Froth flotation.

1. Introduction

The growing demand for minerals and metals in the shift towards cleaner energy sources poses a challenge due to decreasing ore quality. To meet demand effectively, improving the efficiency of current mineral separation techniques while minimizing negative environmental impact is crucial. Froth flotation is the largest tonnage separation process. Given the large-scale nature of this process, even a small improvement in the separation efficiency can result in a substantial increment in mineral recovery (Ferreira & Loveday, 2000).

Effectively controlling the process is difficult due to its complex and dynamic nature (Quintanilla et al., 2021a) and process disturbances, such as feed flowrate, particle size, and feed grade. The traditional control method used in this process is Proportional-Integral (PI) control, primarily used for regulatory control. However, PI controllers alone are usually ineffective in optimizing key performance indicators, especially under process disturbances, leading to suboptimal outcomes. Advanced control and optimization strategies, particularly Model Predictive Control (MPC), have gained significant attention for improving process performance in froth flotation. MPC uses a dynamic model of the process to predict future behavior and optimize control actions, balancing performance while satisfying constraints. However, despite the potential benefits of MPC strategies in flotation, their full utilization has been hindered by the complexity of modeling process dynamics and instabilities. The kinetic models used in previous studies (e.g. Maldonado et al. (2007); Putz & Cipriano (2015); Riquelme et al. (2016)) are insufficient in modeling complex froth phase phenomena, which are critical drivers of the process performance. New advancements in flotation modeling for control that incorporate the froth phase phenomena can be found in Oosthuizen et al. (2021), and Quintanilla et al. (2021b, c).

Economic model predictive control (E-MPC) is a strategy to optimize control actions based on economic objectives. As such, it is a promising solution for enhancing flotation process efficiencies. E-MPC introduces the economic optimization layer into traditional model predictive control, allowing for direct integration of process economics and feedback control (Ellis et al., 2014). This approach considers both technical and economic variables as performance indices and uses nonlinear programming techniques to optimize the set points of control loops.

Our study validates an E-MPC strategy previously developed by Quintanilla et al. (2023a). The strategy was tested in a flotation rig described in Quintanilla et al. (2023b). We used a novel dynamic model incorporating froth physics, which was previously calibrated and experimentally validated. We selected the objective function based on sensitivity analyses, considering air recovery (a measurement of froth stability, directly linked to the flotation performance), separation efficiency (mineral recovery) and product quality (concentrate grade) as a proxy of economic performance.

2. Materials and Methods

2.1. Model overview and definition of control variables

We use a nonlinear, dynamic model developed and experimentally validated by Quintanilla et al. (2021a, b). This model consists of a system of Differential and Algebraic Equations with a total of $26 + 5K + 10I$ equations and $29 + 5K + 12I$ variables, where K is the number of bubble size classes, and I is the number of mineralogical classes. Here, we assumed K=10 and two mineralogical classes (I=2): Chalcopyrite (valuable mineral) and gangue (waste rock with physical properties similar to quartz). As shown in Quintanilla et al. (2023a), the model is normalized to enhance the solver convergence and robustness. Important control variables of the model are given in Table 1.

Table 1: Variables used in control.

Variable	Definition	Variable	Definition
Air recovery (α)	Fraction of air fed into the cell that overflows	Tails flowrate (Q_{tails})	Flowrate of the tailings stream
Mass (M_i)	Mass of the mineralogical classes i	Superficial air velocity (j_g)	Air velocity injected into the flotation cell.
Gas holdup (ϕ_k)	Volume fraction of gas of each bubble size class k	Grade (G_{conc})	Concentration of valuable minerals in the output stream (concentrate)
Pulp height (h_p)	Pulp level	Recovery (Rec)	The proportion of valuable minerals retrieved from the total available.

2.2. E-MPC strategy

The optimal control problem of the dynamic optimization is formulated as a nonlinear programming problem (NLP) using full discretization with orthogonal collocation over finite elements, and it was implemented in MATLAB R2021B with automatic differentiation via CasADi (Andersson et al., 2019). The optimal control problem was successfully implemented using the Interior Point Optimizer (IPOPT) solver. The sampling time was set at one second, and each iteration's solution time was, on average, 0.6 seconds. The general form of the NLP with normalized variables $(\tilde{\cdot})$ is given by:

$$\begin{aligned} &\min_{\tilde{\boldsymbol{x}} \in \mathbb{R}^{N_x}, \tilde{\boldsymbol{z}} \in \mathbb{R}^{N_z}, \boldsymbol{u}_n \in \mathbb{R}^{N_U} \text{ for } n=0,\dots,N_p} J(\tilde{\boldsymbol{x}}, \boldsymbol{y}, \tilde{\boldsymbol{z}}, \boldsymbol{u}, \boldsymbol{\beta}, \tilde{t}) \\ &\text{s.t. } \boldsymbol{h}(\tilde{\boldsymbol{x}}, \boldsymbol{y}, \tilde{\boldsymbol{z}}, \boldsymbol{u}, \boldsymbol{\beta}, t) = 0, \tilde{t} \in \left[t_0, t_{N_p}\right] \\ &\quad \boldsymbol{g}(\tilde{\boldsymbol{x}}, \boldsymbol{y}, \tilde{\boldsymbol{z}}, \boldsymbol{u}, \boldsymbol{\beta}, t) \leq 0, \tilde{t} \in \left[t_0, t_{N_p}\right] \\ &\quad \boldsymbol{u}(\tilde{t}) = \boldsymbol{u}_n \quad \tilde{t} \in [t_n, t_{n+1}] \quad n = 0,\dots,N_p - 1 \end{aligned} \tag{1}$$

where the normalized time $(\tilde{t})$ limits are $t_0 = 0$ and $t_{N_p} = 1$, the state vector is $\tilde{\boldsymbol{x}} := [\widetilde{M_\iota}, \widetilde{\phi_K}, \widetilde{h_p}, \tilde{Q}_{tails}]^T$, the process variables vector is $\mathbf{y} := [\alpha, G_{conc}, Rec]^T$, the algebraic variable vector is $\tilde{\boldsymbol{z}} := [\alpha, \alpha^*]^T$, the decision variable vector is $\boldsymbol{u}_n := \left[j_g^{SP}, h_p^{sp}\right]^T$(the superscript SP indicates that the variable is a set point for regulatory controllers), the weight vector is $\boldsymbol{\beta} := \left[\beta_\alpha, \beta_{G_{conc}}, \beta_{Rec}, \beta_{u_n}\right]^T = [10^8, 10^6, 10^8, 10^6, 10^2]^T$, $\boldsymbol{h}$ is the dynamic model from Quintanilla et al. (2021b, c), and $\boldsymbol{g}$ are the process constraints defined in Quintanilla et al. (2023a).

The objective function was selected via sensitivity analyses with respect to the decision variables, as discussed in Quintanilla et al. (2023b), and is defined as:

$$J = \int_{t_0}^{t_{N_p}} \left(\beta_{G_{conc}} G_{conc}(t) - \beta_\alpha \alpha(t)\right) dt - Rec\left(t_p\right) + \sum_{n=0}^{N_p-1} (\Delta \boldsymbol{u}_n^T \boldsymbol{\beta}_u \Delta \boldsymbol{u}_n), \tag{2}$$

where $G_{conc}(t)$ is the dynamic concentrate grade, $\alpha(t)$ is the dynamic air recovery, $Rec(t_{N_p})$ is the mineral recovery at the end of the prediction horizon (t_{N_p}), and $\boldsymbol{\Delta u_n}$ are the decision variable vectors. It is important to note that the metallurgical recovery (*Rec*) is only meaningful at a steady state, which is why it is maximized at the end of the prediction horizon. To balance the trade-off between metallurgical recovery and concentrate grade, we propose to minimize the dynamic concentrate grade in the objective function (Eq. (2)) while imposing a process constraint where $G_{conc}(t) \geq 20\%$ to ensure minimum quality.

2.3. Experimental rig and E-MPC implementation

The experimental setup consists of a 30-litre tank, as described by Quintanilla et al. (2023b). The tank includes an airflow control system, peristaltic pumps for feed and pulp level regulation, and a sensor to measure the pulp level. Online measurement of air recovery is also available. The instrumentation links to Proficy Machine Edit ion software, which connects to MATLAB via an I/O Server. This configuration allows real-time data acquisition to feedback the model and implement the controlled variables (j_g^{SP} and h_p^{sp}), as shown in Figure 1.

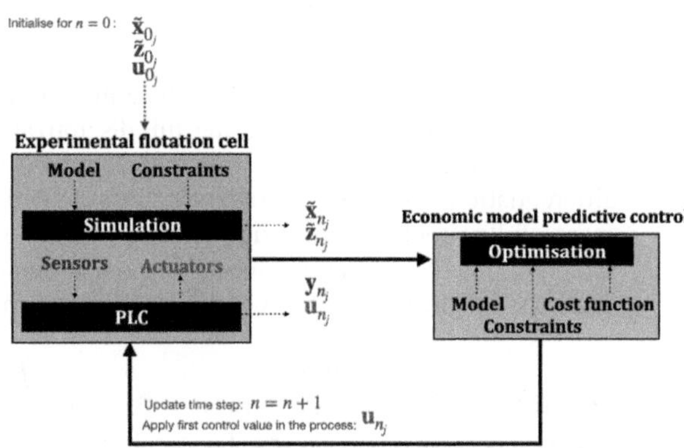

Figure 1: Implementation framework of the E-MPC strategy at laboratory scale. The E-MPC determines the optimal control actions u_{n_j} set points, which are then sent to the Programmable Logic Controller (PLC). The PLC signals the actuators (valves) to reach these set points.

The feed flowrate (Q_{feed}) is a measurable process disturbance. To test the robustness of the EMPC under disturbances, we performed step changes to the feed flowrate using four different values: 52.5, 56, 63, and 66.5 liters per minute [lpm]. Each feed flowrate was kept constant for 5 minutes, and each iteration was implemented every 1 minute in the laboratory-scale flotation rig.

3. Results and discussions

Figure 2 shows that mineral recovery was improved between +9% and +29% for the different conditions in feed flowrates. The concentrate grade was near 20% in most iterations, having some lower concentrate grades for the lowest feed flowrate (i.e., the first and third values). This issue is related to the five tuning parameters of the model remaining constant throughout all feed flow rate values.

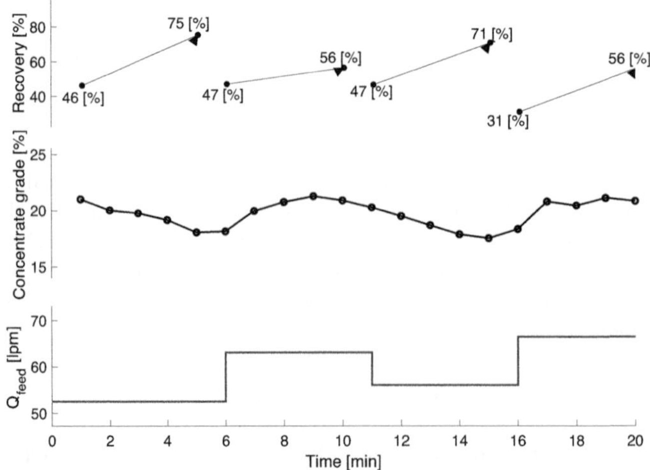

Figure 2: Mineral recovery and concentrate grade for changes in feed flowrates (Q_{feed}).

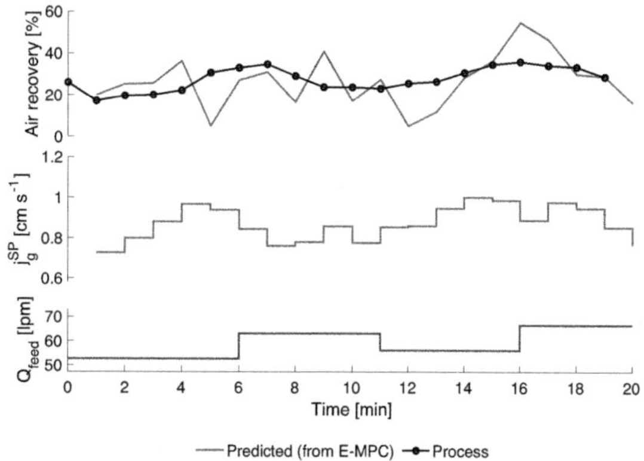

Figure 3: Air recovery and superficial air velocity (j_g) for feed flow rate changes (Q_{feed}).

As shown in Figure 3, air recovery generally followed the trends predicted by the E-MPC strategy, given the different values of superficial air velocity. Moreover, it can be observed that the highest air recoveries were obtained for the highest values of feed flowrates (63 and 66.5 [lpm]), which coincides with the highest pulp heights (see Figure 4). According to what was observed during the experiments, the increase in air recovery may be related to increments in overflowing froth velocity due to shallower froth depths.

Figure 4 shows the level control for the different pulp height setpoints sent from the E-MPC. While the trends of the pulp heights in the systems are the same as the setpoints, the values are usually different, which may be related to the differences between the parameters of the Proportional-Integral (PI) in the laboratory-scale system and the model used for the E-MPC. Those parameters are different because the sampling times are not the same in both cases, i.e. the PI controller had a sampling time of 1 second, while the model used in the E-MPC strategy corresponded to 10 seconds.

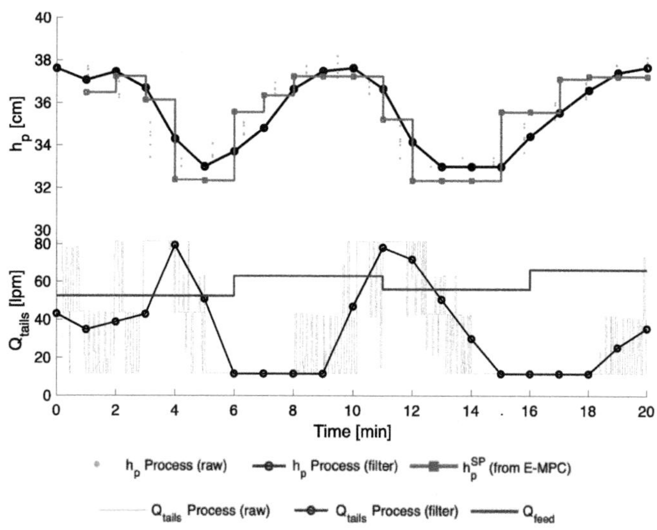

Figure 4: Control level using tail flowrates(Q_{tails}). Red lines are set points from E-MPC optimizatior and blue lines are filtered pulp height (h_p) in process.

4. Conclusions

This study validates an E-MPC strategy in a laboratory-scale flotation cell using a novel dynamic model that considers froth physics. The results of the experiments reveal that the E-MPC approach has led to higher metallurgical recoveries and has also shown its potential to handle feed flowrate disturbances efficiently. Further research will validate the E-MPC strategy in a laboratory-scale flotation bank (i.e. several tanks interconnected in series) to mimic the systems found in industrial-scale operations.

References

Andersson, J. A. E., Gillis, J., Horn, G., Rawlings, J. B., & Diehl, M. (2019). CasADi: a software framework for nonlinear optimization and optimal control. *Mathematical Programming Computation*, *11*, 1–36. https://doi.org/10.1007/s12532-018-0139-4

Ellis, M., Durand, H., & Christofides, P. D. (2014). A tutorial review of economic model predictive control methods. *Journal of Process Control*, *24*(8), 1156–1178. https://doi.org/10.1016/j.jprocont.2014.03.010

Ferreira, J. P., & Loveday, B. K. (2000). An improved model for simulation of flotation circuits. *Minerals Engineering*, *13*(14–15), 1441–1453. https://doi.org/10.1016/S0892-6875(00)00129-1

Maldonado, M., Sbarbaro, D., & Lizama, E. (2007). Optimal control of a rougher flotation process based on dynamic programming. *Minerals Engineering*, *20*(3), 221–232. https://doi.org/10.1016/j.mineng.2006.08.015

Oosthuizen, D. J., le Roux, J. D., & Craig, I. K. (2021). A dynamic flotation model to infer process characteristics from online measurements. *Minerals Engineering*, *167*, 106878. https://doi.org/10.1016/j.mineng.2021.106878

Perez-Correa, R., Gonzalez, G., Casali, A., Cipriano, A., Barrera, R., & Zavala, E. (1998). *Dynamic modelling and advanced multivariable control of conventional flotation circuits*. *11*(4), 333–346.

Putz, E., & Cipriano, A. (2015). Hybrid model predictive control for flotation plants. *Minerals Engineering*, *70*, 26–35. https://doi.org/10.1016/j.mineng.2014.08.013

Quintanilla, P., Navia, D., Neethling, S. J., & Brito-Parada, P. R. (2023a). Economic model predictive control for a rougher froth flotation cell using physics-based models. *Minerals Engineering*, *196*, 108050. https://doi.org/10.1016/J.MINENG.2023.108050

Quintanilla, P., Navia, D., Moreno, F., Neethling, S. J., & Brito-Parada, P. R. (2023b). A methodology to implement a closed-loop feedback-feedforward level control in a laboratory-scale flotation bank using peristaltic pumps. *MethodsX*, *10*. https://doi.org/10.1016/j.mex.2023.102081

Quintanilla, P., Neethling, S. J., & Brito-Parada, P. R. (2021a). Modelling for froth flotation control: A review. *Minerals Engineering*, *162*, 106718. https://doi.org/10.1016/j.mineng.2020.106718

Quintanilla, P., Neethling, S. J., Navia, D., & Brito-Parada, P. R. (2021b). A dynamic flotation model for predictive control incorporating froth physics. Part I: Model development. *Minerals Engineering*, *173*(November), 107192. https://doi.org/10.1016/j.mineng.2021.107192

Quintanilla, P., Neethling, S. J., Mesa, D., Navia, D., & Brito-Parada, P. R. (2021c). A dynamic flotation model for predictive control incorporating froth physics. Part II: Model calibration and validation. *Minerals Engineering*, *173*(November), 107190. https://doi.org/10.1016/j.mineng.2021.107190

Riquelme, A., Desbiens, A., Del Villar, R., & Maldonado, M. (2016). Predictive control of the bubble size distribution in a two-phase pilot flotation column. *Minerals Engineering*, *89*, 71–76. https://doi.org/10.1016/j.mineng.2016.01.014

Flavio Manenti, Gintaras V. Reklaitis (Eds.), Proceedings of the 34th European Symposium on Computer Aided Process Engineering / 15th International Symposium on Process Systems Engineering (ESCAPE34/PSE24), June 2-6, 2024, Florence, Italy
 http://dx.doi.org/10.1016/B978-0-443-28824-1.50295-7

Ethanol Increase in Gasoline and its Impacts in Manufacturing and Supply Chains

Mahmoud Ahmednooh,[a,b,c] Brenno C. Menezes,[a,c*]

[a]*Division of Engineering Management and Decision Sciences, College of Science and Engineering, Hamad Bin Khalifa University, Qatar Foundation, Doha, Qatar*

[b]*Production Planning and Scheduling, Um Said Refinery, Qatar Energy, Doha, Qatar*

[c]*Blend-Shops Company, Qatar Science and Technological Park, Qatar Foundation, Doha, Qatar*

bmenezes@hbku.edu.qa

Abstract

Biofuels, such as ethanol (CH_3-CH_2-OH), remain significantly underutilized globally, despite their potential to mitigate environmental effects associated with fossil-fuels' combustion in light fleet vehicles. Ethanol can be seamlessly blended with petroleum-derived gasoline. In regions like the United States and Europe, ethanol finds its place in the market as E5-E10 gasoline (gas or petrol), a blend consisting of 5-10% ethanol (anhydrous) and 90-95% mineral gasoline. Beyond, Brazil mixes 27% of ethanol in gasoline and holds the largest fleet of flex-fuel vehicles, fueled by any combination of both. However, in several Asian and Middle Eastern countries, where solely petroleum-refined gasoline is sold in fuel stations, octane number (ON) boosters such as methyl tert-butyl ether (MTBE) are still necessary. Additionally, in nations overproducing naphtha from refining of petroleum condensates, investments in extra carbon-chain rearrangement units can be an outlet since they produce high-ON streams. This paper proposes a simulation of scenarios of gasoline recipes considering supply chain (SC) dimensions in pure petroleum-refined gasoline (PPRG) manufacturing. These SC dimensions are ethanol, utilization of ON booster, and installation of extra reforming unit for carbon-chain rearranged components, all towards sustainable gasoline value chain worldwide.

Keywords: Biofuels, ethanol, gasoline, sustainability, petroleum refinery.

1. Introduction

Ethanol is an alternative fuel to fossil-fuel products such as gasoline, in its complete replacement or, partially, when mixing ethanol (anhydrous) to mineral gasoline. This can be also an alternative to octane number (ON) additive boosters such as methyl tertiary butyl ether (MTBE) since ethanol (ETH) boasts a typical research octane number (RON) of 108 (Foong et al., 2014) (around 10 points below MTBE, but 40 points above raw naphtha, one of the main precursors of petroleum-refined gasoline). Besides, ETH has the capacity to be blended to petroleum-refined gasoline at concentrations of up to 25% without causing damage to automobile cycle Otto engines (Menezes et al., 2014). Hence, the incorporation of ethanol into gasoline blends contributes to enhancing the octane rating of the fuel (increasing the performance of the motor engine by promoting antiknock or avoidance of spontaneous ignition before the electrical spark) while acting in the reduction of greenhouse gases (GHG) emissions, since it was mostly sequestered during the biomass raw material growth.

Furthermore, for gasoline production in petroleum refineries, naphtha reforming units play a pivotal role in transforming distilled or straight-run raw naphtha into reformate streams to be added in the gasoline pool among the main components for octane rating boosting (not considered as an additive booster of ON as MTBE, but as main component purposed for enhancement of ON). The integration of ethanol to the gasoline recipe provides flexibility in plant operations, which may involve moderating the severity of the reformate process unit since the carbon-chain cycling transformation inside this process reduces the volume of the output reformate stream by producing hydrogen (H_2) as a by-product. Also, a complete shutdown of the reformate unit can be decided, if ON is not an issue in the gasoline production, or this can be extended for BTX (Benzene, Toluene, and Xylene) operational mode given its higher market value (Quintino et al., 2019). This is also valid when a nation has naphtha excess (when processing light crude-oils or condensates) since from a long-term perspective, can be put in place, the installation of an extra reformate unit, avoiding exports of such low-price commodity stream.

2. Manufacturing and supply chain impacts by adding ethanol in gasoline

The integration of ethanol into gasoline blends offers a spectrum of advantages for petroleum refineries. These encompass (1) increased production (by reducing reformate stream losses if in low-ON); (2) enhanced profitability (since the ethanol price is lower than gasoline); (3) mitigated CO_2 emissions by the incorporation of a sustainable fuel component, and (4) the potential to cease the utilization of ON boosters such as MTBE.

The intriguing interplay among gasoline manufacturing, ethanol supply chains, and national policies towards sustainable liquid fuels on gasoline recipes inspires the connection of these additional gasoline component dimensions to the pure petroleum-refined gasoline (PPRG) manufacturing within their degrees-of-freedom to elucidate ethanol increase in gasoline worldwide. There are several trade-offs in the production of PPRG. The reformate unit increased and decreased severity is the most prominent since operational maneuverings in the spatial velocity and temperature in the carbon-chain cycling reactors can increase the conversion of the reactions resulting in more aromatic molecules (therefore higher ON quality) at a cost of higher production of H_2 as a side-effect. It reduces the quantity of the reformate and boosts its ON quality. Other factors such as the selection of the petroleum (and given yields in the distillation columns), ATR routes, CC modes of operations, also play a role in gasoline production. These diverse manufacturing scenarios (endogenous factors), interplaying with outside refinery walls or exogenous choices on supply chain such as ethanol imports for gasoline blending and the banning of MTBE for sustainable liquid fuels, are the object of our study.

The petroleum refinery in the proposed study represents a typical refinery showing the processes and streams related to gasoline production as in Figure 1, whereby 64 possible primary PPRG production solely based on manufacturing-made scenarios are possible. These are generated by the permutation of the two options of the main variations (petroleum crude-oils, ATR routes, CC modes, and REF modes), yielding 2^4 combinations (16 scenarios). A secondary level of the manufacturing-made scenarios creates 3 additional scenarios (ISO, POLY, and both) for each of the 16 previous ones. Therefore, a total number of 64 scenarios are formed, considering 16 without the secondary ones and 48 scenarios when including isomerization (ISO) unit, polymerization (POLY) unit, and both together, to the 16 mains or primary PPRG scenarios, then modifying the gasoline production from 16 to 64 possible scenarios.

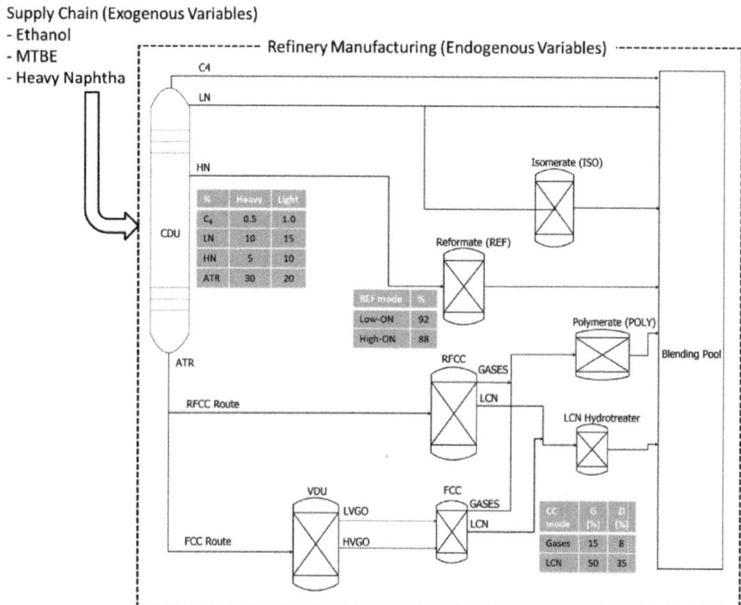

Figure 1. Petroleum refinery network for pure refined gasoline.

To this processing site, supply chain (or outside refinery walls) components like MTBE (ON booster) and ethanol are introduced, along with the construction or installation of another reformate unit, if overproducing of heavy naphtha by processing light petroleum or condensate exists. The refinery involves a distillation column with a capacity of 100,000 barrels per day (BPD), and the focus is on the streams that can be blended into the gasoline pool as seen in Figure 1. Other products such as jet-fuel and diesel are excluded from this discussion. In the reformate unit, an increase (in high-ON) or decrease (in low-ON) of 1.5 point in RON (research octane number) and 0.75 point in MON (motor octane number) is observed to the baseline of typical values. Similarly, for the CC unit, modes in gasoline or diesel, an increase (in gasoline) or decrease (in diesel) of 0.5 point in RON and 0.25 point in MON is found to the baseline of typical values. These typical values can be found in Ali et al. (2022) as well as the equations for the blended gasoline product, used as in a simulation of scenarios as proposed in this study.

3. Results

3.1. Primary manufacturing-made (endogenous) scenarios

In Figure 2, the 16 primary manufacturing-made scenarios for gasoline production, conversion or yield over 100 KBPD are defined on the variations of crude-oils, ATR routes, CC modes, REF modes. As per the scenario tree, the higher conversion is achieved when in light crude-oil (scenarios 1-8) because of the higher amounts of light distillates (15% of LN and 10% of HN, respectively), since these streams can be completely added, directly or indirectly (if processed), in gasoline. Considering ATR stream as 20-30% of the petroleum feed, 50% of VDU converted to FCC feed, and the yields of the RFCC/FCC modes, as in Figure 1, one can calculate the pure petroleum-refined gasoline (PPRG) yields of the 16 primary manufacturing scenarios (seen in Figure 2).

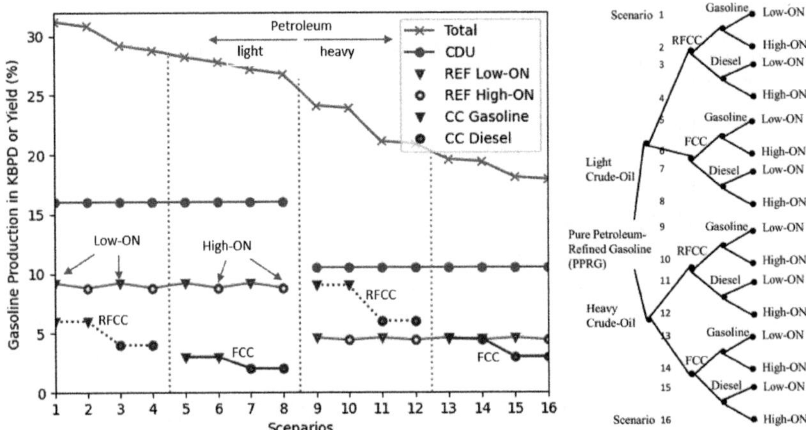

Figure 2. Gasoline yields (%) in the primary manufacturing-made scenarios for PPRG.

In terms of properties, the main concern on any gasoline mix is the ON since it reflects the performance of the motor engine by promoting antiknock or avoidance of spontaneous ignition before the electrical spark. Figure 3 shows the gasoline production/yield and the calculated RON for the 16 scenarios split in groups of 4. The 4 groups (with 4 scenarios in each) have light/RFCC selections in group 1 (scenarios 1-4) and light/FCC in group 2 (scenarios 5-8). Group 3 (scenarios 9-12) has heavy/RFCC and group 4 (scenarios 13-16) has heavy/FCC. These 4 groups are formed by distillation streams on CDU's light/heavy yields and ATR routes (RFCC or FCC). In group 1, the variations on CC and REF modes creates, for example, scenarios 1-2 (CC mode in gasoline) and scenarios 3-4 (CC mode in diesel). The differences in yields and RON between 1-2 and 3-4 are the due to the REF modes. The same CC and REF variations and results apply to the other groups.

Comparing the 4 groups, the higher yields of gasoline are in light petroleum by the high production of light and heavy naphtha (LN and HN), considering all LN is added to the gasoline pool. HN is the feed of REF units, and the low- and high-ON modes are reflected in the 8 pairs of 16 scenarios. Always the first scenario has higher gasoline yield and lower ON when compared to the counterpart in the pair. Within the same pair, the only difference between is the REF mode since the petroleum, ATR route, CC mode are equal.

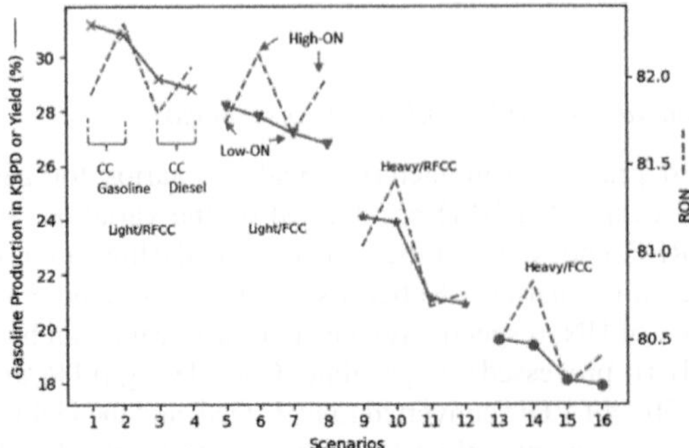

Figure 3. Yield and RON in the primary manufacturing-made scenarios for PPRG.

3.2. Secondary manufacturing-made (endogenous) scenarios

Figure 4 shows the gasoline production/yield and RON for the 16 primary manufacturing-made scenarios by adding the ISO and POLY units (the secondary manufacturing-made selections). These units promote increased ON streams by rearranging linear to ramified naphtha molecules in the ISO or grouping of C_2-C_3 olefins in the POLY. For the ISO, since it uses LN as feed, no difference is found in gasoline yields. What is fed of LN into the ISO, the same is reduced in the final gasoline pool, as in Figure 1. Due to both the reduction of a low ON stream as LN and the addition of the isomerate stream (higher ON), it increases RON by roughly 5 points in all scenarios. For the POLY, gasoline yield increases by adding a new stream from the GASES feed. It increases RON by 0.25-0.5 points in scenarios 1-8 and 0.5-1.0 points in scenarios 9-16. This is expected to occur since the more spherical conformation on the polymers from POLY has more effect is non-linear molecules in the gasoline with higher concentrations of CC streams as in scenarios 9-16. It is considered 30% of LN feeds the ISO and 50% of GASES to POLY.

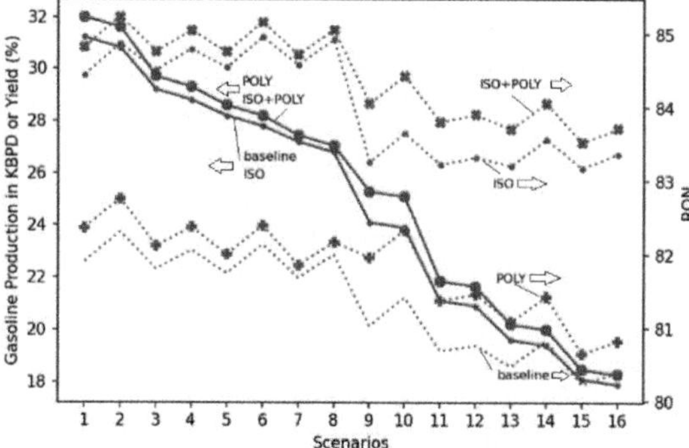

Figure 4. Yield and RON in the secondary manufacturing-made scenarios (Full PPRG).

3.3. Supply chain-related (exogenous) scenarios

Figure 5 shows the RON for the 16 scenarios with ISO and POLY units (full PPRG) by adding 5% and 15% of MTBE and 10% and 25% of ETH to the full PPRG. These MTBE and ETH values are found in the literature or are practices in the nations and are used to evaluate the influence of MTBE and ETH (exogenous SC variables) in the full pure refined gasoline (primary and secondary manufacturing-made or endogenous variables).

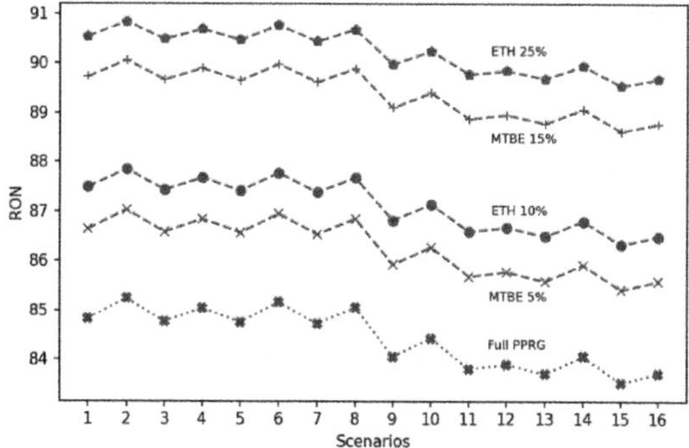

Figure 5. RON in the full PPRG, adding MTBE at 5-15% and ETH at 10-25%.

3.4. Full PPRG, MTBE, ETH, and Extra Reformate (REF2) unit

To reach regular gasoline RON at 91, a gasoline production may consider MTBE at 5% and ethanol (ETH) at 10%. Another SC variable can be an extra reformate unit added up to 15% in volume of the gasoline until it reaches the aromatic content limit at 25% in volume, which is the typical maximum allowed content, as seen in Figure 7. Considering the variations of 91 to 95 RON, for a petroleum refinery producing fuels as gasoline, in a process scheduling perspective, the production of higher grades of gasoline as 95-98 RON is possible by reducing the LN content in the gasoline pool.

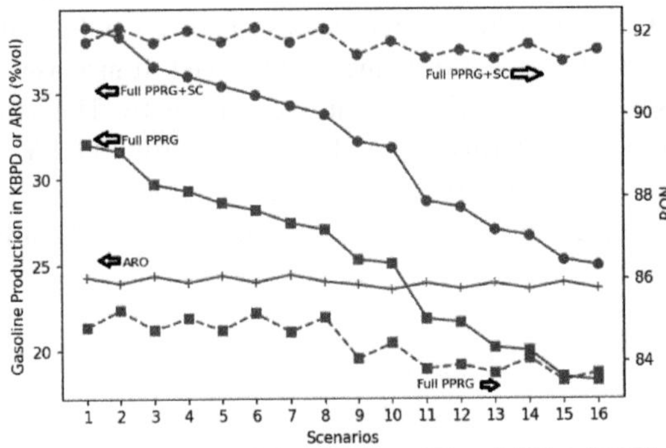

Figure 7. RON in the blend of the full PPRG, ETH at 10%, MTBE at 5%, and extra reformate stream at 15% in volume.

4. Conclusion

Among the nations several reasons are the causes of their current state of ethanol content in gasoline. They are arable land for ethanol production, public policies towards renewables and de-risking dependence on fossil-fuels, overproduction of light petroleum (crude-oil and condensate streams), and the banning MTBE from the gasoline pool. Considering all manufacturing and supply chain variations as presented in this work to reach the octane number (ON) required for antiknock or avoidance of spontaneous ignition before the electrical spark in the gasoline motor engines (Otto cycle), there are several ways (from strategic to operational) to meet the requirements of ON. The primary manufacturing-made gasoline includes crude-oil raw materials (light or heavy), ATR routes (if RFCC or FCC), RFCC/FCC modes in gasoline and diesel, and reformate units in low- or high-ON. Besides, strategic, tactical, operational decisions can include ISO and POLY units by their installation or operation (turn on or off) can be put in place. Limits of supply chain related variations as MTBE, ETH, and extra reformate must be accounted for in this gasoline recipe towards sustainable liquid fuels worldwide.

References

B. C. Menezes, L. F. L. Moro, W. O. Lin, R. A. Medronho, F. L. P. Pessoa, 2014, Nonlinear Production Planning of Oil-Refinery Units for the Future Fuel Market in Brazil: Process Design Scenario-Based Model, Industrial & Engineering Chemistry Research, 53, 11, 4352-4365.

T. M. Foong, K. J. Morgant, M. J. Brear, G. da Silva, Y. Yang, F. L. Dryer, 2014, The octane numbers of ethanol blended with gasoline and its surrogates, Fuel, 115, 727-739.

A. Quintino, M. Catalão-Lopes, J. C. Lourenço, 2019, Can switching from gasoline to aromatics mitigate the price risk of refineries?, Energy Policy, 134, 110963.

T. H. M. Ali, R. E. Franzoi, B. C. Menezes, 2022, Surrogate modeling for nonlinear gasoline blending operations, Computer Aided Chemical Engineering, 49, 1783-1788.

Flavio Manenti, Gintaras V. Reklaitis (Eds.), Proceedings of the 34th European Symposium on Computer Aided Process Engineering / 15th International Symposium on Process Systems Engineering (ESCAPE34/PSE24), June 2-6, 2024, Florence, Italy
 http://dx.doi.org/10.1016/B978-0-443-28824-1.50296-9

Optimal flexible operation of an AICR for P2A

Joachim Weel Rosbo[a*], Anker D. Jensen[a] , John Bagterp Jørgensen[b], Jakob K. Huusom[a]

[a]*Dept. of Chemical and Biochemical Engineering, Technical University of Denmark,*
[b]*Dept. of Applied Mathematics and Computer Science, Technical University of Denmark,*
**jwro@kt.dtu.dk*

Abstract.

In this paper, we propose a strategy for optimal and safe operation of an adiabatic indirect cooled reactor (AICR) for Power-to-Ammonia (P2A). The intermittent nature of renewable energies requires P2A plants to operate over a wide operating window between 30% to 130% of the nominal load. We formulate a rigorous transient model of a three-bed AICR in an ammonia synthesis loop. The AICR operating conditions are optimized over the entire operating window. We set up a simple MIMO control structure for flexible operation of the AICR. This uses decentralised PI loops for regulatory control with setpoints from a supervisory optimisation over the operational window. The control structure is tested under extreme load variations and displays good performance.

Keywords: P2A, modelling, flexible operation, control.

1. Introduction

Power-to-X (P2X) technologies receive widespread recognition as one of the fundamental pillars of a future CO2-neutral society based on renewable energy sources. Of the P2X technologies especially green ammonia from power-to-ammonia (P2A) is perceived as one of the most promising species for energy storage, and decarbonizing fertilizer production and maritime transportation. The intermittent nature of renewable energy sources requires P2A plants to operate over a wide operating window between 30% to 130% of the nominal load. The traditional production of ammonia via the Haber Bosch process relies on a stable supply of reactants (nitrogen and hydrogen). Therefore, several papers describe optimal steady state operation of ammonia reactors (Khademi & Sabbaghi, 2017; Shamiri & Aliabadi, 2021). Few papers describe the transient behaviour of ammonia reactors, but dynamic simulations of an Adiabatic Qunch Cooled Reactor (AQCR) are presented in Morud & Skogestad (1998). In Rosbo et al. (2023b) we present a dynamic model of an AQCR and propose an optimal operating strategy specifically for P2A with a simple regulatory control structure. However, today modern ammonia plants are equipped with AICRs, which yield a higher reactor conversion but also a more complicated design compared with the AQCR. This paper aims to identify the optimal operation strategy for an AICR over the entire P2A operational window. Moreover, we aim to establish a robust control structure capable of regulating the reactor safely between optimal operating points under varying loads from renewable sources.

2. AICR model and the case study

Figure 1 shows a schematic illustration of the ammonia synthesis loop considered in this work. The ammonia is produced via the Haber-Bosch process in an AICR. A relatively large recycle (stream 3) is used as the single-pass conversion of the reactor is around 30%

due to equilibrium limitations. A fraction of the recycle is purged (Stream 8) to avoid accumulating inert gases (argon).

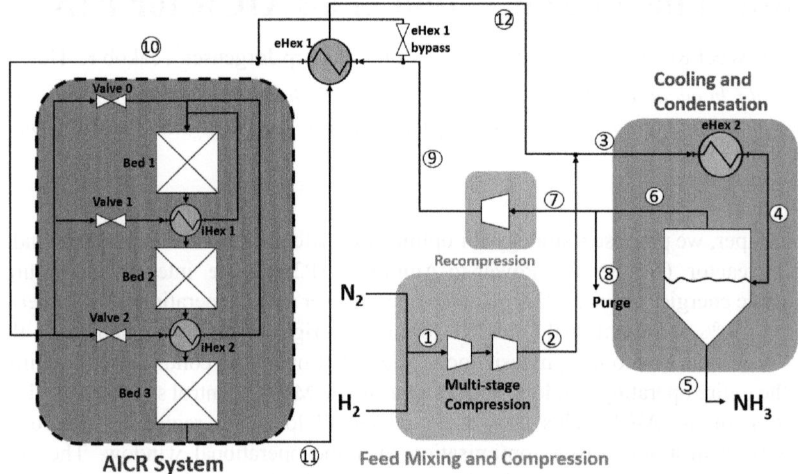

Figure 1: Synthesis loop of a P2A plant with an adiabatic indirect cooled reactor (grey box), compressors (orange boxes), and separator (blue box). The AICR is equipped with two internal heat exchangers (iHex 1 and iHex 2) and three valves for feed split. The AICR feed is pre-heated over the external feed-effluent heat exchanger eHex1. The streams are numbered from 1 to 12.

2.1. *AICR model*

The governing equations of the units in the AICR system (catalytic fixed beds and heat exchangers) are presented in Rosbo et al. (2024). In this paper, we add a dynamic term to the heat exchanger model only described with static equations in Rosbo et al. (2024),

$$\frac{dT_c^{out}}{dt} = \frac{1}{\tau_{Hex}}\left(T_c^{out,SS} - T_c^{out}\right), \qquad \frac{dT_h^{out}}{dt} = \frac{1}{\tau_{Hex}}\left(T_h^{out,SS} - T_h^{out}\right) \tag{1}$$

Where T_c^{out} and T_h^{out} are respectively the cold and hot side heat exchanger outlet temperatures, and $T_c^{out,SS}$ and $T_h^{out,SS}$ are the corresponding steady state temperature found via an effectiveness NTU-model (Saari, 2011). τ_{Hex} is the heat exchanger time constant based on the thermal inertia of the heat exchanger.

2.2. *The case study: 100 MW P2A plant*

The case study is based on the P2A case presented in Rosbo et al. (2024) defining a plant connected to a 250 MW renewable energy source with a capacity factor (CF) of 0.4. This corresponds to an average power supply of 100 MW to the P2A plant. The ammonia reactor volume is dimensioned based on 120% of the average power input to accommodate operation at periods with a power supply above the average load.

Tabel 1: Dimensions of the AICR beds, heat exchangers and nominal feed flow and compositions.

Bed dimensions		**Nominal reactor flow**		**Heat exchangers**	
Porosity	0.33	Total flow, [kmol/h]	5846	A_{iHex1}, [m^2]	89.0
Volume, [m^3]	6.63	x_{N_2}	23.8 %	A_{iHex2}, [m^2]	66.4
bed 1, [m^3]	0.998	x_{H_2}	71.4 %	τ_{iHex1}, [s]	120
bed 2, [m^3]	2.13	x_{NH_3}	4.15 %	τ_{iHex2} [s]	90
bed 3, [m^3]	3.50	x_{Ar}	0.60 %		

Rosbo et al. (2024) describe dimensioning of the heat exchangers to accommodate flexible operation. Table 1 summarizes the dimensions of the beds, heat exchangers, and nominal reactor flow for the AICR. Rosbo et al. (2023a) found that 91% of the total power input is consumed for the hydrogen production. Thus, the reactor load (RL) is defined based on the hydrogen flow to the reactor,

$$RL = \frac{F_{Rf,\mathrm{H_2}}}{F_{Rfn,\mathrm{H_2}}} \tag{2}$$

where $F_{Rf,\mathrm{H_2}}$ is the reactor feed flow of hydrogen and $F_{Rfn,\mathrm{H_2}}$ the nominal flow. The reactor is operated at stoichiometric conditions, $F_{Rf,\mathrm{N_2}} = \frac{1}{3} F_{Rf,\mathrm{H_2}}$. The argon flow in the reactor feed stream is assumed constant over the operating window as a larger recycle ratio yields better loop efficiency at lower load (Rosbo et al., 2023a). Assuming the separator is at constant temperature and equilibrium conditions, the mole fraction of ammonia exiting the flash drum and entering the reactor is constant,

$$F_{Rf,\mathrm{NH_3}} = F_{Rfn,\mathrm{NH_3}} \left(\frac{F_{Rf,\mathrm{H_2}} + F_{Rf,\mathrm{N_2}} + F_{Rf,\mathrm{Ar}}}{F_{Rfn,\mathrm{H_2}} + F_{Rfn,\mathrm{N_2}} + F_{Rfn,\mathrm{Ar}}} \right) \tag{3}$$

3. Steady state optimal operation

3.1. Optimisation algorithm

The optimal AICR configuration maximises reactor conversion. We consider the bed inlet temperatures as unbound optimisation variables. The optimization problem is formulated as a constrained minimisation in Eq. 4-5,

$$\min \quad F_{\mathrm{H_2}}^{out}\left(T_1^{in}, T_2^{in}, T_3^{in}\right) \tag{4}$$

$$s.t. \quad f(\mathbf{x},\mathbf{y}) = 0, \quad g(\mathbf{x},\mathbf{y}) = 0 \tag{5}$$

In which T^{in} is the bed inlet temperatures. The functions $f(\boldsymbol{x},\boldsymbol{y})$ and $g(\boldsymbol{x},\boldsymbol{y})$ refers to the formulation of the bed model in Rosbo et al. (2023b) as a differential algebraic equations system where $\boldsymbol{x}$ contains the states, $\boldsymbol{y}$ contains the algebraic variables, f represents the balance equations and g is the algebraic equations. Eq. 4-5 is solved at nominal load via Matlab's optimiser *fminsearch* yielding,

$$\left[T_1^{in}, \quad T_2^{in}, \quad T_3^{in}\right] = [700.3\,K, \quad 704.2\,K, \quad 695.0\,K] \tag{6}$$

Figure 2a displays the temperature and conversion profile along the reactor volume for the optimized AICR at nominal load. The AQCR data from Rosbo et al. (2023b) is added to the graphs to illustrate the conversion advantage of the AICR at around 10 % higher relative conversion. Higher conversion is achieved in the AICR as all the reacting gas is passing through all the beds and the bed inlet temperatures can be optimised independently. Contrary, the AQCR only have two degrees of freedom for manipulating the bed inlet temperatures (Rosbo et al., 2023a), Figure 2b shows the graphs for reactor conversion versus temperature along with contours of reaction rate. The equilibrium line clearly illustrates how the multi-bed reactor design facilitates further conversion by inter-bed cooling. We observe that the conversion versus temperature curve for the AICR is generally located closer to the maximum reaction rate curve compared to the curve for the AQCR.

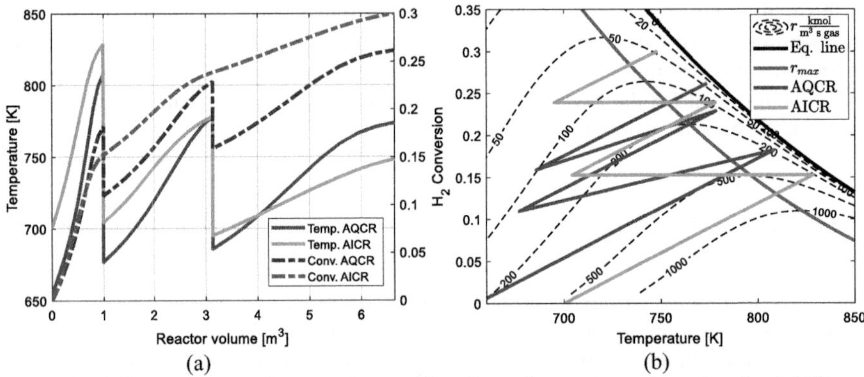

Figure 2: a) Temperature and conversion profiles along the reactor volume for the AQCR and AICR. b) Reactor conversion versus temperature curves plotted with contours of reaction rate.

3.2. Optimal static operation over the P2A operating window

We optimize the AICR by solving Eq. 4-5 over the entire operating window from 30% to 130% of nominal load. Figure 3a) shows the reactor conversion and Figure 3b) the optimal bed inlet temperatures over the operating window. The maximum reactor conversion is higher at lower loads as relatively more catalyst mass is available per reactant gas flow (higher residence time). From Figure 2b, we observe that decreasing the bed inlet temperatures creates more room for reactor conversion reaching before the equilibrium curve. However, this can only be realized if the bed residence time is sufficient to balance the decreased reaction rate at lower temperatures. Thus, the optimal bed inlet temperatures are colder at lower loads (longer residence time) as seen in Figure 3b.

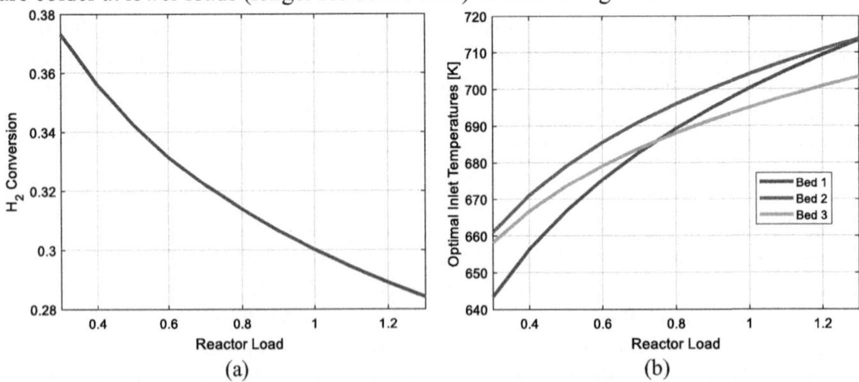

Figure 3: a) Reactor conversion for the optimized reactor, and b) optimal bed inlet temperatures over the operating window.

4. Control of the AICR under variable load operation

The optimisations in Sec. 3.2 compose a supervisory control layer for the optimal setpoints over the P2A operational window. A regulatory control structure is proposed for regulating the AICR safe and efficiently between the optimal static operating points.

4.1. Control structure

Returning to Figure 1, we observe four obvious valves for manipulating the bed inlet temperatures: The three internal reactor valves and the bypass over the external heat exchanger. We neglect the fast valve dynamics and regard the reactor feed split fractions

q_{Rf} as the manipulated variables (MVs). Thus, the degrees of freedom are reduced by one as the feed split fractions sum to 1, $\Sigma q_{Rf} = 1$. To confine the case to control of the reactor system, we assume the reactor feed temperature can be controlled instantaneously by the reactor bypass valve over the external heat exchanger. This allows us to regard the reactor feed temperature as a manipulated variable. These manipulated variables are naturally strongly crosscoupled to the bed inlet temperatures (controlled variables). Thus, we employ a static decoupler to compensate for cross effects. The manipulated variables, u, is given from the controller outputs, v, through,

$$u = [T_{Rf};\ q_{Rf1};\ q_{Rf2}] = Dv$$

Where D is a static decoupler matrix. Table 2 summarizes controlled variables (CV), controller outputs and controller parameters for the control loops. The controller parameters are determined via the SIMC tuning rules proposed by Skogestad (2004).We specify control loop 1 as a pure integral controller with a very fast time constant for the desired closed loop response, τ_c. This is advantages as v_1 has a pure gain influence on the bed 1 inlet temperature, which facilitates very aggressive integral control. Consequently, we expect the bed 1 inlet temperature to be tightly controlled, while the bed 2 and 3 inlet temperature display a more conservatively controlled response towards the set points.

Tabel 2: Control loops and parameters.

	CV	v	τ_c	K_c	τ_I
Control loop 1	T_1^{in}	v_1	2 s	0	0.45 s
Control loop 2	T_2^{in}	v_2	90 s	$-7.7 \cdot 10^{-3}$ [1/K]	120 s
Control loop 3	T_3^{in}	v_3	90 s	$-6.1 \cdot 10^{-3}$[1/K]	90 s

4.2 Closed loop reactor operation

The controller performance is tested by simulating the closed loop response to a series of step changes in the reactor load. The supervisory control layer specifies the optimal set points for bed inlet temperatures given the reactor load.

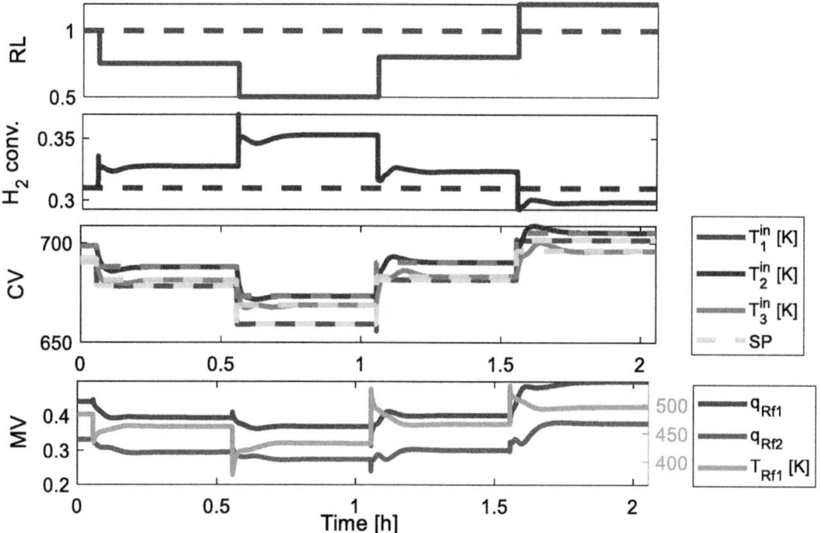

Figure 4: Closed loop response of the AICR system to extreme changes in reactor load.

Figure 4 displays the closed loop response of the AICR system. The four load steps of 25-30 % over only 2 hours are both larger and more frequent than what would be experienced in a real P2A plant. Thus, this provides an extreme test case for the controllers over the entire operating window. The proposed decoupled control structure performs quite well at stabilizing the reactor and tracking the optimal operating temperatures. As intended for the controller design, the bed 1 inlet temperature is controlled tightly and reaches the set point fast. The inlet temperatures to bed 2 and 3 respond slower as intended and display a efficiently controlled path towards the optimal bed inlet temperatures. The decoupling strategy appears to work well as no significant crosscoupling interactions are observed in the closed loop response.

5. Conclusion

In this paper, we have identified the optimal operating conditions of an AICR over an operating window between 30% to 130% of nominal load relevant for P2A. A MIMO control structure with centralized PI control was proposed for safely regulating the AICR between optimal operating points under varying load. We tested the control structure for a case with extreme and frequent variations in load. Even for this demanding case, the control structure performed well at regulating the reactor between the optimal operating points.

References

Khademi, M. H., & Sabbaghi, R. S. (2017). Comparison between three types of ammonia synthesis reactor configurations in terms of cooling methods. *Chemical Engineering Research and Design*, *128*, 306–317.

Morud, J. C., & Skogestad, S. (1998). Analysis of Instability in an Industrial Ammonia Reactor. *AIChE Journal*, *44*(4), 888–895. https://doi.org/10.1002/aic.690440414

Rosbo, J. W., Ritschel, T. K. S., Hørsholt, S., Jensen, A. D., Jørgensen, J. B., & Huusom, J. K. (2023). Optimal power distribution in a P2A plant. In *Computer Aided Chemical Engineering* (Vol. 52, Issue 2022). Elsevier Masson SAS.

Rosbo, J. W., Ritschel, T. K. S., Hørstholt, S., Huusom, J. K., & Jørgensen, J. B. (2023). Flexible operation, optimisation and stabilising control of a quench cooled ammonia reactor for Power-to-Ammonia. *Computers & Chemical Engineering*, *176*(108316).

Rosbo, J. W., Jensen, A. D., Jørgensen, J. B., & Huusom, J. K. (2024). Design and comparison of ammonia reactors for Power-to-Ammonia. *Submitted to Chemical Engineering Journal.*

Saari, J. (2011). Heat Exchanger Dimensioning. Lappeenranta-Lahti University of Technology

Shamiri, A., & Aliabadi, N. (2021). Modeling and Performance Improvement of an Industrial Ammonia Synthesis Reactor. *Chemical Engineering Journal Advances*, *8*, 100177.

Skogestad, S. (2004). Simple analytic rules for model reduction and PID controller tuning. *Modeling, Identification and Control*, *25*(2), 85–120.

Flavio Manenti, Gintaras V. Reklaitis (Eds.), Proceedings of the 34th European Symposium on Computer Aided Process Engineering / 15th International Symposium on Process Systems Engineering (ESCAPE34/PSE24), June 2-6, 2024, Florence, Italy
 http://dx.doi.org/10.1016/B978-0-443-28824-1.50297-0

Optimization of biomass-to-green methanol production: Techno-economic and environmental analysis

Chanmok Kim,[a] Chanhee You,[a] Hyeon Yang,[a] Jiyong Kim[a,*]

[a] *School of Chemical Engineering, Sungkyunkwan University, Suwon 16419, Republic of Korea*

[*]*Corresponding Author's E-mail: jiyongkim@skku.edu*

Abstract

To address the problem of global warming, environmental pollution, and energy source depletion, the transition to renewable and sustainable energy source from fossil fuels is so critical. Biomass is one of promising renewable and sustainable energy sources that can replace existing fossil fuels. In the chemical industry, methanol is used as an important intermediate for producing synthetic hydrocarbons and regarded as a future energy carrier. Recently, green methanol production from biomass is a promising alternative for green and sustainable methanol production compared to traditional methanol synthesis from fossil fuels. Since the syngas derived from biomass gasification does not meet the optimal syngas composition for methanol synthesis, the syngas composition needs to be adjusted by injecting hydrogen into the syngas. This study aims to identify the optimal design and operation strategy of green methanol production system. To achieve this goal, we developed process simulation model for green methanol production from biomass by using commercial process simulator Aspen plus to obtain the sizing and equipment costing data, and mass and energy flow data. Then, we developed sequential quadratic programming optimization model implemented in Aspen plus based on these data. The objective function of the optimization model is to minimize the unit production cost of the produced green methanol considering various constraints such as hydrogen price, and biomass price. As a result, we identified the optimal system configuration and operation strategy for green methanol production from biomass. In addition, the identified optimal system by optimization model is analyzed with technical, environmental, and economic metrics.

Keywords: biomass, green methanol, optimization, optimal design, operation strategy

1. Introduction

In response to the problems of global warming, environmental pollution and the depletion of energy sources, the transition to renewable and sustainable energy source from conventional fossil fuels is crucial. Biomass is recognized as an alternative energy source for producing sustainable liquid fuels, including methanol and Fischer-Tropsh fuels (Ostadi et al., 2023). Methanol is an important feedstock in the chemical industries and a key component in the production of synthetic hydrocarbons. Green methanol production from biomass not only replaces conventional fossil fuels in the transportation sector, but also reduces air pollution and greenhouse gas emissions (Ostadi et al., 2023, and Sollai et al., 2023). Therefore, transitioning to green methanol from biomass is not an innovative approach but a necessary step towards a sustainable and environmentally conscious energy future. In this work, we aim to identify the optimal design and operation strategy for green methanol production system. To achieve this goal, the technology overview, analysis method and methodology are presented in Section 2. In Section 3, the optimal design and operation strategy of the process proposed by the developed optimization model are presented. The optimal design includes the split ratio for the water gas shift (WGS), injected hydrogen amount, equipment size, and process configuration. The operation strategy includes biomass gasification temperature, WGS temperature, and WGS steam-to-carbon monoxide ratio. In addition, a techno-economic-environmental evaluation including the unit production cost, net CO_{2eq} emissions, and process energy efficiency was performed.

2. Technology overview and methodology

2.1. Technology overview

Fluidized biomass gasification: Gasification converts solid biomass into syngas at high temperatures through controlled reactions with gasification agents, involving stages such as drying, pyrolysis, partial combustion, and reduction. Fluidized bed gasifiers (FBG) enhance this process through fluidization, which involves transforming a bed of solid particles into a fluid-like state using gas. This technique ensures uniform temperatures due to excellent gas-solid mixing, achieves high carbon conversion rates, and produces low amounts of tar. (De et al., 2019).

Table 1. Ultimate and Proximate analysis (Güleç et al., 2022)

Material	Ultimate analysis (wt.%)					Proximate analysis (wt.%)			HHV
	N	C	S	H	O	Ash	VM	FC	kJ/g
Eucalyptus chips	0.14	44.77	0.15	6.33	48.6	1.9	79	19.1	16.49

In this study, the feedstock to the biomass-to-green methanol is 111.26 t/h eucalyptus chips biomass. The biomass characteristics including composition and heating value are provided in Table 1.

Water-gas shift (WGS): In WGS process, CO reacts with H_2O to produce CO_2 and H_2.

$$CO + H_2O \leftrightarrow CO_2 + H_2,\ \Delta H_{298K} = -41\ \text{kJ/mol} \quad (1)$$

This WGS process is conducted in two stages: high and low temperature stage. The high-temperature stage employs $Fe_2O_3/Cr_2O_3/CuO$ catalysts, operating within a temperature range of 250 to 400°C and a pressure range of 1 to 20 bar. For the low-temperature stage, $Cu/ZnO/Al_2O_3$ catalysts are utilized, with operational parameters set between 170°C and 250°C for temperature and maintaining the pressure within the 1 to 20 bar range (Do et al., 2023).

Acid gas removal (AGR): For the acid gas removal unit process, CO_2 capture is efficiently achieved using the MEA-based chemical absorption-desorption process, recognized as the most mature technology. In this method, CO_2 is absorbed in the absorber through a counter-current flow of the gas mixture and MEA solvent, facilitating enhanced interaction and CO_2 capture. Subsequently, in the stripper, reverse reactions release CO_2 and regenerate the solvent, allowing for its recirculation and maintaining an optimal system efficiency for CO_2 removal (Do et al., 2023, and Zhang et al., 2020).

Methanol synthesis (MS): Methanol is synthesized from syngas with the $Cu/ZnO/Al_2O_3$ catalysts at 250°C and 50 bar. The reaction appears as follows.

$$CO + 2H_2 \leftrightarrow CH_3OH, \Delta H_{298K} = -90.5 \text{ kJ/mol} \quad (2)$$
$$CO_2 + 3H_2 \leftrightarrow CH_3OH + H_2O, \Delta H_{298K} = -49.5 \text{ kJ/mol} \quad (3)$$
$$CO_2 + H_2 \leftrightarrow CO + H_2O, \Delta H_{298K} = 41 \text{ kJ/mol} \quad (4)$$

The stoichiometric number SN (defined as $(H_2-CO_2)/(CO+CO_2)$) of the syngas injecting into the methanol reactor needs to be slightly above 2.

2.2. Analysis method

In this work, the proposed process was evaluated in various criteria such as unit production cost (*UPC*), net CO_{2eq} emission (*NCE*), and energy efficiency (*EEF*).
In evaluating the economic feasibility of green methanol production, the *UPC* serves as a pivotal metric. The *UPC* calculation includes both the total capital investment cost (*TCI*) and total operating cost (*TOC*) of the process. *TCI* is derived from equipment costs obtained via the Aspen Process Economic Analyzer and reference values using the Lang factor for accurate estimation. The annualized capital investment cost (*ACI*) is then computed considering the *TCI*, along with the applicable interest rate (i) and plant lifespan (l). The *ACI* is expressed in Eq. (5). As shown in Eq. (6), *TOC* is the sum of variable operating costs (*VOC*) related to raw materials and utilities, and fixed operating costs (*FOC*) such as labor, maintenance, and overheads. The final *UPC* for green methanol is determined by dividing the total production cost by the annual production rate (*APR*) of methanol as shown in Eq. (7).

$$ACI = TCI \times \frac{i \times (1+i)^l}{(1+i)^l - 1} \quad (5)$$
$$TOC = VOC + FOC \quad (6)$$
$$UPC = \frac{ACI + TOC}{APR} \quad (7)$$

In assessing the environmental impact of green methanol production, the *NCE* is crucial. The *NCE* calculation includes three main components: 1) the CO_{2eq} of raw material inventory (*RM*); 2) direct CO_{2eq} emissions (*DCE*) from the process such as vent-out or purge gas; and 3) indirect CO_{2eq} emissions (*ICE*) derived from the use of conventional utilities. The overall *NCE* for green methanol production provides a comprehensive measure of its environmental footprint, considering both direct and indirect carbon emissions associated with the production process (Do et al., 2022, and Do et al., 2023).
In the technical evaluation of process efficiency, the *EEF* is critical metric. The *EEF* assesses how efficiently the energy utilized in the process is converted within the products.

2.3. Optimization methodology

$$\underset{x,y \in R^n}{\text{Minimize}} \{\text{UPC of methanol}\}$$

Subject to:

$$\begin{matrix} h(x,y) = 0 \\ g(x,y) \le 0 \end{matrix} \left\{ \begin{matrix} \text{Limits of operating conditions } (T, P) \\ \text{Mass and energy balance} \\ \text{Split fraction for purge} \\ \text{The optimal stoichiometric number} \\ \text{Non-negative constraints} \end{matrix} \right\} \quad (8)$$

$x \in R^n, y \in R^n$

The optimal design and operation strategy were identified via an optimization model developed to minimize UPC of green methanol, as given in equation (8), which is subjected to the set of quality ($h(x, y) = 0$) and inequality ($g(x, y) \leq 0$) constraints. The operation variables ($x, y \in R^n$) are determined to obtain the optimal value of the objective function within the constraint boundaries.

3. Results and discussion

3.1. Optimal configuration

Table 2. Summary of results for optimal design and operation strategy

Design		**Operation strategy**			
Split ratio for WGS	Injected H_2 (kmol/h)	Gasification temperature (°C)	HT-WGS temperature (°C)	LT-WGS temperature (°C)	Steam/CO ratio
0.36	89	840	289	170	1.03

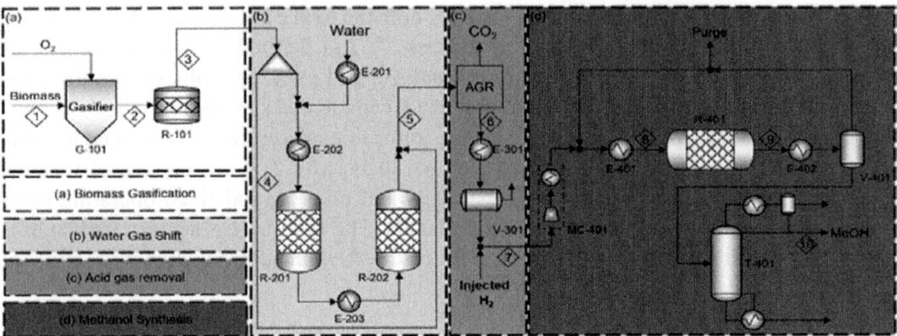

Figure 1. Process flow diagram identified by the optimization

The proposed biomass-to-green methanol process was modeled and simulated using Aspen Plus V.12 software. In this study, we assumed that the price and the CO_{2eq} inventory of renewable hydrogen were 2 \$/kg and 0 kg CO_{2eq}/kg H_2, respectively. Then, we developed an optimization model for identifying optimal design and operation strategy. Note that decision variables for the design and operation strategy include the split ratio for WGS process, injected amount of H_2, gasification temperature, WGS reactor temperature, and steam-to-CO ratio.

With developed optimization model, we could identify the optimal design variable and operation strategy, as summarized in Table 2. The process flow diagram which is identified by the optimization model is provided in Figure 1. The SN of the syngas produced after biomass gasification is not suitable for methanol production. Additional hydrogen must be supplied to adjust SN to be 2. There are two main strategies for supplementing hydrogen in this process: producing hydrogen through the WGS process, or externally injecting hydrogen. Here, the two strategies are simultaneously used to minimize the UPC of green methanol in this study. For example, the split ratio for the WGS process is set at 0.36, meaning that 36% of the syngas from biomass gasification undergoes the WGS process, while the remaining stream is bypassed and directed into the AGR process. Moreover, 89kmol/h of renewable hydrogen is injected externally. It is also identified that the optimal operation strategy includes the high temperature operation of gasification process. For instance, the optimal operating condition is determined to be operating the gasification temperature at 840°C. This is because the high operating temperature of the gasification process reduces the formation of tar, thereby increasing the hydrogen ratio in the syngas.

3.2. Techno-economic and environmental analysis

Table 3. Process energy flow and energy efficiency

Energy flow (MWy)	
(a) Feed (MWy)	
Biomass	411,740
H_2	56,341
(b) Utility (MWy)	
Fired heat	25,716
High-pressure steam	34,819
Medium-pressure steam	46,610
Low-pressure steam	40,067
Electricity	32,568
(c) Product (MWy)	
Methanol	383,002
Energy efficiency (EEF-%)	
EEF (=(c)/((a)+(b)))	**59**

We analyzed the energy efficiency of the optimal process as summarized in Table 3. As shown in Table 3, the proposed process requires various utilities from electricity to different steams. When analyzing energy consumed by utilities, there is no significant difference between the consumed amounts. Especially, huge requirement of MPS is due to CO_2 separation in the AGR to adjust the proper syngas ratio, followed by LPS mostly used in methanol purification. Overall, the energy efficiency of the process is analyzed to be 59%.

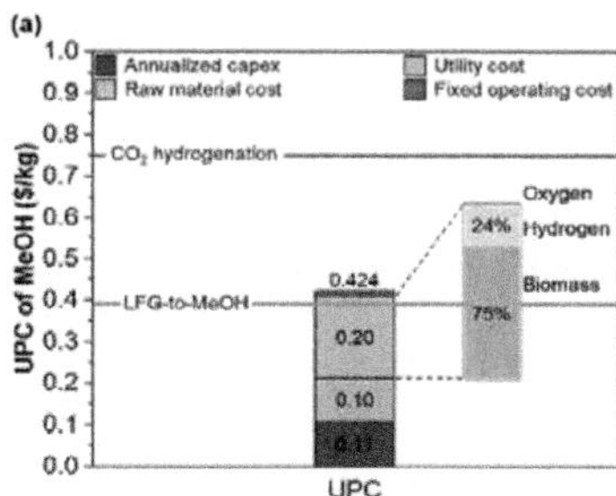

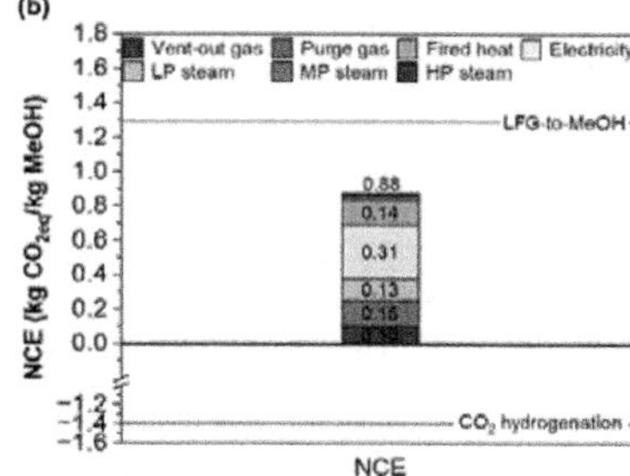

Figure 2. (a) UPC and (b) NCE of produced green methanol

To evaluate the economic feasibility of the optimal process, we analyzed the breakdown in UPC of green methanol as shown in Fig. 2 (a). UPC is broken down into annualized capex and operating cost contributions of utility costs, raw material costs, and fixed operating costs. It is identified that the UPC of optimal process exhibits 0.424 $/kg. The raw material cost is the main cost driver of UPC, accounting for 47% of the total cost. The biomass cost is the dominant cost component in raw material costs. This is because the substantial amount of biomass is required to produce green methanol due to the low carbon efficiency of the process. Which means that the biomass cost and the carbon efficiency are sensitive to the UPC of green methanol produced in the process.

To evaluate the environmental impacts, we conducted an environmental analysis as depicted in Fig. 2 (b). The NCE is broken down into ICE from the consumed utilities (e.g., fired heat, electricity, low-pressure steam, medium-pressure steam, and high-pressure steam), and DCE involving vent-out gas and purge gas. It is identified that ICE has become a major contributor, accounting for 95% of the NCE. This is because the biomass-to-green methanol process operates under high temperatures and pressures, leading to considerable utilization of heat and electricity as utilities.

Figure 2 also shows the UPC and NCE of other resources-based methanol production processes, namely CO_2 and landfill gas (LFG). The UPC of biomass-to-green methanol is slightly higher than that of LFG-to-methanol but lower than that of direct CO_2 hydrogenation. This is because LFG contains a large amount of CH_4, hydrogen can be produced inexpensively via steam methane reforming (SMR), thereby reducing the UPC of methanol. In contrast, significant amounts of renewable hydrogen are required to synthesize green methanol via the direct CO_2 hydrogenation, resulting in higher UPC compared to biomass-to-green methanol.

The biomass-to-green methanol shows higher NCE compared to the direct CO_2 hydrogenation that the feed inventory is represented as negative metrics due to the direct utilization of CO_2 as a feedstock. On the other hand, the NCE of biomass-to-green methanol is lower than that of LFG-to-MeOH. This is attributed to the SMR process used in LFG-to-MeOH, which operates at temperatures exceeding 800°C and utilizes fired heat as a utility.

4. Conclusions

In this study, we developed biomass-to-green methanol simulation model and an optimization model with an objective function of min UPC of green methanol. Then, we identified the optimal design and operation strategy of biomass-to-methanol system. Furthermore, we conducted techno-economic-environmental evaluation. The energy efficiency of the optimal process was 59%. In the economic evaluation, the UPC of green methanol was 0.424 $/kg, and the main cost driver was raw material cost due to the low carbon conversion to green methanol. In the environmental assessment, the NCE was 0.88 $kgCO_2/kgMeOH$ and ICE was the major contributor.

5. References

M. Ostadi, L. Bromberg, D.R. Cohn, E.Gençer, 2023, Flexible methanol production process using biomass/municipal solid waste. Fuel, 334, 126697

S. Sollai, A. Porcu, V. Tola, F. Ferrara, A. Pettinau, 2023, Renewable methanol production from green hydrogen and captured CO_2: A techno-economic assessment. Journal of CO2 Utilization, 68, 102345

S. De, A.K. Agarwal, V.S. Moholkar, B. Thallada, Coal and Biomass Gasification Recent Advances and Future Challenges. 2019, Springer Nature, 69-70

F. Güleç, D. Pekalsan, O.Williams, E.Lester, 2022, Predictability of higher heating value of biomass feedstocks via proximate and ultimate analyses – A comprehensive study of artificial neural network applications. Fuel, 320, 123944

TN. Do, YG. Hur, H. Chung, J. Kim, 2023, Potentials and benefit assessment of green fuels from residue gas via gas-to-liquid. Renewable and sustainable Energy Reviews, 182, 113388

H. Zhang, L. Wang, M. Perez-Fortes, J.V. Herle, F. Maréchal, U. Desideri, 2020, Techno-economic optimization of biomass-to-methanol with solid-oxide electrolyzer. Applied Energy, 258, 114071

TN. Do, YG. Hur, HE. Jeong, JW. Chung, W. Won, J. Kim, 2022, Rethinking of conventional Gas-to-liquid via dimethyl ether intermediate incorporating renewable energy against Power-to-Liquid. Energy Conversion and Management, 261, 115643

TN. Do, H. Kwon, M. Park, C. Kim, YT. Kim, J. Kim, 2023, Carbon-neutral hydrogen production from natural gas via electrified steam reforming: Techno-economic-environmental perspective. Energy Conversion and Management, 279, 116758

Flavio Manenti, Gintaras V. Reklaitis (Eds.), Proceedings of the 34th European Symposium on Computer Aided Process Engineering / 15th International Symposium on Process Systems Engineering (ESCAPE34/PSE24), June 2-6, 2024, Florence, Italy
 http://dx.doi.org/10.1016/B978-0-443-28824-1.50298-2

A Reinforcement Learning Framework for Online Batch Process Scheduling

Syu-Ning Johnn, Vassilis M. Charitopoulos *

Department of Chemical Engineering, The Sargent Centre for Process Systems Engineering, University College London, Torrington Place, London WC1E 7JE, United Kingdom

* *v.charitopoulos@ucl.ac.uk*

Abstract

Optimisation-based batch scheduling methods serve as a practical response strategy in the process industries as a coordination of planning and execution. The efficiency and adaptability of the method are of paramount importance, especially when dealing with frequent modifications to existing decisions caused by uncertainties and unforeseen real-world disturbances, with goal of achieving substantial financial profitability.

Reinforcement Learning, compared to many classic techniques, has the advantages of learning from existed experiment and generalise to unknown scenarios, and thus automating the process with higher flexibility and adaptability. In this work, we propose a RL-based method by transferring a batch process scheduling problem into a Markov Decision Process framework and train the agent to learn to build up task sequences to optimise the production schedule. The results show that our method achieves good computational efficiency and adaptability.

Keywords: Autonomous Online Scheduling, Reinforcement Learning (RL), Neural Network, Optimisation, Batch Processing.

1. Introduction

Batch process scheduling constitutes a fundamental problem in the process industries. Optimising the coordination of planning and execution is imperative for enhancing scheduling efficiency, yet it necessitates frequent modifications owing to unforeseen real-world disturbances. Diverse sources of uncertainty encompassing market demand fluctuations, due date adjustments, equipment reliabilities, and regulatory changes in a dynamic industrial environment pose the potential to swiftly render any pre-established optimal schedule inefficacious or obsolete (Gupta et al., 2016). As a result, optimisation-based scheduling methods serve as a practical response strategy deployed to address uncertainties with the aim of achieving substantial financial profitability.

When uncertainty is considered, existing approaches can be grouped into preventive or reactive based (Castro et al., 2018). Many studies in the literature aim to address the challenges associated with tackling the batch scheduling model and minimising the disparity between the theoretical models and their industrial applicability (Basán et al., 2020). In recent years, the integration of Machine Learning (ML) into process scheduling receives emerging attention (Hubbs et al., 2020). The ML techniques, especially those in the field of Reinforcement Learning (RL), have demonstrated the potential to effectively handle uncertainties with lower evaluation expense. In this work, we introduce deep Q-learning, a model-free RL technique, to address the batch process scheduling problem.

We formulate the problem as a Markov Decision process (MDP), based on which the learning takes place to train a neural network as a function approximator to estimate the optimal decision for building up the task sequence to form a schedule. From our case study, our RL-based approach achieves good adaptability for online schedule optimisation while preserving reasonably high solution quality.

As a popular training approach, RL learns optimal strategies through trial-and-error by interacting with a dynamic environment, and unlike traditional rule-based systems, RL exhibits the potential to discover optimal decision-making strategies generalised from its learned experiences. In the literature, Wang et al. (2023) formulated a flow-shop scheduling problem as a MDP for a deep RL algorithm with long short-term memory network to capture state sequences. Yang et al. (2023) applied Graph Neural Network for learning representation in RL to address a dynamic scheduling problem with the objective of minimising makespan. Additionally, Ren et al. (2021) tackled the scheduling problem by transforming it into a directed graph and applied RL technique for multistage sequential decision-making, utilising a nonlinear state-and-action neural network to approximate the reward function.

2. Methodology

2.1. Markov Decision Process

RL is a learning method mapping states to actions to maximise the expected future rewards (Sutton and Barto, 2018). Markov Decision Process (MDP) is a fundamental mathematical framework that models a sequential decision-making process, based on which we can apply the RL techniques.

An MDP can be represented by a tuple (S, A, P, R), where a state $s \in S$ is a representation of the specific time step within the environment that the agent can be in. At each non-terminal state s, the agent selects an action $a \in A$ from the set of actions $A(s)$ available at this state and receives a reward r according to a given reward function $R(s, a)$, which is the immediate benefit for taking the state-action pair. Afterwards, the agent reaches a new state based on the transition probability that describes the likelihood of moving from one state to another given an action. The key defining feature of an MDP is the Markov property, that the future state of the system is solely dependent on the preceding state-action pair, rendering the history of events irrelevant.

The agent engages with the environment through episodes, each of which encapsulates the agent's interactions over time as a sequential chain of states, actions, and rewards. By receiving feedback in the form of rewards from the environment, the agent is trained to refines its strategy with actions in dynamic states and formulate an optimal policy $\pi(a|s)$ that dictates the agent's behaviour to maximise the cumulative future rewards. Central to this learning is the state-action value function $Q(s, a)$, also denoted as Q-values, which quantify the expected rewards associated with taking any particular state-action pair by following π.

2.2. Problem Formulation

We transform the batch process scheduling problem with continuous time into an episodic task trajectory, incorporating node insertion as the action. Figure 1 provides the visualisation of a sample process schedule involving 2 machines and 2 lines of tasks, which has a problem size equals 2 for simplicity. The schedule illustrates the execution sequence as well as the corresponding processing machine for all tasks. The notation for each task follows a specific format: (flow sequence index, machine index, copy index), representing the ranking of each task in its respective line, the assigned machine's index, and the copy index of the task, respectively. For instance, $T_{1,2,3}$ signifies the first task in the sequence within an individual production line that is processed by the second machine, and this task is the third copy of its kind in the entire production process. All tasks scheduled on the same line are sequentially connected, and all tasks assigned to the same machine must be processed with no time overlapping.

Bringing in the MDP terminology, each state is a tuple (G, X, ϕ), wherein the graph G contains all the existing tasks (represented by nodes) and the sequence between them (represented by arcs), the feature matrix X contains information for the node process sequence, the number of copies, and the starting time t for each task. The starting time for each task is computed by $t(T_{i,j,c}) = \max[t(T_{i-1,j,c}), t(T_{i,j-1,c})]$ if assigned to any machines that is not the first to run, and $t(T_{i,1,c}) = t(T_{i-1,1,c})$ for all tasks assigned to the first machine. Finally, ϕ is a Boolean variable indicating whether a state is a terminal one. The agent's set of actions involves inserting nodes with increasing copy index into the feasible arc within the graph, ensuring compliance with machine availability capacity and time restrictions imposed by the given time horizon. Notably, we require that any additional copy $c + 1$ cannot occur earlier than the existing copy c.

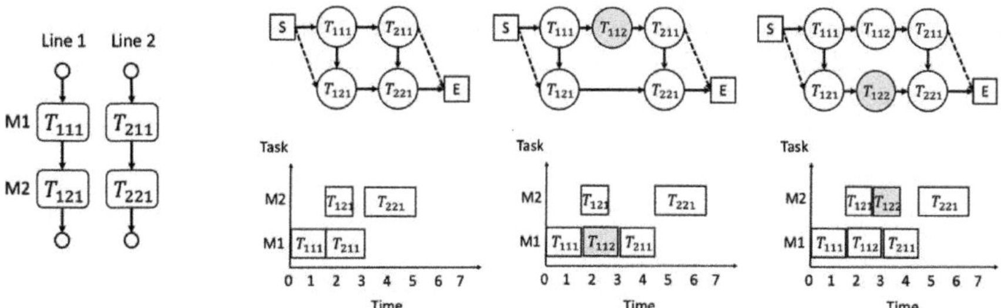

(Left) Figure 1. A sample batch process problem of size 2; (Right) Figure 2. Batch process in a MDP framework as a directed graph from start node S to end node E.

The upper row in Figure 2 illustrates part of an episodic task spanning 3 sequential episodes, where the agent iteratively makes 3 node insertions according to its learnt policy. The bottom row depicts the timeline with the task schedules, categorised by the allocated machine. We start from the left-most column of graphs where there are four tasks, each of which has a single copy. We assume an inventory consumption of 1 unit for each task, and the processing times are at 1.5h for both tasks on machine 1, and for machine 2 the tasks are set to be 1h and 2h.

In the leftmost upper graph in Figure 2, the initial sequence can be written as $[(T_{111}, T_{211}), (T_{121}, T_{221})]$, with the list of starting times as $[(0, 1.5), (1.5, 3)]$. Based on flow balance and machine availability, the agent at this state is given two actions: to insert another copy of either T_{11} or T_{21} into the graph. The agent selects T_{11}, creating T_{112} as a new copy of task and transitioning to the second graph with a processing sequence of $[(T_{111}, T_{112}, T_{211}), (T_{121}, T_{221})]$ and an updated processing time $[(0, 1.5, 3), (1.5, 4.5)]$. At this state, the agent is presented with the options to insert another copy of T_{11}, T_{21} or T_{12} into the graph and it chooses to create another copy of task T_{12}, hence transitioning to the third graph. This process continues until reaching a terminal state where no additional node can be inserted without violating the machine availability or inventory flow balance. The reward for the episode is computed as the improvement in total production at the terminal state s_* compared to the initial state s_0 using the reward function $R = F(s_*) - F(s_0)$, and $R = 0$ for the non-terminal states.

2.3. Q-Learning

Q-learning (Watkins and Dayan, 1992) is a popular model-free RL approach employed to solve MDPs by iteratively updating the Q-values according to the rule:

$$Q^{new}(s,a) \leftarrow Q(s,a) + \alpha \left(r + \gamma \cdot \max_{a} Q(s',a) - Q(s,a) \right) \quad (1)$$

where $Q(s,a)$ is the previous Q-value, the term $\max Q(s',a)$ denotes the maximum Q-value amongst all the available actions in the subsequent state s', and r represents the immediate reward the agent receives by performing the (s,a) pair. The discount factor γ balances immediate rewards against future rewards, influencing the agent's preference for short-term gains versus long-term benefits. Through the iterative refinement in the MDP, the agent refines its policy to estimate the optimal Q-values.

Deep neural networks are frequently utilised as function approximators for the $Q(s,a)$ function, which facilitates the generalisation of Q-values across states that share common characteristics and therefore may consequently yield similar future rewards. Function approximation is particularly advantageous for problems with large state spaces, which contrasts with the traditional Q-table approach: Unlike Q-tables that explicit record Q-values for every state-action combination, DQN provides a more scalable and efficient means of approximating the Q-values by bypassing the memory challenges associated with maintaining extensive records.

We employ the Deep Q-Network (DQN) by Mnih et al. (2015) for agent training, incorporating key techniques including the replay buffer and target network. During training, the DQN algorithm samples iterative batches of previously taken actions from the replay buffer to train the main network. In this step, the algorithm takes the current state of the environment as input and outputs a vector of Q-values corresponding to the list of available actions. The main network parameters are periodically transferred to the target network at every certain number of episodes to stabilise the training process. The target network remains consistent over this certain interval and is used to predict the future Q-values for state-action pairs.

3. Case Study

3.1. Experiment Setup

For the neural network in the DQN algorithm, the main network parameters are updated by stochastic gradient descent using the Q-learning loss. We employ 3 hidden layers with the first layer containing 512 neurons and half the size for the subsequent layers, followed by a ReLU activation function. The feature matrix inputted into the network encompasses task-related information for each state, including the node sequence, number of copies for each task, and the starting time for each task. Prior to input for the training, the feature matrix associated with each state is flattened into a vector, undergoes one-hot encoding, and normalised using the min-max normalisation function.

The training steps is linear to the instance size, increasing by 1000 for every 1 additional production line or machine included. The evaluation contains 500 steps for all instances.

We apply a learning rate $\alpha = 0.0002$, the epsilon initial value of 0.1 that decreases by 0.00005 until either reaching a threshold of 0.01 or when the first 20% of the steps are completed. The replay buffer contains 900 steps and each time a random sample batch of 300 is generated for training the main network. For the parameter setting, each task requires one inventory unit from the preceding task, the task processing time is randomly generated uniformly from interval $[1, 5]$. The time horizon is 10 times the size of instance.

3.2. Results

3.2.1. Evaluation Result

From the evaluation result in Figure 3, the RL agent is able to cumulate reward for all different instance sizes by sequencing tasks to maximise final products whereas the random agent fails to secure any positive sum of reward. Both agents in Figure 4 have a confidence interval of 99%. Despite the large variation caused by randomly generated processing time, the RL agent produced a higher objective value on average for all instance sizes.

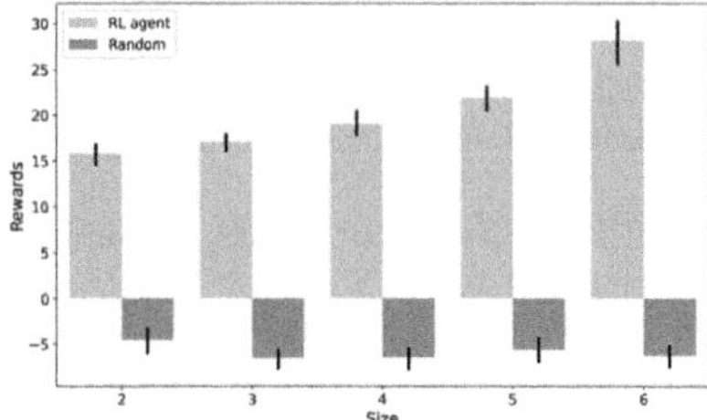

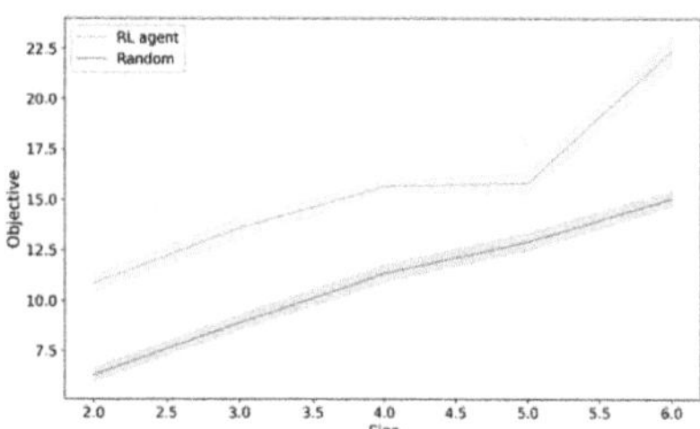

(Left) Figure 3. Reward evaluation for the RL-based agent and random agent; (Right) Figure 4. Objective function evaluation for the RL-based agent and random agent.

3.2.2. Computational Time

The computational time from Table 2 indicates that our RL framework is time efficient in the way that once trained, the agent is able to build up task sequences within 1.5 seconds on average for an instance with 6 machines and 6 jobs.

Table 1. Computational time (second) consumed by 500 evaluation steps for the RL-based agent and the random agent without prior-training. Equivalent to solving the batch process problem for 500 times.

	Size = 2	**Size = 3**	**Size = 4**	**Size = 5**	**Size = 6**
DQN	21.72	44.84	111.89	311.07	632.83
Random	19.94	33.37	72.1	172.35	379.45

4. Conclusions

In conclusion, we have addressed a batch process scheduling problem by first formulating it into a Markov Decision Process. We subsequently employ deep Q-Learning to estimate the expected future rewards for each action and train the agent to build up the production schedule in an online manner by iteratively engaging in trial-and-error interactions with the environment. Preliminary experiment results demonstrate the ability of our learning-based approach in solving the problem with good computational efficiency and model adaptability.

Plans for future research involve the generalisation of learning framework to larger industrial instance size, the adaptation of a larger action set, and the hybridisation of RL-based learning approach with mixed-integer linear programming models to reach optimality more efficiently.

Acknowledgement

Financial support from the Engineering & Physical Sciences Research Council grant EP/V051008/1 is gratefully acknowledged by the authors.

References

N. Basán, M. Cóccola, A. del Valle, C. Méndez, 2020, Scheduling of flexible manufacturing plants with redesign options: A MILP-based decomposition algorithm and case studies, Computers & Chemical Engineering, 136, p.106777

P. Castro, I. Grossmann, Q. Zhang, 2018, Expanding scope and computational challenges in process scheduling, Computers & Chemical Engineering, 114, pp.14-42

D. Gupta, C. Maravelias, J. Wassick, 2016, From rescheduling to online scheduling, Chemical Engineering Research and Design, 116, pp.83-97

C. Hubbs, C. Li, N. Sahinidis, I. Grossmann, J. Wassick, 2020, A deep reinforcement learning approach for chemical production scheduling, Computers & Chemical Engineering, 141, p.106982

V. Jain, I. Grossmann, 2001, Algorithms for hybrid MILP/CP models for a class of optimization problems. INFORMS Journal on computing, 13(4), pp.258-276.

S. Jiang, C. Xu, L. Zhang, Y. Ma, 2023, A decomposition-based two-stage online scheduling approach and its integrated system in the hybrid flow shop of steel industry. Expert Systems with Applications, 213, p.119200.

C. Maravelias, I. Grossmann, 2004, A hybrid MILP/CP decomposition approach for the continuous time scheduling of multipurpose batch plants, Computers & chemical engineering, 28(10), pp.1921-1949

V. Mnih, K. Kavukcuoglu, D. Silver, A. Rusu, J. Veness, M. Bellemare, A. Graves, M. Riedmiller, A. Fidjeland, G. Ostrovski, S. Petersen, 2015, Human-level control through deep reinforcement learning, Nature, 518(7540), pp.529-533

J. Ren, C. Ye, F. Yang, 2021, Solving flow-shop scheduling problem with a reinforcement learning algorithm that generalizes the value function with neural network, Alexandria Engineering Journal, 60(3), pp.2787-2800

R. Sutton, A. Barto, 2018, Reinforcement learning: An introduction. MIT press

Z. Wang, B. Cai, J. Li, D. Yang, Y. Zhao, H. Xie, 2023, Solving non-permutation flow-shop scheduling problem via a novel deep reinforcement learning approach, Computers & Operations Research, 151, p.106095

C. Watkins, P. Dayan. 1992, Q-learning, Machine Learning, 8(3-4):279–292

Z. Yang, L. Bi, X. Jiao, 2023, Combining Reinforcement Learning Algorithms with Graph Neural Networks to Solve Dynamic Job Shop Scheduling Problems, Processes, 11(5), p.1571

Flavio Manenti, Gintaras V. Reklaitis (Eds.), Proceedings of the 34th European Symposium on Computer Aided Process Engineering / 15th International Symposium on Process Systems Engineering (ESCAPE34/PSE24), June 2-6, 2024, Florence, Italy
 http://dx.doi.org/10.1016/B978-0-443-28824-1.50299-4

Role of the Throughput Manipulator on Economic and Sustainable Process Operation

Aayush Gupta[a], Prakhar Srivastava[a], Nitin Kaistha[a*]

[a] *Department of Chemical Engineering, IIT Kanpur 208016,India*
[*]*nkaistha@iitk.ac.in*

Abstract

This study investigates the pivotal role of the throughput manipulator (TPM) in designing the material balance control structure of an integrated plant. Two industrial processes, ester purification and acetone manufacturing, are assessed under three different regulatory control structures (CS1, CS2, CS3) with distinct TPM choices, fresh feed, first major unit inside the recycle loop, and the bottleneck capacity constraint. Economic impact is rigorously evaluated in two operational modes. Results underscore that locating the TPM at the bottleneck within the material recycle loop (CS3) yields substantial energy savings (9.72% and 4.24% in Mode I) and increased maximum throughput (5.8% and 4.67% in Mode II) compared to a conventional structure (CS1) for ester purification and acetone manufacturing process, respectively. This highlights the considerable economic and sustainability benefits associated with positioning the TPM inside the material recycle loop, particularly when bottleneck is identified and within the recycle loop.

Keywords: Quality control, Throughput maximization, Material balance control

1. Introduction

Liquid surge capacities, like the reflux drum or bottom sump in a distillation column, are essential in a plant for smoothing flow transients. Non-self-regulatory liquid hold-up (inventory) in a surge capacity requires an inventory controller to ensure long-term material balance closure (inflow equals outflow). Inventory (material balance) regulation emerges as a primary objective in integrated plants with multiple surge capacities, aiming to automatically close the material balance across individual plant units and the entire plant.

Considering total material balance control on an individual unit, often processing liquid for cost-effectiveness, a SISO (Single input single output) PI controller manipulates the connected process stream flow rate to maintain the total material inventory. However, this flow manipulation acts as a material balance disturbance to the connected unit, prompting adjustments in its inventory controller. This initiates the propagation of flow transients across a series-cascade of units. The severity of transients depends on the 'tightness' of inventory control and the MV-CV (manipulated variable - controlled variable) pairings on individual units, known as the material balance control structure (Buckley, 1964).

In designing the material balance control structure, the throughput manipulator (TPM) is a critical decision. The chosen independent flow rate becomes the TPM, setting the material processing rate (throughput) of the cascade. The location of the TPM affects the orientation of individual unit material balance controllers and the direction of transient propagation. The outwardly radiating control structure implies that flow transients move away from the TPM (Kaistha, 2021). This direction impacts the magnitude of flow variability experienced by different plant units.

Flow transients become particularly relevant in material recycle systems, where positive feedback due to recycle can amplify flow variability. This variability significantly contributes to variations in key process variables (PVs) constrained at maximum or minimum values for economic/sustainability optimization. Key PVs, such as guaranteed minimum product quality and bottleneck capacity constraints, require optimal operation close to these limits without violation, necessitating a back-off that represents an economic loss. Mitigating flow variability, a significant

contributor to variability in key constraint PVs, reduces this back-off and economic loss (Downs & Skogestad., 2011).
This study explores the role of the material balance control structure with alternative TPM locations in mitigating flow variability and enhancing sustainable/economic operation performance. The major contribution is a quantitative demonstration that locating the TPM inside the material recycle loop results in significant energy savings (up to 9.7%) and higher production (up to 5.4%).
The article proceeds with detailed case studies on two integrated processes—an ester recovery process and an acetone manufacturing process—to quantitatively evaluate the impact of the material balance control structure on economic/sustainable process operation.

2. Process Case Studies

We conduct detailed case studies on the ester purification process (Ojasvi & Kaistha, 2016) and the acetone manufacturing process (Luyben, 2011) to assess the economic and sustainability benefits of a regulatory control structure at various TPM locations. Our focus is on mitigating product quality variability and addressing plant capacity bottleneck constraints to enhance throughput and sustainability. The analysis encompasses two operational modes: Mode I, featuring a specified nominal throughput with minimum product quality as the primary constraint, and Mode II, operating at the maximum achievable throughput with bottleneck equipment capacity as an additional constraint.
We explore three control structures at different TPM locations: (i) fresh feed, (ii) feed to the first unit operation inside the recycle loop, and (iii) bottleneck capacity constraint inside the recycle loop. To evaluate operational profitability, we introduce time-series and sinusoidal inputs at various plant locations. Economic metrics include total energy consumed in Mode I and maximum product rate in Mode II

2.1. Case Study 1: Ester Purification Process

In the ester purification process, a ternary ethyl acetate-ethanol-water fresh feed, combined with an ester-rich recycle stream, is introduced at the bottom of a liquid-liquid extractor (LLX).

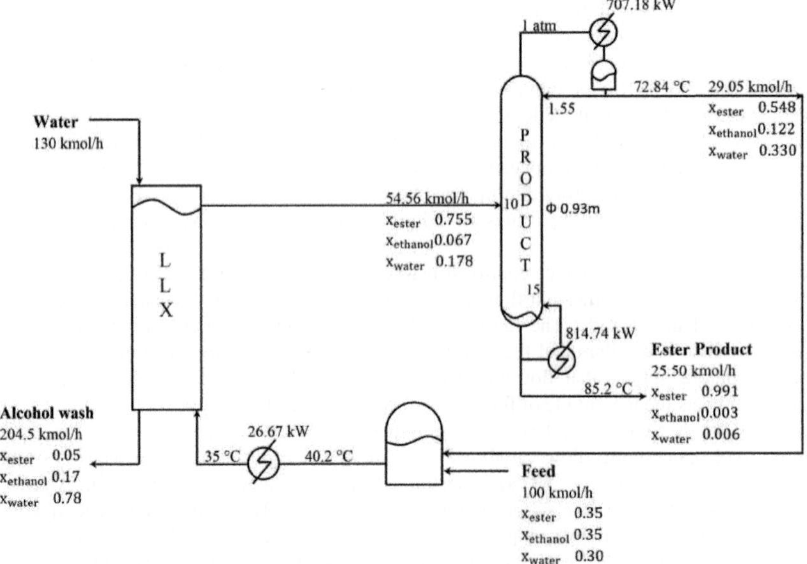

Figure 1: Nominal design and operating condition of ester purification process

Table 1: Mode 1 result for ester purification process

Control Structure	Δx^*_{prod} (10^{-3})	Q_{tot} (kW)	Energy Savings (%)
CS1	3.57	904.5	0.00
CS2	2.62	854.4	5.54
CS3	0.33	816.6	9.72

* No back-0ff x^{min}_{prod}=0.991

Simultaneously, a water solvent stream is introduced at the LLX's top to extract alcohol, leaving the bottoms as the alcohol wash stream. The light organic raffinate stream exiting the LLX top is subjected to distillation column to obtain nearly pure ester product in the bottoms, and the distillate is recycled back to the LLX as shown in figure 1. The maximum production is constrained by the solvent rate to the LLX, and the distillation column approaches the flooding limit, serving as the bottleneck capacity constraint.

Three alternative control structures, CS1 (TPM at the fresh feed), CS2 (TPM at the total feed (F_{tot}) to the LLX), and CS3 (TPM at the column boil up, U), are evaluated.

In CS1, the control strategy involves regulating the LLX feed tank level by manipulating the tank exit stream valve. The LLX feed stream temperature is maintained by adjusting the LLX feed cooler duty. The raffinate rate is adjusted to keep the organic-aqueous interface level near the top of the LLX, given the continuous nature of the aqueous phase in the LLX. On the distillation column, the column pressure is controlled by adjusting the condenser duty, while the bottom sump and reflux drum levels are managed by adjusting the bottoms and distillate rates, respectively. The reflux is maintained in ratio with the distillate, and the sensitive stripping tray 14 temperature is regulated by adjusting the column reboiler duty.

In CS2, with F_{tot} as the TPM, the LLX feed tank level is regulated by manipulating the fresh feed rate, while other control loops remain unchanged from CS1. In CS3, where the TPM is the column boil-up (U), tightly controlled by adjusting the column reboiler duty, Product column sensitive tray temperature is regulated by the column feed rate. The organic-aqueous interface in the LLX is controlled using F_{tot}, and the LLX feed tank level is adjusted by manipulating the fresh feed rate. The inventory control system upstream of the TPM operates in the reverse direction of process flow, but other loops are consistent with CS1.

In Mode I dynamic results, obtained for a continuous 48-hour operation at an average feed processing rate (throughput) of 100 kmol/h, the minimum back-off in the product column stripping tray temperature setpoint is ensured to avoid violating the minimum product purity constraint. Table

Table 2: Mode II result for ester purification process

Control Structure	Δx^*_{prod} (10^{-3})	$U^{\#}$ (10^3 kg/h)	Fresh Feed (kmol/h)	Throughput benefit (%)
CS1	4.27	9.65	105.2	0.00
CS2	3.73	9.76	107.0	1.71
CS3	0.43	10.3	111.3	5.80

* No back-0ff x^{min}_{prod}=0.991, #maximum boil-up U^{max} = 10340 kg/h

1 summarizes the backed-off average ester product purity (x_{prod}), total duty (Q_{tot}), and energy savings for the three control structures—CS1, CS2, and CS3. Among them, CS3 exhibits the lowest total duty (Q_{tot}), followed by CS2 and then CS1. In comparison to the conventional CS1, CS2 and CS3 achieve energy savings of 5.54% and 9.72%, respectively.

For Mode II, focused on throughput maximization, results are obtained with minimum back-off in both x_{prod} and the column boil-up U from the bottleneck capacity constraint U_{max} for CS1, CS2, and CS3. Table 2 summarizes the average values for x_{prod}, U, and F. CS3 attains the highest maximum throughput, followed by CS2 and then CS1. Relative to CS1, CS2 and CS3 achieve higher maximum throughputs by 1.71% and 5.8%, respectively.

2.2. Case Study 2: Acetone Process

Figure 2 shows the nominal and operating condition of the acetone process, which is produced via the dehydrogenation of isopropyl alcohol (IPA). A near-azeotropic IPA-water feed, combined with a similar recycle stream, undergoes vaporization and superheating before entering an oil-heated packed bed reactor. The endothermic dehydrogenation reaction occurs, producing acetone and hydrogen. The reactor effluent is cooled, and condensed, and the resulting condensate is collected in a flash drum. The H_2-rich non-condensable gas is absorbed in an absorber using water solvent. The lean gas exits, while the absorber and flash drum liquids are mixed and fed to a product column, recovering pure acetone at the top. An overhead vapor vent release uncondensed H_2 gas. The acetone-free bottom is further processed in a recycle column to separate wastewater, with the IPA-water azeotrope distillate recycled to the vaporizer. Three plantwide regulatory control structures, CS1, CS2, and CS3, are under consideration. CS1 employs a conventional approach with the TPM at the fresh IPA-water feed. Downstream inventory controllers follow the process flow direction. Key control points include manipulating heat duty for vaporizer level, adjusting reactor preheater duty for feed stream temperature, controlling reactor exit stream temperature by manipulating reactor heat duty, and adjusting cooling duties for reactor effluent two-stage cooling. Absorber

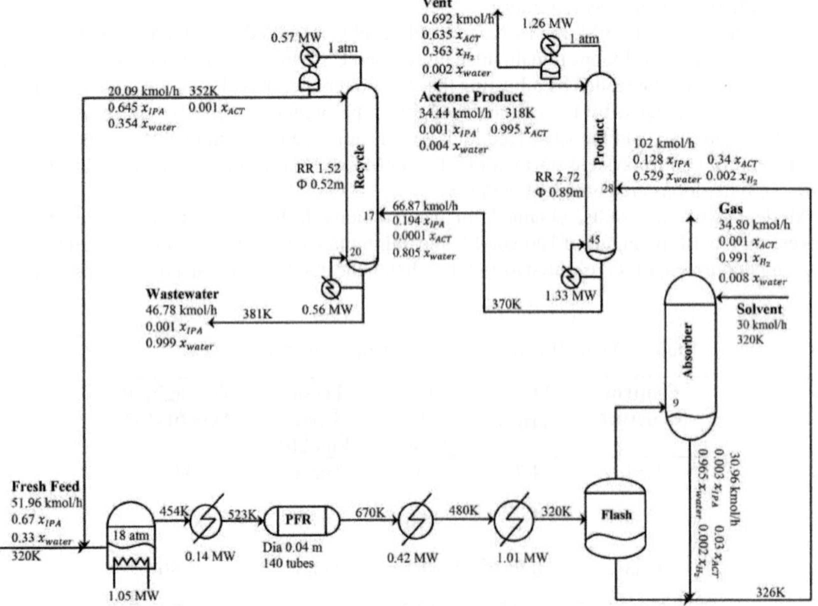

Figure 2: Nominal design and operating condition for acetone manufacturing process

Table 3: Mode I result for acetone manufacturing process

Control Structure	Δx^*_{prod} (10^{-3})	Q_{tot} (kW)	Energy Savings (%)
CS1	2.0	3112.6	0.00
CS2	1.1	3005.2	3.45
CS3	0.8	2980.5	4.24

* No back-0ff x^{min}_{prod}=0.995

pressure is maximized by keeping the flash drum vapor exit valve fully open, regulated by manipulating the absorber exit lean gas valve. All levels are controlled using liquid outflow valves, and condenser pressure is regulated by condenser duty on both columns. Sensitive stripping tray temperature is adjusted by manipulating the reboiler duty. Reflux is controlled in ratio with distillate on the product column and in ratio with column feed rate on the recycle column. Product purity on the product column is controlled through biasing the L/D ratio multiplier output.

CS2 places the TPM at the total (fresh + recycle) feed to the vaporizer, controlled by manipulating the fresh feed rate. All other control loops mirror those of CS1.CS3 designates the product column pressure drop (ΔP_{col1}) as the TPM, tightly controlled by manipulating the product column reboiler duty. However, since the reboiler duty is unavailable for stripping tray temperature control, CS3 adjusts the sensitive stripping tray temperature by manipulating the upstream flash drum effluent control valve position. Vaporizer and flash drum levels are controlled by manipulating the fresh IPA feed and vaporizer duty, respectively. All inventory controllers upstream of the product column TPM are in the reverse direction of process flow, while the remaining control loops remain consistent with CS1.
In Mode I dynamic results, with minimal back-off from the minimum acetone product purity constraint (x^{min}_{prod}), CS1, CS2, and CS3 are evaluated for process operation. The chosen TPM setpoint value ensures an average feed processing rate of 51.96 kmol/h (nominal value). Table 3 outlines the average values of x_{prod}, and total duty (Q_{tot}) over a 48-hour operation period. In terms of energy consumption, CS1 performs the least favorably, while CS2 and CS3 achieve energy savings of 3.45% and 4.24%, respectively, compared to CS1.
For Mode II backed-off maximum throughput dynamic results, CS1, CS2, and CS3 are assessed by setting appropriate setpoint values for x_{prod} and TPM to touch, but not violate, x^{min}_{prod} and ΔP^{max}_{col1} during transients. Table 4 summarizes average values of x_{prod}, ΔP_{col1}, and throughput (F). CS1 exhibits the lowest maximum throughput, while CS2 and CS3 achieve higher throughputs by 1.2% and 4.6%, respectively.

Table 4: Mode II result for acetone manufacturing process

Control Structure	Δx^*_{prod} (10^{-4})	$\Delta P_{col1}{}^{\#}$ (bar)	Fresh Feed (kmol/h)	Throughput benefit (%)
CS1	4.1	0.96	58.41	0.00
CS2	3.4	0.97	59.12	1.22
CS3	3.0	1.02	61.14	4.67

* No back-0ff x^{min}_{prod}=0.995, #maximum pressure drop ΔP^{max}_{col1} = 1.022 bar

3. Conclusion

The economic and sustainable performance of three control structures, CS1 (TPM at fresh feed), CS2 (TPM at feed to the first major unit inside the recycle loop), and CS3 (TPM at the bottleneck capacity constraint inside the recycle loop), is assessed for ester purification and acetone manufacturing processes. In Mode I , CS2 demonstrates energy savings of 5.54% and 3.45% over CS1 for the two processes, while CS3 achieves savings of 9.72% and 4.24%, respectively. In Mode II (maximum throughput), CS2 achieves higher throughputs by 1.71% and 1.22%, and CS3 by 5.80% and 4.67%, compared to CS1. From an economic and sustainability perspective, both in Mode I and Mode II, the evaluated structures rank as CS3 > CS2 > CS1.CS2 and CS3 notably outperform CS1 in both modes, as the TPM inside the recycle loop transforms material balance flow transients out of the loop, mitigating flow variability and resulting in lower variability in product quality (in both modes) and the bottleneck capacity constraint (Mode II). The results underscore the significant impact of TPM location on the outwardly radiating material balance control structure, emphasizing the importance of strategic choices and tuning to maximize realized benefits.

References

Buckley, Page S. "Techniques of process control." (1964).

Downs, James J., and Sigurd Skogestad. "An industrial and academic perspective on plantwide control." Annual Reviews in Control 35, no. 1 (2011): 99-110.

Kaistha, Nitin. "Liquid level control in a recycle loop." Journal of Process Control 104 (2021): 11-27.

Luyben, William L. "Design and control of the acetone process via dehydrogenation of 2-propanol." Industrial & engineering chemistry research 50, no. 3 (2011): 1206-1218.

Ojasvi, and Nitin Kaistha. "Plantwide control for maximum throughput operation of an ester purification process." Industrial & engineering chemistry Research 55, no. 47 (2016): 12242-12255.

Flavio Manenti, Gintaras V. Reklaitis (Eds.), Proceedings of the 34th European Symposium on Computer Aided Process Engineering / 15th International Symposium on Process Systems Engineering (ESCAPE34/PSE24), June 2-6, 2024, Florence, Italy
 http://dx.doi.org/10.1016/B978-0-443-28824-1.50300-8

Integrated Urban Energy System for Metropolitan Area: Optimization and Sensitivity Analysis

Mohammadamin Zarei[a], Meshkat Dolat[a], Chul-Jin Lee[b,c], Michael Short[a,d*]

[a]*School of Chemistry and Chemical Engineering, University of Surrey, Guildford GU2 7XH, UK*

[b]*School of Chemical Engineering and Materials Science, Chung-Ang University, 84 Heukseok-ro, Dongjak-gu, Seoul, Republic of Korea*

[c]*Department of Intelligent Energy and Industry, Chung-Ang University, 84 Heukseok-ro, Dongjak-gu, Seoul, Republic of Korea*

[d]*Institue for Sustainability, University of Surrey, Guildford GU2 7XH, UK*

**m.short@surrey.ac.uk*

Abstract

Energy demand continues to rise, intensifying fossil fuel crises impacts. Power plants contribute significantly to meeting energy demand, highlighting the urgency of introducing more renewable energy solutions like combined heat and power (CHP). However, imbalanced supply and demand necessitates incorporating thermal energy storage (TES) to enhance flexibility. This study proposes a mixed integer linear programming model that optimally integrates TES with CHP to meet electricity, heat, and gas demands in an urban area. It adopts a novel dynamic efficiency approach for TES, which considers high discharge rates as the tanks gradually empty, and low charging rates as the tanks reach full capacity. To demonstrate the effectiveness of the model, Seoul, a metropolitan city, is used as a representative case study. Results showcase substantial cost savings through seamlessly integrating CHP with TES. Furthermore, a sensitivity analysis evaluates supply uncertainties' implications.

Keywords: energy system, thermal energy storage, energy optimization, distributed generation, combined heat and power

1. Introduction

The UN predicts that by 2050, 67% of the global population will reside in cities, posing challenges in energy supply and environmental impact. Increasing urban energy efficiency is crucial to address these issues without compromising economic and quality of life (Colmenar-Santos et al., 2016). CHP systems could play a crucial role in meeting future urban energy demands. These systems satisfy different energy demands simultaneously, including heat, electricity, and possibly cooling (Morvaj et al., 2016). Distributed energy resources (DER) employ a wider range of technologies than central energy supply systems, and include CHP systems and several commercially available energy storage technologies(Yang et al., 2015).

CHP systems are key components in DER and can reduce pollution and increase energy efficiency due to their high efficiency and low investment costs(Jorbandian, 2014). However, CHP systems have the disadvantage of incompatibility between heat and electricity demand throughout the year since the patterns of heat and electricity demand can vary across regions and seasons. Consequently, the extra thermal load cannot be consumed and may be wasted (Cabeza, 2014). TES can increase the efficiency of CHP systems by storing heat for use in the future. It is primarily designed to overcome the incompatibility between produced and consumed energy(Kalaiselvam & Parameshwaran, 2014).

There have been several investigations that present a mathematical model for DER that uses CHP and renewable resources coupled with TES(Flores & Brouwer, 2018; Jordehi, 2021; Mahani et al., 2020; V. et al., 2020; Zakernezhad et al., 2021), but the efficiency of TES is considered as a constant in these studies. In some more accurate models, input and output temperatures of TES are considered (Steen et al., 2015). However, using temperature not only makes model complicated but it can be computationally expensive.

As it can be seen, previous studies on DER systems with CHP and TES units have primarily focused on energy generation and transmission. In these studies, TES efficiency has been assumed constant over time. However, in practice, TES units behave similarly to capacitors; their charge and discharge rates change dynamically. Specifically, the temperature differential between the TES and the charging/discharging medium decreases over time (Dincer & Zamfirescu, 2011). This leads to declining charge and discharge rates over the duration of the charging and discharging cycles respectively. In other words, TES performance evolves over time. As urban power models continue to develop, detailed modelling of TES performance characteristics and economics will become increasingly important to enable wider adoption.

To address this research gap, this study develops a mixed-integer linear programming (MILP) model to design distributed energy resources with CHP and TES units to meet the gas, heat and electricity of a metropolitan city at the lowest cost. The use of case studies in DER models is helpful for evaluating their effectiveness. Therefore, real data for Seoul as metropolitan city case study was utilized to demonstrate the approach. Based on the analysis, the validity and efficiency of the model have been examined. The contributions of the study, in short, are as follows: 1) proposing DER model with non-constant performance of TES; 2) linearizing TES performance and comparing with constant efficiency model; 3) Applying the model for a Korean case study and analyzing the results.

2. Pattern for District Generation

2.1. Baseline model

In this model, the annual cost has been selected as the objective function. The goal is to minimize the cost of satisfying the gas, electricity, and heating demands. The equipment and technology used in this model are: 1) Small household boilers: This consumes natural gas and produces the heat required in a building; 2)Large steam boilers: it consumes natural gas and produces the heat required for several buildings; 3) Small CHP unit: this consumes natural gas and produces heat and electricity; 4) Medium CHP unit: it consumes natural gas and produces heat and electricity for several simultaneous production units.

A mass and energy balance are shown in Equation (1) for the source *r* in district *i* and for time *t* based on production, storage, transport, import, and export.

$$P_{r,i,t} - D_{r,i,t} + Tr_{r,i,t} + Im_{r,i,t} - Le_{r,i,t} - E_{r,i,t} = 0 \quad (1)$$

where *P* is the net production rate of resources, *D* is demand, *Tr* is the transfer rate of resources, *Im* is the import rate, Le is the loss rate, and *E* is the export rate. The objective function in this model is shown by Equation (2):

$$Min\ (Cost) = \sum_{\mu} W_{\mu}\,(C_{\mu}^{p} + C_{\mu}^{Tr} + C_{\mu}^{Im} + C_{\mu}^{E} + C_{\mu}^{S}) \tag{2}$$

where μ is the metric performance indicator, with $W\mu$ as its objective function weight. Various factors contribute to μ: production technologies (c_{μ}^{p}), import (C_{μ}^{Im}), export (C_{μ}^{E}), storage technologies (C_{μ}^{S}), and their impact on the metric's performance.

2.2. Using TES in DER

The energy stored in TES is made up of three parts: charging, storing and discharging energy. In the charging phase, energy enters the system. In the storing phase, the energy is saved and in the discharge phase, the energy will transfer to the system. The amount of stored and discharged energy is different over time. To obtain performance curve of energy storage, the system requires determination of the efficiency curve over time. Performance can be split into two aspects: 1) Energy efficiency is based on the First Law of thermodynamics; 2) Exergy efficiency is based on the Second Law of thermodynamics (Dincer & Rosen, 2002). As the model presented in this work is energy-based, the first law is used to evaluate the performance of TES energy. In this work, water is used for sensible energy storage due to its ease of access and thermal conductivity. In this work, two scenarios with linear formulations are generated based on non-TES and TES with non-constant efficiency.

2.2.1. TES with Constant Efficiency

In this section, TES is considered with constant efficiency. Equations are described below:

$$P_{r,i,t} - D_{r,i,t} + Tr_{r,i,t} + Im_{r,i,t} - Le_{r,i,t} - E_{r,i,t} = \Delta S_{r,i,t} \tag{3}$$

$$S_{r,i,t}^{ini} + \Delta S_{r,i,t} = S_{r,i,t}^{f} \tag{4}$$

$$S_{r,i,t}^{f} = \eta S_{r,i,t-1}^{ini} \tag{5}$$

Mass and energy balance modified by equation (3) where ΔS is the amount of exchanged energy. Equation (4) shows change in energy level of TES where S^{ini} is initial energy level at the beginning of time period, and S^{f} is the energy level at the end of time period of TES. Based on equation (5), every time period has a lower energy level than the previous time period considering energy degradation. Here η denote degradation percentage.

2.2.2. TES with Non-Constant Efficiency

The heat flow rate between thermal energy storage (TES) and connected systems follows nonlinear dynamics per the standard heat transfer equation, as the product of mass flow and temperature differential. However, studies show TES units generally operate around 50% of capacity for charge and discharge(Romanchenko et al., 2018). Moreover, TES shows similar behavior to capacitors - charge/discharge rates are high when empty/full but taper as storage becomes more filled/empty. Thus, a reasonable simplifying assumption is to constrain the TES charge/discharge to 50% of capacity per time period, though this omits nonlinear effects. This enables cleaner mathematical formulation and linear constraints on heat flows rather than reliance on dynamic nonlinear products. Thus, this assumption aligns with common real-world TES performance while allowing simplified linear heat flow constraints. Consequently Equation (4) is modified by Equation (6):

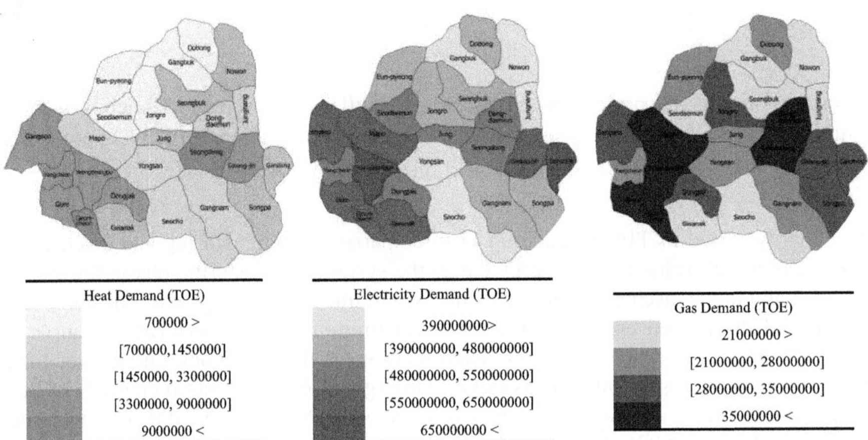

Figure 1. Energy demands for each district in Seoul.

$$N_{i,stor}S^{max} - S^{ini}_{r,i,t} < \Delta S_{r,i,t} \tag{6}$$

where $N_{i,stor}$ is Number of storage technologies of type stor in district i, $S^{max}$is maximum capacity of storage.

3. Case study

The proposed model is implemented in a real case study of distributed generation in metropolitan city Seoul. The objective of this project is to minimize the total cost of providing electricity, heating, and natural gas in the city. The city is divided into districts, with each having specific demands. Through the heat network, electricity and gas can be exchanged between districts. To demonstrate the effectiveness of the proposed model, Seoul is divided into 25 districts and demands for each of them is shown in Figure 1(*Seoul Statistics Integrated Platform*, 2023). Two boilers with different capacities of 0.025MW and 6.2MW are considered. Moreover, two types of CHP with 1 and 10MW capacity are assumed. The storage tanks considered in this study have 2, 3, and 4 MWh capacity.

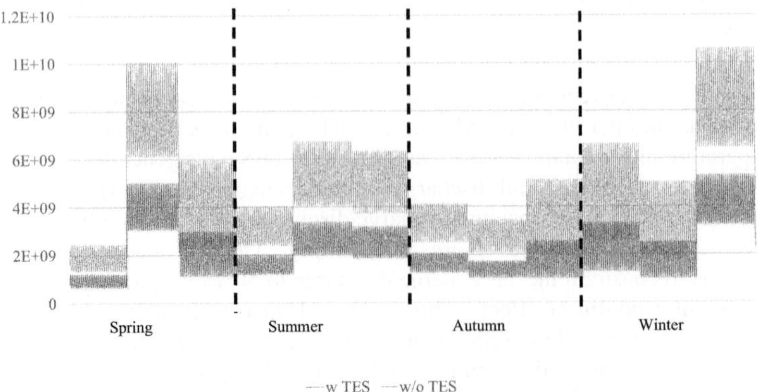

Figure 2. Energy loss in energy system.

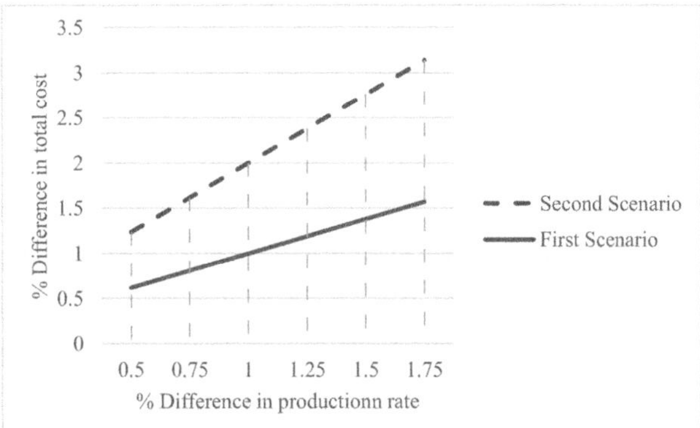

Figure 3. Impact of sensitivity energy production on the total annualized cost.

4. Results and discussion

The optimization model was coded in Python using Pyomo and solved with IBM CPLEX on a standard laptop (16GB RAM, Intel Core i5 CPU). It included over 20,000 variables and 592,000 constraints. Two scenarios were analyzed: 1) DER without TES, and 2) incorporating TES with non-constant charge/discharge efficiency.

The minimum annualized cost computed for Scenario 1 is $2.62 billion, comprising 94% energy production costs, 5.6% import costs, and 4% transmission costs between districts. As shown in Figure 1, the highest electricity/heating demands occur in the southeast districts, aligning with the localization of generation assets in Dongjak, Gwangjin, Yangcheong, Gwanak, Seodaemun, Yeongdeungpo.

For Scenario 2, integrating TES decreases the total annual costs by 9% to $2.37 billion. The largest shares of costs are energy production, imports, transmission, and TES operation, respectively. Figure 2 illustrates how TES reduces transmission losses, especially in summer when heating demands are lower. The loss differential between scenarios is least in winter as heating needs spike.

Sensitivity analyses in Figure 3 indicate production costs become more impactful with TES present. This highlights the value of accurate technical data for storage performance in optimization models. Additional analyses could examine using higher-resolution demand data or new storage mediums.

5. Conclusions

This study presented an MILP model for optimizing DERs in metropolitan cities, considering CHP systems alongside TES. The key novelty was incorporating a linearized, non-constant thermal storage efficiency function to better represent real-world charge/discharge performance over time.

Results demonstrated a 9% cost reduction by integrating thermal storage versus the scenario without storage. In terms of costs, energy production accounted for 94%, followed by imports (5.6%) and transmission (4%). By increasing system flexibility, thermal storage enabled better demand-supply alignment and reduced losses. The sensitivity analysis showed production costs have a greater influence on overall costs when storage is present. This highlights the importance of accurate technical performance data for storage systems in optimization models.

References

Cabeza, L. F. (2014). *Advances in thermal energy storage systems: Methods and applications*. Elsevier.

Dincer, I., & Rosen, M. (2002). *Thermal energy storage: systems and applications*. John Wiley & Sons.

Dincer, I., & Zamfirescu, C. (2011). *Sustainable energy systems and applications*. Springer Science & Business Media.

Fazlollahi, S., Becker, G., & Maréchal, F. (2014). Multi-objectives, multi-period optimization of district energy systems: II—Daily thermal storage. *Computers & Chemical Engineering*, *71*, 648–662. https://doi.org/https://doi.org/10.1016/j.compchemeng.2013.10.016

Flores, R. J., & Brouwer, J. (2018). Optimal design of a distributed energy resource system that economically reduces carbon emissions. *Applied Energy*, *232*, 119–138. https://doi.org/https://doi.org/10.1016/j.apenergy.2018.09.029

Jorbandian, S. (2014). *Urban energy management based on Combine heat and power systems*. Mazandaran University of Science and Technology.

Jordehi, A. R. (2021). Scheduling heat and power microgrids with storage systems, photovoltaic, wind, geothermal power units and solar heaters. *Journal of Energy Storage*, *41*, 102996. https://doi.org/https://doi.org/10.1016/j.est.2021.102996

Kalaiselvam, S., & Parameshwaran, R. (2014). *Thermal energy storage technologies for sustainability: systems design, assessment and applications*. Elsevier.

Koltsaklis, N. E., Kopanos, G. M., & Georgiadis, M. C. (2014). Design and Operational Planning of Energy Networks Based on Combined Heat and Power Units. *Industrial & Engineering Chemistry Research*, *53*(44), 16905–16923. https://doi.org/10.1021/ie404165c

Mahani, K., Jamali, M. A., Nazemi, S. D., & Jafari, M. A. (2020). Economic and Operational Evaluation of PV and CHP combined with Energy Storage Systems considering Energy and Regulation Markets. *2020 IEEE Texas Power and Energy Conference (TPEC)*, 1–6. https://doi.org/10.1109/TPEC48276.2020.9042537

Morvaj, B., Evins, R., & Carmeliet, J. (2016). Optimising urban energy systems: Simultaneous system sizing, operation and district heating network layout. *Energy*, *116*, 619–636. https://doi.org/https://doi.org/10.1016/j.energy.2016.09.139

Romanchenko, D., Kensby, J., Odenberger, M., & Johnsson, F. (2018). Thermal energy storage in district heating: Centralised storage vs. storage in thermal inertia of buildings. *Energy Conversion and Management*, *162*, 26–38. https://doi.org/https://doi.org/10.1016/j.enconman.2018.01.068

Seoul Statistics Integrated Platform. (2023, May 18). Https://Stat.Eseoul.Go.Kr/.

Steen, D., Stadler, M., Cardoso, G., Groissböck, M., DeForest, N., & Marnay, C. (2015). Modeling of Thermal Storage Systems in MILP Distributed Energy Resource Models. *Applied Energy*, *137*, 782–792. https://doi.org/10.1016/j.apenergy.2014.07.036

V., A. K., Sharma, S., & Verma, A. (2020). Optimal DER Sizing and Dispatch of CHP for a Remote Educational Microgrid. *2020 IEEE 9th Power India International Conference (PIICON)*, 1–6. https://doi.org/10.1109/PIICON49524.2020.9113059

Watanabe, Y., & Iwafune, Y. (2014). Method for evaluating the relationships between urban forms and energy system. *ENERGYCON 2014 - IEEE International Energy Conference*, 1004–1011. https://doi.org/10.1109/ENERGYCON.2014.6850548

Yang, Y., Zhang, S., & Xiao, Y. (2015). Optimal design of distributed energy resource systems coupled with energy distribution networks. *Energy*, *85*, 433–448. https://doi.org/https://doi.org/10.1016/j.energy.2015.03.101

Zakernezhad, H., Nazar, M. S., Shafie-khah, M., & Catalão, J. P. S. (2021). Optimal resilient operation of multi-carrier energy systems in electricity markets considering distributed energy resource aggregators. *Applied Energy*, *299*, 117271. https://doi.org/https://doi.org/10.1016/j.apenergy.2021.117271

Printed and bound by CPI Group (UK) Ltd, Croydon, CR0 4YY

03/10/2024

01040328-0004